S0-BYM-305

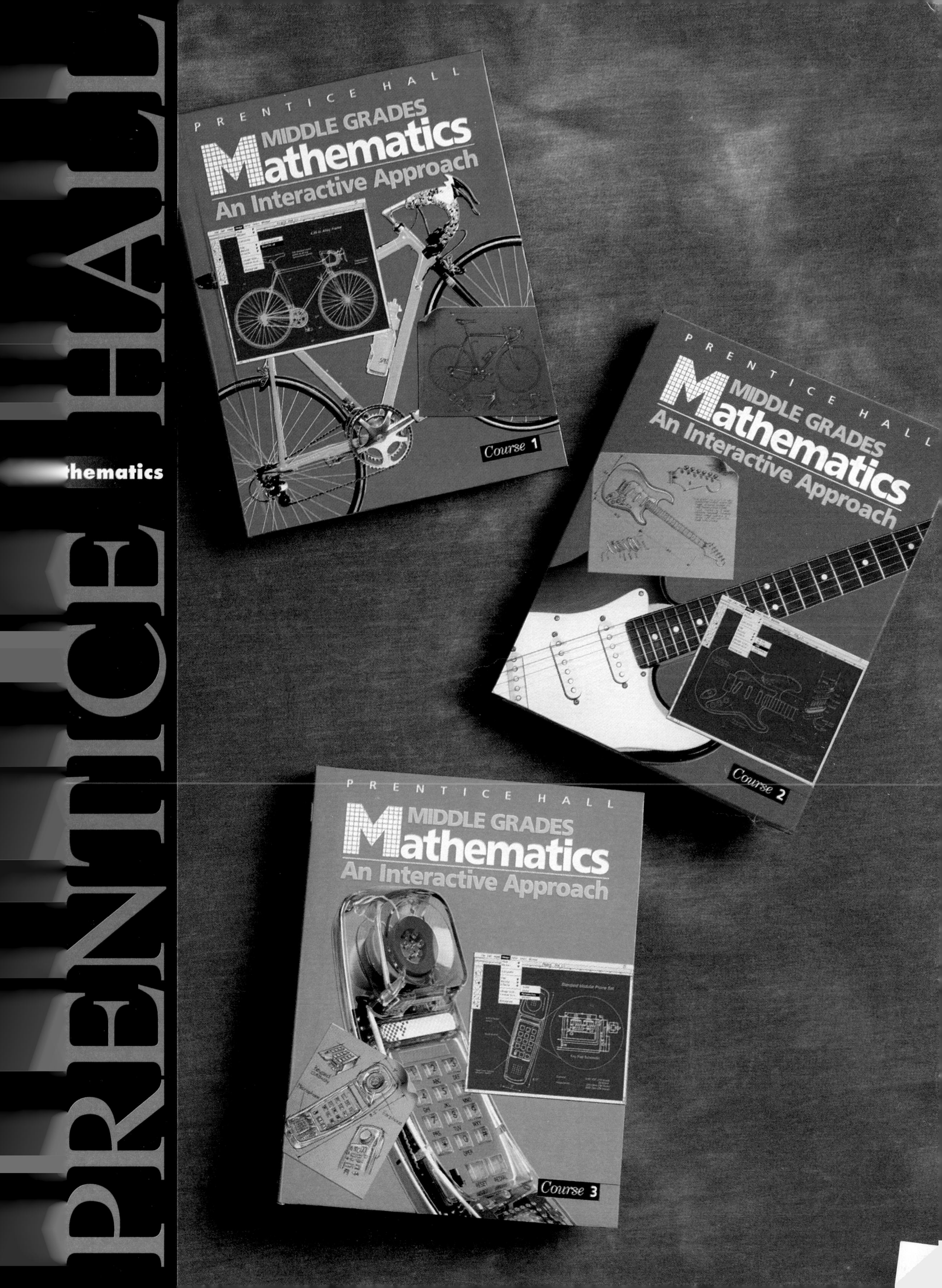

PRENTICE HALL
thematics
PRENTICE HALL
MIDDLE GRADES
Mathematics
An Interactive Approach
Course 1
PRENTICE HALL
MIDDLE GRADES
Mathematics
An Interactive Approach
Course 2
PRENTICE HALL
MIDDLE GRADES
Mathematics
An Interactive Approach
Course 3

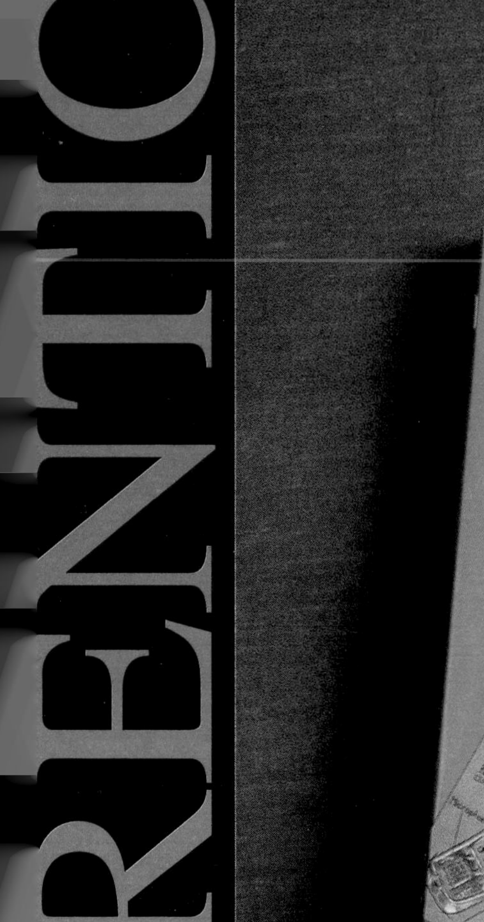

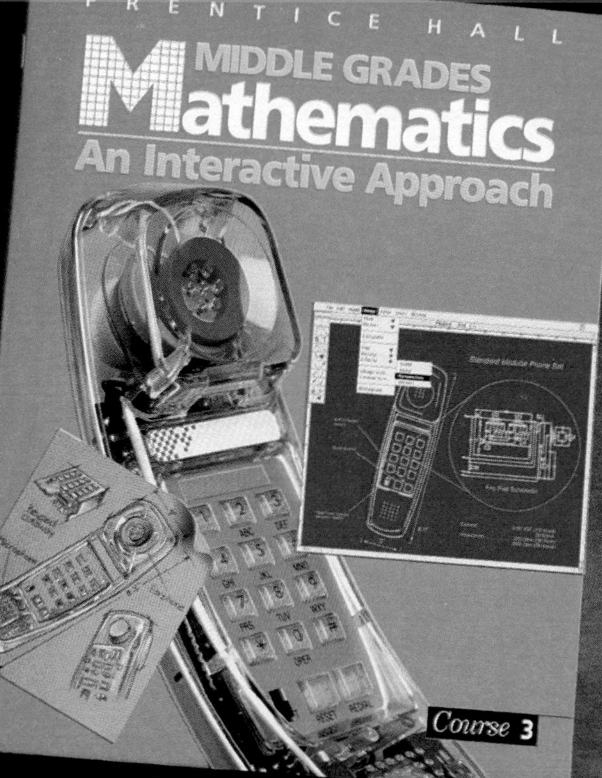

Introducing the first middle grades program to bring math to life.

From the acknowledged leader in middle grades education, a highly involving, entirely new program for today's classroom.

- This is the first program ever to integrate fully print components with state-of-the-art technology for a math experience students will remember.
- An interactive learning system, Middle Grades Mathematics is built to meet even the most diverse learning and teaching styles of the middle grades.
- It's totally new and fully aligned with local and national standards for curriculum and instruction.

Pupil Editions That Excite the Curious Middle Grade Student.

Uses the energy of the typical middle grade student in a variety of ways, including long-term investigations and projects.

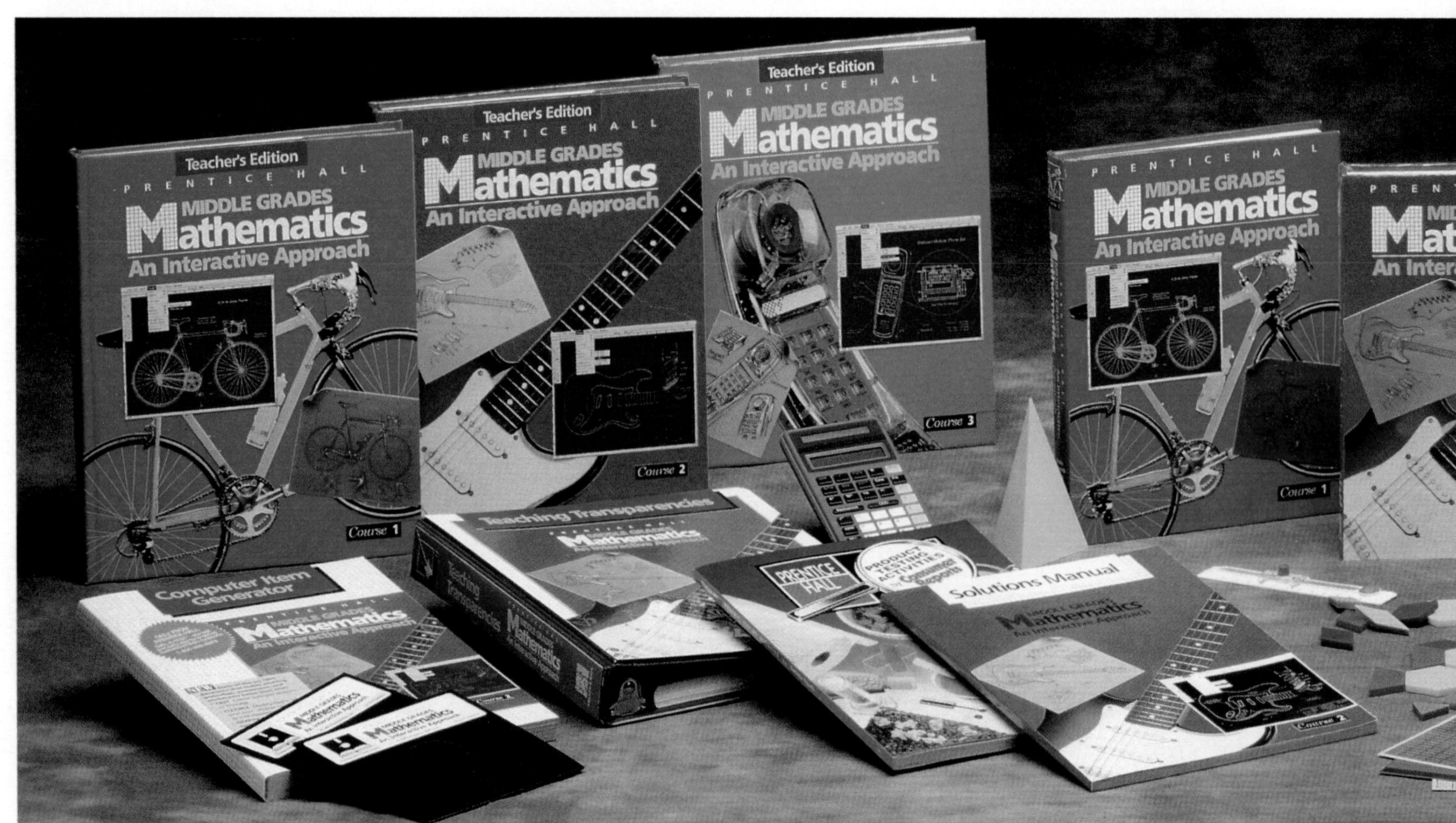

Course 1

Chapter

1 Representing Data
2 Geometry Concepts
3 Adding and Subtracting Decimals
4 Multiplying and Dividing Decimals
5 Patterns, Functions, and Equations
6 Measurement
7 Fraction Concepts
8 Fraction Operations
9 Ratio, Proportion, and Percent
10 Probability
11 Integers and Coordinate Graphing

Course 2

Chapter

1 Interpreting Data
2 Geometry
3 Applications of Decimals
4 Introduction to Algebra
5 Measurement
6 Patterns and Functions

Teacher Editions That Give You What You Want When You Need It.

Designed for use in today's interactive classrooms, teaching notes mimic the format of each student page at its point of use.

Teaching Resources

Organized chapter by chapter, this extensive Teaching Resources package combines everything you need in one place. Many sections are translated into Spanish.

Multimedia Math Package Stresses Flexibility

The first and only original multimedia package specifically designed to work simultaneously with the new **Middle Grades Mathematics** program. Now you will have the opportunity to merge print and media together easily. For those who have access to CD-ROM equipment, **Middle Grades Mathematics** provides an optional level of integrated classroom technology.

Imagine a learning tool that combines motion, sound, photography, graphics, and text to bring math to life.

Complete Course Offers:

- Teaching Transparencies
- Solution Key
- Computer Item Generator
- Professional Development Portfolio
- Manipulative Kits
- Calculator Packages
- Interdisciplinary Units
- Write-On/Wipe-Off Wall Charts
- Product Testing Activities by *Consumer Reports*

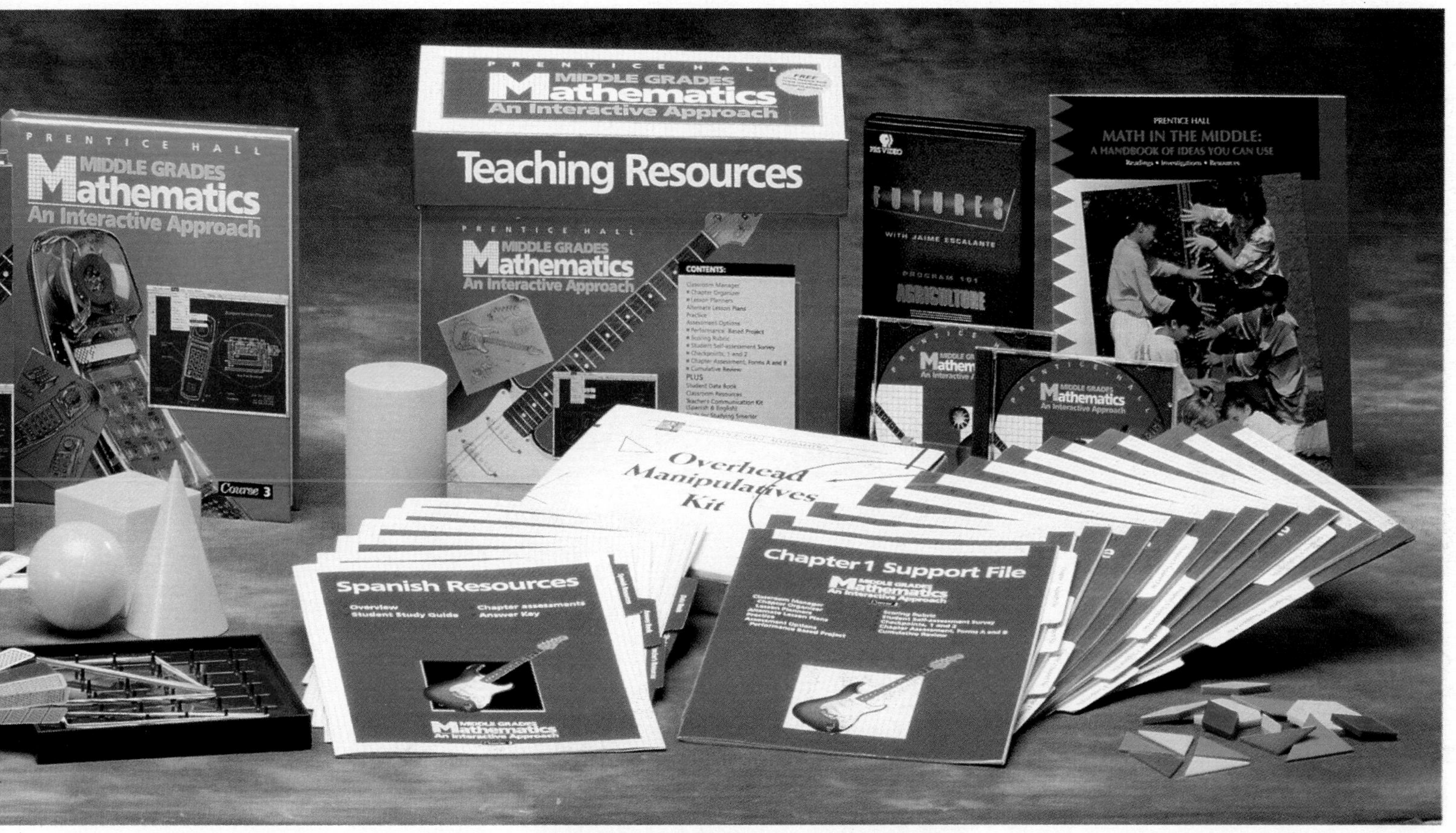

7	**Number Theory**
8	**Fraction Applications**
9	**Reasoning with Proportions**
10	**Probability**
11	**Graphing in the Coordinate Plane**

Course 3

Chapter

1	**Drawing Conclusions from Data**
2	**Patterns in Geometry**
3	**Integers and Variable Expressions**
4	**Algebraic Equations and Inequalities**
5	**Graphing in the Coordinate Plane**
6	**Functions**
7	**Rational Numbers**
8	**Applications of Proportions**
9	**Probability**
10	**Applications of Percent**
11	**Geometry and Measurement**

PRENTICE HALL

MIDDLE GRADES Mathematics

An Interactive Approach

Component	Course 1 ISBNs	Course 2 ISBNs	Course 3 ISBNs
Student Edition	0–13–031105–7	0–13–031121–9	0–13–031147–2
Teacher's Edition	0–13–031113–8	0–13–031139–1	0–13–031154–5
Teaching Resources	0–13–805201–8	0–13–805193–3	0–13–805185–2
Teaching Transparencies	0–13–828047–9	0–13–828054–1	0–13–828062–2
Solution Key	0–13–812769–7	0–13–812777–8	0–13–812801–4
Interdisciplinary Units	0–13–812736–0	0–13–812744–1	0–13–812751–4
Computer Item Generator	0–13–816588–2	0–13–816596–3	0–13–816604–8
Multimedia Math	0–13–828211–0	0–13–828229–3	0–13–328899–4
Teacher's Demonstration Manipulatives Kit	0–13–828096–7	0–13–828096–7	0–13–828096–7
Student Core Manipulatives Kit	0–13–828104–1	0–13–828104–1	0–13–828104–1
Overhead Manipulatives Kit	0–13–828088–6	0–13–828088–6	0–13–828088–6
Fraction Calculator Package	0–13–828443–1	0–13–828443–1	0–13–828443–1
Scientific Calculator Package	0–13–828435–0	0–13–828435–0	0–13–828435–0
Write On/Wipe Off Wall Charts	0–13–828070–3	0–13–828070–3	0–13–828070–3
Professional Development Portfolio	0–13–812322–5	0–13–812322–5	0–13–812322–5
Product Testing Activities by Consumer Reports	0–13–988072–0	0–13–988072–0	0–13–988072–0

PRENTICE HALL
Simon & Schuster Education Group
Englewood Cliffs, NJ and Needham, MA
1-800-848-9500

Teacher's Edition

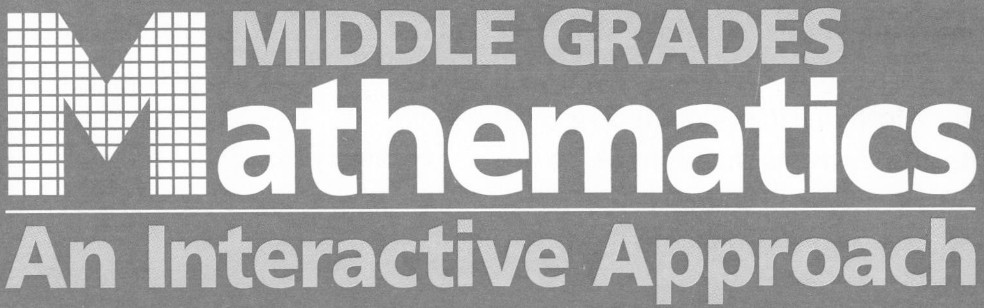

PRENTICE HALL MIDDLE GRADES Mathematics: An Interactive Approach

Suzanne H. **Chapin**

Mark **Illingworth**

Marsha S. **Landau**

Joanna O. **Masingila**

Leah **McCracken**

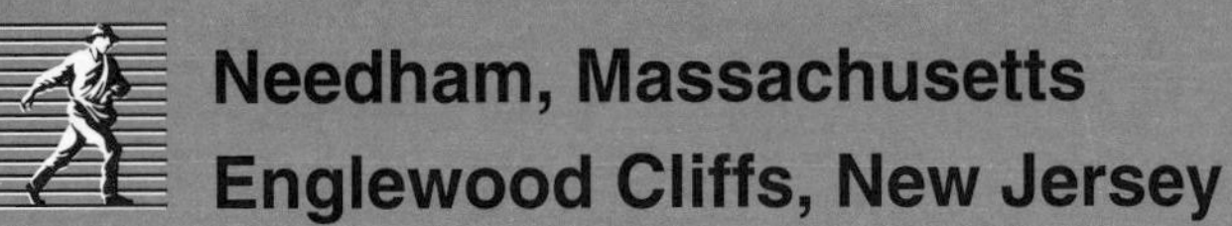

Needham, Massachusetts
Englewood Cliffs, New Jersey

The authors and consulting authors on Prentice Hall *Middle Grades Mathematics: An Interactive Approach* team worked with Prentice Hall to develop an instructional approach that addresses the needs of middle grades students with a variety of ability levels and learning styles. Authors also prepared manuscript for strands across the three levels of *Middle Grades Mathematics*. Consulting authors worked alongside authors throughout program planning and all stages of manuscript development offering advice and suggestions for improving the program.

Authors

Suzanne H. Chapin, *Ed.D., Boston University, Boston MA;* Proportional Reasoning and Probability strands

Mark Illingworth, *Hollis Public Schools, Hollis, NH;* Graphing strand

Marsha S. Landau, *Ph.D., National Louis University, Evanston, IL;* Algebra, Functions, and Computation strands

Joanna O. Masingila, *Ph.D., Syracuse University, Syracuse, NY;* Geometry strand

Leah McCracken, *Lockwood Junior High, Billings, MT;* Data Analysis strand

Consulting Authors

Sadie Bragg, Ed.D., Borough of Manhattan Community College, The City University of New York, New York, NY

Vincent O'Connor, Milwaukee Public Schools, Milwaukee, WI

We are grateful to our reviewers who read manuscript at all stages of development and provided invaluable feedback, ideas, and constructive criticism to help make this program one that meets the needs of middle grades teachers and students.

Reviewers

All Levels

Ann Bouie, Ph.D., Multicultural Reviewer, Oakland, CA

Mary Lester, Dallas Public Schools, Dallas, TX

Dorothy S. Strong, Ph.D., Chicago Public Schools, Chicago, IL

Course 1

Darla Agajanian, Sierra Vista School, Canyon Country, CA

Rhonda Bird, Grand Haven Area Schools, Grand Haven, MI

Leroy Dupee, Bridgeport Public Schools, Bridgeport, CT

Jose Lalas, California State University, Dominguez Hills, CA

Richard Lavers, Fitchburg High School, Fitchburg, MA

Course 2

Raylene Bryson, Alexander Middle School, Huntersville, NC

Sheila Cunningham, Klein Independent School District, Klein, TX

Natarsha Mathis, Hart Junior High School, Washington, DC

Jean Patton, Sharp Middle School, Covington, GA

Judy Trowell, Little Rock School District, Little Rock, AR

Course 3

Michaele F. Chappell, Ph.D., University of South Florida, Tampa, FL

Bettye Hall, Math Consultant, Houston, TX

Joaquin Hernandez, Shenandoah Middle School, Miami, FL

Dana Luterman, Lincoln Middle School, Kansas City, MO

Loretta Rector, Leonardo da Vinci School, Sacramento, CA

Anthony C. Terceira, Providence School Department, Providence, RI

ISBN 0-13-031113-8

Printed in the United States of America

5 6 7 8 01 00 99 98 97 96 95

Table of Contents

P R E N T I C E   H A L L

Middle Grades Mathematics: An Interactive Approach

TEACHER SUPPORT

- ✔ Mimics the organizational design of the student page.
- ✔ Provides helpful suggestions right where you need them.
- ✔ Offers instructional strategies to meet the needs of diverse populations.

ASSESSMENT

- ✔ *Journal and Ongoing Assessment* options offer authentic opportunities to evaluate student progress.
- ✔ Short sets of *Try These* skill-based and application exercises allow for immediate assessment.

CONNECTIONS

- ✔ Integrating strands like geometry, number sense, and data make mathematics-to-mathematics connections real!

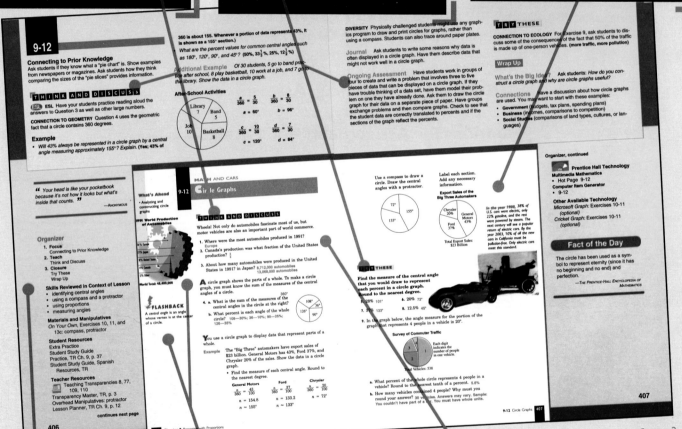

Teacher Edition pages are from Course 2 and are shown reduced.

TEACHER SUPPORT

- ✔ Lesson planning suggestions at your fingertips.
- ✔ Time-saving instructional model, skills review, and resources listed at point of use.

APPROPRIATE CONTENT

- ✔ One of many opportunities for just-in-time reviews. *Flashbacks* remind students of previously learned facts.
- ✔ Motivational art relevant to the mathematical content on the page makes math interesting.
- ✔ Interactive photo captions get students involved.

COMMUNICATION

- ✔ *Think and Discuss* Sections
  - Include interactive questioning as part of the lesson development.
  - Provide a unique opportunity to assess student progress on an ongoing basis.

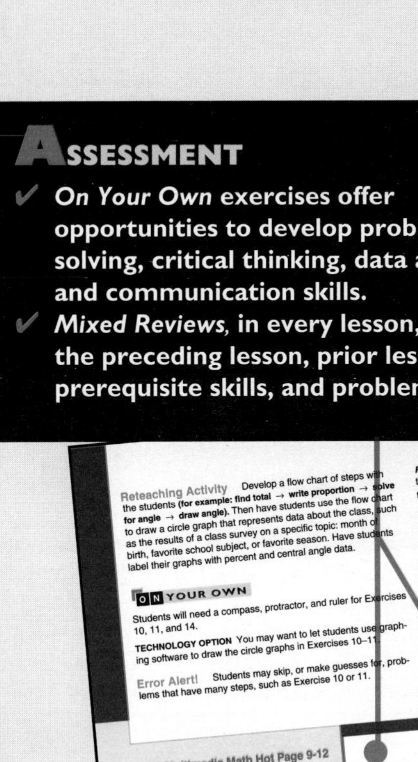

ASSESSMENT

- ✔ *On Your Own* exercises offer opportunities to develop problem solving, critical thinking, data analysis, and communication skills.
- ✔ *Mixed Reviews*, in every lesson, review the preceding lesson, prior lessons, prerequisite skills, and problem solving.

TEACHER SUPPORT

- ✔ Teaching Notes suggest varied instructional strategies to make math accessible to all students.

Reteaching Activity Develop a flow chart of steps with the students **(for example: find total → write proportion → solve for angle → draw angle).** Then have students use the flow chart to draw a circle graph that represents data about the class, such as the results of a class survey on a specific topic: month of birth, favorite school subject, or favorite season. Have students label their graphs with percent and central angle data.

ON YOUR OWN

Students will need a compass, protractor, and ruler for Exercises 10, 11, and 14.

TECHNOLOGY OPTION You may want to let students use graphing software to draw the circle graphs in Exercises 10–11.

Error Alert! Students may skip, or make guesses for, problems that have many steps, such as Exercise 10 or 11.

Remediation Have students plan the necessary steps before they begin to solve the problem. A plan for Exercise 11 might be this: $\frac{part}{whole}$, percent, central angles, circle graph.

TACTILE LEARNERS Ask students to draw their graph for Exercise 10 as a large circle on a transparency. Then have them color the sections and label them. Provide scissors so they can cut out the circles and the sections. Invite someone to reassemble the graph on the overhead while explaining what each section represents.

Exercise 12: As an extension, invite your students to find out the laws in your state about minimum driving ages and report their findings to the class.

CRITICAL THINKING In Exercise 13c, have students give reasons for the changes they suggest in the Millers' budget. Ask them if some changes are easier to make than others.

WRITING For Exercise 15, have students name another type of graph they could use for the first survey. **(bar graph)**

Decision Making

Research information about cars is available from the reference librarian at the public library. Numerous publications (books and magazines such as *Consumer Reports*) rate the different makes and models of cars each year and give statistics for different features such as average miles per gallon.

Since many people buy used cars, encourage students to consider this option. Information is available on used cars in many of the same publications mentioned above.

Have students share their information in groups, and have each group compare data on their cars.

You may wish to ask students the following questions to get them started:

- *What are some factors that people might consider when buying a car?* **(price, size, safety record, fuel efficiency, style, type, reputation, color, repair record, appearance, know someone with same type, financing plan, read article about it)**
- *How will you organize the collection of data about the factors?* **(Make a chart or list with all factors and record responses.)**

ESL Some students may be confused by the use of the word "factor." Go over the difference between its meaning in mathematics and its meaning as used in the questions.

DIVERSITY Be sensitive to the different economic backgrounds of your students. You may wish not to use personal data but instead assign students some criteria ahead of time to avoid embarrassment. For example, a family of six wants a large, safe, used car and can spend no more than $8,000; or a single woman wishes to buy a sporty car for under $6,500. Students often buy a first car for much less using newspaper ads as a source of information.

PH Multimedia Math Hot Page 9-12

Assignment Options

Core: 10, 12, 14, DM all, MR all	
Reinforce: 11	Enrich: 13, 15

Teacher Edition pages are from Course 2 and are shown reduced.

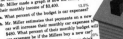

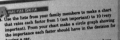

TECHNOLOGY

- ✔ *Multimedia Math* **CD-ROM** technology enables students to interact with electronic *Hot Pages* using *Math Tools* to explore and develop concepts.
- ✔ Long-term Multimedia Math *Investigations* can be linked with the *Math Tools* to explore and connect concepts.
- ✔ *Technology Options* suggest opportunities to integrate the use of various multimedia tools while developing lesson concepts.

TEACHER SUPPORT

- ✔ *Teaching Resources* organized chapter-by-chapter offer an abundance of options for assessment, review, and so much more, in a variety of formats.

Chapter Support File

Classroom Manager
- Chapter Organizer
- Lesson Planners

Alternate Lesson Plans

Practice

Assessment Options
- Performance Based Project
- Scoring Rubric
- Student Self-Assessment Survey
- Checkpoints
- Chapter Assessments
- Cumulative Review

Minds on Math available in Teaching Transparencies

Math Minutes

Have the students draw an example of each kind of angle and name its properties. (Check students' drawings.)

1. acute angle **measures > 0° and < 90°**
2. right angle **measures 90°; sides are ⊥**
3. obtuse angle **measures > 90° and < 180°**

Materials for 10-1
- number cubes

ACTIVE APPROACH

- ✔ Students experience mathematics with these cooperative learning activities.

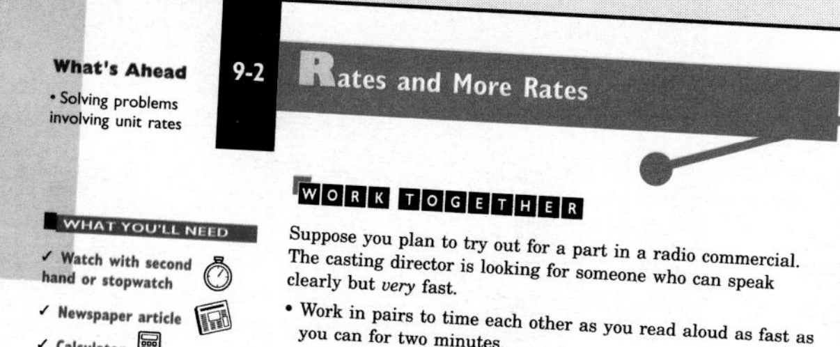

What's Ahead
- Solving problems involving unit rates

9-2 **Rates and More Rates**

WHAT YOU'LL NEED
- ✔ Watch with second hand or stopwatch
- ✔ Newspaper article
- ✔ Calculator

WORK TOGETHER

Suppose you plan to try out for a part in a radio commercial. The casting director is looking for someone who can speak clearly but *very* fast.

- Work in pairs to time each other as you read aloud as fast as you can for two minutes.
- After the two minutes, count the number of words that you read.

Pupil Edition page is from Course 2 and is shown reduced.

Bringing Math to Life!

At a Glance and Varied Instructional Approaches

CONNECTIONS

✔ Graphic representation of possible student responses when asked to connect the chapter title to other math content, real life applications, and the content of other disciplines.

CONNECTIONS

✔ A lesson-by-lesson correlation to current educational issues, NCTM Standards, and so much more, found in every Chapter Planning Guide.

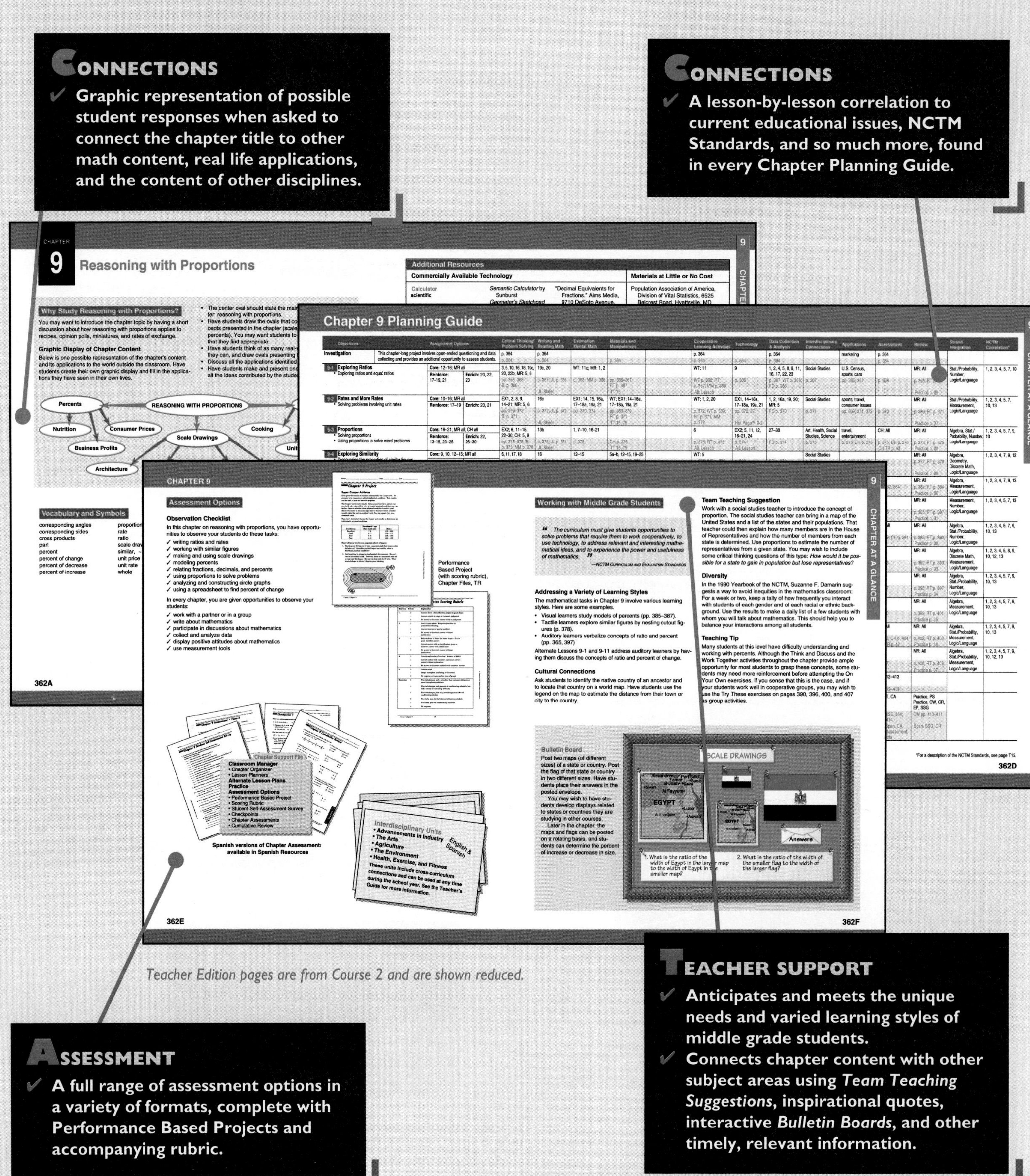

Teacher Edition pages are from Course 2 and are shown reduced.

ASSESSMENT

✔ A full range of assessment options in a variety of formats, complete with Performance Based Projects and accompanying rubric.

TEACHER SUPPORT

✔ Anticipates and meets the unique needs and varied learning styles of middle grade students.

✔ Connects chapter content with other subject areas using *Team Teaching Suggestions*, inspirational quotes, interactive *Bulletin Boards*, and other timely, relevant information.

Making Math Accessible!

P R E N T I C E H A L L

Middle Grades Mathematics: A Program to Meet All Your Needs

Our Unique Program contains:	*Check it out:*
Appropriate Content	
• that is motivational	✔ pp. 380–383, 395–398
• that connects to other disciplines, other math topics, and multicultural topics	✔ pp. 380–383, 386; TE: 361, 396–397
• that is relevant to the real world and diverse student populations	✔ pp. 360–361, 383; TE: 389, 392
• for diverse learning styles	✔ pp. 384–386, 399–401; TE: 373, 381
• that reflects NCTM and local curriculum objectives	✔ TE: pp. C–D, T17–T20
Active Approach for Instruction and Learning	
• to develop and apply problem solving skills	✔ pp. 373–375, 376
• to employ small group activities	✔ pp. 363, 366, 378
• to engage students in hands-on activities	✔ pp. 364, 385, 399–400
• to encourage students to explore topics through long-term projects	✔ pp. 362, 372, 386, 404
• to develop conceptual understanding through interactive questioning	✔ pp. 377–378, 384–385, 391–392
Integrated Technology	
• throughout the program	✔ pp. 388, 395; TE: 381, 388
• for exploration and discovery	✔ pp. 377–379; TE: 366, 369, 377
• as a means of instruction	✔ TE: pp. 366, 369, 377
Assessment	
• to maintain and reinforce skills	✔ pp. 371–372, 390
• as an integrated aspect of instruction	✔ TE: pp. 384, 385
• to utilize a variety of assessment techniques	✔ TE: pp. C–D, E
• to incorporate assessment that is authentic	✔ pp. 362, 386, 394
Teacher Support	
• for the changing role of the teacher	✔ TE: pp. E–F, 384–385, 391–393
• for managing multiple components	✔ TE: pp. C–D
• for incorporating technology	✔ TE: pp. T12–T13, B, C–D, 369, 381, 388

Using Technology with Prentice Hall Middle Grades Mathematics

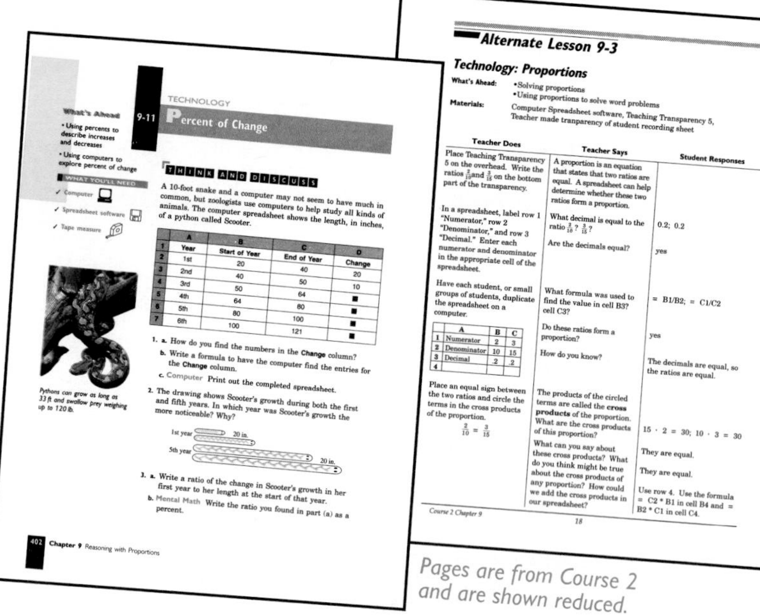

What's Ahead

- Using percents to describe increases and decreases
- Using computers to explore percent of change

WHAT YOU'LL NEED

✓ Computer

✓ Spreadsheet software

✓ Tape measure

TECHNOLOGY

9-11 Percent of Change

THINK AND DISCUSS

A 10-foot snake and a computer may not seem to have much in common, but zoologists use computers to help study all kinds of animals. The computer spreadsheet shows the length, in inches, of a python called Scooter.

	A	B	C	D
1	Year	Start of Year	End of Year	Change
2	1st	20	40	20
3	2nd	40	50	10
4	3rd	50	64	■
5	4th	64	80	■
6	5th	80	100	■
7	6th	100	121	■

Pythons can grow as long as 33 ft and swallow prey weighing up to 120 lb.

1. a. How do you find the numbers in the **Change** column?
   b. Write a formula to have the computer find the entries for the **Change** column.
   c. Computer Print out the completed spreadsheet.
2. The drawing shows Scooter's growth during both the first and fifth years. In which year was Scooter's growth the more noticeable? Why?

1st year 20 in.

5th year 20 in.

3. a. Write a ratio of the change in Scooter's growth in her first year to her length at the start of that year.
   b. Mental Math Write the ratio you found in part (a) as a percent.

402 **Chapter 9** Reasoning with Proportions

Alternate Lesson 9-3

Technology: Proportions

What's Ahead: •Solving proportions •Using proportions to solve word problems

Materials: Computer Spreadsheet software, Teaching Transparency 5, Teacher made tranparency of student recording sheet

Teacher Does	Teacher Says	Student Responses
Place Teaching Transparency 5 on the overhead. Write the ratios $\frac{2}{10}$and $\frac{3}{15}$ on the bottom part of the transparency.	A proportion is an equation that states that two ratios are equal. A spreadsheet can help determine whether these two ratios form a proportion.	
In a spreadsheet, label row 1 "Numerator," row 2 "Denominator," and row 3 "Decimal." Enter each numerator and denominator in the appropriate cell of the spreadsheet.	What decimal is equal to the ratio $\frac{2}{10}$? $\frac{3}{15}$?	0.2; 0.2
	Are the decimals equal?	yes
Have each student, or small groups of students, duplicate the spreadsheet on a computer.	What formula was used to find the value in cell B3? cell C3?	= B1/B2; = C1/C2
(spreadsheet below)	Do these ratios form a proportion?	yes
	How do you know?	The decimals are equal, so the ratios are equal.
Place an equal sign between the two ratios and circle the terms in the cross products of the proportion. $\frac{2}{10} = \frac{3}{15}$	The products of the circled terms are called the **cross products** of the proportion. What are the cross products of this proportion?	15 · 2 = 30; 10 · 3 = 30
	What can you say about these cross products?	They are equal.
	What do you think might be true about the cross products of any proportion?	They are equal.
	How could we add the cross products in our spreadsheet?	Use row 4. Use the formula = C2 * B1 in cell B4 and = B2 * C1 in cell C4.

	A	B	C
1	Numerator	2	3
2	Denominator	10	15
3	Decimal	.2	.2
4			

Course 2 Chapter 9 18

Pages are from Course 2 and are shown reduced.

How does the Student Edition address technology?

The authors of *Middle Grades Mathematics* expect all students to use calculators and have written the textbook so that calculator use is integrated throughout. In addition, there is one technology-based lesson in every chapter. Labeled computer exercises also appear whenever appropriate.

Are there any other materials available?

The Teaching Resources contain one lesson based on technology for every chapter in the student text of *Middle Grades Mathematics*. Each of these lessons is an alternative to a non-technology-based lesson that appears in the student text.

What support does the Teacher's Edition give for technology use?

Teaching notes about the student technology lessons and computer exercises help teachers to teach the concepts as well as manage technology use in the classroom. Technology Option sections indicate what other exercises might be done with technology. Each lesson's side column identifies the Hot Pages, Math Investigations, Math Tools, and alternate technology lessons that are appropriate to use with that lesson.

A list of all Prentice Hall technology products that can be used with a chapter appears on the pages preceding the chapter. The Chapter Planning Guide also references opportunities for technology use in the student edition, teacher's edition, and all other components of the program.

What software does Prentice Hall produce?

Prentice Hall Multimedia Math is a technology package created to integrate with the Prentice Hall *Middle Grades Mathematics* program. Multimedia Math uses interactive software and video to encourage students to take an active role in their learning. The Multimedia Math package includes CDs containing Hot Pages, Math Investigations, and Math Tools, as well as a User's Guide for each component.

Hot Pages are electronic representations of student edition lessons that provide an alternate development of content. Each Hot Page has an interactive math area and at least two cooperative learning activities. One of the activities is based on a video on the page.

Math Investigations are interactive software activities for students and are designed to reinforce and enhance specific mathematical ideas and concepts from the Prentice Hall *Middle Grades Mathematics* program.

Math Tools are a set of electronic tools that interact with each other. Students can use the Math Tools to explore and enhance their understanding of mathematical concepts.

The **Text** tool is a simple word processor that contains standard word processing capabilities.

The **Spreadsheet** is a tool used for manipulating numerical data and formulas.

The **Calculation** tool can be used as a standard calculator, a fraction calculator, an algebraic calculator, or a graphing calculator.

The **Geometry** tool allows the user to create and experiment with geometric figures.

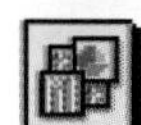
The **Graphs** tool enables the user to make bar graphs, pictographs, line graphs, circle graphs, coordinate graphs, and line plots.

The **Manipulative** tool allows the user to explore math concepts using manipulatives.

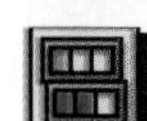
Fraction Strips give a graphic representation of fractional relationships.

The **Probability** tool includes spinners and number cubes. The user can collect probability data, which can then be output to a spreadsheet and displayed as a graph.

The **Frames** tool provides graphical representations of addition, subtraction, and multiplication.

How can you use Prentice Hall Multimedia Math in the classroom?

Prentice Hall Multimedia Math has been designed to give teachers flexibility and can be used in any classroom configuration.

Computer Lab, but No Computers in the Classroom

Ways to use a computer lab:

- **for cooperative learning activities**
Groups of students can discover and extend concepts using the Math Tools, the Hot Page activities, or the Math Investigations.

One Computer in the Classroom

Ways to use one computer:

- **as a teacher demonstration tool with an LCD and an overhead projector**
Teachers can demonstrate concepts using the Math Tools or introduce a lesson by using a Hot Page.

- **to initiate classroom discourse**
Teachers can manipulate the Math Tools, the interactive math area of the Hot Pages, or the video portion of the Hot Pages and then ask questions such as "What do you expect to happen when I change ...?" and "What should I do to get ..."?

- **for cooperative learning activities**
One group of students can work on the Hot Page activities or the Math Investigations, while other groups work at their desks.

- **as a discovery tool for students**
One student or group of students can discover math concepts with the Math Tools or the interactive area of the Hot Pages, while other students work at their desks.

- **for additional work**
When students have completed a class assignment, they can take turns using the Math Tools, Hot Pages, or Math Investigations to reinforce the lesson concepts or to explore concepts in more depth.

About Four Computers in the Classroom

Ways to use about four computers:

- **for cooperative learning activities**
Medium-sized groups of students can work at each computer and use the Math Tools, the Hot Page activities, or the Math Investigations to discover and extend concepts.

- **for small groups of students**
Half of the class can use the computers to discover and extend concepts using the Math Tools, the Hot Page activities, or the Math Investigations, while other students work at their desks, either individually or in groups.

Tips for installing computers in the classroom

1. Put computers in a well-lighted area.
2. Keep computers away from dust and magnetic sources.
3. Place computers so there is no glare from outside.
4. Keep cords away from paths that students walk.
5. Store disks nearby for easy access.
6. Display rules for computer use and care near each computer.
7. Anchor computers or cover the bottom of windows to prevent theft.

Ten or More Computers in the Classroom

Ways to use ten or more computers:

- **for cooperative learning activities**
The entire class can be divided into small groups of students who work at the computers and use the Math Tools, the Hot Page activities, or the Math Investigations to discover and extend concepts.

- **for individual student work**
About half of the class can use the computers to reinforce the lesson concepts or to discover new concepts with the Math Tools, Hot Pages, or Math Investigations, while the other students are working at their desks, either individually or in groups.

Using Materials and Manipulatives with Prentice Hall Middle Grades Mathematics

Prentice Hall's Middle Grades Mathematics program encourages student discovery by use of a variety of manipulatives and everyday materials. Below is a list of the materials suggested for this book. A list specific to each chapter appears on the "A" page preceding the chapter. The manipulative kits that Prentice Hall offers to accompany the *Middle Grades Mathematics* program are described for your convenience.

Materials and Manipulatives for Course 1

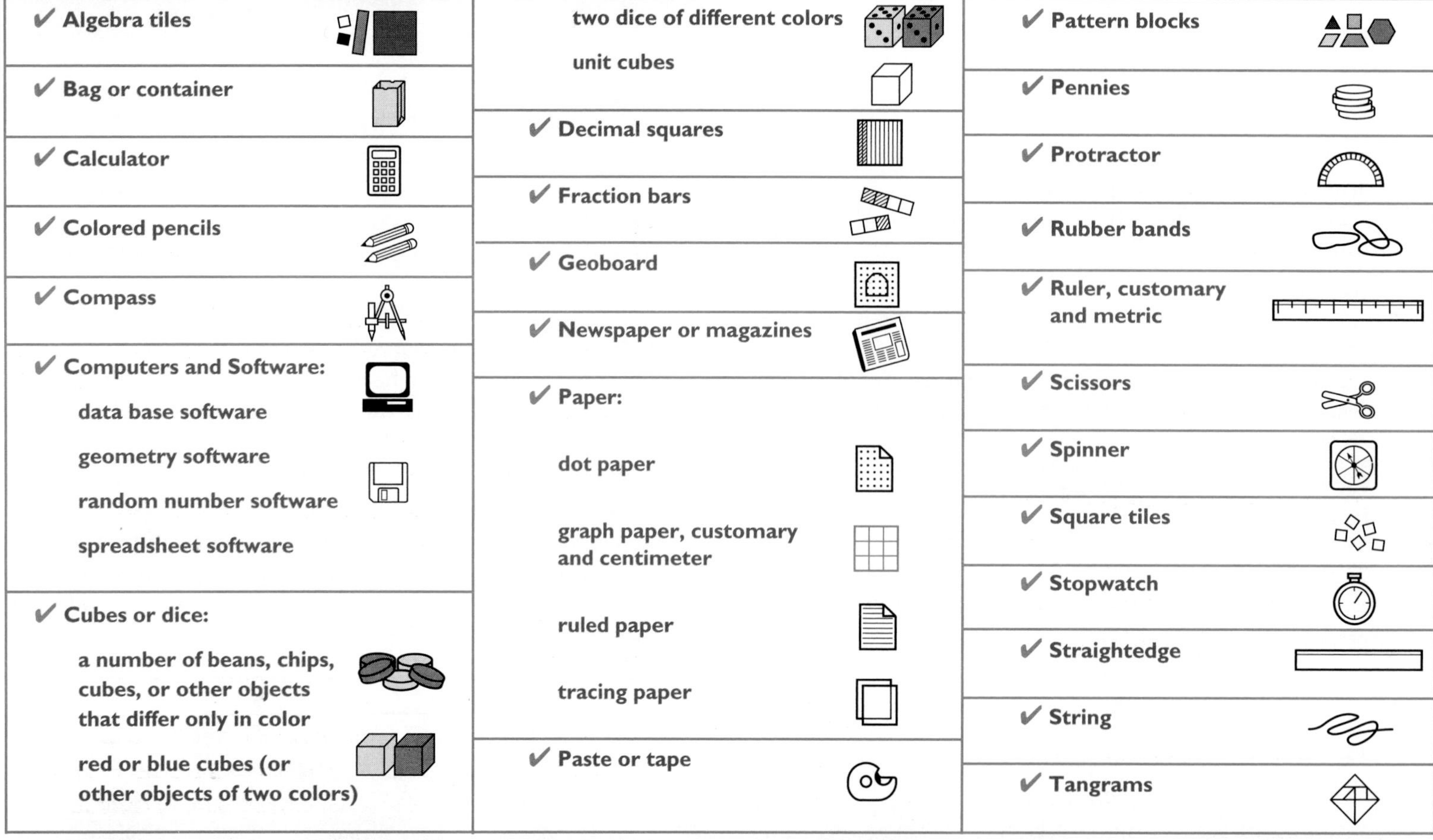

- ✔ Algebra tiles
- ✔ Bag or container
- ✔ Calculator
- ✔ Colored pencils
- ✔ Compass
- ✔ Computers and Software:
  - data base software
  - geometry software
  - random number software
  - spreadsheet software
- ✔ Cubes or dice:
  - a number of beans, chips, cubes, or other objects that differ only in color
  - red or blue cubes (or other objects of two colors)
  - two dice of different colors
  - unit cubes
- ✔ Decimal squares
- ✔ Fraction bars
- ✔ Geoboard
- ✔ Newspaper or magazines
- ✔ Paper:
  - dot paper
  - graph paper, customary and centimeter
  - ruled paper
  - tracing paper
- ✔ Paste or tape
- ✔ Pattern blocks
- ✔ Pennies
- ✔ Protractor
- ✔ Rubber bands
- ✔ Ruler, customary and metric
- ✔ Scissors
- ✔ Spinner
- ✔ Square tiles
- ✔ Stopwatch
- ✔ Straightedge
- ✔ String
- ✔ Tangrams

Student Manipulatives Core Kit

Algebra Tiles
Compasses (safety)
Decimal Squares
Fraction Bars
Geoboard with bands (11 x 11)
Measuring Cups
Mirrors
Number Cubes (regular and blank)
Pattern Blocks
Protractors
Spinners (blank)
Tangrams
Tape Measures

Overhead Manipulatives Kit

Algebra Tiles
Geoboard (11 x 11)
Pattern Blocks
Spinner (clear)
Tangrams

Teacher's Demonstration Manipulative Kit

Balance with weights
Compass for chalkboard
Geometric models

Teaching Transparencies

(selected ones for the overhead projector)

Balance Scale
Circle with tic marks
Coordinate Plane
Decimal Squares
Dot Paper (isometric and square)
Fraction Bars
Graph Paper
Number Lines
Protractor with 1 swinging ray
Shape Tracers
Spreadsheet (blank grid)
Venn Diagram

NCTM Standards for School Mathematics

Curriculum Standards

The Chapter Planning Guide on pages "C" and "D" preceding each chapter indicates the standards that are covered in that chapter.

1 Mathematics as Problem Solving
2 Mathematics as Communication
3 Mathematics as Reasoning
4 Mathematical Connections
5 Number and Number Relationships
6 Number Systems and Number Theory
7 Computation and Estimation
8 Patterns and Functions
9 Algebra
10 Statistics
11 Probability
12 Geometry
13 Measurement

Standards for Teaching Mathematics *

1 Worthwhile Mathematical Tasks
Teachers should choose and develop tasks that are likely to promote the development of students' understandings of concepts and procedures in a way that also fosters their ability to solve problems and to reason and communicate mathematically.

2 The Teacher's Role in Discourse
One aspect of the teacher's role is to provoke students' reasoning about mathematics. A second feature of the teacher's role is to be active in a different way from that in traditional classroom discourse. A third aspect of the teacher's role in orchestrating classroom discourse is to monitor and organize students' participation.

3 Students' Role in Discourse
Students should engage in making conjectures, proposing approaches and solutions to problems, and arguing about the validity of mathematical tools. They should learn to verify, revise, and discard claims on the basis of mathematical evidence and use a variety of mathematical tools.

4 Tools for Enhancing Discourse
Various means for communicating about mathematics should be accepted, including drawings, diagrams, invented symbols, and analogies. Teachers should also help students learn to use calculators, computers, and other technological devices as tools for mathematical discourse.

5 Learning Environment
This standard focuses on key dimensions of a learning environment in which serious mathematical thinking can take place: a genuine respect for others' ideas, a valuing of reason and sense-making, pacing and timing that allow students to puzzle and to think, and the forging of a social and intellectual community.

6 Analysis of Teaching and Learning
Assessment of students and analysis of instruction are fundamentally interconnected. Mathematics teachers should monitor students' learning on an ongoing basis in order to assess and adjust their teaching.

Assessment Standards *

1 Important Mathematics
Assessment should reflect the mathematics that is most important for students to learn.

2 Enhanced Learning
Assessment should enhance mathematics learning.

3 Equity
Assessment should promote equity by giving each student optimal opportunities to demonstrate mathematical power and by helping each student meet the profession's highest expectations.

4 Openness
All aspects of the mathematics assessment process should be open to review and scrutiny.

5 Valid Inferences
Evidence from assessment activities should yield valid inferences about students' mathematical learning.

6 Consistency
Every aspect of an assessment process should be consistent with the purposes of the assessment.

* Excerpts from: *Professional Standards for Teaching Mathematics* (NCTM: Reston, VA, 1991) and *Assessment Standards for School Mathematics* (NCTM working draft: Reston, VA, October 1993).

Options for Assignments and Pacing

Assignments

Assignment Options are listed in the side column of each lesson and in the Chapter Planning Guide before each chapter. The chart contains assignments of exercises from the On Your Own, Checkpoint, Mixed Review, and Decision Making sections.

Core: 11, 12, 15b, 17, 23, 24, DM all, MR all	
Reinforce: 13, 14, 15a	**Enrich:** 16, 18–22

sample of an Assignment Options chart

The Assignment Options chart has three sections: Core, Reinforce, and Enrich. Every exercise is listed in the chart, but in only one category, to allow you to customize your assignments to meet the needs of your students. All students should be able to complete the Core exercises. The Reinforce exercises provide additional work on the lesson concepts for students who need additional practice or for review at a later time. Students who want an extra challenge would benefit from completing the Enrich exercises.

Pacing

The pacing chart shows one way to cover the eleven chapters in the student text. The suggested number of days for each chapter is based on the traditional 50 min class period. You should customize the pacing to suit your individual class needs. The chart includes 160 days to accommodate shortened days, assemblies, or other special days that vary from school to school. Two days per chapter have been allotted to the chapter Investigation, its follow up activities, and the additional projects. Other opportunities to work on the Investigation are included within the chapter.

		Days
CHAPTER 1		11
Investigation	1	
Chapter work, review, and assessment	9	
Putting It All Together	1	
CHAPTER 2		17
Investigation	1	
Chapter work, review, and assessment	15	
Putting It All Together	1	
CHAPTER 3		15
Investigation	1	
Chapter work, review, and assessment	13	
Putting It All Together	1	
CHAPTER 4		15
Investigation	1	
Chapter work, review, and assessment	13	
Putting It All Together	1	
CHAPTER 5		14
Investigation	1	
Chapter work, review, and assessment	12	
Putting It All Together	1	
CHAPTER 6		15
Investigation	1	
Chapter work, review, and assessment	13	
Putting It All Together	1	
CHAPTER 7		15
Investigation	1	
Chapter work, review, and assessment	13	
Putting It All Together	1	
CHAPTER 8		15
Investigation	1	
Chapter work, review, and assessment	13	
Putting It All Together	1	
CHAPTER 9		16
Investigation	1	
Chapter work, review, and assessment	14	
Putting It All Together	1	
CHAPTER 10		13
Investigation	1	
Chapter work, review, and assessment	11	
Putting It All Together	1	
CHAPTER 11		14
Investigation	1	
Chapter work, review, and assessment	12	
Putting It All Together	1	
TOTAL NUMBER OF DAYS		160

Scope and Sequence for Prentice Hall Middle Grades Mathematics

Course	1	2	3
Algebra			
Properties			
of whole numbers			
of integers			
of rational numbers			
Expressions			
order of operations			
evaluate			
simplify			
write from word phrases			
Equations			
solve one-step equations			
solve two-step equations			
solve equations with integer solutions			
solve systems of linear equations			
write from word sentences			
formulas			
Functions			
write a rule			
input-output tables			
linear			
quadratic			
absolute value			
direct variation			
inverse variation			
step			
Graphing			
integers			
inequalities			
ordered pairs			
equations			
functions			
slope			
Inequalities			
write			
solve one-step inequalities			
solve two-step inequalities			
Integers			
read and write			
absolute value			
compare and order			
add and subtract			
multiply and divide			
equations			
Rational numbers			
simplify			
compare and order			
add and subtract			
multiply and divide			
equations			
Irrational numbers			
Real numbers			

Course	1	2	3
Communication			
Create written and oral problems			
Interpret mathematical ideas through discussing, listening, modeling, questioning reading, viewing, and writing			
Make convincing arguments using mathematical ideas			
Relate mathematical language to everyday language			
Relate topics to the history of mathematics			
Use writing to clarify ideas			
Verbalize and define concepts			
Work in groups			
Decimals			
Read and write			
Place value			
Compare and order			
Equivalent decimals			
Add and subtract			
Multiply and divide			
decimal by whole number			
two decimals			
decimal by power of 10			
Estimate			
rounding			
operations			
Convert decimals to fractions			
Convert decimals to percents			
Terminating and repeating			
Scientific notation			
Estimation			
Decimals			
decimal number			
operations			
Dimensional analysis			
Fractions			
proper, improper, and mixed numbers			
operations			
Geometry			
angle measure			
length			
area			
volume			
Integers			
sums and differences			
products and quotients			
Number lines			
Percent			
Proportions			

Introduce *Develop* *Maintain and Apply*

Course	1	2	3
Estimation (cont.)			
Solutions of equations			
Square roots			
Strategies			
choose the computation method			
clustering			
compatible numbers			
front-end			
rounding			
Whole numbers			
whole number values			
operations			
Fractions			
Equivalent fractions			
Simplest form			
Mixed numbers and improper fractions			
Compare and order			
Add and subtract			
like denominators			
unlike denominators			
mixed numbers			
Reciprocal			
Multiply and divide			
whole number and fraction			
fraction and fraction			
whole number and mixed number			
fraction and mixed number			
mixed numbers			
Estimate			
rounding			
operations			
Convert fractions to decimals			
Convert fractions to percents			
Geometry			
Angles			
classify			
measure			
estimate measure			
Constructions			
congruent segments			
parallel lines			
perpendicular lines			
perpendicular bisector			
angle bisector			
congruent angles			
Polygons			
identify			
classify triangles			
Pythagorean theorem			
classify quadrilaterals			
Congruence			
Similarity			
Symmetry			
Tessellations			
Translations and reflections			

Course	1	2	3
Geometry (cont.)			
Rotations			
Three-dimensional figures			
Measurement			
Customary system			
use customary units of length, area, volume, weight, and capacity			
choose appropriate units			
convert within customary system			
Metric system			
use metric units of length, area, volume, mass, and capacity			
choose appropriate units			
convert within metric system			
Length			
estimate			
perimeter			
radius, diameter, and circumference			
Area			
estimate area of irregular figures			
of squares and rectangles			
of parallelograms and rhombuses			
of triangles			
of trapezoids			
of circles			
of composite figures			
Surface area			
of prisms			
of cylinders			
Volume			
estimate			
of prisms			
of cylinders			
of cones and pyramids			
of spheres			
Relate perimeter and area			
Relate perimeter, area, and volume			
Temperature			
Time			
convert units of time			
estimate			
elapsed time			
time zones			
Mental Math			
Divisibility			
Solving equations			
Strategies			
choose the computation method			
compatible numbers			
patterns			
use properties			
Modeling			
Decimals			
Distributive property			

Introduce *Develop* *Maintain and Apply*

Course	1	2	3

Modeling (cont.)

	1	2	3
Equations			
one-step			
two-step			
Exponents			
Factors			
Fractions			
Geometry			
area			
surface area			
volume			
Integers			
absolute value			
add and subtract			
opposites			
zero			
Number patterns			
Percent			
Probability			
outcomes			
simulations			
Problem Solving			
Pythagorean theorem			
Ratio			
Rational numbers			
Variable expressions			

Number Sense

	1	2	3
Read and write numbers			
Place value			
whole number			
decimal			
Compare and order			
whole numbers			
decimals			
fractions			
integers			
rationals			
irrationals			
Divisibility rules			
Factors			
Prime and composite numbers			
Prime factorization			
Greatest common factor			
Multiples			
Least common multiple			
Exponents			
positive			
negative			
Scientific notation			
Square numbers and square roots			

Patterns and Functions

	1	2	3
Geometric patterns			
Pascal's triangle			
Sequences			
recognize and complete			

Course	1	2	3

Patterns and Functions (cont.)

	1	2	3
arithmetic			
geometric			
Fibonacci sequence			
Strategy: look for a pattern			
Tessellations			
Functions			
linear			
quadratic			
absolute value			
direct variation			
inverse variation			
step			
graph			
interpret graphs			
write a rule			
input-output tables			

Probability

	1	2	3
Simple probability			
Counting principle			
Tree diagrams			
Odds			
Independent and dependent events			
Experimental probability			
Theoretical probability			
Probability of complements			
Conduct experiments			
use samples to predict			
random samples			
random numbers			
simulate a problem			
conduct a survey			
fair and unfair games			
use a computer			
Factorial notation			
Permutations			
Combinations			
Pascal's triangle			

Problem Solving

	1	2	3
Analyze and make decisions			
find and classify data			
interpret data			
determine trends from data			
make predictions from data			
decide how to present data			
Strategies			
draw a diagram			
guess and test			
look for a pattern			
make a model			
make a table			
simulate a problem			
solve a simpler problem			
too much, too little information			
use logical reasoning			

Introduce *Develop* *Maintain and Apply*

Course	1	2	3

Problem Solving (cont.)

	1	2	3
use multiple strategies			
use a proportion			
work backward			
write an equation			
Use a calculator			
Use a computer			
Use estimation			
Use formulas			
Use graphs			

Ratio, Proportion, Percent

	1	2	3
Ratio			
read and write			
equal ratios			
the golden ratio			
Rate			
unit rate			
unit price			
distance, rate, time problems			
dimensional analysis			
Proportion			
solve proportions			
estimate solutions to proportions			
Proportions in similar figures			
find missing parts			
scale drawings			
scale factor			
ratio of sides and areas			
ratio of sides and volumes			
indirect measurement			
Sine, cosine, and tangent			
Reason with proportions			
Percent			
understand concept			
write as ratio and decimal			
greater than 100			
less than one			
estimate			
find using a proportion			
find using an equation			
find percent of a number			
find percent one number is of another			
find number when percent is known			
percent of change			
Applications of percent			
markup			
discount			
commission			
sales tax			
simple interest			
compound interest			

Reasoning

	1	2	3
Construct Venn diagrams			
Justify answers			
Make and test conjectures			
Make generalizations			

Course	1	2	3

Reasoning (cont.)

	1	2	3
Reason from graphs			
Reason with proportions			
Recognize patterns			
Use logical reasoning			
Use spatial visualization			

Statistics

	1	2	3
Analyze data			
mean, median, and mode			
range			
quartile			
outlier			
Collect data from a variety of sources			
Conduct surveys			
analyze questions			
population			
sample			
random sample			
Organize and display data			
tables and charts			
frequency tables			
line plots			
histograms			
bar graphs			
double bar graphs			
stacked bar graphs			
sliding bar graphs			
line graphs			
multiple line graphs			
circle graphs			
scatter plots			
stem-and-leaf plots			
back-to-back stem-and-leaf plots			
box-and-whisker plots			
Choose an appropriate graph or statistic			
Identify misleading graphs and statistics			
Reason from graphs			
Make predictions from data			

Technology

	1	2	3
Use a calculator			
for computation			
for problem solving			
for algebra			
for geometry and measurement			
for statistics			
to evaluate square roots			
to evaluate trigonometric functions			
special keys			
Use a computer			
to create a spreadsheet			
to display data in graphs			
to draw and measure geometric figures			
to graph equations			
to generate random numbers			
to simulate problems			

Introduce *Develop* *Maintain and Apply*

PRENTICE HALL

MIDDLE GRADES Mathematics

An Interactive Approach

Suzanne H. **Chapin**

Mark **Illingworth**

Marsha **Landau**

Joanna O. **Masingila**

Leah **McCracken**

PRENTICE HALL

MIDDLE GRADES Mathematics

An Interactive Approach

Course **1**

Needham, Massachusetts
Englewood Cliffs, New Jersey

The authors and consulting authors on *Prentice Hall Mathematics: An Interactive Approach* team worked with Prentice Hall to develop an instructional approach that addresses the needs of middle grades students with a variety of ability levels and learning styles. Authors also prepared manuscript for strands across the three levels of Middle Grades Mathematics. Consulting authors worked alongside authors throughout program planning and all stages of manuscript development offering advice and suggestions for improving the program.

Authors

Suzanne Chapin, *Ed.D., Boston University, Boston MA;* Proportional Reasoning and Probability strands

Mark Illingworth, *Hollis Public Schools, Hollis, NH;* Graphing strand

Marsha S. Landau, *Ph.D., National Louis University, Evanston, IL;* Algebra, Functions, and Computation strands

Joanna Masingila, *Ph.D., Syracuse University, Syracuse, NY;* Geometry strand

Leah McCracken, *Lockwood Junior High, Billings, MT;* Data Analysis strand

Consulting Authors

Sadie Bragg, Ed.D., Borough of Manhattan Community College, The City University of New York, New York, NY

Vincent O'Connor, Milwaukee Public Schools, Milwaukee, WI

ISBN 0-13-031105-7

Printed in the United States of America

4 5 98 97 96 95

Reviewers

All Levels

Ann Bouie, Ph.D., Multicultural Reviewer, Oakland, CA
Mary Lester, Dallas Public Schools, Dallas, TX
Dorothy S. Strong, Ph.D., Chicago Public Schools, Chicago, IL

Course 1

Darla Agajanian, Sierra Vista School, Canyon Country, CA
Rhonda Bird, Grand Haven Area Schools, Grand Haven, MI
Leroy Dupee, Bridgeport Public Schools, Bridgeport, CT
Jose Lalas, California State University, Dominguez Hills, CA
Richard Lavers, Fitchburg High School, Fitchburg, MA

Course 2

Raylene Bryson, Alexander Middle School, Huntersville, NC
Sheila Cunningham, Klein Independent School District, Klein, TX
Natarsha Mathis, Hart Junior High School, Washington, DC
Jean Patton, Sharp Middle School, Covington, GA
Judy Trowell, Little Rock School District, Little Rock, AR

Course 3

Michaele F. Chappell, Ph.D., University of South Florida, Tampa, FL
Bettye Hall, Math Consultant, Houston, TX
Joaquin Hernandez, Shenandoah Middle School, Miami, FL
Dana Luterman, Lincoln Middle School, Kansas City, MO
Loretta Rector, Leonardo da Vinci School, Sacramento, CA
Anthony C. Terceira, Providence School Department, Providence, RI

We are grateful to our reviewers who read manuscript at all stages of development and provided invaluable feedback, ideas, and constructive criticism to help make this program one that meets the needs of middle grades teachers and students.

Staff Credits

Editorial: Carolyn Artin, Alison Birch, Judith D. Buice, Kathleen J. Carter, Linda Coffey, Noralie V. Cox, Edward DeLeon, Audra Floyd, Mimi Jigarjian, John A. Nelson, Lynn H. Raisman
Marketing: Michael D. Buckley, Bridget A. Hadley
Production: Jo Ann Connolly, Gabriella Della Corte, David Graham, Virginia Shine
Electronic Publishing: Will Hirschowitz, Pearl Weinstein
Manufacturing: Roger Powers
Design: Betty Fiora, Russell Lappa, L. Christopher Valente, Stuart S. Wallace

Prentice Hall dedicates this interactive mathematics series to all middle level mathematics educators and their students.

TABLE OF CONTENTS

CHAPTER 1 Representing Data

Look for photos with captions that bring math to life in every chapter!

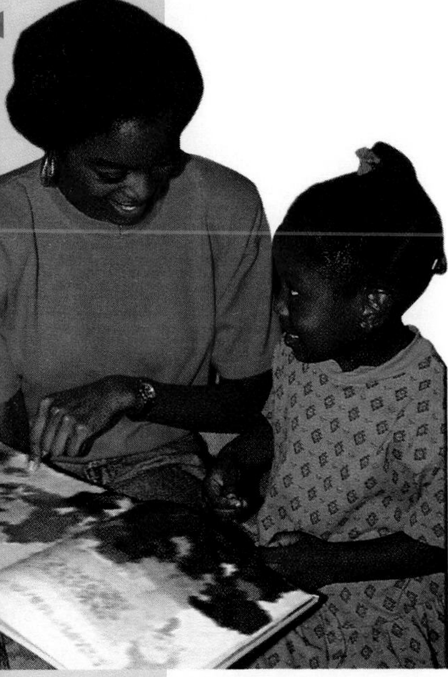

Aja Henderson has a collection of over 1,000 books! Aja lends them out to neighborhood kids who can't get to the public library.

✱ ***Hot Page™ Lesson***

CHAPTER 2

Geometry Concepts

Look for the Who?, What?, Why?, Where?, When?, and How? features in every chapter!

WHAT? A harlequin was a quick-witted clown from the Italian theater. He wore a suit of bright silk diamonds, sometimes with lace and ruffles. He also carried a "wand" which he used to signal the change of scene.

Source: *The Oxford Companion to the Theater*

✳ ***Hot Page™ Lesson***

CHAPTER 3

Adding and Subtracting Decimals

Look for newspaper clippings that bring math to life in every chapter!

Light-Years Away

The brightest star in the sky is Sirius, which is about 8.7 light-years from Earth. The stars Alpha Centauri A and B are each about 4.37 light-years from Earth. Proxima Centauri is about 4.28 light-years away. Other star neighbors are 61 Cygni B, about 11.09 light-years away, and Procyon B, about 11.4 light-years away.

If you could drive to Alpha Centauri at 55 mi/h, the trip would take about 52 million years!

CHAPTER 4

Multiplying and Dividing Decimals

Look for photos with captions that bring math to life in every chapter!

Earth's crust continually moves, causing earthquakes, forming mountains, and separating continents.

Look for relevant quotations in every chapter!

> *Mathematics, rightly viewed, possesses not only truth but also supreme beauty — a beauty . . . like that of sculpture.*
> —Bertrand Russell (1872-1970)

✱ ***Hot Page™ Lesson***

CHAPTER 5

Patterns, Functions, and Equations

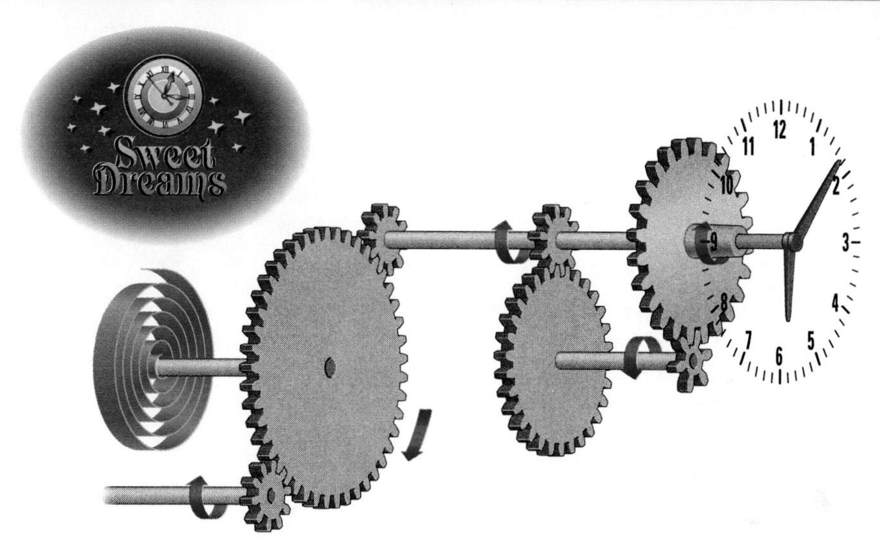

Look for the Flashback (just-in-time review) features in every chapter!

FLASHBACK

A number in standard form is separated into groups of three digits by commas.

Look for the Mixed Review in every lesson to maintain problem solving and computational skills!

Mixed REVIEW

Round to the nearest tenth.

1. 44.68
2. 8.146

Find each answer.

3. $59.36 ÷ $7.42
4. $189.32 + $33.79

Write each decimal in words.

5. 0.73
6. 386.908

7. Maria spent $35 on a pair of jeans and $18 on a shirt. She has $24 left. How much money did she start with?

* *Hot Page™ Lesson*

CHAPTER 6

Measurement

Look for the Who?, What?, Why?, Where?, When?, and How? features in every chapter!

The Great Wall of China spans 2,971 km. The wall is 14 m high and 7 m thick in some places. **If you traveled along the wall at 10 km/h, how long would it take you to travel its length?**

Source: *A Ride Along the Great Wall*

✱ ***Hot Page™ Lesson***

CHAPTER 7 Fraction Concepts

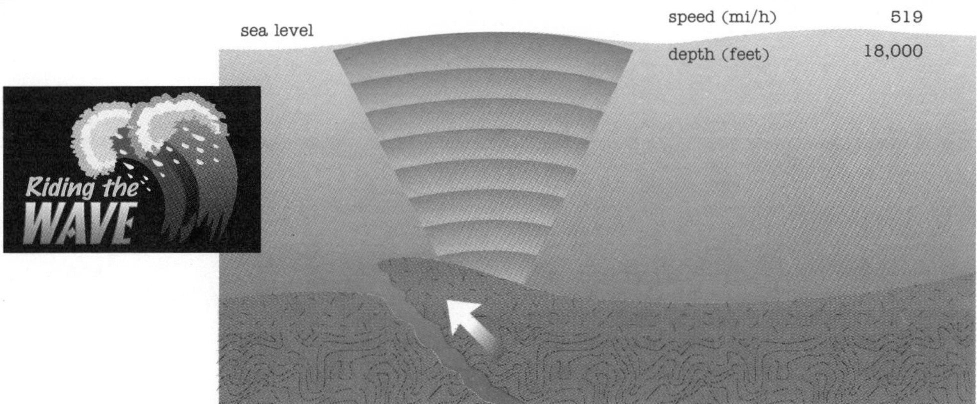

✱ ***Hot Page™ Lesson***

Look for Problem Solving Hints in every chapter!

Problem Solving Hint

Make an organized list.

Look for long term investigations in every chapter!

Mission: Make a list of objects you could use to represent whole numbers 0 through 9. Anyone looking at an object should easily understand the number it represents. Decide how to use the objects to represent the numbers 10 through 20. Make a poster displaying your own personalized numeration system.

CHAPTER 8 Fraction Operations

✸ ***Hot Page Lesson***

Look for photos with captions that bring math to life in every chapter!

***The National Wheelchair Athletic Association** was founded in 1957 and has about 1,500 members.*

CHAPTER 9 Ratio, Proportion, and Percent

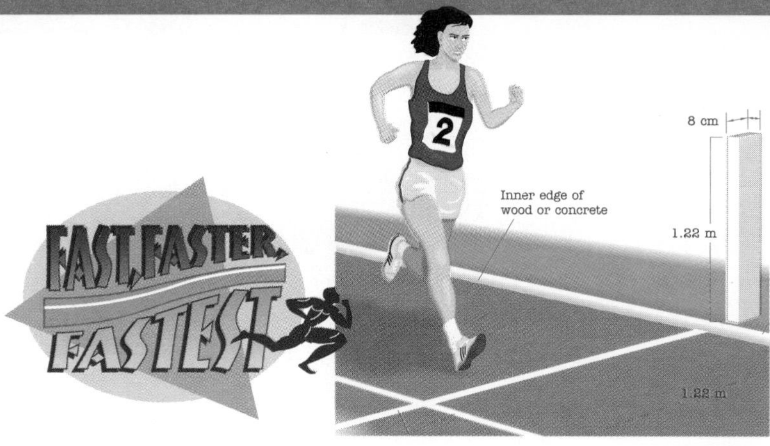

Look for frequent use of real data in every chapter!

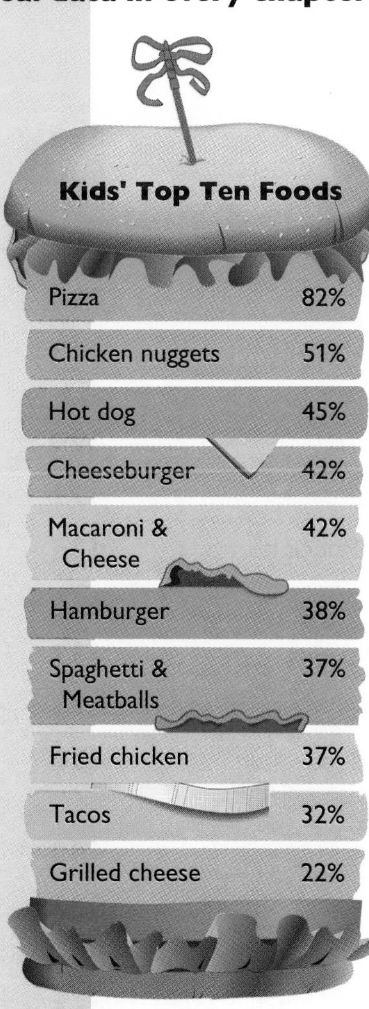

Source: *Gallup Organization*

✷ ***Hot Page™ Lesson***

CHAPTER 10

Probability

Earthquake Zones in the United States

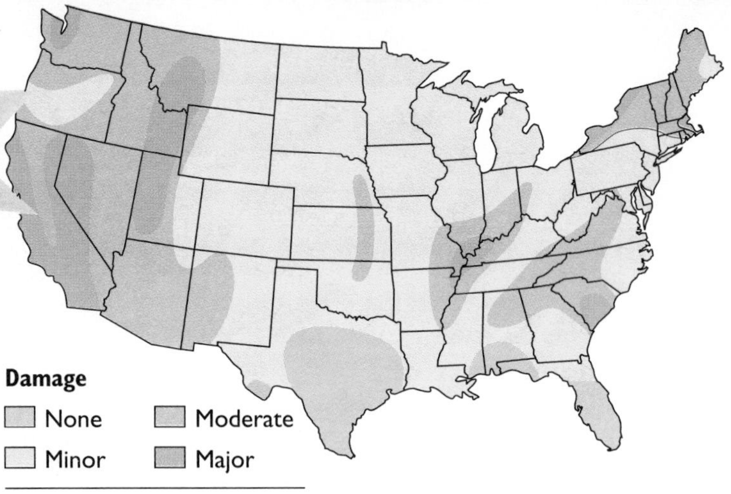

Damage

None
Moderate
Minor
Major

Source: *Earthquakes*, Seymour Simon

SHAKE, RATTLE, & ROLL

Look for Great Expectations career letters throughout the book!

GREAT EXPECTATIONS

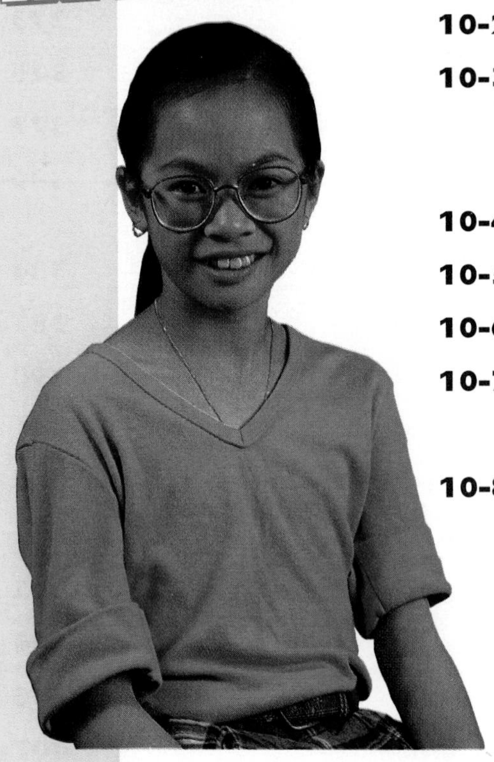

✱ ***Hot Page™ Lesson***

CHAPTER 11

Integers and Coordinate Graphing

✱ ***Hot Page™ Lesson***

Look for What You'll Need materials lists in every chapter!

WHAT YOU'LL NEED

✓ Geoboard 

✓ Rubber bands 

Look for the World View feature in every Data File!

Hawaii is moving *toward* Japan at a rate of over 4 in. per year. North America and Europe are moving *apart* at a rate of about 1 in. per year.

CHAPTER

1 Representing Data

Why Study Representing Data?

If students ask this question, you may want to mention these areas where data are represented: checkbook balances, sports, political polls, temperature trends, crime statistics, gross national product statistics, college enrollment, insurance statistics, sales and profit.

Graphic Display of Chapter Content

Below is one possible representation of the chapter's content and its applications to the world outside the classroom. Have students create their own graphic display and fill in applications that they have seen in their own lives.

- The center oval should state the main concept of the chapter: representing data.
- Have students draw the oval with the next level of concepts presented in the chapter (line graphs, bar graphs, averages, frequency tables, and spreadsheets). You may want students to add any other topics that they think are appropriate.
- Ask students to draw as many application ovals as they can.
- Discuss all the applications that students identify.
- Have students make and present one display that includes all the students' ideas.

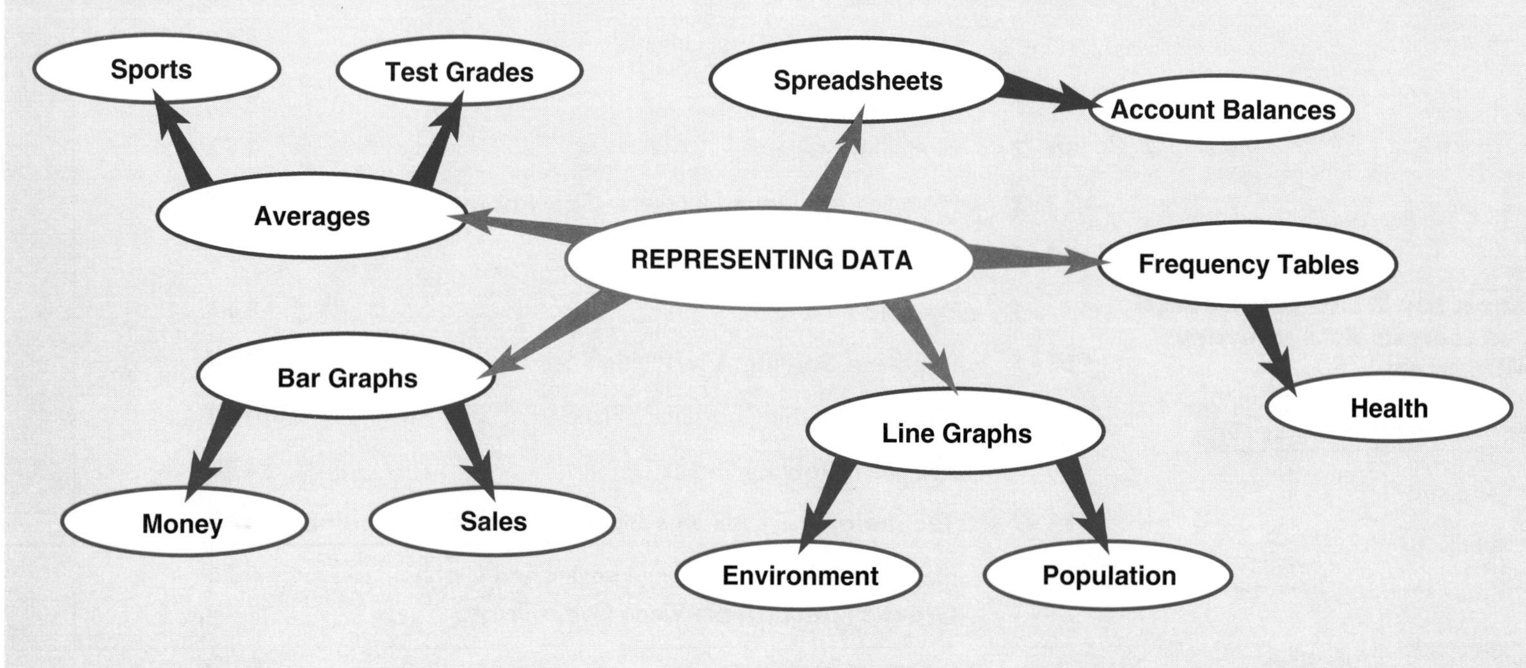

Graphic Display available as a Teaching Transparency

Vocabulary and Symbols

bar graph
cell
circle graph
formula
frequency table
line graph
line plot
mean
median
mode
primary colors
range
spreadsheet

Materials and Manipulatives

	computer		scissors
	graph paper		spreadsheet software

Additional Resources

Commercially Available Technology

Calculator
calculator

Software
spreadsheet software
- *Another Option for Spreadsheets* by AppleWorks
- *Excel; Works* by Microsoft

other
- *Cricket Graph*
- *Data Insights* by Sunburst
- *Microsoft Graph*

Other Media
"Spreadsheet Activities in Middle School Mathematics." Reston, VA: NCTM, 1992.
"Graphic Description." Films Inc Video, 5547 N. Ravenswood Ave., Chicago, IL 60640. (800) 343-4312.
"Time Graph." Films Inc Video, 5547 N. Ravenswood Ave., Chicago, IL 60640. (800) 343-4312.

Materials at Little or No Cost

Lunch Lines. Unified Science and Mathematics. Newton, MA: EDC. Available through ERIC.
Bureau of the Census, Data User Services Division, Washington, DC 20233. Education Hotline—(301) 763-1510. Classroom investigations based on census data.

Bibliography

For Teachers
Curcio, Frances R. *Developing Graph Comprehension: Elementary and Middle School Activities*. Reston, VA: NCTM, 1989.
Product Testing Activities by Consumer Reports. Englewood Cliffs, NJ: Prentice Hall, 1993.
Zawojewski, Judith S., et al. *Dealing with Data and Chance: Addenda Series, Grades 5–8*. Reston, VA: NCTM, 1991.

For Students
Burns, Marilyn. *The I Hate Mathematics Book*. Boston: Little, Brown, 1975.
Fekete, Irene and Jamine Deyer. *Mathematics*. NY: Facts on File, 1990.
Siegel, Alice and Margo McLoone Basta. *The Information Please Kids' Almanac*. Boston: Houghton Mifflin, 1992.

Prentice Hall Technology 

Multimedia Math
- Math Tools, Graphs
- Math Tools, Spreadsheet
- Hot Page™ 1-3
- Hot Page™ 1-5
- Hot Page™ 1-7
- Math Investigations, Hazard City Messengers
- Math Investigations, Mission: Mars

Computer Item Generator
- Chapter 1

Community Resources

Field Trips
- a newspaper to the graphic arts department
- a store that does phone sales
- a campaign headquarters

Guest Speakers
- a baseball reporter
- a statistician

Backpack Take-Home Activities

Materials
- newspaper
- scissors
- tape
- paper
- pencil

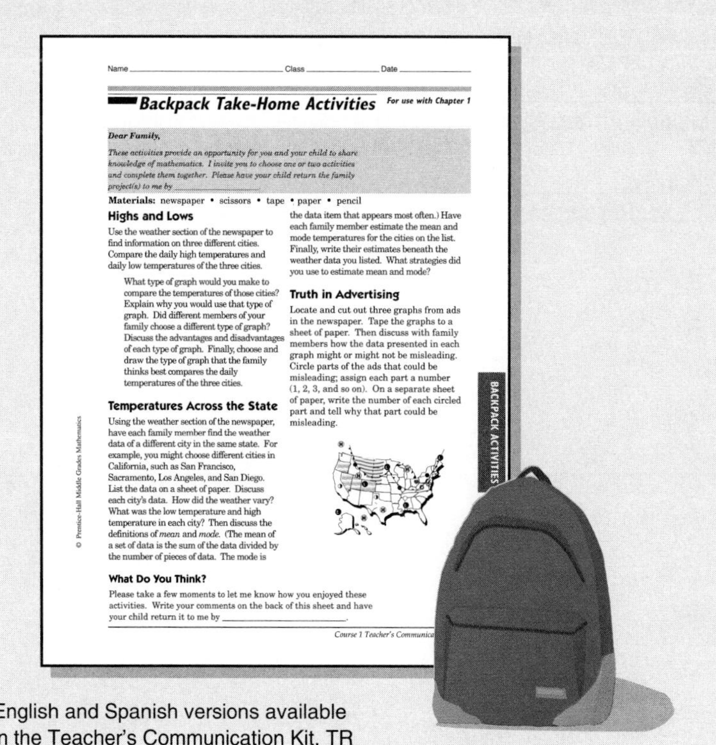

Name ______ Class ______ Date ______

Backpack Take-Home Activities *For use with Chapter 1*

Dear Family,

These activities provide an opportunity for you and your child to share knowledge of mathematics. I invite you to choose one or two activities and complete them together. Please have your child return the family project(s) to me by ______

Materials: newspaper • scissors • tape • paper • pencil

Highs and Lows

Use the weather section of the newspaper to find information on three different cities. Compare the daily high temperatures and daily low temperatures of the three cities.

What type of graph would you make to compare the temperatures of those cities? Explain why you would use that type of graph. Did different members of your family choose a different type of graph? Discuss the advantages and disadvantages of each type of graph. Finally, choose and draw the type of graph that the family thinks best compares the daily temperatures of the three cities.

Temperatures Across the State

Using the weather section of the newspaper, have each family member find the weather data of a different city in the same state. For example, you might choose different cities in California, such as San Francisco, Sacramento, Los Angeles, and San Diego. List the data on a sheet of paper. Discuss each city's data. How did the weather vary? What was the low temperature and high temperature in each city? Then discuss the definitions of *mean* and *mode*. (The mean of a set of data is the sum of the data divided by the number of pieces of data. The mode is the data item that appears most often.) Have each family member estimate the mean and mode temperatures for the cities on the list. Finally, write their estimates beneath the weather data you listed. What strategies did you use to estimate mean and mode?

Truth in Advertising

Locate and cut out three graphs from ads in the newspaper. Tape the graphs to a sheet of paper. Then discuss with family members how the data presented in each graph might or might not be misleading. Circle parts of the ads that could be misleading; assign each part a number (1, 2, 3, and so on). On a separate sheet of paper, write the number of each circled part and tell why that part could be misleading.

What Do You Think?

Please take a few moments to let me know how you enjoyed these activities. Write your comments on the back of this sheet and have your child return it to me by ______.

BACKPACK ACTIVITIES

© Prentice-Hall Middle Grades Mathematics

Course 1 Teacher's Communica

English and Spanish versions available in the Teacher's Communication Kit, TR

Chapter 1 Planning Guide

Objectives	Assignment Options	Critical Thinking/ Problem Solving	Writing and Reading Math	Estimation Mental Math	Materials and Manipulatives
Investigation	This chapter-long project involves open-ended questioning and data collecting and provides an additional opportunity to assess students.	p. 4 p. 4	p. 4		p. 4
1-1 Frequency Tables and Line Plots • Organizing data in frequency tables and line plots	**Core:** 7–11, 15; MR all **Reinforce:** 12, 14 **Enrich:** 13	3, 5, 6, 7b, 9, 11, 12, 13c, 14c; MR: 5 p. 5; BI p. 6	7b, 11, 14c p. 7; JL p. 7 JL Sheet	MM p. 7	9, 13a, 14b TT 31, 34, 96–101 Alt. Lesson
1-2 Problem Solving: Make a Table • Solving problems by making a table	**Core:** 14–16, 18, 19, 21; MR all **Reinforce:** 17, 22 **Enrich:** 20	All; MR: 4 p. 8; BI p. 9	All JL p. 9 JL Sheet	MR: 3	pp. 8, 10 TT 31
1-3 Three Kinds of Averages • Finding mean, median, and mode • Deciding which average is most appropriate for a given situation	**Core:** 8, 10–13, 16; MR all; CH all **Reinforce:** 9 **Enrich:** 14, 15	1b, 3, 7, 9b–c, 10–13, 15; CH: 6; MR: 5 pp. 11, 12, 14; BI p. 13	8c, 15 pp. 13, 14; JL p. 13 JL Sheet	MR: 1–4 MM p. 14	EX1; 14; CH: 3 p. 12; RT p. 13; CH p. 14 TT 1, 31
1-4 Technology: Computer Spreadsheets • Organizing data in a spreadsheet • Using spreadsheets to explore averages	**Core:** 9, 11a, 13, 15, 16, 18; MR all **Reinforce:** 11b, 14, 17 **Enrich:** 10, 12	WT: 4a–b, 5, 6; 11, 14–16, 17d, 18; MR: 5 WT p. 17; BI p. 18; MM p. 19	WT: 4a; 16 p. 17; JL p. 17 JL Sheet	MR: 1	WT: 4c, 7, 8; 10a, 12, 17a pp. 16–19; RT p. 18 TT 4, 5, 32 Alt. Lesson
1-5 Reading and Understanding Graphs • Reading graphs for information • Determining the most appropriate graph to represent data	**Core:** 14, 16–22, 27; MR all **Reinforce:** 23–26 **Enrich:** 15	3b–c, 6, 11, 15–17, 22–26; MR: 4 pp. 20, 21; BI p. 22; MM p. 23	15, 16 p. 23; JL p. 21 JL Sheet	7, 20 p. 20	TT 32, 35, 102–110
1-6 Constructing Bar and Line Graphs • Constructing bar and line graphs	**Core:** 6–9, 12; MR all; CH All **Reinforce:** 11 **Enrich:** 10	1, 2, 3b, 4a, 10, 11c–d; CH: 1; MR: 4 p. 26; BI p. 27; MM p. 28	10 p. 27; JL p. 26 JL Sheet		5, 8, 9, 11a–b, 12; CH: 2 p. 26; RT p. 27 TT 33, 35, 102–110
1-7 Math and Advertising: Analyzing Graphs • Analyzing the effect of different scales and intervals on graphs • Recognizing misleading graphs	**Core:** 7; DM all; MR all **Reinforce:** 8 **Enrich:** 9	1–3; WT: 4–6; DM: 1, 2, 4, 6, 7c; MR: 2 p. 29; BI p. 30; DM p. 31	9 p. 31; JL pp. 29–30 JL Sheet		WT: 6; 7, 8; DM: 7a–b; MR: 1 pp. 29, 30; RT p. 30 TT 33
Putting It All Together	These pages include a Follow-Up to the Investigation and other projects, which provide additional opportunities to assess the students.	pp. 34–35 pp. 34–35	pp. 34–35 p. 35	p. 34	pp. 34–35 pp. 34–35
Chapter Resources		PS Practice, CW, CA, CR PS Practice p. 15; CW pp. 32–33; CA p. 36; CR p. 37	PS Practice, CW, CA p. 2B; PS Practice p. 15; CW pp. 32–33; CA p. 36		pp. 2A, 2B Backpack Activities, Manip. Kits TT 30

Student Edition (question numbers)
Teacher's Edition (page numbers)
Other Components

BI—What's the Big Idea? **CA—Chapter Assessment** **CH—Checkpoint**
CG—Computer Item Generator **CR—Cumulative Review** **CW—Chapter Wrap Up**
DM—Decision Making **EP—Extra Practice** **EX—Example** **FD—Fact of the Day**

Cooperative Learning Activities	Technology	Data Collection & Analysis	Interdisciplinary Connections	Applications	Assessment	Review	Strand Integration	NCTM Correlation*
p. 4		p. 4	Science, Health	biology, health	p. 4			
p. 4		p. 4			p. 4			
14	9	5, 10, 13, 14, 15	Art, Social Studies	art, geography, literature, sports		MR: All	Stat./Probability, Discrete Math, Logic/Language	1, 2, 3, 4, 8, 10, 13
pp. 5, 7; WT p. 6; RT p. 7 Alt. Lesson	pp. 5, 7	p. 7; WT p. 6; FD p. 6	p. 7	pp. 5, 7	p. 6	RT p. 7 Practice p. 21		
		9		money, travel		MR: All	Stat./Probability, Discrete Math, Logic/Language	1, 2, 3, 4, 8, 10, 12, 13
		FD p. 9	p. 9	p. 9	p. 8	p. 8; RT p. 9 Practice p. 22		
8b; WT	EX1; 14; CH: 3	1, 3, 7–9, 14, 16; CH: 3–6		weather, sports, entertainment, music	CH: All	MR: All	Stat./Probability, Discrete Math, Logic/Language	1, 2, 3, 4, 5, 7, 8, 10, 13
pp. 12–14; WT p. 11; RT p. 13	p. 12; CH p. 14 Hot Page™ 1-3	pp. 13, 14; FD p. 12		pp. 11, 13	p. 12; CH p. 14 CH TR p. 32	p. 11; RT p. 13 Practice p. 23		
WT: 4–8	All	WT: 5, 6; 11a, 17, 18		music, money		MR: All	Stat./Probability, Discrete Math, Logic/Language	1, 2, 3, 4, 5, 7, 8, 10
WT pp. 17–18; RT p. 18	pp. 16–19	FD p. 17	Alt. Lesson	p. 18	p. 18	p. 16; RT p. 18 Practice p. 24		
WT: 12, 13		1, 2, 3c, 4, 5, 7–11, 14–22		recycling, recreation, sports, education		MR: All	Stat./Probability, Discrete Math, Logic/Language	1, 2, 3, 4, 5, 7, 8, 10, 12, 13
p. 21; WT p. 22; RT p. 23	Hot Page™ 1-5	p. 21; FD p. 21	p. 22	pp. 22, 23	p. 21	RT p. 23 Practice p. 25		
		3, 10a, 11c–d, 12; CH: 3, 4	Science, Social Studies	environment, architecture, education	CH: All	MR: All	Stat./Probability, Discrete Math, Logic/Language	1, 2, 3, 4, 5, 7, 8, 10, 12, 13
p. 28; RT p. 27	p. 26 Alt. Lesson	pp. 26, 28; FD p. 26; RT p. 27	pp. 25, 27	p. 27 Alt. Lesson	p. 26; CH p. 28 CH TR p. 32	p. 25; RT p. 27 Practice p. 26		
WT: 4–6; DM: All		1; WT: 4–6; DM: All		advertising, hobbies, money		MR: All	Stat./Probability, Discrete Math, Logic/Language	1, 2, 3, 4, 5, 7, 8, 10, 12, 13
p. 29; WT p. 30; RT p. 30; DM p. 31	p. 30 Hot Page™ 1-7	p. 29; FD p. 30; DM p. 31		pp. 29, 30	p. 29	p. 29; RT p. 30 Practice p. 27		
pp. 34–35		pp. 34–35	Science, Health	biology, music, weather	pp. 34–35			
p. 35	p. 34	pp. 34–35			pp. 34–35			
IN, PT		Data File 1	Physical Science, Social Studies	television, entertainment, advertising	IN, PT, CA	Practice, PS Practice, CW, CR, EP, SSG		
pp. 2–4; PT pp. 34–35 Backpack Activities	p. 2B Multimedia Math, CG	pp. 2–3	pp. 2F, 2–3 Interdisciplinary Units	pp. 2A, 2F, 2–3 Backpack Activities, Projects, Interdisciplinary Units	pp. 2E, 4; CW pp. 32–33; PT pp. 34–35; CA p. 36 CA, Span. CA, Self Assessment, Projects	CW pp. 32–33 Span. SSG, CR		

GE—Great Expectations IN—Investigation JL—Journal MM—Math Minutes
MR—Mixed Review PS—Problem Solving PT—Putting It All Together RT—Reteaching Activity
SSG—Student Study Guide TT—Teaching Transparency WT—Work Together

*For a description of the NCTM Standards, see page T15.

Assessment Options

Observation Checklist

In this chapter on representing data, you have opportunities to observe your students do these tasks:

- ✓ read and construct frequency tables and line plots
- ✓ use tables and other organizing strategies to solve word problems
- ✓ find the mean, median, and mode of a set of data
- ✓ use computer spreadsheets and formulas to compute statistics
- ✓ interpret bar, circle, and line graphs
- ✓ collect data and display it in bar and line graphs

In every chapter, you are given opportunities to observe your students:

- ✓ work with a partner or in a group
- ✓ write about mathematics
- ✓ participate in discussions about mathematics
- ✓ collect and analyze data
- ✓ display positive attitudes about mathematics
- ✓ use measurement tools

Name ______ Class ______ Date ______

Chapter 1 Project

Fund-raising

Each year in December, the sixth grade at Wayside Middle School raises money. The money goes to a Toys-for-Children program that buys holiday toys for needy children. Most of the money that the sixth graders raise is change that they collect at lunchtime every day for a week.

Each year's sixth graders try to raise more money than the previous year's sixth graders. Last year the class raised $157.28. This year's group hopes to do better.

Emilio and Tamlyn are in charge of making a chart that shows how much money has been raised this year. First they thought of making a pie chart like the one below, but they decided against it.

Fri, Mon, Thurs, Tues, Wed

Money Raised

Show all work on a separate sheet of paper

1. Do you think that Emilio and Tamlyn were right to decide against using a pie chart? Explain.
2. Tamlyn suggested a line graph like the one below, which would show the total raised each day.

Dollars Raised: 0, 5, 10, 15, 20, 25, 30
Day: Mon, Tues, Wed, Thurs, Fri

What is a good feature of the line graph? What is a weakness?

3. Emilio suggested a bar graph like the one below, which would have a bar for each day.

Course 1 Chapter 1

© Prentice-Hall Middle Grades Mathematics

Performance Based Project (with scoring rubric), Chapter Files, TR

...g Rubric

Exercise	Points	Explanation
1.	1	Good explanation of why pie chart is inappropriate
	0	No response OR other response
2.	2	Strength: shows daily amounts; weakness: total
	1	Strength OR weakness correctly given
	0	No response OR other response
3.	2	Strength: shows daily amounts; weakness: total
	1	Strength OR weakness correctly given
	0	No response OR incorrect response
4.	1	Either a yes or no answer; justification given
	0	No response OR a yes or no answer without justification
5.	4	Correct graph for both Monday and Friday; clear labels
	3	Correct graph for either Monday or Friday with clear labels but incomplete or incorrect graph for the other day OR correct graphs for both days but labels missing
	2	Graphs for both days incomplete but some correct elements
	1	Graphs for both days are so incomplete that they lack correct elements.
	0	No response OR response does not contain graphs
Excursion	5	Creative and interesting way to track money raised
	4	Correct way to track money but lacking creativity OR creative method that does not show money being tracked
	3	Incomplete presentation of an adequate design
	2	Method is incorrect.
	1	Response does not contain a visual element but is somewhat related to task OR response contains a visual element but is not related to task.
	0	No response OR other response.

Course 1 Chapter 1

© Prentice-Hall Middle Grades Mathematics

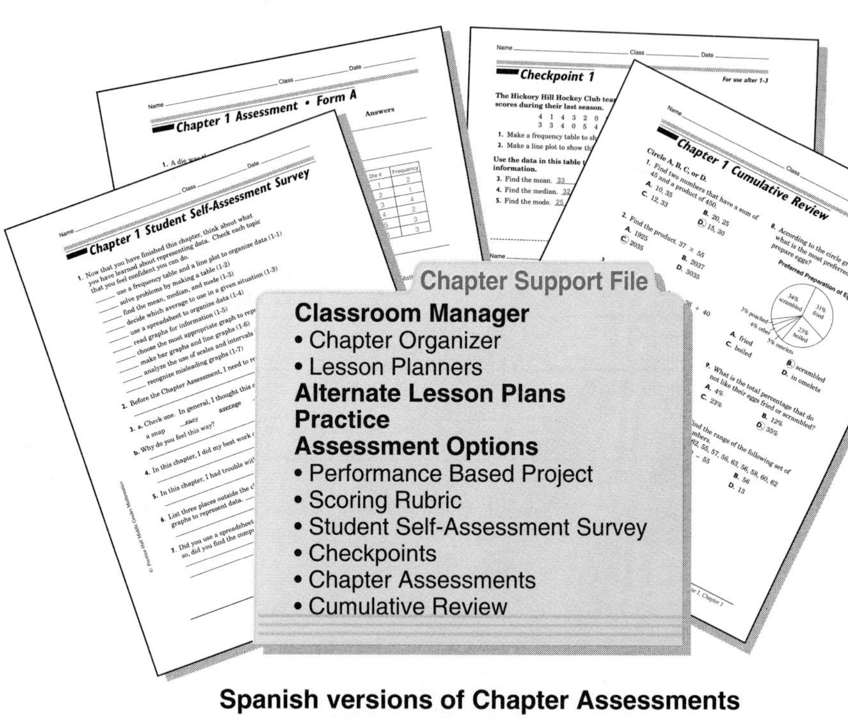

Chapter 1 Assessment • Form A
Checkpoint 1
Chapter 1 Student Self-Assessment Survey
Chapter 1 Cumulative Review
Chapter Support File
Classroom Manager
• Chapter Organizer
• Lesson Planners
Alternate Lesson Plans
Practice
Assessment Options
• Performance Based Project
• Scoring Rubric
• Student Self-Assessment Survey
• Checkpoints
• Chapter Assessments
• Cumulative Review

Spanish versions of Chapter Assessments available in Spanish Resources

Interdisciplinary Units

- **Travel and Geography**
- **Space Exploration**
- **Sports**
- **Consumer Awareness**
- **The Great Outdoors**

English & Spanish

These units include cross-curriculum connections and can be used at any time during the school year. See the Teacher's Guide for more information.

Working with Middle Grade Students

> *"Instruction in statistics should focus on the active involvement of students in the entire process: formulating key questions; collecting and organizing data; representing the data using graphs, tables, frequency distributions, and summary statistics; analyzing the data; making conjectures; and communicating information in a convincing way."*
>
> —NCTM Curriculum and Evaluation Standards

Addressing a Variety of Learning Styles

The mathematical tasks in Chapter 1 involve various learning styles. Here are some examples.

- Visual learners create line plots (p. 6) and spreadsheets (p. 18).
- Tactile learners make bar graphs to display data (p. 25) and use computers (p. 17).
- Auditory learners discuss various ways of solving problems (p. 5), discuss the advantages of different methods, and describe patterns (p. 9).
- Kinesthetic learners survey people to collect data on eye blinks (p. 7) and on finger snapping (p. 14).

Alternate Lessons 1-1 and 1-4 address tactile learners by having them use manipulatives.

Cultural Connections

Have each student find out the population, area, and flag of a different country. Then pool this information and have the class plan three bar graphs to display population, area, and population density (population divided by area) for the countries chosen. Have students draw the flag of each country under the bars that represent data for that country. Discuss the data displayed in the graphs.

Team Teaching Suggestion

Working with the school librarian, have the students use a frequency table to display data collected about how often students frequent the library, which types of books are checked out most frequently, which classes utilize the library the most, and how often books are not returned. Have the students make a presentation to the administration on behalf of the library staff.

Innumeracy

Innumeracy, according to John Allen Paulos, author of *Innumeracy* and *Beyond Numeracy*, is "an inability to deal comfortably with the fundamental notions of number and chance." The assumption that some unevenly distributed math ability is the basis of doing well at mathematics is uniquely American. In other countries and cultures, the assumption is that everyone can do well at mathematics if they work hard at it, according to *Everybody Counts—A Report to the Nation on the Future of Mathematics Education.*

Teaching Tip

There are many activities listed in Marilyn Burns' book *Math Solutions* that suggest topics for frequency tables with middle school students. Plan a once-a-week chart that may list favorite hamburger shops, favorite movie stars, or times the students go to sleep at night.

Bulletin Board

Choose a topic of student interest to investigate. This bulletin board shows juice consumption. Each day poll students and keep a tally. In this case, tally the juice servings consumed by the class each day. Have students bring in juice labels or pictures of fruit from magazines. At the end of the week have students copy and complete the frequency table and make a line plot. Then complete the frequency table and line plot on the bulletin board and have students check their work. Discuss the results.

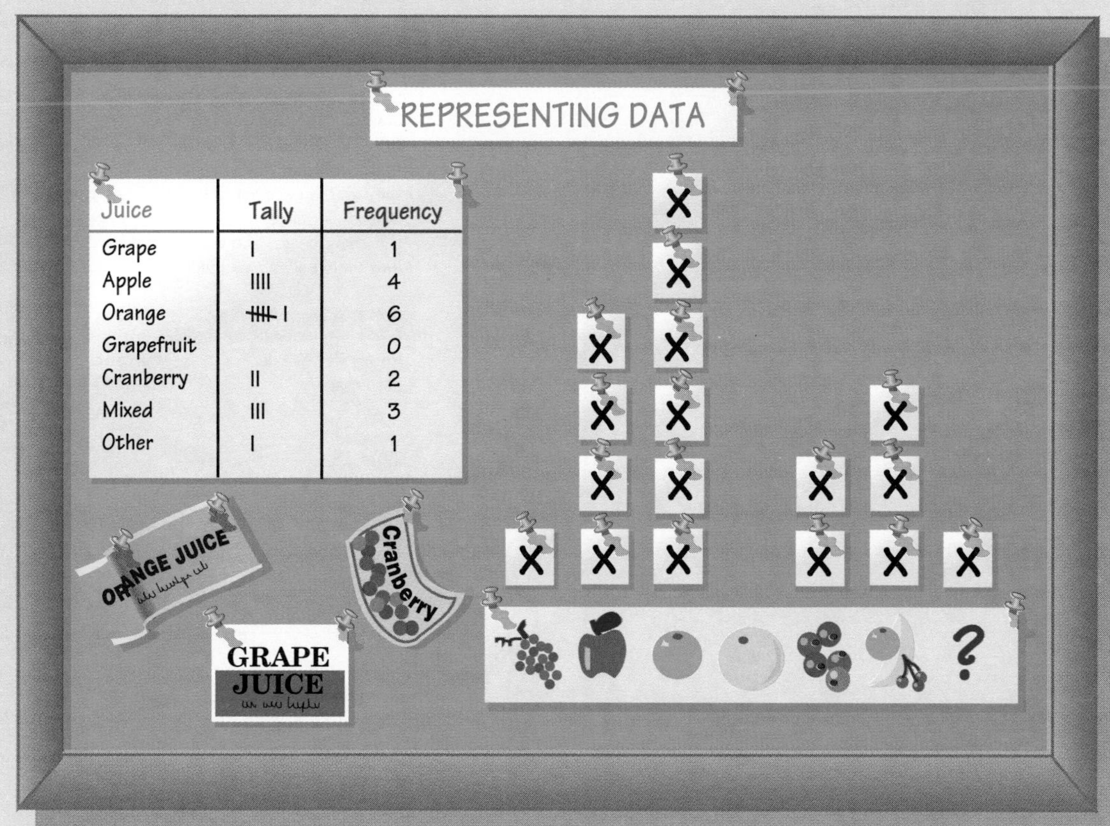

CHAPTER 1 Representing Data

Cultural Connections Although some may think of television as primarily a visual medium, in recent years the possibilities of television have been expanded to include many segments of our society that have previously had problems enjoying television. Closed captioning has enabled members of the audience who are hearing impaired to understand the verbal aspects of many programs. For those members of the audience who are visually impaired, there are now broadcast narratives describing the pictures that enable them to have a greater grasp of what is happening in a television program.

WORLD VIEW In the United States, children between the ages of 2 and 11 view an average of about 31.5 hours of television each week. During the Super Bowl broadcast in 1991, the advertising rate for 30 seconds of television time was $800,000.

Digging for Data Ask the students to use the graphs and other data in the file to answer these questions:

- *What percent of households report watching 15 h or more of TV each week?* **(53%)**
- *How many persons view TV in prime time on Sunday?* **(107.2 million)**

Ask each student to survey at least five people about their TV watching and to make a chart of hours per week.

Collect and graph class results on the chalkboard. Discuss the results with the class and how to design labels for the axes. Ask students to compare the class results with those shown in the data file.

Chapter 1 Contents

Data File Questions

pp. 14, 23, 49, 56, 104, 386, 401, 486

Data File 1

CHAPTER 1 Representing Data

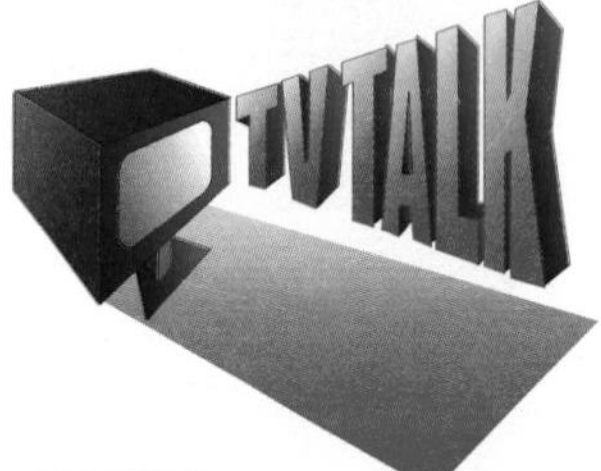

Today 98% of United States households own at least one TV. More than half the households surveyed reported they watch between 7 h and 21 h of TV each week. Look at the chart below and decide into which group you fit.

How Much TV Do We Watch?

Hours Per Week	Percent
Less than 7	17
7 to 14	29
15 to 21	22
22 to 28	12
29 to 35	9
36 to 42	4
43 to 49	2
50 to 70	3
71 or more	1
No response	1

Source: *TV Guide*

How Many Own Televisions?

Homes with:	Number
Color sets	90,258,000
Black and white sets	1,842,000
2 or more sets	59,865,000
1 set	32,235,000
Cable	56,235,340
Any type of set	92,100,000

Sources: *Information Please Almanac; World Almanac; Nielsen Media Research.*

How an Interactive Network Might Work

1. Viewer uses home unit to send information about choices from on-screen menu.
2. Ground based receiver gets data and sends it to a satellite.
3. Satellite receives data, transmits it to an office for processing, and then receives further instructions.

Journal Activity Ask students to read the chapter objectives given in What You Will Learn and to write responses to these questions:

- *What do you think is meant by the word "data"? Give some examples of data.*
- *Which of these four topics sounds most interesting to you, and why?*
- *Which kind of graph shown in the data file do you think is easiest to read: the table, the bar chart, or the circle graph? Why?*

Interdisciplinary Connection [Physical Science] Ask students to follow the cycle of how an interactive network might work. Suggest that they research in science texts or the encyclopedia to find out more information about how a television camera, transmitter, and set work.

WHAT YOU WILL LEARN

- how to gather data and display it in a graph
- how to find and use mean, median, and mode
- how to use technology to analyze data
- how to solve problems by making a table

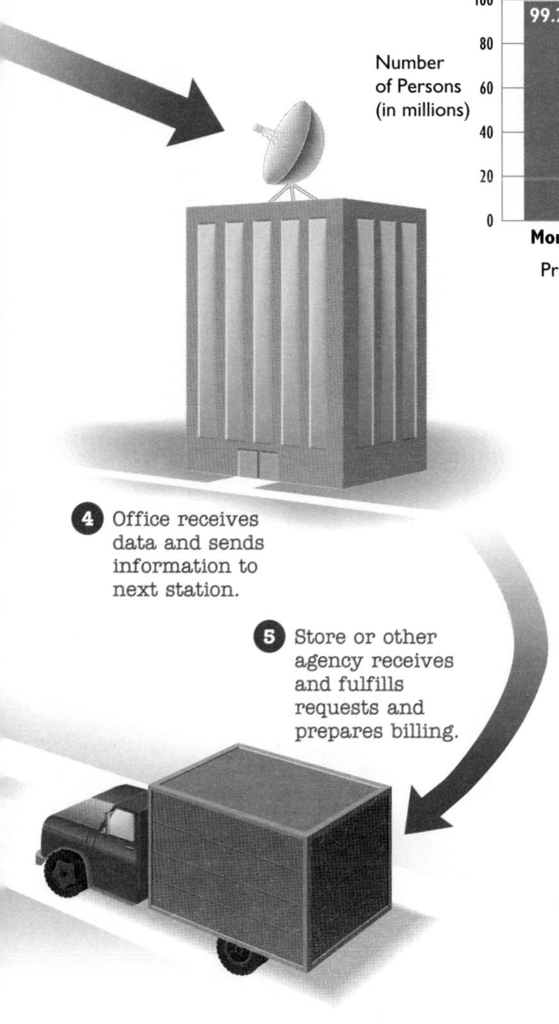

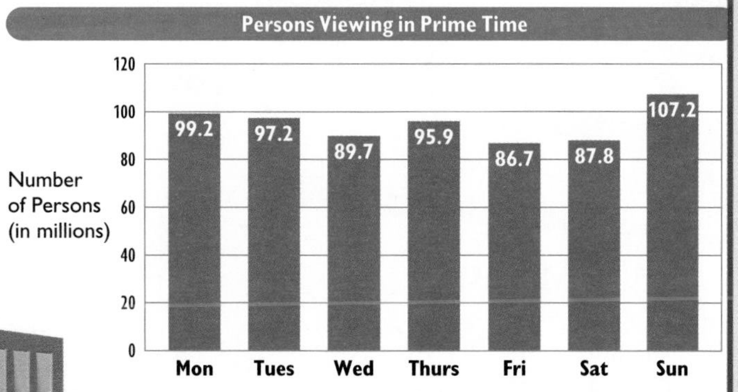

Persons Viewing in Prime Time

Number of Persons (in millions)

Mon	99.2
Tues	97.2
Wed	89.7
Thurs	95.9
Fri	86.7
Sat	87.8
Sun	107.2

Prime time is 8-11 P.M. (EST) Mon–Sat and 7-11 P.M. on Sun.

WORLD VIEW The Japanese government spends $17.71 per person on public television. The Canadians spends $32.15 and the United States spends only $1.06.

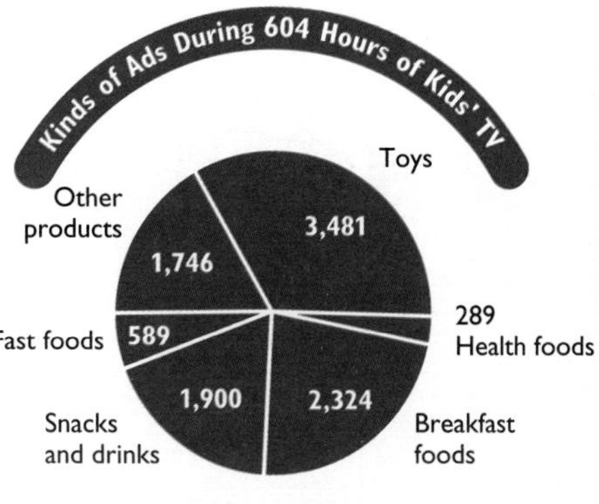

4 Office receives data and sends information to next station.

5 Store or other agency receives and fulfills requests and prepares billing.

Kinds of Ads During 604 Hours of Kids' TV

Kind	Ads
Toys	3,481
Health foods	289
Breakfast foods	2,324
Snacks and drinks	1,900
Fast foods	589
Other products	1,746

Total Ads: 10,329

Source: *Dynamath*

Fact of the Day

The average child in the United States sees at least 26,000 murders on television in the first 18 years of life (reported in 1988).

—*Guinness Book of Records*

CHAPTER 1

INVESTIGATION

Memo

Discuss with students the biological facts about the human heart. Include information about its size (that of a closed fist) and its purpose (to send impure blood from the body to the lungs, exchanging waste products for oxygen, and to pump blood throughout the body).

Mission

Before they begin work on the project, students should experiment to find their own pulses. Then they should look for the pulses of classmates. Encourage students to take all pulses under similar conditions, "equalizing variables" as much as possible.

After about half the chapter has been completed, have students show you their work on the project. If they are behind schedule, you may want to give them intermediate deadlines in order to check their work.

Additional Leads to Follow

- *What can you do to collect all of your data under conditions that are as uniform as possible?*
- *What should you do if your research has a wide range of pulse rates?*

Keeping a Project Notebook

Some suggestions for students' notebooks include the following:

- Include the categories of data you will record. Possibilities: date, time, person's name, number of beats, length of test, general comments. Include categories you aren't sure that you will need; you can always discard them later.
- List the dates and results of all discussions about the project.
- Write down all ideas relating to how you might interpret or display the data.

Project Organizer

Related Exercises
p. 14
p. 28

Follow Up
p. 34

Teacher's Notes
pp. 4, 14, 27

Community Resources
- physician
- nurse
- emergency medical technician

Materials and Manipulatives
- watch with second hand
- art materials

Resources
- *Prentice Hall Product Testing Activities* by Consumer Reports

Memo

The human heart may be the world's most amazing machine. It weighs only about half a pound, yet it can pump blood through some 12,000 mi of bloodways in the human body. It never rests or stops for repairs. In a single year your heart pumps around a million gallons of blood through your body. In an average person's lifetime a heart beats more than 2 billion times.

Mission: Find the pulse rates (beats per minute) of your classmates. Then make a poster displaying your results. Describe how you conducted your investigation and tell how you interpreted the results.

- ✓ For how many students should you find the pulse rate?
- ✓ How many times should you take each student's pulse?
- ✓ What kind of information about pulse rates should you display on your poster?

1-1

Connecting to Prior Knowledge

Ask students to name places where they have seen data presented in an organized fashion, such as in a newspaper. Encourage students to think of reasons why data might need to be organized (for example, to make a point; so that it can be grasped quickly and accurately; so that a particular piece of data, such as a score, can be found easily). Then challenge students to think of some specific types of organization that they have seen used, such as tables, graphs, and charts.

THINK AND DISCUSS

ESL Help students with limited English proficiency by seating them near the front, or where there is a minimum of distractions. Encourage them to start a personal glossary of terms. Review their written definitions to make sure they understand the meaning of these terms: "favorite," "primary colors," "frequency table," "line plot," "horizontal line," and "range."

VISUAL LEARNERS Have a group of students use poster paints to demonstrate that the other colors mentioned as favorites in WHAT? can be made from the three primaries. (White and red make pink; blue and red make purple; yellow and red make orange.)

KINESTHETIC LEARNERS Make a tally similar to that for Questions 1–3 by having students stand, as you name each primary color, to show their favorites.

TECHNOLOGY OPTION Have the class create a database containing the names of the class members to be used throughout the chapter. A committee of students could decide the responses that might be interesting.

- *Would a line plot be a good way to display the heights of students in the entire school? Why or why not?* **(Probably not; there would be too many x's to read easily.)**

What's Ahead

- Organizing data in frequency tables and line plots

1-1 Frequency Tables and Line Plots

THINK AND DISCUSS

You can make any color paint by mixing the colors blue, red, and yellow. These colors are the *primary colors.* An art teacher asked students in her class to name their favorite primary color. She organized their responses in the *frequency table* below. A **frequency table** shows the number of times each piece of data occurs.

Favorite Primary Color	Tally	Frequency
blue	𝍸 ||||	9
red	𝍸 𝍸	10
yellow	|	1

WHAT? Blue is the favorite color of most Americans. In order, the next favorite colors are red, green, white, pink, purple, orange, and yellow.

Source: 3-2-1 *Contact*

1. What does each tally mark, or |, represent? one student
2. How is the frequency in the third column determined? by adding the tally marks for each response
3. **Discussion** How many students are in the class? Describe two ways you can find this number. 20 students; count all the tally marks in the second column or add all the frequencies in the third column.

A *line plot* is another way you can organize data. A **line plot** displays data on a horizontal line.

Heights of Students in a Math Class (in.)

55	56	57	58	59	60	61	62	63	64	65
x	xx	xxx	xx	xxx	xxx	xxxx	xx	xxx	x	x

4. What does each × represent? one student
5. **Discussion** How many students are in the math class? Explain how you found this number. 25 students; count all the x's

"You can teach a student a lesson for a day; but if you can teach him to learn by creating curiosity, he will continue the learning process as long as he lives."

—Clay P. Bedford

Organizer

1. **Focus**
   Connecting to Prior Knowledge
2. **Teach**
   Think and Discuss
   Work Together
3. **Closure**
   Wrap Up

Vocabulary/Symbols
primary colors
frequency table
line plot
range

Materials and Manipulatives
- graph paper (for each student)

On Your Own Exercise 9: calculator; Exercises 13–14: graph paper

Student Resources
Extra Practice
Student Study Guide
Practice, TR Ch. 1, p. 21
Student Study Guide, Spanish Resources, TR
Alternate Lesson, TR Ch. 1, pp. 9–12

continues next page

WORK TOGETHER

Have each pair of students prepare a frequency table before beginning their surveys. They can then keep a running tally in their tables. Writing the paragraph to describe the results is a valuable conclusion to this activity. It not only has students use their communication skills for math topics, it shows the value of relating math information to observations and conclusions.

Error Alert! Students may lose track of the classmates they have surveyed for the Work Together activity. ***Remediation*** Have students compare their responses to the total number of people in the class to check that they have surveyed everyone.

ESL **DIVERSITY** As the students record data about the class, listen for any responses or remarks that may indicate negative feelings or attitudes towards other cultures, languages, or customs. Help students address these issues by open discussions about the value and fun of increasing their knowledge about others. You may want to set up a buddy system to increase interaction between students of different backgrounds.

Ongoing Assessment Have each student interview the same partner used for the Work Together activity. Have students pose questions requiring the interviewees to describe what they learned in the activity and to evaluate results they obtained. Challenge students to name ways they could have made the activity easier or more efficient. As students talk to each other, circulate and identify those who ask good questions and respond well, as well as those who need further help or reteaching.

Wrap Up

What's the Big Idea? Ask students to describe how to organize data in frequency tables and line plots.

Organizer, continued

Teacher Resources

Teaching Transparencies 31, 34, 96–101

Lesson Planner, TR Ch. 1, p. 2

Prentice Hall Technology

Computer Item Generator

- 1-1

Other Available Technology

calculator

Works by Microsoft: Think and Discuss activity *(optional)*

Fact of the Day

Visible light is electromagnetic radiation with a wavelength between 410 nanometers and about 770 nanometers. Yellow light falls between 540 and 600 nm.

—ACADEMIC AMERICAN ENCYCLOPEDIA

Assignment Options

Core: 7–11, 15, MR all	
Reinforce: 12, 14	**Enrich:** 13

Mixed REVIEW

Find each answer.

1. 243 + 43 + 817 + 36 1,139
2. 96 + 17 + 89 + 16 218
3. 23,427 − 4,798 18,629
4. 592 − 418 174
5. Vivian has six coins that total 52¢. What coins, and how many of each, does she have?

5. 1 quarter, 2 dimes, 1 nickel, and 2 pennies

WORK TOGETHER

Answers may vary.

- Make a frequency table in which you can record the birth months of the students in your math class.
- Have each student in your class tell in what month he or she was born. Fill in your frequency table with the responses.
- Display the results in a line plot.
- Work with a partner to write a short paragraph describing the results.

The **range** of a set of data is the difference between the greatest value and the least value in a set of numerical data.

6. In 1852, surveyors made these six measurements of Mt. Everest to determine the height of the mountain.

28,990 ft	28,992 ft	28,999 ft
29,002 ft	29,005 ft	29,026 ft

a. What was the greatest height measured? the least height measured? 29,026 ft; 28,990 ft

b. Find the range of the measurements. 36 ft

ON YOUR OWN

7. **Social Studies** There is a town in Wales named Llanfairpwllgwyngyllgogerychwyrndrobwllllantysiliogogogoch.

a. Copy and complete the frequency table at the left using the name of the Wales town. See left.

b. Describe the data recorded in your frequency table. See left.

Letter	Tally	Frequency
a	|||	3
e	■	■ 1
i	■	■ 3
o	■	■ 6
u	■	■ 0

7.b. Answers may vary. Sample: There is a total of thirteen vowels in the name of the town. There are three a's, one e, three i's, six o's and zero u's.

8. **Literature** The number of letters in each of the first twenty-five words of the book *The Story of Amelia Earhart* are shown below. Make a frequency table. See Solution Key.

6 3 4 2 3 5 3 7 3 4 3 3 4

3 3 3 6 6 3 5 3 2 3 7 5

9. **Calculator** NASA requires that an astronaut be at least 58.5 in. and at most 76 in. tall. Find the height range. 17.5 in.

Journal Tell students to write a response to the following question: *You are in charge of ordering clothes for a department store. How would a frequency table or line plot help you to take inventory and place orders?*

Connections Have students discuss the use of frequency tables and line plots outside the classroom, perhaps including these areas:

- **Health** (comparing bacteria counts in samples, evaluating physical therapy progress, estimating calorie intake by day)
- **Construction** (comparing costs of types of lumber, comparing square feet of rooms, or numbers of rooms)
- **Sports** (finding frequency of free throw percentages, batting averages, yardage gained)

Reteaching Activity Ask students to create a line plot of the data for Questions 1–3 and to create a frequency table of the data for Questions 4 and 5. Ask them to find the range for the height data **(10).**

ON YOUR OWN

WRITING Question 11 can lead to a class discussion about how to create a frequency table that has frequencies arranged horizontally rather than vertically.

ACTIVITY For Exercise 14, suggest that students design and conduct a similar survey with a different letter.

CONNECTION TO GEOGRAPHY Exercise 14 helps create awareness of various states. Have a map available to help students locate these states.

WRITING For Exercise 14c, challenge students to supply explanations for their observations.

CHAPTER INVESTIGATION For Exercise 15, provide time for students to record the number of times ten classmates blink in a minute.

10. a. What information is displayed in the line plot? grades on a science test

b. How many test grades are recorded in the line plot? 16 grades

c. How many students received a grade of C or better? 13 students

Science Test Grades

A	B	C	D	F
	×			
	×			
×	×			
×	×	×		
×	×	×	×	
×	×	×	×	×

11. Writing How are frequency tables and line plots alike? How are they different? See right.

11. Answers may vary. Sample: Both are ways to organize data in a visual way that allows for easy and quick comparison and reading of data. Each uses different notation to represent one item. A frequency table contains a column of numerical data, a line plot does not.

12. Sports The ticket prices available for a Milwaukee Brewers' baseball game are \$14, \$12, \$4, \$15, \$8, \$7, and \$11. Find the range. \$11

13. Social Studies The birth states of the 42 Presidents of the United States are shown below.

Presidential Birth States

State	Tally	State	Tally	State	Tally
VA	卌 III	KY	I	CA	I
MA	IIII	OH	卌 II	NE	I
SC	I	VT	II	GA	I
NY	IIII	NJ	II	IL	I
NC	II	IA	I	AR	I
NH	I	MO	I		
PA	I	TX	II		

a. Make a line plot of the data. See Solution Key.

b. In what four states were the most presidents born? VA, MA, NY, OH

c. Is it possible to find the range for these data? Explain. No; the data are not numerical.

14. Activity There are 8 states that begin with the letter *M*.

a. Ask 20 people who are not in your math class to name as many states that begin with the letter *M* as they can. Record the states that each person correctly names in a frequency table.

b. Display your results in a line plot.

c. Writing Describe the results of your survey. What state was most often missed? Answers may vary. Check student's work.

15. Investigation (p. 4) Collect data on the number of times 10 people blink their eyes in one minute. Display your results in a frequency table. Answers will vary. Check students' work.

Franklin D. Roosevelt *was born in New York and was president longer than any other person. He was elected four times and served more than twelve years.*

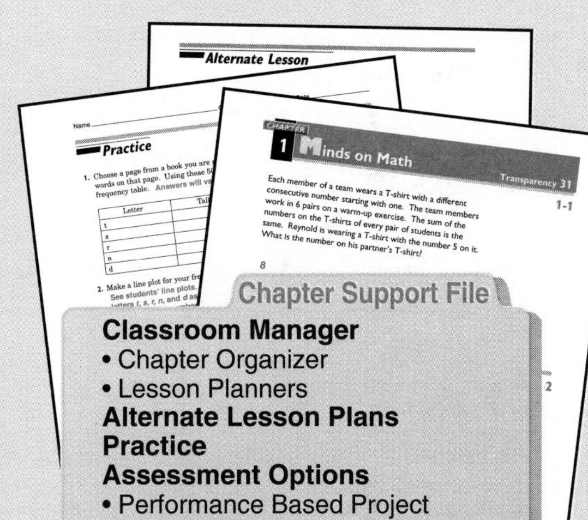

Chapter Support File

Classroom Manager
- Chapter Organizer
- Lesson Planners

Alternate Lesson Plans

Practice

Assessment Options
- Performance Based Project
- Scoring Rubric
- Student Self-Assessment Survey
- Checkpoints
- Chapter Assessments
- Cumulative Review

Minds on Math available in Teaching Transparencies

Math Minutes

Evaluate each of the following operations for $n = 6$.

Multiply n by 4 and add 6. **30**
Multiply n by 9 and add 12. **66**

1-2

Connecting to Prior Knowledge

Have students brainstorm for ways they could use frequency tables to solve problems. Encourage students to think of problems that they have experienced outside the classroom, such as putting together a class or work schedule, or choosing clothes.

Error Alert! For Questions 1–11, some students may ask for a rule that can be used to solve every problem with no further judgment needed on their part. ***Remediation*** Acknowledge their discomfort with problems that are not one step/one method/one answer but encourage them to explore different possibilities for arranging their tables. Praise their attempts and persistence. Working in groups also helps to alleviate this anxiety.

Additional Problem *The school Math Club is having a picnic. Members make their own sandwiches for lunch by picking two of the following ingredients: tuna fish, ham, lettuce, avocado, and tomato. How many different sandwiches can be made?* **(ten)**

Ongoing Assessment Have students examine the tables they made for the Additional Problem. Ask students to evaluate their work based on the following questions:

- *Is the table clear and well-organized?*
- *Are all the ingredients labeled?*
- *Is every possible combination accounted for?*
- *Are repeated combinations eliminated?*

TRY THESE

Exercises 12–13: Encourage students to use the checklist from the Ongoing Assessment to help them make the tables.

ESL **TACTILE LEARNERS** Provide real or play coins so that students can model Questions 12 and 13 and check their answers. Review the name and value of each coin.

"A good leader inspires people to have confidence in the leader; a great leader inspires people to have confidence in themselves."

—ANONYMOUS

Organizer

1. **Focus**
   Connecting to Prior Knowledge
2. **Teach**
3. **Closure**
   Try These
   Wrap Up

Skills Reviewed in Context of Lesson

- making a table

Student Resources

Extra Practice
Student Study Guide
Practice, TR Ch. 1, p. 22
Student Study Guide, Spanish Resources, TR

Teacher Resources

Teaching Transparency 31
Lesson Planner, TR Ch. 1, p. 3

Prentice Hall Technology

Multimedia Math

- Math Investigations, Mission: Mars

Computer Item Generator

- 1–2

What's Ahead

- Solving problems by making a table

PROBLEM SOLVING

1-2 Make a Table

Mr. Mon E. Bags has a pocket full of coins. He says that he can show you all possible ways to make 18¢. How many ways should you expect Mr. Mon E. Bags to show you if what he says is true?

READ Read and understand the given information. Summarize the problem.

Think about the information you are given and what you are asked to find.

1. What does the problem ask you to find? **how many ways there are to make 18¢**
2. What type of coins must Mr. Mon E. Bags have in his pocket? What is the value of each of these coins? **pennies, nickels, and dimes; 1¢, 5¢, and 10¢ respectively**

PLAN Decide on a strategy to solve the problem.

You can make a table to help you organize the possible ways to make 18¢.

3. a. Mr. Mon E. Bags puts 1 dime on the table. How many pennies must he put on the table to make 18¢? **8 pennies**
   b. What is another way that Mr. Mon E. Bags could make 18¢ after putting 1 dime on the table? **add 1 nickel and 3 pennies**
4. Mr. Mon E. Bags uses only pennies to show you 18¢. How many pennies are on the table? **18 pennies**

SOLVE Try out the strategy.

Make a table like the one below to form an organized list of all possible ways to make 18¢.

Dimes	Nickels	Pennies
1	0	8
:	:	:
:	:	:
0	0	18

5. Copy and complete the table above. **See Solution Key.**

The most popular coin is the Lincoln head penny. Since 1909 over 250 billion pennies have been minted. If stacked, they could reach from Earth to the moon.

Source: *Guinness Book of Records*

Journal Have students describe the difficult aspects of making a table to solve a problem. Start students by asking them if they find it hard to make the first step of determining what kind of table could display the required information. Encourage students to list ways they overcome the difficulties they mention.

Wrap Up

What's the Big Idea? Ask students to explain how making a table can solve a problem.

Connections Have a discussion about how tables are used. You may want to start with these examples:

- **Business** (organizing availability of employees, taking inventory, planning possible store displays or promotions)
- **Household** (planning possible meals for the week from groceries, finding times for family activities)
- **Science** (recording multiple sets of experimental data, comparing samples)

Reteaching Activity Point out to students that tables are particularly useful for finding the possible combinations of a set of items. Have students draw and label a table for Question 5 that has the labels "Dimes, Nickels, Pennies" in the first column at the left and use it to complete the problem.

ON YOUR OWN

ESL **ESL** Students may need some help with the vocabulary in the exercises. Give students opportunities to work in small groups with students who have the same language background as well as with students who are proficient in English. Encourage them to discuss and understand the story in the problem before they go on to do the math on their own.

CONNECTION TO GEOMETRY Exercise 17 reviews geometric concepts by having students find triangles in a design.

6. Why does the number 2 not appear in the column labeled *dimes*? Two dimes is 20¢. Since 20¢ > 18¢, it would not be a way to make 18¢.
7. Discussion Why is it easier to determine first the number of dimes needed rather than the number of pennies? Use an example to support your answer. See right.
8. Count the number of ways that Mr. Mon E. Bags can make 18¢. 6 ways

7. Answers may vary. Sample: There are fewer combinations of dimes with other coins than there are combinations of pennies with other coins.

You can use the table you made to answer many other questions.

9. Discussion Are there any patterns in the numbers that appear in your table? If so, describe the patterns. See right.
10. To make 18¢, what is the minimum number of coins needed? the maximum number of coins needed? 5 coins; 18 coins
11. Ten coins total 18¢. What types of coins are they? 2 nickels and 8 pennies

LOOK BACK

Think about how you solved this problem.

9. Answers may vary. Sample: The number of pennies always ends in a 3 or an 8.

TRY THESE

Make a table to solve each problem.

12. How many possible ways are there to make 28¢? 13 ways
13. There are 16¢ in a bag. There are more nickels than pennies.
    a. What types of coins are in the bag? nickels and pennies
    b. How many of each type of coin are in the bag? 3 nickels and 1 penny

ON YOUR OWN

Use any strategy to solve each problem. Show all your work.

14. Michael has a paper route. He earns 15¢ for each daily paper and 35¢ for each Sunday paper he delivers. Michael delivers twice as many daily papers each week as Sunday papers. How many of each type of paper does he deliver if he earns $13 each week? 40 daily papers and 20 Sunday papers

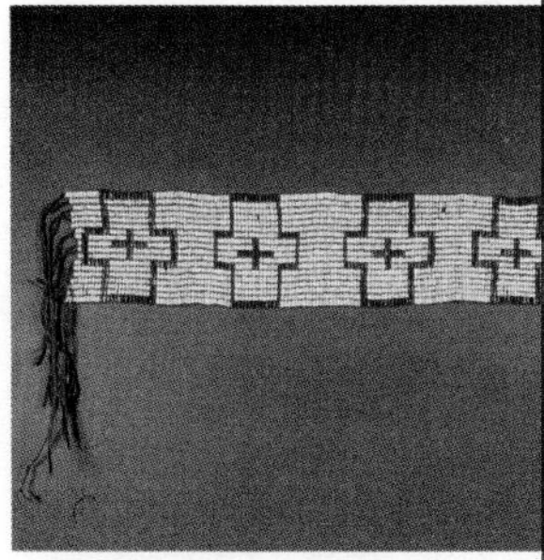

Wampum belts made of beads were used by Native Americans as money. They traded wampum with American settlers for goods. Five purple beads equaled one English penny.

Source: *Reader's Digest Book of Facts*

Fact of the Day

The United States Bureau of Engraving and Printing prints 16 million bills of money every day. Over 8 million of them are $1 bills.

—*In One Day*

Assignment Options

Core: 14–16, 18, 19, 21, MR all	
Reinforce: 17, 22	**Enrich:** 20

KINESTHETIC LEARNERS Remind these students that they can act out Exercise 20 by using floor tiles as blocks.

CONNECTION TO PATTERNS Exercise 21 has students evaluate a pattern.

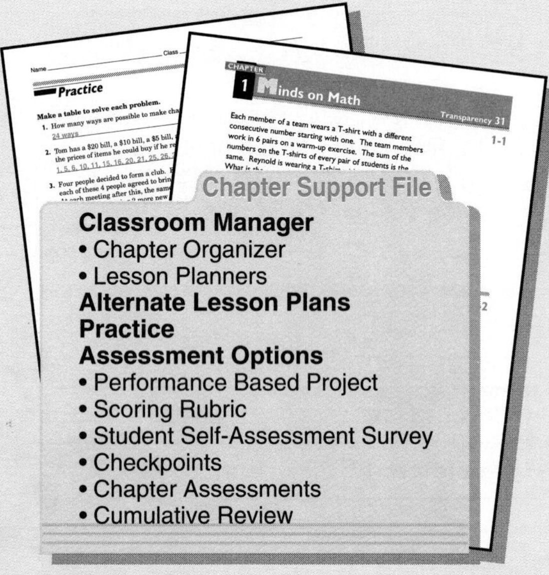

Minds on Math available in Teaching Transparencies

Math Minutes

For each situation described, choose the appropriate graph.

1. You own a fish store. You want to compare one week's sales of salmon and swordfish. **bar graph**
2. You have examined your diet and want to show what part of the foods you have consumed come from each of the four food groups. **circle graph**

Materials for 1-3

- graph paper
- scissors

Caitrin McKiernan wrote and produced a TV news report on homeless children when she was just ten years old. She hopes to become a broadcast journalist when she gets older.

Source: *National Geographic World*

20. Answers may vary. Sample: walk 2 blocks south, then 5 blocks west; walk 5 blocks west, then 2 blocks south; walk 1 block south, 5 blocks west, then 1 block south

See Solution Key for Exercises 1 and 2 in the Mixed Review.

Mixed REVIEW

Use the data for Exercises 1–3. Student heights (in.): 53, 55, 60, 53, 57, 55, 52, 54, 53, 55

1. Make a frequency table.
2. Make a line plot.
3. Find the range. 8 in.
4. Andrés is starting a book-trading group. He is the only member now, but he plans to have each member find an additional 3 new members each month. How many members does Andrés expect to have after 6 months? 4,096 members

15. Yasmine, Fiona, and Carmen graduated from college. They have degrees in engineering, nursing, and law. Yasmine and the engineer plan to share an apartment. The nurse helps Carmen pack. Fiona's law firm specializes in corporate law. Who is the engineer? Carmen
16. Mr. Odina's class is sponsoring an auction to raise money for the homeless. Each class member is assigned to make tags. Chen's task is to make three-digit number tags using the digits 3, 7, and 8. How many number tags can Chen make using each digit exactly once on each tag? 6 tags
17. How many triangles are contained in the floor tile below? 16 triangles

18. Find the smallest number that meets all these conditions. 43
    - When you divide the number by 7, there is 1 left over.
    - When you divide the number by 9, there is 7 left over.
    - When you divide the number by 11, there is 10 left over.
19. A printer uses 121 pieces of type to number the pages of a book. The first page is numbered one. How many numbered pages are in the book? 65 numbered pages
20. Thelma and her brother Otis visit their grandmother and uncle each Friday. From their apartment they walk three blocks north and four blocks west to their grandmother's. They then continue one block south and nine blocks east to their uncle's. What are three ways Thelma and Otis can return home by walking a total of seven blocks? See left.
21. Buses leave Boston for New York every 40 min. The first bus leaves at 5:10 A.M. What is the departure time closest to 12.55 P.M.? 1:10 P.M.
22. The carnival has two types of rides for children. Each race car seats 4 children and each tug boat seats 6 children. Altogether there are 28 race cars and tug boats that seat a total of 136 children. How many of each are there? 16 race cars and 12 tug boats

1-3

Connecting to Prior Knowledge

Ask students to think of places they have seen averages used, such as in finding their grade for a class or batting averages or average price of a house. Have students name ways to find an average.

WORK TOGETHER

Have students work in groups of four or five. Each student can start a list with his or her name and then pass the strips around the group until each student has a complete list of the group members' names. Students in each group can then compare their lists when finding the average length of the names. Point out that one way to average is to take away from one and give to another until all have the same number. This kind of averaging (finding the mean) is the same as distributing the items evenly among all the members.

DIVERSITY if some students are sensitive about their names due to ethnic background or some other reason, consider substituting another set of words such as names of cities or states.

THINK AND DISCUSS

Example 1

You may wish to have students convert the table and the mean into approximate hours.

(South Korea ≈ 3.0 h, Switzerland ≈ 4.2 h, Taiwan ≈ 3.4 h, Jordan ≈ 3.0 h, US ≈ 3.8 h, F ≈ 3.8 h; mean ≈ 3.5 h)

Additional Example *Find the mean test score of a student with test scores of 78, 85, 94, 88, and 90.* **(87)**

Example 2

Ask students to describe median in their own words. **(middle number or value, center, and so on)** Then ask students how a

What's Ahead

- Finding mean, median, and mode
- Deciding which average is most appropriate for a given situation

WHAT YOU'LL NEED

✓ Graph paper

✓ Scissors

1-3 Three Kinds of Averages

WORK TOGETHER

- Write the names of the students in your group on strips of graph paper like the sample shown below.

L	I	S	A						
A	N	T	O	N	I	O			
I	A	N							
C	H	R	I	S	T	I	N	A	
A	L	E	X	A	N	D	E	R	

Check student's work.

- Find the average length of the names of the students in your group. Describe how your group found this number.
- Compare your work with other groups. Did everyone find the average length of the names the same way? Explain.

Answers will vary. Check student's work.

THINK AND DISCUSS

You can make general statements about data using the averages *mean, median,* and *mode.* The **mean** of a set of data is the sum of the data divided by the number of pieces of data.

Math In the World

Country	Minutes in Math Class Each Week
South Korea	179
Switzerland	251
Taiwan	204
Jordan	180
United States	228
France	230

Example 1 Find the mean number of minutes students spend in math class each week.

- Find the sum of the data.

179 + 251 + 204 + 180 + 228 + 230 = 1272

- Divide the sum by the number of pieces of data.

1272 ÷ 6 = 212

Students spend about 212 min in math class each week.

"By the work one knows the workman."

—LA FONTAINE

Organizer

1. **Focus**
   Connecting to Prior Knowledge
2. **Teach**
   Work Together
   Think and Discuss
3. **Closure**
   Try These
   Wrap Up

Vocabulary/Symbols

mean
median
mode

Skills Reviewed in Context of Lesson

- adding, dividing whole numbers
- ordering whole numbers
- reading line plots

Materials and Manipulatives

- graph paper (for each group)
- scissors (1 pair for each group)

On Your Own Exercise 14: calculator

Student Resources

Extra Practice
Student Study Guide
Practice, TR Ch. 1, p. 23
Student Study Guide, Spanish Resources, TR
Checkpoint, TR Ch. 1, p. 32

continues next page

median number is like the dividing median on a highway. **(in the middle of a range)**

Additional Example *Find the median of the ticket prices to a basketball game: $12, $7, $50, $60, and $25.* **($7, $12, $25, $50, $60; the median is $25.)**

Example 3

You may wish to mention to students that surveys of preferences or purchases are often reported using the mode.

VISUAL LEARNERS Line plots should appeal to these learners. Have them describe the plot to auditory learners.

Additional Example *A survey of students' favorite colors in a class resulted in four answers of purple, two orange, five black, one pink, eight blue, six red, and seven green. Name the mode. Could you also find the median and mean? Explain.* **(blue; no; the mean and median are found for numerical data.)**

ESL Error Alert! Students may use the words "average," "mean," "median," and "mode" incorrectly. ***Remediation*** Explain that the English word for "average" is often used for any one of the three mathematical terms. Frequently "average" is used for "mean," but "average" is also used for "mode" and "median." Encourage students to use the precise mathematical terms instead of the ambiguous "average." Flashcards may prove to be a helpful way to reinforce this vocabulary.

TECHNOLOGY OPTION Students should be encouraged to use a spreadsheet. Students can enter a formula for finding mean, they can use the internal function for "average," and they may use the "sort" option to order the data for finding median and mode.

Ongoing Assessment Have students work in pairs on this problem. Listen as they discuss the answers: *A baseball player recorded the number of hits she got in each game. Her record was 1, 3, 0, 1, 3, 2, 2, 1, 4, 3. Name the mean, median, and mode(s).* **(mean: 2; median: 2; modes: 1 and 3)**

Organizer, continued

Teacher Resources

Teaching Transparencies 1, 31
Transparency Masters, TR p. 2
Lesson Planner, TR Ch. 1, p. 4

Prentice Hall Technology

Multimedia Math
- Hot Page 1-3

Computer Item Generator
- 1-3

Other Available Technology
calculator
Excel; Works by Microsoft: Exercises 4–7 *(optional)*

Fact of the Day

The United States Postal Service prints 93 million postage stamps every day. If they were laid flat, the stamps would cover 22 acres.

—*In One Day*

Average Monthly Temperatures (°F) for St. Louis, MO

29	34	43	56	66	75
79	77	70	58	45	34

Aja Henderson has a collection of over 1,000 books! Aja lends them out to neighborhood kids who can't get to the public library.

You can also describe data by finding the *median.* The **median** is the middle number in a set of ordered data.

Example 2 The average daily temperatures (°F) for one week are 86, 78, 92, 79, 87, 91, and 77. Find the median.

Order the data and choose the middle number.

77 78 79 (86) 87 91 92

The median temperature is 86°F.

You can find the median when there is an even number of data items by adding the two middle numbers and dividing by 2.

1. The average monthly temperatures (°F) for St. Louis, Missouri, are shown at the left.
   a. Find the mean and median. 55.5°F; 57°F
   b. **Discussion** Which average better describes the temperatures in St. Louis over a year? Explain. Answers may vary.

Data can also be described by the *mode.* The **mode** is the data item that appears most often. The mode is especially helpful when the data are not numerical.

Example 3 The line plot shows the items collected by a group of students. Find the mode.

Collectibles

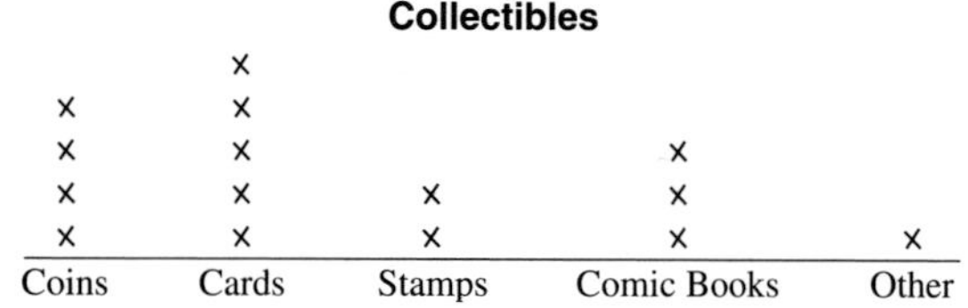

The mode is cards because it appears most often.

A set of data can have more than one mode. There is no mode when all the data items are listed the same number of times.

2. Suppose a student who collects stamps collects coins instead. Find the mode. coins and cards

3. **Discussion** Describe the line plot if the data has no mode. Each data item would appear three times.

TRY THESE

Journal Ask students to write stories that include an appropriate use of all three kinds of averages, perhaps as they describe their school to a penpal in another country.

Wrap Up

What's the Big Idea? Ask students to explain how to find mean, median, and mode. Then have students describe how to decide which average is most appropriate for a given situation.

Connections Have a discussion about how averages are used. You may want to start with these examples:

- **Media** (describing an average consumer or voter's concerns, averaging reader profiles for marketing purposes)
- **Business** (finding average sales to estimate business trends, comparing stocks, comparing employees' efficiency and wages)
- **Household** (averaging bill payments, salary, and expenses in order to plan ahead for each month)

Reteaching Activity Bring to class examples of averages from newspapers and magazines. Share the examples with students. Ask students to describe the averages as means, medians, or modes. Have students explain why the particular kind of average was used in each case.

ON YOUR OWN

ACTIVITY For Exercise 8b, suggest that students also research the lengths of science fiction movies by using a film guide from the library.

TRY THESE

Find the mean, median, and mode of each set of data.

4. 15 12 20 13 17 19 16; 16; no mode
5. 95 80 92 91 98 94 94 92; 94; 94
6. Sports In professional baseball, a baseball is used for an average of five pitches. What are seven numbers that have a mean of 5? Answers may vary. Sample: 4, 5, 5, 4, 6, 6, 5
7. Which average would best describe the favorite subject of students in your math class? Explain. Mode; the data are not numerical.

ON YOUR OWN

8. a. Entertainment Describe the average length of a comedy movie using mean, median, and mode. 99 min; 100 min; 101 min
   b. Activity Visit a nearby video store. Record the lengths in minutes of 20 science fiction movies. Analyze your data using mean, median, and mode. Answers will vary.
   c. Writing Use mean, median, and mode to compare the lengths of science fiction and comedy movies. Answers will vary. Check student's work.
9. Music The line plot shows the number of songs on 27 recently released rock CDs.

Number of Songs on Rock CDs

9	10	11	12	13	14	15
x x	x x x x x	x x x x x x x	x x x x x x x x	x x	x x	x

   a. Find the median and mode. 11 songs; 12 songs
   b. What average do you think best reflects the number of songs on a rock CD? Explain. See right.
   c. Critical Thinking Would it make sense to use the mean to describe this data? Why or why not? No; the mean does not represent a whole number of songs.

Lengths of 20 Comedy Movies (min)

102	111	105	100	100
99	107	104	101	89
101	90	92	87	96
92	95	101	110	98

9.b. Mode; it is the most frequent number of songs appearing on CDs.

Mixed REVIEW

Find each answer.

1. 718 + 46 764
2. 2,057 − 569 1,488
3. 114 × 12 1,368
4. 248 ÷ 8 31
5. At one point on a mountain road, the elevation is 4,000 ft. Two miles up the road, the elevation is 5,200 ft. If this pattern continues, what will the elevation be six miles up the road from the starting point? 7,600 ft

PH Multimedia Math Hot Page™ 1-3

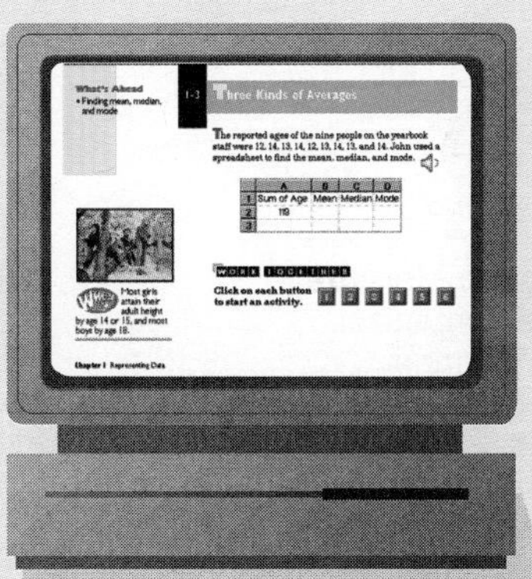

Assignment Options

Core: 8, 10–13, 16, MR all, CH all	
Reinforce: 9	Enrich: 14, 15

WRITING Have students present their comparisons for Exercise 8c in a bulletin board display.

CONNECTION TO STATISTICS Exercise 9 reviews the use of line plots and the idea of central tendency.

CRITICAL THINKING Have students suggest ways they might try to find the mean for Exercise 9c.

CRITICAL THINKING For Exercises 11–13, have students list the disadvantages of the kinds of averages they found to be inappropriate.

WRITING For Exercise 15, suggest that students get ideas for their situations from newspapers and magazines.

CHAPTER INVESTIGATION Arrange students in groups of six for Exercise 16. Have group members pair off so that each group member collects data on the other five. Have groups compare results, and gather them into one graphic to display in the classroom.

CHECKPOINT

CALCULATOR Have students show their steps for Question 3.

CONNECTION TO STATISTICS Questions 3–6 have students use different measures of central tendency.

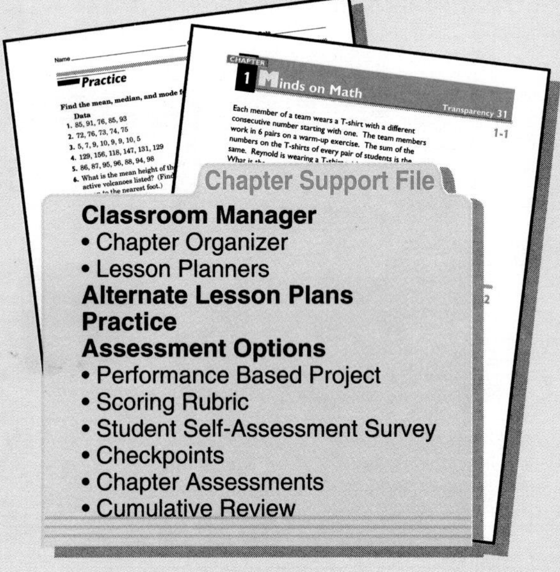

Chapter Support File

Classroom Manager
- Chapter Organizer
- Lesson Planners

Alternate Lesson Plans

Practice

Assessment Options
- Performance Based Project
- Scoring Rubric
- Student Self-Assessment Survey
- Checkpoints
- Chapter Assessments
- Cumulative Review

Minds on Math available in Teaching Transparencies

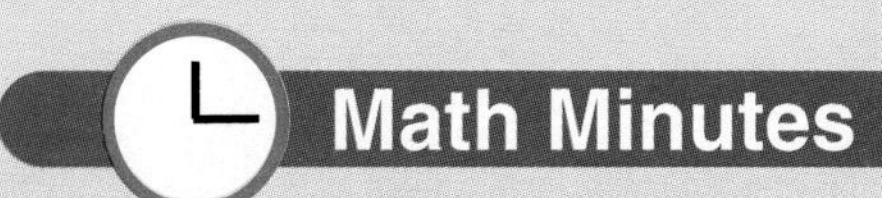

Math Minutes

Express each fraction as a decimal and then find their sum. $\frac{1}{2}, \frac{1}{4}, \frac{1}{8}, \frac{1}{8}$.

0.5 + 0.25 + 0.125 + 0.125 = 1

Materials for 1-4
- calculator
- computer *(optional)*
- spreadsheet software *(optional)*

WHAT? Math was chosen as the favorite subject in a recent survey of 10,832 junior high students.

Source: *Scholastic Math*

15. Answers may vary. Sample: The mean would be appropriate for test scores, the median for heights of students in your class, and the mode for a survey of favorite colors.

Sport	Players on a Team
American Football	11
Volleyball	6
Basketball	5
Soccer	11
Ultimate Frisbee	7
Ice Hockey	6
Softball	9
Field Hockey	11
Speedball	11
Baseball	9

10. Choose A, B, C, or D. Suppose Leotie's teacher allows students to decide whether to use mean, median, or mode as their test average. Leotie finds that she will receive the highest average if she uses the mean. Which set of test grades are Leotie's? A

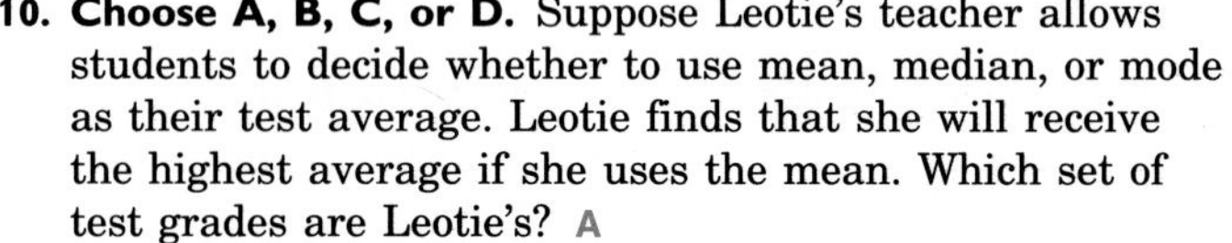

A. 74, 80, 92, 82, 92 **B.** 74, 80, 74, 82, 85
C. 74, 80, 92, 85, 74 **D.** 74, 80, 70, 71, 80

Critical Thinking **What average is most appropriate for each situation? Explain.** Answers may vary. Sample given.

11. the favorite subject of students in your grade
Mode; the data are not numerical.

12. the snowfall for the month of December in Lansing, MI
Mean; the snowfall for all 31 days must be considered.

13. the cost of houses in your community
Median; the average cost will not be influenced by extremes.

14. Data File 1 (pp. 2–3) Use a calculator to find the mean number of people viewing TV during prime time Monday through Friday. about 93.74 million people

15. Writing Describe a situation that would be most appropriately described by each average: mean, median, and mode. See left.

16. Investigation (p. 4) Collect data on the number of times ten people can snap their fingers in one minute. Find the mean, median, and mode of your results. Answers may vary. Check student's work.

CHECKPOINT

Use the following data for Questions 1 and 2.

Grams of fat per serving for 25 popular breakfast cereals:
0, 1, 1, 3, 1, 1, 2, 2, 0, 3, 1, 3, 2, 0, 1, 0, 2, 1, 1, 0, 0, 0, 2, 1, 0

1. Make a frequency table. See Solution Key.

2. Make a line plot. See Solution Key.

Use the table at the left for Questions 3 through 6.

3. Calculator Find the mean number of players. 8.6 players

4. Find the median. 9 players

5. Find the mode. 11 players

6. Which average best describes the number of players on a sports team? Explain. Answers will vary. Sample: mode; it is the most frequent number of players appearing in the data.

CHAPTER 1

PROBLEM SOLVING PRACTICE

This page provides a variety of problems that can be used to reinforce and enhance the students' problem solving skills. Encourage students to read each problem carefully. Then have them refer to the list of problem solving strategies to help them decide how to solve the problems.

Point out, however, that not all questions require a strategy for solving, nor are all the strategies in the list used on this page.

CALCULATOR Have students describe in words the pattern for Exercise 5.

Exercise 6: Encourage students to model the problem with blocks or markers.

Problem Solving Practice

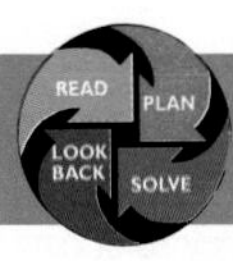

PROBLEM SOLVING STRATEGIES

Make a Table
Use Logical Reasoning
Solve a Simpler Problem
Too Much or Too Little Information
Look for a Pattern
Make a Model
Work Backward
Draw a Diagram
Guess and Test
Simulate a Problem
Use Multiple Strategies

Solve. The list at the left shows some possible strategies you can use.

1. You have been given five single gold links. A jeweler charges $1 to cut and mend a link. What is the minimum cost the jeweler will charge to make the five links into a single gold chain? $2

2. Solve this riddle: "I think of a number, add 6, multiply by 4, divide by 8, and subtract 3. The answer is 2." What is the original number? 4

3. There are two children in the Jackson family. The sum of their ages is 15, and their product is 54. How old are each of the children? 6 y and 9 y

4. Zahur's favorite game uses a velcro board, like the one below, and three velcro darts. When a dart lands on a line, the higher value is counted. What possible scores can Zahur get if all three darts hit the board? 45, 40, 35, 30, 25, 20, or 15

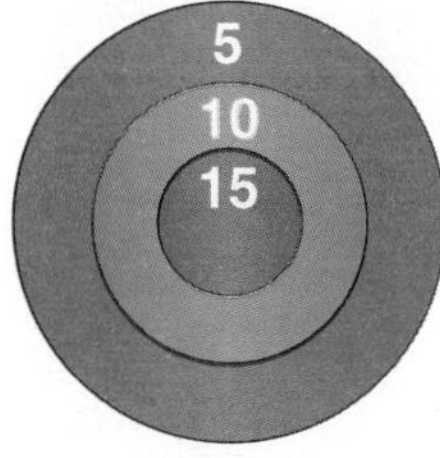

WHAT? Velcro was invented by Georges de Mestral, a Swiss engineer. He got his idea from nature after examining how burrs stuck so well to his woolen socks.

Source: *How in the World?*

5. Calculator Divide 3 by 11. What number would be in the 50th decimal place? 7

6. Six apples weigh the same as two oranges and two kiwi. An orange weighs the same as eight kiwi. How many kiwi equal the weight of an apple? 3 kiwi

1-4

Connecting to Prior Knowledge

Discuss spreadsheets with students. Find their level of experience, if they have used any applications with a spreadsheet, and whether they are clear about the purpose of spreadsheet calculations.

THINK AND DISCUSS

For the computer exercises in this section, students can use any spreadsheet software for exploring the mean. Set up a spreadsheet like the first one on the pupil page. Start with all the cells blank, and slowly enter column and row headings to make sure all the students understand the table. As you continue the discussion, include these points:

- There are five musical categories, with four disks in each category.
- The number of minutes of music is shown for each disk.
- The CDs are not named; they are called Disk 1, 2, 3, and 4.
- The last column (F) will show the mean of the four times in each category.

ESL TACTILE LEARNERS Have students trace column D and then row 4 on the table in the pupil book. Then have the students use both of their index fingers to trace column D and row 4 simultaneously, noting the cell where the two fingers meet. Let them practice finding other cells by touching the table in the book as a cell is named.

Question 2: Make sure that students are able to understand that the name for each of the cells in row 2 has a 2 in it and that the name for each of the cells in column C has a C in it.

Error Alert! In Questions 2 and 3, students may attempt to use the letters A–F along the top and the numbers 1–6 along the side as data. ***Remediation*** Make sure that the students understand that these are used to identify columns and rows.

“The trouble with facts is that there are so many of them.”

—SAMUEL CROTHERS

Organizer

1. **Focus**
   Connecting to Prior Knowledge
2. **Teach**
   Think and Discuss
   Work Together
3. **Closure**
   Wrap Up

Vocabulary/Symbols
spreadsheet
cell
formula

Skills Reviewed in Context of Lesson
- finding the mean for whole numbers

Materials and Manipulatives
- computer (1 per group; *optional*)
- spreadsheet software (1 per group; *optional*)

On Your Own Exercises 10–12: computer and spreadsheet software *(optional)*; Exercise 17: calculator

Student Resources
Extra Practice
Student Study Guide
Practice, TR Ch. 1, p. 24
Student Study Guide, Spanish Resources, TR
Alternate Lesson, TR Ch. 1, pp. 13–16

continues next page

TECHNOLOGY

1-4 Computer Spreadsheets

What's Ahead
- Organizing data in a spreadsheet
- Using spreadsheets to explore averages

WHAT YOU'LL NEED
✓ Computer 
✓ Spreadsheet software

THINK AND DISCUSS

A compact disk can hold nearly 80 min of music. Do your CDs have room for more songs? Do some types of CDs contain more music than other types?

The *spreadsheet* below shows the length of 20 CDs from five different musical categories. You can use a **spreadsheet** to organize and analyze data.

	A	B	C	D	E	F	
1	Music Type	Disk 1 (min)	Disk 2 (min)	Disk 3 (min)	Disk 4 (min)	Mean Length (min)	
2	Rock/Pop	40	44	45	47		44
3	Rap	47	53	55	41	49	
4	Country	32	34	30	36	33	
5	Classical	45	73	51	59	57	
6	Jazz	41	58	44	77	55	

***A compact disk** holds 3 mi of playing track. CDs can never get scratched because no needle ever touches the surface.*

Data are arranged in a spreadsheet in columns and rows.

1. a. How are columns identified in a spreadsheet? by letters
   b. How are rows identified in a spreadsheet? by numbers

A **cell** is the box where a row and column meet. For example, the box where column E and row 3 meet is called cell E3. The value in cell E3 is 41.

2. a. What value is in cell D4? What does this number mean? 30; the length of one country music CD is 30 min
   b. What cells are in row 2? A2, B2, C2, D2, E2, and F2
   c. What cells are in column C? C1, C2, C3, C4, C5, and C6
3. a. Which cell contains the greatest value? the least value? E6; D4
   b. What type of music is on the CD which contains the greatest amount of music? the least amount of music? jazz; country

WORK TOGETHER

WRITING For Question 4a, students may be confused by the term *mean length.* Remind them that this is the mean of the lengths.

Question 4b: Have students first describe the process for finding the mean using the values in row 2. Then substitute the cell names for the values. Explain the purpose of the parentheses and the "division" sign in the formula.

COMPUTER For Question 4c, students who are unfamiliar with spreadsheet programs may need extra help when setting up the problem.

- Enter the headings for rows and columns.
- Enter the data in columns B–E.
- Enter the formula for cell F2 using the = sign.
- Have the program generate the repeated formulas for the rest of column F.

Alternate Approach If a computer is not available, have students do the exercises with paper and pencil. Ask them to use calculators so the lesson can continue at a faster pace. If you are not using calculators, have different groups of students calculate different rows so that each student does just one calculation of the mean length.

Journal Have the students write a paragraph telling which method they prefer, computer or calculator computation, or using pencil and paper. Ask them to give specific reasons.

CRITICAL THINKING For Question 5, make sure students read and use the PROBLEM SOLVING HINT in the margin.

COMPUTER For Question 7, change the values in the cells back and forth, so that the students can see how the changes made to the cells are reflected by the cells that contain the formulas. In this way, students can begin to understand the formula process.

WORK TOGETHER

A spreadsheet program can save you a lot of time and effort. For example, the computer can automatically fill in the values for an entire column of your spreadsheet if you tell it what calculations to do. A **formula** is a set of instructions that tells the computer what to do.

Work with a partner to answer each question.

4. a. Writing Cell F2 displays the mean length of the four rock/pop CDs. Describe how you would calculate this value without using a computer. See right.
   b. Discussion With a spreadsheet program you can enter the formula =(B2+C2+D2+E2)/4 into cell F2. How is this formula like the description you wrote? How is it different? See right.
   c. Computer Set up a spreadsheet like the one on the previous page. Enter the formulas for cells F2 through F6. What are the mean lengths for each of the five types of music? See spreadsheet on p. 16.
5. Critical Thinking Determine what will happen to the value in F4 if each of the following occurs.
   a. the value in cell C4 gets larger increase
   b. the value in cell B4 gets smaller decrease
   c. the value in cell B3 gets larger stay the same
6. Discussion How would the formulas that are now in column F change if there were five disks representing each type of music instead of four? The sum of five values would be added together and then divided by 5.
7. Computer Suppose the length of the first classical CD was entered incorrectly. Change the value in cell B5 to 65. How did the spreadsheet change when you made this correction? The value in cell F5 changed to 62.
8. Computer Add a row 7 to your spreadsheet.
   a. Include these data about four CDs that hold movie soundtracks: 31 min, 48 min, 32 min, 49 min.
   b. What formula did you put in cell F7?
   c. What is the mean length of the movie soundtrack CDs?

8.b. =(B7+C7+D7+E7)/4 40 min

The word *cell* comes from the Latin word *cella,* meaning "room."

Source: *The Oxford Dictionary of English Etymology*

4.a. Answers may vary. Sample: Add the values in cells B2, C2, D2, and E2. Then divide by 4.

Problem Solving Hint

You can substitute appropriate values into each cell to see what happens to the value in cell F4.

4.b. Answers may vary. Sample: The formula is like the description because it adds the values in cells B2, C2, D2, and E2 and then divides the sum by 4. It is different because it is written using math symbols instead of words.

Organizer, continued

Teacher Resources

Teaching Transparencies 4, 5, 32
Transparency Masters, TR p. 5
Lesson Planner, TR Ch. 1, p. 5

Prentice Hall Technology

Multimedia Math

- Math Tools, Spreadsheet
- Math Investigations, Hazard City Messengers

Computer Item Generator

- 1-4

Other Available Technology

calculator
Excel; Works by Microsoft *(optional)*

Fact of the Day

The world's largest private record collection belongs to Stan Kilarr of Klamath, Oregon. It contains about 500,000 albums.

—GUINNESS BOOK OF RECORDS

COMPUTER For Question 8, have students practice the process of inserting additional rows. ***Alternate Approach*** Have students work in pairs, one to make changes in the cells of the paper spreadsheet, the other to play the part of the computer by making the corresponding changes in the mean.

Ongoing Assessment

On the chalkboard, set up a similar table with three values that need averaging. Ask students questions about the cells, the formula, and the mean as you change the values in each of the cells.

Wrap Up

What's the Big Idea?

How do you calculate the mean on a computer spreadsheet?

Connections

Have students discuss the use of spreadsheets when exploring averaging for the following occupations:

- **Machinist** (averaging number of defects for items manufactured)
- **Project Director** (averaging hours worked on a project by a group)
- **Researcher** (averaging the data collected for experiments as a part of the analysis process)

Reteaching Activity

Using colored blocks, have students calculate the mean for four groups. Place blocks into four groups (for example: use 5, 3, 2, and 6). Have the students rearrange the groups by changing the blocks from one group to another. When the students have arranged the piles into equal amounts of cubes **(4),** they will have had a hands-on experience with averaging. Then give students groups of 5, 4, 2, and 6 and have them rearrange them. Discuss the problem of the one extra block and help them see that this mean will be a fraction. **($4\frac{1}{4}$)**

Assignment Options

Core: 9, 11a, 13, 15, 16, 18, MR all	
Reinforce: 11b, 14, 17	**Enrich:** 10, 12

9. Subtract the value in cell B2 from the value in cell C2; multiply the value in cell D2 by 6.

11.a. No; it would calculate Tamara working a negative ten hours instead of the two hours she worked.

ON YOUR OWN

Use the information below for Exercises 9–12.

Tamara works part-time at Rad Sounds music store, where she gets paid $6 per hour. She set up a spreadsheet to keep track of the time she works and the money she earns. The spreadsheet below shows a typical schedule for a week.

	A	B	C	D	E
1	Day	Time in (PM)	Time Out (PM)	Hours Worked	Amount Earned
2	Monday	3	5	■	■
3	Wednesday	4	6	■	■
4	Friday	3	6	■	■
5	Saturday	1	6	■	■
6			Total:	■	■
7			Mean:	■	■

9. How can you calculate the value of cell D2? cell E2? See left.
10. a. Computer Make a spreadsheet like Tamara's. Use your answer to Exercise 9 to write formulas in columns D and E. See Solution Key.
    b. How many hours does Tamara work in a typical week? 12 h
    c. What is the mean number of hours Tamara works each shift? 3 h
    d. How much does Tamara earn in a typical week? $72
    e. What is the mean amount Tamara earns each shift? $18
11. a. Would your formula for cell D2 still work if Tamara arrived at the store at 11 A.M. and left at 1 P.M.? Why or why not? See left.
    b. Critical Thinking How would you change your spreadsheet so it could handle morning and afternoon hours? Answers may vary. Sample: input hours in military time using the numbers 1 through 24.
12. Computer Determine Tamara's weekly earnings if she has the same schedule except that she receives a $2 per hour raise. $96

*In **Denmark,** Tamara would earn about 42 kroner per hour.* ***How many kroner equal one dollar?*** 7 kroner

ON YOUR OWN

COMPUTER In Exercise 10, point out to students that the averaging is now done vertically. Students may need to practice vertical calculation before they are assigned the exercises. ***Alternate Approach*** If you are not using computerized spreadsheets, continue the same process using pencil and paper. Although students will not see the effect of changing a value without having to set up a new spreadsheet or repeat tedious calculations, they will be able to see the applications for spreadsheets.

Exercise 11: Have a clock (with hands) to help the students visualize what happens as the time reaches noon. Students may want to use one formula to describe the calculation for time that stretches across noon, or may want to separate the formulas into two parts. Some spreadsheet programs allow you to enter A.M. and P.M. times, but they may not allow operations with numbers expressed as clock times.

COMPUTER In Exercise 12, encourage students to experiment with other changes in the hourly rate.

Exercise 14: Students can use trial and error if they are using computers or calculators or may choose to work backward for a problem solving activity.

AUDITORY LEARNERS Students often find it helpful to narrate softly what cells are involved as they move through a spreadsheet. Encourage them to talk to themselves as they work on all these problems.

Use the information below for Exercises 13–18.

It's music video month in Ms. Houston's class. Each group of students creates a video and receives three scores from 0 to 100 for originality, effort, and technical quality. Ms. Houston entered all the scores on a spreadsheet, but a "bug" in her computer erased some of the data.

	A	B	C	D	E	F
1	Group	Originality	Effort	Quality	Total	Mean Score
2	Red	90	■ 85	80	■ 255	85
3	Orange	90	90	■ 60	■ 240	80
4	Yellow	95	100	75	■ 270	■ 90
5	Green	■ 65	80	80	■ 225	75
6	Blue	85	■ 85	85	■ 255	85

13. Write the formulas that Ms. Houston could have used to determine the values for cells E2 to E6. =B2+C2+D2; =B3+C3+D3; =B4+C4+D4; =B5+C5+D5; =B6+C6+D6

14. **Choose A, B, or C.** What formula could Ms. Houston *not* have used to determine the value for cell F2? B

A. =E2/3

B. =(B2+B3+B4)/3

C. =(B2+C2+D2)/3

15. Was it necessary for Ms. Houston to include column E in her spreadsheet to determine the mean score for each group? Explain. No; she could have added the scores for each group and divided by 3

16. Writing Explain how you can find the value in cell D3. See right.

17. a. Calculator Copy and complete the spreadsheet above. See spreadsheet above.

b. Which group created the most original video? yellow

c. Which group put the least effort into creating their video? green

d. Which group did the best job overall on their video project? Explain. yellow; they had the highest mean score

18. Critical Thinking Why does the value in cell B5 have to be less than 80? Answers may vary. Sample: if the value in cell B5 is greater than or equal to 80, the mean score would be greater than 75.

Rear Admiral Grace Hopper (1907–1992) was the first person to use the phrase "computer bug" to describe computer errors.

Source: *The Book of Women*

16. Answers may vary. Sample: Multiply the mean score in cell F3 by 3 and subtract the values in cells B3 and C3.

Use the data: 37, 11, 15, 16, 19, 11, 13, 20, 11

1. Find the range. 26
2. Find the mean. 17
3. Find the median. 15
4. Find the mode. 11
5. At 9:00 P.M. the temperature was 42°F. Between 9:00 P.M. and midnight, the temperature dropped 8°. Between midnight and 10:00 A.M., the temperature rose 15°. What was the temperature at 10:00 A.M.? 49°F

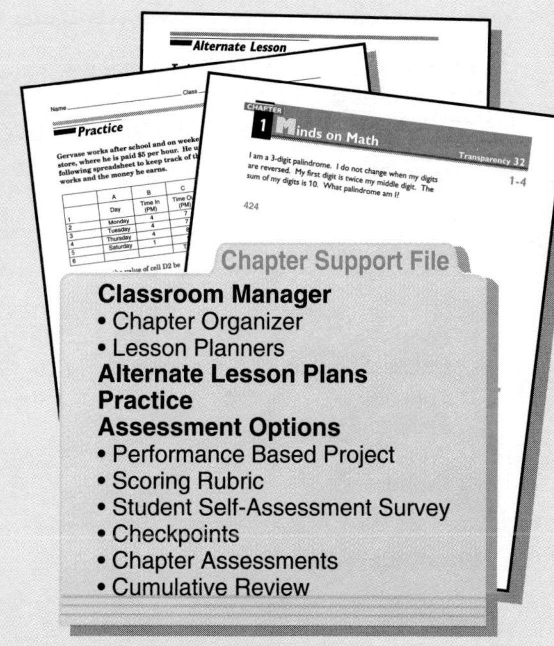

Minds on Math available in Teaching Transparencies

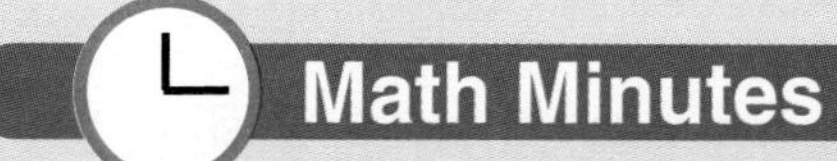

Coach Brown bought six T-shirts for her volleyball players for $47.88. What was the price per shirt? **$7.98**

1-5

Connecting to Prior Knowledge

Ask students to name ways they have seen data organized other than in tables. Have students describe these other methods. Remind them of data they might have seen reported in newspapers.

THINK AND DISCUSS

VISUAL LEARNERS Begin the discussion by asking which bar, in the graph for Question 1, is the shortest and which is the longest. Ask students to estimate how many of the shortest bars it would take to form the tallest. **(about five)** Ask if they compared visually or if they counted the horizontal sections. Point out that both approaches are valid and that different people will think differently on such tasks.

Question 2: Begin by having students explain all the labels.

After students have answered Question 4, you may wish to ask some additional questions based on the bar graph.

- *If the club collects 3 T of white ledger paper, how much money will they receive?* **($135)**
- *If they collect a half ton of cardboard boxes, how much money will they receive?* **($17.50)**
- *A ton of cardboard boxes is worth how much more than a ton of newspapers?* **($25)**
- *What do you think accounts for the different dollar amounts for each type of paper?* **(Answers will vary.)**

ESL **AUDITORY LEARNERS** Have students read the labels on the graphs for Question 5 aloud, to practice reading large numbers.

ESTIMATION For Question 7, have students compare the plotted point to the nearest displayed number. You may wish to have students give estimates for the other years shown. Make sure that students are able to justify their estimates.

" Natural abilities are like natural plants; they need pruning by study. "

—Francis Bacon

Organizer

1. **Focus**
   Connecting to Prior Knowledge
2. **Teach**
   Think and Discuss
   Work Together
3. **Closure**
   Wrap Up

Vocabulary/Symbols
bar graph
line graph
circle graph

Student Resources
Extra Practice
Student Study Guide
Practice, TR Ch. 1, p. 25
Student Study Guide, Spanish Resources, TR

Teacher Resources

Teaching Transparencies 32, 102–110
Lesson Planner, TR Ch. 1, p. 6

Prentice Hall Technology
Multimedia Math
- Math Tools, Graphs
- Hot Page™ 1-5

Computer Item Generator
- 1-5

What's Ahead
- Reading graphs for information
- Determining the most appropriate graph to represent data

1-5 Reading and Understanding Graphs

THINK AND DISCUSS

You can display data in many different ways. The type of graph you choose depends on the type of data you have collected as well as the idea you want to communicate. A **bar graph** is used to compare amounts.

Money for Recycling

Dollars (per ton): 0, 5, 10, 15, 20, 25, 30, 35, 40, 45

Type of Paper: Cardboard boxes, Newspapers, White ledger

3.b. Answers may vary. Sample: It is easy to make comparisons by comparing the heights of the bars.

4.a. cardboard boxes—$35 per ton; newspapers—$10 per ton; white ledger—$45 per ton

Paper has been made from recycled materials throughout history. The Chinese invented paper in 105 A.D., using discarded rags and fishing nets. Trees were not cut down for paper-making until the 1850s.

Source: *Origins of Everything Under, and Including, the Sun*

1. What information does the bottom of the graph show? types of recyclable paper
2. What do the numbers on the left side of the graph represent? dollars per ton of recyclable paper
3. a. Without finding the dollar amounts, order the types of paper from highest to lowest dollar amount per ton. white ledger, cardboard boxes, newspapers
   b. **Discussion** How does the bar graph allow you to make these comparisons quickly? See left.
   c. Describe the relationship between the heights of the bars and the dollars per ton of paper. The taller the bar the greater the dollars per ton of paper.
4. a. How much is each type of paper worth? See left.
   b. The Neighborhood Club collects 15 T of newspaper. About how much money will they receive? $150

After students have answered Question 8, you may wish to ask some additional questions based on the line graph.

- *Between what two years was there the smallest increase in the number of in-line skaters?* **(1989 and 1990)**
- *How many more in-line skaters were there in 1992 than in 1991?* **(about 3,500,000)**

After students have answered Question 11, you may wish to use questions such as the ones that follow to generate a discussion on the appropriateness of each graph for the given data. Such a discussion will prepare students for the Work Together activity.

- *Would a line graph be appropriate for the recycling data? Why or why not?*
- *Would a bar graph be appropriate for the in-line skater data? Why or why not?*
- *Would a line graph be appropriate for the mountain bike data? Why or why not?*

Refer students to the definitions of each kind of graph.

Ongoing Assessment Have pairs of students interview each other on what they have learned about graphs. Encourage students to ask the following questions for each graph:

- *Describe the shape of the graph.*
- *Where are the data labels for the graph?*
- *What kind of relationship does the graph show?*
- *What does each part of the graph represent?*
- *What conclusion can you draw from the graph?*

Have students evaluate each other's answers and review the material as needed.

Journal Ask students to imagine that they were writing to a friend who cannot see the graphs. Ask them to select one of the graphs shown and to describe it in words.

DIVERSITY Explain to students that, just as their physical characteristics differ, they also have developed different ways of thinking. Some people prefer to get data as pictures or graphs,

You can also display data in a *line graph.* A **line graph** shows how an amount changes over time.

5. a. What trend does the line graph above show? See right.
   b. How does the line graph visually display this trend? the line moves upward
6. **Discussion** Why might someone find the line graph more helpful than a table of data? See right.
7. **Estimation** About how many skaters were there in 1991? 6,000,000 skaters
8. Between what two years was there the greatest increase? How can you tell without calculating? 1991 and 1992; the line moves upward quicker

5.a. The number of in-line skaters has increased from 1989 to 1992.

6. Answers may vary. Sample: The line graph makes the trend of in-line skaters more apparent than does a table of data.

A **circle graph** compares parts to a whole. The entire circle represents the whole. Each wedge in the circle graph represents a part of the whole.

9. On what type of surface do the most mountain biking accidents occur? downhill
10. On what type of surface do the fewest mountain biking accidents occur? uphill
11. Describe the relationship between the size of the wedges and the number of accidents in each category. The larger the wedge, the greater the number of accidents.

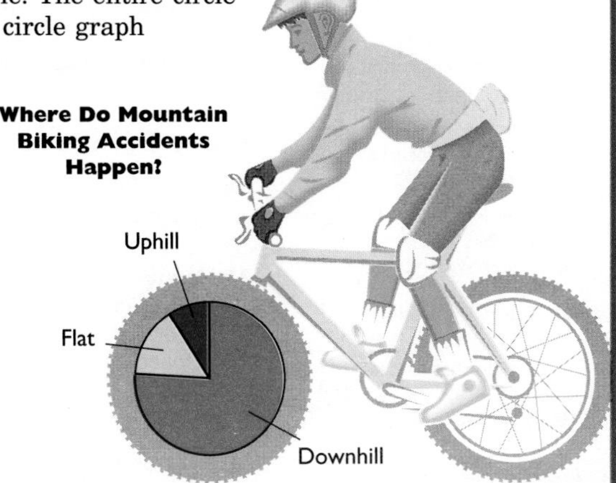

Fact of the Day

It takes 70% less energy to produce a ton of paper from recycled paper than from trees.

—*Academic American Encyclopedia*

others would rather have tables of numbers. Help students explore their own preferences and processes and to accept those that differ from their own.

WORK TOGETHER

Make sure each pair of students has two sets of answers for Question 13. Encourage students to share and discuss their explanations for Questions 12 and 13.

Error Alert! Students may have trouble comparing a bar graph and a line graph for Questions 12 and 13. ***Remediation*** Point out to students that both graphs display amounts. However, a bar graph displays a set of different amounts, and a line graph shows a change in one amount over time. Help students see this difference by pointing out that line graphs can always be continued, for example, with the next year's data. A bar graph, in contrast displays a static set.

Wrap Up

What's the Big Idea? Ask students to describe how to read graphs for information. Then ask students how they determine the most appropriate graph to represent a set of data.

Connections Have a discussion about how graphs are used. You may want to start with these examples:

- **Government** (displaying census information, describing the budget deficit, keeping track of money spent in different departments)
- **Social studies** (comparing populations in terms of culture, language, or geography, comparing the types of land in different regions, tracking world population growth)
- **Media** (displaying complicated information, breaking up lines of type with eye-catching informational graphs)

PH Multimedia Math Hot Page™ 1-5

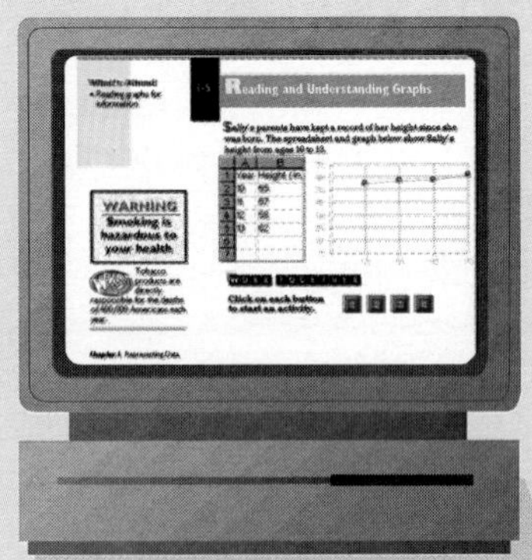

Assignment Options

Core: 14, 16–22, 27, MR all	
Reinforce: 23–26	**Enrich:** 15

Angel Falls is the highest waterfall in the world. It is located in Venezuela and is 1,000 m high.

Source: *The Information Please Almanac*

12.a. Answers may vary. Sample: circle graph; parts are being compared to a whole.

12.b. Answers may vary. Sample: a line graph; the data consists of change over time.

12.c. Answers may vary. Sample: a bar graph; ten different heights are being compared.

WORK TOGETHER

Work with a partner.

12. Choose the most appropriate graph to display each set of data. Support your answer. See left.

a. the students from each grade that are in the chorus

b. the school enrollment for each year from 1980-present

c. the heights of the ten highest waterfalls in the world

13. Describe two situations that would best be displayed in each type of graph. Ask your partner to identify the most appropriate graph for each situation.

a. bar graph b. line graph c. circle graph

Answers may vary. Check student's work.

ON YOUR OWN

Go for the Gold!

Beginning in 1994, Olympic winners will receive money as well as medals. The amount will be based on the type of medal won. The U.S. Olympic Committee says the awards will provide "a way to pay for training, to stay in the sport longer."

Olympic Awards

Medal: Bronze, Silver, Gold

0, 5,000, 10,000, 15,000

Dollars

Sports **Use the article above for Questions 14–16.**

14. How much money will an Olympic gold medalist receive? a silver medalist? a bronze medalist? $15,000; $10,000; $7,500

15. **Writing** Would a line graph also be appropriate for displaying this data? Why or why not? No; the data do not reflect change over time.

16. Describe the relationship between the length of the bar and the dollar amount for each type of Olympic medal. The longer the bar the greater the dollar amount.

Mixed REVIEW

Complete. spreadsheet

1. A table made on a computer is known as a ■.

2. A box where a row and column meet in a spreadsheet is a ■. cell

3. A ■ is a set of formula instructions that tells the computer what to do.

4. The mean average of three test scores is 85. Is it possible that the test scores are 92, 77, and 86? Why or why not?

Yes; the mean of the test scores is 85.

Reteaching Activity Challenge students to think of information that could be displayed as a graph. Then have them name the most appropriate type of graph for the data. Start students with a few examples:

- Comparing the numbers of types of reptiles at the zoo. **(bar graph)**
- Describing the composition of a pencil. **(circle graph)**
- Charting the amount of money made by the highest-grossing film of each year. **(line graph)**

ON YOUR OWN

WRITING In Exercise 15, have students try to describe what type of graph other than a bar graph would be appropriate.

CONNECTION TO SPORTS Exercises 14–20 have students read graphs that provide data on sporting events.

Exercises 23–26: Encourage students to describe the usefulness of each type of graph they mention.

VISUAL LEARNERS In Exercises 23–26, students may find it helpful actually to sketch a possible graph to help them decide.

Sports **Use the line graph below.**

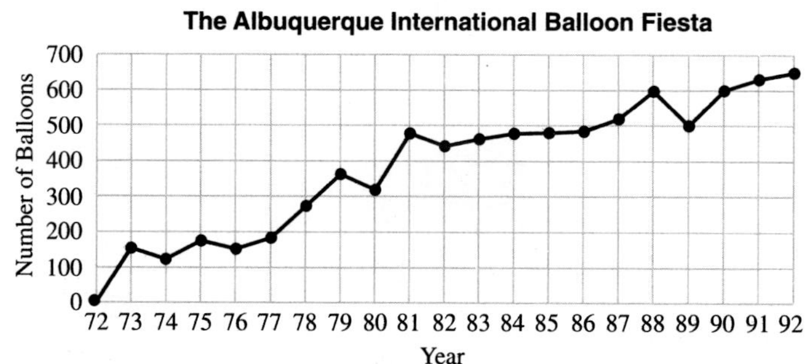

The Albuquerque International Balloon Fiesta draws entries from more than 15 countries.

17. What overall trend does the line graph show? the number of balloons in the fiesta has increased over the past 20 y
18. During what three years did the number of balloons taking part in the fiesta remain about the same? 1984, 1985, and 1986
19. During what years did the number of balloons taking part in the fiesta increase the most? 1980 to 1981
20. About how many balloons took part in the fiesta in 1992? 650 balloons

Education **Use the circle graph at the right.**

21. How many teachers do most middle grade students have? 5 teachers
22. Do about the same number of middle grade students have one teacher as have four teachers? Explain. No; the wedge for 4 teachers is much larger than the wedge for 1 teacher

Number of Teachers for the Typical Middle Grade Student

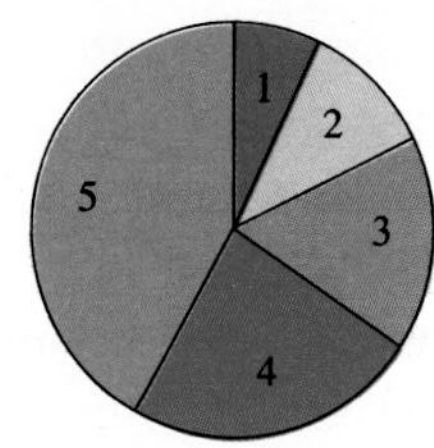

Choose the most appropriate graph to display each set of data. Support your answer. Answers may vary. Sample given.

23. the number of left-handed students and the number of right-handed students in your math class circle graph; two parts are being compared to a whole
24. the number of cases of measles in the United States for the years 1930, 1940, 1950, 1960, 1970, 1980, and 1990 line graph; the data show change over time
25. the life spans of selected animals bar graph; several life spans are being compared
26. the average temperature of Earth for each year from 1980 to the present line graph; the data show change over time
27. Data File 1 (pp. 2–3) What kind of ad appears most frequently during kid's TV? toy ads

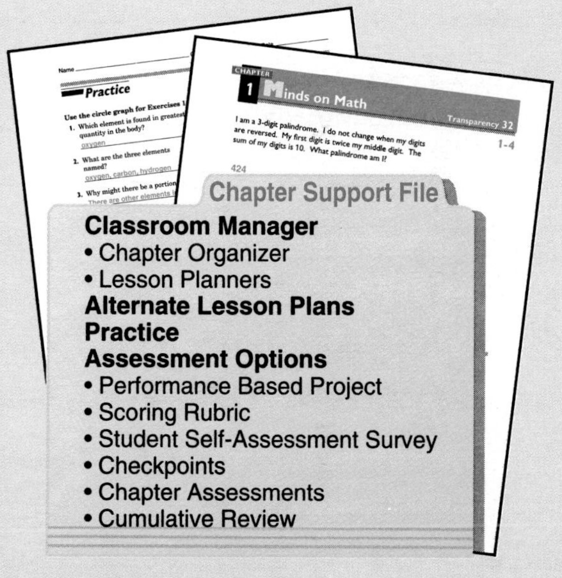

Chapter Support File

Classroom Manager
- Chapter Organizer
- Lesson Planners

Alternate Lesson Plans

Practice

Assessment Options
- Performance Based Project
- Scoring Rubric
- Student Self-Assessment Survey
- Checkpoints
- Chapter Assessments
- Cumulative Review

Minds on Math available in Teaching Transparencies

Math Minutes

Mari packaged 14 seashells in a box. If she had 360 seashells, how many full boxes did she have? How many shells were left over after the boxes were filled? **25; 10**

Materials for 1-6

- graph paper

CHAPTER 1 PRACTICE

This page provides practice on the skills learned up to this point in the chapter. Daily cumulative practice can be found in the Mixed Reviews that appear in every lesson.

Resources
Extra Practice
Student Study Guide
Student Study Guide, Spanish Resources, TR

24

Practice

Use the data in the table at the right.

1. Make a line plot. See Solution Key.
2. Find the median and mode. 198 mi/h; 196 mi/h
3. Find the range. 14 mi/h

Ten Fastest Laps of the Daytona 500 (mi/h)

196	196	199	202	205
205	210	197	197	196

Make a frequency table for each set of data.

4. $125, $122, $138, $135, $125, $122, $122 See Solution Key.
5. 800, 900, 700, 700, 800, 800, 800, 800 See Solution Key.

Find the mean, median, and mode.

6. 85, 73, 93, 74, 71, 101, 71, 90, 98 84; 85; 71
7. 1,216; 4,891; 2,098; 3,662; 5,748 3,523; 3,662; no mode

Name the type of graph most appropriate for each situation. Support your answer.

8. average cost of lunch at six restaurants bar graph
9. change in taxes paid from 1950 to 2000 line graph
10. number of senior citizens, adults, and children visiting Paramount Parks in one day circle graph

Use the bar graph at the right.

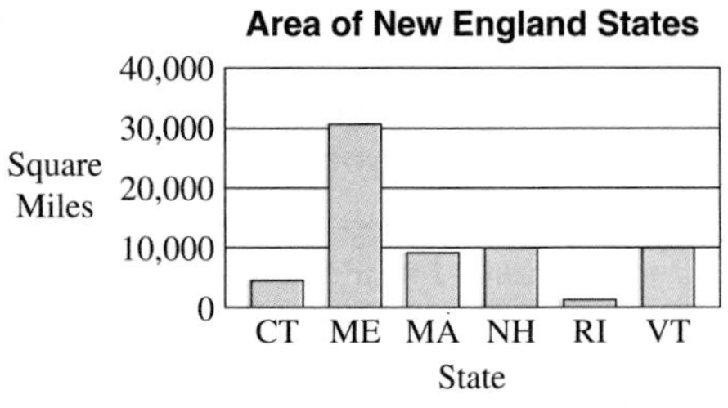

11. Which New England state has the greatest amount of land? the least amount of land? ME; RI
12. Which New England states have about the same amount of land? MA, NH, and VT
13. Compare the amount of land in Maine to the amount of land in Vermont. Maine has about 3 times as much land as Vermont.

Area of New England States

Make a table to solve.

14. Mr. Humphrey has 14 animals in his barnyard. Some are chickens, and some are goats. Simone counted 38 legs in all. How many of the animals are chickens? goats? 9 chickens; 5 goats

1-6

Connecting to Prior Knowledge

Ask students what they would do to make any of the graphs they have studied. Encourage students to express difficulties they expect and how they might overcome these problems.

THINK AND DISCUSS

Example 1

Amphibians are animals such as frogs, toads, and salamanders that usually begin life as tadpoles with gills and later develop lungs.

Make sure that students can see the relationship between the numbers in the table and the lengths of the bars in the graph. You may also wish to ask students the following questions.

- *What does the label "No. Endangered" mean?* **(number of animals endangered)**
- *Is the title for the graph clear?* **(Answers may vary.)**

Additional Example *Describe how to display the data in the table as a bar graph.*

1990 Population Per Sq. Mi of the Most Populous States

State	Population
California	190
New York	380
Texas	65
Florida	239
Pennsylvania	265

- **Draw horizontal and vertical axes.**
- **Put the name of each state on the horizontal axis.**
- **Choose a scale. The data go from 65 to 380. Draw and label a scale from 0 to 400 using intervals of 50.**
- **Draw a bar to show the number of people per square mile in each state.**
- **Label the axes. Label the graph.**

ESL Explain the words "trend," "horizontal," "vertical," and "scale." Have students copy the graph in Example 2 and write these words in appropriate places on the graph.

What's Ahead

- Constructing bar and line graphs

1-6 Constructing Bar and Line Graphs

THINK AND DISCUSS

Many animals face the danger of disappearing forever. Environmental changes, such as climate and geology, are the main causes. However, human activities like hunting, pollution, and land clearing also contribute. The table shows the number of animals endangered in the United States.

U.S. Endangered Animals

Type of Animal	Number Endangered
Mammals	36
Birds	53
Reptiles	18
Amphibians	10
Fish	70

Example 1 Draw a bar graph to display the data at the left.

- Draw the horizontal and vertical axes. Put the name of each type of endangered animal on the horizontal axis.
- Choose a scale for the vertical axis. The data go from 10 to 70. Draw and label a scale from 0 to 70, using intervals of 10.
- Draw a bar to show the number of each type of endangered animal.
- Label the horizontal and vertical axes. Give your bar graph a title.

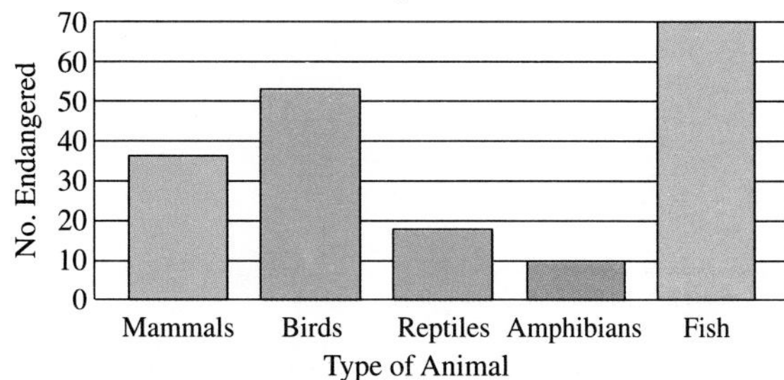

1. **Discussion** How would you display this data in a bar graph where the bars are horizontal? **See below.**
2. Suppose the graph was drawn using intervals of 5. What are the advantages and disadvantages of using intervals of 5, instead of 10? **See Solution Key.**

The long fight to save wild beauty represents democracy at its best. It requires citizens to practice the hardest of virtues—self-restraint.

—Edwin Way Teale (1899–1980)

1. Answers may vary. Sample: The vertical axis is labeled 'Type of Animal.' The horizontal axis is labeled 'No. Endangered.' The bars are parallel to the horizontal axis.

"Mathematics is like checkers in being suitable for the young, not too difficult, amusing, and without peril to the state."

—Plato

Organizer

1. **Focus**
   Connecting to Prior Knowledge
2. **Teach**
   Think and Discuss
3. **Closure**
   Try These
   Wrap Up

Skills Reviewed in Context of Lesson

- identifying bar graphs
- identifying line graphs

Materials and Manipulatives

- graph paper (3 pieces for each student)

On Your Own Exercises 8, 9, 11, 12: graph paper

Student Resources

Extra Practice
Student Study Guide
Practice, TR Ch. 1, p. 26
Student Study Guide, Spanish Resources, TR
Alternate Lesson, TR Ch. 1, pp. 17–20
Checkpoint, TR Ch. 1, p. 32

continues next page

Example 2

- *What does the line graph display?*
  (change in United States population per square mile)
- *In 1990, did every square mile contain 70 people?*
  (No; 70 is an average; some square mile areas were more crowded and some were less crowded)
- *What trend does the graph reveal?*
  (steady increase in population)

TECHNOLOGY OPTION Students can use the computer with programs that make graphs from data. Many spreadsheets, word processing programs, and integrated programs offer this option. There are also programs designed specifically for drawing graphs.

Ongoing Assessment Have the students help you write a brief outline on the chalkboard of the steps needed to construct bar and line graphs. Encourage students to identify similarities and differences in the procedures.

Journal Encourage students to describe how the appearance of each type of graph shows the purpose of the graph. For example, a line graph shows downward trends with a downward slope. Ask them to explain how a graphic display gives a "picture" of the data.

TRY THESE

Exercise 4: Refer to the graphs for Examples 1 and 2 and review the rationale that was used for determining the scales.

Error Alert! Students may be unsure about an interval to use for Exercises 4 and 5. ***Remediation*** Tell students to study the range of the data. A good height for a graph is about ten intervals. Ask students to round the greatest piece of data and divide by ten. Students can use the rounded results for their intervals.

Organizer, continued

Teacher Resources

Teaching Transparency 33
Transparency Masters, TR p. 2
Lesson Planner, TR Ch. 1, p. 7

Prentice Hall Technology

Multimedia Math
- Math Tools, Graphs
- Math Tools, Spreadsheet

Computer Item Generator
- 1-6

Other Available Technology

Data Insights by Sunburst: Exercise 5 *(optional)*
Microsoft Graph: Exercises 5, 8, 9, 11, 12 *(optional)*
Cricket Graph: Exercises 5, 8, 9, 11, 12 *(optional)*

Fact of the Day

At the end of the Permian Period (280 million to 225 million years ago), more than 90% of all existing species of marine life disappeared. It was the greatest mass extinction in history.

—ACADEMIC AMERICAN ENCYCLOPEDIA

The table shows the United States population per square mile for selected years from 1930.

United States Population Per Square Mile	
Year	Population
1930	35
1940	37
1950	43
1960	51
1970	58
1980	64
1990	70

Example 2 Draw a line graph to display the data at the left.

- Draw the axes. Then write the years on evenly spaced intervals on the horizontal axis.
- Choose a scale for the vertical axis. The data go from 35 to 70. Draw and label a scale from 0 to 70, using intervals of 10.
- Place a point on the graph for the population for each year. Connect the points.
- Label the horizontal and vertical axes. Give your line graph a title.

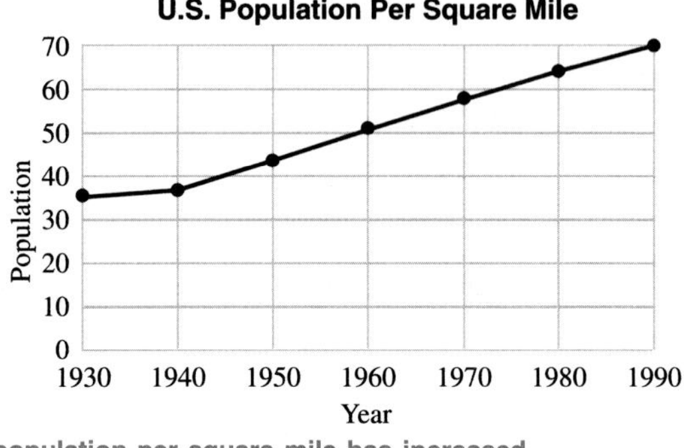

3. a. What trend does the line graph show? The U.S. population per square mile has increased from 1930 to 1990.
   b. Would changing the intervals on the vertical axis affect the trend? Explain. No; an increase in population per square mile would still be shown regardless of the interval on the vertical axis.

4.a. Answers may vary. Sample: scale from 0 to 60, using intervals of 10.
4.b. Answers may vary. Sample: horizontal axis—Average speed (mi/h); vertical axis—Type of Animal

TRY THESE

4. Suppose the average speeds of five animals range from 25 mi/h to 60 mi/h.
   a. What scale would you use to display the data in a horizontal bar graph? Why? See left.
   b. How would you label the horizontal and vertical axes? See left.
5. Display the data at the left in a line graph. See Solution Key.

Sailboats Built in the United States	
Year	Number
1988	14,510
1989	11,790
1990	11,709
1991	8,672
1992	11,264

Wrap Up

What's the Big Idea? Ask students to explain how to construct bar and line graphs.

Connections Have students brainstorm about ways line graphs and bar graphs could be used in the following areas:

- **Baseball** (numbers of hits by players; hitting trends over the course of the season)
- **Music** (compare sales of cassettes, records, CDs, and singles, the sales of compact discs over years)
- **Business** (sales of colors of cars; sales trends)

Reteaching Activity Ask students to name the type of graph that would best compare numbers of boys and girls in the classroom. **(bar graph)** Have students construct bar graphs to compare the male and female populations of the room. Ask students to explain how they determined their scale. Have them compare graphs.

VISUAL LEARNERS Ask students to compare the ease of finding the largest and smallest in a table or from a graph. Use this as a motivator for creating graphs.

ON YOUR OWN

CONNECTION TO SOCIAL STUDIES Exercises 9 and 10 have students compare the changes in population of two American cities.

WRITING For Exercises 10a and b, have students describe the difference in terms of a trend. Then have students tell how a line graph could show the trend.

WRITING Have students describe how the graph reveals a trend for Exercise 11d.

CHAPTER INVESTIGATION For Exercise 12, have students in groups of four compare data that they have acquired outside of class. Students could count fists of family members and friends.

ON YOUR OWN

Architecture **Use the table below for Exercises 6–8.**

Five Highest Buildings in New York City		
Building	**Stories**	**Height (ft)**
World Trade Center (North)	110	1,368
World Trade Center (South)	110	1,362
Empire State Building	102	1,250
Chrysler Building	77	1,046
American International Building	67	950

6. What intervals would you use to construct a bar graph displaying the number of stories in each building? Answers may vary. Sample: intervals of 10
7. What intervals would you use to construct a bar graph displaying the heights of the buildings? Answers may vary. Sample: intervals of 200
8. Construct a bar graph displaying the number of stories in New York City's five highest buildings. See Solution Key.

Social Studies **Use the table below for Exercises 9 and 10.**

Population of Ohio Cities		
Year	**Cleveland**	**Columbus**
1950	914,808	375,901
1960	876,050	471,316
1970	751,000	540,000
1980	574,000	565,000
1990	505,616	632,958

9. Construct a line graph for the population of Cleveland. What trend does your line graph show? See Solution Key for line graph. The population declined from 1950 to 1990.
10. a. Writing How is the data for the population of Cleveland different from the data for the population of Columbus? See right.
    b. Writing How would this difference be displayed on a line graph? A line for the population of Columbus would move upward; a line for the population of Cleveland would move downward.

Mixed REVIEW

For Exercises 1–3, name the type of graph that would be most appropriate.

1. frequency with which students in your class rent movie videos bar graph
2. average monthly rainfall in Seattle, Washington
3. change in home prices from 1980 to the present line graph
4. Find two consecutive numbers whose product is 462. 21 and 22

2. bar graph

10.a. The population of Cleveland decreased over the same time period as the population of Columbus increased.

Ohio is situated between Lake Erie and the Ohio River. The state's name comes from an Iroquois word meaning "great river."

Source: *Encyclopedia Americana*

Assignment Options

Core: 6–9, 12, MR all, CH all	
Reinforce: 11	**Enrich:** 10

CHECKPOINT

Exercise 1 is an enhanced multiple choice question.

CONNECTION TO HISTORY After Exercises 3 and 4, challenge students to find out the history of the Vietnam War and report to the class.

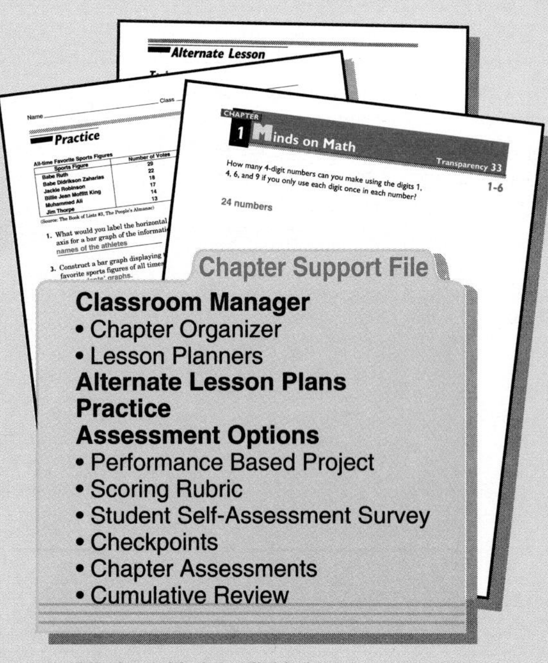

Minds on Math available in Teaching Transparencies

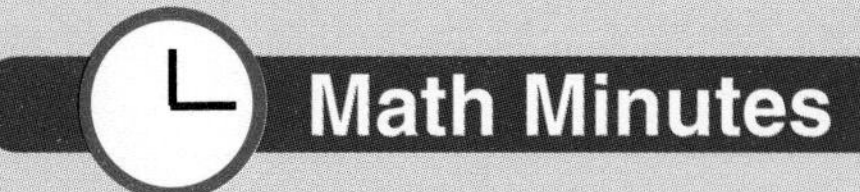

What combination of 2 bills and 3 coins can be used to make $15.45?
one $10 bill, one $5 bill, 1 quarter, 2 dimes

Materials for 1-7

- graph paper

Cost of a College Education

School Year	Public ($)	Private ($)
1984–1985	3,682	8,451
1986–1987	4,138	10,039
1988–1989	4,678	11,474
1990–1991	5,243	13,237
1992–1993	6,125	15,255

11. Education Use the table at the left.

a. Construct a line graph displaying the cost of a public college education. See Solution Key.

b. Construct a line graph displaying the cost of a private college education. Use the same intervals as the ones you used to construct a line graph in part (a). See Solution Key.

c. Describe the trend(s) shown in your line graphs. See left.

d. Which type of college education has increased at a higher rate? private

e. How is this shown on the graph? The line on the graph is steeper.

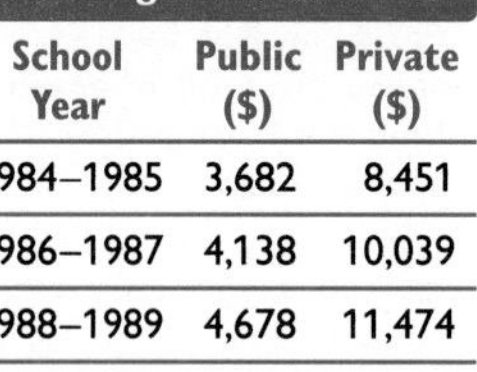

12. Investigation (p. 4) Collect data on the number of times 10 people open and close their fists in one minute. Choose the most appropriate graph to display your data. Answers may vary. Check student's work.

11.c. Both the cost of a public college education and a private college education are increasing.

CHECKPOINT

Use the spreadsheet below.

	A	B	C	D	E	F
1	Student	Test 1	Test 2	Test 3	Test 4	Mean Score
2	Justin	80	78	94	88	■
3	Elizabeth	64	78	82	80	■
4	Naomi	94	84	88	82	

1. **Choose A, B, or C.** What formula could you use to determine the value in cell F4? C
   A. =(B2+B3+B4)/3
   B. =(A4+B4+C4+D4+E4)/5
   C. =(B4+C4+D4+E4)/4

2. Construct a bar graph displaying the mean scores for the students listed in the spreadsheet. See Solution Key.

Medals of Honor Awarded for Service in Vietnam

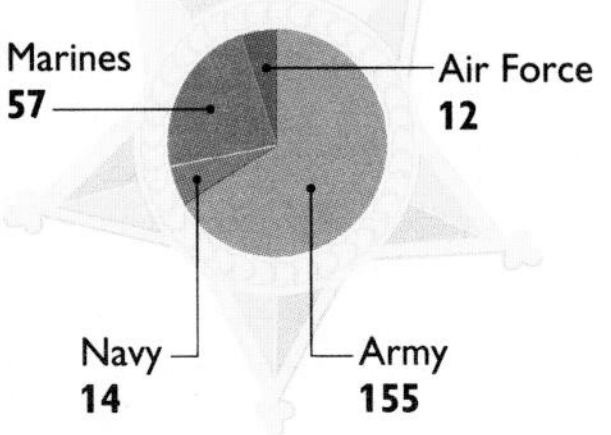

Use the circle graph at the left.

3. Which branch received the most medals of honor for service in the Vietnam War? Army

4. How many medals of honor were awarded for service in the Vietnam War? 238 medals of honor

1-7

Connecting to Prior Knowledge

Ask students to share strategies they used to make sure the graphs they constructed were clear and accurate. Then have students brainstorm for ways the same strategies could be used to make graphs misleading.

THINK AND DISCUSS

Question 1b: Have students outline the differences in the graphs shown in the textbook. Have them describe the visual differences and identify what possible effects each might have for the reader.

ESL **DIVERSITY** All students may not have access to newspapers and magazines. Ask the library for a collection of materials suitable for cutting out pages. This gives all students access to graphs used in advertising. Tell students that examples from publications in languages other than English are welcome, especially if they can explain the titles and labels. Use this as an opportunity to point out that math is a language that can often be understood with little translation.

VISUAL LEARNERS These students often enjoy collecting graphs used in advertising and displaying them for others in the class. Ask students to evaluate the aesthetic qualities of the graphs. Which are pretty and which grab the viewer's attention?

ESL **ESL** If students have difficulty reading the text for Questions 1–6, encourage them to use their bilingual dictionaries. Classmates who are fluent in English should be encouraged to help ESL students with these problems.

Ongoing Assessment Have students assess their own understanding of the ways to analyze graphs. Ask students to write a list of what they have learned. Challenge students to think of ways they could apply this knowledge.

Journal Ask students if they think it is easier to present data to one's own advantage or to present data objectively. Ask them

---

What's Ahead

- Analyzing the effect of different scales and intervals on graphs
- Recognizing misleading graphs

MATH AND ADVERTISING

1-7 Analyzing Graphs

THINK AND DISCUSS

You can represent data in many different ways. Companies often display data in a way that presents their best image and persuades you to see things their way. The table at the left shows the basic monthly rate for Quality Cable Company.

See left.

1. Suppose Quality Cable Company wants to raise the monthly charge.
   a. What graph might the cable company use to persuade you that an increase is justified? Explain.
   b. What graph might the customers use to argue that an increase is not justified? Explain.

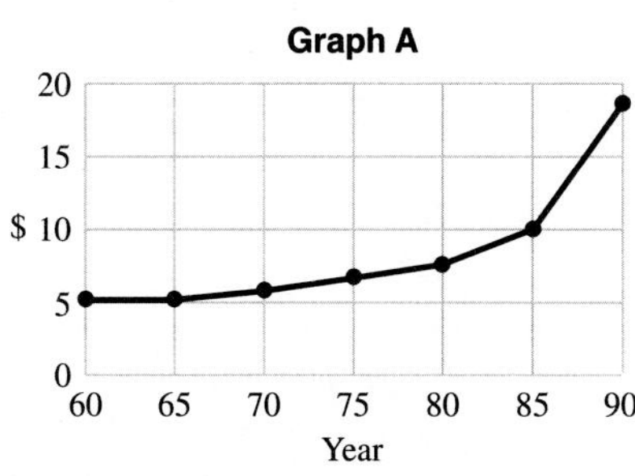

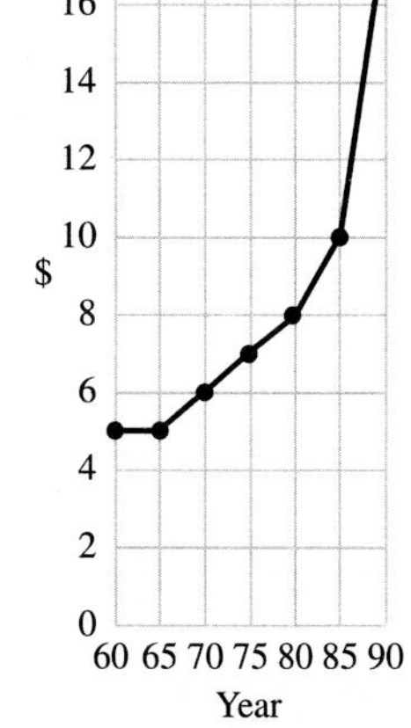

Quality Cable Company

Year	Monthly Charge
1960	$5
1965	$5
1970	$6
1975	$7
1980	$8
1985	$10
1990	$18

1.a. Graph A; it appears the cost has not increased much over 30 y.

1.b. Graph B; it appears the cost has increased a lot over 30 y.

2.a. The smaller the interval, the greater any changes in data appear and the steeper the line on the graph.

2. a. How does the appearance of a set of data displayed in a line graph change as the intervals on the vertical scale decrease? See left.
   b. **Discussion** How would the appearance of a set of data displayed in a vertical bar graph change as the intervals on the vertical scale increase? As the intervals increase, the height of the bars decrease.
3. How does the appearance of a set of data displayed in a line graph change as the data items on the horizontal scale are spaced farther apart? The line becomes flatter and therefore shows a more gradual increase or decrease.

> *"A fact in our lives is valuable not so far as it is true, but as it is significant."*
> —JOHANN WOLFGANG VON GOETHE

Organizer

1. **Focus**
   Connecting to Prior Knowledge
2. **Teach**
   Think and Discuss
   Work Together
3. **Closure**
   Wrap Up

Skills Reviewed in Context of Lesson
- reading a line graph

Materials and Manipulatives
- graph paper (for each student)

On Your Own Exercises 7, 8: graph paper

Student Resources
Extra Practice
Student Study Guide
Practice, TR Ch. 1, p. 27
Student Study Guide, Spanish Resources, TR

Teacher Resources
Teaching Transparency 33
Transparency Masters, TR p. 2
Lesson Planner, TR Ch. 1, p. 8

continues next page

to write a story about a person asked by a boss to create a misleading graph as part of the job.

WORK TOGETHER

Have students work in pairs to check each other's answers. Encourage each pair to work together on Question 6.

Error Alert! Students may not be able to answer Questions 4 and 5 without having another graph for a comparison. ***Remediation*** Encourage students to draw a rough sketch of a graph of the data without a gap in the vertical axis.

Wrap Up

What's the Big Idea? Ask students to describe how to analyze the effects of different scales and intervals on graphs. Have students explain how to recognize misleading graphs.

Connections Have a discussion about how analyzing graphs can be useful. You may want to start with these examples:

- **Business** (reviewing contract bids, deciding on a shipping line or a service technician based on their ads or portfolios)
- **Consumer** (comparing products with conflicting claims, finding a plumber or mechanic through advertisements)

Reteaching Activity Bring to class copies of advertisements that include graphs. Show these to students and ask them if they can find any distortion in the graphs. Ask them to explain how they would redraw the graphs to eliminate distortions.

ON YOUR OWN

TECHNOLOGY OPTION For Exercises 7 and 8, students could use the computer with programs that have graphing options and scales that can be altered.

Organizer, continued

Prentice Hall Technology

Multimedia Math
- Math Tools, Graphs
- Math Tools, Spreadsheet
- Hot Page™ 1-7
- Math Investigations, Hazard City Messengers

Computer Item Generator
- 1-7

Other Available Technology

Another Option for Spreadsheets by AppleWorks: Exercises 7, 8 *(optional)*

Fact of the Day

A television image must flash on and off at least 25 times per second to give the illusion of continuous motion.

—The Way Things Work

PH Multimedia Math Hot Page™ 1-7

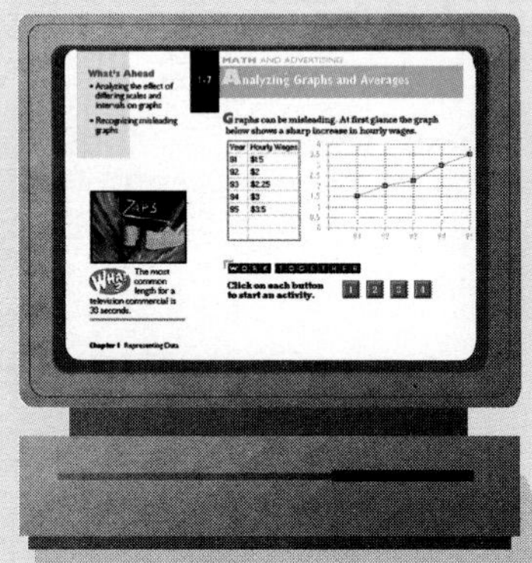

The American Tour de Sol is an annual pollution-free car race. Its purpose is to educate the public about non-polluting alternatives to gasoline-fed automobiles.

Source: AAA World

WORK TOGETHER

A car dealership claims that it has dramatically increased its business over the past three months. One of their advertisements shows the graph at the right.

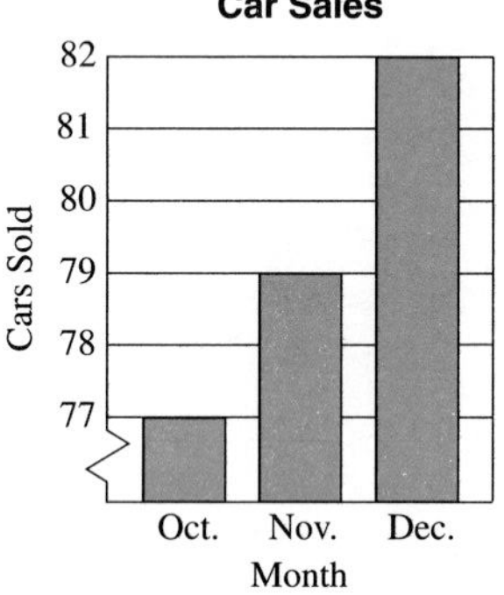

4. Do you agree or disagree with their claim? Explain. See Solution Key.
5. a. There is a gap in the scale, which begins at 77 instead of 0. How is this gap represented? a broken line
   b. How does a gap affect the appearance of the data? See Solution Key.
6. Suppose the company wants to show that car sales have been constant over the past three months. Draw a bar graph to support this claim. See Solution Key.

DECISION MAKING

Polling Your Peers

COLLECT DATA

Collect data about the favorite pastimes of 25 of your classmates. You may want to limit the choices to seven or eight different pastimes. Some choices may include reading, exercising, shopping, and dancing.

1. What other choices could you include in your survey? Answers may vary. Sample: sports, talking on the phone
2. a. Describe how you will organize the responses of the 25 classmates. Answers will vary. Sample: use a frequency table
   b. Is there more than one way that you could organize the responses? Explain. Yes; use a frequency table or a line plot

ANALYZE DATA

3. What was chosen as the favorite pastime of your classmates? Answers will vary. Check student's work.

WRITING For Exercise 9, have students compare the procedures and effects of the graphs.

Decision Making

Students could begin their surveys by making a table to record responses. Students can then make a new table for Exercise 5. Have students compare their graphs for Exercise 7.

ON YOUR OWN

Use the table below.

Money Raised in a National Telethon			
Year	Dollars	Year	Dollars
1983	30,691,627	1988	41,132,113
1984	32,074,566	1989	42,209,727
1985	33,181,652	1990	44,172,186
1986	34,096,773	1991	45,071,857
1987	39,021,723	1992	45,759,368

7. Draw a line graph showing that the money raised increased dramatically each year. See Solution Key.
8. Draw a line graph showing that the money raised increased at a fairly slow rate. See Solution Key.
9. Writing Explain how you constructed the graphs in Exercises 7 and 8 to achieve the desired results. See Solution Key.

Mixed REVIEW

1. Draw a bar graph to display the data below.

City	Average Snowfall
Albany, NY	65.5 in.
Boston, MA	41.8 in.
Juneau, AK	102.8 in.
Omaha, NE	31.1 in.

2. Sumi earns $4.50 an hour baby-sitting. She is saving to buy a tape player that costs $89.95. For how many hours will she have to baby-sit to earn enough money to buy the tape player? 20 h

1. See Solution Key.

Assignment Options

Core: 7, DM all, MR all	
Reinforce: 8	Enrich: 9

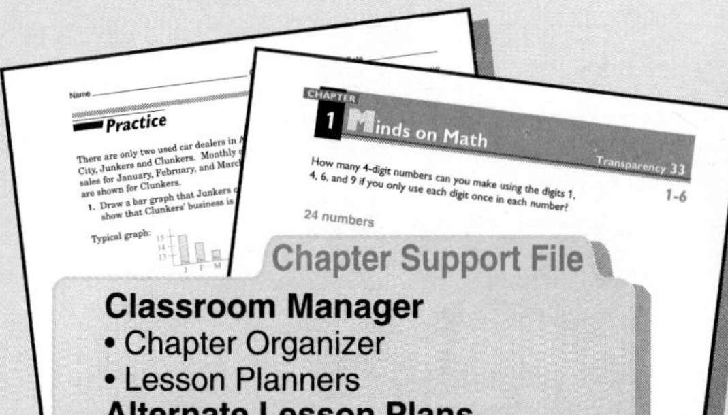

Classroom Manager
- Chapter Organizer
- Lesson Planners

Alternate Lesson Plans
Practice
Assessment Options
- Performance Based Project
- Scoring Rubric
- Student Self-Assessment Survey
- Checkpoints
- Chapter Assessments
- Cumulative Review

Minds on Math available in Teaching Transparencies

Answers will vary for Exercises 4–7. Check student's work.

4. Was any one pastime a lot more popular than the others? If so, which one? Why do you think so?
5. Order the pastimes according to popularity.

MAKE DECISIONS

6. What type of graph would be most appropriate to display your data? Explain.
7. Suppose you have to make a presentation to the school principal about the favorite pastimes of your classmates.
   a. Draw a bar graph showing that there is a wide variety in the pastimes of your classmates.
   b. Draw a bar graph showing that all pastimes are liked about the same by your classmates.
   c. Explain how you constructed each graph to achieve the desired results.

Listening to music is a favorite pastime for people of all ages.

Math Minutes

Find three numbers between 400 and 410 that are divisible by 3. **402, 405, 408**

CHAPTER 1 WRAP UP

Exercises 1–2: You may want to suggest that students count vowels and words in the given paragraph more than once, and perhaps in more than one order, to make sure of counting accurately.

Ongoing Assessment

Have students work with partners or in groups on the exercises involving graphs.

Exercises 3–4: Have students decide in groups what row and column headings to use in their tables. Circulate and see who needs help.

Exercises 5–6: You may need to remind the students that the mean is computed by adding the data values and then dividing by the number of data values.

Exercises 7–9: You may want to review how cells are labeled.

Vocabulary/Symbols

bar graph
cell
circle graph
formula
frequency table
line graph
line plot
mean
median
mode
primary colors
range
spreadsheet

Materials and Manipulatives

- graph paper

Answers to Problems Unique to Spanish Edition

1.

Vocal	Conteo	Frec.
a	𝍸𝍸𝍸𝍸 III	23
e	𝍸𝍸𝍸𝍸𝍸 II	27
i	𝍸 I	6
o	𝍸𝍸𝍸	15
u	𝍸𝍸𝍸	15

2.

```
        x
        x
    x   x
x   x   x
---------
el una de
```

Frequency Tables and Line Plots 1-1

A ***frequency table*** lists data and uses a tally system to show the number of times each response or item occurs. A ***line plot*** displays data above a horizontal line.

1. Make a frequency table showing the number of times each vowel appears in the paragraph above. See Solution Key.
2. Make a line plot showing the number of times the words *the, and, a,* and *are* appear in the paragraph above. See Solution Key.

Make a Table 1-2

You can make a table to organize the possible solutions to a problem.

3. In how many ways can you make 21¢? 9 ways
4. In how many ways can you make $1.00 using only dimes, quarters, and half-dollars? 6 ways

Three Kinds of Averages 1-3

The ***mean*** is a number around which the numbers in a set seem to cluster. The ***median*** is the middle number in a set of data. The ***mode*** is the data item that appears most often.

Find the mean, median, and mode of each set of data.

5. scores: 34, 49, 63, 43, 50, 50, 26 45; 49; 50
6. rainfall in centimeters: 3, 7, 1, 9, 9, 5, 8 6; 7; 9

Technology: Computer Spreadsheets 1-4

A ***spreadsheet*** is an electronic table. A ***cell*** is the box where a row and column meet. Cells can hold data or formulas.

	A	B	C	D	E
1	Date	Kite Sales ($)	String Sales ($)	Book Sales ($)	Total Sales ($)
2	9/9/93	500	85	145	■
3	9/10/93	750	65	125	■

Getting Ready for Chapter 2

The skills previewed will help students understand and solve problems involving triangles, circles, and quadrilaterals.

7. What does the number in cell C3 mean?
   String sales on 9/10/93 totaled $65.
8. How can you calculate the value of cell E2? =B2+C2+D2
9. What is the value of cell E3? $940.00

Bar Graphs and Line Graphs — 1-5, 1-6, 1-7

We use ***bar graphs*** to show numerical data that captures a moment in time. We use ***line graphs*** to show data that changes over time. The intervals you use on the graph's scales can affect the graph's appearance.

Choose the most appropriate graph to display each set of data. Support your answer.

10. the distance from your town to the best colleges in your state bar graph
11. your height on each birthday from birth to the present line graph
12. the sales of different types of lunches in the cafeteria circle graph

Graph each data set using the most appropriate graph.

13. the data you compiled in the frequency table in Exercise 1
14. the cost of tickets showing a dramatic price increase
15. the cost of tickets showing a slight price increase

13–15. See Solution Key for graphs.

Year	Ticket Cost
1970	10.00
1975	15.00
1980	20.00
1985	25.00
1990	30.00

GETTING READY FOR CHAPTER 2

Geometric shapes are all around us. Many everyday objects rely on geometry for good design.

Identify each plane figure.

1. triangle
2. rhombus, parallelogram, square, rectangle

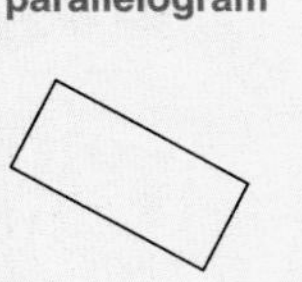

3. rectangle parallelogram

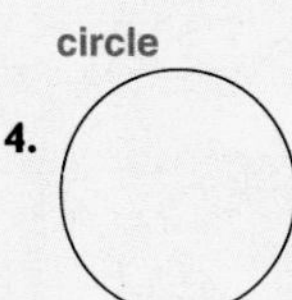

4. circle

Name an object that has the given geometric shape. Answers will vary. Sample given.

5. triangle tip of an arrowhead
6. square tile
7. circle pizza
8. rectangle photograph

Student Resources

Practice, p. 24
Problem Solving Practice, p. 15
Extra Practice
Student Study Guide
Student Study Guide, Spanish Resources, TR
Tools for Studying Smarter, TR
Student Self-Assessment Survey, TR Ch. 1, p. 31 *(see below)*

Name ____ Class ____ Date ____

Chapter 1 Student Self-Assessment Survey

1. Now that you have finished this chapter, think about what you have learned about representing data. Check each topic that you feel confident you can do.
   ____ use a frequency table and a line plot to organize data (1-1)
   ____ solve problems by making a table (1-2)
   ____ find the mean, median, and mode (1-3)
   ____ decide which average to use in a given situation (1-3)
   ____ use a spreadsheet to organize data (1-4)
   ____ read graphs for information (1-5)
   ____ choose the most appropriate graph to represent data (1-5)
   ____ make bar graphs and line graphs (1-6)
   ____ analyze the use of scales and intervals in graphs (1-7)
   ____ recognize misleading graphs (1-7)
2. Before the Chapter Assessment, I need to review ____
3. a. Check one. In general, I thought this chapter was
   a snap ____ easy ____ average ____ hard ____ a monster ____
   b. Why do you feel this way? ____
4. In this chapter, I did my best work on ____
5. In this chapter, I had trouble with ____
6. List three places outside the classroom where people use graphs to represent data. ____
7. Did you use a spreadsheet on the computer? ____ If so, did you find the computer helpful? ____ Explain. ____

ASSESSMENTS

31 Course 1 Chapter 1

CHAPTER 1 PUTTING IT ALL TOGETHER

The projects on these pages can be used in a variety of ways.

- alternative assessment
- portfolio ideas
- additional assignments for gifted and talented students
- extra credit for all students

Follow Up

Suggest that students look for characteristics linking people with similar pulse rates. For example: a person's physical condition can affect the pulse rate (the more efficiently a person's heart-lung system operates, the lower the pulse rate).

EXCURSION Students should expect to have their highest pulse rates during periods of physical activity and their lowest rates during sleep. Rates will usually increase at times of stress or anxiety.

"And the winner is . . ."

TECHNOLOGY OPTION If a computer is available, have the students use the capabilities of a graphing program to organize the results of the survey.

Students can make presentations to the class about their survey and the graphs they chose to display the data.

- For oral presentations, students can include an enlarged version of their graphs.
- For presentations in a notebook, have the students include all written explanations and graphs.
- For presentations with a computerized version of their data, have the students include a written explanation.
- For video presentations, have the students include oral explanations about how they conducted the survey and explanations about their graphs. Students may wish to work in groups in order to plan the interviews, obtain the video equipment, and decide on the appropriate taping procedures.

Materials and Manipulatives

Follow Up *Excursion*
- stop watch
- graph paper

And the winner is . . .
- graph paper

Data Duels
- newspapers or magazines

Ups and Downs
- graph paper

Measuring Up
- ruler, measuring tape, or yardstick
- graph paper

Prentice-Hall Technology

And the winner is . . .
Multimedia Math
- Math Tools, Graphs
- Math Tools, Text

Other Available Technology

And the winner is . . .
- *Word* by Microsoft
- *WriteNow* by Wordstar
- *II Write* by American School Publishers
- *Bank Street Writer* by Broderbund

(all optional)

Follow Up *Excursion*
Microsoft Graph (optional)
Cricket Graph (optional)

And the winner is . . .
Microsoft Graph (optional)
Cricket Graph (optional)

PUTTING IT ALL TOGETHER

Follow Up

Have a Heart

In this chapter you learned ways to analyze and display data. Look back at the poster you made to display the results of your pulse-rate survey. How could you better analyze the data? How could you display your results in a more meaningful way? Revise your poster using what you have learned. You may want to use the following suggestions to improve your poster.

✓ Use a frequency table.
✓ Use averages.
✓ Use an appropriate graph.

The problems preceded by the magnifying glass (p. 7, # 15; p. 14, # 16; and p. 28, # 12) will help you complete the investigation.

The blood that your heart pumps throughout your body is rich in oxygen from your lungs. The better your physical condition the more efficiently your heart and lungs work together to process and transport oxygen. Would you expect a professional athlete to have a higher or lower pulse rate than that of the average person?

Excursion: When is your pulse rate higher than average? When is it lower? Sketch a graph showing your estimated pulse rates over a 24-hour period. The graph should begin when you wake up and extend to the same hour the next day.

"And the winner is..."

Take a survey. Ask 20 students in your school to name their favorite musical group. Organize the results of your survey onto a graph, table, or line plot. Write a brief summary explaining the results of your survey. Tell why you chose to display your data the way you did.

34

Data Duels

RESEARCH An excellent resource for bar and line graphs can be found in the newspaper *USA Today*. Not only do the graphs contain relevant and up-to-date data, the graphs are interesting to investigate because of their unique graphics. Ask a library to save old copies for you so that you can cut out the graphs and use them for class.

If any of the students find graphs that contain data relevant to teenagers, display the graphs and their corresponding math problems on the walls outside of the classroom so that other students can have a chance to read them between classes.

Ups and Downs

If the students have friends or relatives in other parts of the country, have the students collect out-of-state data and graph the results.

Measuring Up

COOPERATIVE GROUPS Have students work in groups of three. While one student is being measured, the second student measures; the third student's job is to hold the measuring instrument and record the data. As each student is measured, the other jobs rotate, so that everyone in the group will eventually do each job.

DATA DUELS
Collect examples of bar graphs, line graphs, circle graphs, and tables from newspapers and magazines.
Select one bar graph, one line graph, one circle graph, and one table from your collection.
Write several math problems that can be solved by using the data represented in each graph or table. Challenge others to solve your problems.
UPS & DOWNS
Record the high and low temperatures each day for one week. The information can be obtained from radio broadcasts or newspapers. Use your data to construct a line graph with two lines. One line will show the high temperatures and another will show the low temperatures. Explain your graph to a friend.
measuring UP
Try this with your group.
Use a ruler or yardstick to measure the height of each member of your group.
Record your data and display it on a horizontal bar graph.
Find the average height of the members of your group. Draw a vertical line down the graph, showing the average height.
35

Ups and Downs
Microsoft Graph (optional)
Cricket Graph (optional)

Measuring Up
Microsoft Graph (optional)
Cricket Graph (optional)

CHAPTER

1 ASSESSMENT

Writing Questions allow students to describe more fully their thinking and understanding of the concepts they've learned. Exercises 5b and 6 are writing questions.

ESTIMATION For Exercise 2, ask students to estimate the mean before computing it. This will help them to see whether their answers are reasonable.

Exercise 3: Point out that an outfit consists of a top, a pair of pants or shorts, and a pair of shoes. You may want to review the use of a table to organize data.

Exercise 10: Ask students to write down estimates of the number of students enrolled at each grade level before attempting to answer the questions.

Resources

Performance Based Project, TR Ch. 1, pp. 28–30
Chapter Assessment, Forms A and B, TR Ch. 1, pp. 33–36
Spanish Chapter Assessment, Spanish Resources, TR
Computer Item Generator

CHAPTER 1

Assessment

1. The sizes of 15 families living on Pike Road are 1, 3, 2, 1, 3, 1, 2, 6, 2, 3, 3, 4, 3, 4, and 5. See Solution Key.

a. Make a frequency table.

b. Make a line plot. See Solution Key.

2. Find the mean, median, mode, and range of each set of data.

a. 12, 7, 8, 6, 9, 7, 10, 8, 11, 8 8.6; 8; 8; 6

b. \$31, \$45, \$20, \$22, \$31, \$48, \$27 \$32; \$31; \$31; \$28

3. Elena packs black shorts, jeans, and red pants. She adds a yellow T-shirt, a green tank top, and a white blouse. For shoes, she packs sneakers and sandals. How many different outfits will she have for her trip? 18 outfits

4. Choose A, B, or C. If all the numbers in a set of data occur the same number of times, then the set has no ■. C

A. median **B.** mean **C.** mode

5. Use the circle graph below.

How Students Get to School

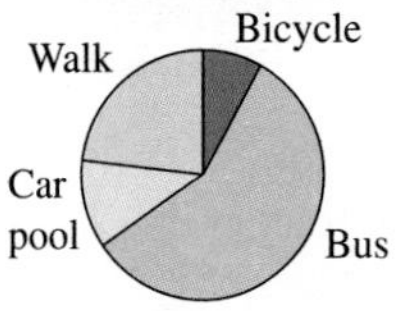

school bus; bicycle

a. What method do students use *most* to commute to school? *least?*

b. **Writing** Would a bar graph have been appropriate for displaying this data? Explain. Yes; a bar graph is used to compare amounts.

6. **Writing** The ages of students at a school dance are 14, 13, 12, 12, 13, 12, 15, 16, 14, 13, 13, and 14. Which average would best describe this data: mean, median, or mode? Explain. Answers will vary.

7. The table below shows the colonial population from 1700 to 1740. Display the data in a line graph. See Solution Key

1700	1710	1720	1730	1740
250,900	331,700	466,200	629,400	905,600

8. Average daily temperatures (°F) for one week are 60, 59, 58, 61, 63, 59, and 64. Find the median. 60°F

9. List a set of data with six numbers in which the mean is 40, the median is 41, and the range is 18. Answers may vary. Sample: 48, 45, 42, 40, 35, and 30.

10. Use the bar graph below.

School Enrollment

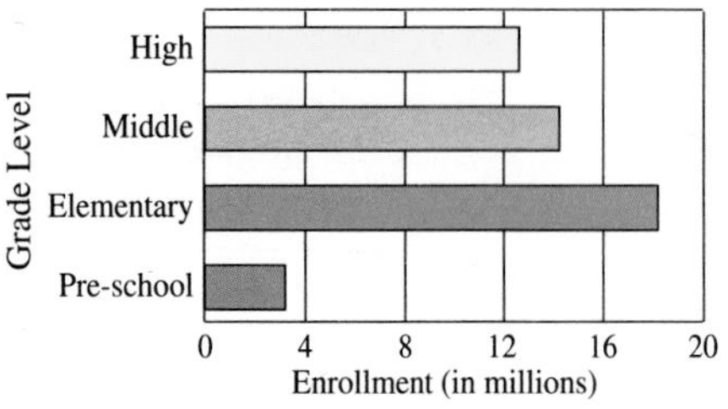

a. Which grade level has the least number of students enrolled? Pre-schoo

b. Estimate the mean. 12 million

c. Estimate the median. 13 million

d. Estimate the range. 15 million

CHAPTER 1

CUMULATIVE REVIEW

Exercise 3, Exercise 6, and Exercise 8 are enhanced multiple choice questions.

For Exercise 8, have students actually redraw the graph in each of the ways suggested.

Item(s)	Review Topic	Chapter
1, 6	kinds of averages	1
2	number problem	pre-book
3, 7	analyzing graphs	1
4	estimating	pre-book
5	finding range	1
8	constructing graphs	1

CHAPTER 1

Cumulative Review

Choose A, B, C, or D.

1. Which measure is the greatest for the data: 81, 70, 95, 73, 74, 91, 86, 74? A
   - **A.** mean **B.** median
   - **C.** mode **D.** range

2. When a number is divided by 13, the quotient is 15 and the remainder is less than 4. Which could be the number? A
   - **A.** 198 **B.** 200 **C.** 190 **D.** 206

3. What information does the bar graph shown *not* give you? C

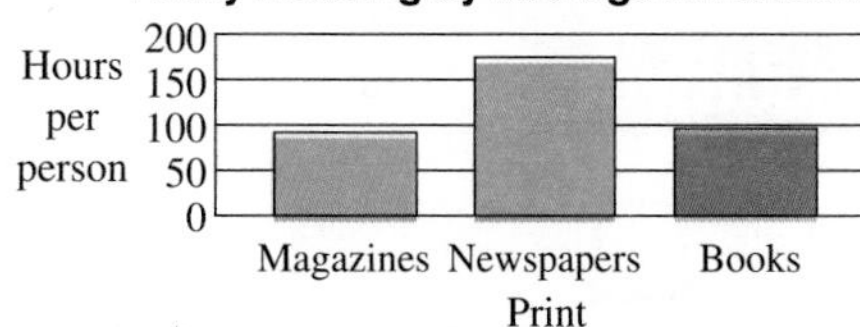

   - **A.** Americans spend more time reading newspapers than books.
   - **B.** Americans spend about the same time reading magazines as books.
   - **C.** Majority of Americans read the Sunday newspaper.
   - **D.** Americans spend twice as much time reading newspapers as books.

4. Which product gives the best estimate of the product 519 × 36? C
   - **A.** 500 × 30 **B.** 550 × 40
   - **C.** 500 × 40 **D.** 550 × 30

5. In one store boom boxes sell for $90, $109, $79, and $60. Find the range. C
   - **A.** $60 **B.** $109 **C.** $49 **D.** $19

6. The mean of three numbers is 19 and the median is 22. What do you know about the other two numbers? D
   - **A.** They are both between 19 and 22.
   - **B.** The numbers must be 17 and 18.
   - **C.** At least one of the numbers is between 19 and 22.
   - **D.** If one number is 24, the other must be 11.

Use the line graph for Questions 7–8.

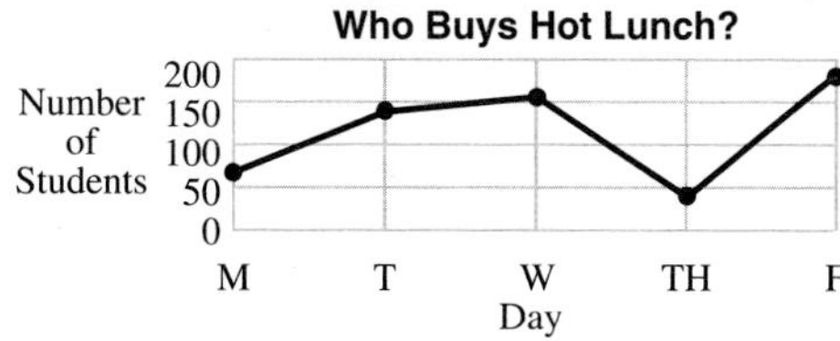

7. Estimate the median number of students buying hot lunch? B
   - **A.** 70 **B.** 140 **C.** 150 **D.** 120

8. How could you redraw the graph so it appears that about the same number of students buy lunch each day? C
   - **A.** Begin the vertical scale at 50.
   - **B.** Use intervals of 10, instead of 50.
   - **C.** Use intervals of 100, instead of 50.
   - **D.** Display the data in a circle graph.

Resources

Cumulative Review, TR Ch. 1, pp. 37–38
Transparency Masters, TR p. 35

CHAPTER 2 Geometry Concepts

Why Study Geometry?

If students ask this question, you may want to mention these areas in which geometry concepts are used: gymnastics, science, architecture, art, and traffic signs. Geometry is everywhere. Once students become aware of the possibilities, they have only to look around to see polygons with congruence, similarity, and symmetry. Artists, builders, designers, and machinists all use geometric concepts on the job.

Graphic Display of Chapter Content

Below is one possible representation of the chapter's content and its applications to the real world. Have students create their own graphic display and fill in applications that they have seen in their own lives.

- The center oval states the main concept of the chapter: geometry.
- Have students draw the ovals with the next level of concepts presented in the chapter (polygons, points, lines, planes, circles, and congruency and similarity). You may want students to add any other topics that they think are appropriate.
- Ask students to draw as many application ovals as they can.
- Discuss all the applications that students identify.
- Have students make and present one display that includes all the students' ideas.

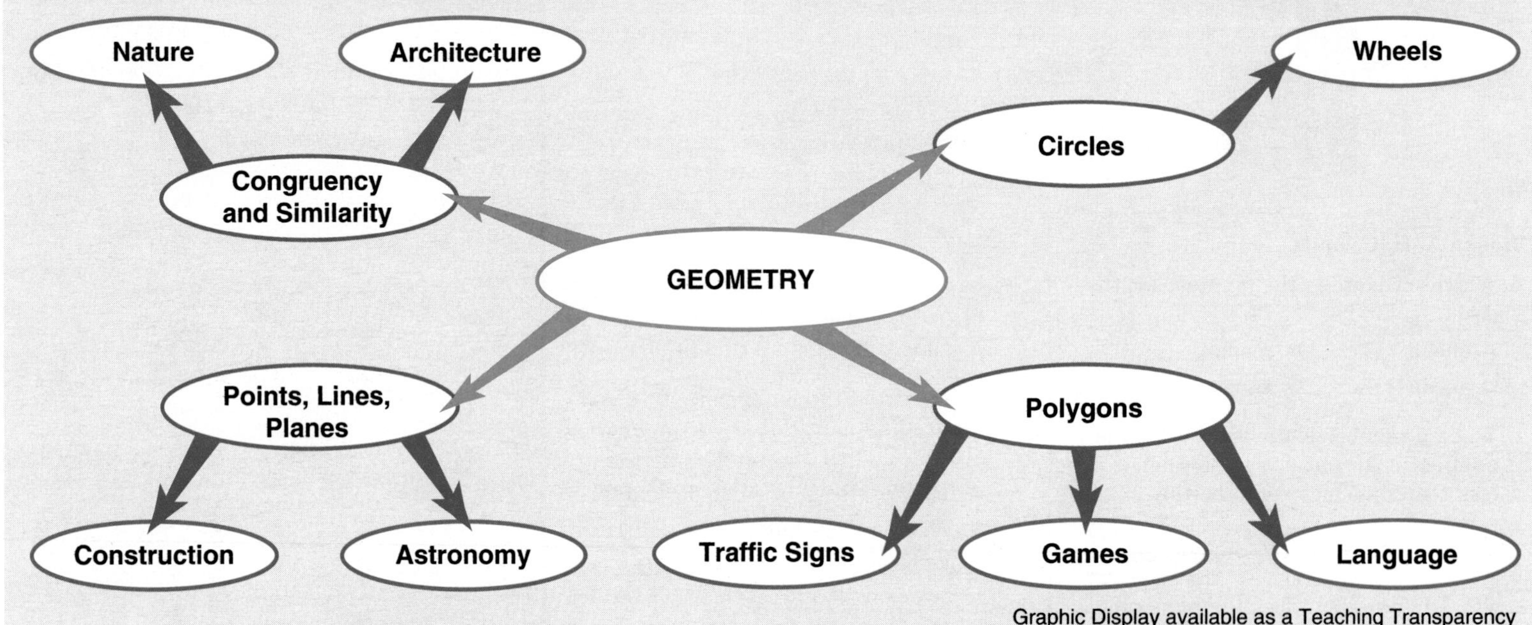

Graphic Display available as a Teaching Transparency

Vocabulary and Symbols

acute angle
acute triangle
angle, $\angle$
arcs
center
central angles
chord
circle
collinear
compass
congruent
congruent angles
congruent segments
construct
convex
degree, °
diameter
endpoints
equilateral triangle
isosceles triangle
line symmetry
line *RS*, $\overleftrightarrow{RS}$
logical reasoning
noncollinear
obtuse angle
obtuse triangle
parallel lines
parallel segments
parallelogram
perpendicular
plane
point
polygons
protractor
radii
radius
ray
rectangle
rhombus
right triangle
scalene triangle
segment *RS*, $\overline{RS}$
sides
similar
square
straight angle
straightedge
tessellations
trapezoid
Venn diagrams
vertex

Materials and Manipulatives

compass	computer
dot paper	geoboard
protractor	rubber bands
ruler	scissors
software	straightedge
tangram	tracing paper

Additional Resources

Commercially Available Technology

Calculator
calculator

Software
geometry software
The Geometer's Sketchpad by Key Curriculum Press

Other Media
"Points and Lines." Films Inc Video, 5547 N. Ravenswood Ave., Chicago, IL 60640. (800) 343-4312.

"S for Symmetry." Films Inc Video, 5547 N. Ravenswood Ave., Chicago, IL 60640. (800) 343-4312.

"Snap and Click Math." Tom Snyder Productions, 80 Coolidge Hill Road, Watertown, MA 02172. (800) 342-0236.

Materials at Little or No Cost

Association for Supervision and Curriculum Development, 1250 N. Pitt St., Alexandria, VA 22314. (703) 836-7921. Newsletter *Curriculum Update.*

Learning Team, 10 Long Pond Rd., Armonk, NY 10504. (914) 273-2226. *MathFINDER Sourcebook: Collection of Resources for Mathematics Reform.*

Bibliography

For Teachers
Pohl, Victoria. *How to Enrich Geometry Using String Designs.* Reston, VA: NCTM, 1986.
Geddes, Dorothy et al. *Geometry in the Middle Grades: Addenda Series, Grades 5–8.* Reston, VA: NCTM, 1992.

For Students
Sakade, Florence. *Origami, Japanese Paper Folding.* Boston: C.E. Tuttle, 1992.
Shaw, Sheila. *Kaleidometrics: The Art of Making Beautiful Patterns from Circles.* NY: Parkwest Publications, 1986.
Walter, Marion. *The Mirror Puzzle Book.* NY: Parkwest Publications, 1985.

Prentice Hall Technology 

Multimedia Math
- Math Tools, Geometry
- Hot Page™ 2-2
- Hot Page™ 2-4
- Hot Page™ 2-11
- Math Investigations, Mission: Mars
- Math Investigations, The Pythagorean Theorem

Computer Item Generator
- Chapter 2

Community Resources

Field Trips
- visit new houses being built
- visit a beehive to see honeycombs
- visit a museum to see geometry in art

Guest Speakers
- a bricklayer
- a carpenter
- a civil engineer

Backpack Take-Home Activities

Materials
- pad of paper
- pencil

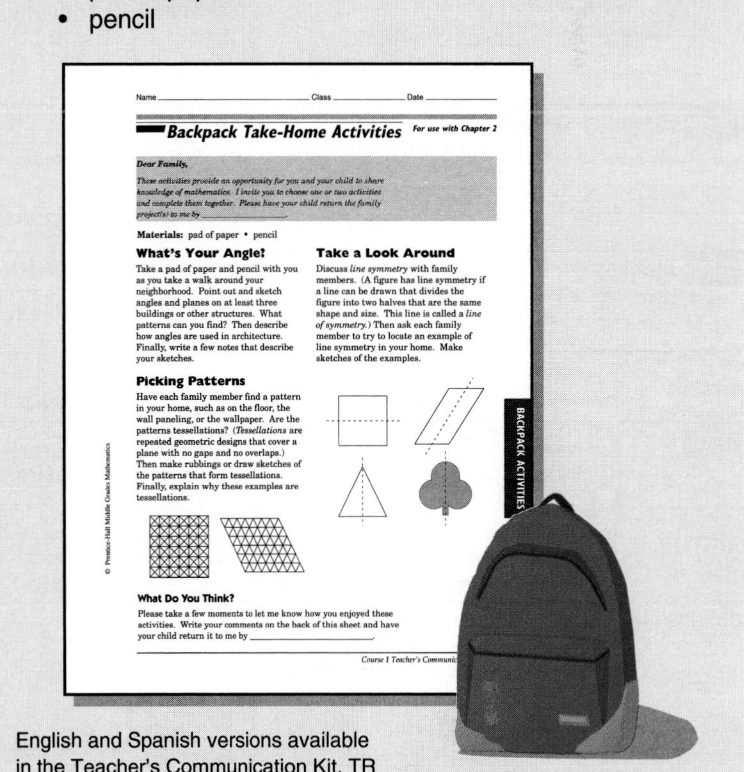

Name ______________ Class ______________ Date ______________

Backpack Take-Home Activities *For use with Chapter 2*

Dear Family,

These activities provide an opportunity for you and your child to share knowledge of mathematics. I invite you to choose one or two activities and complete them together. Please have your child return the family project(s) to me by ______________.

Materials: pad of paper • pencil

What's Your Angle?
Take a pad of paper and pencil with you as you take a walk around your neighborhood. Point out and sketch angles and planes on at least three buildings or other structures. What patterns can you find? Then describe how angles are used in architecture. Finally, write a few notes that describe your sketches.

Take a Look Around
Discuss *line symmetry* with family members. (A figure has line symmetry if a line can be drawn that divides the figure into two halves that are the same shape and size. This line is called a *line of symmetry.*) Then ask each family member to try to locate an example of line symmetry in your home. Make sketches of the examples.

Picking Patterns
Have each family member find a pattern in your home, such as on the floor, the wall paneling, or the wallpaper. Are the patterns tessellations? (*Tessellations* are repeated geometric designs that cover a plane with no gaps and no overlaps.) Then make rubbings or draw sketches of the patterns that form tessellations. Finally, explain why these examples are tessellations.

What Do You Think?
Please take a few moments to let me know how you enjoyed these activities. Write your comments on the back of this sheet and have your child return it to me by ______________.

BACKPACK ACTIVITIES

© Prentice-Hall Middle Grades Mathematics

Course 1 Teacher's Communic

English and Spanish versions available in the Teacher's Communication Kit, TR

Chapter 2 Planning Guide

Objectives	Assignment Options			Critical Thinking/ Problem Solving	Writing and Reading Math	Estimation Mental Math	Materials and Manipulatives
Investigation	This chapter-long project involves open-ended questioning and data collecting and provides an additional opportunity to assess students.			p. 40 p. 40	p. 40		p. 40 p. 40
2-1 Points, Lines, and Planes • Identifying and working with points, lines,	**Core:** 21–26, 29–33; MR all	**Reinforce:** 27, 28, 34–36	**Enrich:** 37, 38	10; WT: 12, 13b; 20b, 38; MR: 5 pp. 41, 42, 44; BI p. 43; MM p. 44	20, 37 p. 44; JL p. 43 JL Sheet	MR: 1, 2	7, WT: 11a, 12a, 13a; 29–30, 38 pp. 41, 44; WT p. 42, RT p. 43 TT 2, 37
2-2 Exploring Angles • Estimating, measuring, and drawing angles • Classifying angles as acute, right, obtuse, or straight	**Core:** 11–13, 16–19, 23–27; MR all	**Reinforce:** 14, 15, 20–22, 28, 29, 31	**Enrich:** 30	2, 3b, 4b, 5, 8, 15, 29, 30; MR: 6 p. 45, 50; BI p. 47	30 p. 48; JL p. 47 JL Sheet	16–22 pp. 45–48, BI p. 47; MM p. 49	4, 6, 12a, 13, 14, 20–27, 31a–d, WT pp. 45–48; RT p. 48 TT 6, 37
2-3 Constructing Segments and Angles • Constructing a segment congruent to a given segment • Constructing an angle congruent to a given angle	**Core:** 6, 7, 10; MR all	**Reinforce:** 8, 9	**Enrich:** 11	5, 11; MR: 7 pp. 51, 53; BI p. 52; MM p. 53	11 p. 53; JL p. 51 JL Sheet		1–4, 6–10 pp. 51, 53; WT p. 52; RT p. 53 TT 2, 6, 37
2-4 Exploring Triangles • Identifying triangles by their angles • Identifying triangles by their sides	**Core:** 12–18, 21–23; MR all; CH all	**Reinforce:** 19, 24–29	**Enrich:** 20	1; EX; 6–11, 19, 20; CH: 13; MR: 5 pp. 54, 55, 57; BI p. 55	19 p. 56; JL p. 55 JL Sheet		WT; 12, 20–29; CH: 10–12 pp. 54–57; WT p. 54; CH p. 57 TT 8, 9, 38, 40
2-5 Exploring Polygons • Determining if a figure is a polygon • Identifying triangles, quadrilaterals, pentagons, hexagons, octagons, and decagons	**Core:** 6–12a, 16–18; MR all	**Reinforce:** 12b, 13, 19	**Enrich:** 14, 15, 20	WT: 1, 2; 5, 13d, 19, 20d; MR: 5 pp. 58, 60; BI p. 59; MM p. 61	WT: 1c; 12b, 20d pp. 58, 60; JL p. 59 JL Sheet	MR: 1, 2	12, 16–18, 20b–c pp. 59–61; WT p. 58; RT p. 60 TT 38; Alt. Lesson
2-6 Special Quadrilaterals • Identifying and classifying special quadrilaterals	**Core:** 12–17, 21, 25–28, 34, 35; MR all	**Reinforce:** 18–20, 22, 29–33	**Enrich:** 23, 24	2, 3a–b, 4; EX; 5–10, 18–20, 22, 23c, 34; MR: 5 pp. 62, 63, 65; BI p. 64	22 p. 64; JL p. 64 JL Sheet	MR: 1, 2	12–17, 24, 35 pp. 62, 64, 65; WT p. 63; RT p. 64 TT 38
2-7 Problem Solving: Using Logical Reasoning • Solving problems by using logical reasoning	**Core:** 10, 13; MR all	**Reinforce:** 11	**Enrich:** 12	All; MR: 7 pp. 66, 67; BI p. 68	All JL p. 68 JL Sheet	MR: 1, 2 MM p. 68	p. 66; RT p. 68 TT 7, 38
2-8 Congruent and Similar Figures • Determining whether figures are congruent • Determining whether figures are similar	**Core:** 7, 8, 12, 14, 16; MR all	**Reinforce:** 9–11 15, 18	**Enrich:** 13, 17, 19	13, 15, 17b–c, 18, 19; MR: 3–5 p. 72; BI p. 71; MM p. 73	13 p. 72; JL p. 71 JL Sheet	MR: 1, 2	WT: 1, 2; 14, 17a, 19 pp. 70–72; WT p. 70; RT p. 72 TT 8, 9, 39, 41
2-9 Exploring Symmetry • Determining whether a figure has line symmetry	**Core:** 6–11, 16; MR all; CH all	**Reinforce:** 12–14, 17, 18, 20	**Enrich:** 15, 19	5, 15c, 17, 18; CH: 4, 5, 7; MR: 7 p. 74; BI p. 75; CH p. 76	15c; CH: 4 p. 76; JL p. 75; CH p. 76 JL Sheet	MR: 1, 2	2, 3, 6–14, 15a–b, 19, 20 pp. 74–76; WT p. 74; MM p. 77 TT 20, 21, 39
2-10 Technology: Exploring Circles • Identifying and working with parts of a circle	**Core:** 10–15, 18, 19, 24; MR all	**Reinforce:** 16, 17, 20, 22	**Enrich:** 21, 23	1d, 2c, 6, 8a; WT: 9b; 16a, 17, 18, 22, 23; MR: 5, 6 p. 78; WT p. 79; BI p. 79; MM p. 81	16a, 19, 20 p. 80; JL p. 79 JL Sheet		2b, 3b, 4, 5; WT: 9a; 17, 21–24 pp. 78–80; RT p. 80 TT 10, 39 Alt. Lesson
2-11 Math and Design: Exploring Tessellations • Drawing tessellations	**Core:** 7–9, 11, 14; DM all; MR all	**Reinforce:** 10, 13	**Enrich:** 12	3, 4; WT: 6d; 10e, 12, 13; DM: All pp. 83, 84; BI p. 83	10e JL p. 83 JL Sheet		2; WT: 5, 6; 7–11, 14; DM: 1 p. 83; WT p. 82; TT 6, 39
Putting It All Together	These pages include a Follow-Up to the Investigation and other projects, which provide additional opportunities to assess the students.			pp. 88–89 pp. 88–89	p. 88		pp. 88–89 p. 89
Chapter Resources				PS Practice, CW, CA, CR PS Practice p. 50; CW pp. 86–87; CA p, 90; CR p. 91	PS Practice, CW, CA p. 38B; PS Practice p. 50; CW pp. 86–87; CA p. 90		pp. 38A, 38B Backpack Activities, Manip. Kits TT 36

Student Edition (question numbers)
Teacher's Edition (page numbers)
Other Components

BI—What's the Big Idea? CA—Chapter Assessment CH—Checkpoint
CG—Computer Item Generator CR—Cumulative Review CW—Chapter Wrap Up
DM—Decision Making EP—Extra Practice EX—Example FD—Fact of the Day

Cooperative Learning Activities	Technology	Data Collection & Analysis	Interdisciplinary Connections	Applications	Assessment	Review	Strand Integration	NCTM Correlation*
p. 40 p. 40		p. 40		design, flags	p. 40 p. 40			
WT: 11–13 p. 41; WT p. 42; RT p. 43 Alt. Lesson	p. 44 Alt. Lesson	FD p. 42	Science p. 43	astronomy pp. 41, 43	p. 41	MR: All RT p. 43 Practice p. 25	Geometry, Logic/Language	1, 2, 3, 4, 8, 12
WT p. 46; WT pp. 46–47; RT p. 48	p. 47 Hot Page™ 2-2	28 FD p. 46	Science p. 48	archaeology, advertising pp. 45, 48	p. 46	MR: All p. 45; RT p. 48 Practice p. 26	Geometry, Stat./Probability, Logic/Language	1, 2, 3, 4, 7, 8, 10, 12
WT WT p. 52; RT p. 53	p. 53	FD p. 52		pp. 51, 52	p. 51	MR: All p. 51; RT p. 53 Practice p. 27	Geometry, Measurement, Logic/Language	1, 2, 3, 8, 12, 13
WT p. 55; WT p. 54; RT p. 56	WT p. 54; MM p. 57 Hot Page™ 2-4	MR: 2 FD p. 55		p. 56	CH: All p. 55; CH p. 57 CH TR p. 40	MR: All p. 54; RT p. 56 Practice p. 28	Geometry, Measurement, Logic/Language	1, 2, 3, 8, 12, 13
WT: 1, 2 p. 61; WT p. 58; RT p. 60		FD p. 59	Language Arts, Science p. 59 Alt. Lesson	earth science, environment pp. 58–60	p. 59	MR: All RT p. 60 Practice p. 29	Geometry, Measurement, Logic/Language	1, 2, 3, 8, 12, 13
WT pp. 62, 65; WT p. 63	p. 64; WT p. 63	21, 35 p. 65; FD p. 63		recreation, architecture p. 64	p. 62	MR: All p. 62; RT p. 64 Practice p. 30	Geometry, Logic/Language	1, 2, 3, 8, 12
p. 67; RT p. 68		p. 66; FD p. 67; RT p. 68	p. 68	jobs, hobbies pp. 66, 68	p. 67	MR: All p. 66; RT p. 68 Practice p. 31	Geometry, Discrete Math, Logic/Language	1, 2, 3, 4, 5, 7, 8, 9, 10, 11, 12, 13
WT: 1, 2 p. 71; WT p. 70; RT p. 72	WT p. 70	FD p. 71		p. 72	p. 71	MR: All p. 70; RT p. 72 Practice p. 32	Geometry, Logic/Language	1, 2, 3, 8, 12
WT p. 76; WT p. 74; RT p. 75		FD p. 75	Science, Art, Language Arts p. 75	biology, art, design p. 75	CH: All p. 74; CH p. 76 CH TR p. 40	MR: All p. 74; RT p. 75 Practice p. 33	Geometry, Stat./Probability, Logic/Language	1, 2, 3, 4, 7, 8, 12
WT: 9; 16b pp. 80, 81; WT p. 79; RT p. 80	All p. 80; WT p. 79	FD p. 79	p. 80	design, engineering, entertainment pp. 78, 80, 81 Alt. Lesson	p. 79	MR: All p. 78; RT p. 80 Practice p. 34	Geometry, Measurement, Logic/Language	1, 2, 3, 4, 8, 12, 13
WT: 5, 6; DM: All p. 84; WT p. 82; RT p. 83; DM p. 84	Hot Page™ 2-11	DM: All FD p. 83; DM p. 84		design pp. 82–84	p. 82	MR: All p. 82; RT p. 83 Practice p. 35	Geometry, Discrete Math, Logic/Language	1, 2, 3, 4, 5, 7, 8, 10, 12, 13
pp. 88–89 p. 88		pp. 88–89 pp. 88–89	Art	design	pp. 88–89 pp. 88–89			
IN, PT pp. 38–40; PT pp. 88–89 Backpack Activities	p. 38B Multimedia Math, CG	Data File 2 pp. 38–39	Science pp. 38F, 38–39 Interdisciplinary Units	entertainment, design pp. 38A, 38–39 Backpack Activities, Projects, Interdisciplinary Units	IN, PT, CA pp. 38E, 40, 86–90 CA, Span. CA, Self Assessment, Projects	Practice, PS Practice, CW, CR, EP, SSG CW pp. 86–87 Span. SSG, CR		

GE—Great Expectations IN—Investigation JL—Journal MM—Math Minutes
MR—Mixed Review PS—Problem Solving PT—Putting It All Together RT—Reteaching Activity
SSG—Student Study Guide TT—Teaching Transparency WT—Work Together

*For a description of the NCTM Standards, see page T15.

Assessment Options

Observation Checklist

In this chapter on geometry, you have opportunities to observe your students do these tasks:

- ✓ identify points, lines, planes, angles, rays, polygons, and parts of a circle
- ✓ estimate, measure, draw, and classify angles
- ✓ use Venn diagrams and logical reasoning to solve word problems
- ✓ construct duplicate segments and angles using compass and straightedge
- ✓ recognize special quadrilaterals
- ✓ determine whether figures are congruent or similar
- ✓ find lines of symmetry
- ✓ draw tessellations of the plane

In every chapter, you are given opportunities to observe your students:

- ✓ work with a partner or in a group
- ✓ write about mathematics
- ✓ participate in discussions about mathematics
- ✓ collect and analyze data
- ✓ display positive attitudes about mathematics
- ✓ use measurement tools

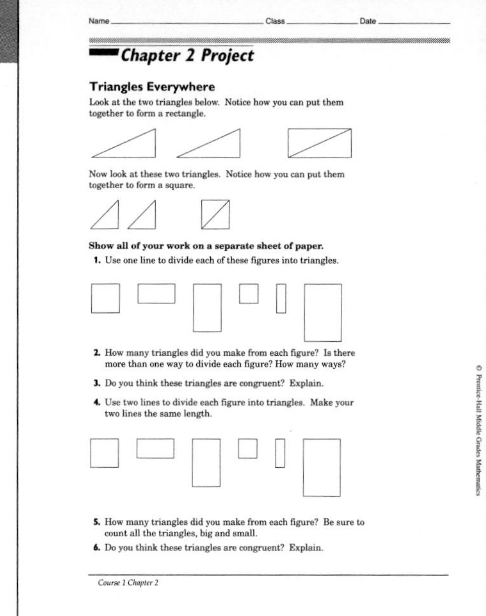

Name ______ Class ______ Date ______

Chapter 2 Project

Triangles Everywhere

Look at the two triangles below. Notice how you can put them together to form a rectangle.

Now look at these two triangles. Notice how you can put them together to form a square.

Show all of your work on a separate sheet of paper.

1. Use one line to divide each of these figures into triangles.
2. How many triangles did you make from each figure? Is there more than one way to divide each figure? How many ways?
3. Do you think these triangles are congruent? Explain.
4. Use two lines to divide each figure into triangles. Make your two lines the same length.
5. How many triangles did you make from each figure? Be sure to count all the triangles, big and small.
6. Do you think these triangles are congruent? Explain.

Course 1 Chapter 2

© Prentice-Hall Middle Grades Mathematics

Performance Based Project (with scoring rubric), Chapter Files, TR

...ere Scoring Rubric

Exercise	Points	Explanation
1.	1	Figures correctly divided into triangles
	0	No response OR other response
2.	1	Two triangles; yes, two ways to do it
	0	No response OR other response
3.	1	Triangles considered congruent and justification given
	0	No response OR other response
4.	1	Figures correctly divided into triangles
	0	No response OR other response
5.	1	Response of eight triangles (not all the same size)
	0	No response OR other response
6.	1	Same sizes: yes; different sizes: no; justification given
	0	No response OR other response
7.	1	Figure divided into triangles, using three lines
	0	No response OR other response
8.	1	Responses should be accurate in terms of drawing.
	0	No response OR other response
9.	1	Responses will vary; explanation of the method given.
	0	No response OR other response
10.	1	Explanation of how lines can be added indefinitely
	0	No response OR other response
Excursion	5	Complex puzzle with good explanation of answer
	4	Complex puzzle with adequate explanation OR less complex puzzle with good explanation
	3	Less complex puzzle with adequate explanation OR complex puzzle with weak explanation
	2	Less complex puzzle with weak explanation
	1	Puzzle with no explanation
	0	No response

Course 1 Chapter 2

© Prentice-Hall Middle Grades Mathematics

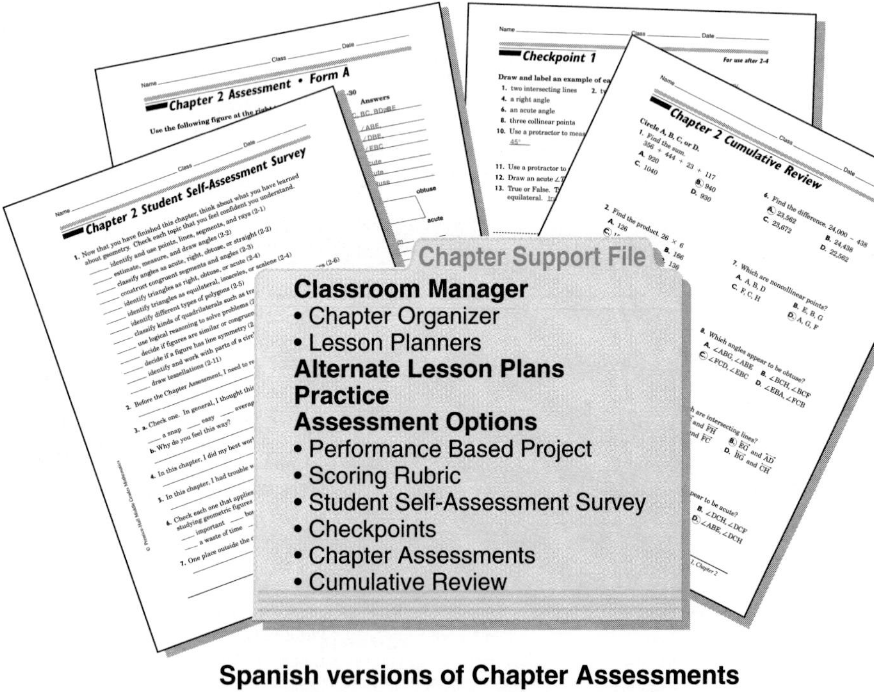

Chapter 2 Assessment • Form A
Chapter 2 Student Self-Assessment Survey
Checkpoint 1
Chapter 2 Cumulative Review
Chapter Support File
Classroom Manager
• Chapter Organizer
• Lesson Planners
Alternate Lesson Plans
Practice
Assessment Options
• Performance Based Project
• Scoring Rubric
• Student Self-Assessment Survey
• Checkpoints
• Chapter Assessments
• Cumulative Review

Spanish versions of Chapter Assessments available in Spanish Resources

Interdisciplinary Units

- **Travel and Geography**
- **Space Exploration**
- **Sports**
- **Consumer Awareness**
- **The Great Outdoors**

English & Spanish

These units include cross-curriculum connections and can be used at any time during the school year. See the Teacher's Guide for more information.

Working with Middle Grade Students

> *"People are usually more convinced by reasons they discovered themselves than by those found by others."*
>
> —Blaise Pascal

Addressing a Variety of Learning Styles

The mathematical tasks in Chapter 2 involve various learning styles. Here are some examples.

- Visual learners classify polygons (p. 59) and look for special quadrilaterals in architecture (p. 65).
- Tactile learners use tangram pieces to form quadrilaterals (p. 63) and make tessellations (p. 83).
- Auditory learners describe inscribed polygons (p. 79) and share their definitions of polygon with the class (p. 58)
- Kinesthetic learners check congruency by cutting out triangles (p. 70), and explore symmetry with folding (p. 77).

Alternate Lessons 2-5 and 2-10 address tactile learners by having them use manipulatives.

Cultural Connections

Have each student choose a country. (More than one student may choose the same country.) Ask each student to locate his or her country on a map or globe and draw a picture of its shape. Then have students combine simple shapes (triangles, polygons, and circles) to model approximately the shapes of their countries. Have students exhibit and name the parts of their models, and arrange a display of them in the classroom.

Team Teaching Suggestion

Work with a science teacher to introduce the concept of geometric figures found in nature:

- Students can observe fruits and vegetables in order to find polygon shapes, often seen in cross sections.
- Students can observe geometric patterns found in spider webs.

Cooperative Groups

Middle school students often learn well in cooperative groups, where they can interact with their peers. In order to have effective groups, students must practice the skills for group dynamics. For an early meeting, set a goal that everyone in the group will be able to name all the other members of the group. Have each person talk to one other person in the group and share a little-known fact about themselves such as "I used to live in Hawaii," or "I own a python." These facts should be true, but not embarrassingly personal. Then each class member introduces his or her partner to the rest of the class by giving the name and telling the fact. Discuss with the class that the goal is to make everyone feel welcome, recognized, and accepted.

Teaching Tip

Middle school students become acutely aware of cars in their pre-driving years; however, this interest may show more in boys than in girls. Include those less interested in the mechanics by discussing the aesthetic and design aspects of cars. By connecting the study of geometry to the discussion, you provide more motivation for student discovery. Incorporate a discussion of and examples from computer assisted design (CAD) for cars, if possible.

Bulletin Board

Display examples of hub cap designs that can be found on cars and trucks, as shown. Have students cut and paste at least two pictures of hub caps from newspapers or magazines. For each hub cap design have students identify the lines of symmetry and the geometric shapes they see. Then ask students to create their own hub cap designs. Encourage students to use color in their designs.

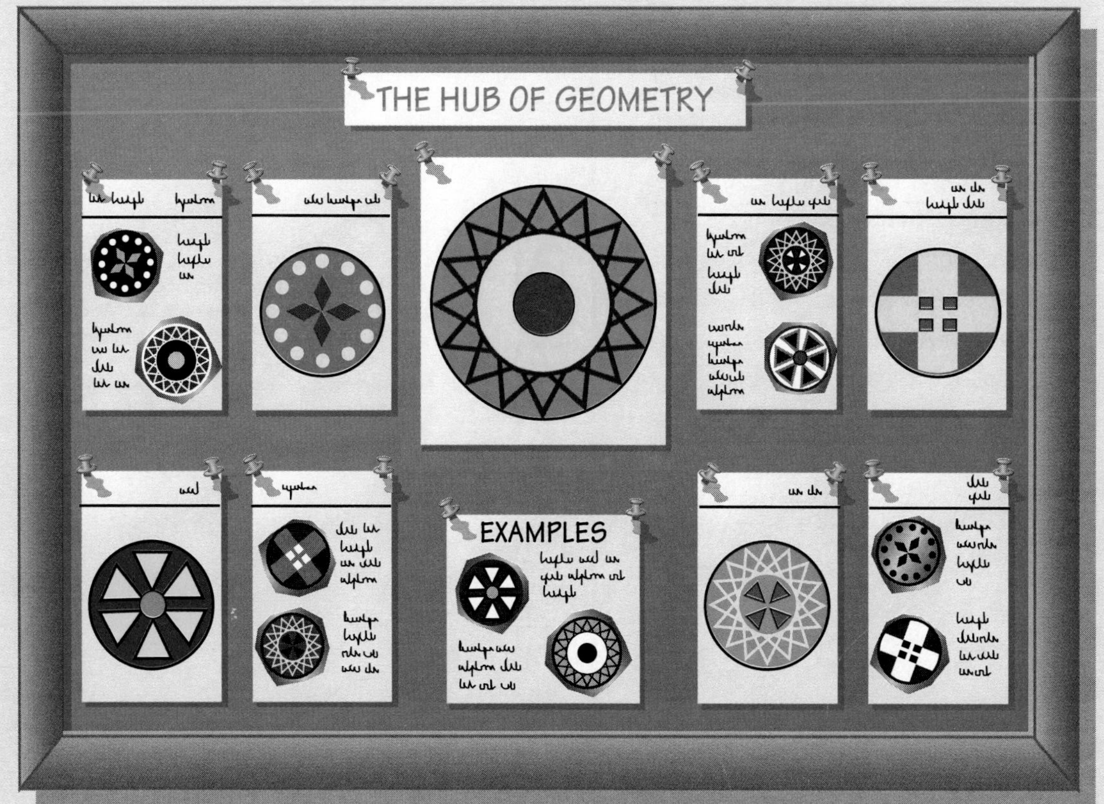

CHAPTER 2 Geometry Concepts

Cultural Connections The amusement parks listed are privately owned, but the United States government also owns parks that are part of the national park system. There are ten National Seashores, including ones in Florida (Canaveral), Texas (Padre Island), and California (Point Reyes). The park system includes National Parks, such as Yellowstone (in Idaho, Montana, and Wyoming) and Carlsbad Caverns (in New Mexico). The Hawaii Volcanoes National Park contains two active volcanoes, Kilauea and Mauna Loa.

WORLD VIEW In 1970, Expo '70 (a World's Fair) was held in Osaka, Japan. More than 65 million people attended.

Digging for Data Ask the students to use the bar graph and table to answer these questions:

- *Which country has the highest ride?* **(Japan)**
- *Which state has the ride that lasts the shortest time?* **(Ohio)**

Group students into teams of four or five people. Each student asks six people if they have been on an amusement park ride and if they have been on a water slide or water ride. As part of planning this survey, students need to design a way to report their results, and to divide assignments so that they do not survey the same people twice. Groups can present their results to the class and design questions that can be answered by their data.

Chapter 2 Contents

Data File Questions

pp. 114, 131, 190, 206, 332

Data File 2

CHAPTER 2 Geometry Concepts

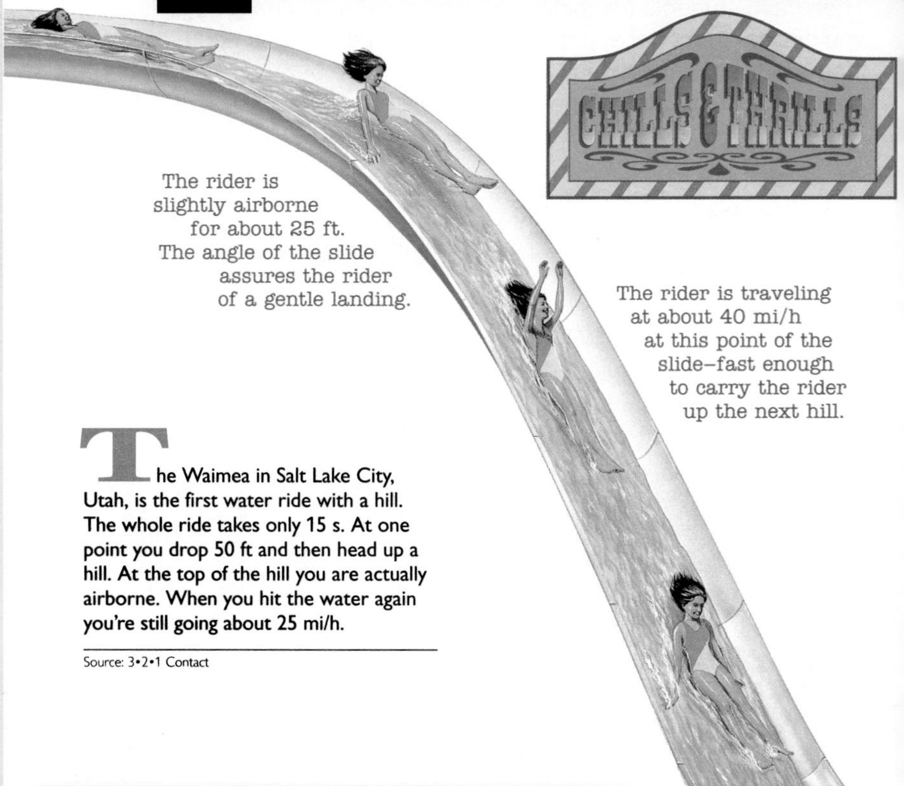

CHILLS & THRILLS
The rider is slightly airborne for about 25 ft. The angle of the slide assures the rider of a gentle landing.
The rider is traveling at about 40 mi/h at this point of the slide–fast enough to carry the rider up the next hill.
The rider sees only sky on the way up the hill. This makes the ride more scary.

The Waimea in Salt Lake City, Utah, is the first water ride with a hill. The whole ride takes only 15 s. At one point you drop 50 ft and then head up a hill. At the top of the hill you are actually airborne. When you hit the water again you're still going about 25 mi/h.

Source: 3•2•1 Contact

Great Rides

Ride	Location	Height (ft)
The Viper	Six Flags Valencia, CA	188
The Beast	King's Island, OH	141
Cyclone	Coney Island, NY	85
Shockwave	Six Flags Gurnee, IL	170
Moonsault Scramble	Kawaguchi, Japan	206.7

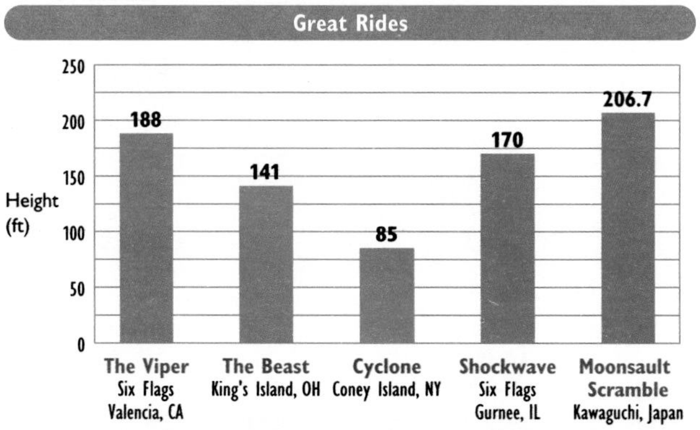

Journal Activity Ask students to read the four objectives in What You Will Learn. Have them write about which they are most interested in and which sound least interesting to them. Ask them to give reasons.

Interdisciplinary Connection [Science] Water is a vital resource for life on this earth. Our bodies are over 90% water. Even a small leak in a faucet wastes a lot of water. A leak that takes 10 minutes to fill a coffee cup wastes over 3,000 gallons of water in a year. That's enough to provide 65 glasses of water every day for a year.

WHAT YOU WILL LEARN

- how to recognize geometric figures
- how to use tools to draw geometric figures
- how to use technology to explore geometry
- how to solve problems by using logic

Favorite Amusement Park Rides

Park (annual attendance)	Admission	Ride	Wait Time (min)	Ride Time (min)
Walt Disney World Lake Buena Vista, FL. (30 million)	Adult: $32.75 Child: $26.40	Space Mountain	45:14	2:36
		Captain EO	14:29	16:47
		For kids: Peter Pan	20:37	3:09
Knott's Berry Farm Buena Park, CA. (4 million)	Adult: $21.00 Child: $16.00	XK-1	2:30	1:30
		Timber Mountain Log	9:22	4:25
		Montezooma's Revenge	1:30	0:37
		For kids: Red Baron	0:55	2:00
Kings Island Kings Island, OH (3.2 million)	Adult: $20.95 Child: $10.45	The Beast	45:00	4:30
		Vortex	30:00	2:30
		The Racer	15:00	2:15
		For kids: Beastie	10:00	1:30
Cedar Point Sandusky, OH (3.2 million)	Adult: $19.95 Child: $10.95	Demon Drop	30:00	0:15
		Cedar Downs	5:00	2:30
		For kids: Sir Rub-a-Dub's Tubs	15:00	3:00

Source: *Money*

On the final hilltop, the rider rises from one inch to six inches off the slide in a state of near weightlessness.

The rider travels at 40 mi/h down the last hill before a gentle landing in a breaking pool.

In 1851 London hosted the first international fair in the Crystal Palace. The exhibition attracted 6,039,195 people.

Fact of the Day

Humans can exist on about 1.5 liters of water per day if the water is used only for drinking. In the United States, the water usage per person averages over 2,000 liters per day.

—Life Science

39

CHAPTER 2 INVESTIGATION

You may wish to bring examples of visual patterns to class in the form of magazines, catalogs, and other printed materials.

Have students describe the patterns shown in the text:

- *What patterns are repeated in each design?*
- *Find patterns in the room that are similar to the patterns found in the teacher's examples.*

Before students begin work, be sure they understand the various ways that motifs can be repeated in a design.

Students can draw scaled designs of the patterns that they analyze. They can modify the ones they like best before deciding on their favorite. This one can be used as the pattern for a final version of the flag.

After half of the chapter has been completed, have students show you their work on the project. If they are behind schedule, give them intermediate deadlines in order to check their work.

Additional Leads to Follow

- *Look at examples of flags of nations. Which do you like best, the simple or elaborate ones?*
- *What materials would you use to make your flag?*

Keeping a Project Notebook

Some suggestions for students' notebooks are:

- Keep a list of all design elements (figures, logos, school symbols) mentioned in discussions with group members.
- Keep sketches showing how figures can be repeated to produce patterns.
- List the dates and results of all discussions about the project.

Project Organizer

Related Exercises
p. 65
p. 81
p. 85

Follow Up
p. 88

Teacher's Notes
pp. 40, 65, 81, 84, 88

Community Resources
- graphic designer

Materials and Manipulatives
- art materials
- magazines
- catalogs

Memo

When a figure is repeated in a design, a *visual pattern* results. Patterns in designs are all around you. The design shown here consists of a flower repeated again and again. The Canadian flag design consists of two halves, each the reverse of the other. If the flag is folded along the dotted line, the two halves match each other. The logo for the Data Processing Corporation consists of two ***d***'s. The second ***d*** is turned upside-down to form a ***p***. Each of these designs displays a pattern.

Mission: Find examples of patterns in visual designs. Some patterns you can find simply by looking around your classroom. Others you can find by looking in books and magazines and by brainstorming with your group. Study the designs. Then create a design for a flag for your class or school. Your design should display a visual pattern.

✓ Which designs do you like best? Which are the most memorable? What can you do to create a likable, memorable design for your flag?

✓ What would you like to say about your class or school that you can represent in a design?

2-1

Connecting to Prior Knowledge

Have students think about the general shape of a house. Ask students how the shape of the house differs from the shape of a tree. **(Students should mention the straight lines and exact measurements that go into building a house.)** Ask students how the distinctive shape of a house can be made. **(accurate measurements of lines and planes)**

THINK AND DISCUSS

DIVERSITY Ask students to sketch the shape of different kinds of dwellings. **(tents, teepees, hogans, igloos, and so forth)** Then ask them to point out and name the geometric shapes in each. Challenge students to name and locate the places in the world where various dwellings are used.

Ongoing Assessment Ask students to describe the difference between a line, a line segment, and a ray. Then ask students to describe the difference between a line and a plane.

ESL Provide models for a point, line, plane, segment, and ray. Give the geometric name for each of the models and have the students repeat the name. Write the names on index cards and ask students to match models with geometric names.

TACTILE LEARNERS Have students find and cut out pictures of objects from newspapers or magazines. Have students identify and describe points, lines, and planes in the objects.

Error Alert! Students may write or name the letters of a ray in the incorrect order. ***Remediation*** Have students name a ray (for example, $\overrightarrow{AB}$) and then draw the ray (starting with the endpoint A). This can be repeated several times so that students can see that a ray has a beginning point and the beginning point needs to be named first.

What's Ahead

- Identifying and working with points, lines, segments, and rays

2-1 Points, Lines, and Planes

THINK AND DISCUSS

What geometric figures do the following everyday items suggest: a straight road? a tabletop? a pencil? a sunbeam?

A **point** has no size, only location. A very small dot made by a pencil tip can represent a point. You can name points by a capital letter. Points A, B, and C are shown.

1. Name something else that could be a physical model of a point. Sample: a pinhole in a piece of paper

A **line** continues without end in opposite directions. It has no thickness. You can name a line by using two points on the line. For example, one name for this line is $\overleftrightarrow{DE}$ (read as "line DE").

2. What are some other names for the line? $\overleftrightarrow{DF}$, $\overleftrightarrow{EF}$, $\overleftrightarrow{ED}$, $\overleftrightarrow{FD}$, $\overleftrightarrow{FE}$
3. Name something that could be a physical model of a line. Sample: a tightly stretched wire

A **plane** is a flat surface that extends indefinitely in four directions. It has no thickness.

4. Name something that could be a physical model of a plane. Sample: top of a desk

A **segment** is part of a line. It is made up of two points and all the points of the line that are between the two points. You name a segment by the two *endpoints*. This is $\overline{RS}$ (read as "segment RS").

5. Give another name for $\overline{RS}$. $\overline{SR}$
6. Name something that could be a physical model of a segment. Sample: a toothpick
7. Draw a line and label several points on it. Name four different segments. See Sol. Key.

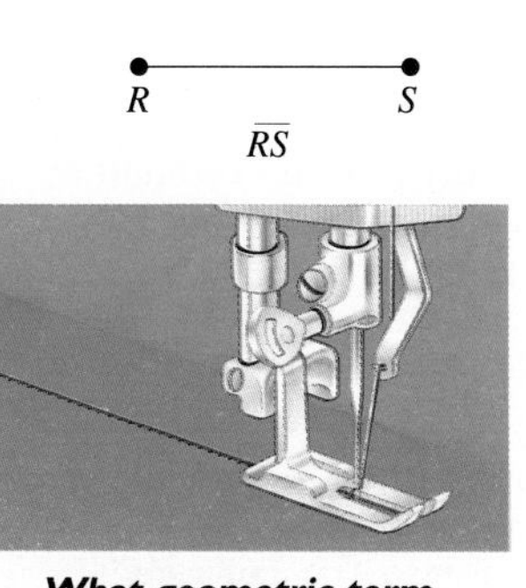

What geometric term does the stitching represent? a line

> *Knowledge, once gained, casts a faint light beyond its own immediate boundaries. There is no discovery so limited as to not illuminate something beyond itself.*
>
> —John Tyndall

Organizer

1. **Focus**
   Connecting to Prior Knowledge
2. **Teach**
   Think and Discuss
   Work Together
3. **Closure**
   Try These
   Wrap Up

Vocabulary/Symbols
point
line *RS*, $\overleftrightarrow{RS}$
plane
segment *RS*, $\overline{RS}$
endpoints
ray
collinear
noncollinear
parallel lines
parallel segments

Materials and Manipulatives
On Your Own Exercises 29–30, 38: straightedge

continues next page

WORK TOGETHER

Have students work in groups of four. Students will be more inclined to work cooperatively if all the group members are working on the same piece of paper. One person can be the one who draws the points and lines (with the help of other group members). Other group members should organize and record the information. Students should rotate roles for each question.

Questions 12 and 13: Make sure students account for all possible arrangements of the points.

CONNECTION TO SCIENCE Invite students to extend the WHAT? question by bringing in pictures of other constellations and describing them by name and geometric description.

Example

Have students trace $\overleftrightarrow{AB}$ and $\overleftrightarrow{CD}$. Then have students extend the lines by using a straightedge to find the point of intersection. Alternatively, have them position pencils over the line in the text to see that the lines intersect.

Additional Example *Draw four points U, V, W, X so that U, V, W are collinear and $\overleftrightarrow{WX}$ does not pass through U and V.* Draw $\overleftrightarrow{WX}$ and $\overleftrightarrow{UW}$. **(Students' drawings will show lines intersecting at point *W*.)**

TRY THESE

Exercises 14–17: Have students compare the figures to their names and note the visual resemblance.

Exercise 20a: Have students draw a diagram to accompany their descriptions.

CRITICAL THINKING For Exercise 20b, ask students to name other items that are often represented by dots. Ask them to think specifically of symbols on a map.

Organizer, continued

Student Resources
Extra Practice
Student Study Guide
Practice, TR Ch. 2, p. 25
Student Study Guide, Spanish Resources, TR
Alternate Lessson, TR Ch. 2, pp. 13–16

Teacher Resources

Teaching Transparencies 2, 37
Lesson Planner, TR Ch. 2, p. 2

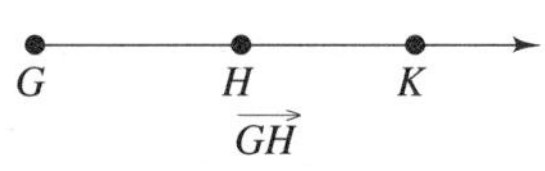
Prentice Hall Technology

Multimedia Math
- Math Tools, Geometry

Computer Item Generator
- 2-1

Other Available Technology
Geometer's Sketchpad by Key Curriculum Press: Exercise 38 *(optional)*

Fact of the Day

On August 4, 1985, Larry Tudor of the United States reached a height of 14,250 ft while hang gliding. On July 3, 1990, Tudor flew 303.35 mi in a straight line before landing.

—GUINNESS BOOK OF WORLD RECORDS

G H K $\overrightarrow{GH}$

A **ray** is part of a line. It consists of one *endpoint* and all the points of the line on one side of the endpoint. To name a ray, you name the endpoint first and then any other point on the ray. This is $\overrightarrow{GH}$ (read as "ray *GH*").

8. If possible, give another name for $\overrightarrow{GH}$. $\overrightarrow{GK}$

9. Name something that could be a physical model of a ray. Sample: a laser beam

X Y

10. Describe $\overrightarrow{YX}$. How is $\overrightarrow{YX}$ different from $\overrightarrow{XY}$? What part of $\overleftrightarrow{XY}$ do $\overrightarrow{YX}$ and $\overrightarrow{XY}$ have in common? Sample: $\overrightarrow{YX}$ begins at point *Y* and continues through point *X* and beyond. The rays have different endpoints and continue in opposite directions. $\overline{XY}$

If a line can be drawn through a set of points, the points are **collinear.** If no line can be drawn through all the points, the points are **noncollinear.**

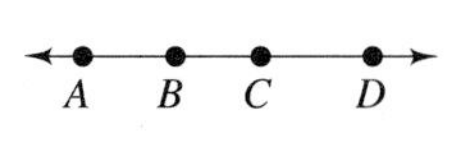

collinear points noncollinear points

WORK TOGETHER

11. a. Draw two points. Then draw all the lines that go through both points. See Solution Key.

    b. If you have two points, how many lines go through the points? one line

12. a. Draw three points. Then draw all the lines that go through two of the points. Is there a different way to arrange the three points so that you get a different number of lines? yes; See Solution Key.

    b. If you have three points, how many lines go through at least two of the points? one line for collinear points, three lines for noncollinear points

13. a. Arrange four points in as many different positions as you can. Draw the lines that go through at least two of the points. See Solution Key.

    b. If you have four points, how many lines go through at least two of the points? 1 line if all pts. are collinear, 4 lines if exactly 3 pts. are collinear, 6 lines if no 3 pts. are collinear. See Sol. Key.

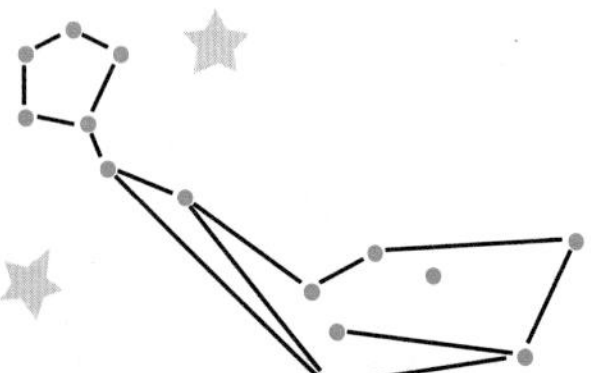

The stars that form the constellation Cetus can be represented by points. These points are connected here with segments to help you identify the shape that is suggested by the constellation's Latin name. **What shape do you see?**

Source: *Encyclopedia Americana*

a whale

Wrap Up

What's the Big Idea? Ask students to describe a point, a line, and a plane, and to give examples of two types of points and two types of lines.

Journal Ask students why they think points, lines, and planes are called the building blocks of geometry. Students should name some things they could build out of these "blocks."

Connections Have a discussion on how points, lines, and planes are used. You may want to start with the following examples:

- **Architecture** (blueprints, models, diagrams)
- **Art** (perspective lines, shading, line sketches)
- **Business** (diagrams of lines of communication or distribution, charts of levels of management or stages in product development)

Reteaching Activity Have students form segments on geoboards and then copy these onto dot paper (or have them begin with dot paper). Students should label endpoints on each segment and name each segment using the proper notation. Have students form as many different arrangements as they can. Students should note significant qualities of their arrangements, such as parallel segments.

There are two possible relationships between two lines that lie in a plane: either they intersect or they are parallel. **Parallel lines** are lines in the same plane that do not intersect. **Parallel segments** are segments that lie in parallel lines.

Example Is each pair of lines parallel or intersecting?

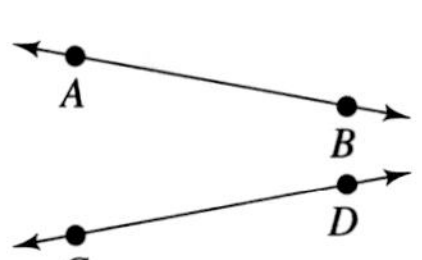

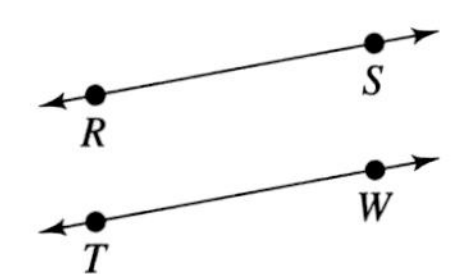

- $\overleftrightarrow{AB}$ and $\overleftrightarrow{CD}$ are intersecting lines, even though the point of intersection is not shown.
- $\overleftrightarrow{RS}$ and $\overleftrightarrow{TW}$ are parallel. No matter how much you extend them, they will not intersect.

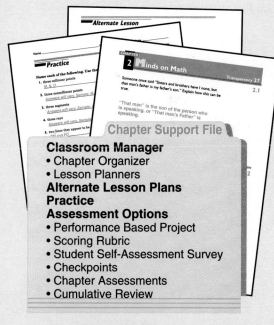

Parallel bars are an event in men's gymnastics. They are a model for parallel segments.

TRY THESE

Match each figure with its name.

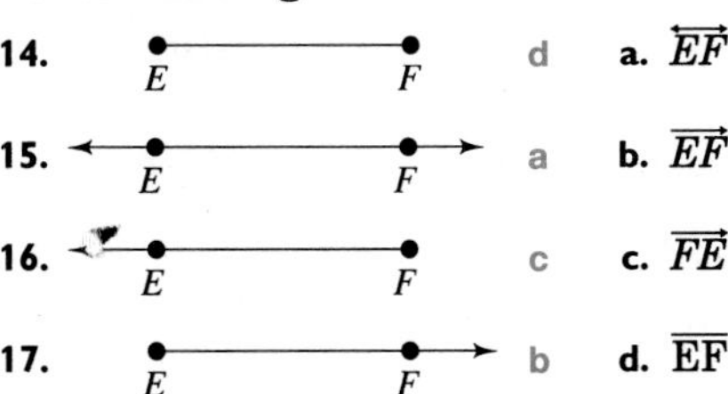

14. d a. $\overleftrightarrow{EF}$
15. a b. $\overrightarrow{EF}$
16. c c. $\overrightarrow{FE}$
17. b d. $\overline{EF}$

18. Name the line in several different ways.
$\overleftrightarrow{AB}$, $\overleftrightarrow{AC}$, $\overleftrightarrow{BC}$, $\overleftrightarrow{BA}$, $\overleftrightarrow{CA}$, $\overleftrightarrow{CB}$
19. Name four different rays.
$\overrightarrow{AB}$, $\overrightarrow{BC}$, $\overrightarrow{CB}$, $\overrightarrow{BA}$

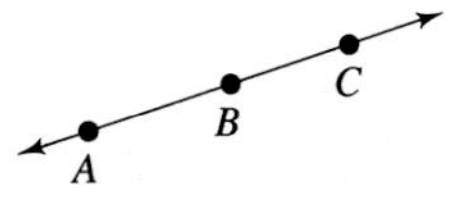

Use the article at the right to answer each question.

20. a. How could you describe geometrically the position of the moon, Earth, and sun during a solar eclipse?
three collinear points
b. **Critical Thinking** Why is it that we can think of heavenly bodies as large as these as points?
We use points to show location of these bodies, not to indicate their size.

Eclipses

Earth is about 248,550 mi from the moon and an amazing 93,000,000 mi from the sun. The diameters of Earth and the moon are about 7,910 mi and 2,200 mi, respectively. The diameter of the sun is about 865,400 mi. A solar eclipse occurs when the moon comes between the sun and Earth.

Assignment Options

Core: 21–26, 29–33, MR all	
Reinforce: 27, 28, 34–36	**Enrich:** 37, 38

Chapter Support File

Classroom Manager
- Chapter Organizer
- Lesson Planners

Alternate Lesson Plans
Practice
Assessment Options
- Performance Based Project
- Scoring Rubric
- Student Self-Assessment Survey
- Checkpoints
- Chapter Assessments
- Cumulative Review

Minds on Math available in Teaching Transparencies

ON YOUR OWN

Students will need dot or graph paper and a straightedge for Exercises 29–30, and 38.

Exercises 22–24: Point out to students that there are more possible answers than are required for these exercises.

Exercise 25: Have students explain their answers.

Exercises 31–36: Have students compare their answers to the figures' definitions.

WRITING For Exercise 37, have students make a numbered list of detailed steps. They can merely estimate the angle measures at this point.

TECHNOLOGY OPTION For Exercise 38, have students use geometry software to draw the sketches. Extend this activity to four lines, five lines, or more. Ask students to describe any patterns.

CRITICAL THINKING For Exercise 38, students should draw a sketch for each case.

Math Minutes

Find out how much money Mark had left if he started with $80.00 at the hardware store. He spent $5.00 on cement, 4 times as much as that on bricks, and bought 3 gallons of paint for $11.00 each. **$22.00**

Materials for 2-2

- protractor

Mixed REVIEW

Use mental math.

1. 24×5 120
2. $160 \div 8$ 20

Use the data: 50, 39, 46, 68, 53, 59, 49.

3. Find the mean. 52
4. Find the median. 50
5. Forty-six members of the hiking club are going camping. Each tent can hold 4 people. How many tents do they need to take with them? 12

ON YOUR OWN

Name each of the following.

21. three collinear points
    A, *B*, and *C*
22. three noncollinear points
    Sample: *A*, *B*, and *D*
23. three segments
    Sample: $\overline{AC}$, $\overline{BD}$, $\overline{DE}$
24. three rays
    Sample: $\overrightarrow{BA}$, $\overrightarrow{BC}$, $\overrightarrow{ED}$
25. two lines that appear to be parallel
    Sample: $\overleftrightarrow{AC}$ and $\overleftrightarrow{DE}$
26. two pairs of intersecting lines
    Sample: $\overleftrightarrow{AC}$ and $\overleftrightarrow{BD}$, $\overleftrightarrow{DE}$ and $\overleftrightarrow{BD}$

Name the segments that appear to be parallel.

27. 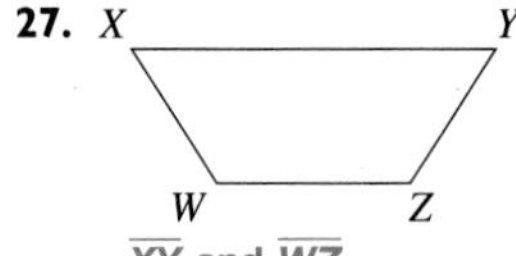

$\overline{XY}$ and $\overline{WZ}$

28. 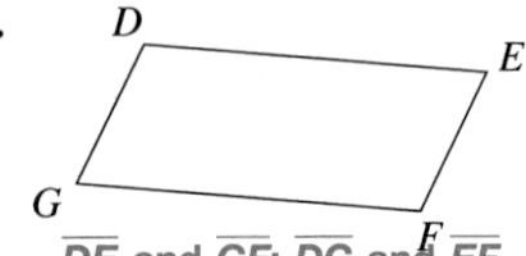

$\overline{DE}$ and $\overline{GF}$; $\overline{DG}$ and $\overline{EF}$

29. Draw five collinear points.
    See Sol. Key.
30. Draw three noncollinear points.
    See Sol. Key.

Complete each sentence with *sometimes, always,* or *never.*

31. Two points are ■ collinear. always
32. Two parallel lines are ■ intersecting. never
33. Four points are ■ collinear. sometimes
34. A segment ■ has two endpoints. always
35. A ray ■ has two endpoints. never
36. A line ■ has two endpoints. never

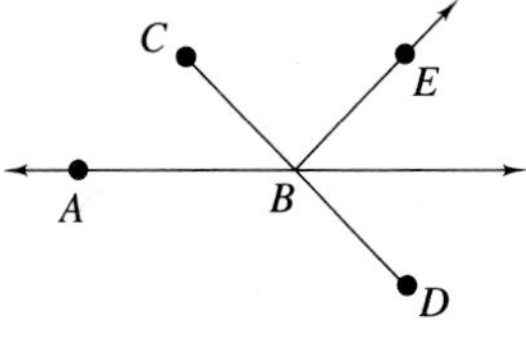

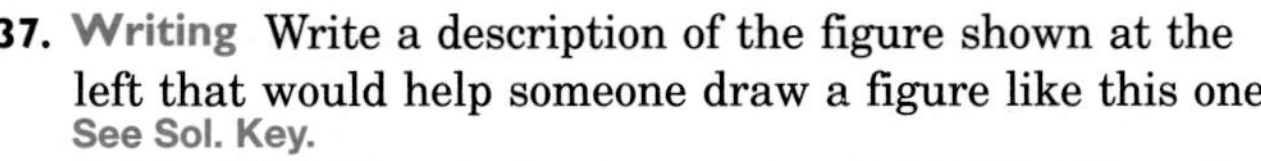

37. **Writing** Write a description of the figure shown at the left that would help someone draw a figure like this one.
    See Sol. Key.
38. **Critical Thinking** In how many ways can three lines that lie on one plane be related? Draw sketches to show all the ways that the lines can intersect or be parallel.
    four ways; See Sol. Key.

2-2

Connecting to Prior Knowledge

Have students consider a skyscraper like the Empire State Building or the Sears Tower. Ask them to give names for the intersections of the lines and planes. **(angles)** Ask students to describe the most common angle used in a house. **(Students may describe the angle as right, square, or perpendicular.)** Ask students why they think that type of angle is so common.

THINK AND DISCUSS

ESL **ESL** Have students practice naming the same angle in a variety of ways such as *∠ABC, ∠CBA, ∠B,* or *∠1.*

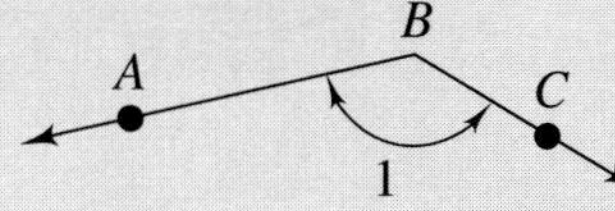

Question 3: Label any point on the bisecting ray as W and ask students to give three different names for the two smaller angles. ***(∠1, ∠STW, ∠WTS; ∠2, ∠WTR, ∠RTW)***

Question 4b: Have students make sure that the base lines of their angles are covered by the base line of the protractor.

Question 4c: Some students may have trouble in reading the scale on the protractor or in estimating between labeled marks. Have students practice measuring angles in pairs so that they can help each other.

Question 6: Some students may ask about angles that are greater than 180°. Tell them that these are called *reflex angles.* Drawings of a reflex angle must be marked with an arrow to show that the angle less than 180° is not meant.

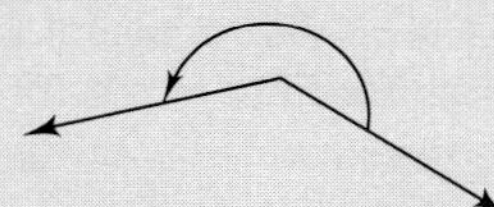

What's Ahead

- Estimating, measuring, and drawing angles
- Classifying angles as acute, right, obtuse, or straight

WHAT YOU'LL NEED

✓ Protractor 

2-2 Exploring Angles

THINK AND DISCUSS

More than 3,000 years ago the Babylonians discovered that it took about 360 days for the sun to travel in a circular path in the sky. As a result of this discovery, the Babylonians divided the circle into 360 equal parts. We now call each of these parts a *degree.*

You measure *angles* in degrees. An **angle** is made up of two rays with a common endpoint, called the *vertex* of the angle. The rays are the *sides* of the angle.

1.b. *X* is the vertex and Y and Z are points on each side.

1. a. Name the vertex and sides of the angle. *X*; $\overrightarrow{XY}$ and $\overrightarrow{XZ}$
   b. One name for the angle is ∠*YXZ*. Describe what the three letters represent. See above.
   c. Can you use three letters to give a different name for the angle? Yes; ∠*ZXY*

Y
X
∠YXZ   Z

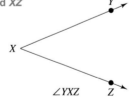

2. Sometimes you can name an angle with a number, like ∠1, or by a single letter. What one-letter name would you use for ∠*YXZ*? Why? ∠*X*; *X* is the vertex.

3. a. How many angles are shown? Name them. 3
   b. Why can't you use a single letter to name any of the angles? The three angles have the same vertex.

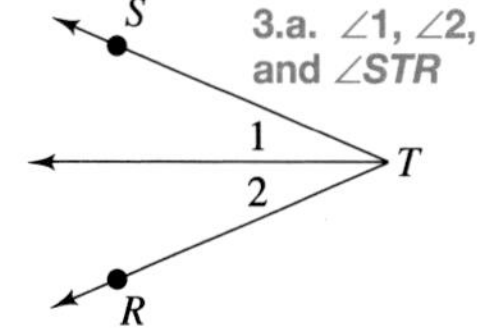

3.a. ∠1, ∠2, and ∠*STR*

You can use a *protractor* to measure the size of an angle in degrees, as shown on the next page.

WHO? The Babylonians used a number system based on the number 60. **How do we use Babylonian ideas to measure time?**

Source: *Historical Topics for the Mathematics Classroom*

60 s = 1 min
60 min = 1 h

> *Education is not to reform students, or amuse them, or to make them expert technicians. It is to unsettle their minds, widen their horizons, inflame their intellects, teach them to think straight, if possible.*
>
> —Robert M. Hutchins

Organizer

1. **Focus**
   Connecting to Prior Knowledge
2. **Teach**
   Think and Discuss
   Work Together
3. **Closure**
   Wrap Up

Vocabulary/Symbols
degree, °
angle, ∠
vertex
sides
protractor
acute angle
right angle
obtuse angle
straight angle
perpendicular

Skills Reviewed in Context of Lesson
- identifying rays and lines

Materials and Manipulatives
- protractor (one for each student)

On Your Own Exercises 13–14: straightedge; Exercises 12, 20–27, 31: protractor

continues next page

ESL Question 7: Ask students for another name for a straight angle.

KINESTHETIC LEARNERS Provide a group of three students with a rope 5 feet in length. Have one student hold the rope at the midpoint while each end of the rope is held by other students. The rope should be held taut to form an angle. As the students holding the ends move, new angles will be formed. Have classmates identify the angles.

ESL TACTILE LEARNERS Extend Question 9 by having students hold two pencils together along $\overrightarrow{ED}$ with both eraser ends at E and points toward D. Tell them to leave one pencil in place, and move the other counterclockwise, keeping the eraser ends together. Ask them to name the kinds of angles formed as they rotate the pencil.

Ongoing Assessment Model angles for students by using two straightedges. Have students describe each angle as acute, right, obtuse, or straight. Then have students estimate the angle measure and use a protractor to draw a similar angle. Have students compare results after each angle.

Error Alert! Students may read the wrong scale on the protractor when measuring angles. ***Remediation*** Have students draw an angle and estimate its measure based on the angle's classification. Then have the students place the protractor in position to measure the angle and decide which scale makes sense for the angle.

WORK TOGETHER

Have students work in pairs. Each pair of students should compare results.

Organizer, continued

Student Resources
Extra Practice
Student Study Guide
Practice, TR Ch. 2, p. 26
Student Study Guide, Spanish Resources, TR

Teacher Resources
Teaching Transparencies 6, 37
Transparency Masters, p. 6
Overhead Manipulatives: protractor
Lesson Planner, TR Ch. 2, p. 3

Prentice Hall Technology

Multimedia Math
- Math Tools, Geometry
- Hot Page™ 2-2
- Math Investigations, Mission: Mars

Computer Item Generator
- 2-2

Other Available Technology
Geometer's Sketchpad by Key Curriculum Press: Work Together activity *(optional)*

Fact of the Day

The Roman calendar was based on a lunar year of 355 days. By the time of Julius Caesar, the Roman civil calendar was three months ahead of the solar year. To fix the problem, Caesar declared that there would be 445 days in the year 46 B.C.

—MAN AND TIME

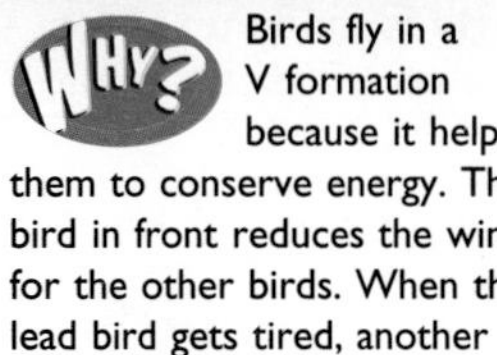

Birds fly in a V formation because it helps them to conserve energy. The bird in front reduces the wind for the other birds. When the lead bird gets tired, another bird takes over.

Source: *The Information Please Kids' Almanac*

4. a. Draw a large angle. To find the measure of the angle, place the center point of your protractor on the vertex of the angle. Make sure that one side of the angle passes through zero on the protractor scale. Check students' work.

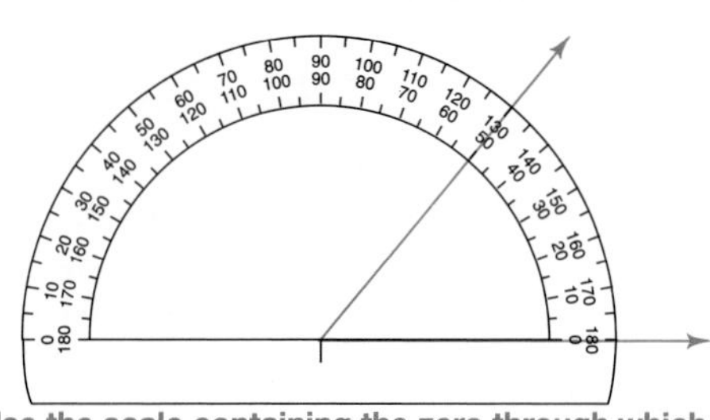

4.b. Use the scale containing the zero through which one side of the angle passes.

b. To find the measure of the angle, you read the scale where it intersects the second side of the angle. Most protractors have two scales. How do you decide which number to read? See above.

c. What is the measure of the angle you drew? Answers will vary.

5. How would you measure an angle with sides that don't extend to the scale of the protractor? Use a straightedge to extend the sides of the angle.

6. Use a protractor to measure each angle.

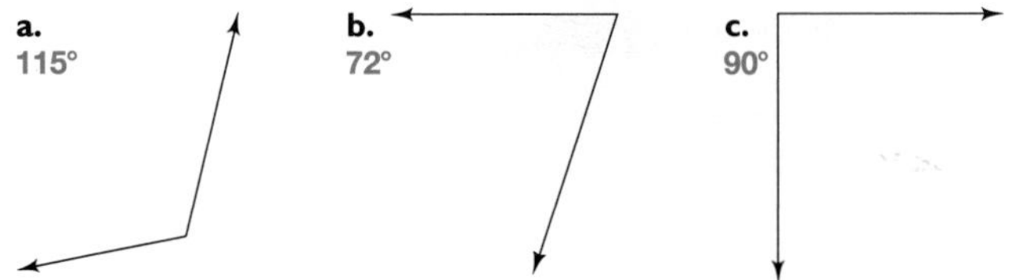

You can classify angles according to their measures.

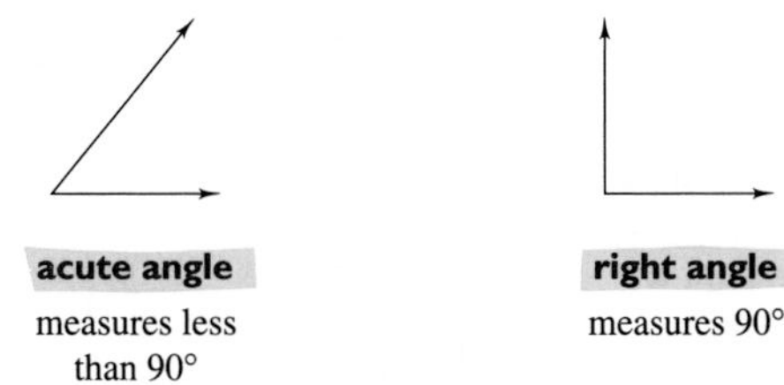

Extend these questions by asking students to match the items in Column A with those in Column B to find a pattern.

A	B
2	135°
$\frac{1}{3}$	60°
$\frac{1}{2}$	45°
1	90°
$\frac{2}{3}$	30°
$1\frac{1}{2}$	180°

Then ask students to describe the pattern.

(2 times 90° = 180°, $\frac{1}{3}$ of 90° = 30°, $\frac{1}{2}$ of 90° = 45°, 1 times 90° = 90°, $\frac{2}{3}$ of 90° = 60°, $1\frac{1}{2}$ times 90° = 135°)

DIVERSITY Have students work in pairs when using protractors so that students with fine motor difficulties who have problems aligning protractors can obtain assistance from their partners.

TECHNOLOGY OPTION For the Work Together activity, students can draw the angles using geometry software. You may also have students draw series of angles that differ by 1°, 5°, and 10°. Then have students estimate the size of each angle to see whether they can distinguish differences.

Journal Ask students to imagine how they could make a (crude) protractor if all they had was a ruler, compass, scissors, pencil, and paper. Have them describe their process in writing.

Wrap Up

What's the Big Idea? Ask students to describe four types of angles and to explain how to estimate, measure, and draw angles.

obtuse angle
measures greater than 90° and less than 180°

straight angle
measures 180°

7. Classify the angles in Question 6 as acute, right, obtuse, or straight. **obtuse; acute; right**

8. You also can use a protractor to draw angles. Describe how you would use your protractor to draw a 110° angle. **See Solution Key.**

Lines that intersect to form right angles are **perpendicular.** You can use the symbol ⌐ to indicate that lines are perpendicular or that an angle is a right angle.

9. Name all the right angles formed by the perpendicular lines, $\overleftrightarrow{AB}$ and $\overleftrightarrow{CD}$, shown. **∠AED, ∠DEB, ∠BEC, ∠AEC**

10. Find examples of perpendicular lines in your classroom. **Sample: adjacent edges of a chalkboard**

WORK TOGETHER

Being able to visualize certain angles will help you estimate angle measures.

- Use a protractor to draw angles with the following measures, but do not draw the angles in the order listed.

  30° 45° 60° 90° 120° 135° 150°

- Exchange papers with a partner.
- Without using a protractor to measure, write the measure of each angle next to the angle.

Did you have more trouble identifying some angles than other angles? If you did, try drawing angles with those measures without using a protractor. Then use your protractor to check how close you got.

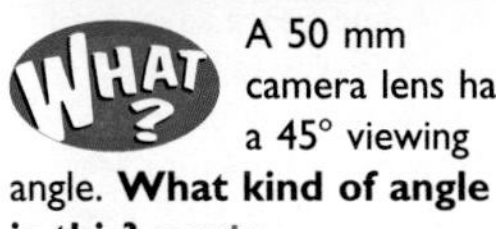

A 50 mm camera lens has a 45° viewing angle. **What kind of angle is this? acute**

Source: *How in the World?*

PH Multimedia Math Hot Page 2-2

Connections

Have a discussion about how angles are used. You may want to start with these examples:

- **Recreation** (racquetball, shooting baskets, diving)
- **Manufacturing** (door hinges, ramps, aerodynamics of a car or an airplane)
- **Science** (determining slope for a physics problem, finding the angle of attachment of atoms in a molecule)

Reteaching Activity

Have students form acute, right, obtuse, and straight angles on geoboards or on dot paper, and trade angles with a partner. Each student should classify and measure the partner's angles.

ON YOUR OWN

Students will need a protractor and straightedge for Exercises 12–13, 20–27, and 31.

Exercise 12b: Have students name the right angles formed.

Exercises 20–22: Have students list their estimates and measurements.

Exercises 23–26: Students should label the angles.

CONNECTION TO SCIENCE Exercise 27 has students apply their knowledge of angles to a scientific theory.

WRITING For Exercise 30, have students draw examples of angles to accompany their explanations.

Assignment Options

Core: 11–13, 16–19. 23–27, MR all	
Reinforce: 14, 15, 20–22, 28, 29, 31	Enrich: 30

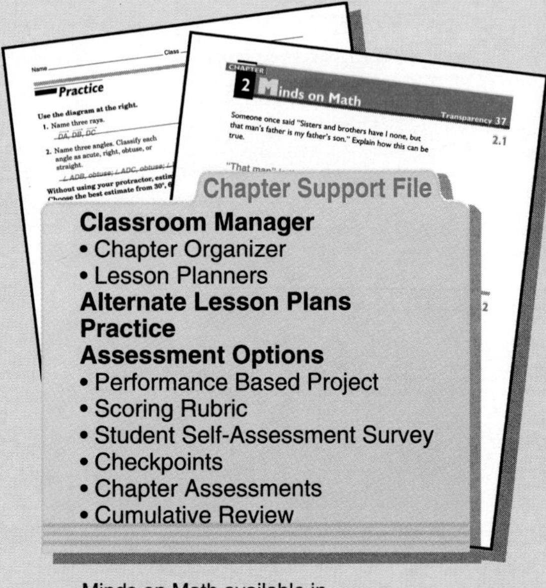

Practice
Minds on Math
Transparency 37
Chapter Support File
Classroom Manager
• Chapter Organizer
• Lesson Planners
Alternate Lesson Plans
Practice
Assessment Options
• Performance Based Project
• Scoring Rubric
• Student Self-Assessment Survey
• Checkpoints
• Chapter Assessments
• Cumulative Review

Minds on Math available in Teaching Transparencies

ON YOUR OWN

11. a. Name three rays. $\overrightarrow{LK}$, $\overrightarrow{LM}$, $\overrightarrow{LN}$
    b. Name three angles. Classify each angle as acute, right, obtuse, or straight.
    ∠MLN: acute; ∠KLM: right; ∠KLN: obtuse

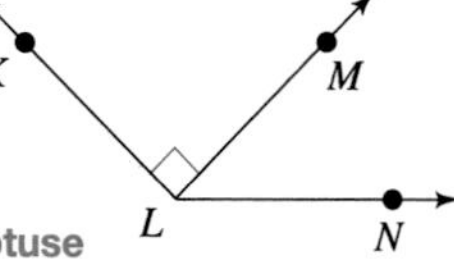

12. a. Draw two perpendicular lines, $\overleftrightarrow{RS}$ and $\overleftrightarrow{TW}$. See Sol. Key.
    b. How many right angles are formed? 4
13. Draw an obtuse ∠*DEF* and an acute ∠*NOP*. See Sol. Key.
14. Without using your protractor, try to draw a 45° angle. Fold a corner of a paper in half and draw along the fold.
15. Are there any angles you can draw accurately without using a protractor? Explain. You need only a straightedge to draw a straight angle; a corner to draw a right angle. Samples: 90°, 180°

Without using your protractor, estimate the measure of each angle. Choose the best estimate from 30°, 60°, 90°, 120°, 150°.

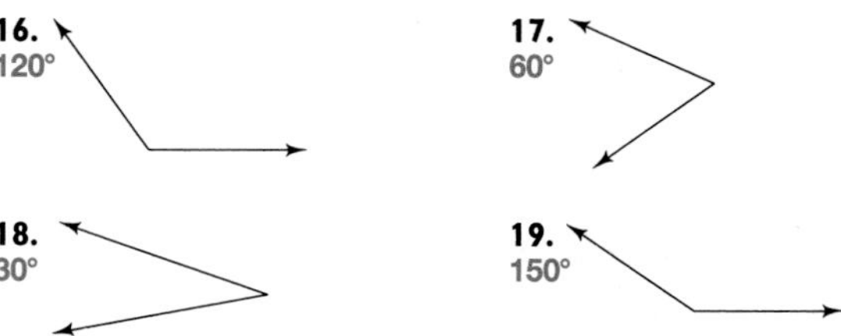

Estimate the measure of each angle. Then use a protractor to find the measure. Classify each angle. Accept reasonable estimates.

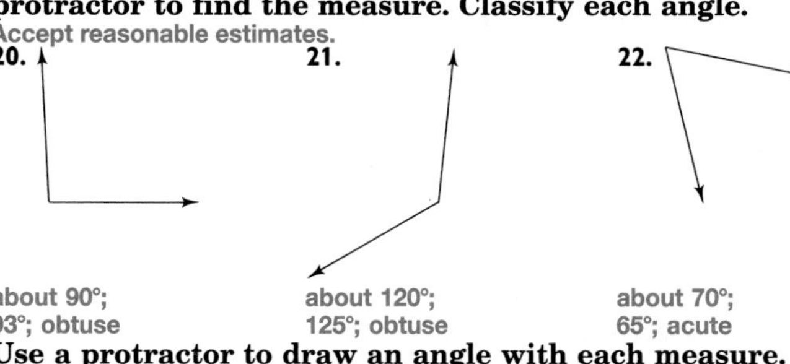

20. about 90°; 93°; obtuse
21. about 120°; 125°; obtuse
22. about 70°; 65°; acute

Use a protractor to draw an angle with each measure.

23. 125° 24. 75° 25. 82° 26. 154°

Check students' work. See Solution Key.

Mixed REVIEW

Find each answer.

1. 918 + 79 997
2. 2,076 − 582 1,494
3. Tell whether mean, median, or mode would best describe the favorite pizza topping of the students in your class. mode

Use the diagram below for Exercises 4 and 5.

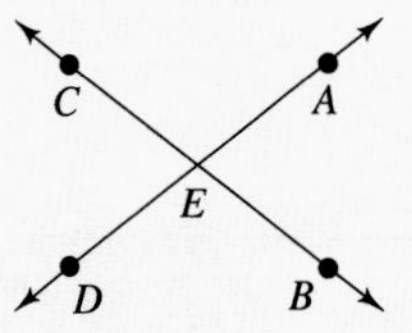

4. Name three noncollinear points. Sample: *A*, *B*, *C*
5. Name two rays on $\overleftrightarrow{BC}$. Sample: $\overrightarrow{BC}$, $\overrightarrow{CB}$
6. A bookstore advertised the following sale: *Buy 3 books, get 1 book free!* How many books do you have to buy to get 4 free books? 12 books

27. What angle does the Tyrannosaurus rex make with the ground in this drawing? 45°

T. Rex on the Prowl

Many museum models of Tyrannosaurus rex show the dinosaur in an upright, tail-dragging position. Scientists now believe that Tyrannosaurus rex actually walked at an angle, using its tail for balance.

28. a. Data File 1 (pp. 2–3) What product was advertised in about one fourth of the commercials during kids' TV shows? breakfast foods

b. What two categories together accounted for about half of the commercials? toys and other products

29. **Choose A, B, C, or D.** Which measure is not a measure of one of the angles shown at the right? A

A. 60° **B.** 90°

C. 120° **D.** 150°

30. Writing Must two acute angles have the same measure? Must two right angles? two obtuse angles? two straight angles? Explain. no; yes; no; yes; All right angles measure 90°. All straight angles measure 180°. Acute and obtuse angles have a range of values.

31. Find the measure of each angle.

a. ∠AGF 180°
b. ∠DGB 70°
c. ∠BGE 120°
d. ∠EGC 90°

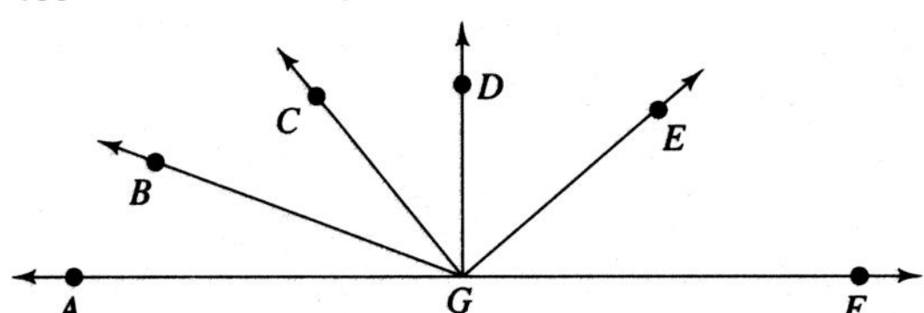

e. List all the obtuse angles shown. ∠AGE, ∠BGE, ∠BGF, ∠CGF

f. List all the right angles shown. ∠AGD, ∠DGF, ∠CGE

g. List all the straight angles shown. ∠AGF

Math Minutes

What number results if you divide 50 by $\frac{1}{2}$ and then subtract 25? **75**

Materials for 2-3

- ruler
- compass
- straightedge
- protractor

CHAPTER 2

PROBLEM SOLVING PRACTICE

This page provides a variety of problems that can be used to reinforce and enhance the students' problem solving skills.

Encourage students to read each problem carefully. Then have them refer to the list of problem-solving strategies to help them decide how to solve the problems.

Point out that not all questions require a strategy for solving. Some questions may require multiple strategies. Not all the strategies in the list are used on this page.

Exercise 2: To solve Exercise 2, have students model their calculations and answers with coins.

Problem Solving Practice

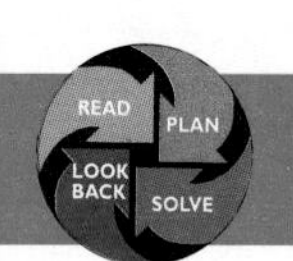

PROBLEM SOLVING STRATEGIES

Make a Table
Use Logical Reasoning
Solve a Simpler Problem
Too Much or Too Little Information
Look for a Pattern
Make a Model
Work Backward
Draw a Diagram
Guess and Test
Simulate a Problem
Use Multiple Strategies

Use any strategy to solve each problem. Show all your work.

1. Under which letter in the chart would you find the number 45? 101? C; E

A	B	C	D	E	F
1	2	3	4	5	6
7	8	9	10	11	12
13	14	15	16	17	18

2. What are the different amounts of money you can make by using any of the following coins: three pennies, two nickels, one dime? 1¢, 2¢, 3¢, 5¢, 6¢, 7¢, 8¢, 10¢, 11¢, 12¢, 13¢, 15¢, 16¢, 17¢, 18¢, 20¢, 21¢, 22¢, 23¢
3. Ewa is selling magazine subscriptions for her class fund raiser. She is trying to sell 26 subscriptions in order to win 10 movie tickets. She has already sold 7 subscriptions. If she is able to sell 3 subscriptions each day, how many days will it take her to reach her goal? 7 days
4. There are 20 students on the intramural tennis team. Eight students play only singles and 8 students play both singles and doubles. How many students play only doubles? 4 students
5. Draw one diagram that contains all the following geometric figures. Read through the list first and draw the minimum number of lines to fulfill all the requirements.
   - at least three segments not all on the same line
   - at least three lines that intersect in one point
   - at least two parallel lines
   - at least three noncollinear points

   Check students' drawings. See Sol. Key.
6. Kyle mowed several lawns after school on Friday. He mowed for 2 h and finished at 5:30 P.M. He did his homework for 50 min before he mowed. At what time did he begin to work on his homework? 2:40 P.M.

The widest lawnmower in the world is 60 ft wide and weighs 5.6 T. The "Big Green Machine" mows an acre in 60 s.

Source: *Guinness Book of Records*

2-3

Connecting to Prior Knowledge

Ask students to consider the piece of furniture called a table. (Point out a specific table if there is one in the classroom.) Have students name qualities of the table that make it stable and well-balanced. **(flat surface, equal leg lengths, equal angle joins)** Ask students to name and evaluate other objects that are stable or well-balanced.

THINK AND DISCUSS

KINESTHETIC LEARNERS Have students use a compass and straightedge to construct line segments and congruent angles.

Questions 1–2: Have students compare their results.

Question 3: Have students compare the measures of the angles with a protractor.

Question 5: Discuss students' answers with the class. If students' answers differ, help the class come to a consensus by reviewing the steps.

Journal Tell students that the compass was long used as a measurement device with ships' navigational charts. Ask students to describe how comfortable they find their own "navigation" with a compass. Have students suggest ways they could improve their skills.

CONNECTION TO MEASUREMENT Question 5 has students distinguish between constructing and measuring segments and angles.

Ongoing Assessment Ask students to describe the process required to construct a congruent segment or a congruent angle. Have students express the steps in their own words.

What's Ahead

- Constructing a segment congruent to a given segment
- Constructing an angle congruent to a given angle

WHAT YOU'LL NEED

✓ Ruler

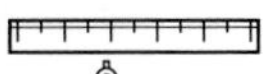

✓ Compass

✓ Straightedge

✓ Protractor

2-3 Constructing Segments and Angles

THINK AND DISCUSS

Do you think that $\overline{UV}$ or $\overline{XY}$ is longer?

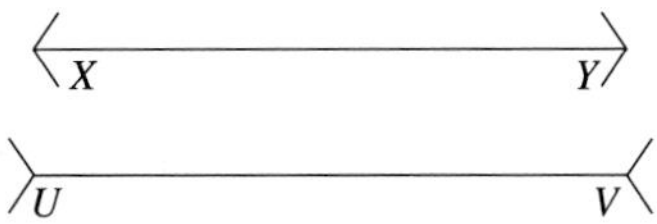

Check your answer by using a ruler to measure the length of each segment. Although $\overline{UV}$ appears to be longer, $\overline{UV}$ and $\overline{XY}$ are actually the same length. Segments that have the same length are **congruent segments.** You can *construct* a segment that is congruent to another segment by using two geometric tools: a compass and a straightedge.

A **compass** is a tool that you can use to draw circles or parts of circles called *arcs*. A **straightedge** is like a ruler but does not have marks that show measurement. You can use a ruler as a straightedge if you ignore the markings.

A B

1. Draw $\overline{AB}$ about as long as shown here. Then follow the steps below to construct a segment congruent to $\overline{AB}$.

C

Step 1 Use your straightedge to draw a ray. Label the endpoint of the ray as C.

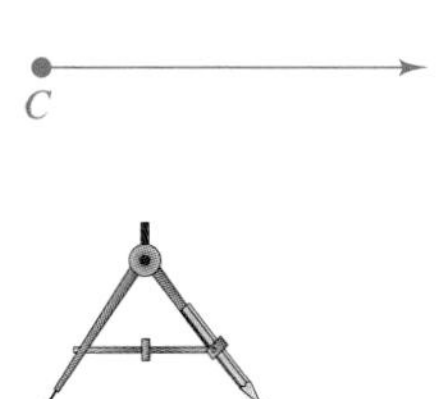

Step 2 Put the tip of the compass at A and open the compass wide enough so that you could draw an arc through B.

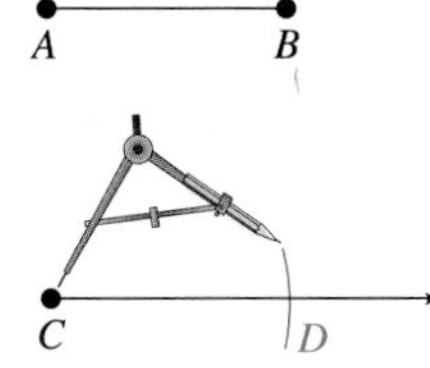

Step 3 Keeping the compass open to the same width, put the tip at C and draw an arc intersecting the ray. Label the point of intersection as D.

You now have constructed a segment, $\overline{CD}$, that is congruent to $\overline{AB}$.

" *Great works are performed not by strength, but by perseverance.* "

—DR. SAMUEL JOHNSON

Organizer

1. **Focus**
   Connecting to Prior Knowledge
2. **Teach**
   Think and Discuss
   Work Together
3. **Closure**
   Wrap Up

Vocabulary/Symbols

congruent segments
construct
compass
arcs
straightedge
congruent angles

Skills Reviewed in Context of Lesson

- identifying line segments, lines, rays, and angles

Materials and Manipulatives

- ruler (one per student)
- compass (one per student)
- straightedge (one per student)
- protractor (one per student)

On Your Own Exercises 6–10: straightedge, compass

continues next page

WORK TOGETHER

Have students work in groups of three or four. Students should complete each step in the activity individually and then confer with their group members after each step. Have each group submit a conjecture.

ESL Remind students that a conjecture is a tentative answer or generalization supported by reasons.

Error Alert! Students may accidentally change the compass width when trying to construct a congruent segment or arc. ***Remediation*** Encourage students to recheck the original compass width every time they make a congruent angle or segment.

ESL Hold up a compass and straightedge and label them. Have students repeat the names after you. You might want to point out that *compass* has another meaning. Demonstrate the words *construct* and *construction.* Encourage students to use these words in context.

Wrap Up

What's the Big Idea? Ask students to describe how to construct a congruent angle and a congruent segment.

Connections Have a discussion about how congruent angles and segments are used. You may want to start with these examples:

- **Manufacturing** (mass production, assembly lines)
- **Architecture** (designing level floor plans, positioning, weight supports)
- **Photography** (printing photographs, enlarging or reducing prints)

Organizer, continued

Student Resources
Extra Practice
Student Study Guide
Practice, TR Ch. 2, p. 27
Student Study Guide, Spanish Resources, TR

Teacher Resources

Teaching Transparencies 2, 6, 37
Overhead Manipulatives: protractor
Lesson Planner, TR Ch. 2, p. 4

Prentice Hall Technology

Multimedia Math
- Math Tools, Geometry

Computer Item Generator
- 2-3

Other Available Technology
Geometer's Sketchpad by Key Curriculum Press: Exercises 6–11 *(optional)*

Fact of the Day

A different kind of compass, called a gyrocompass, is used in navigation. It is a more accurate navigational compass, unaffected by magnetic influence. The gyrocompass points along the meridian.

—THE CONCISE COLUMBIA ENCYCLOPEDIA

Angles that have the same measure are **congruent angles.** You can use a compass and straightedge to construct an angle congruent to a given angle.

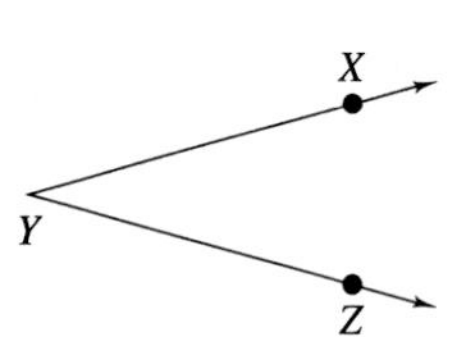

2. Draw an acute angle, $\angle XYZ$. Then follow the steps below to construct an angle congruent to $\angle XYZ$.

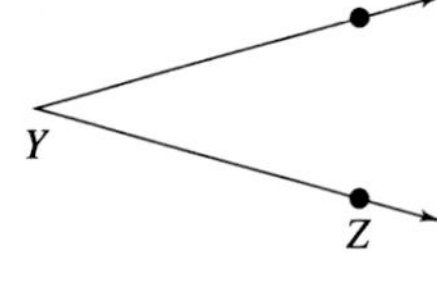

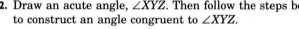

Step 1 Draw a ray. Label the endpoint as S.

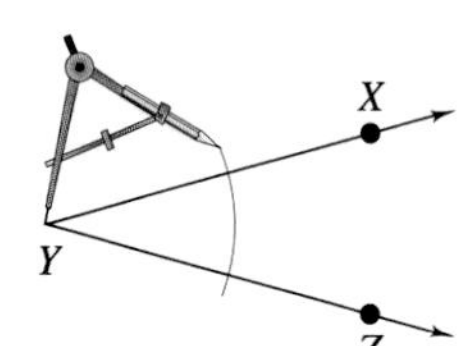

Step 2 Put the compass tip at Y and draw an arc that intersects both $\overrightarrow{YX}$ and $\overrightarrow{YZ}$.

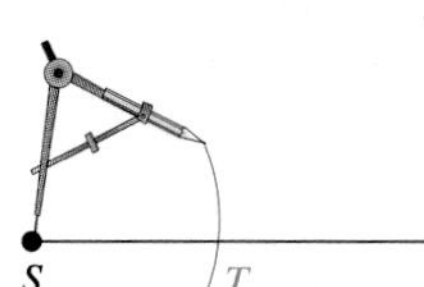

Step 3 Keeping the compass open to the same width, put the tip at S. Draw an arc intersecting the ray at a point you label as T.

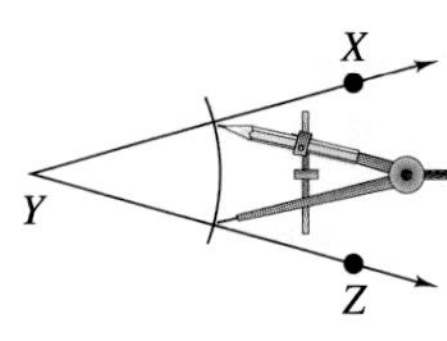

Step 4 Adjust the compass width so that the tip and the pencil are at the points where the arc intersects $\overrightarrow{YX}$ and $\overrightarrow{YZ}$.

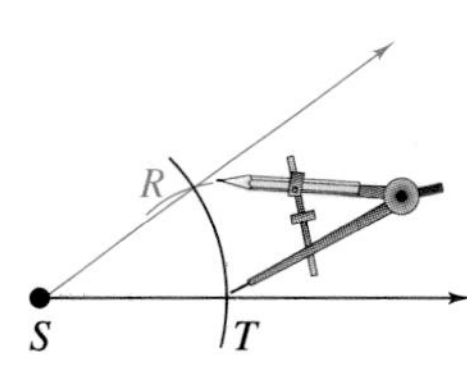

Step 5 Keeping the same compass width, put the tip at T and draw an arc that intersects the first arc. Label the point of intersection as R. Draw $\overrightarrow{SR}$.

You just constructed an angle, $\angle RST$, that is congruent to $\angle XYZ$.

Reteaching Activity Have students draw a 45° angle using a protractor and then follow the steps for constructing an angle congruent to it. Students should then measure the constructed angle with a protractor and compare the two angle measurements.

ON YOUR OWN

Students will need a straightedge and compass for Exercises 6–10.

TECHNOLOGY OPTION For Exercises 6–10, have students do the constructions using geometry software. For Exercise 11, have students experiment with several multiples of the given angle before answering the question.

ESL **Exercises 7 and 8:** Review briefly the definition of acute and obtuse angles.

Exercise 9: Have students think of two ways they can construct a segment that is six times as long as $\overline{GH}$. **(Mark off six lengths congruent to $\overline{GH}$ or mark off two lengths equal to the segment constructed for Exercise 9.)**

WRITING For Exercise 11, have students use their descriptions to construct an angle with a measure three times the measure of $\angle C$. Have students check their drawings with protractors.

3. Draw an obtuse $\angle G$. Then construct an angle, $\angle K$, congruent to $\angle G$. Check students' work. See Sol. Key.
4. Use a protractor to measure your $\angle XYZ$, $\angle RST$, $\angle G$, and $\angle K$. Did you get the same measure for $\angle XYZ$ and $\angle RST$? for $\angle G$ and $\angle K$? What might account for any differences? See below.
5. Do you need to know the length of a segment or measure of an angle to construct a congruent segment or angle? Why or why not? no; Constructions don't use numbers.

4. Answers may vary. Measures may not be exact due to movement of the compass.

WORK TOGETHER

- Use a straightedge to draw a segment. Label it as $\overline{AB}$.
- Open your compass so the tip is on point A and the pencil point is on B. Draw a circle.
- Keeping the compass open to the same width, put the tip at B. Draw an arc that intersects the circle at one point. Label the point of intersection as point C.
- Draw $\overline{AC}$ and $\overline{BC}$. Describe the figure formed by $\overline{AB}$, $\overline{BC}$, and $\overline{AC}$. $\triangle ABC$ is an equilateral triangle.
- Use a protractor to measure $\angle A$, $\angle B$, and $\angle C$. Compare your results with those of your group. Make a conjecture. Each angle has a measure of 60°. Conjecture: A triangle with 3 congruent sides has 3 congruent angles.

ON YOUR OWN

6–10. Check students' drawings. See Sol. Key.

6. Draw a segment and label it as $\overline{KL}$. Construct a segment congruent to $\overline{KL}$.
7. Draw an acute $\angle A$. Construct an angle congruent to $\angle A$.
8. Draw an obtuse $\angle B$. Construct an angle congruent to $\angle B$.
9. Draw a segment, $\overline{GH}$. Construct a segment three times as long as $\overline{GH}$.
10. Draw an angle like $\angle C$. Then construct an angle with measure twice the measure of $\angle C$.
11. *Writing* Describe how to construct an angle with measure three times the measure of $\angle C$. See Sol. Key.

Mixed REVIEW

Complete with <, >, or =.

1. 13 × 7 ■ 120 − 27 <
2. 237 + 338 ■ 25 × 23 =

Use the data: 2, 4, 4, 0, 3, 1, 2, 3, 1, 0.

3. Make a frequency table.
4. Find the range. 4

3. Check students' work.

Use the diagram below for Exercises 5 and 6.

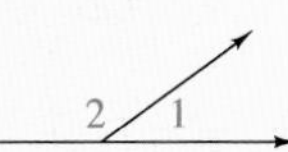

5. Name an acute angle. ∠1
6. If the measure of ∠1 is 35°, find the measure of ∠2. 145°
7. A mountain climber starts at an altitude of 2,830 ft and climbs 4,920 ft. The next day, she climbs another 3,130 ft. What is her final altitude?

10,880 ft

Assignment Options

Core: 6, 7, 10, MR all	
Reinforce: 8, 9	**Enrich:** 11

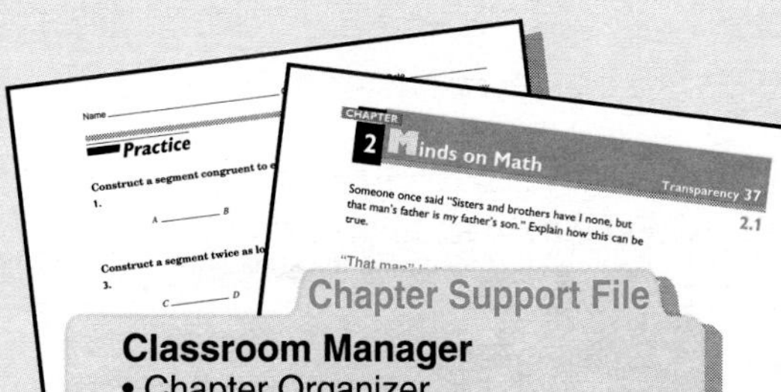

Minds on Math available in Teaching Transparencies

Math Minutes

What math symbol can be placed between 6 and 7 so that the result is a number between 6 and 7? **a decimal point**

Materials for 2-4

- geoboard
- rubber bands
- dot paper

2-4

Connecting to Prior Knowledge

Draw a variety of triangles on the chalkboard. Ask students to discuss the relationship between the triangles and their segments and angles. Encourage students to use and explain any vocabulary they know that names kinds of angles or kinds of triangles.

WORK TOGETHER

Have students work in groups of three or four.

Groups should brainstorm ways of constructing at least two triangles for each description. Use groups' responses to gauge their understanding.

TECHNOLOGY OPTION For the Work Together activity, have students use geometry software to draw several triangles for each part of the activity. Then answer the Think and Discuss Questions 1–5.

THINK AND DISCUSS

ESL **KINESTHETIC LEARNERS** Have each student form acute, obtuse, right, equilateral, isosceles, and scalene triangles on a geoboard. Have students trade geoboards with partners and name the triangles.

Question 5: Discuss students' answers to this question with the class. Have students explain their answers.

Example

- *Why is every equilateral triangle acute?*
  (An obtuse angle would make one side of the triangle greater than the other sides.)
- *Why is every equilateral triangle isosceles?*
  ("Three congruent sides" fits the description of "at least two congruent sides.")

Help students see that the best name is the one that is most specific and gives the most information.

" Man's mind, stretched by a new idea, never goes back to its original dimensions. "

—Oliver Wendell Holmes

Organizer

1. **Focus**
   Connecting to Prior Knowledge
2. **Teach**
   Work Together
   Think and Discuss
3. **Closure**
   Try These
   Wrap Up

Vocabulary/Symbols
acute triangle
obtuse triangle
right triangle
equilateral triangle
isosceles triangle
scalene triangle

Skills Reviewed in Context of Lesson
- working with triangles

Materials and Manipulatives
- geoboard (one per group)
- rubber bands (one dozen per group)
- dot paper (for each student)

On Your Own Exercises 12, 20: centimeter ruler, protractor; Exercises 21–29: straightedge

continues next page

2-4 Exploring Triangles

What's Ahead
- Identifying triangles by their angles
- Identifying triangles by their sides

WHAT YOU'LL NEED
✓ Geoboard
✓ Rubber bands
✓ Dot paper

WORK TOGETHER

Work in groups. On geoboards form as many of the triangles described below as you can. If possible, try to form two triangles with different shapes that fit each description. Record each triangle on dot paper. Check students' work.

a. a triangle with three acute angles
b. a triangle with one right angle
c. a triangle with one obtuse angle
d. a triangle with one right angle and one obtuse angle not possible
e. a triangle with no sides congruent
f. a triangle with exactly two congruent sides

THINK AND DISCUSS

You can classify triangles by angle measures or by the number of congruent sides.

Classifying by Angles

acute triangle
three acute angles

obtuse triangle
one obtuse angle

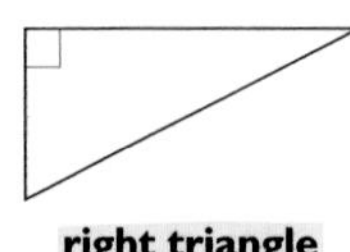

right triangle
one right angle

Classifying by Sides

equilateral triangle
three congruent sides

isosceles triangle
at least two congruent sides

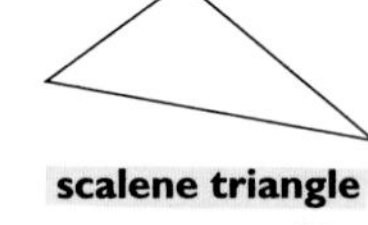

scalene triangle
no congruent sides

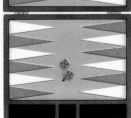

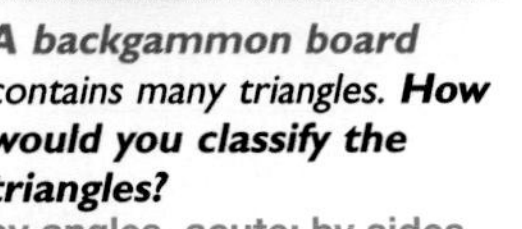

A backgammon board *contains many triangles.* ***How would you classify the triangles?***
by angles, acute; by sides, isosceles

Ongoing Assessment Group students in pairs. Have each student form a triangle on a geoboard for his or her partner to name. The partners should then form a different triangle for the first student to name. Students should repeat the activity until every type of triangle has been formed.

AUDITORY LEARNERS Have each student describe to a partner the attributes of a triangle formed on the geoboard. Have the partner attempt to classify the triangle by its description without looking at it.

Additional Example

- *Judging by appearance, give all the names you can for the triangle below.*

(The triangle is obtuse and scalene.)

TRY THESE

Exercises 6–11: Have students give reasons for their answers.

Error Alert! For Exercise 7, students may ignore the fact that an equilateral triangle is also an isosceles triangle. ***Remediation*** Have students consider a triangle with all sides of length 3 cm. Students should classify the triangle in as many ways as possible according to its sides.

Wrap Up

What's the Big Idea? Ask students to describe six types of triangles.

Journal Invite students to create memory aids, perhaps as rhymes, to help them learn the pronunciation and meaning of terms such as *scalene* and *isosceles*. Some may want to try creating a triangle rap song!

1. It is impossible to have both a right and an obtuse angle in one triangle.

1. Which triangle or triangles described in the Work Together activity could you *not* form on your geoboard? d Why do you think that you were unable to form them? See above.
2. Can an isosceles triangle be an acute triangle? a right triangle? an obtuse triangle? yes; yes; yes
3. Can a scalene triangle be an acute triangle? a right triangle? an obtuse triangle? yes; yes; yes
4. Can an equilateral triangle be an acute triangle? a right triangle? an obtuse triangle? yes; no; no
5. Suppose a triangle is both isosceles and obtuse. What is the best name for it? obtuse isosceles triangle

Example Judging by appearance, give all the names you can for the triangle. What is the best name?

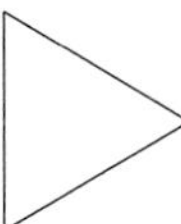

- The triangle is acute, equilateral, and isosceles.
- The best name is equilateral, because every equilateral triangle is acute and isosceles.

A lateen, or triangular sail, allows a boat to sail in any direction—even into the wind.

TRY THESE

Judging by appearance, name all the triangles that fit each description.

6. equilateral triangle d
7. isosceles triangle a, b, d, f
8. scalene triangle c, e
9. acute triangle b, d
10. right triangle a, c
11. obtuse triangle e, f

a.

b.

c.

d.

e.

f.

Organizer, continued

Student Resources
Extra Practice
Student Study Guide
Practice, TR Ch. 2, p. 28
Student Study Guide, Spanish Resources, TR
Checkpoint, TR Ch. 2, p. 40

Teacher Resources
Teaching Transparencies 8, 9, 38, 40
Overhead Manipulatives: geoboard
Lesson Planner, TR Ch. 2, p. 5

Prentice Hall Technology

Multimedia Math
- Math Tools, Geometry
- Hot Page™ 2-4
- Math Investigations, The Pythagorean Theorem

Computer Item Generator
- 2-4

Other Available Technology
Geometer's Sketchpad by Key Curriculum Press: Work Together activity *(optional)*

Fact of the Day

Buckminster Fuller linked together various types and sizes of triangles to form a sphere, thus creating the geodesic dome. This design now is seen in a wide variety of architectural work.

—*MATHEMATICS*

Connections Have a discussion about how triangles are used. You may want to start with these examples:

- **Architecture** (bridge supports, house roofs, chimney covers)
- **Business** (pyramid charts, commercial design measurements)
- **Household** (door wedges, knife blades, needlepoints)

Reteaching Activity Tell students to draw six 60° angles, and then have them use each angle to draw a different type of triangle. Have students share their results.

ON YOUR OWN

Students will need a centimeter ruler and a protractor for Exercises 12 and 20, and a straightedge for Exercises 21–29.

Exercise 12: Students may need tracing paper to be able to copy and extend the angles to make them easier to measure.

Exercise 13: Students may think that a triangle can be formed from any three segments. As an extension, ask them to try drawing triangles with sides of 6 in., 4 in., and 2 in. and one with sides of 3 in., 3 in., and 7 in.
(Both of these are impossible because the sum of any two sides must be greater than the third side.)

WRITING For Exercise 19, have students draw figures to support their answers.

CRITICAL THINKING For Exercise 20, students may need tracing paper to extend and measure the angles. Have students share conjectures during the next class period.

PH Multimedia Math Hot Page™ 2-4

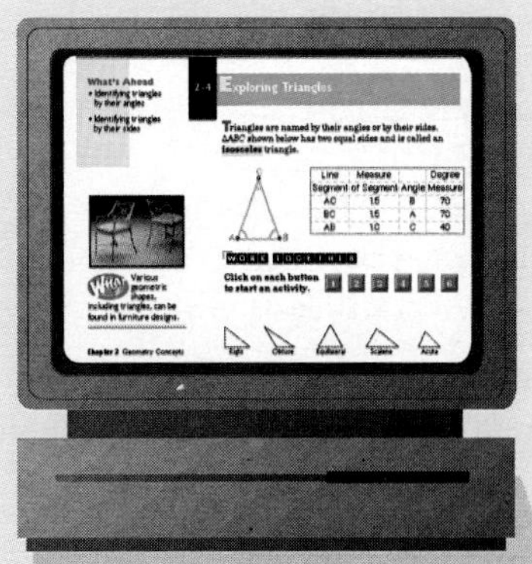

Assignment Options

Core: 12–18, 21–23, MR all, CH all	
Reinforce: 19, 24–29	Enrich: 20

1. 4,527; 3,201; 3,097; 2,852; 2,684; 978

Mixed REVIEW

1. Order the following numbers from greatest to least: 3,201; 2,684; 978; 2,852; 4,527; and 3,097.
2. Data File 1 (pp. 2–3) About how many more people own color sets than black and white sets? about 88 million

Complete.

3. The two geometric tools you use in constructions are the ■ and straightedge. compass
4. Angles that have the same measure are ■ angles. congruent
5. In how many ways can you have coins that total 15¢? 6

ON YOUR OWN

12. Use a centimeter ruler and protractor to measure the sides and angles of each triangle. Classify each triangle according to its angle measures and side lengths. Then choose the best name for each triangle. See Sol. Key.

a. 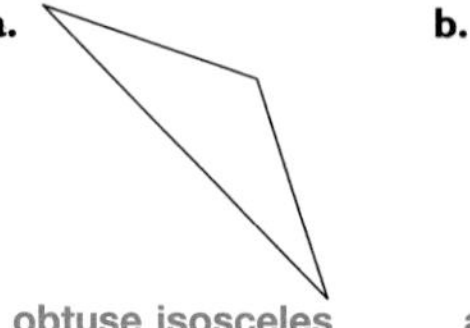
obtuse isosceles

b. 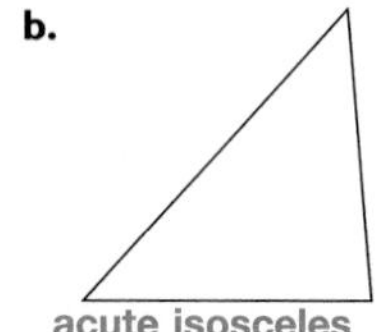
acute isosceles

c. 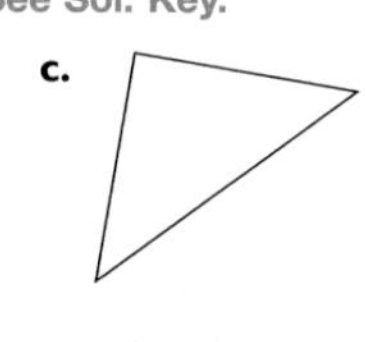
right isosceles

Classify the triangle described as scalene, isosceles, or equilateral.

13. The side lengths are 6, 8, and 6. isosceles
14. The side lengths are 12, 7, and 9. scalene
15. The side lengths are 11, 11, and 11. equilateral

Classify the triangle described as acute, right, or obtuse.

16. The angle measures are 100°, 37°, and 43°. obtuse
17. The angle measures are 56°, 88°, and 36°. acute
18. The angle measures are 50°, 90°, and 40°. right
19. Writing Must an equilateral triangle be an isosceles triangle? Why or why not? Must an isosceles triangle be an equilateral triangle? Why or why not? Yes, it has at least two sides congruent. No, it may only have two congruent sides.
20. Critical Thinking Use a centimeter ruler and protractor to measure the sides and angles of each triangle. Classify each of the triangles by side lengths. Then make a conjecture. All three are isosceles.

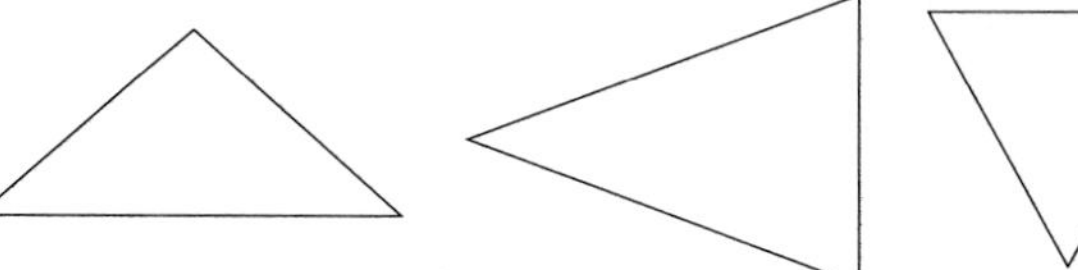

Conjecture: An isosceles triangle has congruent angles opposite its congruent sides.

Exercises 21–29: Have students sketch an example of each figure that does not form a triangle to show that the figure is not a triangle (to show, for example, that two of the sides of the figure do not intersect). Students can use the drawings to check their answers.

CHECKPOINT

Students will need a protractor for Exercises 10–11 and a straightedge for Exercises 11–12.

ESL **Exercise 13:** If students have trouble with this problem, have them draw an example for each of the answers given. Check their drawings and make sure they understand the terms.

If possible, sketch each triangle. If you can't sketch a triangle, explain why.
See Sol. Key.

21. an acute isosceles triangle
22. an obtuse scalene triangle
23. a right isosceles triangle
24. an obtuse equilateral triangle not poss; an equilateral △ has three 60° angles.
25. an acute scalene triangle
26. a right scalene triangle
27. an obtuse isosceles triangle
28. a right equilateral triangle not possible; an equilateral △ has three 60° angles.
29. an acute obtuse triangle not possible; an acute △ has three acute angles.

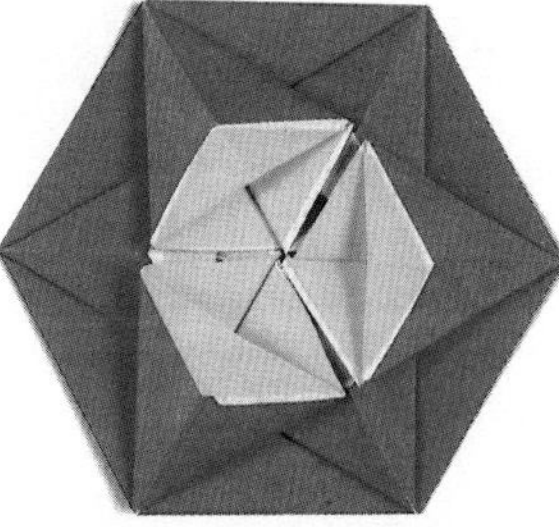

It is a Japanese custom to decorate gifts with noshi cases. These paper decorations symbolize good fortune.

CHECKPOINT

Use the figure at the right to name each of the following.

1. two lines $\overleftrightarrow{LM}$, $\overleftrightarrow{KN}$
2. three rays Sample: $\overrightarrow{JK}$, $\overrightarrow{JL}$, $\overrightarrow{JP}$
3. three segments Sample: $\overline{LM}$, $\overline{JP}$, $\overline{JN}$
4. an acute angle Sample: ∠LJK
5. an obtuse angle Sample: ∠KJM
6. a right angle Sample: ∠LJP
7. a straight angle Sample: ∠LJM
8. three collinear points Sample: L, J, M
9. three noncollinear points Sample: J, P, M
10. Use a protractor to measure ∠*LJK*. 47°
11. Use a protractor to draw an angle with measure 105°. Check students' drawings.
12. Draw an obtuse ∠*E*. Then construct an angle congruent to ∠*E*. Check students' drawings.
13. **Choose A, B, C, or D.** Judging by appearance, classify the triangle. B
    - **A.** right scalene
    - **B.** acute isosceles
    - **C.** equilateral
    - **D.** obtuse isosceles
14. Give examples of three ways triangles might be used in real life. Answers may vary. Sample: quilt designs, tile floors, sails

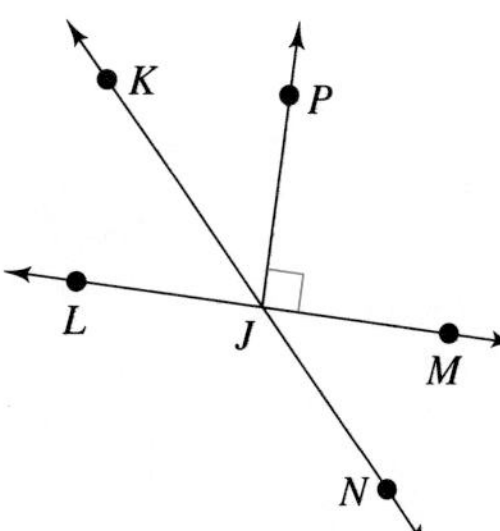

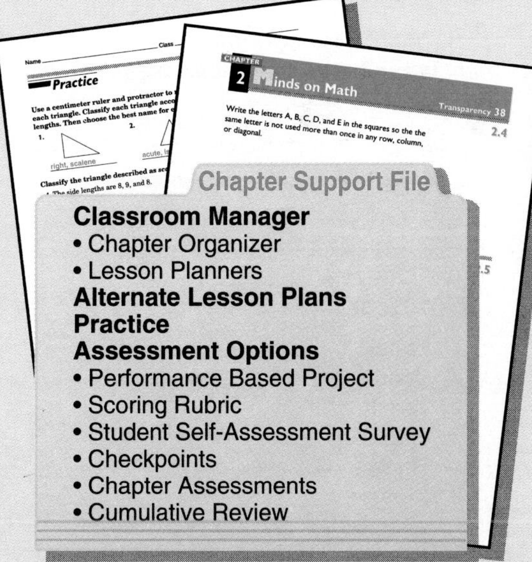

Minds on Math available in Teaching Transparencies

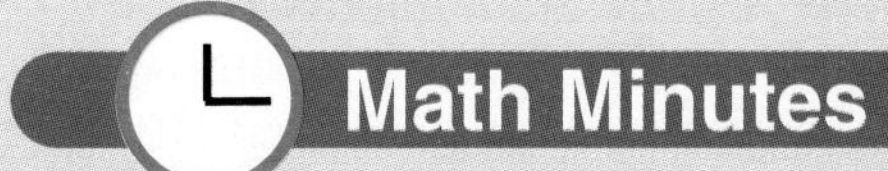

Write $3\frac{1}{7}$ as an improper fraction and then find the decimal equivalent. Use a calculator to decide whether $3\frac{1}{7}$ or π is larger.

$\frac{22}{7}$; 3.1428571; 3.1428571 is larger than π, which is 3.1415927

2-5

Connecting to Prior Knowledge

Have students give examples of figures that have more than three sides. Ask students for examples of polygons they see around them every day.

WORK TOGETHER

Have students work in groups of three or four. Each group should decide on one member to be the recorder, who compiles a list of characteristics for Question 1a and 1b, and writes the definition for Question 1c. The other members draw the diagrams to support the list and definition.

WRITING For Question 1c, encourage students to make their definitions as precise as possible.

Question 2: Have students use the activity to polish their definitions. Groups can then compare their work.

TACTILE LEARNERS Have each student form a figure on a geoboard. Then have the student's partner touch the figure (with eyes closed) to determine whether or not it is a polygon. Have students form some figures that are polygons and some that are not polygons either on geoboards or with twist ties or pipe cleaners.

THINK AND DISCUSS

Question 3: Ask students to name the shape of a traffic sign that says "yield." **(a triangle)**

Question 4: Suggest that students extend the sides of each polygon and notice whether any extended side falls inside the polygon. A *yes* answer says the polygon is not convex.

CRITICAL THINKING For Question 5, have students describe the unusual angle. **(a measure greater than that of a straight angle)** Ask: *Can a convex polygon have obtuse angles?* **(Yes; 3c is such a polygon.)**

"What the superior man seeks is in him; what the common man seeks is in others."

—CONFUCIUS

Organizer

1. **Focus**
   Connecting to Prior Knowledge
2. **Teach**
   Work Together
   Think and Discuss
3. **Closure**
   Wrap Up

Vocabulary/Symbols
polygons
convex

Materials and Manipulatives
On Your Own Exercises 12, 16–18: dot paper, straightedge; Exercise13: ruler; Exercises 13, 16–18: protractor

Student Resources
Extra Practice
Student Study Guide
Practice, TR Ch. 2, p. 29
Student Study Guide, Spanish Resources, TR
Alternate Lesson, TR Ch. 2, pp. 17–20

Teacher Resources

Teaching Transparency 38
Transparency Masters, p. 8
Lesson Planner, TR Ch. 2, p. 6

continues next page

What's Ahead

- Determining if a figure is a polygon
- Identifying triangles, quadrilaterals, pentagons, hexagons, octagons, and decagons

2-5 Exploring Polygons

WHO? Benjamin Banneker helped design the city of Washington, D.C. The map shows the use of geometry in his design.

WORK TOGETHER

Some of the figures shown are *polygons*. The others are not polygons. Work with your group to answer the following questions.

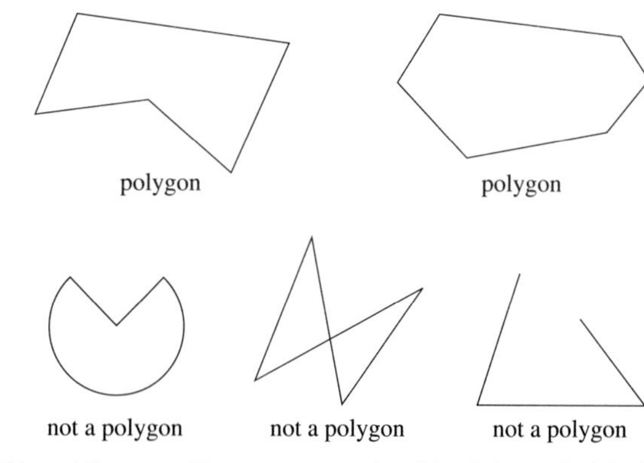

1.a. Closed figures, sides are segments; sides intersect at 1 pt.

1. a. What characteristics do the polygons share?
   b. How do the polygons differ from the figures that are not polygons? refer to 1.a.
   c. **Writing** Formulate a definition for a polygon. Be prepared to share your definition with the class. See below.
2. Use your definition to tell which of these figures are polygons. Does your definition work? If not, how would you change it? b, c, e

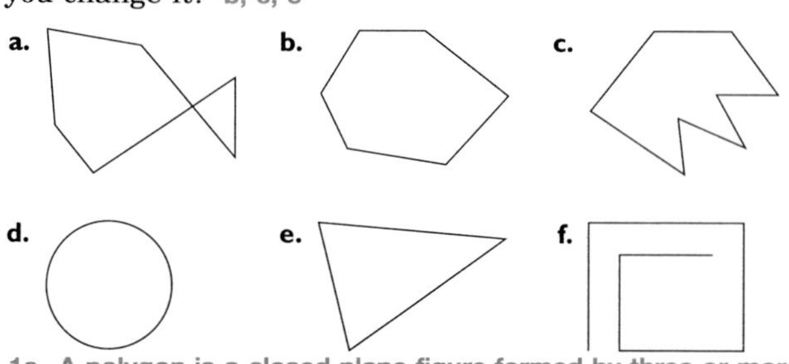

1c. A polygon is a closed plane figure formed by three or more segments that intersect only at their endpoints and none of these segments are collinear.

Point out the sentence following Question 5. Explain to students that this is an agreement made to simplify statements so that "convex" does not have to be written every time before "polygon." The term *polygon* includes both convex polygons and ones that are not convex. Limiting the discussion to convex polygons is just an agreement for now in this text.

ESL Help students make a list of prefixes and write beside the prefix the number it represents. For example *bi*—2, *tri*—3, *quad*—4, and *pent*—5. Generate a list of common words that begin with these prefixes.

Ongoing Assessment Ask students to draw a five-sided figure that is a polygon and a five-sided figure that is not a polygon. Have students name the polygon. **(pentagon)**

DIVERSITY Tell students that Navajo rugs are an example of geometry being used in art. Typical Navajo rugs have geometric designs of brown, black, gray, and occasionally yellow. Provide students with grid art paper. Instruct students to make their own design of a rug on the paper.

Wrap Up

What's the Big Idea? Ask students how they can determine if a figure is a polygon. Have students give the names of six polygons.

Journal Tell students that a seven-sided polygon is a *heptagon* and that a nine-sided polygon is a *nonagon.* Ask students why they think some polygons are more common than others. Then ask them which ones are easier to draw.

Connections Have a discussion about how polygons are used. You may want to start with these examples:

- **Architecture** (many-sided columns, angular staircases, castle towers and keeps)
- **Business** (multi-sided containers designed to be eye-catching, recycling or nutritional symbols, labels)
- **Art** (geometric designs in modern paintings or sculpture, different shaped canvases, stained glass, pottery)

THINK AND DISCUSS

Polygons are named for the number of their sides. Some common names are shown below.

Polygon	Number of Sides	Polygon	Number of Sides
Triangle	3	Hexagon	6
Quadrilateral	4	Octagon	8
Pentagon	5	Decagon	10

3. Classify each polygon as a triangle, quadrilateral, pentagon, hexagon, octagon, or decagon.

a. pentagon

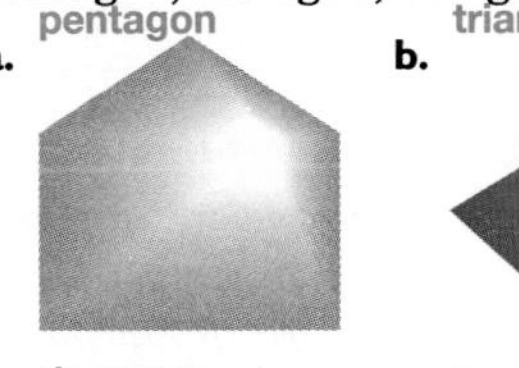

b. triangle

c. octagon

d. decagon

e. hexagon

f. quadrilateral

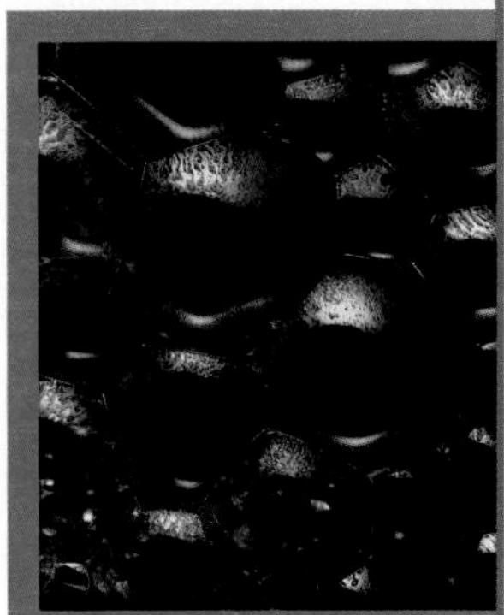

You can see polygons in a cluster of bubbles. ***What kinds of polygons do you see in the photo?*** Answers may vary.

You can think of a **convex** polygon as one that a rubber band could fit around snugly, without any gaps. The polygon shown is not convex because the red band does not fit snugly.

not convex

4. Are any nonconvex polygons shown in Question 3? yes; d, e

5. Critical Thinking How many right angles does the blue polygon appear to have? Does it make sense to talk about the angles of this polygon? Answers may vary. Sample: 3; no

When we talk about a polygon, we will mean a convex polygon.

Organizer, continued

Prentice Hall Technology

Computer Item Generator

- 2-5

Fact of the Day

Pablo Picasso was a famous painter and sculptor who used geometric shapes to emphasize the structure of the human face.

—*ART & IDEAS*

Reteaching Activity Give students a variety of figures (some polygons, some not polygons; some convex, some non-convex) that comprise 3–10 segments. Have students first identify the figures that are polygons. Then have students label the specific polygons. Finally, have them tell which are convex.

ON YOUR OWN

Students will need dot paper for Exercises 12 and 16–18.

Error Alert! Students may think that *pentagon* means that all five sides are congruent when they do Exercise 12. ***Remediation*** Encourage students to be creative and draw polygons with unequal sides, unless the problem requires otherwise.

WRITING Try the following activity for Exercise 12b. To encourage students to think about why a polygon has the same number of sides and angles, have students try to sketch polygons whose sides and angles do not correspond.

CRITICAL THINKING For Exercise 13d, encourage students to brainstorm for a variety of common features shared by the polygons. Students may find only that each polygon has congruent sides or that each polygon has congruent angles, but with encouragement they will find both of these characteristics.

CONNECTION TO LANGUAGE ARTS Exercises 14 and 15 have students use their mathematical knowledge to infer the meaning of the prefixes *tri-* and *quad-*.

Exercises 16–18: Have students share their drawings with the class so that students will see that a variety of polygons can fit the criteria of each exercise.

CONNECTION TO SCIENCE Challenge students to explain the last sentence in the story about the Raft of the Treetops. Suggest that they ask a science teacher or physicist why such a heavy object can be supported by the treetops. Ask students to share their explanation with the class.

Exercises 20b, c: Give students the option of using pattern blocks or geoboards to help them with the activities.

Assignment Options

Core: 6–12a, 16–18, MR all	
Reinforce: 12b, 13, 19	**Enrich:** 14, 15 20

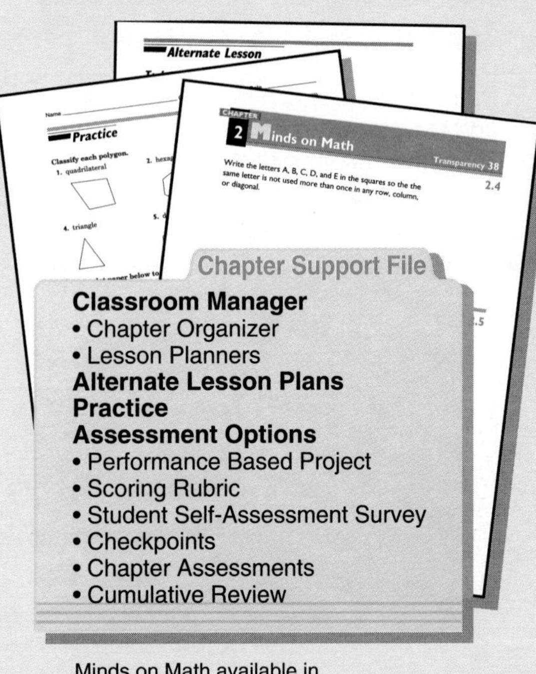

Minds on Math available in Teaching Transparencies

WHAT? *Octos* is a bicycle built for eight. The bicycle is 7 ft wide and can reach a speed of 50 mi/h with strong pedalers. **Why do you think the bicycle was named *Octos*?**

Source: *3-2-1 Contact*

Because octo- means 8.

Mixed REVIEW

Use mental math.

1. 23 × 10 230
2. 1500 ÷ 100 15

Classify each triangle as acute, right, or obtuse.

3. The angle measures are 48°, 53°, and 79°. acute
4. The angle measures are 42°, 104°, and 34°. obtuse
5. Paper cups come in packages of 50. There are 576 students and teachers at Memorial Middle School. How many packages of paper cups should be purchased for the school picnic? 12 packages

ON YOUR OWN

Classify each polygon.

6. pentagon 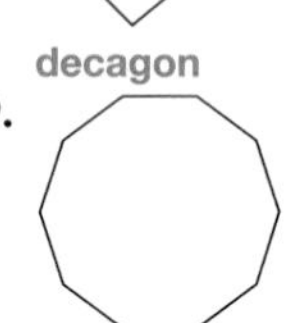
7. hexagon 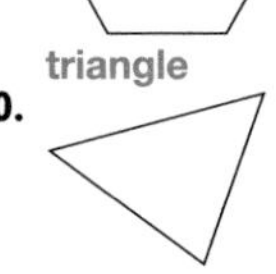
8. quadrilateral 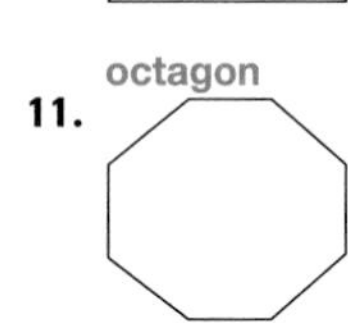
9. decagon
10. triangle
11. octagon

12. Draw a triangle, quadrilateral, pentagon, hexagon, octagon, and decagon on dot paper.
   a. How many angles does each polygon have? 3, 4, 5, 6, 8, 10
   b. **Writing** What is the relationship between the number of sides and the number of angles in a polygon? Why does this relationship exist? The number of sides equals the number of angles.
13. a. What do the triangles shown have in common?

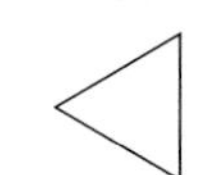  

3 congruent sides and 3 congruent angles

   b. What do the quadrilaterals shown have in common?

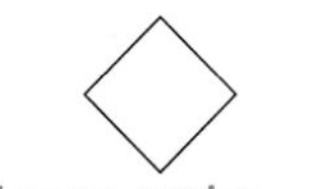 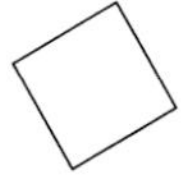

4 cong. sides and 4 cong. angles

   c. What do the pentagons shown have in common?

 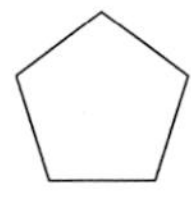

5 cong. sides and 5 cong. angles

   d. **Critical Thinking** What characteristics do the triangles, quadrilaterals, and pentagons share? equal sides and equal angles
14. **Language** List three words, besides triangle, that begin with the prefix *tri-*. Answers may vary. Sample: tricycle, tripod, triathlon, triplet

15. Language List three words, besides quadrilateral, that begin with the prefix *quad-*. Answers may vary. Sample: quadruplet, quadrant, quadriceps

Use dot paper to draw each polygon. Check students' drawings. See Sol. Key.

16. a quadrilateral with exactly two right angles

17. a quadrilateral with no right angles

18. a pentagon with three right angles

19. **Choose A, B, C, or D.** For which polygon shown is the measure of each angle 120°? D

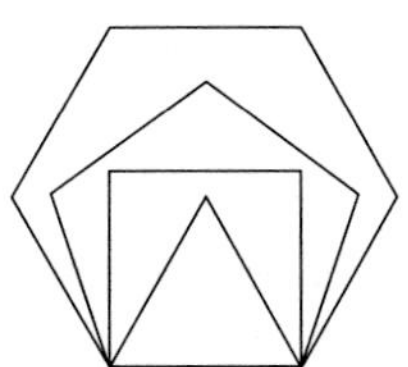

A. triangle **B.** quadrilateral

C. pentagon **D.** hexagon

The Raft of the Treetops

If you've ever climbed a tree, then you know how much fun it is to reach the top. Imagine walking across treetops that are more than 100 ft off the ground! That's what botanist Francis Hallé and his team are doing with the help of their Raft of the Treetops. This "raft" allows the scientists to investigate the top of the rain forest—something only expert tree climbers could do before.

The inflatable platform weighs about 1,650 lb and has an area of about 6,500 ft^2. That's about the size of two tennis courts. The platform looks like a six-sided inner-tube with sausage cross-links and a circus net bottom. Even though the raft sounds heavy, it can spread across the treetops while hardly breaking a twig!

20. **a.** What shape is the platform? hexagon

b. Draw a polygon shaped like the platform. Instead of dividing it into six triangles, divide it into four triangles. Check students' drawings. See Sol. Key.

c. Draw a polygon shaped like the platform. Divide it into a quadrilateral and two triangles. Check students' drawings. See Sol. Key.

d. Why do you think that Francis Hallé designed the platform the way he did? Answers may vary.

Math Minutes

Help Jan figure out how many turns the wheels on her bicycle would make during a 5 km bike ride if it takes about two meters for each complete turn of the wheels. **2,500 turns**

Materials for 2–6

- tangrams

2-6

Connecting to Prior Knowledge

Have students describe the different shapes a quadrilateral might have. Make a drawing of each description on the chalkboard. Having students give instructions out loud will help them become more comfortable with terms such as *parallel sides*. Ask students for drawings until they have named all the types of quadrilaterals they have seen.

THINK AND DISCUSS

ESL Begin the discussion of special quadrilaterals by asking students to describe parallel lines. Then ask students to draw and describe what a polygon would look like if it had two pairs of opposite sides parallel. Have students compare drawings. Help students see that the shapes are not identical.

TACTILE LEARNERS Have students orally define *rhombus* and *square.* Have students form a square with four strips of cardboard fastened at the corners with brads. Have them push on two opposite corners slightly so that the angles are not right angles anymore. Have the students compare and describe the two rhombuses they made.

ESL Use a Venn diagram to show that squares are a subset of rhombuses which are a subset of parallelograms. Use Venn diagrams to show the relationship of rectangles to parallelograms, rhombuses, and squares.

Ongoing Assessment Play a game called Change. Students will be given two special quadrilaterals and must describe the changes required to make the first quadrilateral into the second. Start the first student, for example, with "rhombus into square." He or she must describe the changes to a non-square rhombus to make it a square and then name the target quadrilateral for the next student, such as "rhombus into trapezoid." Play until each student has had a turn.

"A gauge of success is not whether you have a tough problem to solve, but whether it is the same problem you had last year."

—Anonymous

Organizer

1. **Focus**
   Connecting to Prior Knowledge
2. **Teach**
   Think and Discuss
   Work Together
3. **Closure**
   Try These
   Wrap Up

Vocabulary/Symbols
parallelogram
rectangle
rhombus
square
trapezoid

Skills Reviewed in Context of Lesson
- identifying angles, sides, and parallel lines

Materials and Manipulatives
- tangram (one for each group)

On Your Own Exercises 12–17, 24: straightedge; Exercise 24: tracing paper

continues next page

What's Ahead
- Identifying and classifying special quadrilaterals

2-6 Special Quadrilaterals

WHAT YOU'LL NEED

✓ Tangrams 

THINK AND DISCUSS

Certain quadrilaterals have special names because they have characteristics that distinguish them from other quadrilaterals.

A **parallelogram** is a quadrilateral with both pairs of opposite sides parallel.

A **rectangle** is a parallelogram with four right angles.

1. Find several examples of rectangles in your classroom. Sample: door, window

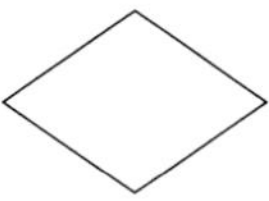

A **rhombus** is a parallelogram with four congruent sides.

2. Can a rhombus be a rectangle? Why or why not? yes; a rhombus can have 4 rt. angles if it's a square.

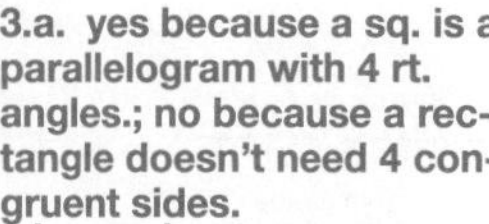

A **square** is a parallelogram with four right angles and four congruent sides.

3. a. Must a square be a rectangle? Must a rectangle be a square? Explain.
   b. Must a square be a rhombus? Must a rhombus be a square? Explain.
   c. What is the best name for a rhombus that is also a rectangle? square

3.a. yes because a sq. is a parallelogram with 4 rt. angles.; no because a rectangle doesn't need 4 congruent sides.
3.b. yes because a square must have 4 congruent sides.; no because a rhombus doesn't need a right angle.

A **trapezoid** is a quadrilateral with exactly one pair of opposite sides parallel.

4. Can a trapezoid be a parallelogram? Why or why not? no; a trapezoid only has one pair of ∥ sides and a parallelogram has two pairs of ∥ sides.

Error Alert! Students may confuse the terms *rhombus* and *trapezoid.* ***Remediation*** Encourage students to create and share with the class any mnemonic devices to help with the distinction.

Example

- *In the example, how can you tell that both pairs of opposite sides are parallel?* **(If you extend the pairs of opposite sides, they will not intersect.)**

Additional Example *Use this description of a polygon to give all the names that apply to the polygon. Then choose the best name.*

- *It has four sides.*
- *Both pairs of opposite sides are parallel.*
- *The four sides are congruent.*
- *The four angles are right angles.*

(The polygon is a quadrilateral, parallelogram, rhombus, rectangle, and square. The best name is square.)

WORK TOGETHER

Each pair of students will need tangram pieces for the activity. After the groups have compared their results, display their tables in the classroom.

TECHNOLOGY OPTION For the Work Together activity, have students use geometry software to draw tangrams and rotate them to form quadrilaterals.

TRY THESE

Exercises 5–10: Have students explain why d. is not used. (It is a pentagon and all the words describe quadrilaterals.)

Wrap Up

What's the Big Idea? Ask students to describe five special quadrilaterals.

Example Judging by appearance, give all the names that apply to the polygon. Then choose the best name.

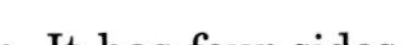

- It has four sides.
- Both pairs of opposite sides are parallel.
- The four sides are congruent.
- The polygon is a quadrilateral, parallelogram, and rhombus.
- The best name is rhombus, because every rhombus is a quadrilateral and a parallelogram.

WORK TOGETHER

You can use tangram pieces to form quadrilaterals. Two ways of forming a parallelogram are shown at the right.

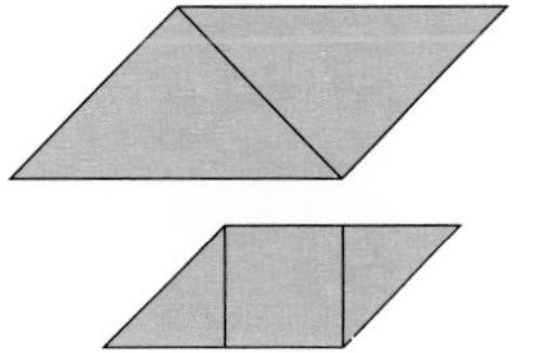

Work with a partner. Record all possible ways you can use tangram pieces to form a parallelogram, rectangle, rhombus, square, and trapezoid. Organize your results in a table. Compare your results with other groups.

TRY THESE

List the letters of all the polygons that have each name.

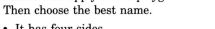

5. quadrilateral
   a, b, c, e, f, g, h, i
6. parallelogram
   a, e, f, g, h, i
7. rhombus
   a, g, h
8. rectangle
   a, e, g
9. square
   a, g
10. trapezoid
    b

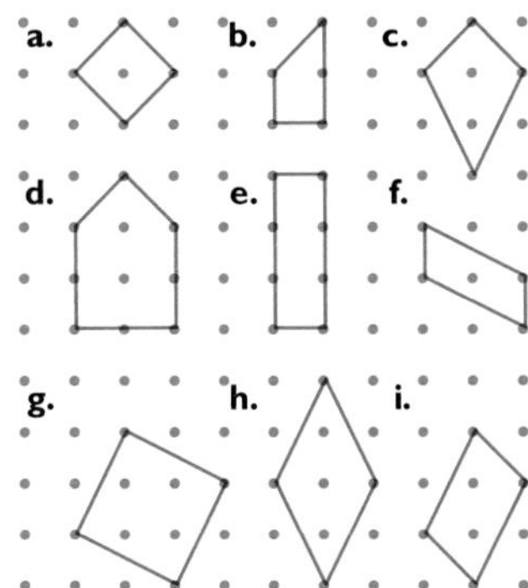

11. For each polygon shown, state the best name.

a. square
d. pentagon
g. square
b. trapezoid
e. rectangle
h. rhombus
c. quadrilateral
f. parallelogram
i. parallelogram

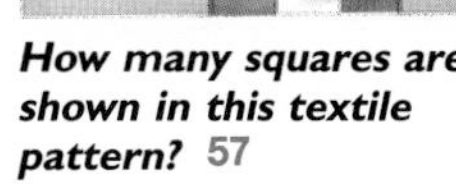

How many squares are shown in this textile pattern? 57

Organizer, continued

Student Resources
Extra Practice
Student Study Guide
Practice, TR Ch. 2, p. 30
Student Study Guide, Spanish Resources, TR

Teacher Resources
Teaching Transparency 38
Transparency Masters, TR p. 9
Overhead Manipulatives: tangram
Lesson Planner, TR Ch. 2, p. 7

Prentice Hall Technology
Multimedia Math
- Math Tools, Geometry

Computer Item Generator
- 2-6

Other Available Technology
Geometer's Sketchpad by Key Curriculum Press: Work Together activity; Exercises 12–17, 24 *(optional)*

Fact of the Day

In 1993, the largest swimming pool in the world was in Casablanca, Morocco. It was 1,574 ft by 246 ft. It had an area of 8.9 acres.

—GUINNESS BOOK OF WORLD RECORDS

Journal Tell students that many of the relationships among the quadrilaterals fall under a logical description of "All A are B, but not all B are A." Give students at least two examples:

- *All squares are rectangles, but not all rectangles are squares.*
- *All chickens are birds, but not all birds are chickens.*

Students then write their own logical statements based on the lesson and on experience outside of class.

Connections Have a discussion about how special quadrilaterals are used. You may want to start with these examples:

- **Trapezoid** (tents, speed bumps)
- **Square** (floor tiles, blueprint grids)
- **Rhombus** (baseball diamond, fabric patterns)
- **Rectangle** (football or soccer field, doors)

Reteaching Activity Give students oral instructions for constructing several different quadrilaterals. Have students form the quadrilaterals on dot paper or geoboards. Students should first identify those that are parallelograms and then label each parallelogram that is a special quadrilateral.

ON YOUR OWN

Students will need tracing paper for Exercise 24.

TECHNOLOGY OPTION For Exercises 12–17 and 24, have students use geometry software to construct the quadrilaterals.

WRITING For Exercise 22, have students use as a basic format for their explanations the logical description they used for the Journal.

Assignment Options

Core: 12–17, 21, 25–28, 34, 35, MR all	
Reinforce: 18–20, 22, 29–33	**Enrich:** 23, 24

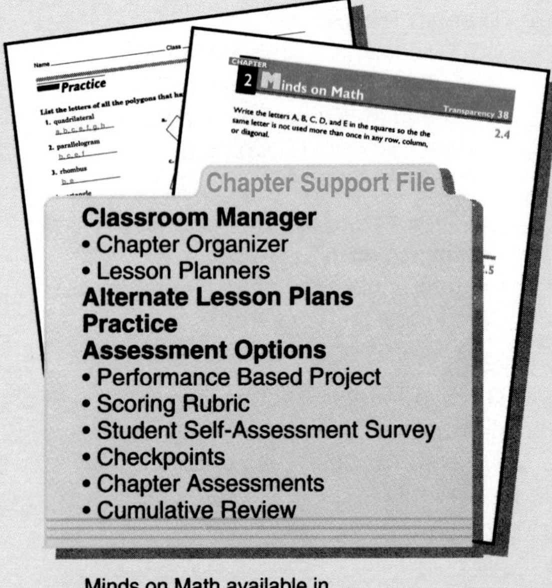

Minds on Math available in Teaching Transparencies

Mixed REVIEW

Find each answer.

1. 116 ÷ 4 29
2. 250 × 100 25,000

Name each polygon.

3. a polygon having 8 sides octagon
4. a polygon having 5 sides pentagon
5. The measure of ∠*A* is twice the measure of ∠*B*. The measure of ∠*B* is three times the measure of ∠*C*. ∠*A* is a right angle. What is the measure of ∠*C*? 15°

ON YOUR OWN

Sketch each quadrilateral. Check students' drawings. See Sol. Key.

12. a parallelogram **13.** a square **14.** a trapezoid

15. a rectangle that is not a square

16. a rhombus that is not a square

17. a quadrilateral that is not a trapezoid or parallelogram

List all the names that appear to apply to each quadrilateral. Choose from parallelogram, rectangle, rhombus, square, and trapezoid. Then circle the best name. 18. trapezoid 19. parallelogram (rectangle) 20. parallelogram rectangle, rhombus, (square)

18. **19.** 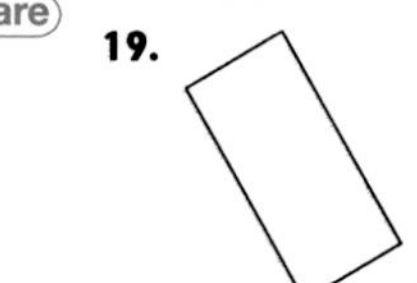 **20.** 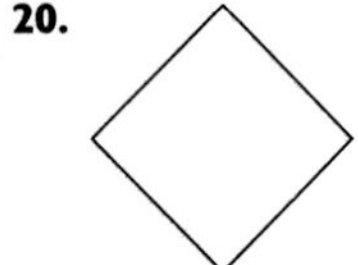

21. Data File 6 (pp. 226–227) What geometric shapes can you find on the bicycle? Sample: circles, segments, angles, triangles

22. Writing Explain the relationship between the following figures: rectangle, rhombus, and square. See Sol. Key. A square is a rectangle and a rhombus.

23. a. Four trapezoids are shown below on dot paper. What do you notice about each pair of nonparallel sides? congruent

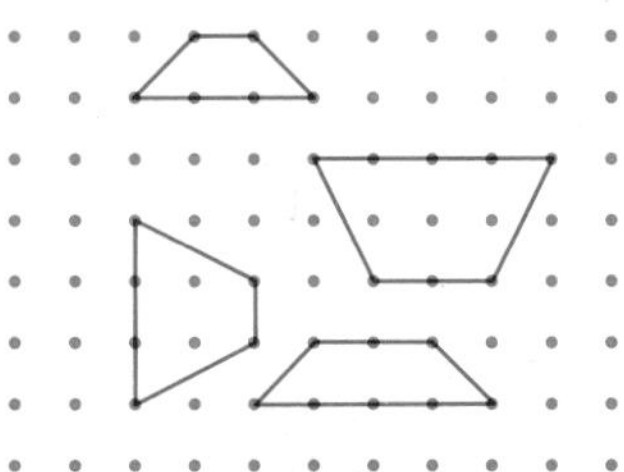

b. When sides of a triangle have this same characteristic, what special name do you give the triangle? isosceles

c. Critical Thinking What special name could you use for trapezoids like this? Why does this name fit? Isosceles trapezoid because two of its sides are congruent.

CRITICAL THINKING For Exercise 23c, have students give a definition for the name they choose.

Exercise 23: Students should be able to use the dot grid to see that the nonparallel sides are congruent. Encourage students to think about the connection between triangles with two congruent sides and a trapezoid with two congruent sides.

Exercises 29–33: Have students make up some of their own sentences that can be completed with *All, Some,* or *No.* Students could exchange these sentences with each other and complete them. A possible sentence is "Some rectangles are squares."

CHAPTER INVESTIGATION For Exercise 35, have students work in groups of four to collect pictures from magazines and newspapers. Ask students to report any trends they find.

24. Make three copies of the trapezoid on tracing paper. Check students' drawings. See Sol. Key.

a. Draw a line through one trapezoid that divides it into two trapezoids.

b. Draw a line through the second trapezoid that divides it into a parallelogram and a triangle.

c. Draw a line through the third trapezoid that divides it into a rhombus and a trapezoid.

Name all the types of quadrilaterals that fit each description.

25. at least two sides parallel parallelogram, rectangle, rhombus, square, trapezoid

26. parallelogram with four right angles rectangle, square

27. parallelogram rectangle, rhombus, square

28. parallelogram with four congruent sides rhombus, square

Complete each sentence with *All, Some,* or *No.*

29. ■ quadrilaterals are parallelograms. Some

30. ■ trapezoids are parallelograms. No

31. ■ parallelograms are quadrilaterals. All

32. ■ squares are rectangles. All

33. ■ rhombuses are rectangles. Some

34. **Choose A, B, C, or D.** Which name does *not* appear to describe quadrilateral *RSTU*? C

A. square **B.** rhombus

C. trapezoid **D.** parallelogram

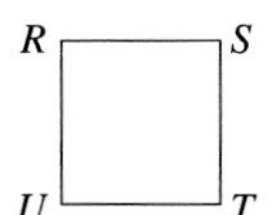

35. Investigation (p. 40) Collect pictures of buildings. Include old buildings as well as new ones. What special quadrilaterals are commonly found in architecture? Sample: rectangles, squares

A harlequin was a quick-witted clown from the Italian theater. He wore a suit of bright silk diamonds, sometimes with lace and ruffles. He also carried a "wand" which he used to signal the change of a scene.

Source: *The Oxford Companion to the Theater*

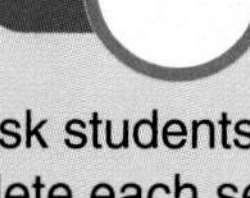

Math Minutes

Ask students to use $<$, $>$, or $=$ to complete each sentence.

If $x < 0$, then 0 ■ x. $>$

If x is any positive integer, then x ■ 0. $>$

If x is any negative integer, then 0 ■ x. $>$

2-7

Connecting to Prior Knowledge

Have students draw a diagram showing the relationship between summer and winter articles of clothing. For example, shoes could be in both categories but swimming suits in most climates would only be in the summer category. Write the categories "Summer," "Winter," and "Both" on the chalkboard and have students provide examples for each category.

Question 1: Challenge interested students to look in books about the history of mathematics to discover where the name "Venn diagram" came from. Have them share their findings with the class.

Additional Problem *The same sixth grade class at Fairfield Middle School surveyed 155 seventh and eighth grade students to find out what sports they played. The survey showed that 25 students play baseball, 16 play basketball, and 39 play football. Also, 6 students play both baseball and basketball, and 9 students play basketball and football. How many students play baseball, basketball, football, or two of the three? How many students do not play a sport?*
(65; 53)

TACTILE LEARNERS Provide students with attribute blocks and rings so they can model the Venn diagram for the situations in Questions 1 and 8.

"Keep trying. It's only from the valley that the mountain seems high."

—Anonymous

Organizer

1. **Focus**
   Connecting to Prior Knowledge
2. **Teach**
3. **Closure**
   Try These
   Wrap Up

Vocabulary/Symbols
logical reasoning
Venn diagrams

Skills Reviewed in Context of Lesson
- addition and subtraction of whole numbers
- identifying quadrilaterals

Student Resources
Extra Practice
Student Study Guide
Practice, TR Ch. 2, p. 31
Student Study Guide, Spanish Resources, TR

Teacher Resources

Teaching Transparencies 7, 38
Lesson Planner, TR Ch. 2, p. 8

Prentice Hall Technology
Computer Item Generator
- 2-7

PROBLEM SOLVING

2-7 Use Logical Reasoning

What's Ahead

- Solving problems by using logical reasoning

You often can use logical reasoning to solve problems involving relationships among groups of objects or people.

> The sixth grade class at Fairfield Middle School surveyed 130 seventh and eighth grade students to find out how they earn money. The survey showed that 45 students baby-sit, 32 have paper routes, 28 do yard work, and 12 have after school jobs at local businesses. Each student who works does only one kind of work except for 15 who baby-sit and do yard work. **How many students earn money by either baby-sitting or doing yard work (or both)? How many students do not earn money?**

READ

Read and understand the given information. Summarize the problem.

1. Think about the information you are given and what you are asked to find.
   a. How many students were surveyed? How did they earn money? **130; baby-sitting, paper route, yard work, local bus.**
   b. How many students did two different kinds of work? **15**
   c. What does the problem ask you to find? **No. of students earning money by baby-sitting or doing yard work (or both) and the no. of students who do not earn money.**

PLAN

Decide on a strategy to solve the problem.

Logical reasoning is a good strategy to use here. You can draw a *Venn diagram* to show the relationships among the different ways students earn money. First draw a rectangle to represent all the seventh and eighth grade students.

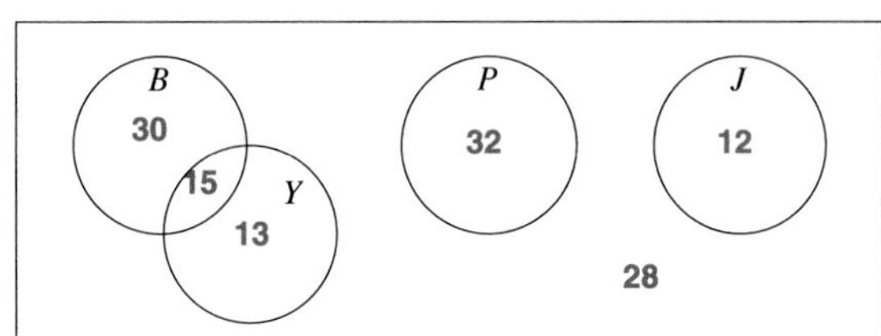

AUDITORY LEARNERS Provide situations involving logical reasoning that can be physically modeled by the students. Choose categories so that some students are in two or three categories, some are in only one, and some are in none. For example: give oral instructions for students to find the set of students wearing belts or wearing the colors white or gray.

DIVERSITY Discourage students from categorizing other students by their physical attributes such as weight or skin color. Also discourage students from categorizing other students by items that are indications of economic status.

Ongoing Assessment Use the Venn diagram for the problem in the textbook to assess students' understanding of the strategy. Ask students what each part of the diagram represents. Each student should make a fully-labeled copy of the diagram.

Error Alert! Students may become confused if the total represented in the circles of a Venn diagram does not equal the total survey population. ***Remediation*** Remind students that there may be members of the population that do not fit into any of the categories. Tell students to think of the area outside of the circles but within the box of a diagram (as shown in Question 8) as the "remainder." Students should label the remainder on their diagrams to avoid confusion.

Then draw a circle, B, to represent the students who baby-sit. Draw another circle, P, to represent the students who have paper routes. Draw a circle, Y, that overlaps B to represent students who do yard work and a circle, J, to represent the students who have jobs at businesses.

2. Why should Y and B overlap? There are students who do both yard wk. and baby-sitting.
3. Why do circles J and P not overlap any other circle? The students in those groups do only one kind of work.

Write 15 where B and Y overlap. Write 32 in P and 12 in J.

SOLVE

Try out the strategy.

4. Find the number of students who only earn money by baby-sitting. Write this number in the part of B that does not overlap Y. 30
5. Find the number of students who only earn money by doing yard work. Write this number in the part of Y that does not overlap B. 13

Use this information to answer the questions in the problem.

6. What numbers can you add to find the total number of students who earn money either by baby-sitting or doing yard work (or both)? What is the total number? 30, 13, and 15; 58
7. a. What does the sum of the five numbers in the Venn diagram circles represent? 7. a. the number of students who earn money
   b. If you subtract the sum from 130, what does the result represent? Write that number inside the rectangle, but not inside a circle. the total no. of students who don't earn money; 28

Look at your Venn diagram and see if all the numbers add up to 130. Make sure that you have stated clearly your answers to the questions in the problem.

LOOK BACK

Think about how you solved this problem.

You can use a Venn diagram to show the relationships among quadrilaterals, rectangles, parallelograms, squares, trapezoids, and rhombuses.

8. Draw a large Venn diagram like the one shown. Label it to show the relationships among types of quadrilaterals.

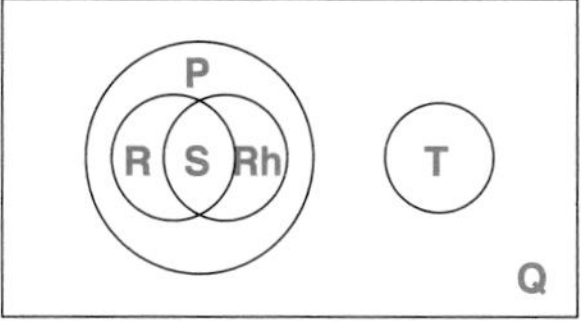

Q = quadrilaterals
P = parallelograms
R = rectangles
S = squares
Rh = rhombuses
T = trapezoids

Fact of the Day

John Venn developed the Venn diagram in 1880. His original diagram showed the relationship between (1) people who were French, (2) people who were generals, and (3) people who wore medals.

—*MATHEMATICS*

Assignment Options

Core: 10, 13, MR all	
Reinforce: 11	**Enrich:** 12

TRY THESE

Exercise 9: Have students think of other questions they can answer by using the Venn diagram.

Wrap Up

What's the Big Idea? Ask students: *How can using logical reasoning with Venn diagrams help you solve problems?*

Journal Ask students to write what they think is the most difficult part of creating a Venn diagram. Then ask students to write the ways in which such a diagram can help them.

Connections Have a discussion about how diagrams are used. You may want to start with these examples:

- **Household** (mapping family trees, charting chore responsibilities, appliance instructions)
- **Science** (mapping genetic traits, understanding chemical bonds)
- **Social Sciences** (showing population growth, language distribution, or clan boundaries)

Reteaching Activity Give students a Venn diagram with several circles (at least two overlapping) and a description of a situation. Have students match the circles with information in the situation and describe what the rectangle represents. A possible diagram could be a description of students' shoes in the classroom by color and type.

ON YOUR OWN

Encourage students to use some type of diagram for each exercise. Exercise 11 is especially suited to be solved by using a Venn diagram.

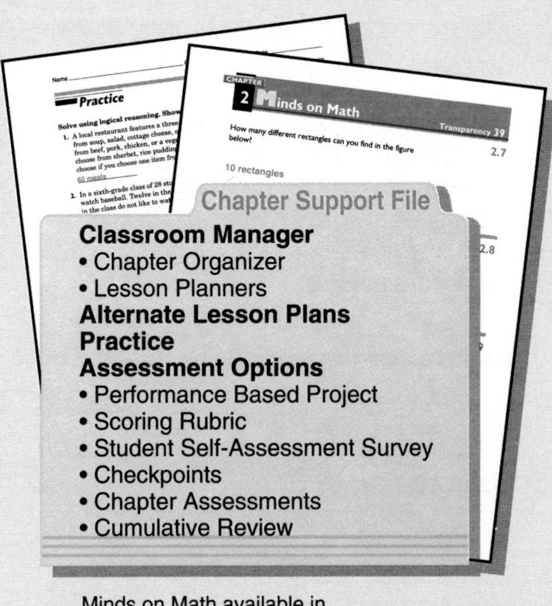

Minds on Math available in Teaching Transparencies

Math Minutes

Ask students to list the possible values for y, if $|y| = 5$. **−5, +5**

Materials for 2–8

- dot paper
- scissors
- tracing paper

Mixed REVIEW

Use mental math.

1. 30 × 21 630
2. 20 × 19 380

Use the data: 8, 11, 9, 17, 18, 7, and 8.

3. Find the range. 11
4. Find the median. 9

State the best name for each figure.

5. trapezoid
6. rhombus

7. Carla got test scores of 76, 89, and 81. What is Carla's mean score? 82

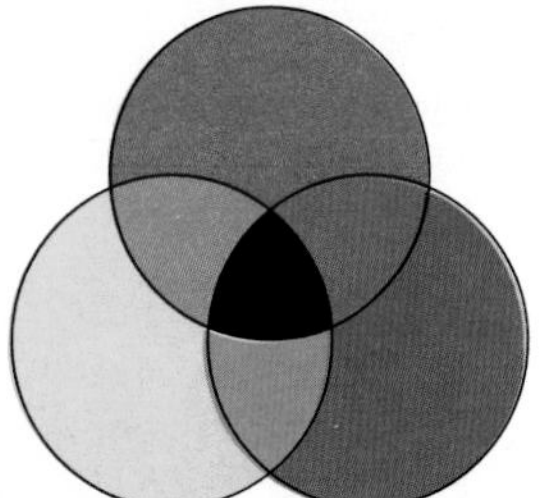

Red, yellow, and blue are the primary colors. *What color do you get when you mix blue and red?* purple

TRY THESE

Solve using logical reasoning.

9. In a box of 39 buttons there are 25 that have four holes, 18 that are red, and 13 that have four holes and are also red. The rest of the buttons have two holes or are colors other than red.
   a. How many buttons have four holes but are not red? 12
   b. How many red buttons have two holes? 5
   c. How many buttons do not have four holes and are not red? 9

ON YOUR OWN

Use any strategy to solve each problem. Show all your work.

10. If you have three pairs of pants, four sweaters, and five shirts, how many days can you wear an outfit consisting of a pair of pants, a sweater, and a shirt before you wear the same outfit again? 60 days

11. In a restaurant, 37 customers ordered lunch between 11:30 A.M. and 12:30 P.M. Twenty-five of the customers ordered soup with their lunch, 16 ordered salad with their lunch, and 8 ordered both soup and salad.
    a. How many customers ordered soup but no salad with their lunch? 17
    b. How many customers did not order soup or salad? 4

12. Suppose you have a baseball card collection and you decide to sort your cards. When you put your cards in piles of two, you have one left over. You also have one left over when you put the cards in piles of three or piles of four. But when you put them in piles of seven, you have none left over.
    a. What is the least number of cards in your collection? 49
    b. Name two other possibilities for the number of cards in your collection. Answers may vary. Sample: 217, 385

13. In what ways can you have coins that total exactly 17¢?
    17 pennies; 12 pennies, 1 nickel; 7 pennies, 1 dime; 7 pennies, 2 nickels; 2 pennies, 1 dime, 1 nickel; 2 pennies, 3 nickels

CHAPTER 2 PRACTICE

This page provides practice on the skills learned up to this point in the chapter. Daily cumulative practice can be found in the Mixed Reviews that appear in every lesson.

Error Alert! Students may still be confused on Exercises 7–12 when reading a protractor. They may read the same scales when reading left to right, as well as right to left.

Practice

Name each of the following. Answers may vary. Sample given.

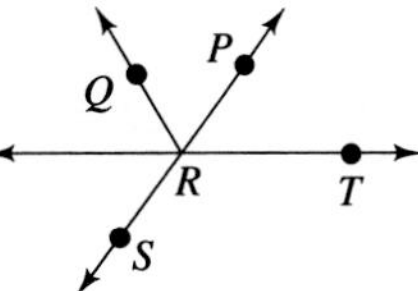

1. three collinear points
   S, R, P
2. four noncollinear points
   Q, R, S, T
3. three segments
   $\overline{RQ}$, $\overline{SR}$, $\overline{PR}$
4. four rays
   $\overrightarrow{RS}$, $\overrightarrow{RT}$, $\overrightarrow{RP}$, $\overrightarrow{RQ}$
5. an acute angle
   ∠QRP
6. an obtuse angle
   ∠QRT

Use a protractor to find the measure of each angle.

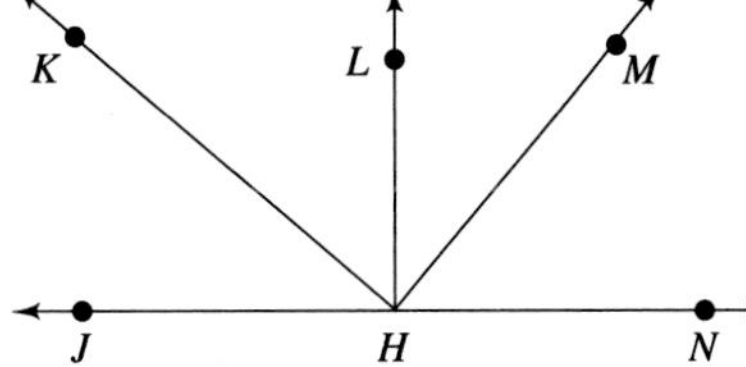

7. ∠KHL 50°
8. ∠NHM 50°
9. ∠KHN 140°
10. ∠JHN 180°
11. ∠LHM 40°
12. ∠LHJ 90°

13. Use a protractor to draw a 115° angle. Check students' drawings.

14. Draw a segment, $\overline{GH}$. Construct a segment twice as long as $\overline{GH}$. Check students' work.

15. Draw an obtuse ∠A. Construct an angle congruent to ∠A. Check students' work.

Classify the triangle with the given side lengths as scalene, isosceles, or equilateral.

16. 6 cm, 6 cm, 6 cm
    equilateral
17. 6 in., 8 in., 6 in.
    isosceles
18. 17 m, 15 m, 8 m
    scalene

Classify the triangle with the given angle measures as acute, obtuse, or right.

19. 60°, 90°, 30°
    right
20. 40°, 100°, 40°
    obtuse
21. 60°, 70°, 50°
    acute

Sketch each of the following. Check students' drawings.

22. a pentagon
23. an octagon
24. a hexagon

True or False?

25. All squares are rectangles.
    true
26. Some rectangles are parallelograms.
    true
27. No rhombuses are trapezoids.
    true
28. All rectangles are quadrilaterals.
    true

Resources
Extra Practice
Student Study Guide
Student Study Guide, Spanish Resources, TR

2-8

Connecting to Prior Knowledge

Ask students to name two objects in the classroom, such as two desks, that are identical. Ask students why they think the objects are the same, and how they could measure each to verify their opinions.

WORK TOGETHER

Encourage students to draw irregular triangles, such as obtuse and scalene.

Have each pair of students make a conjecture about the relationship between a triangle and the triangles formed by repeatedly copying the original triangle. Have students predict whether this conjecture is true for geometric figures in general.

Question 1a: One way to see the pattern here is to draw an obtuse scalene triangle and join the midpoints of the three sides to form four triangles similar to the original.

ESL **DIVERSITY** Some students will recognize congruent figures more quickly than other students. Provide unusually shaped congruent figures. Encourage students to place figures on top of each other, turn figures around, and flip figures over as they try to determine congruency.

TECHNOLOGY OPTION For the Work Together activity, have students use geometry software to construct several different sets of four identical triangles. Then have students do Question 1 for each set and describe any patterns.

THINK AND DISCUSS

Question 3: Emphasize that a figure may need to be flipped over to make it match another, and the two are still considered congruent.

"What lies behind us and what lies before us are tiny matters compared to what lies within us."

—ANONYMOUS

Organizer

1. **Focus**
   Connecting to Prior Knowledge
2. **Teach**
   Work Together
   Think and Discuss
3. **Closure**
   Wrap Up

Vocabulary/Symbols
congruent
similar

Skills Reviewed in Context of Lesson
- recognizing triangles

Materials and Manipulatives
- dot paper (for each student)
- scissors (one pair for each group)
- tracing paper (for each student)

On Your Own Exercises 7, 12: tracing paper *(optional)*; Exercises 14, 17: dot paper; Exercise 19: protractor

Student Resources
Extra Practice
Student Study Guide
Practice, TR Ch. 2, p. 32
Student Study Guide, Spanish Resources, TR

continues next page

What's Ahead
- Determining whether figures are congruent
- Determining whether figures are similar

WHAT YOU'LL NEED
✓ Dot paper
✓ Scissors

2-8 Congruent and Similar Figures

WORK TOGETHER

Work with a partner.
- Draw a triangle on dot paper.
- Draw three copies of the triangle on dot paper.
- Cut out the four triangles.
- Put the triangles on top of each other to check that they have the same size and shape. See Sol. Key. Sample given.

1. a. Arrange the four triangles so that they form a larger triangle that has the same shape as the original triangle. None of the triangles should overlap.
   b. Draw your arrangement on dot paper. Show how the four smaller triangles fit together to form the larger triangle. How do the lengths of the sides of the original triangle and the larger triangle compare? Each side of the orig. △ is half as long as a side of larg. △.
2. Suppose you have nine triangles that have the same size and shape as your original triangle. On dot paper show how to arrange these triangles to form a larger triangle with the same shape. How do the lengths of the sides of the larger triangle compare to the lengths of the sides of the original triangle? Each side of the larger △ is 3 times as long as a side of orig. △.

Why do you think it is important that parts produced on an assembly line be congruent? Answers may vary.

THINK AND DISCUSS

Figures that have the same size and shape are **congruent.** As you saw in the Work Together activity, two figures can be congruent even if one of the figures is turned. Two figures also can be congruent even if one of them appears to be turned over.

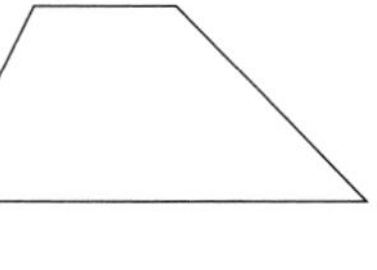

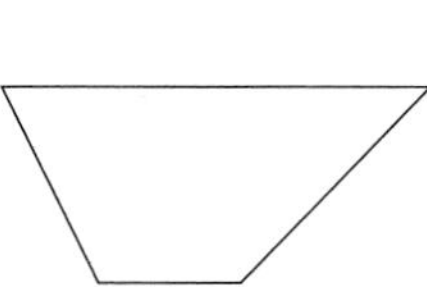

3. How could you check that the trapezoids shown are congruent? Answers may vary. Sample: cut one out and place it on top of the other.

Question 5: Have students support their answers with a drawing.

ESL Have students draw two figures that are congruent. Have students draw another figure that is similar but not congruent. Have students draw a figure that is not similar. Have students label the figures.

Ongoing Assessment Ask students to form congruent rectangles on geoboards or dot paper. Then have them change one of the rectangles so that the two rectangles are only similar. Then ask them to form two rectangles that are neither similar nor congruent. Make sure students understand that congruence depends on shape and size, but that similarity involves only shape and proportional sides.

AUDITORY LEARNERS Have students orally compare and contrast figures that are congruent and figures that are only similar.

TACTILE LEARNERS Encourage students to imagine fitting one figure over another. If they coincide everywhere, the figures must be congruent.

Error Alert! Students may have difficulty recognizing congruence or similarity if one of the figures is turned or turned over. ***Remediation*** Encourage students to use tracing paper or to turn their textbooks to check their answers. Students should also make a mental note of angle and line measurements when determining congruence.

Wrap Up

What's the Big Idea? Ask students: *What does it mean for two figures to be congruent? to be similar?*

Journal Ask students to brainstorm for ways they recognize a certain place or a familiar route. Ask them how they keep from making a mistake or getting lost. Students should also write about how they can keep from getting lost when determining congruence or similarity in class.

4. Which triangles are congruent to the triangle at the right? b, c, d, f

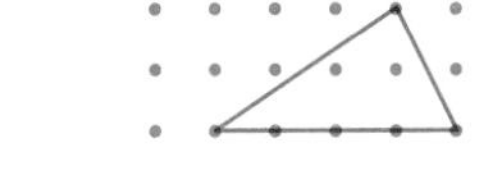

a. b. c.

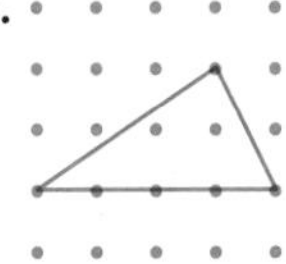

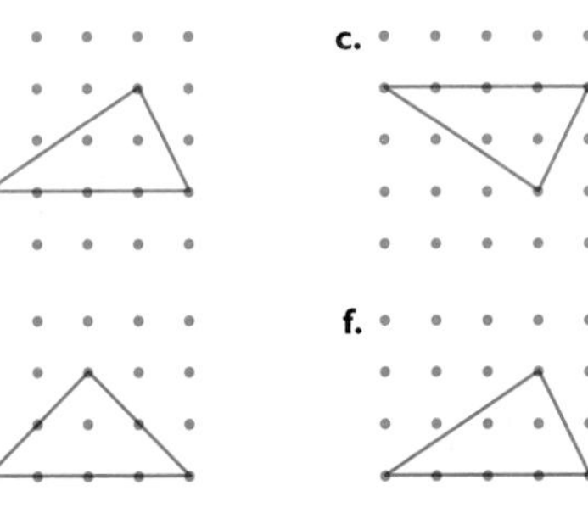

d. e. f.

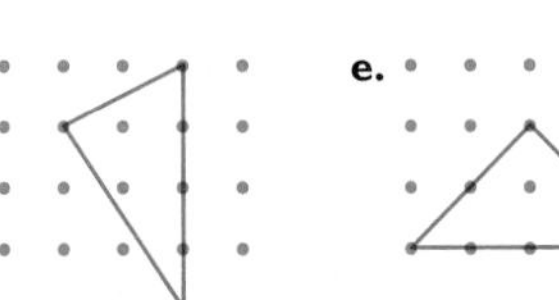

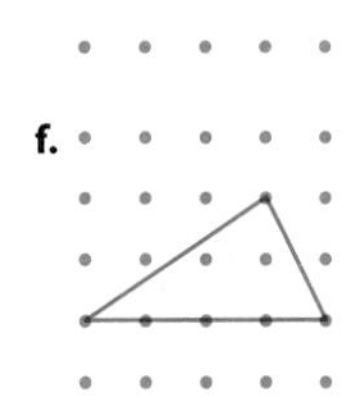

You can see congruent and similar triangles in Arizona's Navajo Bridge. The bridge crosses the Colorado River.

Figures that have the same shape are **similar.** Two figures can be similar even if one is turned or appears to be turned over. The larger triangles you formed in the Work Together activity are each similar to the original triangle. They also are similar to each other.

5. Must two congruent figures be similar? Why or why not? yes; they have the same shape.

6. Which triangles are similar to the triangle at the right? a, c, d, e, f

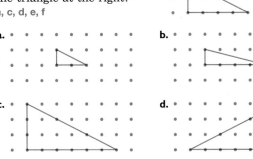

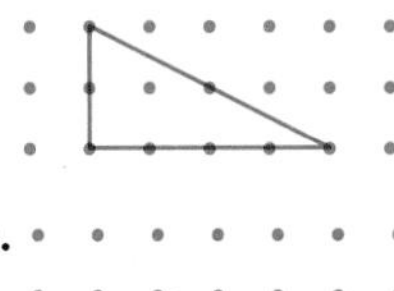

a. b.

c. d.

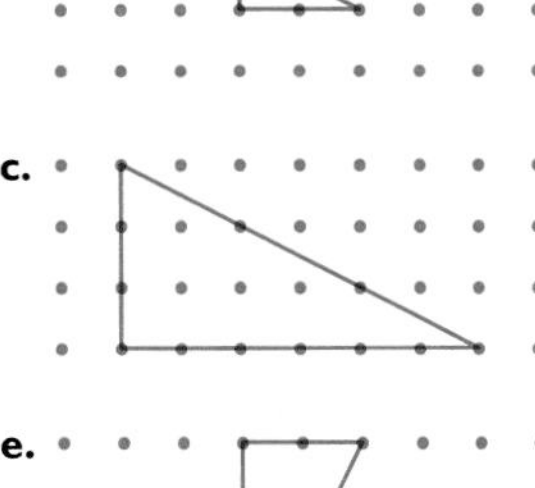

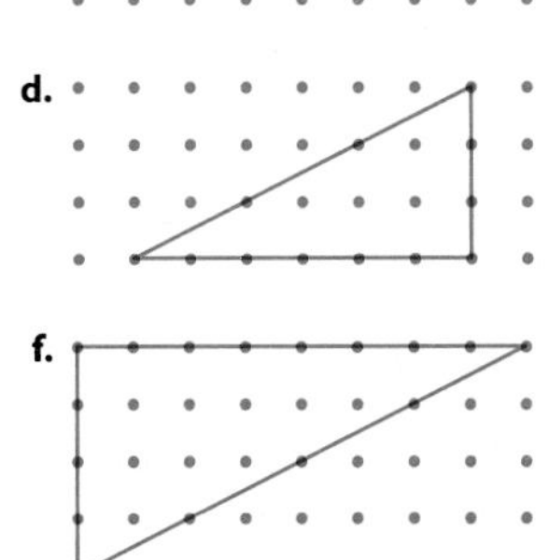

e. f.

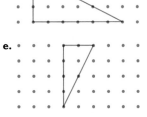

Organizer, continued

Teacher Resources

Teaching Transparencies 8, 9, 39, 41
Transparency Masters, TR p. 19
Lesson Planner, TR Ch. 2, p. 9

Prentice Hall Technology

Multimedia Math
- Math Tools, Geometry

Computer Item Generator
- 2-8

Other Available Technology

Geometer's Sketchpad by Key Curriculum Press: Work Together activity *(optional)*

Fact of the Day

Michelangelo was hired by Pope Julius II to paint the ceiling of the Sistine Chapel. Michelangelo divided the ceiling into geometrical forms, such as the triangle, circle, and square.

—ART & IDEAS

Connections

Have a discussion about how congruence and similarity are used. You may want to start with these examples:

- **Architecture** (blueprints, models, drafting)
- **Manufacturing** (making different sizes of the same dress pattern, making replacement parts for machinery)
- **Recreation** (jigsaw puzzles, computer games)

Reteaching Activity

Have students form congruent figures by using different pattern blocks. Then have students form similar shapes. Have students describe the distinction between the two sets of figures.

ON YOUR OWN

Students may need tracing paper for Exercises 7 and 12. Students will need dot paper for Exercises 14 and 17, and a protractor for Exercise 19.

Exercise 7: Encourage students to consider all possibilities. Have students explain how the figures they choose as congruent can be obtained from the original figure through turning or turning over.

Exercises 9–12 and 15: Have students share their explanations in class. These exercises will indicate whether or not students understand the concept of similarity.

Exercise 16: Students may find it useful to imagine that a smaller figure is to be enlarged on a photocopying machine. Enlarging or reducing by this process produces figures that are similar to the original.

WRITING For Exercise 13, have students support their explanations with a table or Venn diagram.

Exercise 18: Invite students to extend this exercise by creating a similar problem using another letter of the alphabet.

Exercise 19: Have students investigate the process further by using another pair of angle measures.

Assignment Options

Core: 7, 8, 12, 14, 16, MR all	
Reinforce: 9–11, 15, 18	**Enrich:** 13, 17, 19

Mixed REVIEW

Complete with <, >, or =.

1. 24 × 5 ■ 600 ÷ 5 =
2. 1,100 ÷ 100 ■ 110 ÷ 10 =
3. Suppose you ask 100 people whether they prefer blueberry, raspberry, or vanilla yogurt. What type of graph would be appropriate to display your results? Explain. Circle graph

Use the Venn diagram below for Exercises 4 and 5.

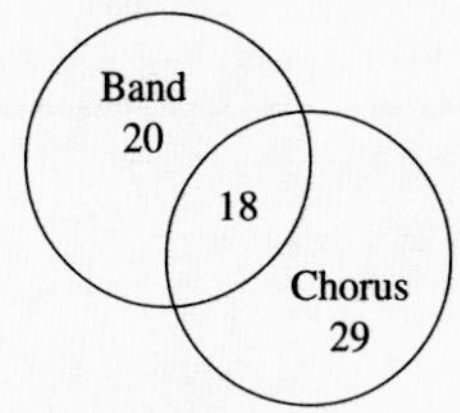

4. How many students play in the band? 38
5. How many students are in both the band and the chorus? 18

ON YOUR OWN

7. Which figures appear to be congruent to the trapezoid at the right? a, d

a. b. c. d.

8. Which rectangles are similar to the rectangle at the right? a, c, d

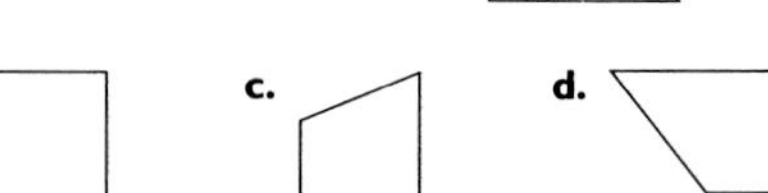

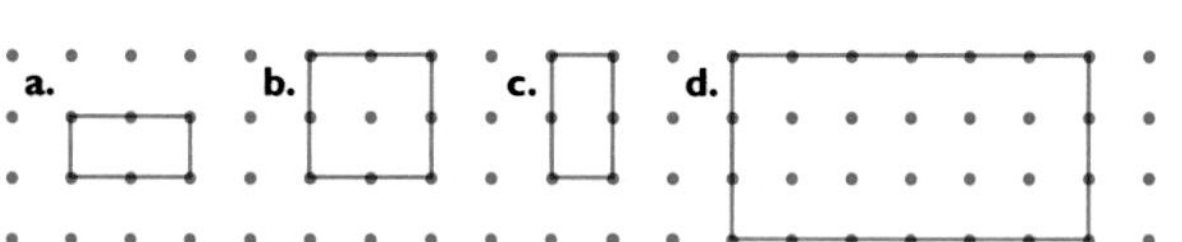

Tell whether the triangles appear to be congruent, similar, or neither.

9. 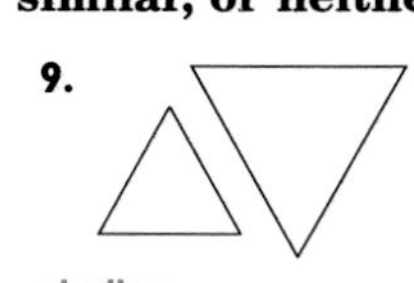 similar

10. 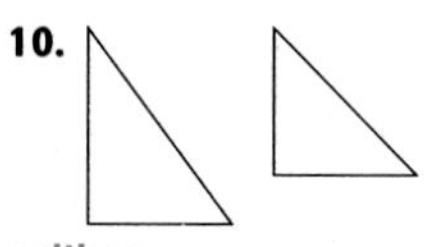 neither

11. 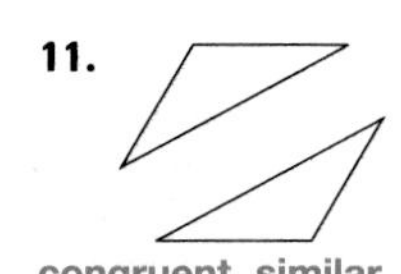 congruent, similar

12. List the pairs of triangles that appear to be congruent. a, d; b, f; c, e

a. b. c.

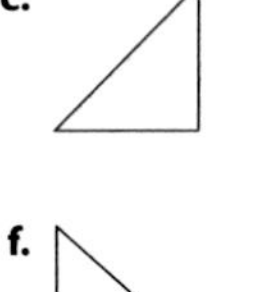

d. e. f.

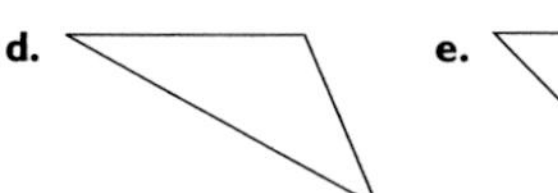

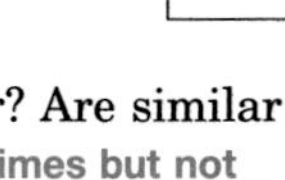

13. **Writing** Are congruent figures similar? Are similar figures congruent? Explain. yes; sometimes but not necessarily; see Sol. Key.
14. Use dot paper to draw four congruent triangles in different positions. Check students' drawings. See Solution Key.
15. Suppose you are replacing a window. Should the replacement be congruent to or similar to the original? Explain your reasoning. Congruent; The window must be the same size and shape to fit in the window opening.

16. List the pairs of figures that appear to be similar. a, f; b, d; c, j; e, l; h, i; g, k

a. b. c.

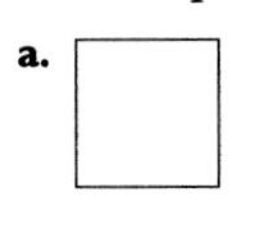
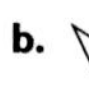
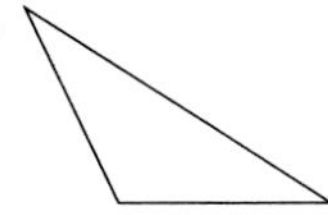

d. e. f.

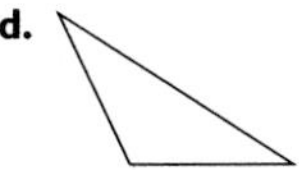
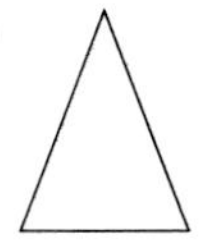

g. h. i.

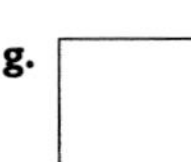
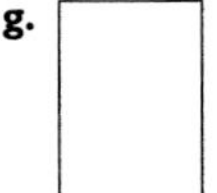
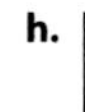
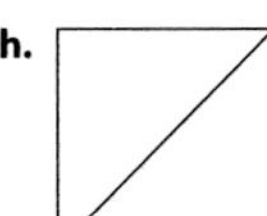
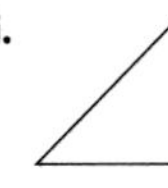

j. k. l.

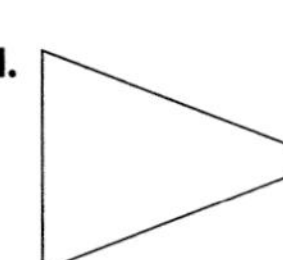

17a. See Sol. Key. 17b. no; rhombuses can be dif. shapes.

17. a. Use dot paper to draw several rhombuses, none of which are congruent. Include squares and nonsquares. If possible, make each one a different shape.
    b. Are all rhombuses similar? Why or why not?
    c. Are all squares similar? Why or why not? yes; they are always the same shape.

18. **Choose A, B, C, or D.** Which figure is not congruent to the figure at the right? C

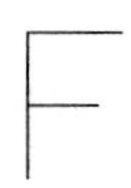

A.  B. 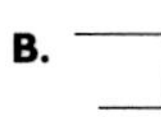 C.  D. 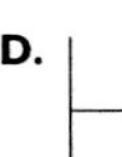

19. Use a protractor to draw a triangle with two angles measuring 45° and 60°. Then draw a second triangle that is not congruent to the first triangle, but that has angles measuring 45° and 60°. What appears to be true of the two triangles? They appear to be similar.

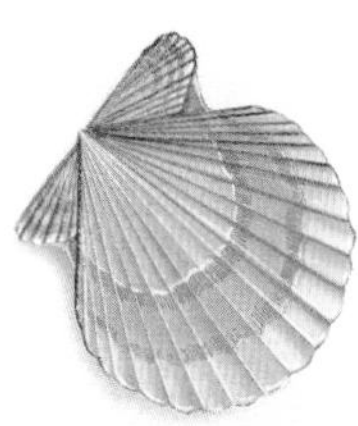

The sea shells** above are an example of similarity in nature.* ***Can you think of another place where similarity is found in nature?
Answers may vary. Sample: leaves, butterflies, insects

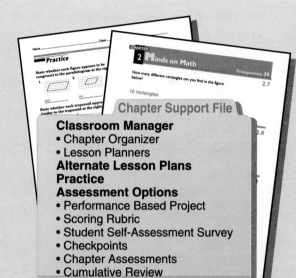

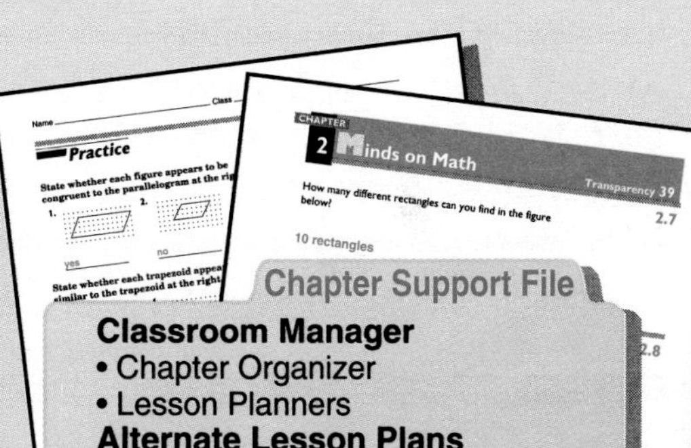

Minds on Math available in Teaching Transparencies

Ask students to compare and contrast the distances on a number line that +9 and –9 are from 0. **Both are the same distance from 0, but the directions are different.**

Materials for 2–9

- tracing paper
- scissors

2-9

Connecting to Prior Knowledge

Ask students if they have ever balanced a spinning basketball on one finger, or seen someone else do it. Then ask students what would happen to the ball if it tilted too far to the left or right. Help students describe the state of balance in terms of the ball's tilt with relation to a vertical line drawn through its center.

WORK TOGETHER

Have each pair of students trace two copies of the equilateral triangle and square. They can cut out one copy and use the other copy for recording lines of symmetry they discover by folding.

ESL **AUDITORY LEARNERS** Encourage students to ask themselves this question softly aloud as a test for symmetry: *If I fold along this line, will the two halves match?*

VISUAL LEARNERS Suggest that students imagine folding along the line of symmetry even when they can't use a cutout model.

THINK AND DISCUSS

Ask students to make a conjecture about whether human faces are symmetrical and, if they think so, where the line(s) of symmetry might be. Ask for suggestions about how they could test their conjectures.

CRITICAL THINKING For Question 5, have students support their answers with example drawings.

Ongoing Assessment Ask students to work in pairs and to draw a figure with exactly two lines of symmetry, a figure with exactly one line of symmetry, and a figure with no lines of symmetry. Then have the pairs join to form groups of four to explain and verify their figures. Listen for correct use of vocabulary and for explanations that involve folding along the lines of symmetry to see that the halves match exactly.

"We neither get better or worse as we get older, but more like ourselves."
—Robert Anthony

Organizer

1. **Focus**
   Connecting to Prior Knowledge
2. **Teach**
   Work Together
   Think and Discuss
3. **Closure**
   Wrap Up

Vocabulary/Symbols
line symmetry
line of symmetry

Skills Reviewed in Context of Lesson
- recognizing polygons

Materials and Manipulatives
- tracing paper (for each student)
- scissors (one pair for each group)

On Your Own Exercises 6–11: tracing paper; Exercises 12–13: dot paper; Exercise 20: scissors

Student Resources
Extra Practice
Student Study Guide
Practice, TR Ch. 2, p. 33
Student Study Guide, Spanish Resources, TR
Checkpoint, TR Ch. 2, p. 40

continues next page

2-9 Exploring Symmetry

What's Ahead
- Determining whether a figure has line symmetry

WHAT YOU'LL NEED
✓ Tracing paper
✓ Scissors

WORK TOGETHER

- Trace the equilateral triangle and the square. Then cut them out.

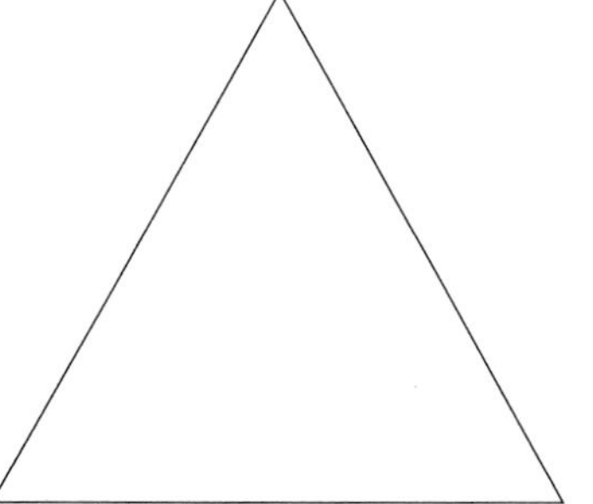

- Fold the triangle in as many ways as you can so that one half matches the other half.
- Repeat for the square.
- Compare your results with a partner's. In how many different ways can you fold each figure? **There are 3 ways to fold the triangle and 4 ways to fold the square.**

THINK AND DISCUSS

You often see symmetry in nature—in the human body, in flowers, insects, birds, and many other natural objects. Because symmetrical designs are appealing to the eye, they often are used in fabrics, flags, carvings, masks, weavings, and pottery.

A figure has **line symmetry** if there is a line that divides the figure into two congruent halves. The line is called a *line of symmetry*.

1. Does the butterfly have any lines of symmetry? How many? **yes; 1**

Error Alert! Students may confuse a line of symmetry with any line that divides a figure in half. Remind students that a line of symmetry divides a figure into two congruent halves, so that both shape and size are important. ***Remediation*** Encourage students to think of a line of symmetry as a mirroring line. Each side of the line should be an exact reflection of the other.

Wrap Up

What's the Big Idea? Have students discuss what it means for a figure to have line symmetry.

Journal Have students think of other ways to describe the line symmetry of a figure. Ask students to choose a description they feel most comfortable with and to explain why the description is a good one.

Connections Have a discussion about how the line symmetry of figures is used. You may want to start with these examples:

- **School Groups** (marching band patterns, cheerleader and dance squad routines)
- **Arts and Crafts** (quilts, paper snowflakes, fabric patterns)
- **Business** (building design, company logos)

Reteaching Activity Have students use a rubber band to create a vertical segment down the center of a geoboard. Students should then use another band to form a figure so that the first rubber band divides the figure into two congruent parts.

ON YOUR OWN

Students will need tracing paper for Exercises 6–11, dot paper for Exercises 12 and 13, and scissors for Exercise 20.

2. How many lines of symmetry does an equilateral triangle have? Draw an equilateral triangle and sketch the lines of symmetry. 3; See Sol. Key.

3. How many lines of symmetry does a square have? Draw a square and sketch the lines of symmetry. 4; See Sol. Key.

4. How many lines of symmetry does each figure have? Describe each line of symmetry as horizontal, vertical, or neither.

a.  1; vertical

b.  1; neither

c.  2; hor., vert.

d. 1; neither

e. 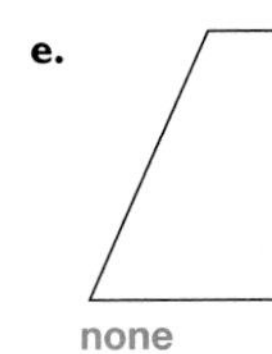 none

f. 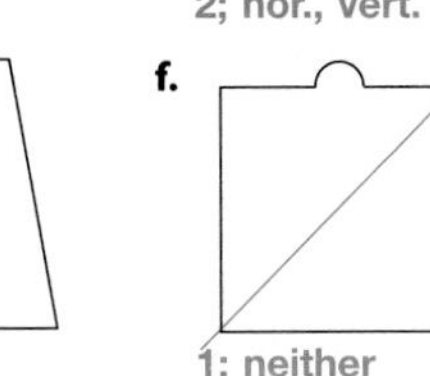 1; neither

5. Critical Thinking How could you check whether a figure has line symmetry? Sample: Fold the figure to form congruent halves to determine whether a figure has line symmetry.

This is a mask from Indonesia. ***How many lines of symmetry does it have?***

one line

ON YOUR OWN

Does the figure have line symmetry? If it does, trace the figure and draw all the lines of symmetry. Check students' drawings.

6. 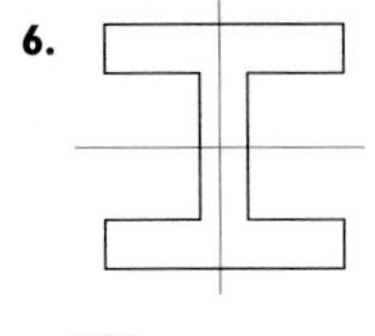 yes

7. 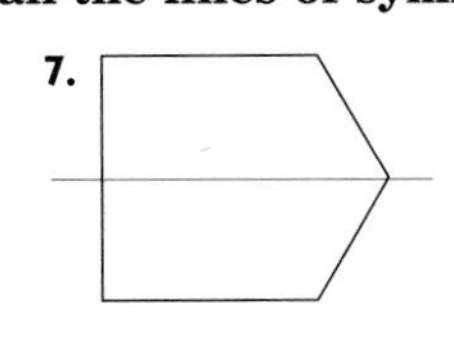 yes

8. 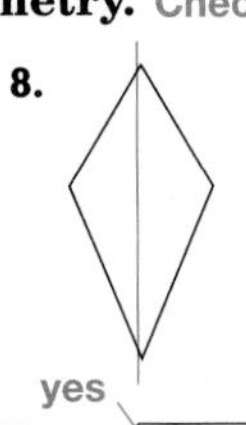 yes

9. yes

10. 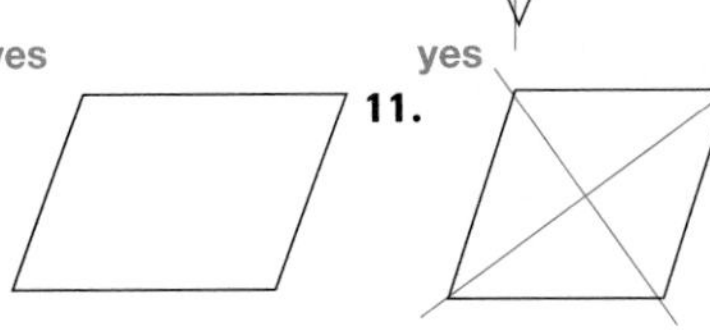 no

11. yes

Organizer, continued

Teacher Resources

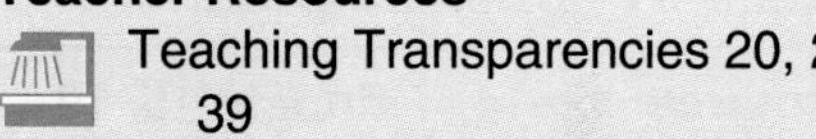

Teaching Transparencies 20, 21, 39

Lesson Planner, TR Ch. 2, p. 10

Prentice Hall Technology

Computer Item Generator

- 2-9

Fact of the Day

The Taj Mahal is the most famous of all Islamic mausoleums. It was built by one of the Moslem rulers in India as a memorial to his wife. Symmetry is seen in the structure of the building and in the reflecting pools.

—Gardner's Art Through the Ages

WRITING For Exercise 15c, have students draw each figure and label its lines of symmetry.

ESL **Exercise 16:** Perhaps each ESL student would like to make a copy of his or her alphabet to share with the class. Students could determine if these letters have line symmetry.

Exercise 19: Display students' flags so that all students can see a variety of figures that have line symmetry.

ACTIVITY For Exercise 20a, encourage students to make two patterns: one simple test pattern, and one more elaborate design.

Exercise 5: Ask students to name several strategies that they might use to work this problem. Be sure that students include making a Venn diagram as one of their strategies.

Exercise 7: Ask students to draw the figures and show the lines of symmetry.

CHECKPOINT

Exercise 7 is an example of an enhanced multiple choice question.

WRITING For Exercise 4, remind students to make their definitions as precise as possible. Encourage students to look for different words and phrases to describe the same qualities.

Assignment Options

Core: 6–11, 16, MR all, CH all	
Reinforce: 12–14, 17, 18, 20	**Enrich:** 15, 19

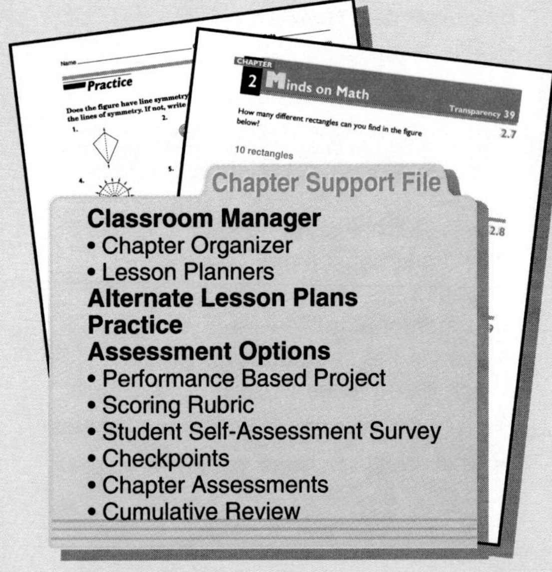

Minds on Math available in Teaching Transparencies

Answers to Problems Unique to Spanish Edition

16. In addition to the letters listed for the English edition, the Spanish letter Ñ also has line symmetry.
17. Sample: DEDO
18. Sample: MUY

Mixed REVIEW

Use mental math.

1. 0 + 332 332
2. 332 ÷ 1 332

Classify each triangle as scalene, isosceles, or equilateral.

3. a triangle having side lengths of 8, 8, and 8 equilateral
4. a triangle having side lengths of 9, 14, and 7 scalene

Use the figures below for Exercises 5 and 6.

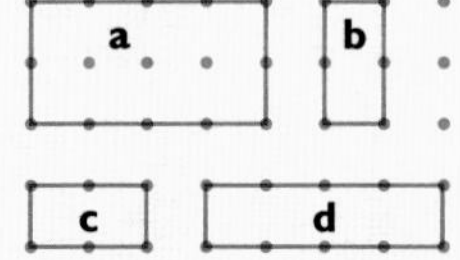

5. Which figures appear to be congruent? c, b
6. Which figures appear to be similar? a, b, c
7. The product of two whole numbers is 35. Their difference is 2. What are the two numbers? 5 and 7

Copy each figure on dot paper. Complete the figure so that the line is a line of symmetry. See Solution Key.

12. 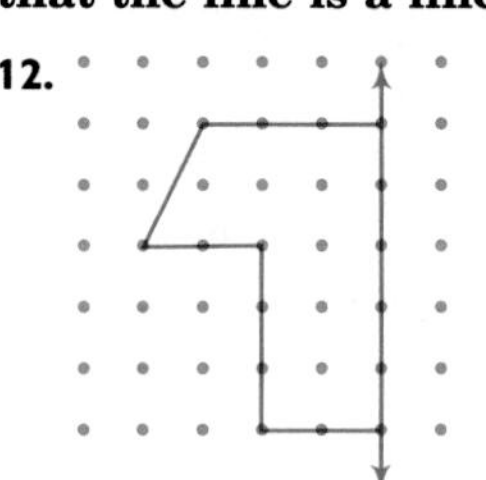

13. 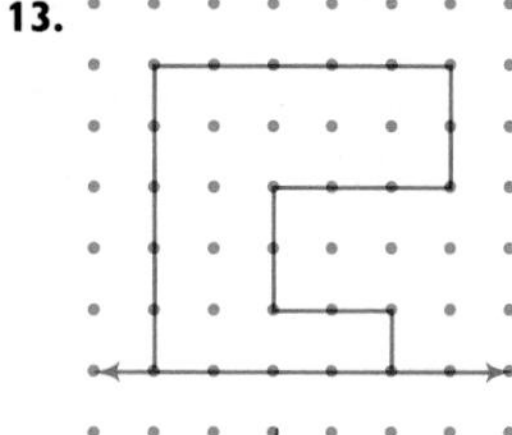

14. Trace the hexagon and draw all the lines of symmetry.

15. a. Draw three or more isosceles triangles like those shown below. Draw all the lines of symmetry for each triangle.

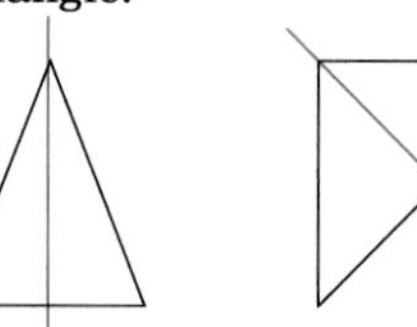

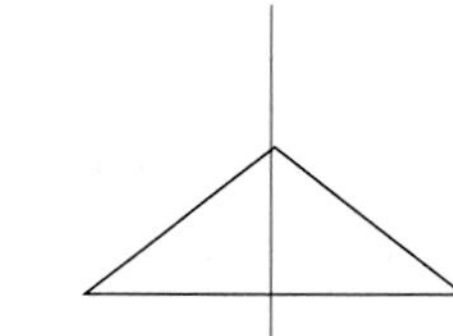

b. Draw three or more scalene triangles. Draw all the lines of symmetry for each triangle. See Sol. Key.

c. *Writing* Describe the lines of symmetry that scalene triangles, equilateral triangles, and isosceles triangles have. See Sol. Key.

16. Which letters of the alphabet, when printed in capital letters, have line symmetry? A, B, C, D, E, H, I, K, M, O, T, U, V,

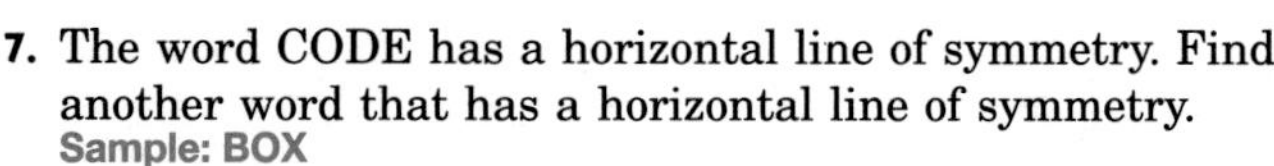

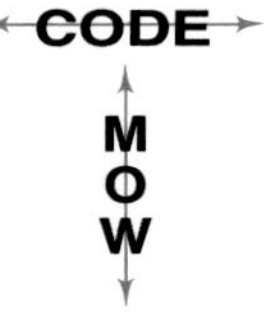

17. The word CODE has a horizontal line of symmetry. Find another word that has a horizontal line of symmetry. Sample: BOX
18. When the word MOW is written in column form, it has a vertical line of symmetry. Find another word like that. Sample: TOY

19. Many flags, such as the Canadian flag shown, have line symmetry. Check students' drawings. See Sol. Key.
   a. Design a flag that has line symmetry.
   b. Design a flag that has no line symmetry.

20. a. Activity Fold a sheet of paper. Cut out a shape that will have the foldline as a line of symmetry.
   b. Fold a sheet of paper into quarters. Cut out a shape that will have two perpendicular lines of symmetry. Check students' work.

Canada's Maple Leaf flag is a symbol of unity.

CHECKPOINT

How many sides does each of the following polygons have?

1. a decagon 10
2. an octagon 8
3. a quadrilateral 4
4. Writing In your own words, define a square. Sample: A square is a figure with four equal sides and four right angles.
5. The Yummyum Cafe had 63 customers for dinner. Twenty of the customers ordered an appetizer with their dinner, 36 ordered dessert with their dinner, and 14 ordered both an appetizer and dessert.
   a. How many customers ordered an appetizer but no dessert with their dinner? 6
   b. How many customers did not order an appetizer or dessert with their dinner? 21
6. a. Which of the figures shown below appear to be congruent? A, B, E
   b. Which figures appear to be similar? A, B, D, E

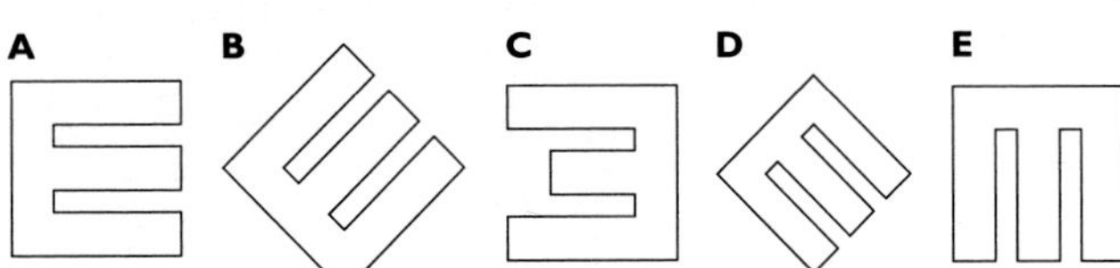

7. **Choose A, B, C, or D.** Which figure has the greatest number of lines of symmetry? A
   A. a square
   B. a right isosceles triangle
   C. a scalene triangle
   D. an equilateral triangle

Math Minutes

On a number line, find the integer at point *A*, if point *A* is 12 units to the left of 4. **–8**

Materials for 2-10

- computer and software *(optional)*
- compass
- ruler

2-10

Connecting to Prior Knowledge

In discussing computer-aided design (CAD), ask: *Why would computers be useful in designing things like Ferris wheels?* **(On a computer, you can change and redraw geometric figures very quickly.)**

THINK AND DISCUSS

As you go over the definitions on the page, have the students make sure that the examples satisfy the definitions. For instance, for diameter $\overline{AE}$ the endpoints *A* and *E* are on the circle and it passes through the center, *O*.

Question 1: Students should see that as they rotate the compass to make a circle, the pencil point stays the same distance from the pivot point.

CRITICAL THINKING To help students who have difficulty seeing why one circle can have an infinite number of radii for Question 1d, review previous discussions about points and lines having zero thickness.

Question 2c: Students may find it easier to explain by demonstrating. Have students support their answers with diagrams.

Question 5: Students should draw longer and longer chords until they see that the longest chord goes through the center of the circle and that such a chord satisfies all the conditions for a diameter.

Error Alert! Students may assume that the sum of angles other than the central angles of a circle equals 360°. Have students use a protractor to measure the outer angles in the Ferris wheel on page 79 in the textbook (angles such as $\angle FED$ or $\angle ABC$). Students should then realize that only the sum of angles around a point equals 360°.

“Hope is the thing with feathers that perches in the soul.”

—Emily Dickinson

Organizer

1. **Focus**
   Connecting to Prior Knowledge
2. **Teach**
   Think and Discuss
   Work Together
3. **Closure**
   Wrap Up

Vocabulary/Symbols

circle
center
radius
diameter
chord
radii
central angles

Skills Reviewed in Context of Lesson

- recognizing line segments
- measurement

Materials and Manipulatives

- computer and software (one per group)
- compass (one per group)
- ruler (one per group)

On Your Own Exercises 17, 21–24: computer or alternate materials

continues next page

TECHNOLOGY

2-10 Exploring Circles

What's Ahead

- Identifying and working with parts of a circle

WHAT YOU'LL NEED

✓ Computer
✓ Software
✓ Compass
✓ Ruler

THINK AND DISCUSS

From factories to Ferris wheels, computers aid in design. Designers and engineers use geometric figures on the computer screen to model real objects. For example, you can model a Ferris wheel with a *circle* and segments inside the circle.

A **circle** is the set of points in a plane that are the same distance from a given point, the *center*. You name a circle by its center. This is circle *O*.

A **radius** is a segment that has one endpoint at the center and the other endpoint on the circle.

$\overline{OG}$ is a radius of circle *O*.

A **diameter** is a segment that passes through the center of a circle and has both endpoints on the circle.

$\overline{AE}$ is a diameter of circle *O*.

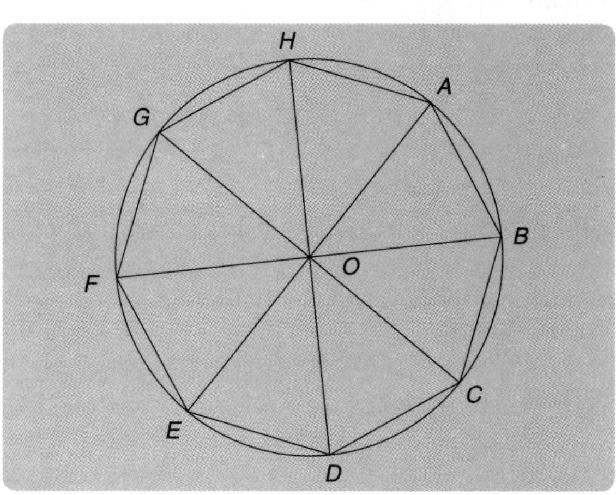

A **chord** is a segment that has both endpoints on the circle.

$\overline{ED}$ is a chord of circle *O*.

The space city *of the future may be built in a wheel shape or torus.*

Ongoing Assessment Have students draw and label a circle with center *X* and four congruent adjacent central angles with the points *Q, R, S,* and *T,* in order. Then have them name the angles, four radii, and two diameters. (**∠*QXR*, ∠*RXS*, ∠*SXT*, ∠*TXQ*; $\overline{XR}$, $\overline{XS}$, $\overline{XQ}$, $\overline{XT}$; $\overline{QS}$ or $\overline{SQ}$, and $\overline{RT}$ or $\overline{TR}$**) Ask: *What are the measures of the central angles?* (**90°**)

WORK TOGETHER

COMPUTER For making and testing conjectures about circles, in Question 9a, students can use geometry software packages. Encourage students to try changing the size of the circle, the size of the central angles, and the number of central angles the circle is divided into. If the software has table (spreadsheet) capability, have the students set up a table to record some of their trials. ***Alternate Approach*** If you are not using computers, have the students use compasses, straightedges, and protractors to draw and measure different configurations of central angles. To save time, each student in the group should try out a different configuration (with different numbers and sizes of central angles). Students can then draw central angles that are easy to measure and add.

CRITICAL THINKING For Question 9b, have students list as many possibilities as they can think of, and then evaluate their lists.

Wrap Up

What's the Big Idea? Ask students to describe the parts of a circle.

Journal Ask students to describe any problems they have with circles or computers. Ask students to list possible solutions to explain how they can overcome any frustration they may feel.

Use a compass to draw a circle. Label the center as *S*.

1. a. Name a radius of circle *O* other than $\overline{OG}$. Sample: $\overline{OA}$
   b. Draw a radius of your circle. Label it as $\overline{ST}$.
   c. Did everyone draw $\overline{ST}$ the same way? no
   d. **Critical Thinking** The plural of radius is *radii.* How many different radii can a circle have? infinitely many
2. a. Name two diameters of circle *O* other than $\overline{AE}$. Sample: $\overline{BF}$, $\overline{CG}$
   b. Choose any point on your circle other than *T*. Label it as *U*. Draw diameter $\overline{UV}$. How many times longer is $\overline{UV}$ than $\overline{ST}$? 2
   c. Is the length of any radius of a circle always half the length of any diameter of that circle? Why or why not? yes; 2 times the length of any radius = the length of a diameter.

> *A circle may be small, yet it may be as mathematically beautiful and perfect as a large one.*
> —Isaac D'Israeli (1766–1848)

The length of a radius of a circle is *the radius* of the circle. The length of a diameter is *the diameter.*

3. a. If the diameter of circle *O* is 6 cm, what is the radius? 3 cm
   b. Find the diameter and radius of circle *S*. Check students' work.
4. Draw $\overline{UT}$ in your circle. What do you call this type of segment? a chord
5. Draw and measure several chords of circle *S*. What is the longest chord of a circle called? diameter
6. A computer model of a 6-car Ferris wheel, like the one at the right, contains many angles. Some of the angles, like ∠*APB*, are *central angles.* Why do you think they have this name? the vertex of the angle is the center of the circle.

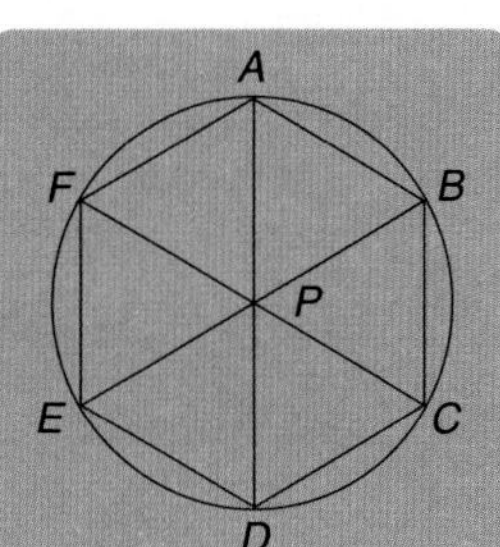

7. a. List the 6 acute central angles shown in circle *P*. See below.
   b. What is the sum of their measures? 360°
   c. These central angles are congruent. What is the measure of each angle? 60°
8. a. Describe the triangles shown for circle *O* on the facing page. Answers may vary. Sample: All eight triangles are isosceles.
   b. What is the measure of ∠*AOB* of circle *O*? 45°
   c. Judging by appearance, classify the triangles shown for circle *P*. equilateral and equiangular

7a. ∠*APB*, ∠*BPC*, ∠*CPD*, ∠*DPE*, ∠*EPF*, ∠*FPA*

Organizer, continued

Student Resources
Extra Practice
Student Study Guide
Practice, TR Ch. 2, p. 34
Student Study Guide, Spanish Resources, TR
Alternate Lesson, TR, Ch. 2, pp. 21–24

Teacher Resources

Teaching Transparencies 10, 39
Lesson Planner, TR Ch. 2, p. 11

Prentice Hall Technology
Multimedia Math
- Math Tools, Geometry

Computer Item Generator
- 2-10

Other Available Technology
Geometer's Sketchpad by Key Curriculum Press *(optional)*

Fact of the Day

The architect Frank Lloyd Wright designed the original Solomon R. Guggenheim Museum. It is a circular building with a dome height of 92 ft and a diameter of approximately 100 ft. Within the room, a ramp spirals for 6 stories. It rises at a 3 percent grade. It goes from a width of 17 ft at the lowest level to about 35 ft at the top.

—*Art & Ideas*

Connections Have a discussion about how circles are used. You may want to start with these examples:

- **Sports** (marking soccer and lacrosse fields, or ice hockey rinks)
- **Business** (graphs, descriptions of cycles or trends)
- **Science** (culture dishes, mapping rotations or torque)

Reteaching Activity Have students list the parts of a circle, define the terms, and draw examples of each. Have students exchange papers within groups of four so that they can look at different examples and so that each may check the others' work. ESL students should be encouraged to make flashcards to help them with the terms introduced in this section.

ON YOUR OWN

Students will need a computer or alternate materials for Exercises 17 and 21–24.

WRITING In Exercise 16, when students test their directions, they should not react to the person's drawing while it is being made (because over the phone they would not be able to see it). For the purposes of this exercise, however, they can take notes for later use. After testing a complete version, students can use their notes to modify their directions and try them out on someone else.

COMPUTER For Exercise 17, if geometry software is not available, any computer drawing program can be used in its place. ***Alternate Approach*** If you are not using computers, have the students use compasses, straightedges, and protractors to draw their circles.

COMPUTER In Exercise 21, have students use geometry software to design and measure their Ferris wheels. ***Alternate Approach*** If you are not using computers, have the students use compasses, rulers, and protractors to draw and measure their Ferris wheels.

Assignment Options

Core: 10–15, 18, 19, 24, MR all	
Reinforce: 16, 17, 20, 22	**Enrich:** 21, 23

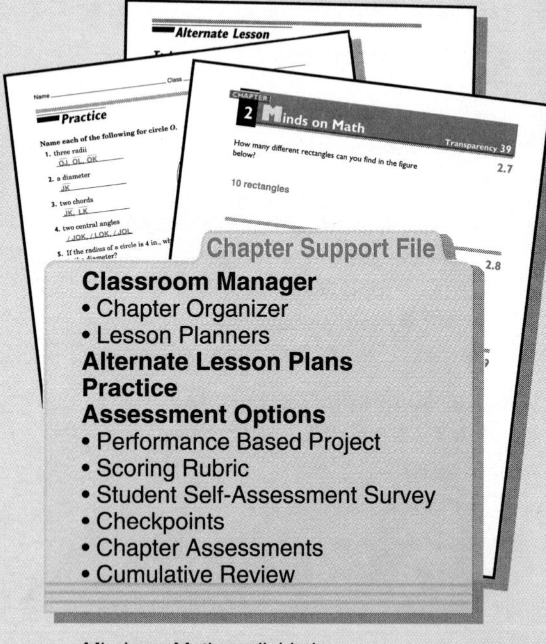

Minds on Math available in Teaching Transparencies

Mixed REVIEW

Compare using <, >, or =.

1. 750 ÷ 150 ■ 80 ÷ 16 =
2. 19 × 17 ■ 176 + 83 >

How many lines of symmetry does each figure have?

3. 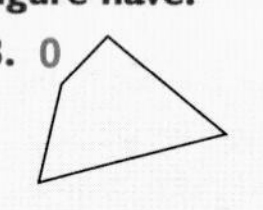 0
4. 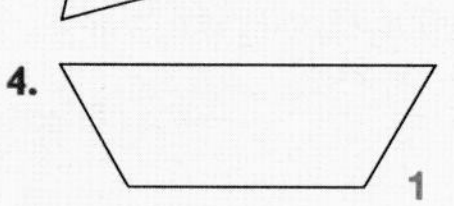 1

Use the figure below for Exercises 5 and 6.

5. How many parallelograms are shown? 16
6. How many rhombuses are shown? 8

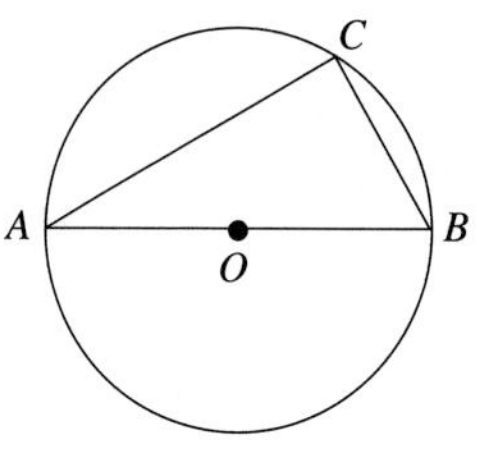

WORK TOGETHER

9. a. **Computer** Make a conjecture about the sum of the measures of the non-overlapping central angles in a circle. Test your conjecture by trying it with different circles and different central angles. Sum = 360°

   b. **Critical Thinking** Suppose you are testing a conjecture on a computer and the sum of the measures of the angles is off by 1°. What could account for that? Sample: This could be due to rounding measures of angles which are not whole numbers.

ON YOUR OWN

Name each of the following for circle *O*.

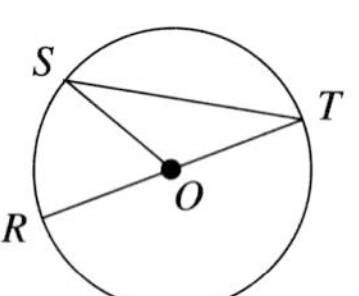

10. three radii $\overline{OR}, \overline{OS}, \overline{OT}$
11. a diameter $\overline{RT}$
12. two central angles $\angle ROS, \angle SOT$
13. two chords $\overline{RT}, \overline{ST}$
14. If the radius of a circle is 8 cm, what is the diameter? 16 cm
15. If the diameter of a circle is 10 in., what is the radius? 5 in.
16. A graphic designer used a computer to create the logo shown at the left. She wants to know what a friend in another city thinks of her design. The fax machine is broken, so she must describe the drawing in words.

    a. **Writing** Write a set of instructions that the graphic designer could give someone over the phone to help him to draw the logo. Use geometric terms like radius, diameter, and chord in your directions. See Sol. Key.

    b. Try out your instructions on a friend or family member. If necessary, revise the instructions.

17. **Computer** Draw a circle and several chords having different lengths. Measure the distance from the center of the circle to each chord. Describe the relationship between the length of the chords and the distances from the center of the circle. Answers may vary. Sample: The shorter the chord, the greater the distance from the center of the circle. The longest chord, the diameter, intersects the center of the circle.

COMPUTER In Exercise 23, students can use geometry software to test their conjectures. ***Alternate Approach*** Have students work in groups to test as many positions as possible for *C*.

Exercise 23: Have students support their answers with examples.

CHAPTER INVESTIGATION Allow students to use real flags as models for Exercise 24. Students could work with partners so that they would have someone to check their work. If possible, each student should print a copy of the flag for the partner to draw a line of symmetry on.

18. Choose A, B, C, or D. The acute central angles of circle P are congruent. What is the measure of $\angle APC$? B

A. 60° **B.** 120°

C. 150° **D.** 180°

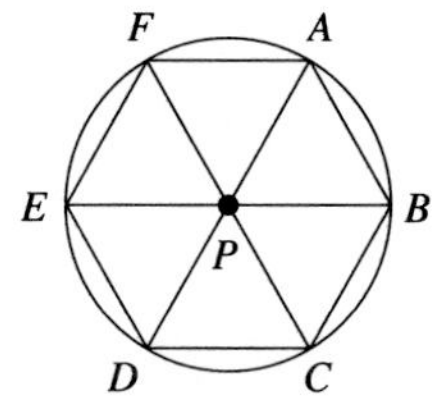

Riding in Circles

The Ferris wheel first appeared at the Chicago World's Fair in 1893, thanks to George Washington Ferris. This mechanical engineer dreamed of designing and building something "original, daring, and unique." Because of this dream, we enjoy his creation at fairs worldwide.

The first Ferris wheel was 265 ft high and had a diameter of 250 ft. That's almost the length of a football field! The 36 cars carried 2,160 passengers high above the crowd. And, unlike today, a single spin took 20 min. The cost of building this Ferris wheel was $385,000.

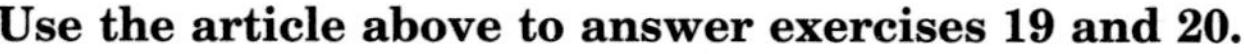

Use the article above to answer exercises 19 and 20.

19. What was the radius of the first Ferris wheel? 125 ft

20. How many people could fit in one car? 60

21. Computer Design your own Ferris wheel using geometric figures. How many cars does it have? What is the measure of each central angle? Check students' drawings. 360 ÷ no. of cars

22. Computer Draw and label a circle. Then draw a central angle of your circle. If you increase or decrease the size of your circle, what happens to the measure of the central angle? unchanged

23. Computer Make and test a conjecture about what happens to $\angle ACB$ as point C moves around the circle. (Hint: What kind of angle is ACB?) $\angle ACB$ is always a right angle.

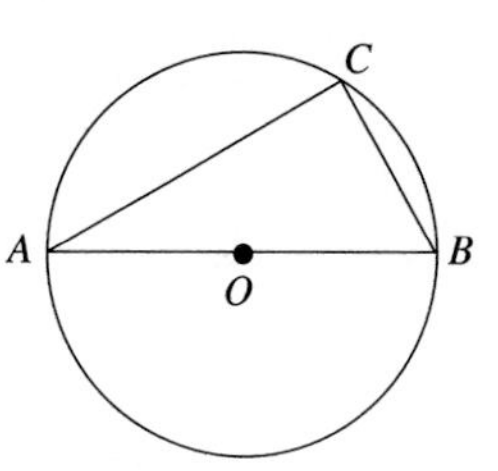

24. Investigation (p. 40) Use the computer to create a flag that has symmetry. Describe the symmetry of your flag. Check students' computer drawings.

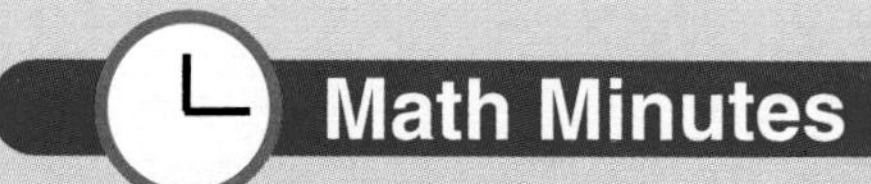

Find two even integers whose sum is 20 and whose product is 96. **8 and 12**

Materials for 2-11

- protractor
- dot paper
- scissors

2-11

Connecting to Prior Knowledge

Have students list examples of tessellations that are found in the classroom and school building. Encourage students to brainstorm as many examples as they can think of.

THINK AND DISCUSS

Question 3: Have students share their descriptions with a partner.

VISUAL LEARNERS Have students use pattern blocks or graph paper and colored pencils to create tessellations.

Ongoing Assessment Ask students to draw an example of repeated uses of a geometric figure that does not form a tessellation. Check students' work to make sure they understand the concept of a tessellation.

DIVERSITY Remind students that many cultures utilize a geometric pattern in their art. Geometric patterns can be found in Maya, Navajo, Islamic, and Congolese art. Encourage students to create their own patterns using geometric shapes. To allow for individual differences in student abilities, emphasize that the patterns may be complex or simple.

WORK TOGETHER

Each pair of students will need scissors and dot paper.

Question 5: One easy way to cut a number of congruent figures is to use a pad of paper and cut several at a time.

Error Alert! For Questions 5 and 6, some students may have difficulty in forming a tessellation with either a triangle or a quadrilateral. ***Remediation*** Encourage them to try to find ways to put congruent sides together.

"Honesty is one part of eloquence. We persuade others by being in earnest ourselves."

—William Hazlitt

Organizer

1. **Focus**
   Connecting to Prior Knowledge
2. **Teach**
   Think and Discuss
   Work Together
3. **Closure**
   Wrap Up

Vocabulary/Symbols
tessellations

Skills Reviewed in Context of Lesson
- working with polygons
- measuring angles
- working with patterns
- recognizing quadrilaterals and triangles

Materials and Manipulatives
- protractor (one for each student)
- dot paper (for each student)
- scissors (one pair for each group)

On Your Own Exercises 7–11: tracing paper; Exercise 14: graph paper

Student Resources
Extra Practice
Student Study Guide
Practice, TR Ch. 2, p. 35
Student Study Guide, Spanish Resources, TR

continues next page

MATH AND DESIGN

2-11 Exploring Tessellations

What's Ahead
- Drawing tessellations

WHAT YOU'LL NEED
✓ Protractor
✓ Dot paper
✓ Scissors

THINK AND DISCUSS

Tessellations are repeated geometric designs that cover a plane with no gaps and no overlaps. Tessellations have been used in designing and decorating buildings, streets, and walkways for a long time. For example, the Sumerians in the Mesopotamian Valley (about 4000 B.C.) decorated their homes and temples with mosaics in geometric patterns. Brick streets, tiled floors, and patios are just a few examples of modern tessellations.

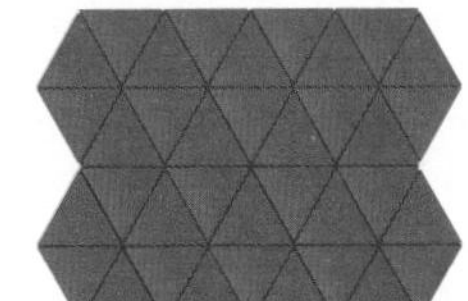

The title of this** art work is "Apple Core." **What two figures tessellate the plane?
the apple and the core

1. Describe the polygons used to form the tessellations above. Answers may vary.
2. Measure the angles of each polygon. For each tessellation what is the sum of the measures of angles that have the same vertex? 360°
3. Describe how you could use a pattern for each polygon to draw the tessellation. Can you draw each of the three tessellations without turning the pattern? no; the bottom right pattern involves rotations.
4. Are any of the tessellations related? In what way? yes; In the bottom rt., six equilateral triangles form a hexagon, which can tessellate the plane as shown in the top pattern.

Wrap Up

What's the Big Idea? Ask students: *What are tessellations and how are they made?*

Journal Have students compare drawing a tessellation to assembling a jigsaw puzzle. Ask students to list some rules of thumb they've discovered that help them with tessellations. Then ask them to describe their reactions when a pattern is slow in forming.

Connections Have a discussion about how tessellations are used or where they are found. You may want to start with these examples:

- **Nature** (honeycomb, sunflower seed pattern)
- **Art** (stained glass, mosaics)
- **Manufacturing** (mattress coils, packaging designs)

Reteaching Activity Have students work with partners to make tessellations using rubber bands and geoboards. Students should design and have their partners examine both triangle and quadrilateral tessellations. Students may need some help seeing the relationship between the sum of the angles of the figure and the fact that there are 360° around a point.

ON YOUR OWN

Students will need tracing paper for Exercises 7–11 and 13, and graph paper for Exercise 14.

Exercises 7–9: Have students explain why each figure can or cannot form a tessellation.

WRITING For Exercise 10e, have students draw designs of each step to accompany their explanations.

WORK TOGETHER

5. Working with a partner, draw an acute scalene triangle and an obtuse scalene triangle on dot paper. Each of you should cut out several congruent copies of one of the triangles and use them to form a tessellation. Copy each tessellation on dot paper. See Sol. Key.

FLASHBACK A scalene triangle has no congruent sides.

6. On dot paper draw a quadrilateral that has no congruent sides. Work with your partner. See Sol. Key.
   a. Cut out nine copies of the quadrilateral.
   b. Experiment to find out how to form a tessellation.
   c. Copy the tessellation on dot paper.
   d. What does your tessellation show about the sum of the measures of the angles of your quadrilateral? Explain your reasoning. 360°; At each vertex, four different angles of the quad. meet without a gap and their sum is 360°.

ON YOUR OWN

Trace each figure. Determine whether you can use the figure to form a tessellation.

7. yes
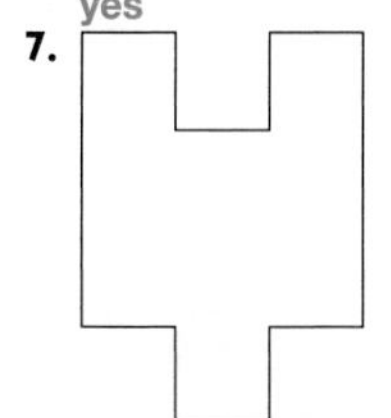

8. no
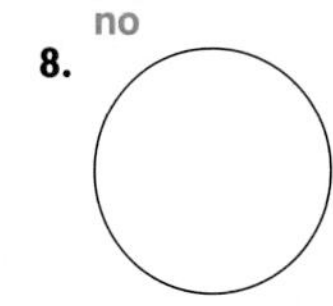

9. yes
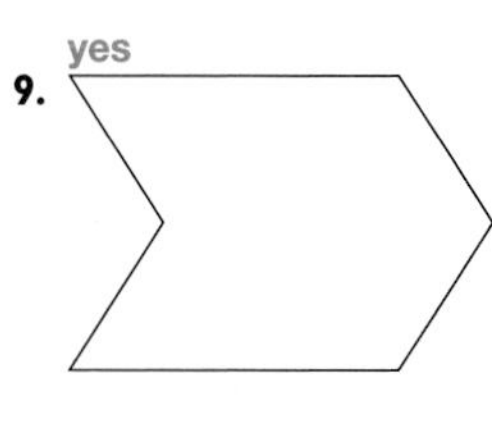

10. You can create your own tessellating figure. Start with a square and follow the steps below. Check students' work.
    a. Cut a shape out of one side of the square.
    b. Tape the shape on the opposite side of the square.
    c. Cut another shape from a different side and tape it to the opposite end.
    d. Trace the new figure repeatedly to form a tessellation.
    e. **Writing** Why does this procedure result in a figure that will form a tessellation? The figures form a tessellation in the same way that squares do. Each cut out is filled by the extension on the figure underneath.

Organizer, continued

Teacher Resources

Teaching Transparencies 6, 39
Overhead Manipulatives: protractor
Lesson Planner, TR Ch. 2, p. 12

Prentice Hall Technology

Multimedia Math
- Hot Page 2-11

Computer Item Generator
- 2-11

Fact of the Day

In ancient Rome, small cubes or pieces of stone were set in cement to create a floor mosaic. Roman artists often used geometric patterns for floor designs and stories and landscapes for wall mosaics.

—*Arts & Ideas*

CRITICAL THINKING For Exercise 12, students should try to create such a tessellation.

CHAPTER INVESTIGATION Have students work in groups of three or four for Exercise 14. Each group should first decide on suitable designs for the letters C, S, and T. Have groups share their designs.

Decision Making

RESEARCH Students can find pictures of tile designs in brochures from tile stores and in reference books.

The Alhambra, built between 1238 and 1358 by the Moors in Granada, Spain, is famous for its tile designs. Students may be able to find pictures of these in a library.

Have students work in groups of four.

Encourage students first to compare in their groups actual tile designs that they have found outside of class. Students can use the designs to help them create their own patterns.

Have each group use as many different shapes as possible. After the groups finish their projects, they can compare their designs.

PH Multimedia Math Hot Page™ 2-11

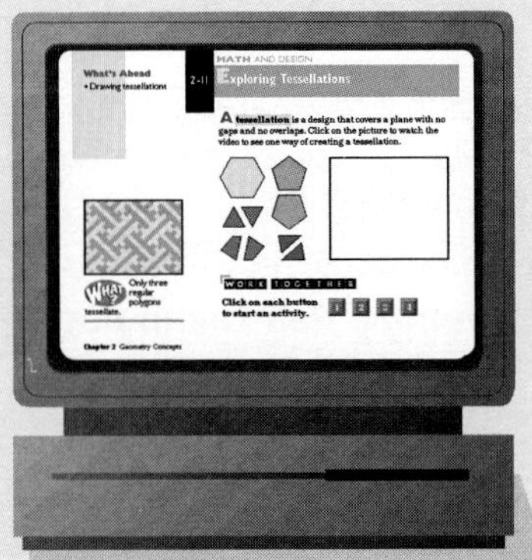

Assignment Options

Core: 7–9, 11, 14, DM all, MR all	
Reinforce: 10, 13	**Enrich:** 12

Mixed REVIEW

Find each answer.

1. 13,789 + 23,653 37,442
2. 34,567 − 27,488 7,079
3. How many more sides does an octagon have than a quadrilateral? 4
4. How many fewer sides does a triangle have than a decagon? 7

Complete.

5. A diameter of a circle is ■ as long as a radius of the circle. twice
6. A ■ is the longest chord of a circle. diameter

11. You can use more than one type of polygon to form a tessellation. By tracing, use two or more of the figures below to create a tessellation. Check students' drawings.

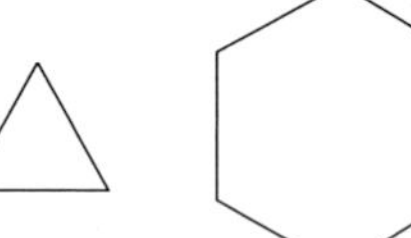
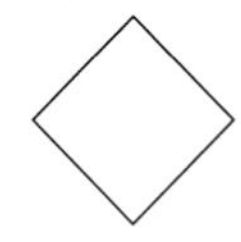
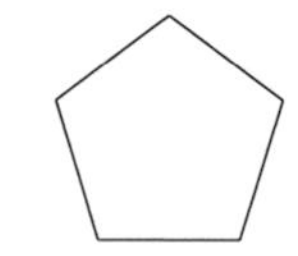

12. Critical Thinking Is it possible to use a figure with curves to form a tessellation? If you think it is possible, sketch an example. If you think it is not possible, explain your reasoning. yes; See Sol. Key.

DECISION MAKING

COLLECT DATA

You can use square tiles to tile a floor. Or you can create a more interesting design by using more than one shape, like those shown below.

6 in.

$5

4 in.

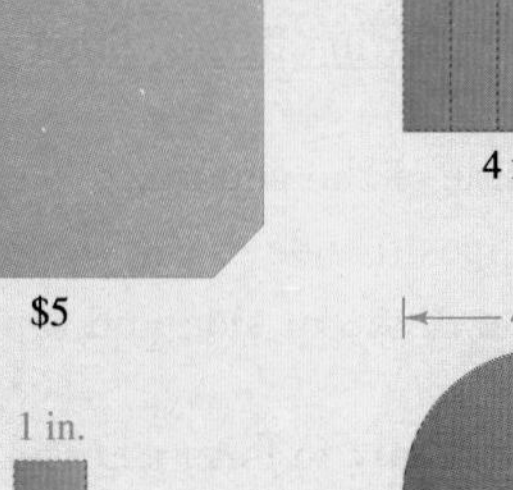

4 for $5

4 in.

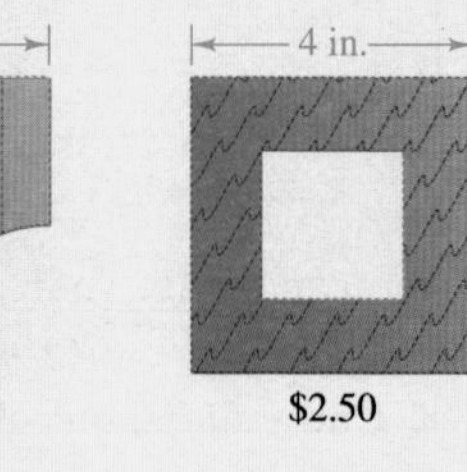

$2.50

1 in.

$1

4 in.

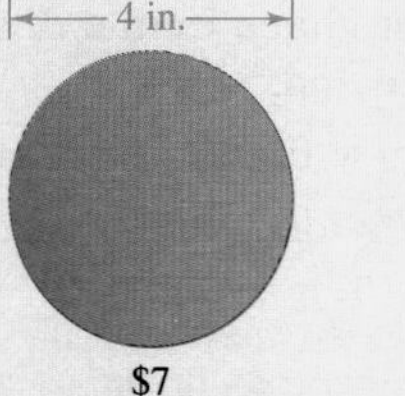

$7

2 in.

$2.50

13. **Choose A, B, C, or D.** Which of the following could you use to tessellate the plane? D

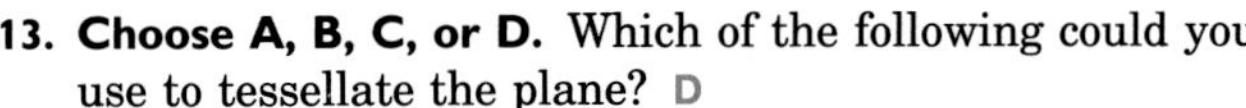

A. 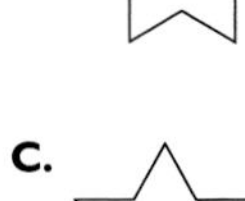

B. 

C.

D. 

14. Investigation (p. 40) You can design the letters C, S, and T to tessellate. Use graph paper to create a tessellation using each letter. Check students' drawings. See Solution Key. Sample given.

Problem Solving Hint

Trace the figures and draw a diagram.

The 1-in. square comes in different colors. The circular tile and 2-in. square come in different designs.

ANALYZE DATA

1. Use tracing paper to draw three designs. For each design use two kinds of tile shown.
2. Suppose you are using each of your designs to tile an area 1 ft by 1 ft square. 2a. 1 in. square, circle
   a. Which tiles, if any, must you cut?
   b. How many of each kind of tile will you need? Answers may vary.

MAKE DECISIONS

3. You want to tile a 12 ft by 8 ft floor. Find the cost for each of your three designs. If you have to use any half or quarter tiles, assume that the cost is one half or one quarter that of a whole tile. Then choose one of your designs and explain why you made that choice. Answers may vary. See Sol. Key.

The word tessellation comes from the Latin tessellare. It means "to pave with tiles." ***What figures tessellate in the photo?***

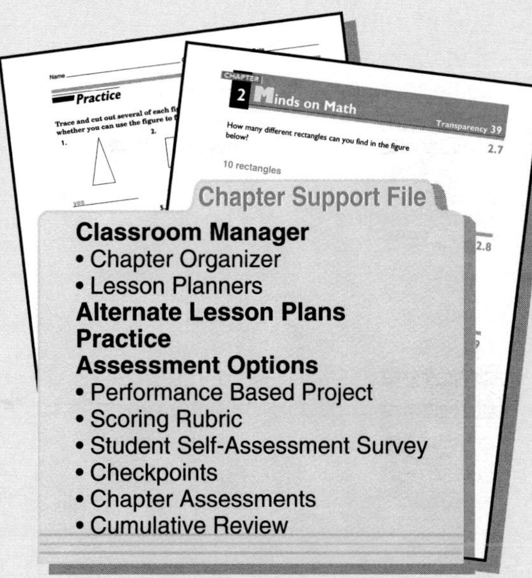

Minds on Math available in Teaching Transparencies

Math Minutes

What is the opposite of each of the following changes?

1. earned \$8.00 **spent \$8.00**
2. decreased 7° **increased 7°**
3. gained 3 kg **lost 3 kg**

CHAPTER 2 WRAP UP

Ongoing Assessment For Exercises 1, 2, and 12, have students compare their drawings and constructions and tell how they are different, or how they are the same.

For Exercise 17, ask students to label their figures and name the congruent segments and angles, if any.

Exercise 13 is an example of an enhanced multiple-choice question.

Vocabulary/Symbols

acute angle
acute triangle
angle, ∠
arcs
center
central angles
chord
circle
collinear
compass
congruent
congruent angles
congruent segments
construct
convex
degree, °
diameter
endpoints
equilateral triangle
isosceles triangle
line of symmetry
line RS, $\overleftrightarrow{RS}$
logical reasoning
noncollinear
obtuse angle
obtuse triangle
parallel lines
parallel segments
parallelogram
perpendicular
plane
point
polygons
protractor
radii
radius
ray
rectangle
rhombus
right triangle
scalene triangle
segment RS, $\overline{RS}$
sides
similar
square
straight angle
straightedge
tessellations
trapezoid
Venn diagrams
vertex

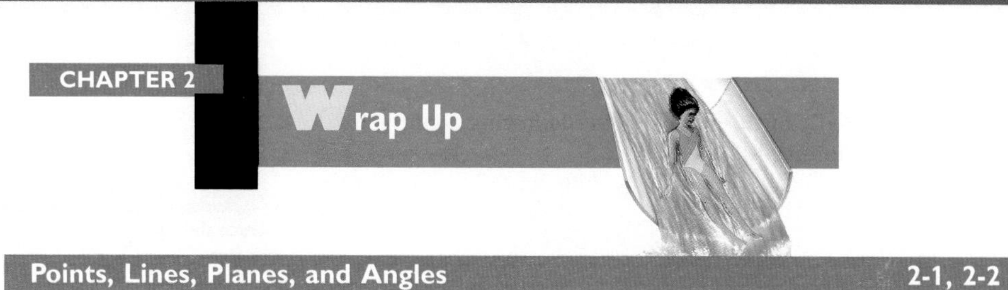

Points, Lines, Planes, and Angles 2-1, 2-2

You can represent ***points, lines,*** and ***planes*** by everyday objects.

A ***segment*** is a part of a line with two endpoints. A ***ray*** is a part of a line with one endpoint.

You can classify angles as ***acute, right, obtuse,*** or ***straight.***

1–2 Check students' drawings.

1. Draw three noncollinear points A, B, and C.
2. Draw parallel lines $\overleftrightarrow{JK}$ and $\overleftrightarrow{MN}$.
3. How many segments are in the figure? how many rays? how many lines? 3; 6; 1

Classify each angle.

4. straight
5. acute
6. obtuse

Circles 2-10

A ***radius*** has one endpoint at the center and one endpoint on the circle. A ***diameter*** has two endpoints on the circle and passes through the center. A ***chord*** has two endpoints on the circle.

Name the following for circle O.

7. three radii Sample: $\overline{OX}$, $\overline{OY}$, $\overline{OV}$
8. a diameter $\overline{XV}$
9. two central angles ∠XOY, ∠VOY
10. three chords $\overline{VW}$, $\overline{WY}$, $\overline{VX}$

Construction 2-3

Figures that are the same size and shape are ***congruent.***

11. Writing Explain how to construct a segment congruent to a given segment. See Sol. Key.
12. Draw an acute ∠Z. Construct an angle congruent to ∠Z. Check students' work. See Sol. Key.

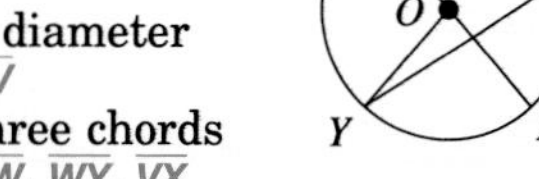

Getting Ready for Chapter 3

The skills previewed will help students understand and solve problems involving place value of decimals.

Polygons, Congruence, and Similarity — 2-4, 2-5, 2-6, 2-8

You can classify triangles as ***acute, obtuse,*** or ***right*** and ***equilateral, isosceles,*** or ***scalene.***

We name polygons for the number of their sides.

Figures that have the same size and shape are ***congruent.*** Figures that have the same shape are ***similar.***

13. **Choose A, B, C, or D.** When $\overline{XZ}$ is drawn in parallelogram *WXYZ*, two congruent equilateral triangles are formed. What kind of figure is *WXYZ*? B

    A. rectangle **B.** rhombus **C.** trapezoid **D.** square

Do the triangles appear congruent, similar, or neither?

14. 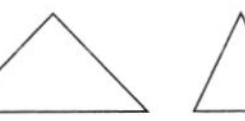 similar

15. neither

Symmetry and Tessellations — 2-9, 2-11

A ***line of symmetry*** divides a figure into two congruent parts.

Tessellations are geometric figures that cover a plane with no gaps or overlaps.

16. How many lines of symmetry does a rhombus that is not a square have? 2

17. Draw a sketch to show how a parallelogram tessellates a plane. Check students' drawings.

Strategies and Applications — 2-7

You often can use logical reasoning to solve problems.

18. Of 26 students, 3 read both "The Black Stallion," and "Island of the Blue Dolphin." Eleven read the first book, but not the second. Seven students read neither book. How many read only the second book? 5

GETTING READY FOR CHAPTER 3

In the number 254, 4 is the units' digit, 5 is the tens' digit, and 2 is the hundreds' digit.

1. In the number 4,908, 9 is the ■ digit. hundreds'

2. Identify the thousands' digit in 36,158. 6

Materials and Manipulatives

- ruler
- protractor

Student Resources

Practice, p. 69
Problem Solving Practice, p. 50
Extra Practice
Student Study Guide
Student Study Guide, Spanish Resources, TR
Tools for Studying Smarter, TR
Student Self-Assessment Survey, TR Ch. 2, p. 39 *(see below)*

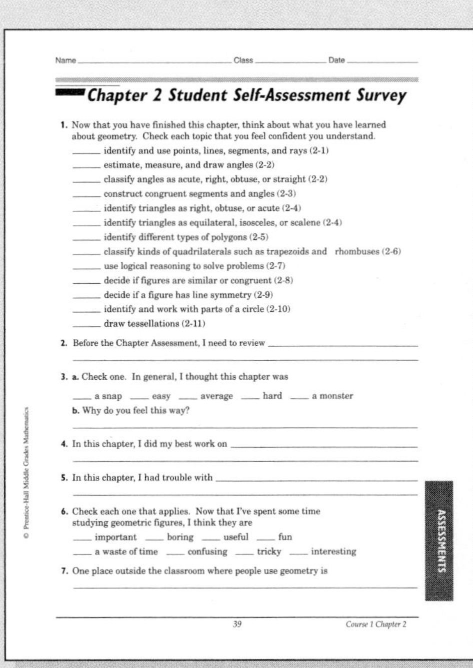

Name ______ Class ______ Date ______

Chapter 2 Student Self-Assessment Survey

1. Now that you have finished this chapter, think about what you have learned about geometry. Check each topic that you feel confident you understand.
   ______ identify and use points, lines, segments, and rays (2-1)
   ______ estimate, measure, and draw angles (2-2)
   ______ classify angles as acute, right, obtuse, or straight (2-2)
   ______ construct congruent segments and angles (2-3)
   ______ identify triangles as right, obtuse, or acute (2-4)
   ______ identify triangles as equilateral, isosceles, or scalene (2-4)
   ______ identify different types of polygons (2-5)
   ______ classify kinds of quadrilaterals such as trapezoids and rhombuses (2-6)
   ______ use logical reasoning to solve problems (2-7)
   ______ decide if figures are similar or congruent (2-8)
   ______ decide if a figure has line symmetry (2-9)
   ______ identify and work with parts of a circle (2-10)
   ______ draw tessellations (2-11)
2. Before the Chapter Assessment, I need to review ______
3. a. Check one. In general, I thought this chapter was
   ___ a snap ___ easy ___ average ___ hard ___ a monster
   b. Why do you feel this way? ______
4. In this chapter, I did my best work on ______
5. In this chapter, I had trouble with ______
6. Check each one that applies. Now that I've spent some time studying geometric figures, I think they are
   ___ important ___ boring ___ useful ___ fun
   ___ a waste of time ___ confusing ___ tricky ___ interesting
7. One place outside the classroom where people use geometry is ______

ASSESSMENTS

39 Course 1 Chapter 2

CHAPTER 2 **PUTTING IT ALL TOGETHER**

The projects on these pages can be used in a variety of ways.

- alternative assessment
- portfolio ideas
- additional assignments for gifted and talented students
- extra credit for all students
- outdoor activity investigation

Follow Up

- Ask students to explain the term *geometrical.* How can they determine whether their flags are geometrical?

COOPERATIVE GROUPS School flags patterned on the Canadian flag and the Data Processing logo will already be symmetrical. Flags that repeat figures to create patterns will need to be redesigned by reversing or rotating the figures in the design.

ESL Students may want to show pictures of flags from their native countries. Students can determine if the designs are symmetrical.

EXCURSION Suggest that students choose the most important figure or symbol from their design. Have the students use the most simplified figure as the basis for their tessellation.

Shape Up

Students may wish to alter the game rules to be able to list objects that are outside the classroom. Have the students discuss the change and have them decide.

For added interest, students may wish to participate in the problem-solving activities of *Odyssey of the Mind.* This international competition includes segments that allow students to brainstorm about shapes, problems, and ideas in an impromptu setting.

Materials and Manipulatives

Follow Up: *Excursion*
- art materials

Shape Up
- watch or clock

123 Symmetry
- dot paper or graph paper

What's Your Angle?
- colored pencil

Portrait of a Polygon
- straightedge
- colored pencils

Prentice Hall Technology

Follow Up
Multimedia Math
- Math Tools, Text *(optional)*

Other Available Technology

- *Word* by Microsoft
- *WriteNow* by Wordstar
- *II Write* by American School Publishers
- *Bank Street Writer* by Broderbund *(all optional)*

Pattern Hunt

At the beginning of this chapter, you and your group designed a flag. Now you have been invited to carry the flag in the parade at the annual Math Fair.

The Fair Committee has stated that the design of each flag must be geometrical and must display symmetry. Take a look at your flag. If it does not display symmetry, redesign it. When you are satisfied with your design, explain how it is geometrical. Do this in one of the following ways.

✓ Make an oral presentation to the committee.
✓ Write a letter to the committee.
✓ Write an article for the school paper.

The problems preceded by the magnifying glass (p. 65, # 35; p. 81, # 24; and p. 85, # 14) will help you complete the investigation.

Excursion: Redesign your flag so that the design is a tessellation.

Who to Talk To:
- an art teacher
- a graphic designer

Rules:
- Play with three or more people
- One player keeps time and assigns a shape to the other players, such as a square.
- Players are given 1 minute to look around the classroom and list as many objects as possible that are in that shape or have that shape in their design.

When time is up, players compare lists to see who was able to find the most objects. The player with the longest list assigns the next shape and serves as timekeeper for the next round of play.

88

What's Your Angle

Have students label their drawings. Suggest that the students use the corner of an envelope as a template for the right angles.

123 Symmetry

You may wish to remind students to think of how numbers are displayed on a digital clock as they draw their numbers. Have students draw lines of symmetry in color.

Portrait of a Polygon

Suggest that students draw two identical pictures. Have the students use one picture to color the angles, lines of symmetry, and parallel lines. The other picture can be dedicated to the colored designs that the students produce with this activity.

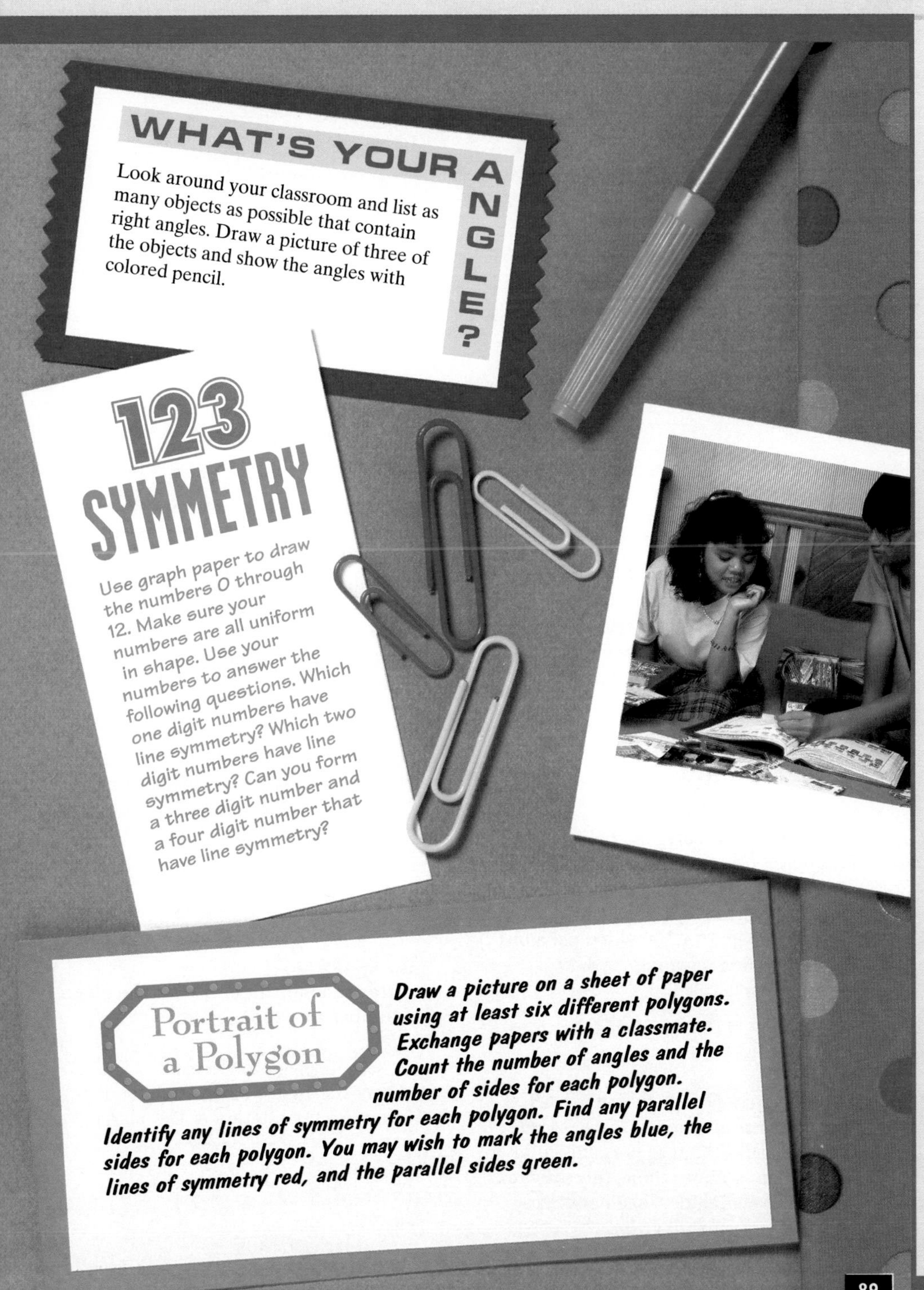

WHAT'S YOUR ANGLE?
Look around your classroom and list as many objects as possible that contain right angles. Draw a picture of three of the objects and show the angles with colored pencil.
123 SYMMETRY
Use graph paper to draw the numbers 0 through 12. Make sure your numbers are all uniform in shape. Use your numbers to answer the following questions. Which one digit numbers have line symmetry? Which two digit numbers have line symmetry? Can you form a three digit number and a four digit number that have line symmetry?
Portrait of a Polygon
Draw a picture on a sheet of paper using at least six different polygons. Exchange papers with a classmate. Count the number of angles and the number of sides for each polygon. Identify any lines of symmetry for each polygon. Find any parallel sides for each polygon. You may wish to mark the angles blue, the lines of symmetry red, and the parallel sides green.
89

CHAPTER 2

ASSESSMENT

Exercise 6 is an example of an enhanced multiple-choice question.

Writing Exercises allow students to describe more fully their thinking and understanding of the concepts they've learned.

Exercise 4 is a writing question.

Exercise 5: Be sure students understand that point O is the center of the circle.

Some students may need extra help with vocabulary. Have students use index cards to make flash cards, one for each definition.

Enhanced Multiple-Choice Questions are more complex than traditional multiple-choice questions, which assess only one skill. Enhanced multiple-choice questions assess the processes that students use as well as the end results. They are written so that students can use more than one strategy to solve the problem. Using multiple strategies is encouraged by the National Council of Teachers of Mathematics (NCTM).

Resources

Performance Based Project, TR Ch. 2, pp. 36–38
Chapter Assessment, Forms A and B, TR Ch. 2, pp. 41–44
Spanish Chapter Assessment, Spanish Resources, TR
Computer Item Generator

CHAPTER 2

Assessment

1. Draw three noncollinear points and label them X, Y, and Z. Draw $\overleftrightarrow{XY}$. Then draw a line through Z that appears to be parallel to $\overleftrightarrow{XY}$. Check students' drawings.
2. **Estimation** The *best* estimate for the measure of $\angle PQR$ is: A
   - **A.** 100°
   - **B.** 80°
   - **C.** 135°
   - **D.** 150°

   R P Q

3. $\triangle ABC$ is isosceles. Copy the triangle and then use a straightedge and compass to construct a triangle congruent to $\triangle ABC$. (*Hint:* First construct an angle congruent to $\angle B$.)

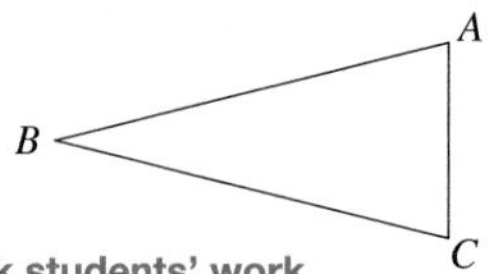

Check students' work.

4. **Writing** In the polygons below, *diagonals* from one vertex are drawn. How many diagonals can you draw from one vertex of a hexagon? a 7-sided polygon? a 100-sided polygon? Explain your reasoning. 3; 4; 97

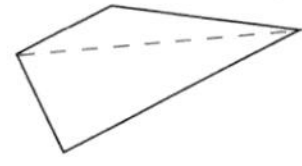
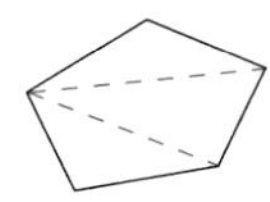

5. Draw a circle O and any chord $\overline{AB}$ that is not a diameter. Draw $\overline{OA}$, $\overline{OB}$, and the radius that is perpendicular to $\overline{AB}$. Make as many conjectures as you can about the angles, segments, and triangles in your diagram. Check students' drawings. See Sol. Key.

6. In order to conclude that $MNOP$ is a rhombus, you have to know that: C
   - **A.** $\overline{MO} \perp \overline{NP}$
   - **B.** $\overline{MO}$ has length 8
   - **C.** $\overline{MP}$ and $\overline{PO}$ have length 8
   - **D.** $\overline{NP}$ and $\overline{MO}$ are congruent

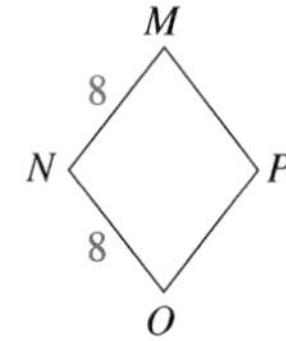

7. Of the 16 boys in Mrs. Stern's math class, 7 play soccer and 5 are in the band. Four play football but they do not participate in any other activity. Two students play soccer *and* play in the band. How many students participate in none of the three activities? 2
8. **a.** Name a pair of triangles that appear to be congruent. Sample: $\triangle ADC$, and $\triangle BCD$

   b. Name a pair of triangles that appear to be similar but not congruent. $\triangle AOB$ and $\triangle COD$

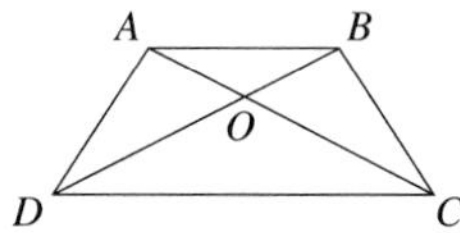

9. Draw a quadrilateral with the given number of symmetry lines.

   a. 0 **b.** 1 **c.** 2 **d.** 4

   Check students' drawings.
10. Copy the figure below and use it to create a tessellation of the plane.

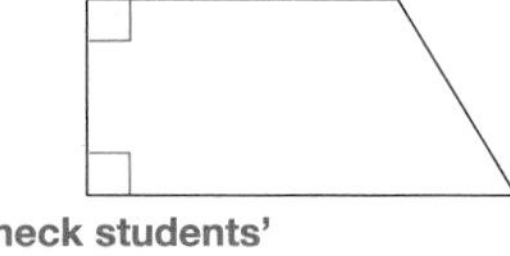

Check students' drawings.

CHAPTER 2

CUMULATIVE REVIEW

Exercise 5 is an example of an enhanced multiple choice question.

Item(s)	Review Topic	Chapter
1	Organizing Data: Frequency Tables	1
2	Exploring Symmetry	2
3	Points, Lines and Planes	2
4	Angles	2
5	Triangles	2
6, 7	Averages	1
8	Number Expressions	pre-book
9	Reading and Understanding Graphs	1
10	Angles	2

CHAPTER 2

Cumulative Review

Choose A, B, C, or D.

1. What can you conclude from the line plot? A
   - **A.** Most absences occurred on Monday and Friday.
   - **B.** The mean number of absences per day was 2.5.
   - **C.** Only one person was absent on Wednesday because of a field trip.
   - **D.** At least one person was absent twice that week.

No. of Students Absent

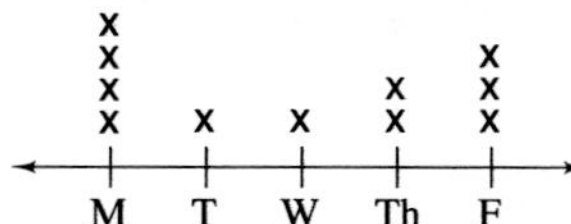

2. How many lines of symmetry does a rectangle that is not a square have? C
   A. 0 **B.** 1 **C.** 2 **D.** 4

3. Which ray does NOT contain C? B
   A. $\overrightarrow{DB}$ **B.** $\overrightarrow{BA}$
   C. $\overrightarrow{AD}$ **D.** $\overrightarrow{BD}$

   A B C D

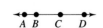

4. Estimate the sum of the measures of an obtuse angle and a right angle. D
   A. less than 90° **B.** equal to 180°
   C. between 90° and 180°
   D. more than 180°

5. What kind of triangle is impossible to draw? D
   A. right scalene **B.** acute isosceles
   C. obtuse isosceles
   D. obtuse equilateral

6. Find the mode of the following temperatures: 100°, 70°, 70°, 85°, 70° A
   A. 70° **B.** 75° **C.** 77° **D.** 79°

7. Find the median of these test scores: 78, 90, 71, 85, 68, 77, 88, 96. A
   A. 81.5 **B.** 78 **C.** 85 **D.** 82

8. If bagels cost \$2 per dozen, how would you find the cost of 5 bagels? B
   A. $\$2 \times 5 \times 12$ **B.** $\$2 \div 12 \times 5$
   C. $\$2 \times 12 \div 5$ **D.** $\$2 \div 5 \times 12$

9. What information does the circle graph NOT tell you? C
   - **A.** Jen purchased lunch more often than she brought it from home.
   - **B.** Jen purchased hot and cold lunches equally often.
   - **C.** Jen brought lunch from home more often than she purchased cold lunch.
   - **D.** Jen purchased hot lunch more often than she brought lunch from home.

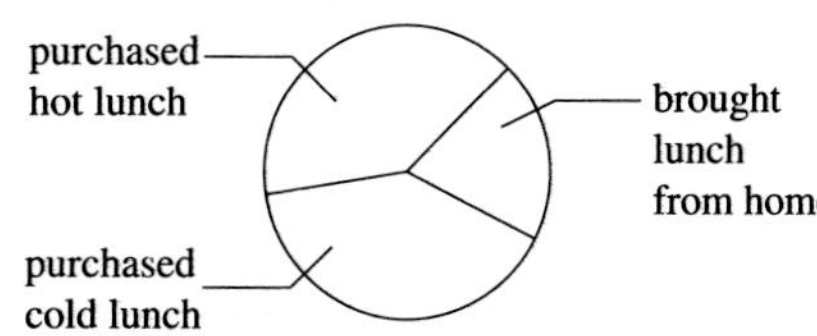

10. How many acute angles can you find in the figure? C
    A. 3 **B.** 4
    C. 5 **D.** 6

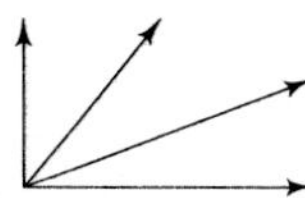

Resources

Cumulative Review, TR ch. 2, pp. 45–46
Transparency Masters, TR p. 35

CHAPTER

3 Adding and Subtracting Decimals

Why Study Decimals?

If students ask this question, you may want to mention these areas in which decimals are used: finance, science, consumer issues, sports, schedules, metric units, weights and measurement, statistics, and manufacturing.

Graphic Display of Chapter Content

Below is one possible representation of the chapter's content and its applications to the world outside the classroom. Have students create their own graphic display and fill in applications that they have seen in their own lives.

- The center oval should state the main concept of the chapter: decimals.
- Have students draw the ovals with the next level of concepts presented in the chapter (adding and subtracting decimals, rounding, comparing and ordering, and metric length). You may want students to add any other topics that they think are appropriate.
- Ask students to draw as many application ovals as they can.
- Discuss all the applications that students identify.
- Have students make and present one display that includes all the students' ideas.

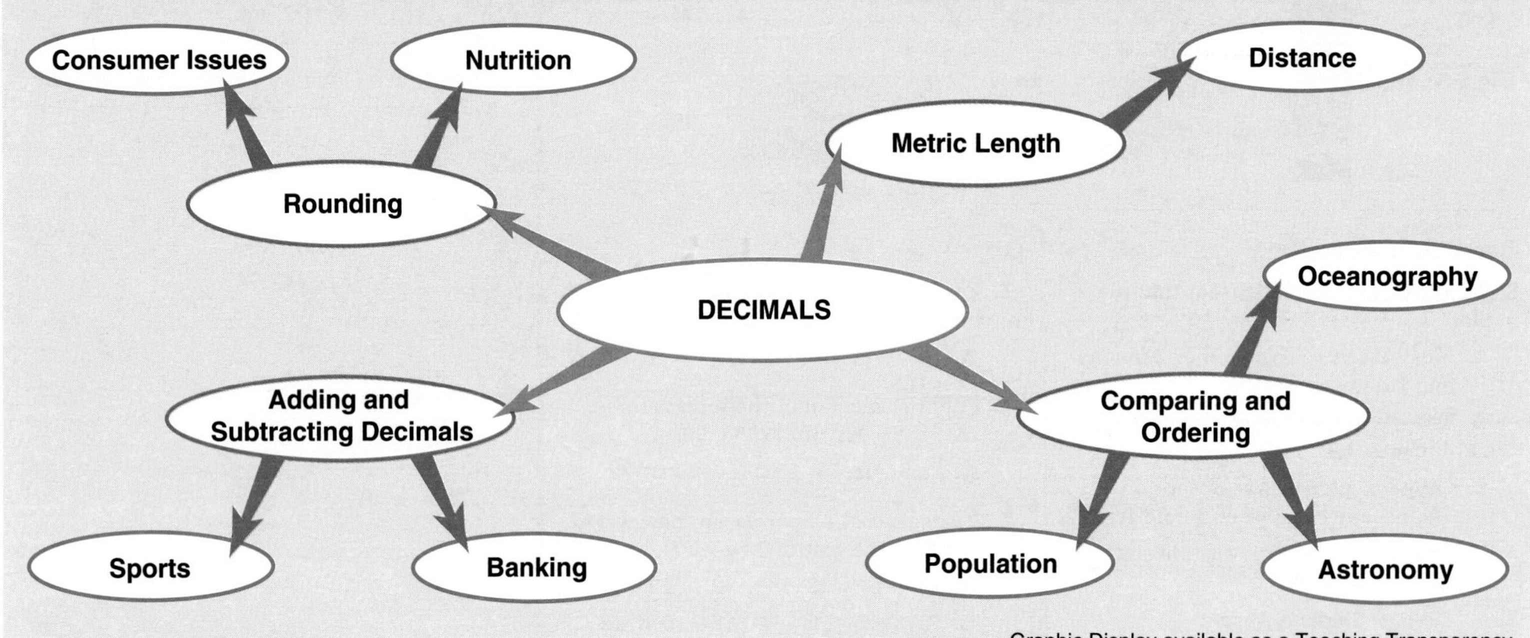

Graphic Display available as a Teaching Transparency

Vocabulary and Symbols

balance
centimeter
deposits
elapsed time
equivalent
expanded form
interest
kilometer
meter
mill
millimeter
one hundredth
one tenth
perimeter
standard form
statement
withdrawals

Materials and Manipulatives

calculator	metric ruler
computer (optional)	graph paper
newspapers or magazines	spreadsheet software (optional)

Additional Resources

Commercially Available Technology

Calculator
scientific

Software
ClarisWorks by Apple
1-2-3 by Lotus
Conquering Decimals (+, –) by MECC
Excel; Works by Microsoft
Word by Microsoft

Other Media
"Decimal Names for Rational Numbers." Aims Media, 9710 DeSoto Avenue, Chatsworth, CA 91311-4409.
"Rounding Decimals." Aims Media, 9710 DeSoto Avenue, Chatsworth, CA 91311-4409.
"The Secret of Vincent's Museum." Tom Snyder Productions, 80 Coolidge Hill Road, Watertown, MA 02172 (800) 342-0236.

Materials at Little or No Cost

Math + Science: A Solution. AIMS Education Foundation, Box 8120, Fresno, CA 93747-8120. Reproducible activities.
Young Astronauts Council, 1308 19th St., N.W., Washington, D.C. 20036. Activities and clubs.

Bibliography

For Teachers
Burton, Grace, et al. *Sixth-Grade Book: Addenda Series.* Reston, VA: NCTM, 1992.
Hiebert, James and Merlyn Behr, eds. *Number Concepts and Operations in the Middle Grades.* Reston, VA: NCTM, 1988.

For Students
Simon, Seymour. *How to Be a Space Scientist in Your Own Home.* NY: Harper, 1989.
Watson, Mark. *Department of the Treasury.* NY: Chelsea House, 1989.
Wilkinson, Elizabeth. *Making Cents: Every Kids' Guide to Money: How to Make It, What to do with It.* Boston: Little, Brown, 1989.

Prentice Hall Technology

Multimedia Math
- Math Tools, Spreadsheet
- Math Tools, Text
- Hot Page™ 3-1
- Hot Page™ 3-5
- Hot Page™ 3-10
- Math Investigations, Hazard City Messengers
- Math Investigations, Mission: Mars
- Math Investigations, Measuring Elephant Populations in Africa

Computer Item Generator
- Chapter 3

Community Resources

Field Trips
- visit a metro system (buses, trolleys, or trains)
- visit a bank or savings-and-loan association
- visit a grocery store

Guest Speakers
- a grocery store manager on the pricing of items
- a banker who makes loans
- the scheduler of a timed metro system

Backpack Take-Home Activities

Materials
- newspaper
- scissors
- paper
- almanac
- tape
- pencil

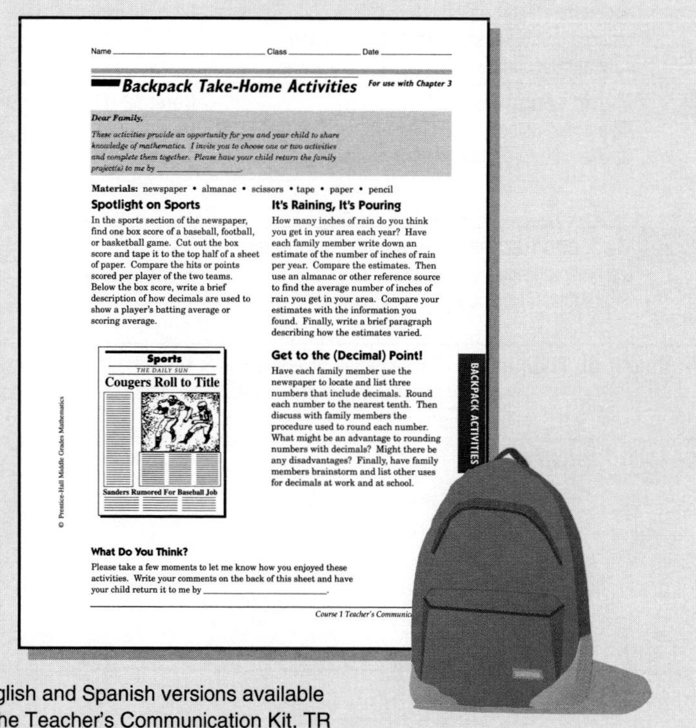

Name ______ Class ______ Date ______

Backpack Take-Home Activities *For use with Chapter 3*

Dear Family,

These activities provide an opportunity for you and your child to share knowledge of mathematics. I invite you to choose one or two activities and complete them together. Please have your child return the family project(s) to me by ______.

Materials: newspaper • almanac • scissors • tape • paper • pencil

Spotlight on Sports
In the sports section of the newspaper, find one box score of a baseball, football, or basketball game. Cut out the box score and tape it to the top half of a sheet of paper. Compare the hits or points scored per player of the two teams. Below the box score, write a brief description of how decimals are used to show a player's batting average or scoring average.

It's Raining, It's Pouring
How many inches of rain do you think you get in your area each year? Have each family member write down an estimate of the number of inches of rain per year. Compare the estimates. Then use an almanac or other reference source to find the average number of inches of rain you get in your area. Compare your estimates with the information you found. Finally, write a brief paragraph describing how the estimates varied.

Get to the (Decimal) Point!
Have each family member use the newspaper to locate and list three numbers that include decimals. Round each number to the nearest tenth. Then discuss with family members the procedure used to round each number. What might be an advantage to rounding numbers with decimals? Might there be any disadvantages? Finally, have family members brainstorm and list other uses for decimals at work and at school.

What Do You Think?
Please take a few moments to let me know how you enjoyed these activities. Write your comments on the back of this sheet and have your child return it to me by ______.

BACKPACK ACTIVITIES

Course 1 Teacher's Communica

English and Spanish versions available in the Teacher's Communication Kit, TR

Chapter 3 Planning Guide

Objectives	Assignment Options	Critical Thinking/ Problem Solving	Writing and Reading Math	Estimation Mental Math	Materials and Manipulatives
Investigation	This chapter-long project involves open-ended questioning and data collecting and provides an additional opportunity to assess students.	p. 94 p. 94	p. 94		
3-1 Exploring Tenths and Hundredths • Exploring decimals with models	**Core:** 9–17, 23, 24; MR all **Reinforce:** 18–22, 25, 26 **Enrich:** 27, 28	7a, 17, 27, 28; MR: 5 BI p. 96; MM p. 97	17, 27 p. 97; JL p. 96 JL Sheet	25, 26 pp. 96, 97	1, 2, 3e, 4, 5g, 9–12, 28a pp. 95, 97; WT p. 96; RT p. 97 TT 1, 11, 12, 43
3-2 Understanding Place Value of Decimals • Writing decimals in standard and expanded forms • Reading and writing decimals	**Core:** 19–28, 30–36, 43; MR all **Reinforce:** 29, 38–42 **Enrich:** 37	4; WT: 5; 29; MR: 7 p. 99; BI p. 99; MM p. 100	29 p. 100; JL p. 99 JL Sheet	WT: 5	1, 2, 19a p. 98; WT p. 98 TT 1, 43, 46
3-3 Comparing and Ordering Decimals • Comparing and ordering decimals • Graphing decimals on a number line	**Core:** 13–19, 22, 23, 28; MR all; CH all **Reinforce:** 21, 24, 25 **Enrich:** 20, 26, 27	6, 7a, 8, 20, 21; MR: 5 pp. 101, 104; BI p. 103	22b, 24–26 JL p. 103 JL Sheet		2, 5, 8, 12, 19 pp. 101, 104; WT p. 103; RT p. 103 TT 1, 12, 15, 43
3-4 Problem Solving: Solve a Simpler Problem • Solving problems by using a simpler problem	**Core:** 11, 14, 15; MR all **Reinforce:** 9, 10, 13 **Enrich:** 12	All; MR: 5 pp. 105–107; BI p. 106; MM p. 107	All JL p. 106 JL Sheet	4a, 11	p. 105 TT 44
3-5 Exploring Addition and Subtraction • Modeling addition and subtraction of decimals	**Core:** 12–17, 20–27; MR all **Reinforce:** 11, 18, 19, 29 **Enrich:** 28	6d–e, 10c, 28, 29; MR: 5 pp. 108, 110; BI p. 109; MM p. 110	4b, 8c, 29 pp. 108–110; JL p. 109 JL Sheet	8b, 10b	1, 3c, 4a, 5, 9, 10a, 11–15, 20–27, 29 pp. 108–110; WT p. 108; RT p. 110 TT 1, 11, 44
3-6 Rounding and Estimating • Rounding decimals • Estimating sums and differences with decimals	**Core:** 19–26, 35–37, 40; MR all **Reinforce:** 27, 29–34, 38, 39 **Enrich:** 28	2b, 3b, 4, 18, 28, 31–33, 36–40; MR: 5 pp. 111, 112; BI p. 113; MM p. 114	34 p. 114; JL p. 113 JL Sheet	5, 6; EX1, 2; 11–14, 16–18, 23–40; MR: 3, 4 pp. 111–114	2b, 3b p. 113; WT p. 112 TT 44
3-7 Adding and Subtracting Decimals • Adding and subtracting decimals	**Core:** 15–23, 25, 31; MR all **Reinforce:** 24, 26–30, 33–35 **Enrich:** 32, 36	2, 3, 7, 14, 26, 31–36; MR: 5 pp. 116, 117; BI p. 117; JL p. 118	36 p. 119; JL p. 118 JL Sheet	1; EX1–3; 8–22, 27–32 pp. 116–119; MM p. 119	EX2; 7–13, 15–22, 24, 25, 31, 32, 34 p. 116; RT p. 118 TT 19, 45
3-8 Technology: Keeping Track of Your Savings • Adding and subtracting decimals in bank accounts • Using a computer spreadsheet to add and subtract decimals	**Core:** 14; MR all **Reinforce:** 15 **Enrich:** 16	2, 5, 7–12, 15a, 16; MR: 5 pp. 120, 122; BI p. 121	WT: 13e; 16 JL p. 121 JL Sheet	MR: 3, 4 p. 120	WT: 13 p. 120; WT p. 121; RT pp. 121–122 TT 4, 5, 45, 47 Alt. Lesson
3-9 Metric Length • Measuring using metric units • Choosing appropriate units of measure	**Core:** 13–17, 21–24; MR all; CH: all **Reinforce:** 18–20, 27–30 **Enrich:** 25, 26	1a–b, 11a, 12, 19, 26; CH: 9; MR: 5 pp. 124, 127; BI p. 125	20, 25 pp. 126, 127; JL p. 125 JL Sheet	5d, 11, 12; CH: 1–4, 9 pp. 124–126; CH p. 127	3, 5, 6, 7a, 13–18 pp. 124–126; WT p. 125; RT p. 126 TT 45
3-10 Math and Parties: Times and Schedules • Determining and using elapsed time • Reading, using, and making schedules	**Core:** 8a, 9a, 10, 11; MR all **Reinforce:** 9b, 12–14 **Enrich:** 8b	1, 3–7, 8b, 9, 12; MR: 3–5 pp. 128, 129, 131; BI p. 130	6b p. 129; JL p. 130 JL Sheet	11, 14 p. 131; MM p. 131	p. 129 TT 45
Putting It All Together	These pages include a Follow-Up to the Investigation and other projects, which provide additional opportunities to assess the students.	pp. 134–135 pp. 134–135	pp. 134–135 p. 134		pp. 134–135
Chapter Resources		PS Practice, CW, CA, CR PS Practice p. 115; CW pp. 132–133; CA p. 136; CR p. 137	PS Practice, CW, CA p. 92B; PS Practice p. 115; CW pp. 132–133; CA p. 136		pp. 92A, 92B Backpack Activities, Manip. Kits TT 42

Student Edition (question numbers)
Teacher's Edition (page numbers)
Other Components

BI—What's the Big Idea? CA—Chapter Assessment CH—Checkpoint
CG—Computer Item Generator CR—Cumulative Review CW—Chapter Wrap Up
DM—Decision Making EP—Extra Practice EX—Example FD—Fact of the Day

Cooperative Learning Activities	Technology	Data Collection & Analysis	Interdisciplinary Connections	Applications	Assessment	Review	Strand Integration	NCTM Correlation*
p. 94		p. 94		music, consumer issues, advertising	p. 94			
p. 94		p. 94			p. 94			
WT				money		MR: All	Geometry, Number, Logic/Language	1, 2, 3, 4, 5, 6, 7, 8, 12, 13
p. 95; WT p. 96; RT p. 97	Hot Page™ 3-1	FD p. 96	p. 96	pp. 95, 96	pp. 95, 96	RT p. 97 Practice p. 24		
WT: 5; 18, 43		24, 37, 43	Science	money, astronomy, biology,		MR: All	Stat./Probability, Measurement, Number, Logic/Language	1, 2, 3, 4, 5, 6, 7, 8, 10, 13
pp. 99, 100; WT p. 98; RT p. 100	p. 98 Alt. Lesson	p. 100; FD p. 99	pp. 99, 100	Alt. Lesson	pp. 98–100 p .99	p. 98; RT p. 100 Practice p. 25		
WT		EX1, 2; 7, 22, 27	Social Studies, Science	astronomy, geography	CH: All	MR: All	Stat./Probability, Discrete Math, Number, Logic/Language	1, 2, 3, 4, 5, 6, 8, 10, 12
p. 104; WT p. 103; RT p. 103	pp. 103, 104	p. 104; FD p. 102	p. 104	pp. 101, 104	p. 102; CH p. 104 CH TR p. 38	p. 101; RT p. 103 Practice p. 26		
	9, 11, 12, 14–16		Science	money, biology, consumer issues,		MR: All	Algebra, Discrete Math, Number, Logic/Language	1, 2, 3, 4, 5, 6, 7, 8, 9, 13
RT p. 107		FD p. 106	pp. 106–107	pp. 105–107	p. 106	p. 105; RT p. 107 Practice p. 27		
WT						MR: All	Number, Logic/Language	1, 2, 3, 4, 5, 6, 7, 8
WT p. 108; RT p. 110	pp. 109, 110 Hot Page™ 3-5	FD p. 109		p. 110	p. 109	p. 108; RT p. 110 Practice p. 28		
WT		27, 29–32, 39	Science	nutrition, consumer issues, entertainment		MR: All	Stat./Probability, Measurement, Number, Logic/Language	1, 2, 3, 4, 5, 6, 7, 8, 10, 13
WT p. 112; RT p. 114	pp. 112, 113	WT p. 112; FD p. 112	p. 114	pp. 111, 113, 114	p. 113	p. 111; RT p. 114 Practice p. 29		
WT	EX2; 7–22, 24, 31, 32, 34	4, 5, 23–27, 34–36	Social Studies	sports, energy, consumer issues		MR: All	Stat./Probability, Measurement, Number, Logic/Language	1, 2, 3, 4, 5, 6, 7, 8, 9, 10, 13
p. 117; WT p. 117	p. 116	WT p. 117; FD p. 117	p. 118	pp. 117, 118 Alt. Lesson	p. 117	p. 116; RT p. 118 Practice p. 30		
WT: 13	All	6–8, 14a		banking		MR: All	Functions, Number, Logic/Language	1, 2, 3, 4, 5, 7, 8, 9, 13
WT p. 121; RT pp. 121–122 Alt. Lesson		FD p. 121		pp. 120, 121 Alt. Lesson	p. 120	p. 120; RT pp.121–122 Practice p. 31		
WT	MR: 5		Social Studies	pets	CH: All	MR: All	Measurement, Number, Logic/Language	1, 2, 3, 4, 5, 6, 7, 8, 12, 13
p. 125; WT p. 125; RT p. 126		p. 125; FD p. 125	pp. 124, 126	pp. 124, 126	p. 125; CH p. 127 CH TR p. 38	RT p. 126 Practice p. 32		
WT		10, 12–14		parties, schedules		MR: All	Measurement, Number, Logic/Language	1, 2, 3, 4, 5, 7, 8, 13
p. 128; WT p. 129	p. 129 Hot Page™ 3-10	p. 131; FD p. 129	p. 130	pp. 128–130; GE pp. 131–132	p. 129	p. 128; RT p. 130 Practice p. 33		
pp. 134–135		pp. 134–135		music, time, consumer issues,	pp. 134–135			
pp. 134–135		pp. 134–135			pp. 134–135			
IN, PT		Data File 3	English	stamps, baseball, money	IN, PT, CA	Practice, PS Practice, CW, CR, EP, SSG		
pp. 92–94; PT pp. 134–135 Backpack Activities	p. 92B Multimedia Math, CG	pp. 92–93	pp. 92F, 92–93 Interdisciplinary Units	pp. 92A, 92F, 92–93 Backpack Activities, Projects, Interdisciplinary Units	pp.92E, 94; pp. 132–136 CA, Span. CA, Self Assessment, Projects	CW pp. 132–133 Span. SSG, CR		

GE—Great Expectations IN—Investigation JL—Journal MM—Math Minutes
MR—Mixed Review PS—Problem Solving PT—Putting It All Together RT—Reteaching Activity
SSG—Student Study Guide TT—Teaching Transparency WT—Work Together

*For a description of the NCTM Standards, see page T15.

Assessment Options

Observation Checklist

In this chapter on adding and subtracting decimals, you have opportunities to observe your students do these tasks:

- ✓ model decimals using graph paper
- ✓ read the names of decimals aloud
- ✓ write decimals in standard and expanded form
- ✓ order decimals by size, and place them on a number line
- ✓ break complicated problems into simpler problems
- ✓ use technology and other methods to add and subtract decimals
- ✓ round decimals and estimate results of calculations
- ✓ choose appropriate metric units for measuring various objects
- ✓ use decimals to solve problems involving times and schedules

In every chapter, you are given opportunities to observe your students:

- ✓ work with a partner or in a group
- ✓ write about mathematics
- ✓ participate in discussions about mathematics
- ✓ collect and analyze data
- ✓ display positive attitudes about mathematics
- ✓ use measurement tools

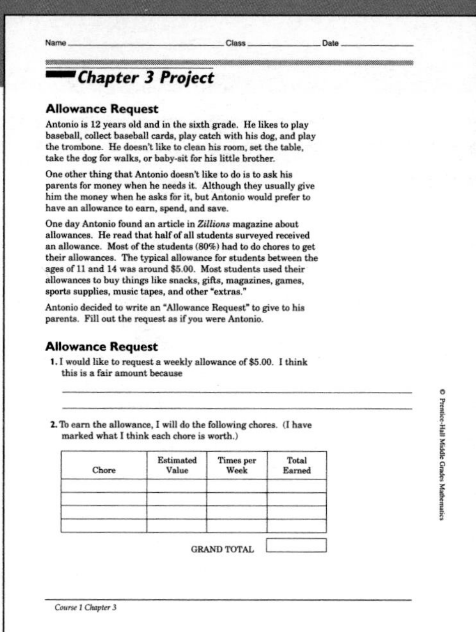

Name ____________ Class ________ Date ________

Chapter 3 Project

Allowance Request

Antonio is 12 years old and in the sixth grade. He likes to play baseball, collect baseball cards, play catch with his dog, and play the trombone. He doesn't like to clean his room, set the table, take the dog for walks, or baby-sit for his little brother.

One other thing that Antonio doesn't like to do is to ask his parents for money when he needs it. Although they usually give him the money when he asks for it, but Antonio would prefer to have an allowance to earn, spend, and save.

One day Antonio found an article in *Zillions* magazine about allowances. He read that half of all students surveyed received an allowance. Most of the students (80%) had to do chores to get their allowances. The typical allowance for students between the ages of 11 and 14 was around $5.00. Most students used their allowances to buy things like snacks, gifts, magazines, games, sports supplies, music tapes, and other "extras."

Antonio decided to write an "Allowance Request" to give to his parents. Fill out the request as if you were Antonio.

Allowance Request

1. I would like to request a weekly allowance of $5.00. I think this is a fair amount because

2. To earn the allowance, I will do the following chores. (I have marked what I think each chore is worth.)

Chore	Estimated Value	Times per Week	Total Earned

GRAND TOTAL

Course 1 Chapter 3

© Prentice-Hall Middle Grades Mathematics

Performance Based Project (with scoring rubric), Chapter Files, TR

Scoring Rubric

Exercise	Points	Explanation
1.	1	Reasonable justification given
	0	No response OR unreasonable response
2.	3	Reasonable values, correct total of at least $5.00
	2	Reasonable values, 1 computation error
	1	Chore list weak and has less than $5.00 total
	0	No response
3.	2	Reasonable amounts assigned to 2 or more categories, correct total of $5.00 or less
	1	Reasonable amounts assigned to 2 or more categories, computation error for total or total over $5.00
	0	No response
4.	2	Reasonable goal (total given); rate per week given, rate times the number of weeks equals goal amount
	1	Goal given, some data missing
	0	No response
5.	2	More than one reasonable idea given, such as: an allowance would help teach him the value of money, help him develop responsibility, or encourage his independence.
	1	One reasonable response is given
	0	No response OR illogical response
Excursion	5	Identification of the person asking for the increase; the amount of the increase; a justification; a plan for earning the increase; a plan for earning and spending the increase.
	4	Identification of the person asking for the increase; the amount of the increase; a justification; a plan for earning the increase; plans for earning or spending are weak or missing.
	3	Identification of the person asking for the increase; the amount of the increase; a justification; a plan for earning the increase; plans for earning and spending are weak or missing.
	2	Identification of the person asking for the increase; the amount of the increase; a justification; a plan for earning the increase; justification and plans for earning and spending are missing.
	1	Answer includes only the description of the increase.
	0	No response

Course 1 Chapter 3

© Prentice-Hall Middle Grades Mathematics

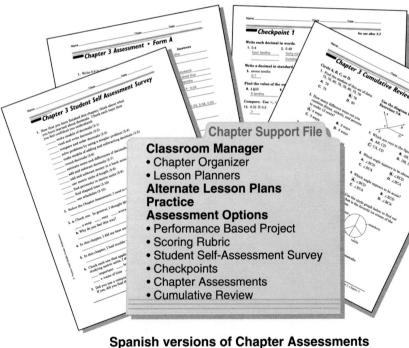

Chapter Support File

Classroom Manager
- Chapter Organizer
- Lesson Planners

Alternate Lesson Plans

Practice

Assessment Options
- Performance Based Project
- Scoring Rubric
- Student Self-Assessment Survey
- Checkpoints
- Chapter Assessments
- Cumulative Review

Spanish versions of Chapter Assessments available in Spanish Resources

Interdisciplinary Units
- Travel and Geography
- Space Exploration
- Sports
- Consumer Awareness
- The Great Outdoors

English & Spanish

These units include cross-curriculum connections and can be used at any time during the school year. See the Teacher's Guide for more information.

Working with Middle Grade Students

> *"Half of the working people in the United States are women, yet girls in school today generally do not believe computers will be useful to them, do not expect to like computing, and see the use of computers as a male-oriented activity."*
>
> —Kay Gilliland

Addressing a Variety of Learning Styles

The mathematical tasks in Chapter 3 involve various learning styles. Here are some examples.

- Visual learners draw decimal models for the values of coins (p. 98) and use charts for decimal place value (p. 96).
- Tactile learners use models for decimal problems (p. 110) and use computers (p. 121).
- Auditory learners discuss the process for finding a median (p. 102) and discuss various models for metric lengths (p. 124).
- Kinesthetic learners conduct a survey (p. 100) and find decimal numbers in newspapers (p. 112).

Alternate Lesson 3-8 addresses tactile learners by having them use manipulatives.

Cultural Connections

The number zero and the decimal point are important to the use of decimals. The zero was invented in Babylonia and in India in the second century B.C. (The Mayans also had a zero.) The decimal point was not invented until the sixteenth century.

Have students collect information about number systems used by the ancient Egyptians, Hebrews, Babylonians, Japanese, Chinese, Mayans, Yoruba, and others. Find out what these systems were like, and what sorts of calculations people did with them.

Team Teaching Suggestion

Work with a science teacher when introducing the metric section of this chapter. Plan a joint project using the metric unit as the focus (for example, measuring bacteria under the microscope).

Using Technology

Equitable use of computers in school is particularly important because research tells us that girls often have fewer opportunities than boys to use computers outside the classroom. Girls may attribute failure to their own inadequacy, and working with computers helps girls discover that making mistakes is essential to the problem-solving process. In general, females respond more positively to cooperative approaches than to competitive ones. It is particularly important, in the middle school years, that girls not be put in situations where they must compete with boys for hands-on experience on the computer. For this reason, you may choose to have technology groups or pairs be single sex rather than mixed.

Teaching Tip

Students of middle grades are generally interested in learning about money. While teaching about decimals, include the buying of articles that are important to middle school students (for example, clothes, shoes, cassettes, CDs, and food).

Bulletin Board

Ask students to bring in grocery tape receipts from home. Sending a class newsletter to inform parents of the ongoing project may be helpful. At the end of each week add up the grocery receipts for that week and record the total. Subtract and indicate whether the week's total is less than or more than the previous week's total. Have students try to predict whether the total will be more or less than the total from the week before.

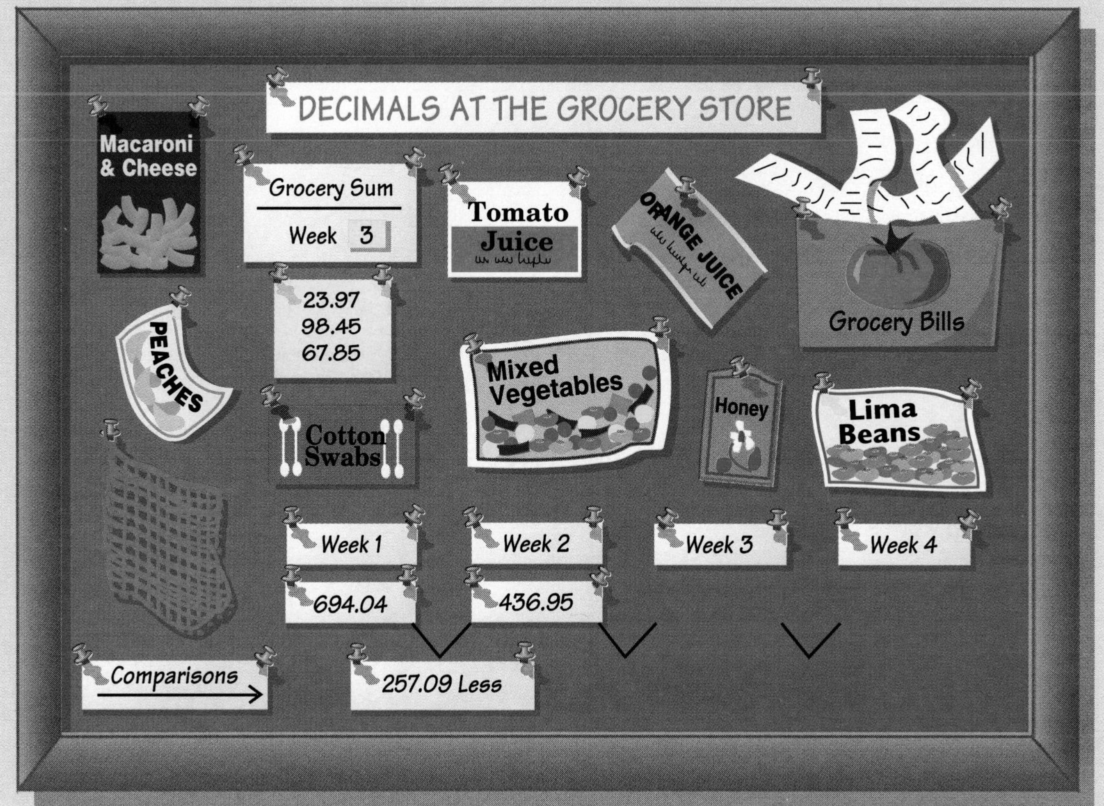

CHAPTER 3 Adding and Subtracting Decimals

Cultural Connections The Inca culture flourished from about 1400 to 1540 in areas of present-day Peru, Bolivia, Ecuador, Chile, and Argentina. The Incas kept careful records using the quipu (pronounced KEE poo), a collection of dyed cotton or wool cords. Knots were tied in the quipu to record numbers such as the census, important dates, and the output of the gold mines. The knots on the quipu used a base-ten number system.

Few sports in the United States are as deeply loved as baseball; over the years, it has woven its place in the country's cultural fabric. The country's shrine to this sport is the National Baseball Museum and Hall of Fame at Cooperstown, New York. Cooperstown was believed to have been the original site where baseball was first played, although this claim was later refuted. The Hall of Fame opened on June 12, 1939, and has been enlarged over time as its popularity has grown. Honus Wagner and Napoleon Lajoie were among the first players chosen to be enshrined and were present at the Hall's opening.

WORLD VIEW A one-penny stamp issued in 1856 by British Guiana (now Guyana, next to Venezuela in South America) is the rarest stamp in the world—only one of its kind is known to exist. The main language of Guyana is English. The name Guiana means "land surrounded by water," in an Indian language, perhaps Arawak.

Digging for Data Ask the students to use the table and other information on the data file to answer these questions:

- *Who printed the Eddie Plank card?*
  (American Tobacco Company)

Chapter 3 Contents

Data File Questions

pp. 114, 236

CHAPTER 3 Adding and Subtracting Decimals

Data File 3

STAMPS

The enlarged stamp shows the possible parts of a postage stamp. The next time you use a postage stamp or open a letter, see how many of the parts you can find.

Source: *Usborne Guide to Stamps and Stamp Collecting*

Margin / Borderline / Country of issue

JERSEY

"CALVADOS"

Centenary - Inauguration

G. DRUMMOND

Designer's name / Purpose of issue

This "stamp-on-stamp" was issued in 1950 to commemorate one hundred years of Spanish stamps. The small stamp in the upper left corner is a copy of the first Spanish stamp issued in 1850.

This 1980 stamp shows some bottles waiting to be picked up by a row boat near Ascension Island. This was the custom 300 years ago, because it was too dangerous for sailing ships to approach the rocky coast.

Source: *Stamps! A Young Collectors Guide*, Brenda Lewis

- *What is the value of the Honus Wagner card and why is it so rare?*
  ($250,000; Wagner, a nonsmoker, demanded that it be removed from circulation by the tobacco company.)

Group students into teams of four or five people. Ask each student to try to collect at least five stamps over a week's time. Encourage them to ask friends for used stamps and to find stamps from different countries. Then have each group prepare a display and a report that shows the stamps collected by the group and includes these items: the country of origin; a map showing the location of the country of origin; a brief comment about what is pictured on the stamp.

Journal Activity Ask students to read the objectives in What You Will Learn. Have them write a list of the decimals they see around them and use every day outside the classroom. Ask them to circle the items in their list that they understand well, and to put a question mark by those about which they would like to know more.

Interdisciplinary Connection [English] The theme of this Data File is Oldies But Goodies. Ask students what oldies but goodies they can think of in other areas. Have them recall favorite songs that they first heard over five years ago. Ask about children's stories or books they remember well. Discuss any literature they have read recently that was written over fifty years ago. You may want to have the class create a list on poster board of oldies but goodies in story and song. This can lead to a discussion of what has to be new to be valid (such as population statistics) and what has to be old to be valuable (antiques) and what can be good regardless of whether or not it is old (such as life skills, wisdom, movies and literature with universal themes).

WHAT YOU WILL LEARN

- how to use and apply decimal concepts
- how to estimate decimal sums and differences
- how to use technology to apply decimal concepts
- how to solve problems using a simpler problem

The world's smallest stamps were issued in Bolivia from 1863 to 1866. They measured 0.31 in. by 0.37 in.

Valuable Baseball Cards

Player's Name	Year(s) Issued	Publisher	Value ($)
Honus Wagner	1909-11	T206	250,000
Napoleon "Larry" Lajoie	1933	Goudey	25,000
Eddie Plank	1909-11	T206	25,000
Mickey Mantle	1951	Bowman	24,000
Robin Roberts*	1951	Topps	15,000
Eddie Stanky*	1951	Topps	12,500
Jim Konstanty*	1951	Topps	12,500
Sherry Magie	1909-11	T206	12,000
Ty Cobb	1911	T3	5,000
Babe Ruth	1933	Goudey	4,500

*All Star card
Note: Cards with the initial "T" refer to cards manufactured by the American Tobacco Company.

Sources: *Baseball Card Price Guide*, Dr. James Beckett; *U.S. News and World Report*

Baseball Cards

The most valuable baseball card is the 1909 Honus Wagner card printed by the American Tobacco Company. There are only six existing cards in excellent condition and about 40 of poorer quality. Few cards remain because Wagner, a nonsmoker, demanded that the American Tobacco Company remove his card from circulation.

Source: *U.S. News and World Report; The Saturday Evening Post*

Fact of the Day

Babe Ruth, perhaps the most famous baseball player of all, is known for his home runs as a batter. He began his career, however, as a pitcher. He could throw two baseballs at the same time so that they followed paths parallel to each other from his hand all the way to the catcher.

—*2201 Fascinating Facts*

93

INVESTIGATION

Memo

You may wish to bring samples of actual cassette/CD club or book club promotional materials to class. Ask students to discuss their music-buying habits:

- *How important are the latest releases to them?*
- *Where do they purchase their tapes or CDs?*
- *What factors enter their decisions to buy tapes?*

Mission

Suggest that groups brainstorm about all the possible costs associated with joining a music club or making purchases at a store. Ask students to include nonfinancial factors (convenience, musician, type of music). Compare student lists.

Additional Leads to Follow

- *What are the advantages and disadvantages of belonging to the Music Club?*
- *What are the advantages and disadvantages of purchasing music locally?*
- *Do you know anyone who belongs to a music club?*

Keeping a Project Notebook

Some suggestions for students' notebooks are:

- Find and keep examples of actual club membership offers, together with analysis of their advantages and disadvantages.
- Record sample club prices and actual local prices of popular tapes and CDs.
- List the dates and results of all discussions about the project.
- Include all calculations, together with explanations of how they were done.

Project Organizer

Related Exercises
p. 100
p. 104
p. 114
p. 131

Follow Up
p. 134

Teacher's Notes
pp. 94, 100, 104, 114, 130, 134

Community Resources
- manager of local tape/CD store

Materials and Manipulatives
- magazine or newspaper ads for music or book clubs

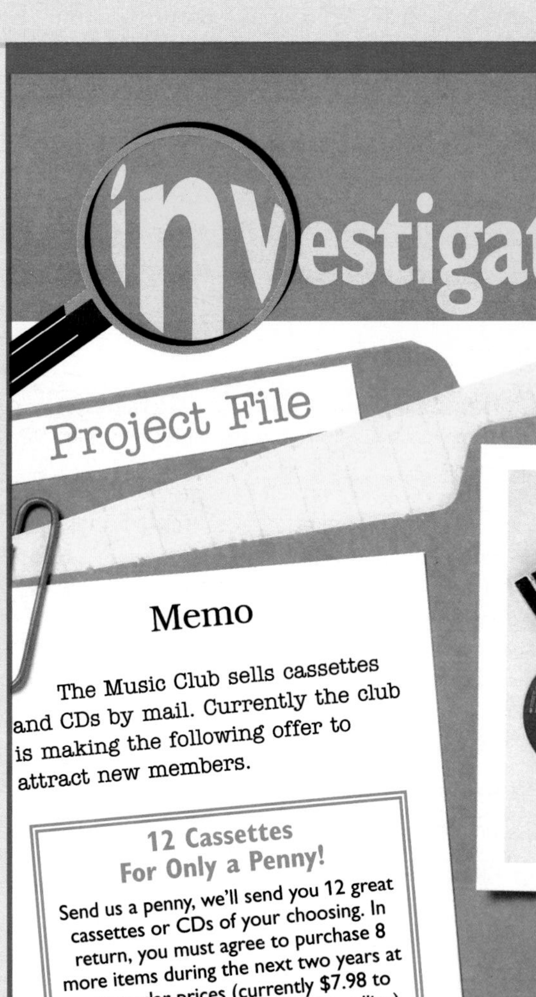

inVestigation

Project File

Memo

The Music Club sells cassettes and CDs by mail. Currently the club is making the following offer to attract new members.

12 Cassettes For Only a Penny!

Send us a penny, we'll send you 12 great cassettes or CDs of your choosing. In return, you must agree to purchase 8 more items during the next two years at our regular prices (currently $7.98 to $11.98, plus $1.79 shipping and handling).

Don't delay! Join today!

Mission: Would it be a good idea to join the Music Club? Or would you be better off buying your cassettes and CDs locally? Your answer should be based on financial considerations, convenience, and any other factors that you feel are important.

LEADS to FOLLOW

- ✓ How many cassettes or CDs are you likely to buy in the next two years?
- ✓ How much does the average cassette or CD cost in your town?
- ✓ How much will you spend to fulfill your obligation to the Music Club?

3-1

Connecting to Prior Knowledge

Ask students if they have ever taught a younger sibling or a friend how to do something, such as shoot a basketball or play checkers. Ask students if they gave only verbal instructions. Get students to reply with examples of gestures that they made, or demonstrations or models that they used. Ask students to decide if it is easier to perform an activity with only verbal instructions or with instructions and a model.

THINK AND DISCUSS

Question 3: Ask students what ten tenths of the cake would equal. **(1)**

VISUAL LEARNERS Have students compare their drawings with the models shown. Ask them if it makes a difference which way the strips go on the tenths' model. **(no)**

Question 5: Ask students what one hundred hundredths of the cake would equal. **(1)**

Error Alert! Students may have trouble reading decimals with zeros in the tenths' place. They may read a decimal such as 0.06 as six tenths and 0.01 as one tenth. ***Remediation*** Refer students to the textbook model. Point out that before any cuts are made there is one piece of cake. Point out that after ten pieces are cut each is one tenth of the original piece, or 0.1 of the whole. Students might find it helpful to think of the tenths' place as being one set of divisions of the whole and the hundredths' place as being the second set of divisions.

Ongoing Assessment Have students work in pairs. Give each partner a blank hundredths' model and the following instructions:

- *Each student shades two different parts of the model.*
- *Exchange models.*

What's Ahead

- Exploring decimals with models

WHAT YOU'LL NEED

✓ Graph paper

3-1 Exploring Tenths and Hundredths

THINK AND DISCUSS

Suppose you are in charge of cutting a huge square birthday cake. There are 100 people that must be served. How would you cut the cake so that each person receives an equal-sized piece?

1. Discussion To model the cake, draw a square on a piece of graph paper. How big will you draw the square?
   Answers may vary. The square will be 10 units by 10 units.
2. Cut the "cake" vertically into ten equal strips. On your model, draw a line for each cut. Check students' drawings.

Tenths' model

One strip is *one tenth* of the cake. You write one tenth as 0.1. Two strips is two tenths, or 0.2, of the cake.

3. a. How many strips is 0.8 of the cake? 8 strips
   b. How many tenths is 0.3 of the cake? 3 tenths
   c. How many strips is all of the cake? 10 strips
   d. Write a decimal that describes half the cake. 0.5
   e. Draw a model for nine tenths of the cake.
   Check students' drawings. See Sol. Key.
4. Now cut the "cake" horizontally so that each vertical strip is cut into 10 squares. On your model, draw a line for each cut. How many pieces of cake do you have?
   See Sol. Key. 100 pieces.

Hundredths' model

One piece is *one hundredth* of the cake. You write one hundredth as 0.01. Two pieces is two hundredths, or 0.02.

5. a. How many pieces is 0.07 of the cake? 7 pieces
   b. How many pieces is 0.43 of the cake? 43 pieces
   c. How many hundredths is 0.09 of the cake? 9 hundredths
   d. How many hundredths is 0.90 of the cake? 90 hundredths
   e. Write a decimal that describes half the cake. 0.50 or 0.5
   f. How many hundredths is one quarter of the cake? 25 hundredths
   g. Draw a model for 0.11 of the cake.
   Check students' drawings. See Sol. Key.

"The way to get things done is not to mind who gets the credit of doing them."
—Benjamin Jowett

Organizer

1. **Focus**
   Connecting to Prior Knowledge
2. **Teach**
   Think and Discuss
   Work Together
3. **Closure**
   Wrap Up

Vocabulary/Symbols
one tenth
one hundredth
equivalent

Materials and Manipulatives
- graph paper (for each student)

On Your Own Exercises 9–12, 28: graph paper

Student Resources
Extra Practice
Student Study Guide
Practice, TR Ch. 3, p. 24
Student Study Guide, Spanish Resources, TR

Teacher Resources
Teaching Transparencies 1, 11, 12, 43
Transparency Masters, TR p. 2
Lesson Planner, TR Ch. 3, p. 2

continues next page

- *Estimate and write the decimal number to show how much of your partner's region is shaded.*
- *Exchange the models again and discuss whether you both agree on each other's estimates and decimal numbers.*

Circulate among the students to check that they understand how to estimate and how to write decimals that represent their estimates.

WORK TOGETHER

Students may create their own models or use five 10 × 10 squares of graph paper and label the back of the squares with the type of coin represented and its decimal value.

ESL Some students will know a coin's value, but will not know the coin's name. Before the Work Together activity, show and name a penny, nickel, dime, and quarter. Write the names and values of the coins on the board. Have students practice saying the names.

Wrap Up

What's the Big Idea? Ask students: *How can you model tenths and hundredths?*

Journal Ask students if they can think of another model for tenths and hundredths. They may first need to analyze the cake model to determine what elements they will need to include. Encourage students to include a visual and a written explanation in their responses.

Connections Have a discussion about how tenths and hundredths are used. You may want to start with these examples:

- **Sports** (timing Olympic races, determining precise auto speed)
- **Science** (measuring earthquakes, or making accurate measurements of rock samples or dinosaur bones)
- **Meteorology** (measuring temperatures, and humidity)

Organizer, continued

Prentice Hall Technology
Multimedia Math
- Hot Page™ 3-1

Computer Item Generator
- 3-1

Fact of the Day

Alabama became the 22nd state of the United States on December 14, 1819. Its capital is Montgomery.

—Information Please Almanac

PH Multimedia Math Hot Page™ 3-1

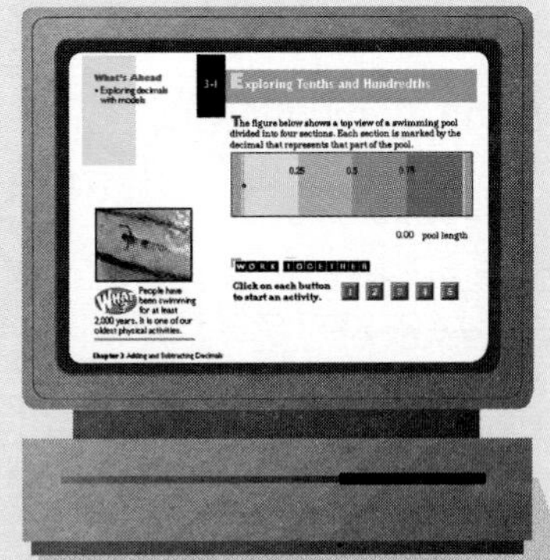

Assignment Options

Core: 9–17, 23, 24, MR all	
Reinforce: 18–22, 25, 26	**Enrich:** 27, 28

On October 18, 1989 a huge cake in the shape of the state of Alabama was made to celebrate the 100th birthday of the town of Fort Payne. The cake weighed 128,238.5 lb, including 16,209 lb of icing. 100-year-old resident Ed Henderson made the first cut.

Source: *Guinness Book of Records*

Two different models for half the cake are shown below.

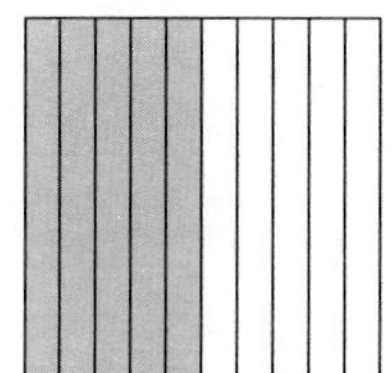

five tenths = 0.5

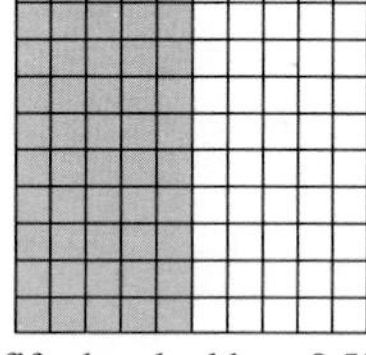

fifty hundredths = 0.50

6. Do the two models represent the same amount of cake? Yes.

Numbers that represent the same amount are **equivalent.** The decimals 0.5 and 0.50 are equivalent.

7. a. How many tenths describe the whole cake? How many hundredths describe the whole cake? Are the numbers equivalent? Why? 10 tenths; 100 hundredths; yes, they both describe the whole cake.

b. What whole number describes the whole cake? 1

8. How many hundredths is equivalent to seven tenths? 70 hundredths

WORK TOGETHER

- Work with a partner. Suppose you have a dime and a penny. Are these coins tenths or hundredths of a dollar? Draw models for one dollar, one dime, and one penny. Write a decimal number for the value of each coin. See left.
- Draw models for one nickel and one quarter. Write the decimal numbers for a nickel and a quarter. Check students' work. nickel - 0.05 quarter - 0.25

- dime; tenths
  penny; hundredths
  Check students' drawings.
  dime - 0.1
  penny - 0.01

Answers to Problems Unique to Spanish Edition
13. ocho centésimas
14. dos décimas
15. cincuenta y seis centésimas
16. treinta centésimas

ON YOUR OWN

Draw a model for each decimal. Check students' models. See Sol. Key.

9. 0.7 **10.** 0.36 **11.** three tenths **12.** four hundredths

Write each decimal in words. 13. eight hundredths

13. 0.08 **14.** 0.2 **15.** 0.56 **16.** 0.30

14. two tenths 15. fifty-six hundredths 16. thirty hundredths

Reteaching Activity

Have students make a tenths' model by drawing a square that contains ten strips. Students should number the strips from left to right: 1, 2, 3, and so on. Ask students to place a decimal point and a zero with each number that represents the value of the whole as measured from the left border of the square: 0.1, 0.2, 0.3, and so on. Ask students if the last number needs a zero to the left of the decimal. **(no)** Have students compare what they wrote for the last number and describe what it represents. **(1.0; the whole)** Have students divide these strips into 10 parts and label at least 3 of them as 0.01, 0.02, and so on. Ask students: *Just as 0.1 equals one tenth, what does 0.01 equal?* **(one hundredth)**

ON YOUR OWN

WRITING For Exercise 17, have students model 0.4 and compare their drawings to the one in the textbook.

ESTIMATION To help students reach an estimate for Exercises 25–26, suggest that they first determine if more or less than half of the region is shaded.

WRITING For Exercise 27, have students model the value of their new coins. Students should compare the value of the new coin with the value of the old ones. If they do not choose a coin whose value divides evenly into 100, then the model may have a different number of strips.

TACTILE AND VISUAL LEARNERS In Exercise 28, students may want to try various shapes, such as an L-shaped piece. Encourage students to create an actual model, and have them share the models with the class.

17. **Writing** Sue thinks this model shows 0.4. Paul thinks it shows 0.40. Do you agree with Sue? with Paul? Explain. Both; 0.4 = 0.40
18. How many tenths is equivalent to sixty hundredths? six tenths

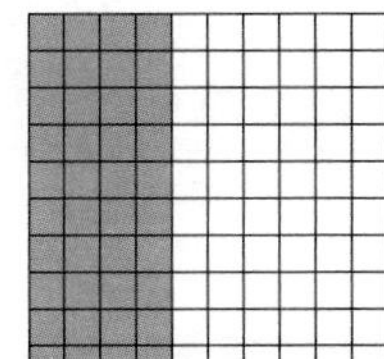

Write a decimal for the given words.

19. four tenths 0.4
20. ninety-six hundredths 0.96
21. six tenths 0.6
22. five hundredths 0.05

Write a decimal for each model.

23. 0.8

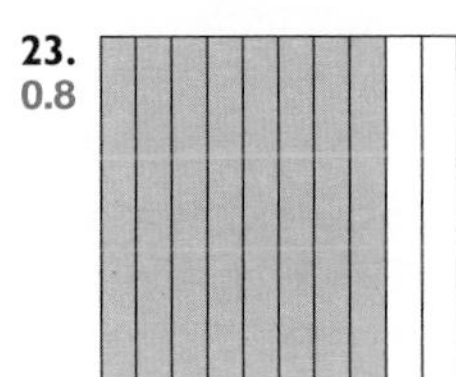

24. 0.42

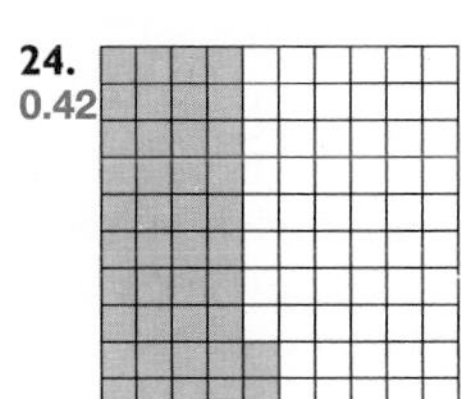

Estimation **Each square model represents 1. Write a decimal to estimate the amount shaded.** Accept reasonable estimates.

25. about 0.25

26. about 0.92

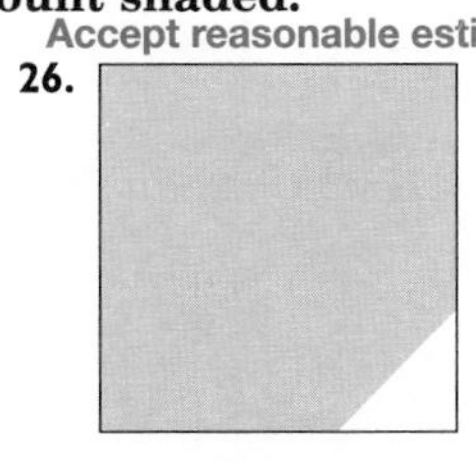

27. **Writing** Imagine you are asked to introduce a new coin into the money system. How much would your coin be worth? Explain your choice and give the coin a name. Answers may vary. Sample: My coin is a "slot" worth 75¢. I chose it because many vending machine items cost 75¢.

28. **Critical Thinking** Suppose you want to cut a square birthday cake into 10 equal pieces. A vertical strip will not fit on a party plate, so you decide on a different shape. Check students' models.
    a. Draw a model that shows how you will cut the cake.
    b. Write a decimal number to represent one piece of cake. 0.1

Mixed REVIEW

Find the mode.

1. 4, 5, 9, 2, 2, 3 2
2. 98, 95, 91, 98, 95, 95 95

Tell whether you could form a tessellation with each figure.

3. □ yes
4. ○ no

5. An ant can lift 50 times its own body weight. Suppose a student weighing 85 lb could do the same. How much could the student lift? 4,250 lb

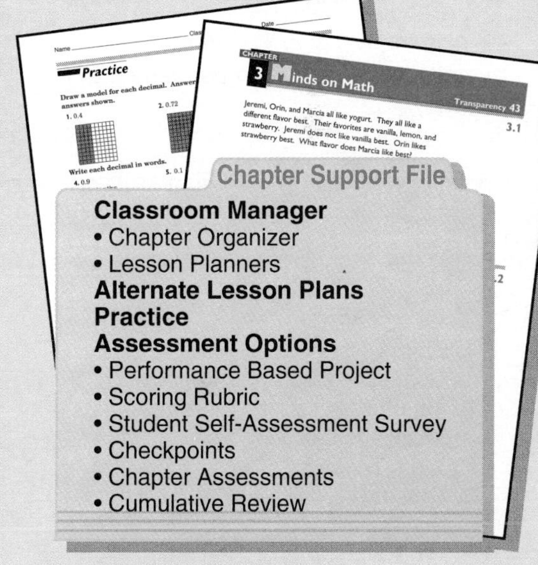

Classroom Manager
- Chapter Organizer
- Lesson Planners

Alternate Lesson Plans
Practice
Assessment Options
- Performance Based Project
- Scoring Rubric
- Student Self-Assessment Survey
- Checkpoints
- Chapter Assessments
- Cumulative Review

Minds on Math available in Teaching Transparencies

Math Minutes

Ask students to draw an 8-slice pizza. Have students determine how many slices will be left for a topping of their choice if they must put only mushrooms on $\frac{1}{4}$ of the slices and only sausages on $\frac{5}{8}$ of them.
1 slice

Materials for 3-2
- graph paper

3-2

Connecting to Prior Knowledge

Ask students to compare the value of one quarter and four nickels. **(The quarter is worth $.25, or twenty-five hundredths of a dollar, more than four nickels.)**

THINK AND DISCUSS

Error Alert! Students may confuse the decimal point in the chart with a position for a number. ***Remediation*** Point out that the decimal point separates the integer part of the number from the part that is less than one.

TECHNOLOGY OPTION For Questions 3 and 4, have students use a spreadsheet to take a number, such as 2,500, and repeatedly divide it by 10. Have students create a vertical place-value chart using the spreadsheet and record each answer, one below another.

Example

Caution students not to add extra "ands" between, for example, the hundredths' place and the tenths' place.

ESL Point out that decimal numbers always end in "th." Have students practice identifying and saying "tens" and "tenths," "hundreds" and "hundredths," and "thousands" and "thousandths."

Additional Example *Read 1.097.* **(one and ninety-seven thousandths)** *Read 26.26.* **(twenty-six and twenty-six hundredths)**

WORK TOGETHER

Have each pair of students use objects, such as pieces of paper or blocks, to model mills.

> *"Nothing will ever be attempted, if all possible objections must be first overcome."*
>
> —Dr. Johnson

Organizer

1. **Focus**
   Connecting to Prior Knowledge
2. **Teach**
   Think and Discuss
   Work Together
3. **Closure**
   Try These
   Wrap Up

Vocabulary/Symbols
expanded form
standard form
mill

Skills Reviewed in Context of Lesson
- modeling decimals

Materials and Manipulatives
- graph paper (for each student)

On Your Own Exercise 19: graph paper

Student Resources
Extra Practice
Student Study Guide
Practice, TR Ch. 3, p. 25
Student Study Guide, Spanish Resources, TR
Alternate Lesson, TR Ch. 3, pp. 12–15

continues next page

What's Ahead
- Writing decimals in standard and expanded forms
- Reading and writing decimals

WHAT YOU'LL NEED
✓ Graph paper

3-2 Understanding Place Value of Decimals

THINK AND DISCUSS

If you use a $1.00 bill to buy a snack for $.75, you get $.25 in change. To model $1.00, draw a hundredths' model.

1. For $.25 change, you might get 2 dimes and 5 pennies. Use graph paper to model this amount. Use tenths and hundredths to describe $.25. **Check students' models. See Sol. Key.**
2. Instead you might get 25 pennies! Use graph paper to model this amount. Use hundredths to describe $.25. **Check students' models. See Sol. Key.**

Two tenths and five hundredths is equivalent to twenty-five hundredths. They describe the same amount. One is expressed in *expanded form* and the other in *standard form.*

Expanded Form	=	**Standard Form**
0.2 + 0.05	=	0.25
two tenths and five hundredths		twenty-five hundredths

A number in **expanded form** shows the place and value of each digit. Look at 0.25 in the place value chart below.

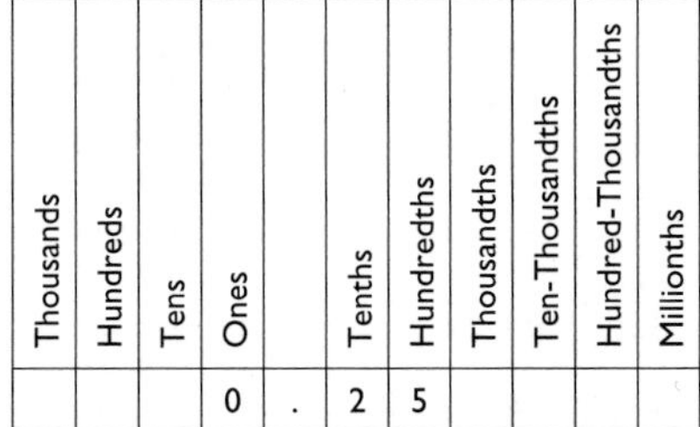

Thousands	Hundreds	Tens	Ones		Tenths	Hundredths	Thousandths	Ten-Thousandths	Hundred-Thousandths	Millionths
			0	.	2	5				

FLASHBACK
The prefix *dec-* means *ten.*

3. In the number 0.25, the digit 2 is in the tenths' place. Its value is two tenths, or 0.2. What is the value of the 5? **5 hundredths or 0.05**
4. **Discussion** As you move from left to right in the place value chart, how do the values increase or decrease? **Each place has a value of one tenth the place to its left.**

Ongoing Assessment
Monitor students' understanding by asking guiding questions such as:

- *How much would more than a thousand mills equal?* **(more than a dollar)**
- *To what value would you round less than five mills?* **(zero, less than a cent)**

After partners have finished this activity, you may wish to have volunteers share how they arrived at their answers.

TRY THESE

AUDITORY LEARNERS Have students work with partners. While one partner reads aloud the decimal number, the other partner writes the number in standard form.

Exercises 14 and 15: Have students discuss the difference an "and" makes.

Wrap Up

What's the Big Idea?
Ask students to explain how to express decimals in standard and expanded forms, and how to read and write decimals.

Journal
Ask students: *Do decimals in expanded and standard forms resemble words when they are abbreviated and written out? Explain the similarities and differences you see.*

Connections
Have a discussion about how decimals can be used. You may want to start with these examples:

- **Household** (determining interest on bank accounts, finding balance of accounts, estimating utility rates)
- **School** (finding grade average, using the Dewey decimal system in the library)
- **Business** (calculating interest on loans or increases in leases, using precise figures for figuring payroll)

When you use standard form to read or write a decimal number greater than or equal to 1, the word "and" tells you where to place the decimal point.

Example **a.** Read 1.897 as "one *and* eight hundred ninety-seven thousandths."

b. Write "three hundred twenty-seven and sixty-four hundredths" in standard form as 327.64.

WORK TOGETHER

Work with a partner. A *mill* is a very small unit of money that state governments sometimes use to calculate taxes. One mill is equivalent to one thousandth of a dollar ($.001). There is no coin to represent one mill.

5. **Money** Write each number of mills as part of a dollar. About how many cents is each number of mills worth?

a. 6 mills **b.** 207 mills **c.** 53 mills **d.** 328 mills

a. 0.006; $.01 b. 0.207; $.21 c. 0.053; $.05 d. 0.328; $.33

TRY THESE

What is the value of the digit 4 in each number?

6. 0.4 — 4 tenths **7.** 3.004 — 4 thousandths **8.** 1.285964 — 4 millionths **9.** 42.39 — 4 tens

Read each number in standard form. 10.–13. See Sol. Key.

10. 352.3 **11.** 6.025 **12.** 11.2859 **13.** 70.009

Write each number in standard form.

14. four hundred seventy-five thousandths 0.475

15. four hundred and seventy-five thousandths 400.075

16. two and six hundred five ten-thousandths 2.0605

17. 1 + 0.6 + 0.03 1.63

18. **Work in pairs** Write a decimal number in standard form. Have your partner write the number in expanded form. Repeat several times, then switch roles. Check students' work.

Gasoline prices are usually calculated to the *thousandths' place.* **How does this work when you pay for gasoline?**

The number of gallons is multiplied by the price. Then the total is rounded up to the nearest cent.

Organizer, continued

Teacher Resources

Teaching Transparencies 1, 43, 46
Transparency Masters, TR pp. 2, 5
Lesson Planner, TR Ch. 3, p. 3

Prentice Hall Technology

Multimedia Math
- Math Tools, Spreadsheet

Computer Item Generator
- 3-2

Other Available Technology

Excel; Works by Microsoft: Questions 3, 4 *(optional)*
1-2-3 by Lotus: Questions 3, 4 *(optional)*

Fact of the Day

The highest-value banknote in the United States is the $10,000 bill, which bears the likeness of Salmon P. Chase. There are only 345 of these bills left in circulation.

—GUINNESS BOOK OF RECORDS

Assignment Options

Core: 19–28, 30–36, 43 MR all	
Reinforce: 29, 38–42	**Enrich:** 37

Reteaching Activity Arrange students in groups of four. On the chalkboard, draw a place value chart extending to millionths. Have students use their own copies of the chart to build a decimal number by taking turns writing a digit from 0 to 9 in any column. For example, one student writes 0 in the tenths' column, another writes 6 in the hundredths' column, and so forth until the decimal number is complete. Then have students read the number aloud.

CHAPTER INVESTIGATION For Exercise 43, arrange students in groups of four. Each group constructs a survey of about three questions. Each student in the group checks the survey to make sure it is clear, inoffensive, and unbiased. Have the groups compare their results.

ON YOUR OWN

WRITING For Exercise 29, have students write the number in expanded form and give the value of each digit. Then they can compare the values of the digits.

RESEARCH Have students use the school library's encyclopedias for Exercise 37. Suggest that students look under the headings "Earth" or "Solar System."

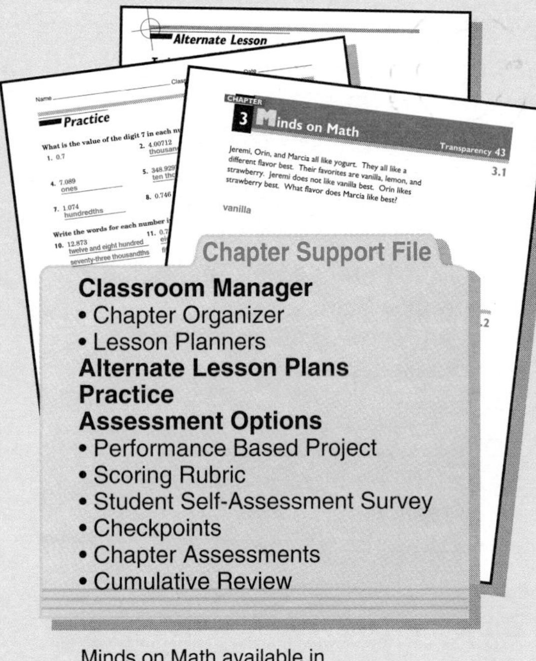

Minds on Math available in Teaching Transparencies

Ask students to order lunch for a field trip. If the order is 300 cheeseburgers and one out of every five must have only mustard on it, how many will have only mustard?
60 cheeseburgers

Materials for 3-3

- graph paper

Answers to Problems Unique to Spanish Edition
30. trescientos cuarenta y dos, y cinco décimas
31. nueve centésimas
32. cuarenta y uno, y doscientas ochenta y tres milésimas
33. una cienmilésima

Mixed REVIEW

Tell whether the angle is acute, obtuse, or right.

1. 67° acute 2. 45° acute

Write each decimal.

3. nine tenths 0.9
4. one and five hundredths 1.05

Write in words.

5. 0.35 6. 2.33 See below.
7. Evan saves two quarters and three nickels each day. At the end of 30 days how much has he saved? $19.50

5. thirty-five hundredths
6. two and thirty-three hundredths

Bees don't really buzz. They flap their wings up to 250 times per second, which makes the familiar buzzing sound.

ON YOUR OWN

19. a. Draw a model for twenty-two hundredths. Write this number in standard form. See Sol. Key. 0.22
  b. In your model, how many tenths and hundredths did you shade? Write the number in expanded form. 2 tenths; 2 hundredths; 0.2 + 0.02

Money **Write each amount as a decimal part of $1.00.**

20. 8 dimes $.80
21. 6 pennies $.06
22. 49 pennies $.49
23. 3 quarters $.75

24. Data File 2 (pp. 38–39) Suppose you plan to take two rides on the Beast at Kings Island Amusement Park. How much waiting time should you expect? 1 h 30 min

What is the value of the digit 5 in each number?

25. 0.5 5 tenths
26. 4.0052 5 thousandths
27. 3.004365 5 millionths
28. 530.34 5 hundred

29. Writing Explain how the value of the digit 2 changes in each place in the number 22.222. In each place the value of 2 is one tenth the value of the digit to the left.

Write the words for each number in standard form.

30. 342.5 See Sol. Key.
31. 0.09
32. 41.283
33. 0.00001

Write each number in expanded form. 36. 10 + 6 + 0.4

34. 4.133
35. 0.2498
36. sixteen and four tenths

34. 4 + 0.1 + 0.03 + 0.003
35. 0.2 + 0.04 + 0.009 + 0.0008

37. Research The Earth revolves around the sun in 365.24 days. Find out what happens to the extra 0.24 day. Every 4 years a day is added. These years are called Leap Years.

Biology **Write each measurement in standard form.**

38. A flea can jump six hundred forty-six thousandths feet. 0.646 ft
39. A goat makes four and seven tenths pints of milk a day. 4.7 pt
40. A tortoise moves seventeen hundredths miles per hour. 0.17 mi/h
41. It takes a housefly about one thousandth of a second to beat its wings once. 0.001 s
42. A bee's wing weighs five hundred-thousandths gram. 0.00005 g

43. Investigation (p. 94) Conduct a simple survey to see if people are interested in joining a music or book club. Check students' work.

3-3

Connecting to Prior Knowledge

Remind students of the importance of order when giving instructions. Ask students if they could bake a cake, for example, if their first instructions were to add the frosting and serve. Then have students review the process they use to compare and order whole numbers. Ask students: *Which is larger, 1,786 or 1,900?* **(1,900)** Have students explain their reasoning.

THINK AND DISCUSS

Question 1: Have students study the models and then answer the following question.

- *Why do the models show only the decimal portion of the populations?*
  (Since the whole number portions were equal, making a model for them would not help determine which number is greater.)

Error Alert! Students may have difficulty comparing two decimal numbers, such as 0.7 and 0.72 in Question 2. ***Remediation*** Remind them that 0.7 equals 0.70. Emphasize to students that they can always add zeros to the right of a decimal number without changing its value.

Example 1

Ask students why it is necessary to line up the decimal points when comparing decimals. **(If they are not lined up, the place values may be confused.)**

VISUAL LEARNERS Write 0.28 and 0.285 on the board. Tell students to line up the decimal points and then to compare the numbers. Ask the students to identify which places have digits that are the same. Ask students to compare the thousandths' place (adding a zero, if necessary). Since $5 > 0$, $0.285 > 0.280$.

DIVERSITY In Example 1, students who have poor fine motor skills may have difficulty aligning the decimal points. Provide students with graph paper. Direct students to select one vertical line

What's Ahead

- Comparing and ordering decimals
- Graphing decimals on a number line

WHAT YOU'LL NEED

✓ Graph paper

3-3 Comparing and Ordering Decimals

THINK AND DISCUSS

Buenos Aires, Argentina, has an estimated population of 12.23 million people. Rio de Janeiro, Brazil, has an estimated population of 12.79 million. To compare the two populations, first look at the whole number parts, 12 and 12. They are the same. Now look at the decimal parts, 0.23 and 0.79.

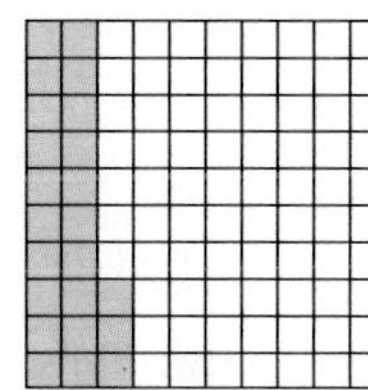

0.23

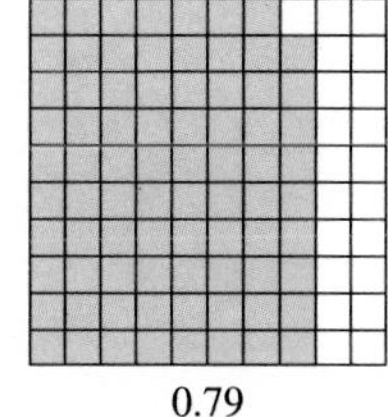

0.79

The model for 0.79 shows more shaded area than the model for 0.23. So 0.79 is greater than 0.23, and $12.79 > 12.23$.

1. **Social Studies** Which city has the greater estimated population, Buenos Aires or Rio de Janeiro? Rio de Janeiro
2. Draw models for 0.7 and 0.72. Which number is greater? Check students' drawings. See Solution Key; 0.72

You can graph decimals on a number line to compare them. Numbers are greater as you move to the right.

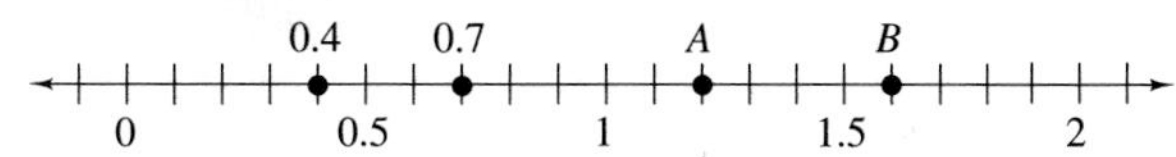

3. Use =, <, or > to make true statements.
   a. 0.7 ■ 0.4 >
   b. 0.4 ■ 0.7 <
4. a. What decimal numbers are at points A and B? 1.2 and 1.6
   b. Write two statements to compare the numbers. $1.2 < 1.6$; $1.6 > 1.2$

FLASHBACK

To compare numbers, use these symbols.

= is equal to
> is greater than
< is less than

" We have admire the other fellow more after we have tried to do his job. "

—La Rochefoucauld

Organizer

1. **Focus**
   Connecting to Prior Knowledge
2. **Teach**
   Think and Discuss
   Work Together
3. **Closure**
   Try These
   Wrap Up

Skills Reviewed in Context of Lesson

- comparing numbers

Materials and Manipulatives

- graph paper (for each student)

Student Resources

Extra Practice
Student Study Guide
Practice, TR Ch. 3, p. 26
Student Study Guide, Spanish Resources, TR
Checkpoint, TR Ch. 3, p. 38

Teacher Resources

Teaching Transparencies 1, 12, 15, 43
Transparency Masters, TR pp. 2, 20
Lesson Planner, TR Ch. 3, p. 4

continues next page

on which always to place the decimal point in a problem. Remind students that only one number goes in each box.

Additional Example *Which number is larger, 0.106 or 0.1039?* **(0.106)**

Example 2

Have students group the numbers in order by the tenths' digits. **(0.28 and 0.205 are greater than 0.018 and 0.013 and 0.035)** Have students then order the numbers in the second group by the hundredths' digits. **(0.035 is greater than 0.018 or 0.013)**

- *Is it necessary to compare the thousandths' digits of the numbers in the second group?* **(yes)**
- *What is the resulting order?* **(0.035, 0.018, and 0.013)**
- *Is it necessary to compare to the hundredths' or the thousandths' digits for the first group?* **(hundredths')**
- *What is the resulting order?* **(0.28, 0.205)**
- *Combine the groups in order from greatest to smallest.* **(0.28, 0.205, 0.035, 0.018, and 0.013)**

Additional Example Order the numbers 213, 211.987, 213.07, and 211.098 from greatest to least. **(213.07, 213, 211.987, 211.098)**

Ongoing Assessment Ask students to group the following decimal numbers in order by the value of the digit in the tenths' place: 0.03, 0.210, 0.2, 0.111, 0.006, 0.001, 0.196, 0.701. **(0.701; 0.210 and 0.2; 0.111 and 0.196; 0.03 and 0.006 and 0.001)** Then ask students to name the group of numbers that must be ordered by looking at the digits in the thousandths' place. **(the group beginning with 0.0)** Ask students to name the smallest number of the entire set. **(0.001)**

Organizer, continued

Prentice Hall Technology

Multimedia Math
- Math Tools, Text

Computer Item Generator
- 3-3

Other Available Technology

Word by Microsoft: Exercises 9–11, 13–18 *(optional)*

Fact of the Day

The Great Salt Lake is 75 miles (121 km) long and has a total area of 1,800 square miles (4,662 km^2).

—INFORMATION PLEASE ALMANAC

Salt per Liter in Major Bodies of Water

Body of Water	Salt per Liter
Black Sea	0.018 kg
Caspian Sea	0.013 kg
Dead Sea	0.28 kg
Great Salt Lake	0.205 kg
Ocean (average)	0.035 kg

Source: *Natural Wonders of the World*

5. Use a number line to compare 0.13 and 0.08. How many hundredths are between the two decimals? five hundredths

You can also use place value to compare decimal numbers. Start at the left and move right, one place at a time.

Example 1 Which body of salt water is saltier, the Dead Sea or the Great Salt Lake? Use the data at the left.

Compare 0.28 and 0.205. Line up decimal points.

0.28 / 0.205 — Compare digits in the ones' place. They are the same.

0.28 / 0.205 — Compare digits in the tenths' place. They are the same.

0.28 / 0.205 — Compare digits in the hundredths' place. $8 > 0$, so $0.28 > 0.205$.

The Dead Sea is saltier than the Great Salt Lake.

LOOK BACK How could you use a model or number line to solve the problem?

6. Discussion Explain how you can use place value to compare 1.679 and 1.697. The digits in the ones' and tenths' places are the same. Compare the digits in the hundredths' place: $7 < 9$, so $1.679 < 1.697$

The Dead Sea between the countries of Israel and Jordan is so salty a person would have no trouble floating in its waters.

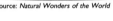

You compare decimals to place them in order.

Example 2 Order the bodies of water in the chart from most salty to least salty.

Compare 0.018, 0.013, 0.28, 0.205, and 0.035.

$0.280 > 0.205$ — Compare the numbers with the greatest tenths' digits.

$0.03 > 0.01$ — Look at the hundredths' digits in the remaining numbers.

$0.018 > 0.013$ — Compare the remaining numbers.

The bodies of water from most salty to least salty are Dead Sea, Great Salt Lake, Ocean, Black Sea, and Caspian Sea.

FLASHBACK

The median is the middle value in a set of ordered data.

7. a. Discussion What must you do first to find the median of the five values given in the chart?

b. Find the median of the five values. 0.035 kg

7. a. The values must be ordered, least to greatest or greatest to least.

WORK TOGETHER

VISUAL AND TACTILE LEARNERS If possible, groups should include one visual and one tactile learner. The visual learner may graph the numbers on a number line. The tactile learner may place the models in order from least to greatest. Have students in each group compare their strategies for each task.

TRY THESE

TECHNOLOGY OPTION For Exercises 9–11, have students use word processing software to enter each value in a column. Then use the decimal tab format to align the decimals by their decimal points. Have students compare the digits in each place to decide which decimal is greater.

Journal Ask students: *In Think and Discuss, you compared decimals using the populations of two large cities. Suppose you saw a CD advertised at three stores for the following prices: $14.98, $14.69, and $14.88. Would you use one of the three methods you learned to compare these prices? Explain your answer.*

Wrap Up

What's the Big Idea? Ask students to explain how to compare and order decimals, and to describe how to graph decimals on a number line.

Reteaching Activity Have students use pennies (or paper coins) to model 0.05, 0.07, 0.12, and 0.10. Then ask them to write these decimals in increasing order of value. Ask them to create their own amounts with the coins and then write the decimals to represent them.

WORK TOGETHER

Work in groups of three. Each member writes down any decimal number between 0 and 1 and draws a model for the number. Assign one of the tasks below to each member.

- Graph the numbers on a number line.
- Place the models in order from least to greatest.
- List the decimals in order from least to greatest.

Make sure your number line, models, and list agree! Repeat this activity until each member has done every task.
Check students' drawings. See Sol. Key.

TRY THESE

8. Discussion Draw models for 0.45 and 0.55. How do the models show which number is greater? Check students' drawings. See Sol. Key.

Compare. Use >, <, or =.

9. 0.06 ■ 0.60 <
10. 3.968 ■ 4.007 <
11. 0.05 ■ 0.050 =

12. Graph 6.4, 6.04, 7.6, 6.59, and 7.2 on a number line. Check students' drawings. See Sol. Key.

ON YOUR OWN

Compare. Use >, <, or =.

13. 0.58 ■ 0.578 >
14. 5.7 ■ 5.70 =
15. 0.37 ■ 0.3651 >
16. 8.009 ■ 8.079 <
17. 6.6 ■ 6.2 >
18. 49.5 ■ 49.05 >

19. Graph 0.49, 0.34, 0.4, 0.3, and 0.38 on a number line. Check students' drawings. See Sol. Key.

20. **Choose A, B, C, or D.** Decimals x, y, and z are graphed on a number line. Read statements I–IV. Which two statements give exactly the same information? C

I. $y < z$ and $z < x$ II. y is less than x and z
III. $y < x$ and $x < z$ IV. $y < z$ and $y < x$

A. I and II **B.** II and III **C.** II and IV **D.** III and IV

21. Critical Thinking Are there only 9 decimals between 0.4 and 0.5? Explain your reasoning. No, the number of decimals between 0.4 and 0.5 is unlimited. Other decimal places can be added to 0.4 such as thousandths, ten-thousandths, etc.

Mixed REVIEW

What angle measure must be added to the angle given to make a right angle?

1. 22° 68° 2. 59° 31°

Find the value of the digit 3 in each number.

3. 108.39 3 tenths 4. 38.22 3 tens

5. A large paving stone weighs 5 times as much as a small brick. Together they weigh 30 lb. What is the weight of the paving stone? 25 lb

Assignment Options

Core: 13–19, 22, 23, 28, MR all, CH all	
Reinforce: 21, 24, 25	**Enrich:** 20, 26, 27

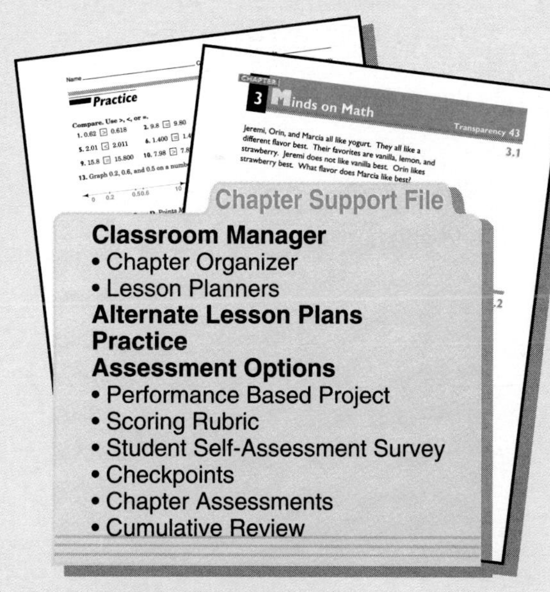

Minds on Math available in Teaching Transparencies

Connections Have a discussion about how comparing and ordering decimal numbers is used. You may want to start with these examples:

- **Sports** (determining league batting title winner, ranking teams by winning percent)
- **Meteorology** (comparing snowfall to averages of other years, establishing rainfall trends for a specific locale)
- **Business** (comparing wages, deciding on a loan or lease plan)

TECHNOLOGY OPTION For Exercises 13–18, have students use word processing software to enter each value in a column. Then use the decimal tab format to align the decimals by their decimal points. Have students compare the digits in each place to decide which decimal is greater.

CRITICAL THINKING For Exercise 21, have students support their answers with a number line representing the range. Challenge students to name and label more than nine decimals.

RESEARCH For Exercise 27, students will be able to find the term *light-year* in a dictionary from the school's library. Remind students that a light-year measures distance, not time. Students interested in the origins of the term should look under "Astronomy" in an encyclopedia.

CHAPTER INVESTIGATION For Exercise 28, have students brainstorm list entries in groups of four. Ask students to think of short-term consequences as well as long-term consequences. Have students consider their own personal priorities when ordering their lists.

ESL **Exercises 12–14:** Students may need to read each number aloud to see the differences.

Math Minutes

Give students the following recipe for a health yogurt shake and ask them to rewrite the quantities in lowest terms:

$\frac{9}{12}$ cup of lowfat milk $\frac{3}{4}$

$\frac{7}{14}$ cup of lowfat plain yogurt $\frac{1}{2}$

$\frac{4}{8}$ cup of pineapple $\frac{1}{2}$

$\frac{2}{8}$ tsp of cinnamon $\frac{1}{4}$

$\frac{20}{32}$ cup of ice $\frac{5}{8}$

Blend and serve.

Answers to Problems Unique to Spanish Edition
1. nueve décimas
2. una centésima
3. setenta y tres centésimas
4. sesenta centésimas

104

Light-Years Away

The brightest star in the sky is Sirius, which is about 8.7 light-years from Earth. The stars Alpha Centauri A and B are each about 4.37 light-years from Earth. Proxima Centauri is about 4.28 light-years away. Other star neighbors are 61 Cygni B, about 11.09 light-years away, and Procyon B, about 11.4 light-years away.

If you could drive to Alpha Centauri at 55 mi/h, the trip would take about 52 million years!

22. Data File 1 (pp. 2–3) a. Sunday, Monday, Tuesday, Thursday, Wednesday, Saturday, Friday

a. List the days of the week in order from most popular to least popular for watching prime-time TV.

b. Writing How does the bar graph model each number? Bar heights show decimals that represent the number of viewers.

23. What decimal numbers do points A, B, and C represent? 0.4; 0.8; 1.1

(Number line with points A, B, C; labels 0.1, 0.5, 1.0)

Astronomy **Read the article at the left. Use the information in Exercises 24–26.**

24. Which star is farthest from Earth? Which is closest to Earth? Procyon B; Proxima Centauri

25. Write the distances from Earth of the six stars in order from least to greatest. 4.28, 4.37, 8.7, 11.09, 11.4

26. Use <, >, and = to write three statements about the distances of any of these stars from Earth. Sample: Distance of Sirius from Earth < distance of Cygni B from Earth.

27. Research Look up the meaning of light-year. Why do you think astronomers use this measure? See left.

28. Investigation (p. 94) List the advantages and disadvantages of belonging to a music or book club. Order the entries from most important to least important. Answers may vary. Sample: Advantages: 12 tapes for a penny, shop at home convenience. Disadvantages: receiving unwanted tapes, required to buy more tapes, tend to buy more than you want.

27. Light-year is the distance light travels in one year; approx. 6 trillion miles. This unit enables astronomers to measure vast distances with smaller, more understandable numbers.

CHECKPOINT

Write each decimal in words.

1. 0.9 **2.** 0.01 **3.** 0.73 **4.** 0.60

1. nine tenths 2. one hundredth 3. seventy-three hundredths 4. sixty hundredths

Write a decimal in standard form.

5. three tenths 0.3 **6.** two hundredths 0.02 **7.** 0.9 + 0.02 0.92

Find the value of the underlined digit.

8. 5.68 **9.** 0.870 **10.** 8.005 **11.** 4.203

8. 6 tenths 9. seven hundredths 10. eight ones 11. three thousandths

Compare. Use >, <, or =.

12. 0.2 ■ 0.29 < **13.** 32.07 ■ 32.070 = **14.** 1.8 ■ 1.08 >

3-4

Connecting to Prior Knowledge

Tell students to pretend that they are in charge of organizing a birthday dinner for a friend. They are expecting twenty guests. Ask students:

- *How could you prepare for the party by dividing this complicated task into simpler components?*
  (Students might mention some basic steps such as sending invitations, preparing enough food, providing the necessary plates and utensils, finding a suitably sized table and room, and so on.)
- *What are some other complicated tasks or problems that can be performed or solved in simpler steps?*
  (Responses will vary, but could include tasks such as planning a large Thanksgiving dinner, deciding upon an in-depth research project, or planning a vacation.)

DIVERSITY While many students are familiar with and may even have sizable collections of computer and video games, you may have students who have had little or no experience with them. If this is possible, consider explaining the Treacherous Tunnel game as though it were a board game.

Video games often include several choices or paths that the player needs to make a decision about. Encourage volunteers to explain how they make their decisions, and if their decisions tend to change as they become more proficient at the game.

TACTILE LEARNERS For Question 4, provide students with chips. Have students arrange chips in stacks of 2, 4, 6, 8, 10, 12, 14, 16, 18, 20. Then have students physically combine pairs of numbers.

Additional Problem *Carlos drives a truck an average of 35 h/wk at an average speed of 30 mi/h. He has to change the oil in the truck approximately every 6,000 mi. About how often, in weeks, does Carlos change the oil in his truck?* **(about every 6 weeks)**

PROBLEM SOLVING

3-4 Solve a Simpler Problem

What's Ahead

- Solving problems by using a simpler problem

When solving a problem, you may find it helpful to solve a similar, simpler problem first.

Imagine you are playing the video game Treacherous Tunnel. You have two choices for entering the next level of the game. You have played before and don't want to use Choice 1, because it takes too long. Your goal is to use Choice 2 and follow the correct path within the time limit.

Treacherous Tunnel

Choose a path. Travel Time: 1 min

Choice 1 This path has diamonds in bunches of 2, 3, 4, and so on, to 100. You must collect all even-numbered bunches. The sum of the bunches instantly appears with each bunch you collect. If you miss any, or if you collect odd-numbered bunches, the game ends.

Choice 2 A three-headed creature guards the path. One of the numbers below is the total number of diamonds you can collect in Choice 1. If you select the wrong number, the creature will not let you pass, and the game ends.

3,129 5,050 4,201 2,550 1,201

READ

Read and understand the given information. Summarize the problem.

Think about the information you have and what you need to find.

1. Read Choices 1 and 2 carefully. What is your goal? **Select the sum of the even-numbered bunches.**
2. What numbers will you add to find the number you should select in Choice 2? **The even numbers from 2 to 100 will be added.**
3. What numbers can you eliminate? Why? **The odd numbers 3,129, 4,201, and 1,201. The sum of the even numbers is an even number.**

"Those who are quite satisfied sit still and do nothing; those who are not quite satisfied are the sole benefactors of the world."

—WALTER LANDOR

Organizer

1. **Focus**
   Connecting to Prior Knowledge
2. **Teach**
3. **Closure**
   Try These
   Wrap Up

Skills Reviewed in Context of Lesson

- adding whole numbers

Student Resources

Extra Practice
Student Study Guide
Practice, TR Ch. 3, p. 27
Student Study Guide, Spanish Resources, TR

Teacher Resources

Teaching Transparency 44
Lesson Planner, TR Ch. 3, p. 5

Prentice Hall Technology

Computer Item Generator

- 3-4

TRY THESE

Exercises 7–8: Have students check their answers with calculators.

Error Alert! Students may find an incorrect number of pairs of whole numbers for Exercise 8. ***Remediation*** Help students realize that there are twice as many pairs of numbers for this problem as there were in Question 5.

Ongoing Assessment Have students write a paragraph explaining how they would solve Exercise 7 if the light had changed every 15 seconds rather than every 30 seconds. Have volunteers share their paragraphs with the class. **(One possible answer is to first find out how many times the traffic light changes in 1 minute, and then in 1 hour. It changes 4 times in a minute and 240 times in an hour. In a 365-day year of 24-hour days, the light will change 2,102,400 times.)**

Wrap Up

What's the Big Idea? Ask students to explain how a complicated problem may be solved by solving a simpler problem.

Journal Ask students to write about an actual problem or complicated task they have encountered. Have students determine if the problem or task could have been divided into simpler steps. Students should write about how they solved the problem and whether they could have approached it differently.

Connections Have a discussion about how the strategy of solving a simpler problem is used. You may want to start with these examples:

- **Science** (performing controlled one-variable experiments, using laboratory models or small-scale tests)

Fact of the Day

Before the 1984 Summer Olympics in Los Angeles, 3,200 computer-linked sensors were installed in the intersections at 800 traffic signals in the city's central, downtown area. A similar system in New York City will be installed in the mid-1990s.

—ACADEMIC AMERICAN ENCYCLOPEDIA

Assignment Options

Core: 11, 14, 15, MR all	
Reinforce: 9, 10, 13	Enrich: 12

PLAN
Decide on a strategy to solve the problem.

One strategy for finding the sum of all even numbers from 2 to 100 is to solve a simpler problem first. Start with all even numbers from 2 to 20: 2, 4, 6, 8, 10, 12, 14, 16, 18, 20. Look for shortcuts for finding this sum.

SOLVE
Try out the strategy.

4. Try adding pairs of numbers.

2 4 6 8 10 12 14 16 18 20

2 + 20

a. Continue to add pairs. What sum do you get each time? 22
b. How many even numbers did you start with? 10
c. How many pairs do you have? 5
d. How can you use the number of pairs to find the sum? Multiply the number of pairs by the sum of a pair.

5. Look at the original problem and use the same procedure.
a. What are the first and last numbers you will add? What is the sum of these two numbers? 2 and 100; 102
b. There are 50 even numbers from 2 to 100. How many pairs can you make? 25
c. Show with examples that each pair has the same sum. See left.
d. What is the sum of all the even numbers from 2 to 100? This is the number you will select in the video game. 2,550

5c. Answers may vary. Sample: 6 + 96 = 102, 10 + 92 = 102, 14 + 88 = 102.

LOOK BACK
Think about how you solved this problem.

6. a. Discussion Explain how solving a simpler problem helped you find the answer to the original problem. See left.
b. Discussion Is this strategy better than finding the sum by hand or with a calculator? Why or why not? Answers may vary. Sample: yes, it takes less time and entry errors on the calculator are avoided.

6a. Answers may vary. Sample: The simpler problem showed a pattern.
7.b. 1,051,200 times a year (1,054,080 times a leap year) 2 changes per min × 60 min/h × 24 h/da × 365(366) da/y

TRY THESE

Solve by using a simpler problem. 7.a. 2 times; 120 times

7. When Ben's bakery opened, a traffic light was installed at the corner. The traffic light changes every 30 s. The bakery has been opened for 1 y. How many times has the traffic light changed since the bakery opened?
a. Break the problem into simpler problems. How many times did the light change in 1 min? in 1 h?
b. Solve the problem and explain your solution.

- **Language Arts** (examining the structure of a sentence by breaking it into parts, using specific words or phrases to determine the tone or purpose of a passage, inferring the meaning of a word by its context)
- **Business** (dividing a complicated procedure into tasks, as with an assembly line)

Reteaching Activity Have students discuss this problem: *You must order school supplies, including textbooks, notebooks, pencils, and paper, for all the students in your class. How would you go about compiling this order?*

Help students realize that if they solve this problem for one student first, they can then easily determine how much they will need for the class.

ON YOUR OWN

ESL **ESL** Students may need assistance on some unfamiliar words, or word meanings, such as *plasma* in Exercise 11 and *flat* in Exercise 13. Ask volunteers to explain the meaning of these words.

CONNECTION TO PROPORTIONS Exercise 11 previews proportions by giving students a known ratio of blood to plasma and having them complete an equivalent ratio for a complete adult blood system.

CONNECTION TO BIOLOGY Exercises 11 and 12 have students use a problem solving strategy to solve problems involving biological data.

CONNECTION TO ECONOMICS Exercises 13 and 15 have students use a problem solving strategy to determine which is the better buy.

8. Find the sum of all whole numbers from 1 to 100.
   a. What smaller set of numbers could you start with? a. Answers may vary. Sample: 1 to 10
   b. How will you make pairs? Order the numbers from 1 to 100. Add the least and greatest numbers.
   c. Solve the problem and explain your solution. Multiply the sum of each pair, 101, by 50 pairs. $101 \times 50 = 5{,}050$

ON YOUR OWN

Use any strategy to solve. Show your work.

9. A line of 1,500 people is waiting to see a museum exhibit. Every 20 min a guard allows 55 people to enter. The exhibit is open for 8 h. Will all 1,500 people get in? No; 1,320 people will get in
10. The International Club serves Chinese, Mexican, German, and Lebanese food. Chris serves German or Lebanese food. Vincent does not serve Chinese food. Louis serves German food. Carla does not serve Mexican or Lebanese food. Each person serves only one kind of food. Who serves each food? Chris—Lebanese, Vincent—Mexican, Louis—German, Carla—Chinese
11. Biology For every quart of blood in your body, you have about 19 oz of plasma. An average adult has about 5 qt of blood. About how many quarts are plasma? About 2.97 qt
12. Biology A baby's heart beats about 120 times per minute. How many times does a baby's heart beat in a year? 63,072,000 beats a year (63,244,800 beats a leap year)
13. Consumer Issues A 3-pack of flowering plants costs $1.59. A flat of the plants costs $11.59. There are 24 plants in a flat. Suppose you want to buy 30 plants. What is the least amount of money you could spend? $14.77: Compare 10 3-packs for $15.90 or a flat plus 2 3-pks, $11.59 + $3.18 = $14.77
14. Ted's car averages 420 mi on 14 gal of gas. How many gallons will the car use if Ted drives 1,080 mi? 36 gal; $420 \div 14 = 30$, $1{,}080 \div 30 = 36$
15. Consumer Issues Tickets to the circus are $6.50 per person. The cost of a ticket decreases to $5.00 per person for groups of ten or more people.
    a. How much do you save over the regular ticket price if you buy 18 tickets? $27
    b. How much would your class save on a trip to the circus? Answers may vary.

Mixed REVIEW

What angle measure must be added to the angles given to form a straight angle?

1. 42°, 60° 78°
2. 90°, 65° 25°

Compare. Use >, <, or =.

3. 0.39 ■ 0.399 <
4. 1.2 ■ 1.02 >
5. A train makes 5 stops. At the first stop there are 3 passengers. At the second 9. At the third 27. Continue the pattern to find the number of passengers at the fifth stop. 243 passengers

In the 1940s Dr. Charles Drew supervised the "Blood for Britain" project. This project preserved and stored blood plasma for transfusions on the battlefield during World War II.

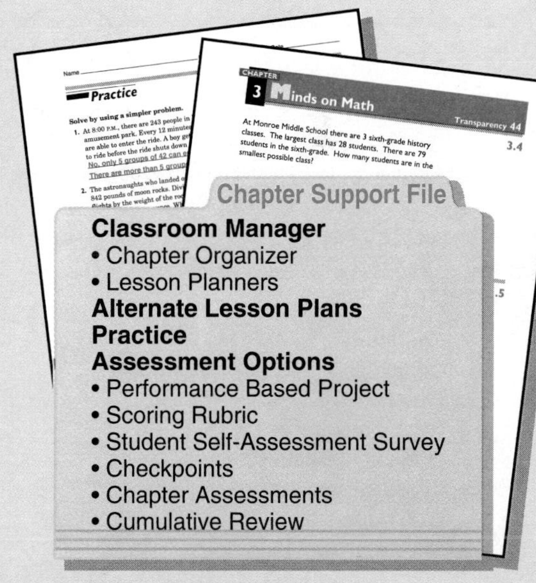

Minds on Math available in Teaching Transparencies

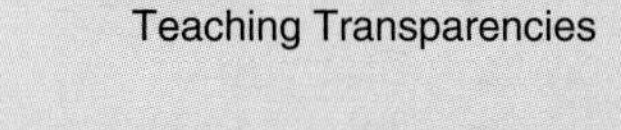

Math Minutes

What fraction of 2 dollars is represented by the total of these coins: 3 quarters, 2 dimes, and 2 nickels? $\frac{21}{40}$

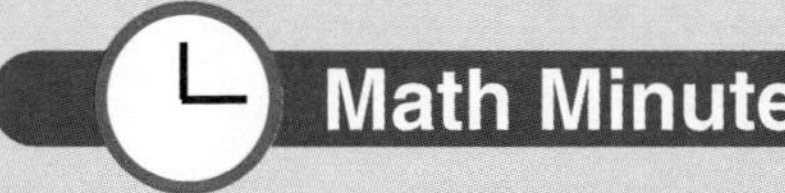

Materials for 3-5

- graph paper

3-5

Connecting to Prior Knowledge

Ask students to describe the decimal models they used in the previous lessons. Then have them consider how these models might help them to add and subtract decimals. Then ask them to answer the following questions:

- *How is the expanded form of a decimal like the addition of two or more decimals?*
  (The expanded form does involve the addition of decimals, but they are decimals with only one non-zero digit, each with a different place value.)
- *How is the comparison of two decimals like the subtraction of one decimal from another?*
  (When comparing, one looks at the difference between two decimals to name the greater or lesser decimal. When subtracting, one actually finds the difference between the two decimals.)

WORK TOGETHER

Remind each pair of students that they must perform four steps for this activity: make a model of 0.63; write 0.63 in expanded form; describe in words 0.63 in two ways; and draw models for the sum 0.6 + 0.03 = 0.63.

THINK AND DISCUSS

Questions 1–10: If decimal squares are not available, have students use copies of tenths' and hundredths' squares or sections of graph paper to sketch the models.

WRITING For Question 4b, students should describe, step by step, the process involved in adding the decimals. Have students write their lists in the form of a set of instructions.

AUDITORY LEARNERS For Questions 5–7, have one student read the problem aloud while other students listen and write the

"Tact is the ability to make advice agreeable."

—ANONYMOUS

Organizer

1. **Focus**
   Connecting to Prior Knowledge
2. **Teach**
   Work Together
   Think and Discuss
3. **Closure**
   Wrap Up

Skills Reviewed in Context of Lesson

- place value for decimals

Materials and Manipulatives

- graph paper (for each student)

On Your Own Exercises 11–15, 20–27, 29: graph paper

Student Resources

Extra Practice
Student Study Guide
Practice, TR Ch. 3, p. 28
Student Study Guide, Spanish Resources, TR

Teacher Resources

Teaching Transparencies 1, 11, 44
Transparency Masters, TR p. 20
Lesson Planner, TR Ch. 3, p. 6

continues next page

What's Ahead

- Modeling addition and subtraction of decimals

3-5 Exploring Addition and Subtraction

WHAT YOU'LL NEED

✓ Graph paper

WORK TOGETHER

Work in pairs. **Check students' drawings. See Sol. Key.**

- Draw a model for 0.63 while your partner writes 0.63 in expanded form. **0.6 + 0.03 = 0.63**
- Agree on two ways of describing 0.63 in words. **See below.**
- Draw models for the sum 0.6 + 0.03 = 0.63.
  Check students' drawings. See Sol. Key.

Sixty-three hundredths or six tenths plus three hundredths

THINK AND DISCUSS

You can use models to find any sum. The models below show 0.4 + 0.3 = 0.7.

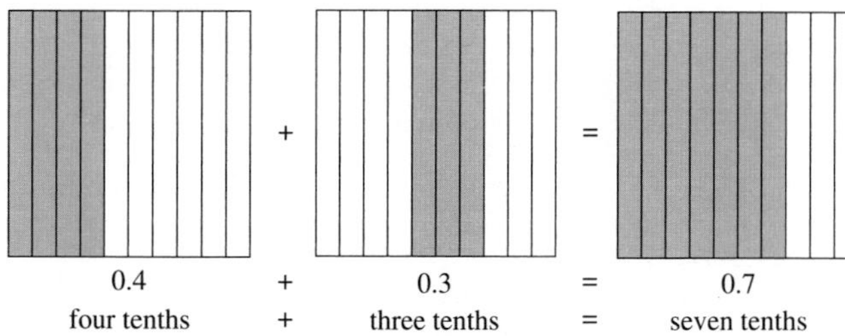

0.4 + 0.3 = 0.7
four tenths + three tenths = seven tenths

FLASHBACK
To find a sum you add. To find a difference you subtract.

1. Use models to find each sum.
   a. 0.1 + 0.8 **0.9** b. 0.3 + 0.09 **0.39** c. 0.44 + 0.23 **0.67**
2. Use words to describe each sum in Question 1.
   a. nine tenths b. thirty-nine hundredths c. sixty-seven hundredths
3. a. Use words to describe 0.8 + 0.5. What is the total number of tenths? **eight tenths plus five tenths; thirteen tenths or 1.3**
   b. Thirteen tenths is equivalent to one and ■ tenths. **3**
   c. You can write the sum as: $\begin{array}{r} 0.8 \\ +\ 0.5 \\ \hline 1.3 \end{array}$
   Draw a model showing that 0.8 + 0.5 = 1.3.
   Check students' drawings. See Sol. Key.
4. a. Draw a model showing 1.6 + 0.8. Find the sum. **2.4**
   b. **Writing** Explain how you found the sum. **See left.**

4b. Answers may vary. Sample: 1.6 equals 16 tenths; 16 tenths plus 8 tenths equals 24 tenths; 24 tenths equals 2 and 4 tenths or 2.4.

3-6

Connecting to Prior Knowledge

Have students relate experiences when they have had to estimate the cost of several items, such as at a grocery store or a take-out restaurant. Ask students to share their strategies. Ask students to answer these questions: *Do you ever overestimate your purchases to make sure you have enough money? Are there times when you must account for tax?*

THINK AND DISCUSS

ESL Attention should be paid to phrases here such as "round up" and "front end"; they may be confusing to some students if read literally. Have students explain the meaning of these phrases in their own words.

CONNECTION TO STATISTICS Questions 1 and 2 relate to work with percents and graphs by having students examine a circle graph.

Example 1

Emphasize to students that the thousandths' place digit of a decimal is irrelevant when rounding the decimal to the nearest tenth.

- *Why is the hundredths' digit compared to the number 5?* **(The number 5 is the lowest number that would make the decimal closer to the higher tenth value. So if the hundredths' place digit were 5 or greater, the decimal would be rounded up.)**

Additional Example *Round 0.349 to the nearest tenth.* **(0.3)**

CRITICAL THINKING For Question 4, have students add the prices together and compare the sum to the estimate.

What's Ahead
- Rounding decimals
- Estimating sums and differences of decimals

WHAT YOU'LL NEED
✓ Newspapers or magazines 

2a. 0.138–0.14; 0.089–0.09; 0.039–0.04; 0.012–0.01; 0.722–0.72

Corn has been an important part of Native American cultures. The kachina represents the spirit of corn to the Hopi tribes.

3-6 Rounding and Estimating

THINK AND DISCUSS

Do you ever wonder what is in the food you eat? The circle graph shows the contents of whole-grain field corn. For example, 0.138 of a kernel of corn is water.

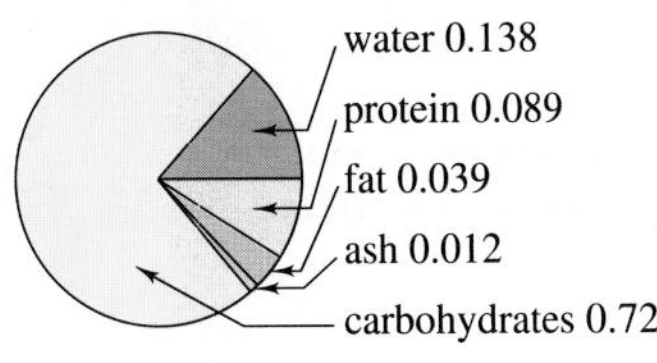

You can round decimals to any place.

1. To round 0.138 to the nearest hundredth do the following.
   a. What digit is in the hundredths' place? 3 After rounding, this digit will stay the same or increase by one. So 0.138 will round to 0.1■ or 0.1■, whichever is closer. 3; 4
   b. Is 0.138 closer to 0.13 or 0.14? Draw a number line to decide. Or, look at the digit 8. Is it 5 or more? Check students' drawings. See Sol. Key; 0.14; yes.
2. a. Round the five decimals in the circle graph to the nearest hundredth.
   b. Discussion To model the five rounded numbers, use graph paper and draw a hundredths' model. Use a different color shading for each rounded number. How is this model like the circle graph? Check students' drawings. See Solution Key. Both show the decimals as a part of the whole number, 1.

Make a tenths' model for the decimals in the circle graph.

Example 1 Round 0.138 to the nearest tenth.

- Find the digit in the tenths' place: 1. So 0.138 rounds to 0.1 or 0.2.
- Since $3 < 5$, 0.138 is closer to 0.1 than 0.2.

To the nearest tenth, 0.138 rounds to 0.1.

3. a. Round the decimals in the circle graph to the nearest tenth. 0.138–0.1; 0.089–0.1; 0.039–0.0; 0.012–0.0; 0.722–0.7
   b. Discussion Draw a tenths' model. Use a different color shading for each rounded number. What do you notice? Check students' drawings. See Sol. Key. Part of the model is not shaded.

"The shortest answer is doing." —Proverb

Organizer

1. **Focus**
   Connecting to Prior Knowledge
2. **Teach**
   Think and Discuss
   Work Together
3. **Closure**
   Try These
   Wrap Up

Skills Reviewed in Context of Lesson
- comparing decimals
- adding whole numbers

Materials and Manipulatives
- newspapers or magazines (3 per group)

Student Resources
Extra Practice
Student Study Guide
Practice, TR Ch. 3, p. 29
Student Study Guide, Spanish Resources, TR

Teacher Resources
Teaching Transparency 44
Lesson Planner, TR Ch. 3, p. 7

continues next page

Questions 4–6: The main idea behind estimating costs of items is to be certain of having enough money. Students should be aware that the practical thing to do is to round the prices up.

TECHNOLOGY OPTION For Questions 1–3, have students use the round function of a spreadsheet. You may want to have students round each decimal to ones, tenths, hundredths, and thousandths.

Example 2

- *How is front-end estimation like the expanded form of a decimal?*
  (In front-end estimation, as in expanded form, each decimal is considered as the sum of the digits in each place value.)
- *Why is it important to group the remaining digits carefully?*
  (This grouping will indicate whether you need to add to your front-end estimate.)

VISUAL LEARNERS For Example 2, have students write the actual cost of each tin of popcorn vertically. Have students use the decimal points to align vertically the four costs. Then have students circle the front-end digits, 1, 1, and 1 to see that 10, 10, and 10 are added.

Additional Example *Use front-end estimation to estimate the total cost of the following school supplies: pen $.95, binder $3.75, book bag $9.89.* **(approximately $15.00)**

WORK TOGETHER

Have each pair of students separate the decimals they find into estimations and measurements. Students should cut the number from the newspapers or magazines and tape or glue the clippings on a separate sheet of paper. Have one pair of students explain to another pair how they determined whether or not each decimal was an estimate.

Organizer, continued

Prentice Hall Technology
Multimedia Math
- Math Investigations, Measuring Elephant Populations in Africa

Computer Item Generator
- 3-6

Other Available Technology
Excel; Works by Microsoft: Questions 1–3, Exercises 7–10 *(optional)*
1-2-3 by Lotus: Questions 1–3, Exercises 7–10 *(optional)*

Fact of the Day

Sugarcane is the major source of the world's sugar. It is thought to have originated in New Guinea, and is now cultivated in tropical and subtropical regions worldwide.

—ENCYCLOPAEDIA BRITANNICA

Popcorn Prices	
1-gal tin	$8.45
2-gal tin	$10.95
3-gal tin	$12.35
6-gal tin	$17.95

You can use rounding to estimate a sum or a difference. To find the total cost of a 1-gallon and a 2-gallon tin of popcorn, round to the nearest dollar.

Round each number to the nearest dollar.

$$\begin{array}{rcr} \$\ 8.45 & \rightarrow & \$\ \ 8 \\ +\ 10.95 & \rightarrow & +\ 11 \\ & & \$\ 19 \end{array}$$

The cost of the two tins is about $19.

4. **Critical Thinking** Is the estimate higher or lower than the actual price? How can you tell? **lower; answers may vary. Sample: $10.95 is closer to $11 than $8.45 is to $8.**
5. Use rounding to estimate the total cost of two 2-gal tins. **$11 + $11 = $22**
6. About how much more does the largest tin of popcorn cost than the smallest tin? Use rounding to estimate. **$18 − $8 = $10**

To estimate sums, you can also use front-end estimation.

Example 2 Estimate the total cost of the four different size tins of popcorn.

$0 + 10 + 10 + 10 = 30$ Add front-end digits.

$8 + 2 + 7 = 17$
$0.45 + 0.35 \approx 1$
$0.95 + 0.95 \approx 2$
Adjust by estimating the sums of the remaining digits.

$30 + 17 + 1 + 2 = 50$ Add the results.

The total cost of the four tins is about $50.

WORK TOGETHER

Work with a partner. Look through newspapers or magazines to find at least five decimal numbers. Complete a table like the one below. Decide whether or not each number is an estimate.

Decimal	Units	Context	Estimate?
47.05	feet	record depth of Mississippi River	no
24.1 million	dollars	profit	yes

Study the information in your table. Make several true statements about your decimals. For example, did you find many estimates? To what place were the decimals rounded? **Answers may vary. Check students' work.**

TRY THESE

TECHNOLOGY OPTION For Exercises 7–10, have students use the round function of a spreadsheet. You may want to have students round each decimal to ones, tenths, hundredths and thousandths.

Error Alert! For Exercises 11–14, students may incorrectly estimate a sum or difference due to a mistake in rounding the numbers. ***Remediation*** Encourage students to keep track of each rounded number by writing them down. Have students similarly keep track of their sums and estimates for Exercises 16–17.

Ongoing Assessment Have students make new estimates for the sums for Exercises 11–14 by using front-end estimation instead of rounding. Have students compare their results to their prior estimates.

Wrap Up

What's the Big Idea? Ask students to explain how to round decimals and how to estimate sums and differences of decimals.

Journal Ask students to compare the two methods of estimating sums and differences of decimals. Ask students to name which method they prefer, and to explain why.

Connections Have students discuss real-life situations where they would estimate decimal numbers, rather than find exact sums and differences.

- **Math** (checking solutions to addition or subtraction problems)
- **Household** (comparing approximate nutritional content of different meal plans, balancing a checkbook mentally, planning a budget)

TRY THESE

Round to the place of the underlined digit.

7. 2.64372 — 2.6437 **8.** 0.5817 — 0.582 **9.** 0.7352 — 0.74 **10.** 3.4746 — 3.47

Round to the nearest dollar to estimate.

11. $14.65 + 3.85 — $19.00 **12.** $9.93 − 3.26 — $7.00 **13.** $16.81 + 11.49 — $28.00 **14.** $12.44 − 8.75 — $3.00

15. Write five different decimal numbers that round to 6.7. Answers may vary. Sample: 6.73, 6.715, 6.74, 6.68, 6.65

Use front-end estimation. Explain how you estimated.

16. 1 + 3 + 8 = 12, 0.29 + 0.52 ≈ 1, 0.89 ≈ 1, 12 + 1 + 1 = 14, about $14

16. $1.29 + $3.52 + $8.89 **17.** $3.89 + $9.95 + $6.59

17. 3 + 9 + 6 = 18, 0.89 + 0.95 + 0.59 ≈ 3, 18 + 3 = 21, about $21

18. Consumer Issues Unleaded gasoline costs $1.259/gal. You pump $5 worth into your automobile. About how many gallons of gasoline did you pump? Accept any reasonable estimate. Sample: about 4 gal

ON YOUR OWN

Round to the place of the underlined digit.

19. 0.087 — 0.1 **20.** 0.6873 — 0.69 **21.** 2.70842 — 2.7084 **22.** 4.0625 — 4.063

Round to the nearest dollar to estimate.

23. $7.28 + 6.87 — $14.00 **24.** $18.42 − 9.88 — $8.00 **25.** $24.66 + 19.55 — $45.00 **26.** $7.42 − 2.58 — $4.00

27. Nutrition Use the chart at the right. Estimate and round to the nearest tenth. a. about 1.8 oz; about 5.2 oz

a. About how much sugar will you have eaten if you have a soft drink and a granola bar? one of everything?

b. About how much more sugar is in one-half cup of sherbet than in 8 oz of yogurt? about 0.2 oz

c. About how much sugar is in the last three items combined? about 3.7 oz

28. Critical Thinking Rounding and front-end estimation are methods for estimating a sum. Think of three decimals that when added give the same estimated sum with both methods. Answers may vary. Sample: 2.9, 7.68, 5.77

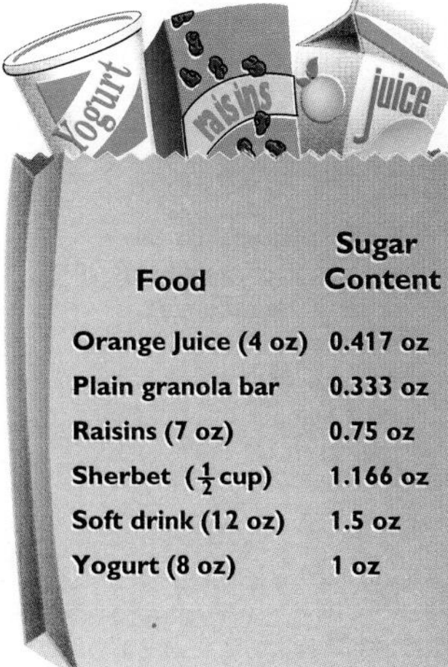

Food	Sugar Content
Orange Juice (4 oz)	0.417 oz
Plain granola bar	0.333 oz
Raisins (7 oz)	0.75 oz
Sherbet ($\frac{1}{2}$ cup)	1.166 oz
Soft drink (12 oz)	1.5 oz
Yogurt (8 oz)	1 oz

Assignment Options

Core: 19–26, 35–37, 40, MR all	
Reinforce: 27, 29–34, 38, 39	Enrich: 28

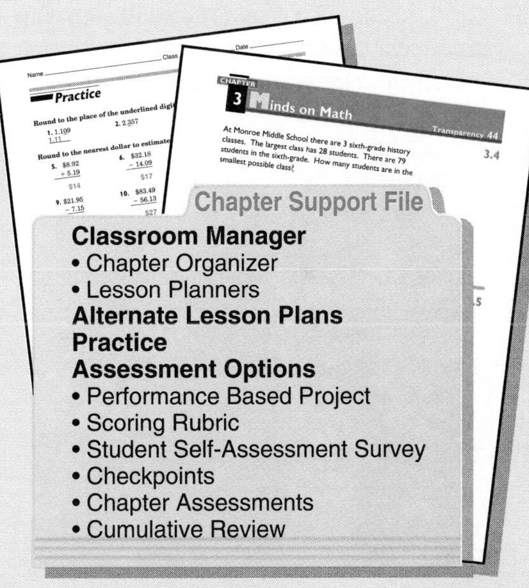

Minds on Math available in Teaching Transparencies

- **Business** (estimating products to be ordered, predicting gains or losses, describing the benefits of plans for the future to boss or stockholders)

Reteaching Activity Tell students they have $13 to spend at a restaurant. Display the following menu:

club sandwich	$2.95
garden salad	$1.50
fruit salad	$2.25
stir-fried vegetables	$3.25
milk	$0.75
juice	$0.95

Have students use estimations to answer the following:

- *Do you have enough money to buy yourself and a friend each a sandwich, garden salad, and juice?* **(Yes; the estimate is $11.00 or $12.00.)**
- *Do you have enough money to buy yourself and a friend each an order of stir-fried vegetables, a fruit salad, milk, and juice?* **(No; the estimate is $14.00 or $15.00.)**
- *About how much money would you expect to have left after a lunch of a club sandwich, a fruit salad, and milk?* **(about $7.00)**

ON YOUR OWN

CONNECTION TO NUTRITION Exercise 27 has students use estimation to evaluate the nutritional content of different foods.

Exercise 33: Encourage students to find a low and high estimate for each choice before they answer the question.

WRITING For Exercise 34, have students compare the situations they mention. Students should explain what difference between the two situations causes a difference in estimation strategies.

CHAPTER INVESTIGATION For Exercise 40, students should include a low estimate, a high estimate, and then a sample total for 8 cassettes.

Math Minutes

A 12 in. submarine sandwich is divided into 6 slices and a second sandwich is divided into 8 slices. Which sandwich has the larger slices? Explain. **(The sandwich with six slices; the sandwich divided into more parts would have smaller portions.)**

Materials for 3-7

- calculator

The largest and most expensive carousel is the Columbia at Paramount's Great America. It is 100 ft high and cost $1.5 million.

Answers may vary. Samples given.

Mixed REVIEW

Use the figure below.

S T U V

1. Name the line three different ways. $\overleftrightarrow{ST}$, $\overleftrightarrow{SU}$, $\overleftrightarrow{SV}$
2. Name three rays. $\overrightarrow{TS}$, $\overrightarrow{TU}$, $\overrightarrow{UV}$

Add or subtract.

3. 2.2 + 0.4 2.6
4. 1.05 − 0.95 0.1
5. A bookcase has three shelves. Each shelf holds 20 books. The maximum number of books is placed on each shelf. What is the total number of books in the case? 60 books

Data File 2 (pp. 38–39) **Use the data for Exercises 29–32.**

29. Use rounding to estimate the cost for a family of two adults and two children to enter Walt Disney World. about $118
30. Use front-end estimation to find the cost for a family of one adult and three children to enter Kings Island. about $52.50
31. Your family plans a trip to Ohio and you decide to save money for admission. Will it cost less to visit Kings Island or Cedar Point? Answers may vary.
32. Choose an amusement park you would like to visit. Estimate the cost of admission for your family. Answers may vary. Check students' work.
33. **Choose A, B, C, or D.** A low estimate of $19 and a high estimate of $22 is a good range for which sum? B

    A. $4.22 + $10.85 + $8.97 **B.** $2.98 + $13.75 + $4.50
    C. $6.05 + $7.86 + $9.22 **D.** $15.32 + $9.63 + $0.45
34. Writing Describe a situation in which you might want your estimate to be high. Then describe one in which you might want your estimate to be low. Answers may vary. See Sol. Key.
35. Use the numbers 13.228, 6.8, 8.87, 3.158, and 5.4.
    a. Which pair of numbers has an estimated sum of 10? 3.158 and 6.8
    b. Which pair has an estimated difference of 6? 13.228 and 6.8
36. Consumer Issues Is $7 enough money to buy cereal for $4.29, milk for $2.47, and strawberries for $.98? Explain. No, $4.29 and $2.47 are rounded down more than $.98 is rounded up.
37. Is an estimate of 22 higher or lower than the sum of 6.83, 9.57, and 4.712? How can you tell? higher; all numbers have been rounded up.
38. Is the statement true or false? Explain your answer.

    Tony has $10 for school supplies. He will have about $1 in change after buying pencils for $2.79, a notebook for $1.39, a ruler for $0.85, and 3 pens for $1.69 each. False; estimate of supplies is $11. He is short $1.
39. Data File 3 (pp. 92–93) How much more valuable is the Honus Wagner card than the Mickey Mantle card? $226,000 more
40.  Investigation (p. 94) Find an estimated range of costs for buying 8 cassettes from the Music Club. Accept any reasonable estimate. Sample: $80–$112

CHAPTER 3 PROBLEM SOLVING PRACTICE

This page provides a variety of problems that can be used to reinforce and enhance the students' problem solving skills. Encourage students to read each problem carefully. Then have them refer to the list of problem solving strategies to help them decide how to solve the problems.

Point out, however, that not all questions require a strategy for solving, nor are all the strategies in the list used on this page.

Exercise 1: Encourage students to trace these trips on a map.

Exercise 4: Students may not know where Nassau is. Help them to find the Bahamas on a map.

DIVERSITY For Exercise 5, many different kinds of occupations may call for a great deal of employee travel. Students may have relatives or family friends who travel frequently for their jobs. Encourage students to brainstorm a list of occupations that could require frequent travel.

Problem Solving Practice

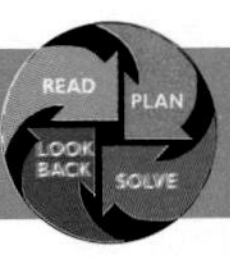

PROBLEM SOLVING STRATEGIES

Make a Table
Use Logical Reasoning
Solve a Simpler Problem
Too Much or Too Little Information
Look for a Pattern
Make a Model
Work Backward
Draw a Diagram
Guess and Test
Simulate a Problem
Use Multiple Strategies

Solve. The list at the left shows some possible strategies you can use.

1. Travel On a business trip, Martha flew 331 mi from Montreal, Canada, to New York City. She flew 10 times that distance from New York to Paris, France. She returned from Paris through New York and then on to Montreal. About how many miles did she fly? 7,282 mi

2. Consumer Issues Mr. Alvarez is purchasing juice in 12-oz cans for the school picnic. There are four 6-packs of juice in a case. For every 5 cases he buys, the store will donate 2 cases. How many cases should Mr. Alvarez buy to have 430 cans of juice? 14 cases

3. Sara, Sue, Steve, and Sam are brothers and sisters. Sam is twice Sue's age, but he is younger than Steve. In four years Sara will be twice as old as Sue, and Sam will be the age Sara is now. Steve is the oldest. List them from oldest to youngest. Steve, Sara, Sam, Sue

4. Travel A ship leaves Miami, Florida, on Friday at 4:40 P.M. The sailing time to Nassau is 16 h 30 min. On what day and at what time is the ship expected to arrive in Nassau? Saturday 9:10 A.M.

5. Travel Keisha has 18,659 frequent flyer miles with an airline. She needs 35,000 mi to qualify for one free round-trip ticket. She flies about 1,500 mi a month. Estimate how long it will be before she can get a free ticket. Accept any reasonable estimate. Sample: about 11 mo

6. Money Terry is saving to buy a new bicycle that costs $120. For every $20 she saves, her parents will contribute $5. She plans to save $20 a month. How long will it take her to save the money for the new bicycle? 5 mo

7. The McCormick family is going to the movies. There are 2 adults and 4 children. The adult tickets cost $7.00, and children go for half price. They brought a coupon for $.75 off each adult ticket and $.50 off each child's ticket. Is $25.00 enough for their admission? Why or why not? Yes; The total cost of the tickets is $28. The estimated discount total is $3.50. $28 − $3.50 = $24.50.

WHEN? In 1894, the Holland Kinetoscope Parlor in New York City charged customers $.25 to view five short films on machines called *kinetoscopes.*

3-7

Connecting to Prior Knowledge

Ask students to recall how to add and subtract decimals by using models. Have students name some important steps in the procedure. **(Line up the decimal points vertically; rename, or add zeros, if necessary; check with an estimate.)**

THINK AND DISCUSS

Example 1

Have students explain how the decimals were rounded to provide an estimate. Review with students also the practice of adding zeros as placeholders onto the ends of decimals.

VISUAL LEARNERS Have students plot on a number line the maximum and minimum weights of a volleyball. Have students connect the two weights with a line segment. Have students draw line segments for the weights of the other balls.

Additional Example *Find the sum 2.49 + 3.011 + 4.8.*

2.490
3.011
+ 4.800
10.301

KINESTHETIC LEARNERS The exercise within the *What?* feature on the student page is especially appropriate for these kinds of learners. Once students have completed their descriptions, have volunteers demonstrate their responses for the class.

Example 2

Make sure students find the same difference on their calculators. Caution students to be careful that they press the decimal point key at the right time.

Additional Example *Find the difference 9.137 − 6.87.*
(9 [.] 137 [−] 6 [.] 87 [=] 2.267)

" It is a good answer that knows when to stop. "

—ITALIAN PROVERB

Organizer

1. **Focus**
   Connecting to Prior Knowledge
2. **Teach**
   Think and Discuss
   Work Together
3. **Closure**
   Try These
   Wrap Up

Skills Reviewed in Context of Lesson
- rounding decimals
- reading tables

Materials and Manipulatives
- calculator (one per group)

On Your Own Exercise 25: graph paper; Exercises 34–36: calculator

Student Resources
Extra Practice
Student Study Guide
Practice, TR Ch. 3, p. 30
Student Study Guide, Spanish Resources, TR
Alternate Lesson, TR Ch. 3, pp. 16–19

Teacher Resources
Teaching Transparencies 19, 45
Lesson Planner, TR Ch. 3, p. 8

continues next page

What's Ahead
- Adding and subtracting decimals

WHAT YOU'LL NEED
✓ Calculator 

3-7 Adding and Subtracting Decimals

THINK AND DISCUSS

Manufacturers often package sports balls in boxes for display. A basketball weighing 21.8 oz is in a box that weighs 2.4 oz.

1. Add to find the total weight of the package. 24.2 oz
2. How can you check to see if your answer is reasonable? Estimate by rounding to the nearest whole number.

Before you add or subtract, it is a good idea to estimate the answer as a check. When you add, line up the decimal points and write zeros to make the columns even.

Example 1 Find the sum 3.026 + 4.7 + 1.38.

Estimate: 3 + 5 + 1 = 9

Add:

3.026	→	3.026
4.7		4.700
+ 1.38		+ 1.380
		9.106

Check 9.106 is reasonable since it is close to 9. ✓

3. Why can you write 4.7 as 4.700? Answers may vary. Sample: 7 tenths has the same area model as 700 thousandths, so 4.7 = 4.700

Most sports equipment sizes follow a standard. The table below lists minimum and maximum weights for sports balls.

Official Standard Weights

Type	Minimum Weight	Maximum Weight
Basketball	21.16 oz	22.93 oz
Baseball	5 oz	5.5 oz
Football	14 oz	15 oz
Softball	6.25 oz	7 oz
Tennis ball	2 oz	2.06 oz
Volleyball	9.17 oz	9.88 oz

A properly inflated basketball should bounce between 1.2 m and 1.4 m on a hard wooden floor if you drop it from a height of about 1.8 m. **Describe a way to test whether a basketball is inflated correctly.**

Source: *The Rules of the Game*

Example 3
Make sure students understand how the difference $20 − $11.78 is obtained from the information.

Additional Example *You use a $5 bill to pay for a bottle of orange juice costing $1.29. How much change will you get?*

$$\begin{array}{r} \$5.00 \\ -\ 1.29 \\ \hline \$3.71 \end{array}$$

Ongoing Assessment Have students in groups of four design receipts reflecting sums and differences of decimals. Each group should create a receipt showing four sales, two returns, and a total. Display the groups' work so that students can compare the receipts.

WORK TOGETHER

Each student should find the range for each sports ball and then compare the data with a partner. Each pair should then create a table that compares the weight of a sports ball to its range of standard weights.

TRY THESE

Error Alert! For Exercise 14, students may include the costs for both 12- and 24-exposure film. ***Remediation*** Remind students to read the problem carefully and to do an estimate first.

Wrap Up

What's the Big Idea? Have students explain how to add and subtract decimals.

Organizer, continued

Prentice Hall Technology
Computer Item Generator
- 3-7

Fact of the Day

The Seikan Tunnel was completed in 1988. It is the world's deepest underwater tunnel and the longest transportation tunnel, with a length of just under $33\frac{1}{2}$ miles (almost 54 km).

—*ACADEMIC AMERICAN ENCYCLOPEDIA*

To find the range of standard weights for a type of sports ball, subtract its minimum weight from its maximum weight.

4. The difference 9.88 − 9.17 is the range of standard weights for which type of ball? Find this range. volleyball; 0.71 oz
5. Is a volleyball weighing 9.02 oz within the range of standard weights? What does this mean? No; The 9.02 oz volleyball could not be used in an official game.

You can use a calculator to add or subtract decimals.

Example 2 Find the difference 10.028 − 3.7.

Estimate: 10 − 4 = 6

10 [.] 028 [−] 3 [.] 7 [=] 6.328

Check 6.328 is close to the estimate 6. ✓

6. When you use a calculator to find 7.87 − 1.47, why will the display show 6.4 instead of 6.40? Answers may vary. Sample: Calculators don't show unneeded zeros.

Sometimes you need to write a whole number as a decimal.

Example 3 You use a $20 bill to pay for a CD costing $11.78. How much change will you get?

Estimate: $20 − $12 = $8

Write $20 as $20.00 and subtract:

$$\begin{array}{r} \$20.00 \\ -\ 11.78 \\ \hline \$8.22 \end{array}$$

Check $8.22 is close to the estimate $8. ✓

You will get $8.22 in change.

No major league pitcher has had 110 no-hitters, 35 perfect games, a lifetime batting average of 0.300, and a fast ball clocked at 118 mi/h. Between 1958 and 1976, a softball pitcher named Joan Joyce accomplished all of this.

Source: *The Superman Book of Super-human Achievements.*

WORK TOGETHER

Work with a partner. Use the chart of standard weights.
- List the names of the sports balls from heaviest to lightest.
- Find the range of standard weights for each sports ball.
- Use your data to decide if the following statement is true or false: The heavier the ball is, the smaller is its range of standard weights. See Sol. Key; false—a volleyball is heavier than a softball but the range is less.

Journal *It is helpful to estimate your answer before adding and subtracting decimals. Explain what you would do if your answer was not close to your initial estimate, and tell why.*

Connections Have a discussion about how decimals are added and subtracted in real life. You may want to start with these examples:

- **Science** (adding weights of solids or liquids; finding the difference in height or weight of animals)
- **Geography** (finding the difference in distance between two locations on a map, gross national product of countries)
- **Consumer Skills** (comparing prices, knowing how much change to expect)

Reteaching Activity Have students use decimal squares or graph paper to find the difference 0.9 − 0.25 and the sum 0.3 + 0.19. Point out that because the operations require the addition of zeros, students need to use hundredths' models to find the difference and the sum.

ON YOUR OWN

ESL Explain the vocabulary in Exercises 23–27 before students try the problems. The term "natural resources" may need some explanation, as well as the items in the table. Encourage students to help each other with this vocabulary.

CONNECTION TO STATISTICS Exercises 23–27 preview students' future work with decimals and graphs by having students analyze a data table that lists the components of total natural resources used to produce energy.

ESTIMATION For Exercise 27, encourage students to round the decimal for each natural resource before they attempt to answer the question.

Assignment Options

<table>
<tr><td colspan="2">Core: 15–23, 25, 31, MR all</td></tr>
<tr><td>Reinforce: 24, 26–30, 33–35</td><td>Enrich: 32, 36</td></tr>
</table>

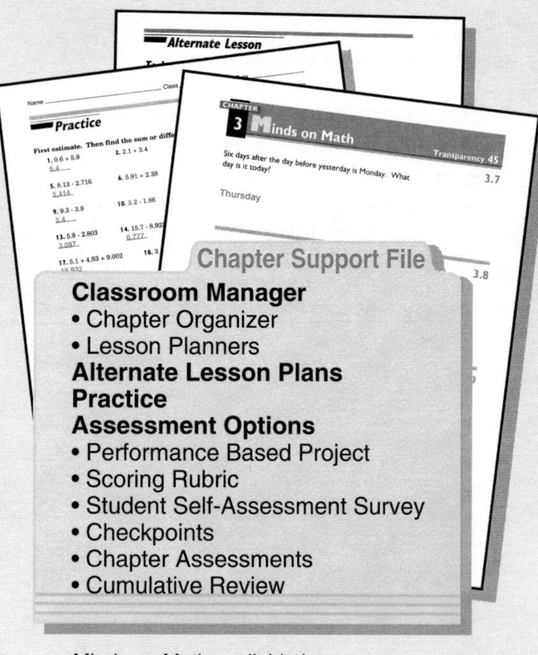

Minds on Math available in Teaching Transparencies

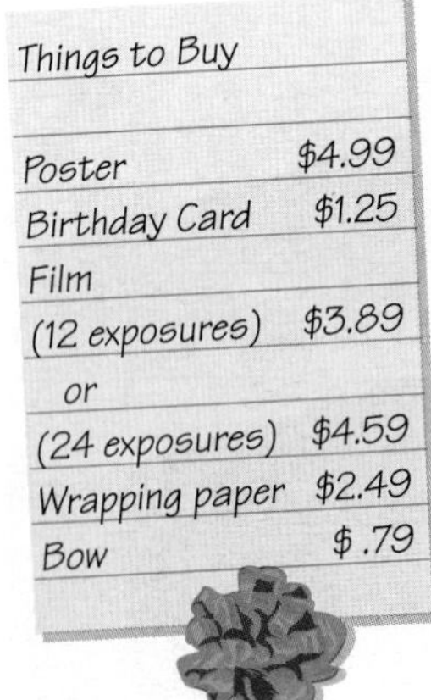

Things to Buy
Poster $4.99
Birthday Card $1.25
Film
(12 exposures) $3.89
or
(24 exposures) $4.59
Wrapping paper $2.49
Bow $.79

TRY THESE

7. The length of the Eurotunnel between England and France is 49.94 km. The Seikan Tunnel in Japan is 53.9 km long. How much longer is the Seikan Tunnel? 3.96 km

First estimate. Then find the sum or difference.
Accept any reasonable estimate. Sample given.

8. 0.6 + 3.4 — 4; 4.0
9. 6.2 − 0.444 — 6; 5.756
10. 8.001 − 0.77 — 7; 7.231
11. 4.035 + 8.99 — 13; 13.025
12. 22.2 − 4.3 — 18; 17.9
13. 9.76 + 3.45 — 13; 13.21

14. Consumer Issues You have a $10 bill and a $5 bill, and you wish to buy all the items on the list shown at the left. Can you buy the 24-exposure film? Yes

ON YOUR OWN

First estimate. Then find the sum or difference.
Accept any reasonable estimate. Sample given.

15. 0.5 + 4.6 — 6; 5.1
16. 8.7 − 0.368 — 9; 8.332
17. 9.011 − 0.45 — 9; 8.561
18. 2.091 + 5.75 — 8; 7.841
19. 8.5 − 5.8 — 3; 2.7
20. 12.34 + 1.68 — 14; 14.02
21. 4.1 + 3.72 + 6.05 — 14; 13.87
22. 7 + 11.436 + 3.08 — 21; 21.516

Use the data at the left for Exercises 23–27.

Part of Energy Supply Produced by Natural Resources	
Oil	0.39
Coal	0.27
Gas	0.17
Nuclear power	0.02
Hydro (water) power	0.02
Firewood/charcoal	0.12
Other	0.01

23. What part of the total energy is produced by coal? 0.27
24. Find the sum of the numbers given in the chart. What is the meaning of this sum? 1; Answers may vary. Sample: This is the total energy produced by all the resources.
25. Make a hundredths' model showing the parts of energy produced by each natural resource. Check students' drawings. See Sol. Key.
26. What part of all the energy is produced from oil and coal? Is it more than half? Explain. 0.66; Yes; 0.5 is half of 1, 0.66 > 0.5
27. Estimation Which two natural resources produce an amount of energy approximately equal to that of coal? gas and firewood/charcoal

Mental Math **Find the missing number.**

28. 6.4 + 3.1 = ■ + 6.4 — 3.1
29. 0.43 + ■ = 0.43 — 0
30. (2.1 + 0.3) + 4 = 2.1 + (■ + 4) — 0.3

MENTAL MATH Hint to students that they should read aloud each equation for Exercises 28–30 before they attempt to answer the question.

Exercise 32: Have students compare any mistakenly computed decimal with the actual decimal.

CONNECTION TO ALGEBRA Exercise 33 uses algebraic concepts by having students substitute numbers for blanks to make a numerical expression.

WRITING Students' examples for Exercise 36 should consist of a comparison of the same orders placed under both plans.

Consumer Issues How much change will you get?

31. At the movie theater, you order popcorn for $2.75 and two drinks for $1.50 each. You pay with a $10 bill. $4.25

Accept any reasonable estimate. Sample given.

32. Pam used a calculator to find the following sums and differences. First estimate to see if the answer is reasonable. If it is not, what did Pam enter incorrectly?

a. $5.85 + 6.24 = 629.85$ a. 12; 6.24 entered as 624
b. $36.8 - 7.2 = 29.6$ b. 30; reasonable

33. **Choose A, B, C, or D.** If you place the digits 1–6 in the boxes ■■.■ + ■.■■ to give the greatest possible sum, the digit in the third box from the left must be: C

A. 2 **B.** 3 **C.** 2 or 3 **D.** 4

Use a calculator and the given information.

When you order by mail, you pay for shipping and handling. The company may base the fee on the amount of the order or on the number of items.

34. **a.** Suppose you order one adult sweatshirt, size XXL, and three child T-shirts. How much do they cost without shipping and handling? $67.45

b. Find the charge for shipping and handling your order in each of the charts. Explain the difference in price. See right.

35. Suppose you order one of each item in size medium. Which shipping and handling method will cost less? Charges based on the dollar amount of the order are less.

36. **Writing** If you were ordering more expensive items, which chart would you prefer? If you were ordering less expensive items, which chart would you prefer? Use examples to explain your answer. See Solution Key.

HAPPY BIRTHDAY SHIRTS
#345 Adult Birthday Tee
(M – XL) $15.00
(XXL) $17.95
#355 Adult Birthday Sweatshirt
(M – XL) $29.50
(XXL) $29.95
#445 Child's Birthday Tee
$12.50
#455 Child's Birthday Sweatshirt
$16.95

Mixed REVIEW

True or False?

1. The letter M has symmetry. True
2. All triangles have symmetry. False

Round to the place of the underlined digit.

3. 1.94872 1.949
4. 23.0384 23.0

5. Jonah had $340 in his bank account. He withdrew $52 and wrote a check for $18.50. Find the balance.

5. $269.50

34b. $6.95; $8.95; One charges by dollar amount, the other by the number of items.

Shipping and Handling Charge by Dollar Amount of Order	
Under $15.00	$2.95
$15.00–$24.99	$3.95
$25.00–$39.99	$4.95
$40.00–$49.99	$5.95
$50.00–$74.99	$6.95
$75.00–$99.99	$7.95
$100.00 and over	$8.95

Shipping and Handling Charge by Number of Items Ordered	
1 Item	$3.15
2 Items	$4.95
3 Items	$6.95
4+ Items	$8.95

Math Minutes

Use mental math to find each product.

$\frac{1}{2} \times 24 = \mathbf{12}$

$\frac{3}{4} \times 24 = \mathbf{18}$

$\frac{1}{4} \times 24 = \mathbf{6}$

$3 \times 24 = \mathbf{72}$

$1\frac{1}{2} \times 24 = \mathbf{36}$

$1\frac{3}{4} \times 24 = \mathbf{42}$

Materials for 3-8

- computer with spreadsheet software *(optional)*

3-8

Connecting to Prior Knowledge

Ask students to recall previous activities in Chapter 1 when they used spreadsheets to organize and manipulate data about lengths of compact discs, hours worked, and scores.

THINK AND DISCUSS

DIVERSITY Students may have varying knowledge of banking and savings accounts. Be aware that some students may have accounts in their own names, while others may have had no experiences with banking.

KINESTHETIC LEARNERS Have students simulate a deposit and a withdrawal from a bank account using play money. For each transaction, complete a table to keep a record of what happened. (Use a model similar to the spreadsheet activity in the student edition, but remove row numbers and column headings.) Make sure students understand that deposits and interests are added and withdrawals are subtracted.

ESL **Question 5:** Students may be unfamiliar with terms such as *monthly, quarterly,* and *annually.* You may want to use a calendar to explain the meaning of these terms.

Error Alert! For the chart following Question 5, some students may become confused about the balances for the end of the day and at the beginning of the next day. ***Remediation*** It may help to draw a chart on the board using the same information in the computer spreadsheet so that students can see the flow between the "end" and "beginning" balances.

Ongoing Assessment Ask: *How did you or how could you have used mental math to find the balance in row 4?* If students feel they need paper and pencil or a calculator, ask them to estimate the answer. If they are having trouble giving a reasonable estimate, they probably need more experience working with written money amounts.

"Experience is a good teacher, but she sends in terrific bills."

—MINNA ANTRIM

Organizer

1. **Focus**
   Connecting to Prior Knowledge
2. **Teach**
   Think and Discuss
   Work Together
3. **Closure**
   Wrap Up

Vocabulary/Symbols
interest
statement
deposits
withdrawals
balance

Skills Reviewed in Context of Lesson
- adding and subtracting decimals

Materials and Manipulatives
- computer and spreadsheet software (one per group; *optional*)

Student Resources
Extra Practice
Student Study Guide
Practice, TR Ch. 3, p. 31
Student Study Guide, Spanish Resources, TR
Alternate Lesson, TR, Ch. 3, pp. 20–23

continues next page

TECHNOLOGY

3-8 Keeping Track of Your Savings

What's Ahead
- Adding and subtracting decimals in bank accounts
- Using a computer spreadsheet to add and subtract decimals

WHAT YOU'LL NEED
✓ Computer 
✓ Spreadsheet software

THINK AND DISCUSS

Suppose you need to save some money to buy a gift.

1. Where would you keep the money you save? How would you keep track of the amount of money you have saved? In a piggy bank; make a list

You could open a savings account at a bank. It is a safe place to keep your money. Also, the bank pays you money, called **interest,** for having a savings account there.

2. Why do you think a bank would pay you interest, rather than charging you a fee, for a savings account? The bank uses the money to make investments.

Banks usually send you a report, or a **statement,** for your account. The statement shows the interest you earned on the account. It also shows **deposits,** money you put into the account, and **withdrawals,** money you take out of the account. A **balance** is the amount of money in the account at a given time.

3. Is interest like a deposit or a withdrawal? a deposit
4. You open an account with a $50 deposit. What is the balance? $50
5. **Discussion** Banks send statements monthly, quarterly, or annually. Why would you want to keep your own account record and check it against the bank statement? Answers may vary. Sample: to make sure the bank statement is correct.

You can use a spreadsheet to keep track of your savings.

	A	B	C	D	E	F
1	Date	Balance	Withdrawal	Deposit	Interest	End Balance
2	11/3	73.47		100.00		173.47
3	11/14	173.47	98.00			75.47
4	11/31	75.47			1.99	77.46

At the age of 11, Andrew J. Burns became president of Children's Bank in Omaha, Nebraska. The bank is part of Enterprise Bank, where Andrew's father is president. Andrew helps young people open bank accounts. In 1993 Children's Bank had 500 accounts!

Source: *National Geographic World*

Journal Ask students to think of some possible errors they might make if they had a savings account. Have students list ways to avoid or minimize these errors.

WORK TOGETHER

Question 13: Have students divide the tasks in their groups. Have one student read the amounts to be recorded into the spreadsheet, another student enter the data into the computer, and a third student check the reasonableness of the balance.

Question 13a: Some students may respond that they would order the transactions by category, such as deposits and withdrawals. Encourage students to examine why bank records are kept in chronological order.

ALTERNATE APPROACH If you are not using a computer, have students do the exercise manually. Although students won't see the power of automatic spreadsheet calculation, they will get the rest of the real-world connections and the mathematical content of the exercise (addition and subtraction of decimals).

Wrap Up

What's the Big Idea? Have students discuss why adding and subtracting decimals are useful when keeping track of a savings account.

Connections Have a discussion about adding and subtracting decimals. You may wish to start with these examples:

- **Weather** (accumulating types of precipitation)
- **Sports** (diving averages, distance timing for running events)
- **Accounting** (tax preparation, payroll preparation)
- **Architecture** (house design)

Reteaching Activity Have students use base ten blocks and calculators to reinforce the concepts of addition and

6. What does the number in cell B2 mean? in cell D2? **amount of money in the account when the bank opens (11/3); amount put into account (11/3)**
7. How was the amount in cell F2 calculated? in F3? in F4? **\$73.47 + \$100.00; \$173.47 − \$98.00; \$75.47 + \$1.99**
8. Which cells show the same amounts? Why? **F2 and B3; F3 and B4; no transactions were made.**
9. **Discussion** How can you use mental math to check the balance at the end of each day? **Sample: estimate, 70 + 100 = 170, 170 − 100 = 70, 70 + 2 = 72**
10. A withdrawal slip and a deposit slip are shown at the right. Show what the next two rows of the spreadsheet will look like after these transactions. **See Sol. Key.**

WITHDRAWAL — DATE 12/4 — ACCOUNT NUMBER 12487592 — AMOUNT \$ 30.00

DEPOSIT — DATE 12/10 — ACCOUNT NUMBER 12487592 — AMOUNT \$ 19.95

11. Suppose your savings account has a balance of \$67.41. You deposit \$37.75 and then withdraw \$37.75. What is the new balance? Would you get the same result if you made the withdrawal first and then the deposit? Explain. **\$67.41; Yes; The amount added and subtracted is the same.**
12. **Critical Thinking** Suppose you deposit \$7.50. In your records, you accidentally subtract \$7.50. By how much will your balance be off? Why? **\$15; The bank adds \$7.50 to your balance and you subtract \$7.50, \$7.50 + \$7.50 = \$15.**

WORK TOGETHER

13. **Computer** Use the five savings account slips and a spreadsheet to make a record for this account. The beginning balance is \$68.74.
    a. How will you order the transactions? **by date**
    b. What is the final balance? **\$74.94**
    c. What is the sum of all the deposits? the sum of all the withdrawals? **\$61.95; \$55.75**
    d. Compute: (Beginning Balance) + (Sum of Deposits) − (Sum of Withdrawals). Compare with the final balance. **\$74.94; same**
    e. **Writing** Describe the relationship you found in part (**d**). How can you use this to check your calculations? **See Sol. Key.**

DEPOSIT — DATE 1/23 — ACCOUNT NUMBER 753164 — AMOUNT \$ 21.95

DEPOSIT — DATE 1/3 — ACCOUNT NUMBER 753164 — AMOUNT \$ 40.00

WITHDRAWAL — DATE 1/9 — ACCOUNT NUMBER 753164 — AMOUNT \$ 13.75

WITHDRAWAL — DATE 1/27 — ACCOUNT NUMBER 753164 — AMOUNT \$ 17.00

WITHDRAWAL — DATE 1/8 — ACCOUNT NUMBER 753164 — AMOUNT \$ 25.00

Organizer, continued

Teacher Resources

Teaching Transparencies 4, 5, 45, 47
Transparency Masters, TR p. 5
Lesson Planner, TR Ch. 3, p. 9

Prentice Hall Technology

Multimedia Math

- Math Tools, Spreadsheet

Computer Item Generator

- 3-8

Other Available Technology

1-2-3 by Lotus
Excel; Works by Microsoft
ClarisWorks by Apple
(all optional)

Fact of the Day

In 1991, the bank with the greatest assets was the Dai-Ichi Bank, Ltd., of Tokyo, Japan, which was worth \$446,221,203,000.

—INFORMATION PLEASE ALMANAC

Assignment Options

Core: 14, MR all	
Reinforce: 15	**Enrich:** 16

subtraction. As the students add decimal equivalents with the blocks, they can simultaneously add the same amounts on calculators (to check for accuracy).

ON YOUR OWN

Exercises 15a–f: Many balance sheets do not include balances that are recorded twice (only the end of the day is recorded). Ask students to discuss how the spreadsheet format and spreadsheet formulas would or would not be affected if the Start of Day column was eliminated. Ask:

- *How would you answer Exercises 15d and e if the Start of the Day column was eliminated?*
  (look at column "End of Day" from the previous row)

Exercise 16: This exercise uses critical thinking skills to evaluate the final results of the program. Students may need some help when attempting to find an alternate method in finding the final balance.

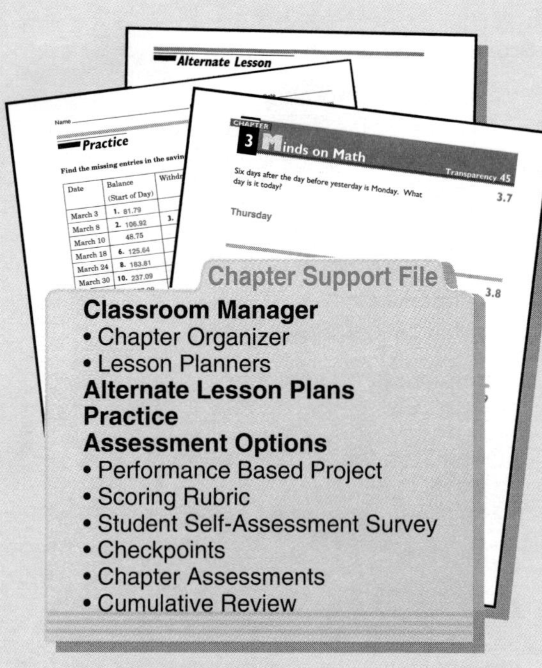

Classroom Manager
- Chapter Organizer
- Lesson Planners

Alternate Lesson Plans

Practice

Assessment Options
- Performance Based Project
- Scoring Rubric
- Student Self-Assessment Survey
- Checkpoints
- Chapter Assessments
- Cumulative Review

Minds on Math available in Teaching Transparencies

Order each set of numbers from least to greatest.

16, 23, 8, 19, 4, 25 **4, 8, 16, 19, 23, 25**

1, 1.4, 1.12, 0.1, 1.43 **0.1, 1, 1.12, 1.4, 1.43**

Materials for 3-9

- centimeter ruler

Mixed REVIEW

Find the mean.

1. 44, 45, 43, 49 **45.25**
2. 2, 9, 7, 3, 2 **4.6**

Add or subtract.

3. 5.31 + 17.04 = **22.35**
4. 10.25 − 6.09 = **4.16**
5. Rod earns $10 for mowing one lawn. After mowing seven lawns, how much money has he earned? **$70**

14a. Yes; 1/17—subtracted 0.14 instead of 14; 1/23—subtracted 37.50 instead of adding.

Ruthie Barrientos is a champion baton twirler. Besides winning many titles, Ruthie finds time to perform while staying active in school affairs and making the honor roll. In 1988 Ruthie was named Athlete of the Year by the Houston Hispanic Chamber of Commerce.

ON YOUR OWN

14. Suppose this bank statement is for your savings account.

Date	Balance	Withdrawal	Deposit	Interest	Balance
1/5	38.64		22.50		61.14
1/11	61.14	21.00			40.14
1/17	40.14	14.00			40.00
1/23	40.00		37.50		2.50

See left.
   a. Are there any errors? If so, how were mistakes made?
   b. Which amounts can you keep track of yourself? Which amounts do you need to get from the statement?
   withdrawals and deposits; interest

15. Rita keeps the money she is saving in a small box in her room. She uses a notebook to keep track of the amount. One day, her dog Rex chewed the notebook.

Date	Start of Day	Took Out	Put In	Comment	End of Day
6/3	**20.00**		4.50	Allowance	24.50
6/8	**24.50**	7.00		Went to a movie	**17.50**
6/9	17.50		1.99	Change from movie	**19.49**
6/10	**19.49**		4.50	Allowance	**23.99**
6/14	**23.99**		9.25	Mowed Miller's lawn	**33.24**
6/15	**33.24**	25.00		Bought gift	**8.24**

   a. Answers may vary. Sample: Data is organized into cells.
   a. **Discussion** How is Rita's record like a spreadsheet?
   b. What does Rita call deposits? withdrawals? balances?
   Put In; Took Out; End of Day
   c. How much money was in the box at the end of June 3? **$24.50**
   d. Was there more or less than that in the box at the start of June 3? How do you know? **less; start of day was $2**
   e. How much was in the box at the start of June 8? **$24.50**
   f. Copy Rita's table and fill in the missing amounts.
   See above.

16. **Writing** How could you check your answers to Exercise 15 by calculating the final balance in a different way?
(Beginning Balance) + (Sum of Deposits) − (Sum of Withdrawals)

CHAPTER 3 PRACTICE

This page provides practice on the skills learned up to this point in the chapter. Daily cumulative practice can be found in the Mixed Reviews that appear in every lesson.

Exercises 1–5: As long as student models are correct, accept any creative version as well as the standard ones.

Exercises 25–28: Remind students that the smaller end of the arrow points to the smaller number.

Practice

Draw a model for each decimal.

1. 0.6 2. 0.27 3. 1.7 4. four tenths 5. ten hundredths

Check students' drawings. See Solution Key.

Write each decimal in words.

6. 0.09 7. 0.5 8. 0.65 9. 0.70 10. 22.75 11. 75.03

6. nine hundredths 7. five tenths 8. sixty-five hundredths 9. seventy hundredths 10. twenty-two and seventy-five hundredths 11. seventy-five and three hundredths

Write a decimal for the given words.

12. three tenths 0.3 13. forty-five hundredths 0.45 14. seven and nine hundredths 7.09

What is the value of the digit 7 in each number?

15. 0.7 16. 5.007 17. 73.59 18. 0.532497 19. 431.07

15. 7 tenths 16. 7 thousandths 17. 7 tens 18. 7 millionths 19. 7 hundredths

Write each number in standard form.

20. one hundred fifty-one thousandths 0.151
21. one hundred and fifty-one thousandths 100.051

Write each number in expanded form.

22. 438.9 23. 38.8015 24. two and one hundred forty-nine thousandths

22. 400 + 30 + 8 + 0.9 23. 30 + 8 + 0.8 + 0.001 + 0.0005 24. 2 + 0.1 + 0.04 + 0.009

Compare. Use >, < or =.

25. 7.7 ■ 7.3 >
26. 0.3978 ■ 0.39 >
27. 81.773 ■ 81.78 <
28. 12.70 ■ 12.7 =

29. Graph 0.59, 0.37, 0.5, 0.3, and 0.33 on a number line. See Solution Key.

Round to the place of the underlined digit.

30. 0.<u>0</u>54 0.1
31. 6.18<u>7</u>9 6.188
32. 7.1<u>3</u>48 7.13
33. 95.3<u>5</u>8 95.36
34. 4<u>5</u>.89 46
35. <u>3</u>.09 3

Round to the nearest dollar to estimate.

36. \$6.27 + 5.73 = \$12.00
37. \$18.79 − 9.78 = \$9.00
38. \$75.12 + 73.81 = \$149.00
39. \$49.02 − 48.13 = \$1.00
40. \$107.55 + .39 = \$108.00

First estimate. Then find the sum or difference.

41. 0.7 + 2.3 3; 3.0
42. 7.8 − 0.375 8; 7.425
43. 9.001 − 0.54 8; 8.461
44. 12.43 + 2.86 15; 15.29
45. 5.13 + 6.4 11; 11.53
46. 8 − 2.3 6; 5.7
47. 12.431 − 6.522 5; 5.909
48. 4.181 + 1.299 5; 5.48

Resources
Extra Practice
Student Study Guide
Student Study Guide, Spanish Resources, TR

Answers to Problems Unique to Spanish Edition
6. nueve centésimas
7. cinco décimas
8. sesenta y cinco centésimas
9. setenta centésimas
10. veintidós, y setenta y cinco centésimas
11. setenta y cinco, y tres centésimas

3-9

Connecting to Prior Knowledge

Ask students to share what they know about the metric system of measurement. Have students estimate the length of a meter, a centimeter, and a millimeter. Have students use their estimates to estimate lengths in the classroom.

THINK AND DISCUSS

ESL Many ESL students are familiar with metric measurement. Have students make a chart that shows how the centimeter, millimeter, kilometer, and meter are related to measurements in the customary system.

DIVERSITY Ask students if they can name countries where the metric system of measurement is used as the standard. Ask them for other countries that use inches, feet, and yards as the standard. **(Almost all countries, for example, Canada, Australia, France, and Mexico use the metric system. The United States and England are still in the process of converting.)**

Question 5: Remind students to line up their rulers as carefully as possible. Accept measurements that do not exactly match the given answers, since some rulers may not be calibrated as precisely as others. Have students answer the following questions:

- *How can you use your ruler to measure a segment to the nearest centimeter?*
  (If the measurement is halfway between two whole centimeters, round up to the next centimeter. If it is less than halfway, round down.)
- *How can you round 13 mm or 26 mm to the nearest centimeter without actually measuring?*
  (If you know that 5 mm is the half-way mark between centimeters then you know that 13 mm is a little more than 1 cm, so the nearest centimeter is 1 cm. You can use similar reasoning to round 26 mm to 3 cm.)

"We can lick gravity, but sometimes the paperwork is overwhelming."
—Werner von Braun

Organizer

1. **Focus**
   Connecting to Prior Knowledge
2. **Teach**
   Think and Discuss
   Work Together
3. **Closure**
   Wrap Up

Vocabulary/Symbols
meter
centimeter
millimeter
kilometer
perimeter

Materials and Manipulatives
- centimeter ruler (one per student)

On Your Own Exercises 13–18: centimeter ruler

Student Resources
Extra Practice
Student Study Guide
Practice, TR Ch. 3, p. 32
Student Study Guide, Spanish Resources, TR
Checkpoint, TR. Ch. 3, p. 38

Teacher Resources
Teaching Transparency 45
Transparency Masters, TR p. 3
Lesson Planner, TR Ch. 3, p. 10

continues next page

What's Ahead
- Measuring using metric units
- Choosing appropriate units of measure.

WHAT YOU'LL NEED
✓ Metric Ruler

3-9 Metric Length

THINK AND DISCUSS

The metric system of measurement, like the decimal system, is based on tens. A *meter* is the basic unit of length. Other units you will use are *centimeter, millimeter,* and *kilometer.*

One centimeter (cm) is one hundredth of a meter (m).

1. a. **Discussion** Suppose you had a strip of paper to represent a meter. What could you do to the paper to model a centimeter? **Divide it into 100 equal parts.**
   b. **Discussion** How is this model similar to the square hundredths' models you have been using? **Each model has 100 equal parts.**
   c. How many centimeters are there in one meter? **100 cm**

One millimeter (mm) is one thousandth of a meter.

2. a. Suppose you want to model millimeters. Into how many equal parts would you divide a segment that represents 1 m? **1,000 equal parts**
   b. How many millimeters are there in one meter? **1,000 mm**
   c. How many millimeters are there in one centimeter? **10 mm**

WHAT? The meter was the first unit of measure based on something other than the body. Today the meter is based on the distance light travels in a certain amount of time.

3. Use your models to complete the following.
   a. 1 cm = ■ m **0.01**
   b. ■ cm = 1 m **100**
   c. 1 mm = ■ m **0.001**
   d. ■ mm = 1 m **1,000**
   e. ■ mm = 1 cm **10**
   f. 1 mm = ■ cm **0.1**

When you need to measure short distances, you can use a centimeter ruler. To measure a segment, align the 0 mark on the ruler with one end of the segment. Then read the length.

The segment is 53 mm, or 5.3 cm long.

KINESTHETIC LEARNERS For Questions 11–12, have students check their estimates by measuring such things as the width of the door and the length of a wall with a meter stick.

Ongoing Assessment Students will need centimeter rulers and meter sticks. Have students work in pairs to measure the items listed and complete the following table:

OBJECT	LENGTH	WIDTH	PERIMETER
desktop			
math textbook			
board eraser			
science textbook			

As students work, note whether they are choosing appropriate units and are using the rulers correctly. Then have students share and compare their measurements.

WORK TOGETHER

You may want to have sets of objects ready so that pairs of students can compare their measurements with others. Objects to measure might include a paper clip, a pencil, a window in the classroom, a textbook, a bulletin board, and a piece of chalk.

Wrap Up

What's the Big Idea? Ask students to describe the metric units of measurement. Then have students define *perimeter* and explain how to decide on an appropriate unit of measure.

Journal Have students compare the metric and ancient Egyptian systems of measurement to the United States units of yard, foot, and inch. Ask students which system they prefer. Have students give reasons for their answers.

4. a. What do the smaller marks on the ruler represent? millimeter
   b. What do the numbers 0, 1, 2, 3, and so on, represent? centimeter

5. Measure each segment in millimeters. Accept any reasonable measure.
   a. ______ 19mm b. ______________ 51mm
   c. ____________________ 74 mm
   d. Estimation What is the length of each segment to the nearest centimeter? a. 2 cm b. 5 cm c. 7 cm
   e. Measure each segment in centimeters. a. 1.9 cm b. 5.1 cm c. 7.4 cm

6. a. Draw a segment that is 16 cm long. Check students' drawings.
   b. Draw a segment that is 128 mm long. See Solution Key.
   c. Which of the segments you drew is longer? 16 cm segment

The **perimeter** of a figure is the distance around it. You find perimeter by adding the lengths of the sides of the figure.

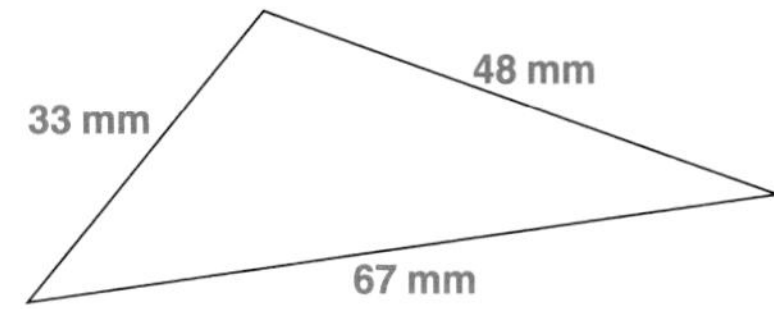

7. a. Measure each side of the triangle in millimeters. See above.
   b. What is the perimeter of the triangle? 148 mm

8. Describe some situations where you might need to know the perimeter of a figure. Answers may vary. Samples: fencing in a yard, buying a wallpaper border

When you measure an object you should first choose an appropriate unit of measure. To measure longer distances you would use kilometers (km). There are 1,000 m in 1 km.

9. Name two objects or distances you would measure using each unit. Answers may vary. Sample: a. swimming pool, room b. book c. stamp, safety pin d. race, distance to school
   a. meter b. centimeter c. millimeter d. kilometer

10. What unit would you use to measure each item?
    a. perimeter of a backyard meter
    b. length of a shirt sleeve centimeter
    c. width of a nailhead millimeter
    d. distance between towns kilometer

Some groups raise funds by sponsoring 10 km (10K) races or walks. A participant asks people to pledge a set amount of money for each kilometer the participant walks.

Organizer, continued

Prentice Hall Technology

Multimedia Math
- Math Investigations, Hazard City Messengers
- Math Investigations, Mission: Mars

Computer Item Generator
- 3-9

Fact of the Day

In 1791, the meter was defined as one ten-millionth of the length of the quadrant of the Earth's meridian. In 1983, it was redefined in terms of the speed of light in a vacuum.

—ACADEMIC AMERICAN ENCYCLOPEDIA

Connections Have students share ideas about when they might apply what they have learned about metric measurement. You may want to start with these examples:

- **Industrial Arts** (measuring construction materials, plumbing supplies, and foreign automotive parts)
- **Art** (drawing accurate diagrams or scale drawings)
- **Geography** (determining distance on maps drawn to scale)
- **Travel** (reading foreign street signs, following directions in another country, translating United States measures into metric measures)

Reteaching Activity Students will need centimeter rulers and strips of paper approximately 5 cm wide and 1 m long.

Have students make their own meter strips. Have them mark 100 cm and the first 10 mm on their strips. Students can then use their meter strips to measure various objects in the room such as pencil lengths, perimeter of windows and doors, and the length of the room. Send students on a Metric Measurement Scavenger Hunt around the room to find objects with approximate given measures, such as 20 cm (approximate width of a sheet of notebook paper).

ON YOUR OWN

CONNECTION TO GEOMETRY Exercises 16 and 17 review geometric concepts by having students add the measures of the sides of a figure to determine the figure's perimeter.

Error Alert! In Exercises 16–19, students may make a mistake in calculating the perimeter of an object. ***Remediation*** Tell students to check their answers for the perimeter of rectangles by comparing the answer to the length and width. The perimeter should equal twice the length plus twice the width.

WRITING For Exercise 20, have students check their estimates by measuring. Students should then evaluate their estimation strategies.

Assignment Options

Core: 13–17, 21–24, MR all, CH all	
Reinforce: 18–20, 27–30	**Enrich:** 25, 26

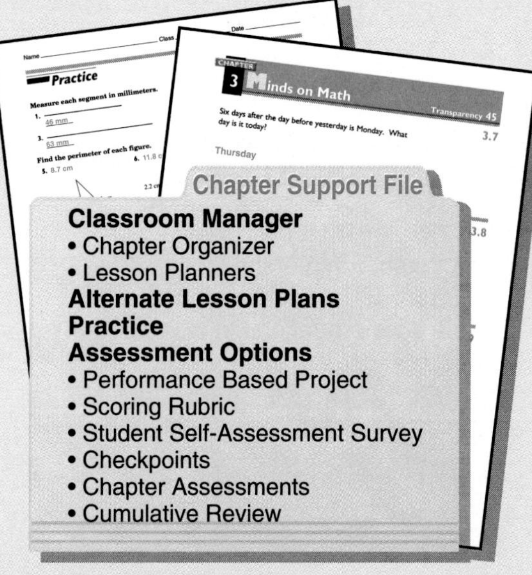

Minds on Math available in Teaching Transparencies

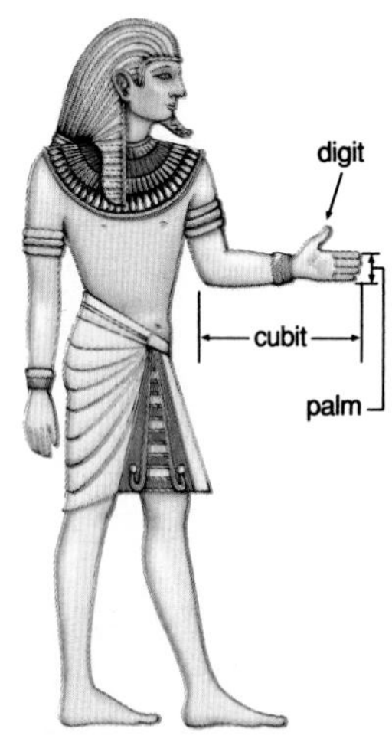

Ancient Egyptians based measures of length on the royal cubit, the palm, and the digit. The cubit (forearm) was the length from the elbow to the fingers. The palm was the width of the palm excluding the thumb. The digit was the width of the finger. **What standard measure is based on the human body?** foot

You can estimate the length or height of an object by using the length or height of an object you know. Answers may vary. Sample: a. Use string to represent the width of the door.

11. a. The width of a door is about one meter. How can you estimate the length of a wall that contains the door?
    b. Estimate the length of your classroom wall using the method you just described. Accept any reasonable estimate. Sample: A 33 m wall is about 33 door widths.
12. The height of a desk or table is about one meter. Explain how to estimate the height of your classroom from the floor to the ceiling using the height of the desk or table. Answers may vary. Sample: Measure the height of the desk using string. Use the string against a wall.

WORK TOGETHER

Work with a partner to create your own set of units. First have your partner measure your handspan, the distance on your hand from the tip of your small finger to the tip of your thumb. Then have your partner measure the width of your finger, and the length of your foot. Use your units to estimate the length of two objects in your classroom. Are your units convenient? Answers may vary. Sample: handspan—20 cm; finger—15 mm; foot—25 cm; a dictionary is about 1 foot; jumbo paperclip is about 3.5 fingers; Yes

ON YOUR OWN

Measure each segment in millimeters.
Answers may vary. Accept any reasonable measure.

13. ________ 28 mm
14. ________ 42 mm
15. ________ 91 mm

Find the perimeter of each figure.

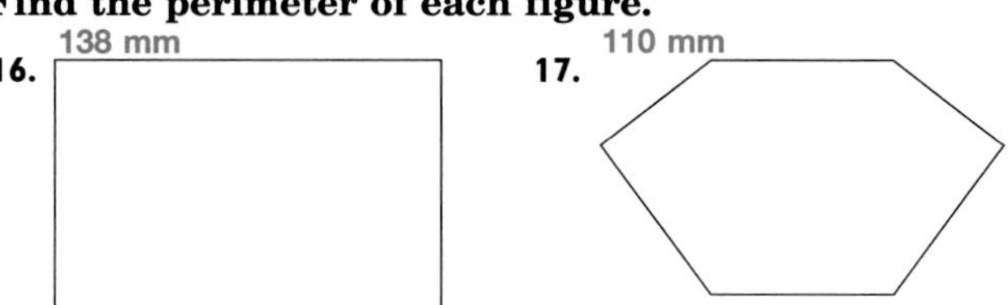

16. 138 mm
17. 110 mm

18. Draw a figure that has a perimeter of 20 cm. Answers may vary. Check students' drawings. See Solution Key.
19. **Pets** A rectangular dog kennel measures 4 m by 5 m. How much fence do you need to enclose the kennel? 18 m

Problem Solving Hint
Try drawing a diagram.

Exercises 21–24: Have students explain why a particular measurement may be unreasonable.

WRITING Students' answers for Exercise 25 should draw from their reading of the article. Encourage students to counter any points against their argument that they can find.

CRITICAL THINKING Students should make drawings of the table to accompany their answers to Exercise 26.

CHECKPOINT

AUDITORY LEARNERS For Exercises 1–4, have students say an estimate out loud before they work the problem, and then use it to check whether their answer is reasonable.

20. **Writing** Explain how you can find the perimeter of the rectangle without measuring. Find the perimeter.
See Solution Key.

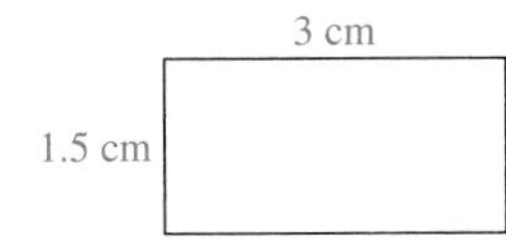

Is each measurement reasonable? If not, give a reasonable measurement.

21. The sidewalk in front of a house is 30 km long. no; 30 m
22. Your friend is about 160 cm tall. yes
23. Your pencil is 18 mm long. no; 18 cm
24. Our kitchen table is about 123 cm long. yes
25. **Writing** Read the newspaper article at the right. List some possible reasons why the metric system is not more widely used in this country. Then tell whether or not you think it should be more widely used. See Solution Key.
26. **Critical Thinking** The perimeter of a rectangular table is 8 m. The table is 1 m longer than it is wide. Find the length of each side. Explain how you got your answer.
2.5 m by 1.5 m; Draw a diagram and guess and check

Choose an appropriate unit of measure for each.

27. your height centimeter
28. Width of a ring millimeter
29. perimeter of your state kilometer
30. height of the ceiling meter

CHECKPOINT

Accept any reasonable estimate. Sample given.

First estimate. Then find the sum or difference.

1. $1.25 + 6.07$ 7; 7.32
2. $9.06 - 0.8$ 8; 8.26
3. $5.59 + 12.6$ 19; 18.19
4. $37 - 7.8$ 29; 29.2

Round to the place of the underlined digit.

5. 12.041 12.04
6. 2.40 2
7. 9.0655 9.066
8. 53.85 53.9
9. **Choose A, B, or C.** Suppose you wish to buy three items priced \$2.09, \$.59, and \$1.46. Which is the best estimate?
A. \$4.00 **B.** \$3.50 **C.** \$5.00 A

U.S. Still Catching Up

The United States officially began to "go metric" in 1973. Since most of the rest of the world's countries were using the metric system, it seemed to be a good idea.

The transition has been very slow. Still, there are signs of metrification on highway signs and on some items on the shelves of supermarkets and hardware stores.

Mixed REVIEW

Find the measure of a supplementary angle.

1. 98° 82°
2. 44° 136°

True or False?

3. Some trapezoids are squares. False
4. All squares are rectangles. True
5. Randa has \$25 in her bank account. She deposits \$33, \$18, and \$19.80. She earns interest of \$3.83. How much money does she have in her account now? \$99.63

Math Minutes

Write the integers described in each case.

1. greater than –3 and less than +5
–2, –1, 0, +1, +2, +3, +4
2. between –6 and –1
–5, –4, –3, –2

3-10

Connecting to Prior Knowledge

Students may at first think math and parties to be an unlikely combination. Have students brainstorm a number of ways math is used to plan and carry out a party. **(Possible answers include planning a budget and calculating costs, determining proportions such as food and utensils for guests, and planning timed activities such as showing a movie or playing games.)**

THINK AND DISCUSS

ESL **Questions 1 and 2:** Have students define *elapsed time* in their own words.

VISUAL LEARNERS Tell students that another way to show elapsed time is with a timeline. Help students draw a timeline and plot the times from the schedule onto the timeline.

KINESTHETIC AND AUDITORY LEARNERS For Question 3c, have a pair of students act out the situation and brainstorm ways to make a new schedule. Encourage auditory learners to give suggestions as they watch and listen.

Question 3c: Students may have creative solutions to the change in schedule. Have volunteers share their answers with the class.

DIVERSITY Be sensitive to the diverse background of students in your class. Some students may have never gone to a birthday party, much less planned one. Others may have long-standing family birthday traditions.

Error Alert! In Questions 6 and 7, students may make the mistake of adding different activities of less than an hour of elapsed time and dividing by 100 to find the time in hours. ***Remediation*** Remind students that time measurement is not a decimal system. Have students make a note of the conversions 60 s = 1 min, 60 min = 1 h, 24 h = 1 d, 7 d = 1 week. Point out that it is difficult to change from a decimal system for measurement to what seems like a less logical timekeeping system.

"Time is like money; the less we have of it to spare, the further we make it go."
—JOSH BILLINGS

Organizer

1. **Focus**
   Connecting to Prior Knowledge
2. **Teach**
   Think and Discuss
   Work Together
3. **Closure**
   Wrap Up

Vocabulary/Symbols
elapsed time

Skills Reviewed in Context of Lesson
- reading a clock

Student Resources
Extra Practice
Student Study Guide
Practice, TR Ch. 3, p. 33
Student Study Guide, Spanish Resources, TR

Teacher Resources

Teaching Transparency 45
Lesson Planner, TR Ch. 3, p. 11

Prentice Hall Technology

Multimedia Math
- Math Tools, Spreadsheet
- Hot Page™ 3-10

Computer Item Generator
- 3-10

continues next page

3-10 Times and Schedules

What's Ahead
- Determining and using elapsed time
- Reading, using, and making schedules

THINK AND DISCUSS

The amount of time between two events is **elapsed time.**
Answers may vary. Sample given.

1. What time do you get up in the morning on a school day? What time does school begin? Find the elapsed time. 6:30 A.M.; 8:10 A.M.; 1 h 40 min
2. How long is your lunch period? Is this elapsed time? 40 min; yes

You can use elapsed time when planning a party.

Party for Joey	
11:00 A.M.	Friends arrive, play outside.
11:30 A.M.	Clown show
12:15 P.M.	Lunch
1:00 P.M.	Open presents
2:00 P.M.	Friends leave

3. You plan a birthday party for your younger brother and make the schedule shown at the left.
   a. For how long do you plan the party to last? 3 h
   b. How much time did you allow for the clown show? for lunch? for presents? 45 min; 45 min; 1 h
   c. The clown calls at 10:30 A.M. to say that he will not be at the party until noon. Make a new party schedule. Answers may vary. See Solution Key.
4. Susan is having a party at 4:00 P.M. On the day of the party she needs to do the following activities:

decorate room (1 h)	mix cake (40 min)
bake cake (35 min)	cool cake (45 min)
frost cake (20 min)	shower (25 min)

   a. If Susan does the activities in the order given, at what time should she begin? 12:15
   b. Look more carefully at the activities. Which activities must be done in order? Could any be done at the same time? Figure out the latest time Susan could begin. See left.
   c. Susan does not want to shower until she has frosted the cake. Does this change your answer? Yes; 1:15 P.M.
   d. Susan decides she needs 25 min before the party to take care of last minute details. When should she begin her activities to allow for the extra 25 min? 1:10 P.M. for part b or 12:50 P.M. for part c

4b. mix cake, bake cake, cool cake, frost cake; decorate room and shower while baking and cooling cake; 1:40 P.M.

Whiteface, Auguste, *and Character are the three types of clowns.* ***Find out what is different about each type of clown.***

DIVERSITY Ask students if they know what the abbreviation RSVP on the invitation stands for, and where it comes from. **(It is short for the French phrase, *repondez s'il vous plait,* meaning, "Please respond." The phrase and its abbreviation came into use in this country during the 19th century.)**

WRITING For Question 6b, have students review the abridged list to make sure that no essential steps have been left out.

Error Alert! For Question 7, students may overlook that the bus schedule includes the times for buses leaving from Kagy Boulevard if they note only the "Leave" and "Arrive" columns, which begin with Willson Street and Kagy Boulevard. ***Remediation*** Encourage students to review the entire schedule before they begin. Some students may find it helpful to draw a simple diagram of the bus "route."

TECHNOLOGY OPTION For Question 7, have students use the date and time functions of a spreadsheet to calculate elapsed time. Students can also create their own schedule for extra practice using the spreadsheet.

Ongoing Assessment Tell students to pretend that each member of the class will be required to give a presentation on their favorite book or film. Each student will have 10 minutes in which to give a presentation. Ask students to determine how many presentations could be given during each class, and how many days it would take to complete all presentations.

WORK TOGETHER

Have each pair of students display the party schedule on a sample invitation that also gives the date, time, and location of the party. Students should then compare invitations. Students should ask themselves the following questions about each invitation:

- *Will I have time to prepare?*
- *Does the party look well planned?*
- *Am I missing any important information?*

Each pair of students should then revise its invitation to accommodate peers' comments and questions.

5. You decide to have a Halloween party. You want the invitations to arrive at least one week before the party. Mail usually takes two days in your city.
   a. By what date should you mail the invitations? **Oct. 22**
   b. **Discussion** What will you need to do before you can mail the invitations? How much time should you allow for these activities? **See right.**
   c. Your invitations ask people to let you know at least two days before the party if they are coming. If the people invited respond by mail or by telephone, between what dates should you hear from them? **Oct. 24 to Oct. 29**

5b. Answers may vary. Sample:
—Make a guest list (15 min)
—Buy invitations (1 h)
—Write invitations (45 min)
—Buy stamps (45 min)
—Put stamps on (5 min)

When you attend a party, you also need to think about time.

6. Suppose you received the invitation shown at the right. It is now 1:30 P.M. on May 15. You make a list and estimate the times for things you must do before the party.

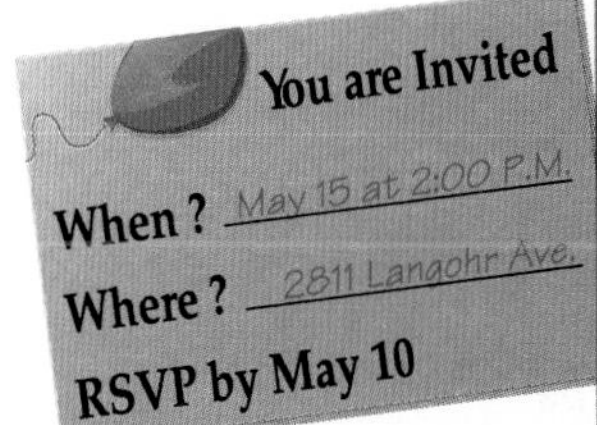

You are Invited
When ? May 15 at 2:00 P.M.
Where ? 2811 Langohr Ave.
RSVP by May 10

Change clothes	5 min
Wrap present	10 min
Ride bike to store	5 min
Buy film at the store	5 min
Ride bike to the party	10 min

   a. Suppose you start to get ready at 1:30 P.M. Will you get to the party on time? **No (5 min late)**
   b. **Writing** Explain how you solved this problem. **Answers may vary. See Solution Key.**

7. Lee is going to a party on Friday at 6:00 P.M. She will take the bus. The schedule is shown at the right. The bus stop at Willson Street is in front of Lee's house. The party is a 5-min walk from the bus stop at Kagy Boulevard.
   a. By what time should Lee catch a bus to arrive at the party in time? **5:20 P.M.**
   b. How many minutes will Lee be on the bus in each direction? how many minutes total? **25 min; 50 min**
   c. By what time should Lee leave the party to catch a bus and be home by 9:00 P.M.? **8:15 P.M.**
   d. Write down a schedule for Lee's travel plans. **See Solution Key.**

WK Bus Line
Buses Run Every 30 Minutes Monday-Friday

Leave	Arrive
Willson St.	Kagy Blvd.
7:20 A.M.	7:45 A.M.
7:50 A.M.	8:15 A.M.
...	...
11:20 P.M.	11:45 P.M.
Kagy Blvd.	Willson St.
7:50 A.M.	8:15 A.M.
8:20 A.M.	8:45 A.M.
...	...
11:50 P.M.	12:15 A.M.

Organizer, continued

Other Available Technology
Excel; Works by Microsoft: Question 7 *(optional)*

Fact of the Day

The Ferris Wheel was invented by the American engineer G. W. Ferris for the 1893 World's Columbian Exposition in Chicago. It could carry more than 2,000 people.

—ACADEMIC AMERICAN ENCYCLOPEDIA

PH Multimedia Math Hot Page™ 3-10

Wrap Up

What's the Big Idea? Have students explain how to determine and use elapsed time. Then ask students how to read, use, and make schedules.

Journal Tell students that one result of a good schedule or organization is that it seems to actually make time. Have students write about the benefits of organizing or planning time. Ask students if they think it is possible to make or save time.

Connections Have a discussion about how reading and using maps, charts, and schedules are useful in real-life situations. You may want to start with these examples:

- **Travel** (planning trips)
- **Social Studies** (understanding current events)
- **Employment** (working as a secretary, travel agent, pilot, railroad worker, nurse, truck driver)

Reteaching Activity Call an airline to ask for information about flights to another city. Share the departure and arrival times with the class. Ask students to explain what happens between the times listed for the two cities. **(The plane is moving from one city to the other.)** Ask students to name a good term for this time. **(elapsed time)** Then have students imagine that they want to travel from the one city to the other. Ask students to determine the elapsed time they should expect the flight to take. Bear in mind that time changes between sections of the country will affect the real elapsed time.

ON YOUR OWN

CRITICAL THINKING For Exercise 8b, have students draw a diagram for the bus route to help them answer the question.

CHAPTER INVESTIGATION Students should identify the elapsed time for Exercise 10 and compare it to the buying obligations of the club.

Assignment Options

Core: 8a, 9a, 10, 11, MR all	
Reinforce: 9b, 12–14	**Enrich:** 8b

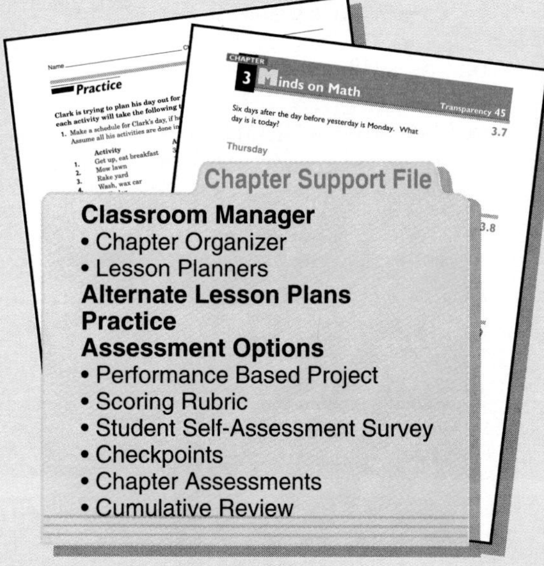

Chapter Support File

Classroom Manager
- Chapter Organizer
- Lesson Planners

Alternate Lesson Plans

Practice

Assessment Options
- Performance Based Project
- Scoring Rubric
- Student Self-Assessment Survey
- Checkpoints
- Chapter Assessments
- Cumulative Review

Minds on Math available in Teaching Transparencies

9b. Answers may vary. Sample:

Ride bike home	3:30 P.M.
Feed dog	3:50 P.M.
Do homework	4:00 P.M.
Play outside	5:00 P.M.
Help make dinner	5:25 P.M.
Eat dinner	6:00 P.M.

WORK TOGETHER

Work with a partner. Plan a party. Decide on an occasion and activities for the party. List all the things you will need to do to plan and have the party. Make a schedule for the party. Answers may vary. Check students' work.

ON YOUR OWN

8. Use the bus schedule on the previous page.
   a. What time does the last bus of the day leave? Where does it end? 11:50 P.M.; Kagy Blvd.
   b. **Critical Thinking** Could only one bus be used for all the scheduled trips? Explain your answer. Answers may vary. Sample: No; Both buses are traveling at the same time.

Ride bike home	20 min
Feed the dog	10 min
Do homework	1 h
Play outside	■
Help prepare dinner	35 min

9. Bonnie does the activities shown at the left after school but before dinner at 6:00 P.M. School is out at 3:30 P.M.
   a. How much time does she have to play outside? 25 min
   b. Make a schedule for Bonnie's afternoon. See left.

GREAT EXPECTATIONS

Astronaut

I, Evin Demirel, would gladly like to be an astronaut. I have always found that space exploration into the unexplored fascinates me. To be on another planet in space would be a wonderous and great feeling. I would like to try to go to space camp in Huntsville to learn about how to be an astronaut. I also would like to learn about the planets. I have always had an interest in space. I took a program about it 2 years ago and decided to have a career in space science. I like to look at the perilous blackness up in the sky at night, and I also like looking at books with pictures of planets and other space objects. Right now, I wish I could be one of the first lucky persons to set foot on Mars and with a lot of determination and hard work, don't doubt me.

Evin Demirel

ACTIVITY Students may benefit from extending Exercise 11 to cover a longer period of time, such as a week. Have students note ways in which they could make better use of their time.

ESTIMATION Students should round the time for Exercise 14 to the nearest quarter of an hour.

Great Expectations

There are many valuable resources available to the students for gathering information about astronauts. Students can write for more information to such places as these:

- Young Astronaut Council
  Box 65432
  1211 Connecticut Avenue, NW, #800
  Washington, D.C. 20036
- National Aeronautics and Space Administration
  Aerospace Education Services Program
  Educational Publishing Services
  Washington, D.C. 20546
- U. S. Space and Rocket Center
  P. O. Box 070015
  Huntsville, AL 35807-7015

Students can also learn from discussions with experts. For example:

- Visit Kennedy Space Center, Houston Space Center or the United States Space and Rocket Center in Atlanta Georgia. All three centers provide guided tours as well as information packets in the education offices.

Discussions with students can include the following topics:

- What degree and what kind of courses one needs to become an astronaut
- The skills needed to predict, calculate, and coordinate data for space flight
- The role of computers and new technology for space flight
- The relationship between the careers of astronaut and pilot

Answers may vary. Sample given.
10. Investigation (p. 94) Identify any time or schedule obligations you make when you join the music club. Does this influence your decision to join or not? 8 tapes must be purchased in 2 years; No, I usually buy 4 tapes a year.
11. Activity Name at least five activities you do between the time you get up in the morning and the time you arrive at school. Estimate the elapsed time for each activity. Time yourself tomorrow morning to see how close your estimates were. Answers may vary. Check students' work.

Data File 2 (pp. 38–39) **Use the data for Exercises 12–14.**

12. Find the total time you would expect to spend for the Montezuma's Revenge ride at Knott's Berry Farm. 2 min 7 s
13. Which ride has a wait time slightly less than ride time? Captain EO, Red Baron
14. Estimation At about 4:50 P.M. you get in line for Captain EO while your sister gets something to eat. At about what time should she meet you after the ride? Accept any reasonable estimate. Sample: about 5:20 P.M.

Classify the triangle with the following angles.

1. 45°, 45°, 90° right
2. 38°, 65°, 77° acute
3. The lengths of the sides of a square are 1.5 mm. Find the perimeter. 6 mm
4. What metric unit would you use to measure the height of your school? meter
5. Joelna has 3 h of homework tonight. She likes to take a $\frac{1}{2}$ h break. What is the latest she can begin studying to finish by 9:30 P.M.? 6:00 P.M.

Math Minutes

In each case, which of the quantities is the most reasonable estimate?

1. shoes: 1 mg, 1 g, 1 kg **1 kg**
2. horse: 500 mg, 500 g, 500 kg **500 kg**
3. bucket: 10 ml, 10 l, 10 kl **10 l**

Dear Evin,

I was completely fascinated by your description of space and your wish to become a future space explorer. The experiences that I have had as a NASA astronaut have allowed me to see things from a slightly different view.

While on orbit inside a Space Shuttle vehicle, I circle the entire earth every 90 minutes, at a speed of about 7 miles every second! My concept of *neighbor* begins to include those living on different continents and in remote and isolated areas. As I view our Earth from space, the land masses are easily recognizable because they look just like the maps I studied in school. There are no boundaries or borders or fences visible from our lofty perch. It is awesome to see it and get the "big picture."

Frederick D. Gregory
NASA Astronaut

CHAPTER 3

WRAP UP

Exercises 1–3: You may need to give students an example of a decimal written in standard form, such as 0.327.

Exercises 13–17: Have students use estimation to check if their answers are reasonable.

Ongoing Assessment Have students work with partners on the exercises.

- After students have done Exercises 21–23, have them take turns asking their partners to choose an appropriate metric unit of length to measure objects they see in their classroom.
- For Exercises 25 and 26, encourage partners to come up with more than one approach to solving the problems.

Vocabulary/Symbols

balance
centimeter
deposits
elapsed time
equivalent
expanded form
interest
kilometer
meter
mill
millimeter
one hundredth
one tenth
perimeter
standard form
statement
withdrawals

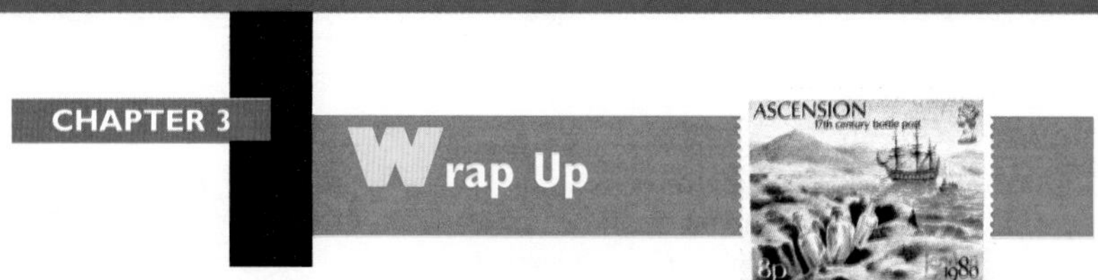

Place Value of Decimals 3-1, 3-2, 3-3

You can write decimals in ***standard form, expanded form,*** or in words. Order decimals by comparing digits that have the same place value. Start with the digit on the left and move one place to the right as needed.

Write each number in standard form.

1. five tenths 0.5
2. forty-eight hundredths 0.48
3. nine and eight ten-thousandths 9.0008

Compare. Use >, <, or =.

4. 1.8392 ■ 1.8382 >
5. 11.721 ■ 6.731 >
6. 0.81 ■ 0.81 =
7. 500.2 ■ 50.02 >

Estimation, Adding and Subtracting Decimals 3-5, 3-6, 3-7, 3-8

You can use ***rounding*** or ***front-end*** estimation to estimate a sum. To estimate a difference, use rounding. Before adding or subtracting decimals, line up decimal points and annex zeros if necessary. Use estimation to check if answers are reasonable.

Money added to a bank account is a ***deposit.*** Money taken out is a ***withdrawal.*** The amount in the account is the ***balance.***

Round to the place value of the underlined digit.

8. $5.69\underline{8}3$ 5.698
9. $0.8\underline{7}624$ 0.88
10. $9.23\underline{5}7$ 9.236
11. $3.\underline{9}876$ 4.0
12. $4\underline{4}.095$ 44

Add or subtract.

13. $0.9 - 0.2$ 0.7
14. $0.72 + 0.96$ 1.68
15. $1.741 - 0.81$ 0.931
16. $62.24 - 8.598$ 53.642
17. $337.4 + 20.08$ 357.48

Complete the spreadsheet.

	A	B	C	D	E	F
1	Date	Start Balance	Withdrawal	Deposit	Interest	End Balance
2	2/5/95	18. ■	20.00	0.00	0.00	65.62
3	2/15/95	19. ■	0.00	40.00	20. ■	106.02

18. 85.62 19. 65.62 20. 0.40

Get Ready for Chapter 4

The skills previewed will help students understand and solve problems involving multiplying and dividing decimals.

Metric Length 3-9

Metric measurement is based on tens. The ***meter*** (m) is the basic unit of length. Other measures include ***millimeter*** (0.001 m), ***centimeter*** (0.01 m), and ***kilometer*** (1,000 m).

Choose the appropriate unit of measure for each.

21. altitude of an airplane meter

22. your height centimeter

23. perimeter of a classroom meter

Times and Schedules 3-10

Elapsed time is the amount of time between two events. You can use elapsed time to help plan your day.

24. It's 6:00 P.M. Can Lori do everything on her schedule and still have time to read for 25 min before her 9:30 P.M. bedtime? At what time will she complete her to-do list if she works continuously? Yes; 8:15 P.M.

Eat dinner	*40 min*
Homework	*55 min*
TV program	*30 min*
Feed dog	*10 min*

Strategies and Applications 3-4

Solving a similar, simpler problem can help you see new ways to solve a given problem.

25. A clock chimes every 30 min. How many times will it chime in the month of June? 1,440 times

26. How many days have passed since you were born? Answers may vary. Check students' work.

GETTING READY FOR CHAPTER 4

Sometimes you can estimate the product or quotient of two decimals by first rounding each decimal to the nearest whole number, and then multiplying or dividing.

Round each decimal to the nearest whole number. Then multiply or divide.

1. 3.5×2.1 about 8

2. 6.3×9.256 about 54

3. 10.1×119.2 about 1,190

4. $80.63 \div 8.9$ about 9

5. $72.4 \div 8.5$ about 8

6. $99.8 \div 9.8$ about 10

7. 32.5×0.55 about 33

8. $230.55 \div 0.95$ about 231

9. 47.8×39.9 about 1920

10. $11.99 \div 4.33$ about 3

11. 70.008×3.15 about 210

12. $2.5 \div 0.99$ about 3

Student Resources

Practice, p. 123
Problem Solving Practice, p. 115
Extra Practice
Student Study Guide
Student Study Guide, Spanish Resources, TR
Tools for Studying Smarter, TR
Student Self-Assessment Survey, TR Ch. 3, p. 37 *(see below)*

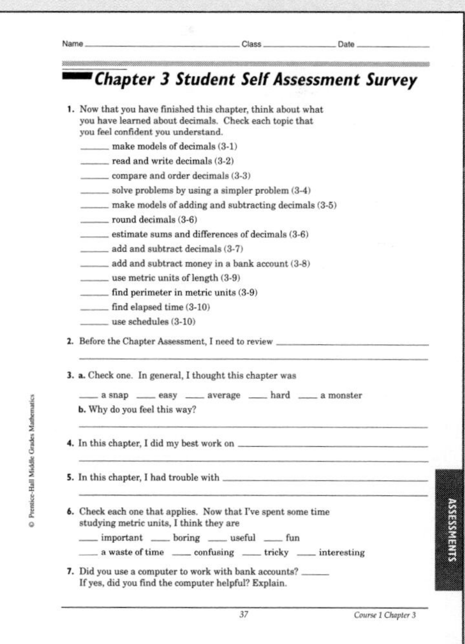

Name ____ Class ____ Date ____

Chapter 3 Student Self Assessment Survey

1. Now that you have finished this chapter, think about what you have learned about decimals. Check each topic that you feel confident you understand.
   ____ make models of decimals (3-1)
   ____ read and write decimals (3-2)
   ____ compare and order decimals (3-3)
   ____ solve problems by using a simpler problem (3-4)
   ____ make models of adding and subtracting decimals (3-5)
   ____ round decimals (3-6)
   ____ estimate sums and differences of decimals (3-6)
   ____ add and subtract decimals (3-7)
   ____ add and subtract money in a bank account (3-8)
   ____ use metric units of length (3-9)
   ____ find perimeter in metric units (3-9)
   ____ find elapsed time (3-10)
   ____ use schedules (3-10)
2. Before the Chapter Assessment, I need to review ____
3. a. Check one. In general, I thought this chapter was
   ____ a snap ____ easy ____ average ____ hard ____ a monster
   b. Why do you feel this way?
4. In this chapter, I did my best work on ____
5. In this chapter, I had trouble with ____
6. Check each one that applies. Now that I've spent some time studying metric units, I think they are
   ____ important ____ boring ____ useful ____ fun
   ____ a waste of time ____ confusing ____ tricky ____ interesting
7. Did you use a computer to work with bank accounts? ____
   If yes, did you find the computer helpful? Explain.

ASSESSMENTS

37 Course 1 Chapter 3

CHAPTER 3

PUTTING IT ALL TOGETHER

The projects on these pages can be used in a variety of ways.

- alternative assessment
- portfolio ideas
- additional assignments for gifted and talented students
- extra credit for all students

Follow Up

- Have students list points from their investigation.
- Ask students to write a rough draft of an article on the Music Club.
- If students have decided not to join the Music Club, ask them to explain how the club could improve its offer so that they would change their minds.

Students can contact local music stores to find CD and cassette prices over the past decade. Motivated students can learn about the Consumer Price Index and use the index to look for price trends.

Newspaper Numbers

COOPERATIVE GROUPS Have students work in pairs, or in groups of three. Once they have compiled their numbers, have one group compare their findings with another group. You may want to have findings presented to the whole class.

To further the activity, have students consider what kinds of decimal numbers they would be likely to find in different sections of the newspaper, such as the sports, business, national/world news, and style/home sections. Again, students should determine whether rounded numbers in each section would affect the reader's understanding. Students could create a chart to present their ideas.

Materials and Manipulatives

Newspaper Numbers
- newspapers

Decimal Derby
- number cubes

In Round Numbers
- papers
- scissors
- ruler

alternate to paper, scissors, and ruler:
3 × 5 index cards

Prentice Hall Technology

Follow Up
Multimedia Math
- Math Tools, Text

Other Available Technology

Follow Up
- *Word* by Microsoft
- *WriteNow* by Wordstar
- *II Write* by American School Publishers
- *Bank Street Writer* by Broderbund
  (all optional)

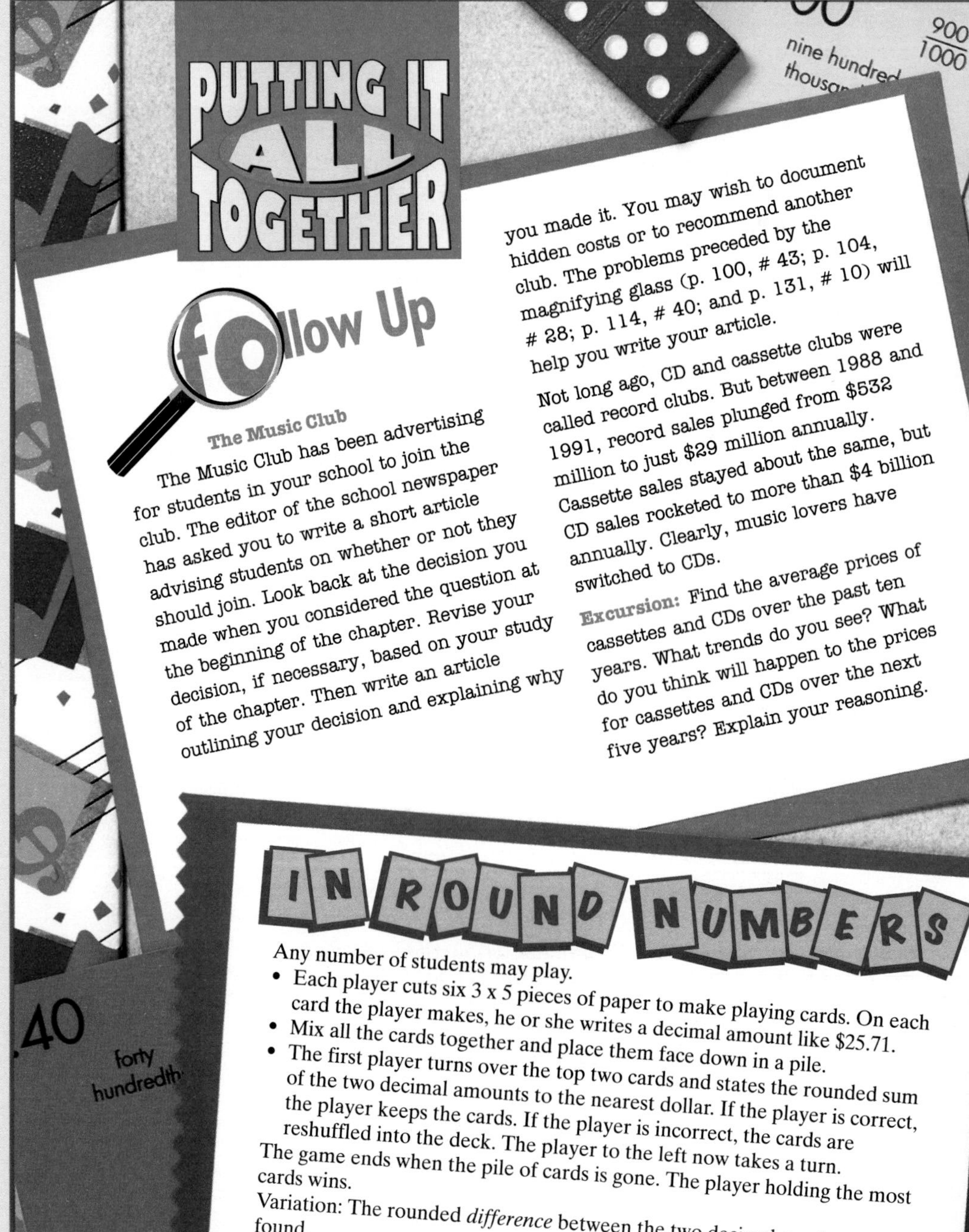

PUTTING IT ALL TOGETHER

Follow Up

The Music Club

The Music Club has been advertising for students in your school to join the club. The editor of the school newspaper has asked you to write a short article advising students on whether or not they should join. Look back at the decision you made when you considered the question at the beginning of the chapter. Revise your decision, if necessary, based on your study of the chapter. Then write an article outlining your decision and explaining why you made it. You may wish to document hidden costs or to recommend another club. The problems preceded by the magnifying glass (p. 100, # 43; p. 104, # 28; p. 114, # 40; and p. 131, # 10) will help you write your article.

Not long ago, CD and cassette clubs were called record clubs. But between 1988 and 1991, record sales plunged from $532 million to just $29 million annually. Cassette sales stayed about the same, but CD sales rocketed to more than $4 billion annually. Clearly, music lovers have switched to CDs.

Excursion: Find the average prices of cassettes and CDs over the past ten years. What trends do you see? What do you think will happen to the prices for cassettes and CDs over the next five years? Explain your reasoning.

IN ROUND NUMBERS

Any number of students may play.
- Each player cuts six 3 x 5 pieces of paper to make playing cards. On each card the player makes, he or she writes a decimal amount like $25.71.
- Mix all the cards together and place them face down in a pile.
- The first player turns over the top two cards and states the rounded sum of the two decimal amounts to the nearest dollar. If the player is correct, the player keeps the cards. If the player is incorrect, the cards are reshuffled into the deck. The player to the left now takes a turn.

The game ends when the pile of cards is gone. The player holding the most cards wins.

Variation: The rounded *difference* between the two decimal numbers is found.

Decimal Derby

Students will realize that they should place what they believe will be the largest number they roll in the tens column of the place value chart.

In Round Numbers

COOPERATIVE GROUPS Students may want to designate one student to confirm whether the answers players give are correct. This role could be rotated among players after each round.

A Time and a Place

VISUAL LEARNERS Students may want to construct a floor plan of the museum first, in order to plan their path to and from exhibits they want to visit. Students may find it helpful to organize the information in a chart, broken into hours or half hours.

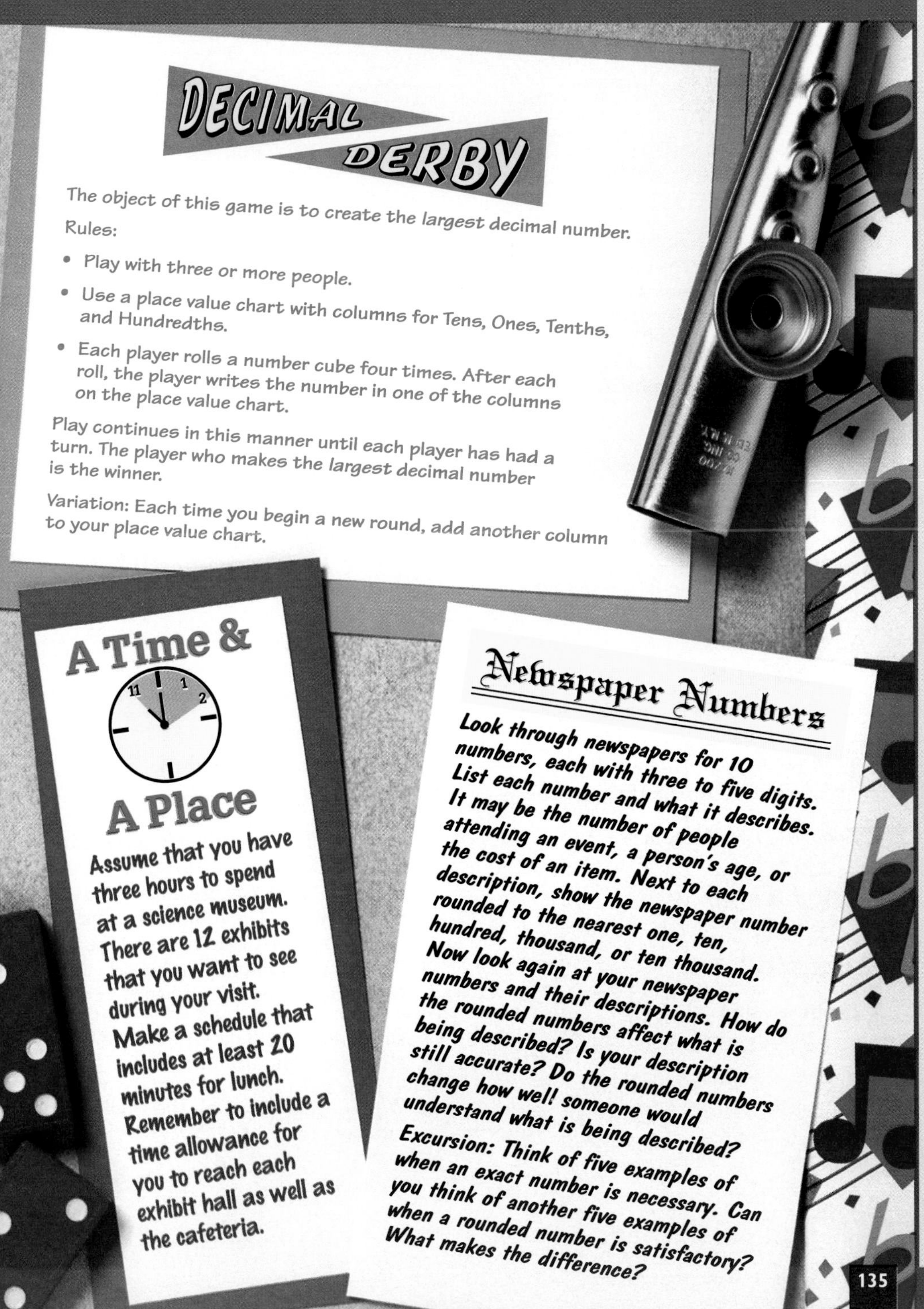

DECIMAL DERBY
The object of this game is to create the largest decimal number.
Rules:
• Play with three or more people.
• Use a place value chart with columns for Tens, Ones, Tenths, and Hundredths.
• Each player rolls a number cube four times. After each roll, the player writes the number in one of the columns on the place value chart.
Play continues in this manner until each player has had a turn. The player who makes the largest decimal number is the winner.
Variation: Each time you begin a new round, add another column to your place value chart.
A Time & A Place
Assume that you have three hours to spend at a science museum. There are 12 exhibits that you want to see during your visit. Make a schedule that includes at least 20 minutes for lunch. Remember to include a time allowance for you to reach each exhibit hall as well as the cafeteria.
Newspaper Numbers
Look through newspapers for 10 numbers, each with three to five digits. List each number and what it describes. It may be the number of people attending an event, a person's age, or the cost of an item. Next to each description, show the newspaper number rounded to the nearest one, ten, hundred, thousand, or ten thousand. Now look again at your newspaper numbers and their descriptions. How do the rounded numbers affect what is being described? Is your description still accurate? Do the rounded numbers change how well someone would understand what is being described?
Excursion: Think of five examples of when an exact number is necessary. Can you think of another five examples of when a rounded number is satisfactory? What makes the difference?
135

CHAPTER 3 ASSESSMENT

Writing Questions allow students to describe more fully their thinking and understanding of the concepts they've learned.
Exercise 1 is a writing question.

Enhanced Multiple Choice Questions are more complex than traditional multiple choice questions, which assess only one skill. Enhanced multiple choice questions assess the processes that students use as well as the end results. They are written so that students can use more than one strategy to solve the problem. Using multiple strategies is encouraged by the National Council of Teachers of Mathematics (NCTM).
Exercise 3 is an enhanced multiple choice question. If students select A, ask them if they read the question carefully.

ESTIMATION For Exercise 6, ask students to round to the nearest one dollar and nearest ten dollars and compare the answers. Have students compare each method and determine which way worked better.

Exercise 7: Have students use estimation to check if answers are reasonable.

Exercise 12: Remind students to use a problem solving strategy to solve the problem.

Resources

Performance Based Project, TR Ch. 3, pp. 34–36
Chapter Assessment, Forms A and B, TR Ch. 3, pp. 39–42
Spanish Chapter Assessment, Spanish Resources, TR
Computer Item Generator

CHAPTER 3

Assessment

1. **Writing** Is the number two hundred thirteen thousandths equal to two hundred and thirteen thousandths? Explain. No; The word "and" means the second number is 200.013.
2. **Choose A, B, C, or D.** The value of the digit 3 in the number 24.1538 is ■. D
   - **A.** three hundreds
   - **B.** three hundredths
   - **C.** three tenths
   - **D.** three thousandths
3. **Choose A, B, C, or D.** Which of the following is *not* true for the number 5.836? B
   - **A.** 5.836 rounds to 5.84.
   - **B.** 5.836 > 5.85
   - **C.** The expanded form is 5 + 0.8 + 0.03 + 0.006.
   - **D.** It is read as "five and eight hundred thirty-six thousandths."
4. Compare. Use >, <, or =.
   - **a.** 2.34 ■ 2.4 <
   - **b.** 8.97 ■ 8.970 =
   - **c.** 32.12 ■ 32.42 <
   - **d.** 12.82 ■ 12.81 >
5. Find each sum.
   - **a.** 3.89 + 15.638 19.528
   - **b.** 8.99 + 6.35 15.34
   - **c.** 0.9356 + 0.208 1.1436
   - **d.** \$4.38 + \$2.74 + \$1.17 \$8.29
6. **Estimation** Suppose your savings account has a balance of \$129.55. You deposit \$17.89 and withdraw \$83.25. What is the approximate balance? about \$65 (Accept any reasonable estimate.)
7. Find each difference.
   - **a.** \$20 − \$15.99 \$4.01
   - **b.** 8.956 − 6.973 1.983
   - **c.** 536.79 − 95.8 440.99
   - **d.** 5.867 − 0.345 5.522
8. Find the perimeter in millimeters. 110 mm

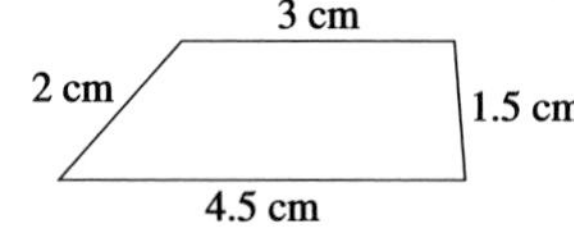

9. What unit of metric measure is appropriate for each item?
   - **a.** length of a pen centimeter
   - **b.** perimeter of a state kilometer
   - **c.** distance around a track meter
   - **d.** width of an automobile centimeter
10. Jackson plans to attend a beach party at 1:00 P.M. He needs to shower and dress (35 min), eat breakfast (25 min), do his chores (1 h 40 min), get his beach supplies (25 min), and bike to the party (20 min). Plan his schedule before he leaves for the beach party. Answers may vary. See Solution Key.
11. Graph 8.1, 8.2, 8.08, 8.15, and 8.03 on a number line. See Solution Key.
12. What is the sum of all the whole numbers from 1 to 300? 45,150

CHAPTER 3

CUMULATIVE REVIEW

Exercise 4 and Exercise 8 are enhanced multiple choice questions.

Item(s)	Review Topic	Chapter
1	writing decimals	3
2	angles	2
3, 5	averages	1
4	symmetry	2
6, 9	triangles	2
7	estimating products	3
8	comparing and ordering decimals	3
10	metric length	3

Resources

Cumulative Review, TR Ch. 3, pp. 43–44
Transparency Masters, TR p. 35

CHAPTER 3

Cumulative Review

Choose A, B, C, or D.

1. Which is the decimal for thirty-four hundredths? B

   A. 0.034 B. 0.34
   C. 3.40 D. 34.00

2. Which angle would have $\overrightarrow{XY}$ as one of its sides? C

   A. $\angle XYZ$ B. $\angle XZY$
   C. $\angle ZXY$ D. $\angle YZX$

3. How would you find the range of five salaries? B

   A. Add the salaries and divide by 5.
   B. Subtract the lowest salary from the highest.
   C. Arrange the salaries in order and choose the middle one.
   D. Choose the salary that occurs more than once.

4. If a quadrilateral has two lines of symmetry, then it *cannot* be which of the following? D

   A. rhombus B. square
   C. rectangle D. trapezoid

5. All five items in a data set are multiplied by 10. How is the mode changed? A

   A. It is multiplied by 10.
   B. It is multiplied by 50.
   C. It is multiplied by 2.
   D. The mode does not change.

6. In $\triangle ABC$, the measure of $\angle A$ is half the measure of $\angle B$. $\angle B$ is a right angle. What is the measure of $\angle A$? A

   A. 45° B. 61° C. 78° D. 59°

7. Unleaded gasoline costs $1.29 per gallon. If you buy 12 gallons, estimate the amount of money you spend. C

   A. $10 B. $29
   C. $14 D. $20

8. If 0.305 is represented by point B, what numbers could be represented by points A and C? D

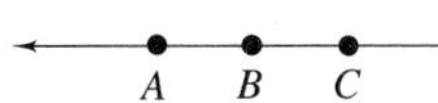

   A. A: 0.051, C: 0.7
   B. A: 0.03, C: 0.06
   C. A: 0.350, C: 0.4
   D. A: 0.29, C: 0.32

9. What is the *best* name for the triangle shown? B

   A. acute B. obtuse
   C. scalene D. right

10. Without measuring, what is the best estimate for the perimeter of the triangle shown in Question 9? B

   A. 7 mm B. 7 cm C. 7 m D. 7 km

CHAPTER

4 Multiplying and Dividing Decimals

Why Study Multiplying and Dividing Decimals?

If students ask this question, you may want to mention these areas in which decimals are used: science, architecture, art, nature, bank balances, foreign currency, problem solving, and financial advising.

Graphic Display of Chapter Content

Below is one possible representation of the chapter's content and its applications to the real world. Have students create their own graphic display and fill in applications that they have seen in their own lives.

- The center oval should state the main concept of the chapter: multiplying and dividing decimals.
- Have students draw the ovals with the next level of concepts presented in the chapter (estimating, order of operations, distributive property, multiplying decimals, and dividing decimals). You may want students to add other topics that they think are appropriate.
- Ask students to draw as many application ovals as they can.
- Discuss all the applications that students identify.
- Have students make and present one display that includes all the students' ideas.

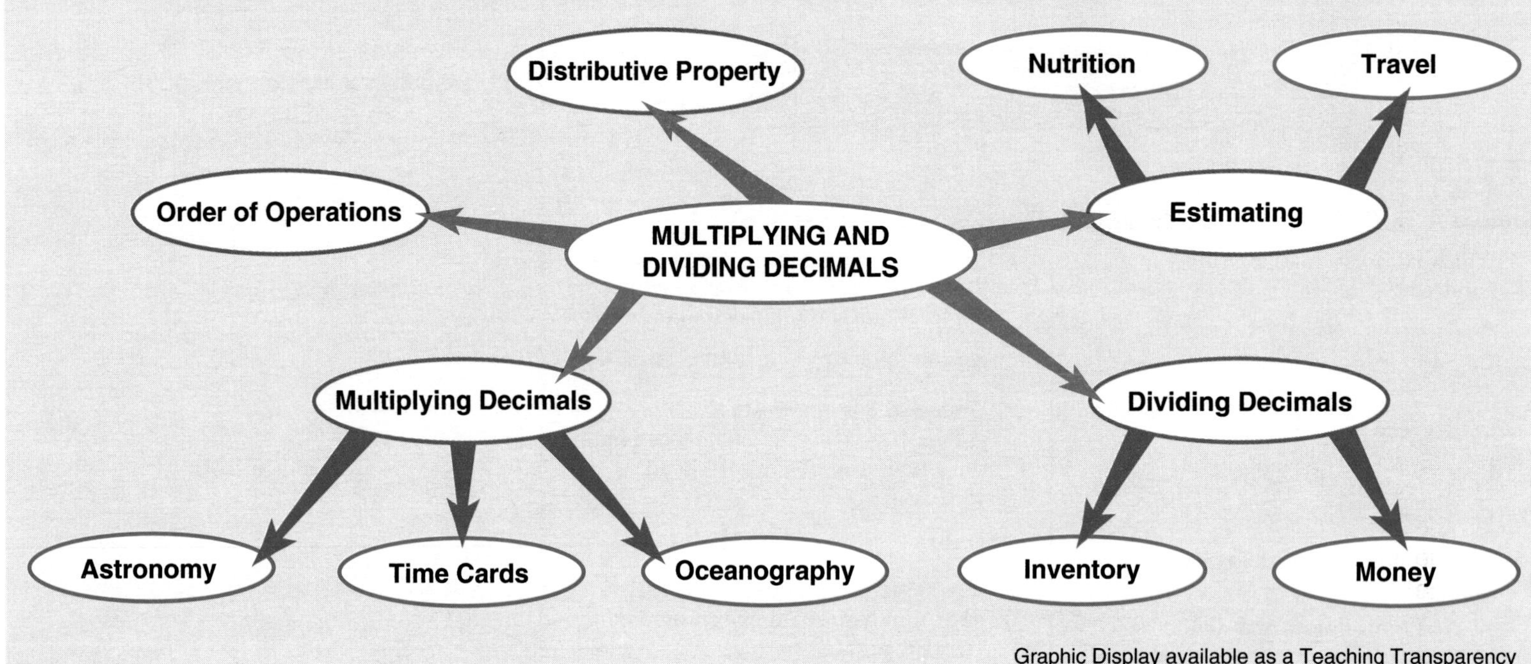

Graphic Display available as a Teaching Transparency

Vocabulary and Symbols

area	field
compatible numbers	order of operations
database	record
distributive property	sort

Materials and Manipulatives

calculator	colored pencils
computer	database or spreadsheet software
decimal squares	graph paper
paper	ruler
scissors	

Additional Resources

Commercially Available Technology

Calculator
fraction

Software
spreadsheet software
Excel; Works by Microsoft
Works by Microsoft

other
Data Insights by Sunburst

Other Media
"Decimals Forever." Films Inc Video, 5547 N. Ravenswood Ave., Chicago, IL 60640. (800) 343-4312.
"Dividing with Decimals." Aims Media, 9710 DeSoto Avenue, Chatsworth, CA 91311-4409.
"Multiplying with Decimals." Aims Media, 9710 DeSoto Avenue, Chatsworth, CA 91311-4409.

Materials at Little or No Cost

American Numismatic Association, 818 N. Cascade Ave., Colorado Springs, CO 80903. Publishes *First Strike* for junior members interested in coins and money.
Center for Multisensory Learning, Lawrence Hall of Science, University of California, Berkeley, CA 94720. Distributes math and science activities for visually impaired and physically challenged learners.

Bibliography

For Teachers
Mathematical Scientists at Work. Washington, DC: Mathematical Association of America, 1992. Distributed by NCTM.
Reys, Barbara J. et al. *Developing Number Sense in the Middle Grades: Addenda Series, Grades 5–8.* Reston, VA: NCTM, 1991.

For Students
Bungum, Jane E. *Money and Financial Institutions.* Minneapolis, MN: Lerner Publications, 1991.
Phillips, Louis. *263 Brain Busters: Just How Smart Are You Anyway?* NY: Viking Kestrel, 1985.
Taylor, Ron. *Through the Microscope.* NY: Facts on File, 1984.

Prentice Hall Technology

Multimedia Math
- Math Tools, Manipulatives
- Math Tools, Math Frames
- Math Tools, Spreadsheet
- Math Tools, Calculation
- Hot Page™ 4-4
- Hot Page™ 4-5
- Hot Page™ 4-10
- Math Investigations, Crisis in Hydrotown

Computer Item Generator
- Chapter 4

Community Resources

Field Trips
- a jewelry store to learn about gem weight
- a branch bank for accounting

Guest Speakers
- a company manager on wages
- a jeweler

Backpack Take-Home Activities

Materials
- newspaper
- pencil
- tape
- paper
- scissors

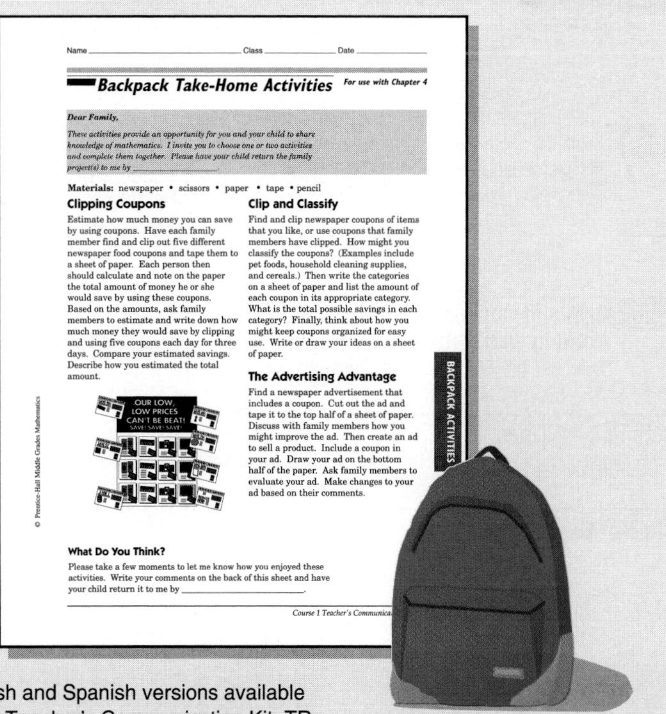

Name ______ Class ______ Date ______

Backpack Take-Home Activities For use with Chapter 4

Dear Family,
These activities provide an opportunity for you and your child to share knowledge of mathematics. I invite you to choose one or two activities and complete them together. Please have your child return the family project(s) to me by ______.

Materials: newspaper • scissors • paper • tape • pencil

Clipping Coupons
Estimate how much money you can save by using coupons. Have each family member find and clip out five different newspaper food coupons and tape them to a sheet of paper. Each person then should calculate and note on the paper the total amount of money he or she would save by using these coupons. Based on the amounts, ask family members to estimate and write down how much money they would save by clipping and using five coupons each day for three days. Compare your estimated savings. Describe how you estimated the total amount.

Clip and Classify
Find and clip newspaper coupons of items that you like, or use coupons that family members have clipped. How might you classify the coupons? (Examples include pet foods, household cleaning supplies, and cereals.) Then write the categories on a sheet of paper and list the amount of each coupon in its appropriate category. What is the total possible savings in each category? Finally, think about how you might keep coupons organized for easy use. Write or draw your ideas on a sheet of paper.

The Advertising Advantage
Find a newspaper advertisement that includes a coupon. Cut out the ad and tape it to the top half of a sheet of paper. Discuss with family members how you might improve the ad. Then create an ad to sell a product. Include a coupon in your ad. Draw your ad on the bottom half of the paper. Ask family members to evaluate your ad. Make changes to your ad based on their comments.

What Do You Think?
Please take a few moments to let me know how you enjoyed these activities. Write your comments on the back of this sheet and have your child return it to me by ______.

© Prentice-Hall Middle Grades Mathematics
Course 1 Teacher's Communica...

English and Spanish versions available in the Teacher's Communication Kit, TR

Chapter 4 Planning Guide

Objectives	Assignment Options	Critical Thinking/ Problem Solving	Writing and Reading Math	Estimation Mental Math	Materials and Manipulatives
Investigation	This chapter-long project involves open-ended questioning and data collecting and provides an additional opportunity to assess students.	p. 140 p. 140	p. 140 p. 140	p. 140	p. 140
4-1 Estimating Products and Quotients • Estimating decimal products and quotients	**Core:** 18–20, 24–26, 32, 33, 35a, 39, 41; MR all **Reinforce:** 21–23, 27–31, 35b, 36, 37 **Enrich:** 34, 38, 40	1–3, 6; EX2; 16, 17, 30, 31, 36–41; MR: 1, 5 pp. 141, 142; BI p. 142	30, 31, 40 p. 144; JL p. 143 JL Sheet	1c, 2, 4; EX1; 5, 6; EX2; 7–41 pp. 141–144; RT p. 143	p. 141 TT 49
4-2 Technology: Decimals in Databases • Using a database to explore applications of decimals	**Core:** 9; MR all **Reinforce:** 11, 12 **Enrich:** 10	1, 3b, 4; WT: 5, 6, 8; 11; MR: 6 pp. 145, 146; BI p. 146; MM p. 147	11 JL p. 145 JL Sheet	MR: 1, 2, 4, 5	WT: 7; 10 pp. 145–147 TT 4, 5, 19, 49
4-3 The Order of Operations • Evaluating expressions using order of operations	**Core:** 8–22, 24–26, 30–33, 36, 37; MR all **Reinforce:** 23, 27, 28, 34, 35, 38–43 **Enrich:** 29, 44	WT: 2b; 4, 23, 29, 44; MR: 1, 2, 6 pp. 148, 150; BI p. 149	23 p. 150; JL p. 149 JL Sheet	5a–c, 6, 7, 9–22; MR: 3–5 p. 150	WT: 1; 36–39 p. 149 TT 19, 49
4-4 The Distributive Property • Using the distributive property	**Core:** 23, 24, 30–33; MR all; CH all **Reinforce:** 20–22, 25–29 **Enrich:** 34	WT: 6; EX1; 7, 22, 34; CH: 10 pp. 151–153; BI p. 152; MM p. 154	34 p. 154; JL p. 153 JL Sheet	17–19, 27–29; CH: 1–9; MR: 1–3 pp. 152, 154	1–3; WT: 4–6; 20, 21 WT p. 151; RT p. 153 TT 1, 50, 52
4-5 Exploring decimal products	**Core:** 6–9, 11–16, 21; MR all **Reinforce:** 10, 17–19 **Enrich:** 20, 22	4, 20, 22; MR: 6 p. 156; BI p. 157; MM p. 157	20 p. 157; JL p. 157 JL Sheet	MR: 4, 5	1–3; WT: 5; 11–19 p. 157; WT p. 156; RT p. 157 TT 1, 11, 12, 50
4-6 Multiplying Decimals • Multiplying decimals	**Core:** 21–34, 43; MR all **Reinforce:** 35–40, 42, 45–47 **Enrich:** 41, 44	WT: 1–4; EX1; 5, 6; EX2; 9, 20, 42–47; MR: 5, 6 pp. 158, 159; BI p. 160; MM p. 161	44–47 p. 161; JL p. 160 JL Sheet	EX2; 7; EX4; 16–20, 25–28; MR: 1, 2 pp. 158–161	WT: 1–4; EX3; 10, 11, 29–36 pp. 159, 160; WT p. 158 TT 19, 50, 53
4-7 Problem Solving: Too Much, Too Little Information • Solving problems with too much or too little information	**Core:** 11–13, 15, 17; MR all **Reinforce:** 9, 10, 14 **Enrich:** 16	All; MR: 4, 7 p. 162; BI p. 163	All p. 164; JL p. 163 JL Sheet		p. 162 TT 51
4-8 Exploring Decimal Quotients • Modeling decimal quotients	**Core:** 9–12, 14–17; MR all **Reinforce:** 13, 18–22 **Enrich:** 23, 24	5, 23; MR: 4, 5 BI p. 167	23 p. 167; JL p. 167 JL Sheet		1d, 2, 4; WT: 6–8; 14–22, 24a pp. 166, 167; WT p. 166; RT p. 167 TT 11, 12, 19, 51
4-9 Dividing Decimals • Dividing decimals	**Core:** 23–31, 35–38, 40; MR all; CH all **Reinforce:** 32–34, 39, 42 **Enrich:** 41, 43	EX1; 5, 6a, 7c, 8–11, 22, 38–43; CH 5; MR: 3 pp. 168, 169, 171; BI p. 170; MM p. 171	41 JL p. 170 JL Sheet	EX1; 8c, 9c, 18–22, 32–37 pp. 168, 170	WT: 2–4; MR: 1, 2 p. 170; WT p. 168; RT pp. 170–171 TT 19, 51, 53
4-10 Math and Consumer Economics: Working with Data • Using decimals in real-world situations	**Core:** 4, 5, 6, 12; MR all **Reinforce:** 9–11 **Enrich:** 7, 8	1–12; MR: 6 pp. 172, 174; BI p. 173; MM p. 175	11 JL p. 173 JL Sheet	2, 7–9, 12b; MR: 1–3 pp. 173, 174	7–10 pp. 172–174 TT 1, 19, 51
Putting It All Together	These pages include a Follow-Up to the Investigation and other projects, which provide additional opportunities to assess the students.	pp. 178–179 pp. 178–179	pp. 178–179		pp. 178–179 pp. 178–179
Chapter Resources		PS Practice, CW, CA, CR PS Practice p. 155; CW pp. 176–177; CA p. 180; CR p. 181	PS Practice, CW, CA p. 138B; PS Practice p. 155; CW pp. 176–177; CA p. 180		pp. 138A, 138B Backpack Activities, Manip. Kits, TT 48

Student Edition (question numbers)
Teacher's Edition (page numbers)
Other Components

BI—What's the Big Idea? CA—Chapter Assessment CH—Checkpoint
CG—Computer Item Generator CR—Cumulative Review CW—Chapter Wrap Up
DM—Decision Making EP—Extra Practice EX—Example FD—Fact of the Day

Cooperative Learning Activities	Technology	Data Collection & Analysis	Interdisciplinary Connections	Applications	Assessment	Review	Strand Integration	NCTM Correlation*
p. 140	p. 140	p. 140 p. 140		paper	p. 140 p. 140			
WT p. 142; WT p. 142; RT p. 143 Alt. Lesson		32–34, 41 FD p. 142	Health, Social Studies pp. 141, 143	money, recreation, nutrition, sports pp. 141, 143 Alt. Lesson	p. 142	MR: All p. 141; RT p. 143 Practice p. 24	Stat./Probability, Measurement, Number, Logic/Language	1, 2, 3, 4, 5, 7, 8, 10, 13
WT: 5–8 p. 145; WT p. 146; RT p. 147	All pp. 146, 147	1–3; WT: 5–8 9–12 p. 145; WT p. 146; FD p. 146	Alt. Lesson	hobbies, marketing, money p. 147	p. 146	MR: All p. 145; RT p. 147 Practice p. 25	Stat./Probability, Discrete Math, Number, Logic/Language	1, 2, 3, 4, 5, 7, 8, 10, 13
WT: 1–3 WT p. 148; RT p. 149	WT: 1; 36–39 p. 149	FD p. 149	p. 149	consumer issues pp. 148, 149	p. 148	MR: All p. 148; RT p. 149 Practice p. 26	Algebra, Number, Logic/Language	1, 2, 3, 4, 5, 6, 7, 8, 9
WT: 4–6 WT pp. 151–152; RT p. 153	Hot Page™ 4-4	FD p. 152		pp. 151, 153	CH: All p. 152; CH p. 154 CH TR p. 38	MR: All p. 151; RT p. 153 Practice p. 27	Algebra, Geometry, Number, Logic/Language	1, 2, 3, 4, 5, 6, 7, 8, 9, 12, 13
WT: 5 p. 156; WT pp. 156–157	Hot Page™ 4-5	FD p. 157	p. 157	p. 157	p. 156	MR: All p. 156; RT p. 157 Practice p. 28	Number, Logic/Language	1, 2, 3, 4, 5, 6, 7, 8
WT: 1–4 p. 159; WT p. 158 Alt. Lesson	WT: 1–4; EX3; 10, 11 pp. 159, 160 Alt. Lesson	41, 45–47 FD p. 159	Geography, Science, Health pp. 160, 161	geography, oceanography, astronomy pp. 160, 161	pp. 159–160	MR: All p. 158; RT p. 161 Practice p. 29	Stat./Probability, Measurement, Number, Logic/Language	1, 2, 3, 4, 5, 7, 8, 10, 11, 13
p. 163; RT p. 163		17 FD p. 163	Science p. 163	hobbies, money, sports, jobs p. 163	p. 162	MR: All p. 162; RT p. 163 Practice p. 30	Stat./Probability, Measurement, Number, Logic/Language	1, 2, 3, 4, 7, 8, 10, 12, 13
WT: 6–8 p. 166; WT p. 166; RT p. 167	1d WT p. 166	FD p. 167		food p. 167	p. 166	MR: All p. 166; RT p. 167 Practice p. 31	Number, Logic/Language	1, 2, 3, 4, 5, 6, 7, 8
WT: 1–4 p. 171; WT p. 168	WT: 2–4 p. 170; WT p. 168	40 p. 171; FD p. 169	p. 170	food, money pp. 168, 170	CH: All pp. 169–170; CH p. 171 CH TR p. 38	MR: All p. 168; RT pp. 170–171 Practice p. 32	Measurement, Number, Logic/Language	1, 2, 3, 4, 7, 8, 13
10 pp. 173, 174; WT p. 172	7, 8 p. 173 Hot Page™ 4-10	1–3; WT: 4–6; 7–10, 12 p. 172; FD p. 173; RT p. 174		economics, jobs, medicine pp. 172–174; GE p. 175	p. 173	MR: All p. 172; RT p. 174 Practice p. 33	Stat./Probability, Discrete Math, Logic/Language	1, 2, 3, 4, 5, 7, 8, 9, 10, 13
pp. 178–179 p. 179	pp. 178–179 pp. 178–179	pp. 178–179 pp. 178–179		sports, money, advertising	pp. 178–179 pp. 178–179			
IN, PT PT pp. 178–179 Backpack Activities	p. 138B Multimedia Math, CG	Data File 4 pp. 138–139	Health, Science pp. 138F, 138–139 Interdisciplinary Units	biology, health pp. 138A, 138F, 138–139 Backpack Activities, Projects, Interdisciplinary Units	IN, PT, CA pp. 138E, 140; pp. 176–180 CA, Span. CA, Self Assessment, Projects	Practice, PS Practice, CW, CR, EP, SSG CW pp. 176–177 Span. SSG, CR		

GE—Great Expectations IN—Investigation JL—Journal MM—Math Minutes
MR—Mixed Review PS—Problem Solving PT—Putting It All Together RT—Reteaching Activity
SSG—Student Study Guide TT—Teaching Transparency WT—Work Together

*For a description of the NCTM Standards, see page T15.

Assessment Options

Observation Checklist

In this chapter on multiplying and dividing decimals, you have opportunities to observe your students do these tasks:

✓ estimate decimal products and quotients
✓ use decimals with database or spreadsheet software
✓ simplify expressions using order of operations and the distributive property
✓ model decimal products and quotients using decimal squares
✓ multiply and divide decimals
✓ solve problems containing irrelevant information
✓ identify problems with too little information
✓ use decimals to solve real-life problems

In every chapter, you are given opportunities to observe your students:

✓ work with a partner or in a group
✓ write about mathematics
✓ participate in discussions about mathematics
✓ collect and analyze data
✓ display positive attitudes about mathematics
✓ use measurement tools

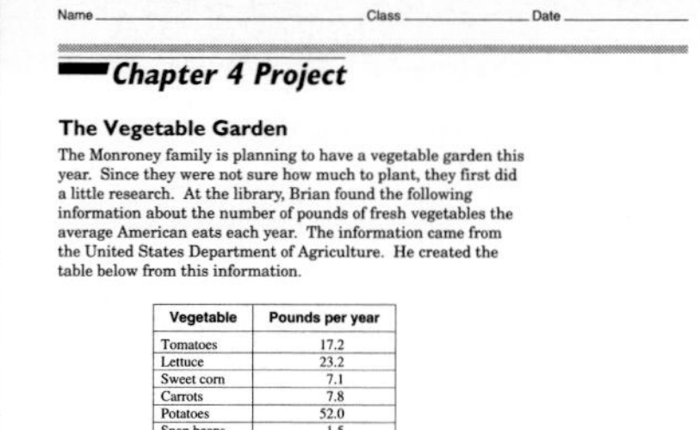

Name ____________ Class ________ Date ________

Chapter 4 Project

The Vegetable Garden

The Monroney family is planning to have a vegetable garden this year. Since they were not sure how much to plant, they first did a little research. At the library, Brian found the following information about the number of pounds of fresh vegetables the average American eats each year. The information came from the United States Department of Agriculture. He created the table below from this information.

Vegetable	Pounds per year
Tomatoes	17.2
Lettuce	23.2
Sweet corn	7.1
Carrots	7.8
Potatoes	52.0
Snap beans	1.5

Brian also gathered the following information about the six people in his family:

- His mother likes all vegetables.
- His father likes everything except beans.
- His grandmother doesn't like tomatoes or carrots.
- His brother doesn't like lettuce.
- His sister doesn't like carrots, potatoes, or beans.
- Brian likes everything.

Brian also discovered that everyone in the family loves sweet corn, so he estimated that his family eats twice the average amount.

To keep track of all this information, Brian made a chart. He decided to put a check for each vegetable that each person likes and an *X* for each vegetable that any person doesn't like. He put double checks for corn. Then he added up the total number of checks for each vegetable.

Course 1 Chapter 4

Performance Based Project (with scoring rubric), Chapter Files, TR

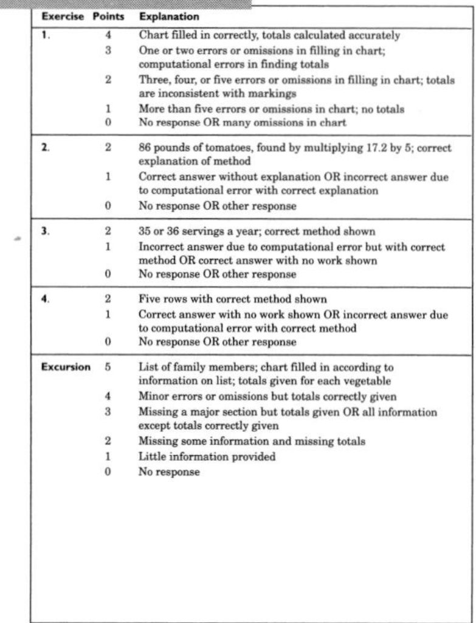

...en Scoring Rubric

Exercise	Points	Explanation
1.	4	Chart filled in correctly, totals calculated accurately
	3	One or two errors or omissions in filling in chart; computational errors in finding totals
	2	Three, four, or five errors or omissions in filling in chart; totals are inconsistent with markings
	1	More than five errors or omissions in chart; no totals
	0	No response OR many omissions in chart
2.	2	86 pounds of tomatoes, found by multiplying 17.2 by 5; correct explanation of method
	1	Correct answer without explanation OR incorrect answer due to computational error with correct explanation
	0	No response OR other response
3.	2	35 or 36 servings a year; correct method shown
	1	Incorrect answer due to computational error but with correct method OR correct answer with no work shown
	0	No response OR other response
4.	2	Five rows with correct method shown
	1	Correct answer with no work shown OR incorrect answer due to computational error with correct method
	0	No response OR other response
Excursion	5	List of family members; chart filled in according to information on list; totals given for each vegetable
	4	Minor errors or omissions but totals correctly given
	3	Missing a major section but totals given OR all information except totals correctly given
	2	Missing some information and missing totals
	1	Little information provided
	0	No response

Course 1 Chapter 4

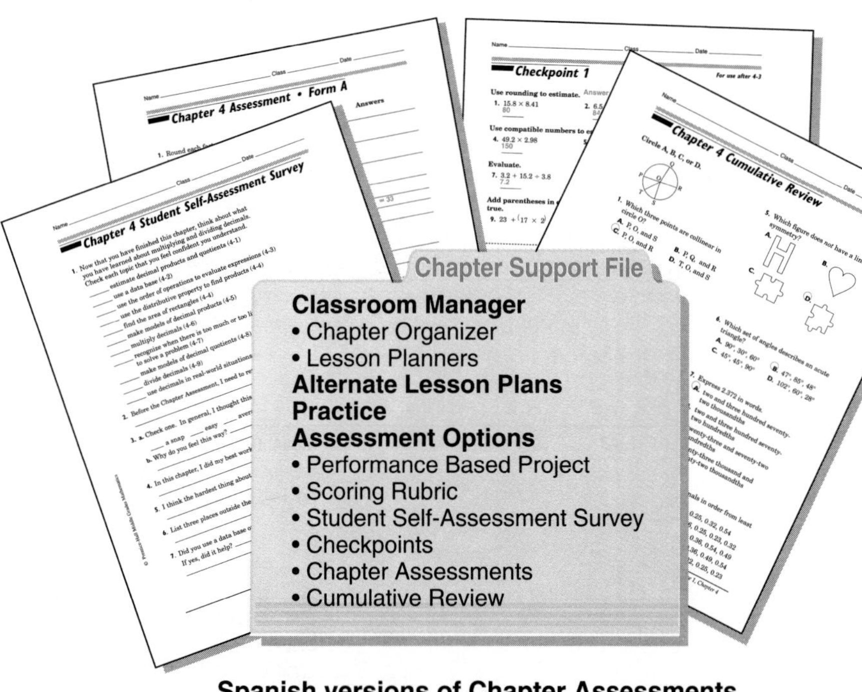

Chapter Support File

Classroom Manager
- Chapter Organizer
- Lesson Planners

Alternate Lesson Plans

Practice

Assessment Options
- Performance Based Project
- Scoring Rubric
- Student Self-Assessment Survey
- Checkpoints
- Chapter Assessments
- Cumulative Review

Spanish versions of Chapter Assessments available in Spanish Resources

Interdisciplinary Units
- **Travel and Geography**
- **Space Exploration**
- **Sports**
- **Consumer Awareness**
- **The Great Outdoors**

English & Spanish

These units include cross-curriculum connections and can be used at any time during the school year. See the Teacher's Guide for more information.

Working with Middle Grade Students

> *"For many students, mathematics in the middle grades has far too often simply repeated or extended much of the computational work covered in the earlier grades. The intent of this standard is to help students broaden their perspective, to view mathematics as an integrated whole rather than as an isolated set of topics, and to acknowledge its relevance and usefulness both in and out of school. Mathematics instruction at the 5–8 level should prepare students for expanded and deeper study in high school through exploration of the interconnections among mathematical ideas."*
>
> —NCTM Curriculum and Evaluation Standards

Addressing a Variety of Learning Styles

The mathematical tasks in Chapter 4 involve various learning styles. Here are some examples.

- Visual learners apply area formulas (p. 152) and use decimal squares (p. 156).
- Tactile learners use calculators (p. 158) and model decimal quotients (p. 166).
- Auditory learners discuss the distributive property (p. 152) and patterns in decimal combinations (p. 168).
- Kinesthetic learners find the thickness of one page of a book (p. 171) and measure the length of their femurs (p. 161).

Cultural Connections

An Australian tribe of the Murray River counts from one to seven like this: enea, petcheval, petcheval enea, petcheval petcheval, petcheval petcheval enea, petcheval petcheval petcheval, petcheval petcheval petcheval enea. If we write "1" for "enea" and "2" for "petcheval," we write: 1, 2, 21, 22, 221, 222, 2221. This system is not positional. That is, 2122, 1222, 1222 and 2221 are all the same number. There is no zero. Using this system, addition is very easy but multiplication is hard. (Try both!)

Team Teaching Suggestion

Work with a kinesiology teacher to introduce the concept of decimal computations found in sports.

- Students can observe baseball players in order to find batting averages and pitching averages.
- Students can observe swimming meets and gymnastics competitions to calculate scores.

Mathematical Connections

This chapter relates decimals to many other school subjects and to life outside the classroom. Many middle school students find security in the clarity of mathematics, and appreciate it as an unambiguous language, available to everyone regardless of their verbal skills.

Teaching Tip

Students in the middle grades are extremely active and often very dramatic in their expressions. By connecting the study of decimals to the construction of theater scenery and its placement on the stage, you provide more motivation for student discovery.

Bulletin Board

Post items (or pictures of items) that students would be interested in purchasing. List prices next to each item. For some of the items supply a price that is for more than one item. (For example, markers are 3 for $1.00.) Each week post a holiday shopping list and a weekly class allowance. Have students find out how much it will cost to purchase everything on the list. Then ask students if their weekly class allowance is enough to pay for it.

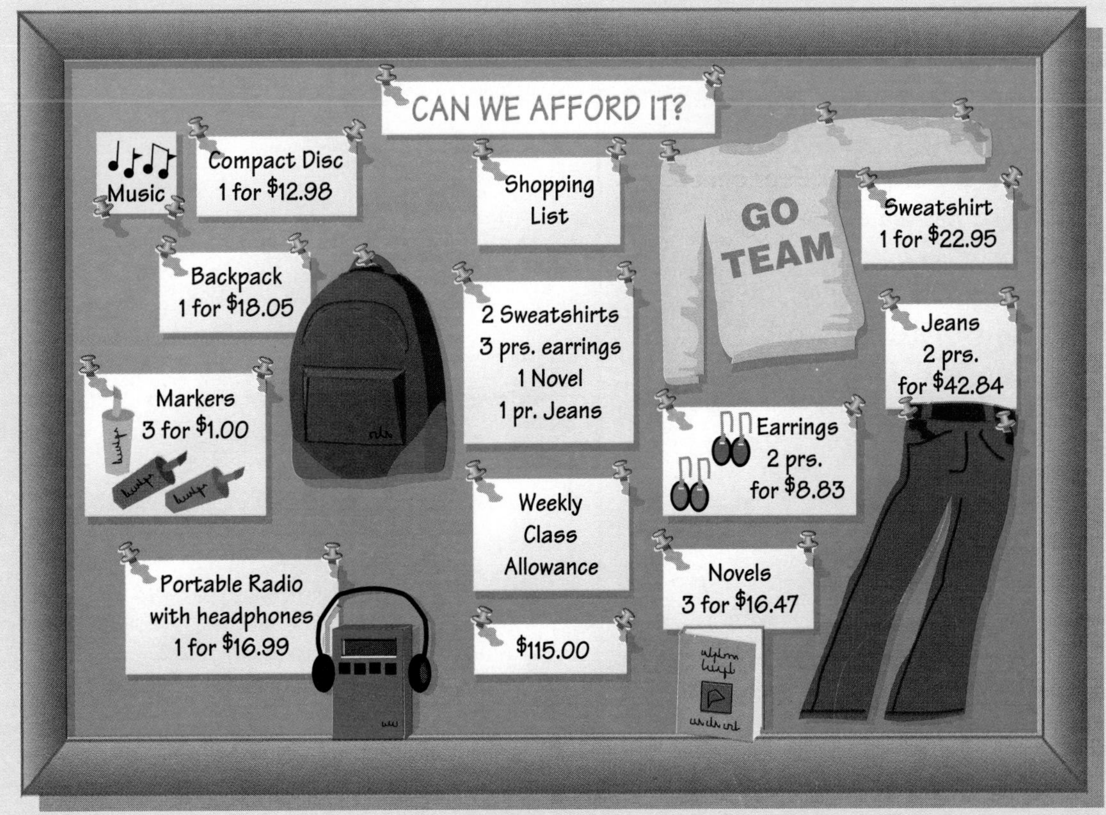

CHAPTER 4 Multiplying and Dividing Decimals

Cultural Connections Johann Friederich Blumenbach (1752–1840) was a German physiologist who had a large collection of human skulls. He made very careful measurements of these skulls and divided humans into five racial groups: Caucasian, Mongolian, Malayan, Ethiopian, and American. Today, race is defined more broadly as a set of shared traits that include characteristics that are passed on genetically, such as blood type, hair texture, and skin color. Characteristics such as language, customs, and religion are parts of culture, rather than race, because they are not inherited. Experts do not agree on how many races exist. Some speak of these nine races: African, Native American, Asian, Native Australian, European, Indian, Melanesian, Micronesian, and Polynesian.

WORLD VIEW The culture of ancient Greece is credited with providing the basis of much of our present-day knowledge. Hippocrates (born 460 B.C.), the son of a physician, reasoned out that time and a proper diet were necessary means for dealing with illnesses. The ethics of the Hippocratic Oath are still embedded in current medical practices.

Digging for Data

Have each student determine what height they will probably be at the age of 18 (from the chart), and do the same for four other students. Make a list of the "now" and "then" heights and then discuss the expected average growth.

- *Name the four types of bones used to determine adult height.* **(humerus, radius, femur, tibia)**
- *Consider the phrase "every bone in my body aches" and list the bones most likely to be the problem.* **(Answers may vary.)**

Chapter 4 Contents

Data File Questions

pp. 161, 496

Data File 4

Measuring Up

In the 16th century, the Germans were using leg splints and arm stretchers to set broken limbs. The Greeks used splints, starched bandages, and clay casts to set broken bones.

It's All in the Bones

When scientists know the gender of a skeleton and the length of the tibia, femur, humerus, or radius, they can estimate the person's height when they were alive. The chart shows the formula used for each gender and bone.

Adult Height (in cm) Based on the Length of Major Bones

Male

(2.9 x length of humerus) + 70.6
(3.3 x length of radius) + 86.0
(1.9 x length of femur) + 81.3
(2.4 x length of tibia) + 78.7

Female

(2.8 x length of humerus) + 71.5
(3.3 x length of radius) + 81.2
(1.9 x length of femur) + 72.8
(2.4 x length of tibia) + 74.8

Source: *Arithmetic Teacher*

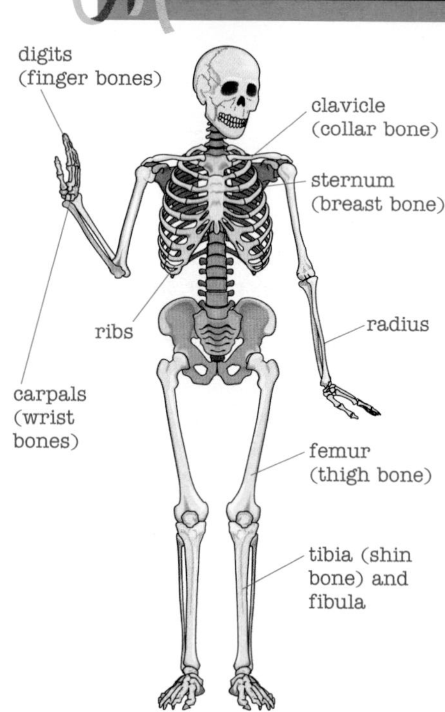

How Many Bones Do You Have?

A baby is born with more than 300 bones—that's more than an adult's 206 bones. As you grow, some of your bones grow together. This is called bone fusion. The last bones to grow together become the collarbone. Different people's bones grow and fuse in different ways. About one person in 20 ends up with an extra rib bone.

Source: *Macmillan Book of Fascinating Facts*

- *If there is an average of 4.5 people in every family, how many bones is that per family?* **(927 if the family members are adults)**
- *Have students call the librarian, veterinarians, or pet shop owners to find out the number of bones in their pets.*

Journal Activity Have students read the four objectives for the chapter and write what they already know about decimals. Ask them to describe any problems they have solved using decimals on a calculator.

Interdisciplinary Connection [Health] The five major kinds of nutrients needed to keep our bodies healthy are proteins, carbohydrates, fats, vitamins, and minerals. A large part of our bones and teeth are made up of minerals which are also an essential part of muscles, blood, and nerves. These minerals are calcium, iron, phosphorus, potassium, sulfur, chlorine, sodium, magnesium, and iodine. A proper balance of a variety of healthful foods usually provides enough of these minerals. Drinking lots of water each day is very important; a person can survive longer without food than without water.

WHAT YOU WILL LEARN

- how to model decimal products and quotients
- how to estimate decimal products and quotients
- how to use technology to create databases
- how to solve problems with too much or too little information

scapula (shoulder blade)
cervical (neck) vertebrae
humerus
pelvis
lumbar vertebrae
tarsals (ankle bones)

How Tall Will You Be?

To estimate your adult height, find your present height on the left side of the graph for your gender. Follow the horizontal line across until you are above your age. Now follow the nearest curve to the column on the right that gives an estimate of your adult height.

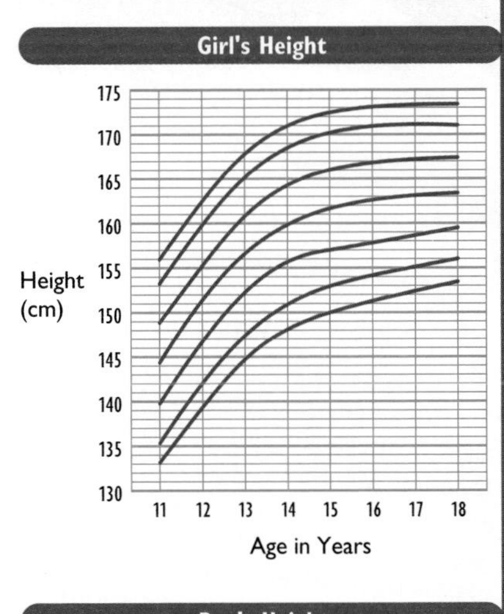

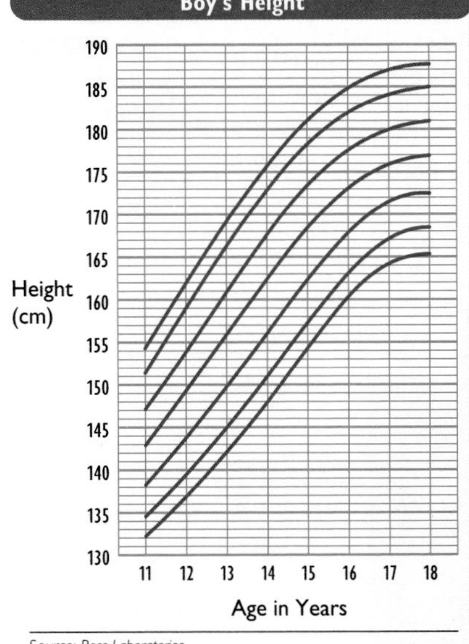

Source: *Ross Laboratories*

Fact of the Day

Giraffes, the tallest of mammals, have exactly the same number of bones in their neck as human beings or shrews.

—*McGraw-Hill Encyclopedia of Science and Technology*

CHAPTER 4

INVESTIGATION

Memo

Students may be perplexed by having to determine the thickness of something so thin as a sheet of paper. Remind them that this kind of problem often can be solved indirectly. Ask this question: *A pillow weighing 5 lb is stuffed with 2,000 feathers. How could you find the weight of 1 feather?* **(Divide 5 lb by 2,000.)**

Mission

Encourage students to be creative in their approaches to the problem. The best ideas are sometimes those that at first seem the most outlandish. Foster an attitude of daring in group problem-solving situations.

After about half the chapter has been completed, have students show you their work on the project. If they are behind schedule, you may want to give them intermediate deadlines in order to check their work.

Additional Leads to Follow

- *How can you use estimation to help you find the thickness of a sheet of paper?*
- *Do different kinds of notebook paper have different thicknesses? If so, how will this affect your choice?*

Keeping a Project Notebook

Some suggestions for students' notebooks are these.

- Decide on the categories of data you will record. Possibilities: date, location of sample, description of sample, measurements of sample. Include categories that you are not sure you will need. You can always discard them later.
- Keep paper samples whenever possible.
- List the dates and results of all project discussions.
- Include all calculations, together with explanations for how they were done.

Project Organizer

Related Exercises
p. 161
p. 171
p. 174

Follow Up
p. 178

Teacher's Notes
pp. 140, 161, 171, 174

Community Resources
- stationery or office supply store
- paper manufacturer
- print shop

Materials and Manipulatives
- ruler (1 per group)
- calculator (1 per group; *optional*)

Memo

You are enrolled in a twelve week study course. Rumor has it that the teacher, Mr. Skim, gives a lot of notes! In fact, students who have taken the class say that Mr. Skim gives an average of four pages of notes each time the class meets and each daily assignment requires about two pages. Thinking this might be a good opportunity to begin practicing organizational skills, you decide to purchase a binder in which to keep your notes and daily assignments for the class. You find that there are 0.5 in., 0.625 in., and 1 in. binders available in the school store.

Mission: Find out what size binder will best hold your notes and daily assignments for the study skills course. Explain in detail how you reached your conclusion.

- ✓ How many sheets of paper will you need altogether for your notes and daily assignments?
- ✓ How thick is one sheet of notebook paper?
- ✓ How would a decision to write on both sides of each sheet of notebook paper affect the size binder you purchase?

140

4-1

Connecting to Prior Knowledge

Ask students to share times when they have made an estimate, such as when making a purchase at a grocery store. Then have students describe why an estimate was helpful in each situation.

THINK AND DISCUSS

VISUAL LEARNERS For Question 2, have students use pencil and paper to round factors up and down. Then have them find each product so they can see how the estimate is affected.

Example 1

- *Why are 3 and 25 compatible numbers?* **(The product of any whole number (such as 3) and 25 ends in 0 or 5 and is also easily found because 25 is one fourth of 100.)**
- *Is the estimate higher or lower than the actual product?* **(lower)**

Additional Example *Estimate the product 49.19 × 4.25.*

$$\begin{array}{r} 49.19 \\ \times\ 4.25 \\ \hline \end{array} \begin{array}{c} \rightarrow \\ \rightarrow \\ \\ \end{array} \begin{array}{r} 50 \\ \times\ 4 \\ \hline 200 \end{array}$$

The product 49.19 × 4.25 is about 200.

AUDITORY LEARNERS Have students explain orally why the compatible numbers 25 and 3 were chosen in Example 1.

DIVERSITY To stimulate interest, you may wish to bring in pictures or examples of paper money from other countries before discussing Example 2.

Example 2

- *How are 90 and 15 compatible numbers?* **(90 is evenly divisible by 15)**

What's Ahead

- Estimating decimal products and quotients

4-1 Estimating Products and Quotients

THINK AND DISCUSS

Lisa works at Downtown Hardware. Her hours vary weekly depending on the amount of work available. Her time card shows her daily and weekly hours worked. Lisa's hourly wage is $4.25. Estimate how much she will earn this week.

DH DH DH DH DH

Downtown Hardware

Employee: Lisa M. Smith

DAY	DATE	HOURS
MON	5/3	2.1
TUE		
WED	5/5	1.7
THU	5/6	3.5
FRI	5/7	4.0
SAT		
SUN		
TOTAL HOURS		11.3

DH DH DH DH DH

1. a. What two numbers would you multiply to find how much Lisa will earn this week? 11.3 and $4.25
   b. Round each factor to the nearest whole number. 11; 4
   c. Estimate Lisa's earnings for the week. about $44
2. Estimate Lisa's weekly earnings two ways. See left.
   a. Round both factors up. Is this estimate higher or lower than Lisa's actual weekly earnings? Explain.
   b. Round both factors down. Is this estimate higher or lower than Lisa's actual weekly earnings? Explain.
3. Is your estimate in Question 1(c) higher or lower than Lisa's actual weekly earnings? Explain. Lower; both factors are rounded down.
4. Estimate the product 12.6 × 1.9. Round each factor to the nearest whole number. about 26

2.a. 12 × 5 is higher
b. 11 × 4 is lower; since 11.3 is between 11 and 12 and 4.25 is between 4 and 5, 11.3 × 4.25 is between 11 × 4 and 12 × 5.

Numbers that are easy to multiply or divide mentally are **compatible numbers.** You can use them to estimate products.

Example 1 Estimate the product 26.03 × 3.31.

$$\begin{array}{r} 26.03 \\ \times\ 3.31 \\ \hline \end{array} \begin{array}{c} \rightarrow \\ \rightarrow \\ \\ \end{array} \begin{array}{r} 25 \\ \times\ 3 \\ \hline 75 \end{array}$$ Change to compatible numbers.

The product 26.03 × 3.31 is about 75.

5. What compatible numbers would you choose to estimate the product 3.89 × 16.03? Explain your choice. Answers may vary. Sample: 4 × 15
6. Is it easier to estimate the product 29.26 × 11.62 by using compatible numbers or by rounding each factor to the nearest whole number? Explain.

Answers may vary. Sample: Using compatible numbers is easier because finding 30 × 10 can be done mentally unlike 29 × 12.

"Perhaps the most valuable result of all education is the ability to make yourself do the thing you have to do, when it ought to be done, whether you like it or not."
—T.H. Huxley

Organizer

1. **Focus**
   Connecting to Prior Knowledge
2. **Teach**
   Think and Discuss
   Work Together
3. **Closure**
   Try These
   Wrap Up

Vocabulary/Symbols
compatible numbers

Skills Reviewed in Context of Lesson
- rounding decimals
- multiplying decimals
- dividing decimals
- reading charts

Student Resources
Extra Practice
Student Study Guide
Practice, TR Ch. 4, p. 24
Student Study Guide, Spanish Resources, TR
Alternate Lesson, TR Ch. 4, pp. 12–15

continues next page

Additional Example *Tickets to a movie matinee cost $2.75. About how many tickets can be purchased with a $20 bill?*

20 ÷ 2.75

21 ÷ 3 = 7 Use compatible numbers

About 7 tickets can be bought with $20.

Error Alert! Students may think that there are established sets of compatible numbers for problems such as the examples. ***Remediation*** Tell students that they choose which numbers are compatible and which are not. Compatible numbers are simply numbers that are easy to multiply or divide mentally.

Ongoing Assessment Group students in pairs. Have each student describe compatible numbers in his or her own words to the other student. Challenge partners to combine and polish their descriptions and provide examples. Make sure partners find that their descriptions match.

WORK TOGETHER

Encourage pairs to organize their lists in tables. Have students give reasons why their estimates are accurate and useful. Ask the pairs of students to compare lists.

ESL Pair each ESL student with a partner who is fluent in English and has good math skills.

TRY THESE

Exercises 10–15: Have students discuss how they chose their compatible numbers.

Wrap Up

What's the Big Idea? Ask students to explain how to estimate decimal products and quotients.

Organizer, continued

Teacher Resources

Teaching Transparency 49

Lesson Planner, TR Ch. 4, p. 2

Prentice Hall Technology

Computer Item Generator

- 4-1

Fact of the Day

The first Soap Box Derby was held in Dayton, Ohio, in 1934. The following year the event was moved to Akron, Ohio, where it has been held every year since, except for four years during World War II.

—*Academic American Encyclopedia*

When you estimate quotients you can use compatible numbers.

Example 2 The largest paper money ever issued was the Chinese one-kwan note. It was issued in the 14th century and was 92.8 cm long. The United States one-dollar bill is 15.6 cm long. About how many times as long as a one-dollar bill was the one-kwan note?

92.8 ÷ 15.6 Write the quotient.

90 ÷ 15 = 6 Use compatible numbers.

The one-kwan note is about six times as long as the one-dollar bill.

Party Supplies	Cost
Streamers (81 ft)	$.79
Paper tablecloths	$1.99
Plain napkins (50)	$2.49
Holiday napkins (8)	$.69
Colored balloons (20)	$2.29
Foil balloons (each)	$1.99
Cardboard cut-outs	$.29
Colored paper (24)	$1.16
Markers (10 colors)	$1.65
Games (4-6 players)	$9.95
Music	$8.78

WT: Sample: Halloween

1 Game	$9.95	≈ $10
Holiday music	$8.78	≈ $9
3 Holiday napkins	$.69	≈ $1
		≈ $1
		≈ $1
2 Foil Balloons	$1.99	≈ $2
		≈ $2
Total		≈ $26

WORK TOGETHER Answers may vary.

Plan a party for your class. Work with a partner. Choose the supplies you need to make the party a success. Keep in mind that your class has to stay within a $26 budget.

- Choose a theme for your class party.
- Decide what you want for the party. Choose from the list at the left.
- How much of each item do you need? Make sure there is enough for everyone in the class.
- Estimate the total cost of the party.

TRY THESE

Round each factor to the nearest whole number. Estimate the product.

7. 15.3 × 2.6 about 45
8. 2.25 × 16.91 about 34
9. 3.5 × 2.72 about 12

Write a pair of compatible numbers. Then use the numbers to estimate. Answers may vary. Accept reasonable estimates.

10. 46.4 ÷ 4.75 about 9
11. 39.3 ÷ 8.7 about 5
12. 39.26 × 1.98 about 80
13. 18.8 × 4.3 about 80
14. 17.33 ÷ 5.49 about 3
15. 2.18 × 24.19 about 50

Journal Have students describe the criteria for choosing compatible numbers. Ask them to give examples for products and quotients.

Connections Have students discuss situations in which they might estimate products or quotients. You may want to start with these examples:

- **Social Studies** (estimating distances on maps, comparing the areas or populations of countries)
- **Consumer Topics** (determining prices, installment payments, and best buys)
- **Carpentry** (estimating the amount of wood needed for a project, dividing a project into tasks that require the same amount of time)

Reteaching Activity Have pairs of students give estimates for the following products and quotients. They should explain to one another how they arrive at each estimate.

6.21×9.59 **(about 60)**
$82.3 \div 8.99$ **(about 9)**
16.11×5.55 **(about 90)**
$80.09 \div 3.66$ **(about 20)**

ON YOUR OWN

Exercises 24–29: Have students note the exercises that required more than rounding the numbers to estimate.

CONNECTION TO STATISTICS Exercises 32–34 have students use a chart to make estimates.

CONNECTION TO SOCIAL STUDIES Exercise 39 has students make estimates in comparing the lengths of two tunnels in different countries.

Answers may vary. Accept reasonable estimates.

16. Luisa earns \$4.75/h mowing lawns. Estimate how much money she will earn in 3.5 h. about \$20

17. Yuri earned \$33.25 in one week baby-sitting. He earns \$3.50/h. Estimate the number of hours he worked. about 10 h

ON YOUR OWN

Round each factor to the nearest whole number. Estimate the product.

18. 0.95×22.8 about 23 **19.** 11.6×3.23 about 36 **20.** 15.25×3.9 about 60
21. 1.79×0.12 about 0 **22.** 4.01×0.62 about 4 **23.** 31.4×3.20 about 93

Use compatible numbers to estimate. Answers may vary. Accept reasonable estimates.

24. 41.5×18.75 about 800 **25.** $15.76 \div 2.51$ about 5 **26.** 3.5×8.9 about 36
27. $65 \div 8.4$ about 8 **28.** 12.2×2.96 about 36 **29.** $37.2 \div 6.12$ about 6

The Soap Box Derby

The Derby held in Akron, Ohio, is a downhill race for cars without motors. The cars are built and driven by young people between the ages of 9 and 16. The cars race on a 953.75 ft downhill track.

Drivers can enter one of three racing divisions. To enter the masters division, the combined weight of the car and its driver must be exactly 236 lb. To compete in the Stock car or Kit Car divisions, the combined weight must be 206 lb. Sometimes the drivers need to add lead weights to the cars to reach the required weight for their division.

In 1992, 70 girls and 133 boys from 35 states and 6 countries entered the race. Carolyn Fox, an 11-year-old from Salem, Oregon, was the winner of the Kit Car division. Her winning time was 28.27 s.

Answers may vary. Accept reasonable estimates.

30. To find speed divide the distance by the time. Estimate Carolyn Fox's average speed. about 30 ft/s

31. Suppose the track is 2.5 times its original length. Carolyn finishes the race in 52.56 s. Find her average speed. about 50 ft/s

Mixed REVIEW

1. A bus trip from Austin to San Antonio takes 2 h 57 min. What time will the bus arrive, if it leaves Austin at 10:35 A.M.? 1:32 P.M.

Complete.

2. ■ m = 54 cm 0.54
3. 18 km = ■ m 18,000
4. 400 mm = ■ cm 40
5. A year has two months in a row with a Friday the 13th. What months must they be? Feb. and Mar.

Assignment Options

Core: 18–20, 24–26, 32, 33, 35a, 39, 41, MR all	
Reinforce: 21–23, 27–31, 35b, 36, 37	**Enrich:** 34, 38 40

WRITING For Exercise 40, make sure students remember that a product or quotient does not have one correct pair of compatible numbers, but rather several reasonable possibilities. Encourage students to think of what the estimates will have in common.

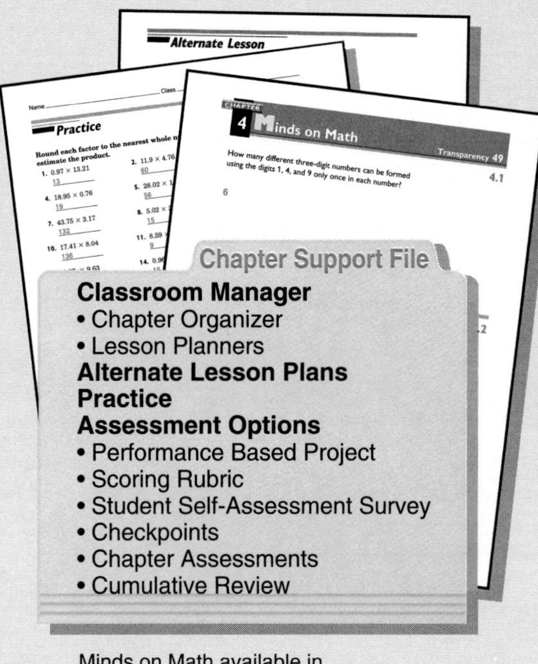

Minds on Math available in Teaching Transparencies

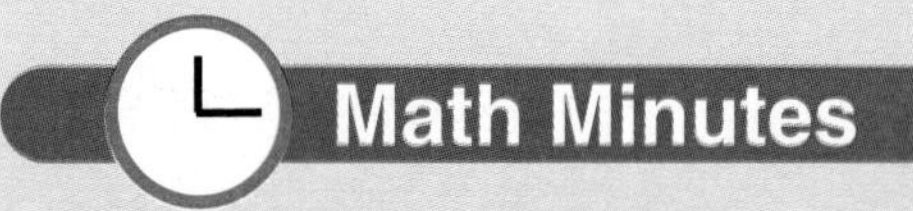

Find the range, mean, median, and mode for the set of numbers 11, 18, 14, 24, 28.
range: 17; mean: 19; median: 18; no mode

Materials for 4-2

- computer
- database or spreadsheet software
- calculator

Use the chart below to answer questions 32–34.

Food	Serving Size	Protein (grams)
American Cheese	1 slice	6.6
Canned Tuna	3 oz (drained)	24.4
Rye Bread	1 slice	2.3
Cheese Pizza	1 slice (14-in. pie.)	7.8

Answers may vary. Accept reasonable estimates.

32. About how many grams of protein are in 2 slices of pizza? about 16 g

33. About how many grams of protein are in 8 slices of pizza? about 64 g

34. Nutrition Estimate how many grams of protein are in a sandwich consisting of 2 slices of rye bread, 2 oz of tuna, and one slice of American Cheese. about 27 g

Protein makes new cells to help your body grow. Most food contains some protein. Meat, fish, nuts, milk, and cheese provide your body with large amounts of protein. A 12-year-old needs about 55 g of protein every day.

Source: *The Usborne Book of Food Fitness & Health*

35. a. Mental Math If you save \$6.25 each week, estimate how much you will save in one year. about \$300

b. Mental Math If you saved \$443.75 in one year, estimate how much you saved each week. about \$9

36. A librarian orders 3 copies of a book. The bill is \$38.85. Estimate the cost of 1 book. Is your estimate higher or lower than the actual cost of the book? Explain. about \$13; higher because \$39 > \$38.85.

37. Choose A, B, or C. Between what two numbers is the quotient 18.7 ÷ 5.4? B

A. 2 and 3 **B.** 3 and 4 **C.** 4 and 5

38. Sports A volleyball weighs 283.5 g and a shipping crate weighs 595.34 g. Estimate the weight of a shipping crate containing 9 volleyballs. about 3,300 g or 3.3 kg

39. Social Studies The Apennine Railroad Tunnel in Italy is 18.5 km long. The Seikan Tunnel in Japan is about 2.9 times as long. Estimate the length of the Seikan tunnel. about 60 km

40. Writing If two different people estimate a product or quotient using compatible numbers, will they always get the same result? Use examples to support your answer. See left.

40. Answers may vary. Sample: Not always; for example, 950 ÷ 28 may be estimated as 1000 ÷ 25 or 900 ÷ 30.

41. Data File 6 (pp. 226–227) Estimate the appropriate seat height for you when riding a bicycle. Answers may vary. Sample: a person with a 25 in. inseam would require a seat height of about 25 in.

4-2

Connecting to Prior Knowledge

Have students recall different uses of decimals from previous sections in the book and elsewhere (newspapers, sports).

THINK AND DISCUSS

TACTILE LEARNERS For Questions 1 and 2, have students use the following process to understand database terminology. Give students a set of five index cards. Have the students survey five people in order to write their favorite sport, favorite color, and favorite type of music on each card.

- The collection of cards is the database.
- Each card is a record.
- Each category of information (sport, music, color) is a field.

ESL The terms "field" and "record" are often confused by beginners. Help students use them correctly in discussion.

Explain that each stamp or comic book in a collection has a record that gives its specific information. Each blank that gets filled in with one piece of information is a field.

DIVERSITY You may wish to use the discussion of databases as an opportunity for allowing students to share information about their special outside interests and hobbies.

AUDITORY LEARNERS Have students identify aloud the fields and records from the table.

Error Alert! Students who want to create their own spreadsheet need to adjust the formatting of the columns so that it will look similar to the one shown on the page.

Journal Have students write about how they could organize or reorganize their school work, rooms at home, or any school club data in a way that would help them manage their time more wisely.

What's Ahead

- Using a database to explore applications of decimals

WHAT YOU'LL NEED

✓ Computer 

✓ Database or spreadsheet software 

✓ Calculator

TECHNOLOGY

4-2 Decimals in Databases

THINK AND DISCUSS

A **database** is a collection of information organized by category. You could use a database to organize recipes or a comic book collection. A **field** is a category in a database. A group of fields relating to one entry is a **record.**

Answers may vary. Sample given.

1. Suppose you have a stamp collection. What are some ways you might organize your collection? Name at least three fields you might use to organize your data. You may organize your collection according to year, worth, or country.

You can use a spreadsheet to organize data as you would in a database. The database below shows one way to organize information about a comic book collection.

2.a. Issue number, Title, Value; condition or year

2. a. What fields are in the database? What other fields could you add to the database?
   b. What information does each record contain? Issue Number, Title, Value of each comic book.

	A	B	C	D
1	Issue Number	Title	Value	
2	270	Batman	35.00	
3	1	Indiana Jones	2.50	
4	314	Justice League	11.00	
5	28	Spiderman	170.00	
6	1	The Atom	300.00	

Source: Wizzard

3. a. Which fields contain numbers? Which fields contain letters or text? Issue Number, Value; Title
   b. **Discussion** How are the records alike? How are they different? Answers may vary. Sample: Each record contains its Issue Number, Title, and Value; The Titles and numbers are not the same for each comic book.

"The keynote of progress, we should remember, is not merely doing away with what is bad; it is replacing the best with something better."

—Edward A. Filene

Organizer

1. **Focus**
   Connecting to Prior Knowledge
2. **Teach**
   Think and Discuss
   Work Together
3. **Closure**
   Wrap Up

Vocabulary/Symbols
database
field
record
sort

Skills Reviewed in Context of Lesson
- reading a chart

Materials and Manipulatives
- computer (1 for each group)
- database or spreadsheet software (for each computer)
- calculator (1 for each student)

On Your Own Exercise 10: computer and database software *(optional)*

continues next page

WORK TOGETHER

Any database software may be used for the computer investigation in Question 7. If students are not familiar with databases, briefly discuss the usefulness of organizing information into records, where each record contains data about a single item. Database software uses organization to make it easier to find the information you need as well as to sort the information by categories.

Ongoing Assessment Have students work in pairs. Have them answer the following questions for each of the fields listed in Questions 5 and 6.

- *Why do you want to compare the information in each of the fields?*
- *Who would want the information for each field? For example: Who would care to know the weight before choosing the appropriate sneaker? Why?*

COMPUTER For Question 7, review or demonstrate how to set up a computerized database.

- Define each field and specify whether it will contain numeric or alphanumeric data.
- Choose a layout for each of the records, providing enough room for the characters that will fit into each field.
- Plan the fields that will be sorted. Some software limits the number of fields that can be sorted.

Alternate Approach If a computer is not available, have students write each record on a separate card or small piece of paper.

- Have different students work on different records.
- Have students sort the cards by hand.

Wrap Up

What's the Big Idea? Ask students: *How can you use a database to organize information?*

Organizer, continued

Student Resources
Extra Practice
Student Study Guide
Practice, TR Ch. 4, p. 25
Student Study Guide, Spanish Resources, TR
Alternate Lesson, TR Ch. 4, pp. 16–19

Teacher Resources

Teaching Transparencies 4, 5, 19, 49
Transparency Masters, TR p. 5
Lesson Planner, TR Ch. 4, p. 3

Prentice Hall Technology
Multimedia Math
- Math Tools, Spreadsheet

Computer Item Generator 4-2

Other Available Technology
- calculator

Works by Microsoft: Question 7, Exercise 10 *(optional)*

Fact of the Day

Deltiology—postcard collecting—is considered the third largest collecting hobby, after stamps and coins.

—*Guinness Book of Records*

Assignment Options

Core: 9, MR all	
Reinforce: 11, 12	**Enrich:** 10

Some computers "talk" and "listen" to users. When "talking," a computer makes words from digital sounds and outputs them to a speaker. When "listening," a receiver recognizes the sounds and translates them so the computer understands.

One advantage of a database is the ability to **sort,** or order, data by field. Computers sort letters or text alphabetically and numbers from greatest to least or least to greatest.

4. How are the comic books sorted? What other ways could you sort the comic book database? By Title; By Value or Issue Number.

WORK TOGETHER

Your group has been asked to recommend a brand of sneakers for the track team. The database shows data for five different sneakers. Testers rated the sneakers on a scale of 1 (very good) to 5 (very poor) for their ability to dry out (evaporation rate) after wearing and for flexibility.

5. What factors are most important in making your recommendation? Answers may vary. Choose from: Brand, Price, Weight, Evaporation Rate, and Flexibility.
6. What other information might you want before making your decision? Answers may vary. Sample: color, tread.
7. **Computer** Enter the information using database software. Sort the information in various ways to get the information you need. Sort the information based on the factors you chose as most important.
8. Prepare a report.
   a. Tell which sneaker you recommend.
   b. Tell which sneaker to avoid.
   c. Give a second choice.
   Answers may vary. Check students' work.

	A	B	C	D	E
1	Brand	Price	Weight	Evaporation Rate	Flexibility
2	Air Jumpers	33.50	13 oz	5.0	1.8
3	Cool Runners	60.00	12 oz	2.5	3.3
4	Floaters	75.95	16 oz	2.6	2.9
5	Foot Lights	125.35	17 oz	3.9	2.7
6	Hi Flyers	135.00	11 oz	1.5	4.1

Connections Have a discussion about how databases are useful. You may wish to start with these examples:

- **Sales** (list of customers, locations, estimated sales for regions)
- **Inventory** (list by part number, wholesale price, retail price, location, damaged products)
- **Universities** (student identification number, degree plan, financial aid plan, library debts, estimated graduation date)
- **Telemarketing Phone Communications** (list of phone numbers, list of possible remarks with appropriate answers)

Reteaching Activity Have students use the table listed in the Work Together section to write every brand, price, weight, evaporation rate, and flexibility on an index card. Let the students sort the cards by price, weight, and then flexibility.

ON YOUR OWN

Exercise 9f: Review the capabilities of the database software for the possibility of adding fields after data has been added to the existing records. Software varies, and it may become too troublesome to add fields at a later time. Ask students to plan, design, and implement a database all at the same time.

COMPUTER In Exercise 10, choosing the database of a gradebook gives students a chance to understand their grades. ***Alternate Approach*** Have students create a one-page design for their database on paper.

ON YOUR OWN

	A	B	C	D
1	Coin	Composition	Condition	Cost
2	1993 United States Silver Eagle	0.999 oz pure silver	brilliant, uncirculated	$8.95
3	1992 Panda	0.999 oz pure silver	gem, brilliant, uncirculated	$18.95
4	Morgan silver dollar, uncirculated	0.90 pure silver	brilliant, uncirculated	$19.95
5	1986 Statue of Liberty silver dollar (2-coin set)	0.90 pure silver	gem, proof set	$29.95
6	1992 Mexico Libertad	0.999 oz pure silver	brilliant, uncirculated	$8.95

Source: *Quality Collectibles, LTD*

9. Use the database above. a. Coin, Composition, Condition, Cost
   a. Name the fields in the database.
   b. How many records are in the database? 5
   c. Suppose you sort the coins by condition. What would be the order? See right.
   d. Suppose you sort the coins by cost. What would be the order? See right.
   e. What is the value of all the coins in the collection? $86.75
   f. What other fields could you add to the database? Answers may vary. Sample: number, value
10. **Computer** Use database software. Choose a topic from the list at the right or one of your own and create a database. Use at least three fields. Answers may vary. Check students' work.
11. **Writing** Where might a database be useful? How might a teacher use a database? Sample: to organize addresses; to organize class attendance lists.
12. **Data File 8 (pp. 316–317)** Answers may vary. See right.
   a. Which data set would be appropriate for a database?
   b. What are three fields the database would have?
   c. What are two ways you might sort the data base?

Mixed REVIEW

Estimate the product.

1. 19.2×9.7 about 200
2. 4.3×6.73 about 28
3. Draw an acute $\angle A$. Construct an angle congruent to $\angle A$. See Solution Key.

Find the difference.

4. $8 - 7.35$ 0.65
5. $25 - 21.984$ 3.016
6. Is $5 enough money to buy yogurt for $2.09, blueberries for $1.49, and bread for $.85? yes

9.c. Answers may vary. Sample: 1993 U.S. Silver Eagle, Morgan silver dollar, 1992 Mexico Libertad, 1992 Panda, 1986 Statue of Liberty silver dollar.

9.d. Answers may vary. Sample: Listed greatest to least: 1986 Statue of Liberty silver dollar, Morgan silver dollar, 1992 Panda, 1993 U.S. Silver Eagle, 1992 Mexico Libertad.

12.a. Top Medal winners in the 1992 Summer Olympics.
b. Number of Gold medals, Silver medals and Bronze medals.
c. By the Number of Gold medals by the Number of Silver medals.

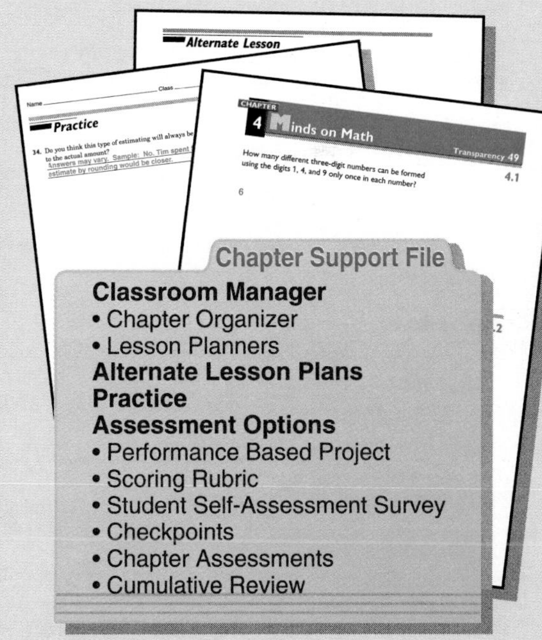

Minds on Math available in Teaching Transparencies

Math Minutes

Write the next four numbers in each pattern.

1. 80, 120, 160, . . . **200, 240, 280, 320**
2. 3.2, 3.7, 4.2, . . . **4.7, 5.2, 5.7, 6.2**
3. 3, 2.9, 2.7, 2.4, . . . **2, 1.5, 0.9, 0.2**

Materials for 4-3

- calculator

4-3

Connecting to Prior Knowledge

Ask students what they think would happen if the traffic lights at a major road intersection went out. Have students give reasons why traffic lights are useful. Then encourage students to list other situations in which rules and order are important, such as in the Senate or in a baseball game.

WORK TOGETHER

Question 1: Students using paper and pencil should ignore the order of operations, working strictly "from left to right."

Question 2: You may wish to have the students within each pair change roles and repeat the activity before going on to Question 3.

THINK AND DISCUSS

Error Alert! Students may have difficulty remembering the order of operations for Questions 4–7 and later problems. ***Remediation*** Have a contest to encourage students to think of mnemonics to help them remember the order of operations. Point out to students that each mnemonic should use the letters *P* (parenthesis), *M* (multiply), *D* (divide), *A* (add), and S (subtract). Have students select their favorites in such categories as Most Creative, Easiest to Remember, and Best Sentence.

Ongoing Assessment Give students the expression $3 + (6 - 2) \times 5$. Have students evaluate the expression by describing each step in terms of their own personal mnemonic for remembering the order of operations. Challenge students to evaluate their procedures for any weaknesses, difficulties, or mistakes. Encourage students to improve on their methods. Then have the class compare answers. **(23)**

"Concentration is my motto—first honesty, then industry, then concentration."

—ANDREW CARNEGIE

Organizer

1. **Focus**
   Connecting to Prior Knowledge
2. **Teach**
   Work Together
   Think and Discuss
3. **Closure**
   Wrap Up

Vocabulary/Symbols
order of operations

Skills Reviewed in Context of Lesson
- operations with whole numbers

Materials and Manipulatives
- calculator (1 for each student)

On Your Own Exercises 36–39: calculator

Student Resources
Extra Practice
Student Study Guide
Practice, TR Ch. 4, p. 26
Student Study Guide, Spanish Resources, TR

Teacher Resources
Teaching Transparencies 19, 49
Lesson Planner, TR Ch. 4, p. 4

continues next page

What's Ahead

- Evaluating expressions using order of operations

WHAT YOU'LL NEED

✓ Calculator

4-3 The Order of Operations

WORK TOGETHER

Work with a partner. One partner uses a calculator and the other uses paper and pencil to find the value of the expressions shown below. Work from left to right. The partner who uses the calculator presses  only after entering the last number.

1. Record the value of each expression.
   a. $18 + 12 \times 5$ 78
   b. $15 - 12 \div 3$ 11
   c. $(6 + 18) \div 3 \times 6$ 48
2. a. Compare your results with your partner's results. Did you both get the same values for the expressions? No
   b. Is it possible to get two different values? Explain. See left.
   c. How might getting two values for one expression cause problems? Sample: You would not know which answer was intended.
3. Look at each calculator result and decide which operation the calculator performed first.
   a. multiplication b. division c. addition

You say you've got a real solution.
Well, you know,
We'd all love to see the plan.
John Lennon

2.b. Yes; your values may be different if you perform operations in different order.

THINK AND DISCUSS

Sometimes getting different solutions to an expression can be confusing. There is a set of rules for evaluating expressions that guarantees everyone gets the same answer. We call this set of rules the **order of operations.**

Order of Operations

1. Do all operations within parentheses first.
2. Multiply and divide in order from left to right.
3. Add and subtract in order from left to right.

AUDITORY LEARNERS Have students explain orally what to do first in Questions 6 and 7.

Wrap Up

What's the Big Idea? Ask students to describe how to evaluate expressions using order of operations.

Connections Have a discussion about how the order of operations is used. You may want to start with these examples:

- **Science** (solving equations involving many operations, finding verifiable and repeatable results)
- **Consumer** (adding the costs of different repeated items at a store)
- **Sports** (evaluating the chances of a come-from-behind victory by adding different numbers of touchdowns, field goals, and extra points needed by a team)

Journal Ask students if rules are necessarily limiting or whether rules sometimes provide opportunities. Start students thinking by asking them if they could play a game without rules. Then ask students: *What kind of opportunities does the order of operations provide you with?*

Reteaching Activity Have students evaluate expressions and show each step. Use examples such as the following:

$18 \div (15 \div 5) - 5$
$18 \div 3 - 5$
$6 - 5$
1

Have students compare their results.

ON YOUR OWN

Students will need calculators for Exercises 36–39.

4. Now look at the expression $3 + 4 \times 5$. What are two possible values you might find for the expression? Which value is correct? Explain. 35; 23; 23 is correct because it follows the order of operations.
5. a. What is the value of the expression $(4 + 5) \times 5$? 45
   b. What is the value of the expression $4 + (5 \times 5)$? 29
   c. What is the value of the expression $4 + 5 \times 5$? 29
   d. What do you notice about the values of each expression in parts (a), (b), and (c)? The expressions in parts (b) and (c) have the same value.
6. Consider the expression $2 + 6 \times 7$.
   a. Which operation would you perform first? multiplication
   b. What would you do next? add
   c. What is the value of the expression? 44
7. Consider the expression $3 + 2 \times 5 \times 4$. See right.
   a. Which operation would you perform first? Why?
   b. Write the expression after the first step. $3 + 10 \times 4$
   c. What would you do next? 10×4
   d. What is the last step and the final value? $3 + 40$; 43

7.a. multiplication (2×5); There are no parentheses, and this is the first multiplication from left to right.

ON YOUR OWN

Which operation would you perform first?

8. $8 - 2 \times 3$ multiplication
9. $(4.6 - 0.6) \div 4$ subtraction
10. $15 \times 8 \div 3$ multiplication
11. $12 - 2 \times 3 \div 5$ multiplication
12. $16 \div 4 \times (3.3 + 0.7) \times 4$ addition

Evaluate.

13. $6 - 2 + 4 \times 2$ 12
14. $3 + 3 \times 2$ 9
15. $(3.3 - 1.4) + 6$ 7.9
16. $4 \div (4.4 - 2.4)$ 2
17. $6 \times (2 \times 5)$ 60
18. $13 - (2.7 + 0.4)$ 9.9

Mental Math **Evaluate.**

19. $5 + 2 \times 0$ 5
20. $(12 - 7) \times 5 + 1$ 26
21. $(6.3 - 4.8) \times 1$ 1.5
22. $18 \div 6 - (5.6 - 4.6)$ 2
23. Writing Explain the steps you would use to evaluate the expression $8 \div 4 \times 6 + (7.5 - 5.5)$. First subtract 5.5 from 7.5; next, divide 8 by 4, multiply the result by 6 and add 2. The result is 14.

Mixed REVIEW

1. Will has 2 copies of a *Batman* comic valued at \$35 each and one *Spiderman* comic valued at \$170. What is the value of his comic collection? \$240
2. How many *Justice League* comics valued at \$11 each would you need to trade to obtain the first issue of *The Atom* worth \$300? 28

Estimate using compatible numbers.

3. 19.43×6.2 about 120
4. 493.8×1.869
5. $203.179 \div 22.039$ about 10
6. The lockers in the sixth grade corridor are numbered 100 to 275. How many lockers are there?

4. about 1000
6. 176 lockers

Organizer, continued

Prentice Hall Technology

Computer Item Generator
- 4-3

Other Available Technology
- calculator

Fact of the Day

Americans use 550,000 bushels of apples (11,000 tons) every day. About half of them are eaten fresh.

—*In One Day*

Assignment Options

Core: 8–22, 24–26, 30–33, 36–37, MR all	
Reinforce: 23, 27 28, 34, 35, 38–43	**Enrich:** 29, 44

MENTAL MATH For Exercises 19–22, have students check their answers and indicate points of difficulty.

WRITING For Exercise 23, have students write their explanations in the form of instructions.

CRITICAL THINKING For Exercise 29, challenge students to support their explanations with examples.

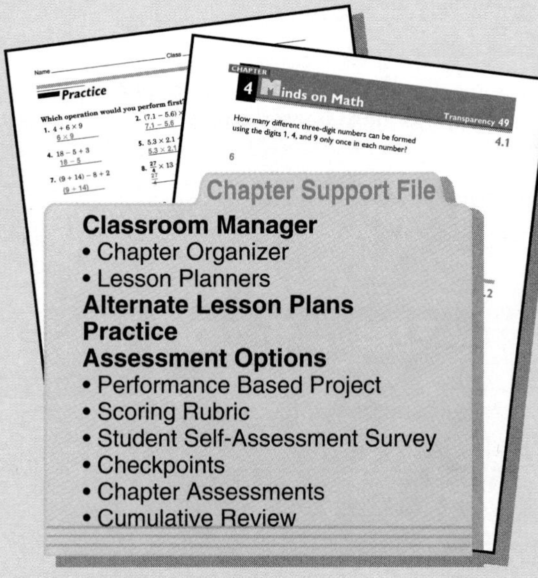

Minds on Math available in Teaching Transparencies

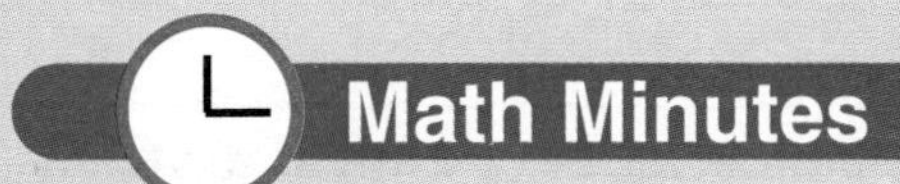

Express 3 yards and 1 foot in inches.
120 inches

Materials for 4-4

- graph paper
- scissors

Replace ■ with <, >, or =.

24. $(3 + 6) \times 4$ ■ $3 + 6 \times 4$ >
25. $(8 - 2) \times (6 + 1)$ ■ $(8 - 2) \times 6 + 1$ >
26. $2 + (12 \div 3)$ ■ $2 + 12 \div 3$ =
27. $7 - 2 \times 3$ ■ $(7 - 2) \times 3$ <
28. $2 \times (15 - 3)$ ■ $2 \times 15 - 3$ <
29. **Critical Thinking** If you follow the order of operations to evaluate expressions, when would you subtract before you multiply? **When the subtraction is in parentheses**

Place parentheses in each expression to make it true.

30. $(12 + 6) \div 2 - 1 = 8$
31. $14 \div (2 + 5) - 1 = 1$
32. $(1 + 2) \times (15 - 4) = 33$
33. $(11 - 7) \div 2 = 2$
34. $14 - 3 - 2 \times 3 = 5$ **no parentheses needed**
35. $5 \times 6 \div 2 + 1 = 16$ **no parentheses needed**

Use a calculator to evaluate.

Sample: $3 \times (5 + 2)$

3 [×] [(] 5 [+] 2 [)] [=] 21

36. $(6.3 + 3.7) \div 5$ **2**
37. $4 \times (13 - 6)$ **28**
38. $13 \times (4.6 - 1.6)$ **39**
39. $(16 \times 4) \div (4.2 + 3.8)$ **8**

Insert operation symbols to make the equation true.

40. 21 ■ 3 ■ 4 = 11 **÷, +**
41. 14 ■ 7 ■ 2 ■ 3 = 7 **÷, +, +**
42. (6 ■ 9) ■ 4 ■ 6 = 10 **+, ×, ÷**
43. (12 ■ 8) ■ (5 ■ 1) = 20 **−, ×, ÷ (or −, ×, ×)**
44. At a local grocery store the price of apples, 49 cents a pound, has been reduced by 20 cents. Next week the manager will double this reduced price.
    a. Should you use $49 - 20 \times 2$ or $(49 - 20) \times 2$ to find next week's price? Explain.
    b. What will the price of apples be next week? **58¢ per lb**

44. a. $(49 - 20) \times 2$; the other expression gives the price if the reduction is doubled.

In 1991, United States farmers received an average price of $.25/lb for apples.

4-4

Connecting to Prior Knowledge

Ask students for examples of products, such as a piece of land, a TV, or a table, that can be described in terms of their length and width. Have students name the word used between the dimension measurements. **(by)** Ask students to describe the symbol used for "by." **(×, multiplication symbol)** Ask students to think of what the product of the two dimensions equals. **(area)**

THINK AND DISCUSS

Error Alert! For problems such as Question 2, students may use the wrong unit of measurement for area. ***Remediation*** Point out to students that an area is composed of squares. An area is thus expressed in square units. If the unit of measurement for length and width is feet, then the area is expressed in square feet, since the product of 1 ft in length and 1 ft in width is 1 sq. ft.

Question 3: Have students compare their measurements and area calculations for a common item, such as a math textbook.

WORK TOGETHER

Provide each pair of students with graph paper. Encourage students to organize their answers to Questions 4–6 with an illustration of the combined rectangles.

KINESTHETIC LEARNERS Help students fix in their minds the meaning of area by having them use blocks, tiles, or squares cut from index cards to cover the entire rectangle. This action will help them distinguish the idea of area from that of perimeter, or walking the border.

Examples

- *In Method 2, why are 3 and 4 added together in parentheses?* **(Together they equal the width of the combined tables, so they must be added together before finding the area.)**

What's Ahead

- Using the distributive property
- Finding areas of rectangles

WHAT YOU'LL NEED

✓ Graph paper

✓ Scissors

Area = length × width
$A = l \times w$

4-4 The Distributive Property

THINK AND DISCUSS

We call the number of square units that cover a rectangle its *area.* The **area** of a rectangle is equal to the product of its length times its width. We express area in square units.

1. Use graph paper to draw a rectangle that is 5 units wide and 6 units long.
   a. Count the number of square units in the rectangle to find its area. **30 square units**
   b. Multiply the length times the width to find the area of the rectangle. Do you get the same result? **Yes.**
   c. Compare parts (a) and (b). Which method appears easier? Explain. **Sample: Even with a 5 × 6 rectangle, using the formula seems quicker. Try a 50 × 60 rectangle.**
2. Find the area of a rectangle 3 ft wide and 6 ft long. **18 ft^2**
3. Measure the length and the width of a binder or notebook. Find the area of the cover. **Answers may vary. Sample: A binder 10 in. wide by 12 in. long has an area of 120 sq in.**

WORK TOGETHER

Work with a partner. Draw a rectangle with the given dimensions on graph paper. Cut out each rectangle.

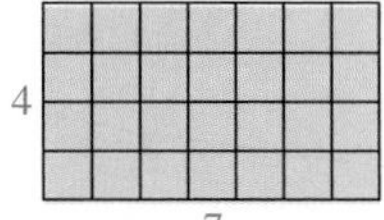

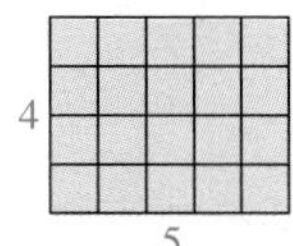

4. Find the area of each rectangle. Record each number. **28 sq. units; 20 sq. units**
5. Put the two rectangles end to end so the sides of equal length touch. What is the length and width of the new rectangle? **12 units; 4 units**
6. Find the area of the new rectangle. How does this area relate to the areas of the two smaller rectangles? **48 sq. units; the area of the new rectangle is the sum of the areas of the two smaller rectangles.**

> *"The general diffusion of knowledge and learning through the community is essential to the preservation of free government."*
>
> —Carl Becker

Organizer

1. **Focus**
   Connecting to Prior Knowledge
2. **Teach**
   Think and Discuss
   Work Together
3. **Closure**
   Try These
   Wrap Up

Vocabulary/Symbols
area
distributive property

Skills Reviewed in Context of Lesson
- multiplying whole numbers
- adding whole numbers

Materials and Manipulatives
- graph paper (1 per group)
- scissors (1 pair per group)
- tiles or squares *(optional)*

Student Resources
Extra Practice
Student Study Guide
Practice, TR Ch. 4, p. 27
Student Study Guide, Spanish Resources, TR

continues next page

Additional Example More guests than expected arrive at the Elliots' cookout. They must cover another table, this one 5 ft long and 3 ft wide. What is the new total area of contact paper needed?

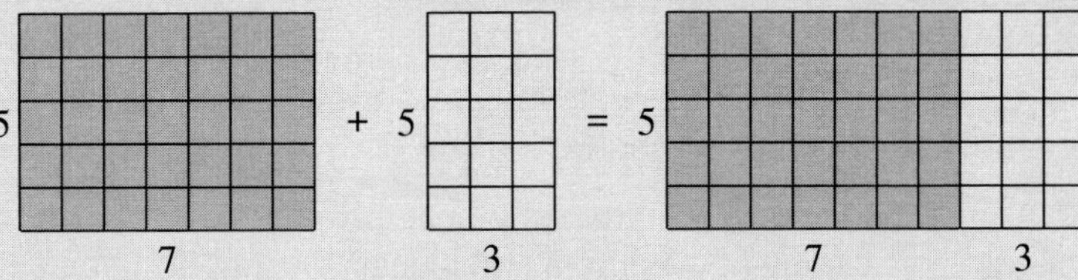

$(5 \times 7) + (5 \times 3) = 5(7 + 3)$

The total area is 5 × 10, or 50 sq. ft.

Additional Example *Use the distributive property to evaluate (8 × 2) + (8 × 4).*

$$\begin{aligned}(8 \times 2) + (8 \times 4) &= 8 \times (2 + 4)\\ &= 8 \times 6\\ &= 48\end{aligned}$$

Ongoing Assessment Have each student write a description of what he or she has learned about the distributive property and its use in finding the areas of rectangles. Collect the descriptions and read samples to the class. Encourage a class discussion on the use of the distributive property.

TRY THESE

MENTAL MATH For Exercises 17–19, have students check their answers by listing the steps they used mentally.

Wrap Up

What's the Big Idea? Ask students to explain how to use the distributive property and how to find the areas of rectangles.

Organizer, continued

Teacher Resources

Teaching Transparencies 1, 50, 52
Transparency Masters, TR p. 2
Lesson Planner, TR Ch. 4, p. 5
Checkpoint, TR Ch. 4, p. 38

Prentice Hall Technology

Multimedia Math

- Math Tools, Frames
- Hot Page™ 4-4

Computer Item Generator

- 4-4

Fact of the Day

Yogurt is made by heating concentrated milk to about 90°C and cooling it to 44°C. Then two forms of cultured bacteria are introduced, which cause the milk to sour and thicken. This process gives yogurt its flavor and acidity and also protects it against pathogens.

—ACADEMIC AMERICAN ENCYCLOPEDIA

Around 300 B.C. Euclid wrote a book called *Elements*. In the book, Euclid shows how the distributive property works for area. "If one large rectangle is divided into 3 smaller ones, the area of the one is equal to the areas of the 3 smaller ones added together!"

There are at least two methods for finding the area of two rectangles with the same length or the same width.

Example 1 The Elliots have to cover two tables for the Memorial Day cookout. One table is 5 ft long and 3 ft wide. The other table is 5 ft long and 4 ft wide. How much contact paper will they need to cover both tables for the cookout?

Method 1 Find the area of each table top. Then add the areas.

Method 2 Place the tables end to end. Find the area of the combined table top.

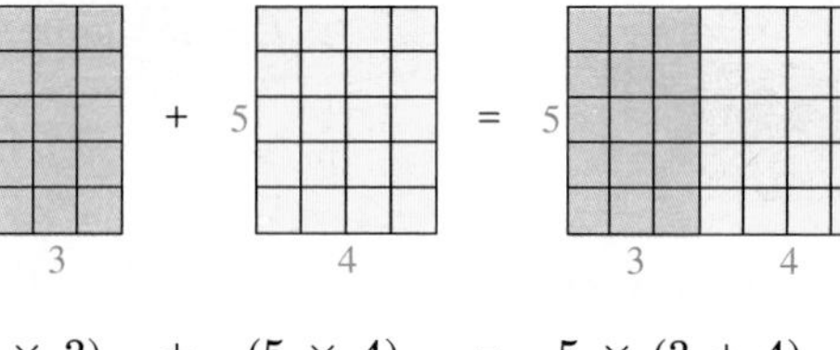

$(5 \times 3) + (5 \times 4) = 5 \times (3 + 4)$

$15 + 20 = 5 \times 7$

$35 = 35$

Both methods give the same total area. Therefore $5 \times (3 + 4) = (5 \times 3) + (5 \times 4)$. This is an example of the **distributive property.** You can use the distributive property to evaluate an expression that involves multiplication and addition.

Example 2 Use the distributive property to evaluate $(3 \times 4) + (3 \times 7)$.

$$\begin{aligned}(3 \times 4) + (3 \times 7) &= 3 \times (4 + 7)\\ &= 3 \times 11\\ &= 33\end{aligned}$$

7. **Discussion** Do you think the distributive property works for multiplication and subtraction? Make a conjecture. Try several examples to test your conjecture. See Solution Key.

8. a. Evaluate $8 \times (100 - 3)$ using the distributive property. 776
   b. Find $100 - 3$, then multiply by 8. Is your answer the same as part (a)? Explain. See left.
   c. In this problem, which method was easier, the method in part (a) or in part (b)? Explain your reasoning. Sample: part (a) because you can multiply mentally.

8.b. Yes; The distributive property and the order of operations should give you the same value of an expression.

Reteaching Activity Arrange students in groups of four. Have each student draw on graph paper two rectangles with a common dimension measurement. Then have students express the total area of both rectangles on a separate sheet of paper as the addition of two multiplication operations, for example, $(5 \times 3) + (5 \times 4)$. Then have students trade papers. Challenge each student to use the distributive property to find the total area of each group member's rectangles, and to check their answers by counting the squares in the graphed figures. Have group members compare results.

Connections Have a discussion about how the distributive property is used. You may want to start with the following examples:

- **Household** (finding the surface area of a table with and without leaves added, estimating the size of a room created by knocking down the wall between two adjacent rooms)
- **Manufacturing** (finding the surface area of several boxes of products for shipping, comparing the area of two products such as a legal notepad and a regular notepad)
- **Construction** (finding the new area of lumber needed if thinner or wider beams are used)

Journal Ask students to look up the word *distributive* or provide them with the definition "sharing evenly." Have students describe how using the distributive property relates to the definition of the word *distributive.*

ON YOUR OWN

CRITICAL THINKING For Exercise 22, have students provide an example of length times width and an example of width times length for the same rectangle.

CONNECTION TO ALGEBRA Exercises 25–26 have students solve for an unknown value.

You can also use the distributive property to help you multiply mentally.

Example 3 Use the distributive property to find 8×56.

$8 \times 56 = 8 \times (50 + 6)$ Think of 56 as 50 + 6.
$= (8 \times 50) + (8 \times 6)$ Multiply mentally.
$= 400 + 48$ Add mentally.
$= 448$

TRY THESE

Write two expressions to describe the total area. Then find the total area.

9. 

$(7 \times 5) + (7 \times 14)$; $7 \times (5 + 14)$; 133 sq. units

10. 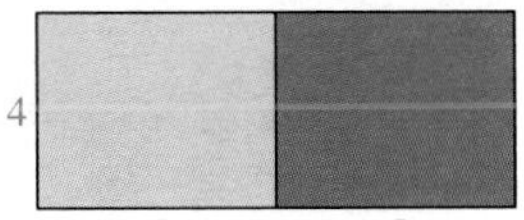

$(4 \times 5) + (4 \times 5)$; $4 \times (5 + 5)$; 40 sq. units

Write the missing numbers.

11. $6 \times (12 + 2) = (■ \times 12) + (6 \times ■)$ 6; 2

12. $(10 \times ■) - (■ \times ■) = 10 \times (6 - 3)$ 6; 10; 3

Use the distributive property to rewrite and evaluate each expression.

13. $(4 \times 6) + (4 \times 3)$ $4 \times (6 + 3)$; 36
14. $6 \times (20 - 4)$ $(6 \times 20) - (6 \times 4)$; 96
15. $12 \times (4 + 10)$ $(12 \times 4) + (12 \times 10)$; 168
16. $(5 \times 3) - (5 \times 2)$ $5 \times (3 - 2)$; 5

Mental Math **Use the distributive property to evaluate.**

17. 6×210 1260
18. 8×109 872
19. 4×75 300

ON YOUR OWN

Draw a rectangular model for each expression.

20. $8 \times (3 + 4)$
21. $(5 \times 8) + (5 \times 2)$

Check students' drawings. See Solution Key.

22. **Critical Thinking** What would happen if you multiplied the width times the length to find the area of a rectangle? Use an example to support your answer. You would get the same area; Example: a rectangle 10 in. long and 5 in. wide has an area of 50 sq in. $10 \times 5 = 50 = 5 \times 10$

Each side of an official singles tennis court is 27 ft wide by 39 ft long. ***Can you use the distributive property to find the area of the entire tennis court?*** yes; $27 \times (39 + 39)$

PH Multimedia Math Hot Page™ 4-4

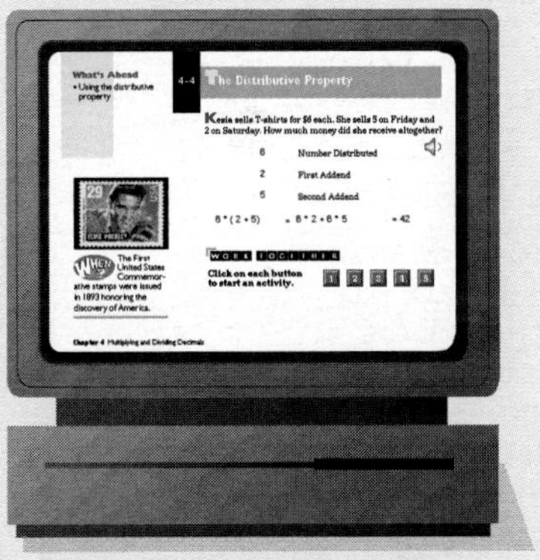

Assignment Options

Core: 23, 24, 30–33, MR all, CH all	
Reinforce: 20–22, 25–29	**Enrich:** 34

MENTAL MATH For Exercises 27–29, have students check their answers by listing the steps they performed mentally.

WRITING Have students write their descriptions for Exercise 34 as a set of instructions for using the distributive property to find the product.

CHECKPOINT

Enhanced multiple choice questions are more complex than traditional multiple choice questions, which assess only one skill. Enhanced multiple choice questions assess the process that students use as well as the end results. They are written so that students can use more than one strategy to solve the problem. Using multiple strategies is encouraged by the National Council of Teachers of Mathematics (NCTM).

Exercise 10 is an example of an enhanced multiple choice question.

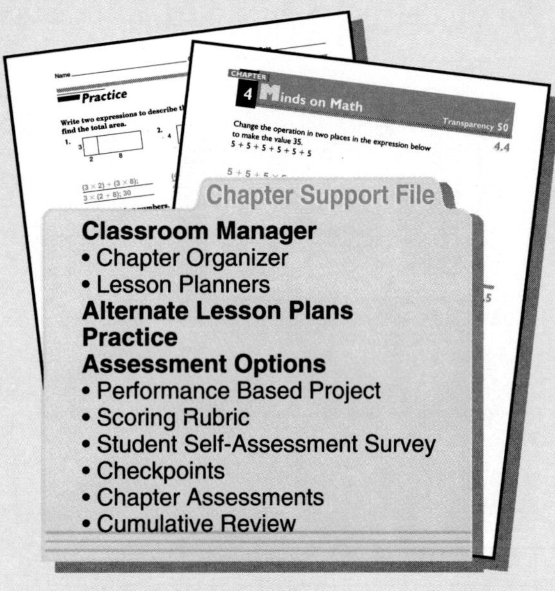

Minds on Math available in Teaching Transparencies

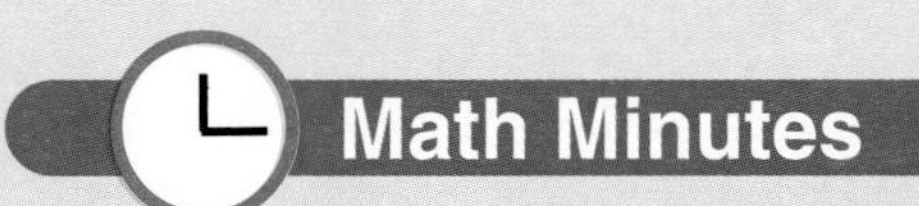

Jake paid $92.40 for 11 yd of fabric. How much did the fabric cost per yard?
$8.40

Materials for 4-5

- decimal squares
- colored pencils
- graph paper

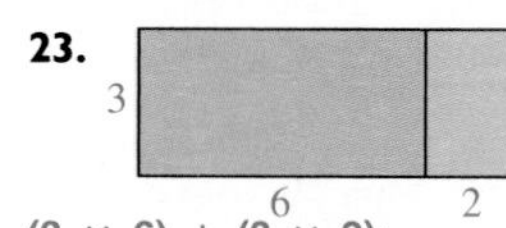

Evaluate. Use the order of operations.

1. 16 − 3 × 2 + 5 15
2. (6.3 + 8.7) − 6 × 2 3
3. 24 ÷ 3 − 2 × 4 0

Organize the data in a frequency table and in a line plot.

4. ages: 16 15 9 10 9 13 9 12 15 11 8 20
5. points: 8.5 8.8 8.4 8.4 8.5 9 8.6 8.1 8.5 9

See Solution Key.

6. Find the mean, median, and mode of each set of data in exercises 4 and 5.

4. See Solution Key.
6. 4. 12.25; 11.5; 9
   5. 8.58; 8.5; 8.5

Write two expressions to describe the total area. Then find the total area.

23. (3 × 6) + (3 × 2); 3 × (6 + 2); 24 sq. units

24. (2 × 1) + (2 × 8); 2 × (1 + 8); 18 sq. units

Complete.

25. (8 × 3) + (■ × 4) = 8 × (■ + 4) 8; 3

26. 3 × (8 − 1) = (■ × 8) − (3 × ■) 3; 1

Mental Math Use the distributive property to evaluate.

27. 8 × 42 336 **28.** 6 × 98 588 **29.** 5 × 112 560

Use the order of operations and the distributive property to evaluate.

30. 8 × (2 + 3) × 6 − 1 239 **31.** (7 + 3) × 2 × 4 80

32. 4 + 2 × 9 × 3 + 1 59 **33.** 7 × (5 − 2) + 7 × 8 77

34. Writing Describe how using the *distributive property* can help you find 9 × 92. Sample: You can write 9 × 92 as 9 × (100 − 8). Then use the distributive property to rewrite the expression as (9 × 100) − (9 × 8) = 900 − 72 = 828.

CHECKPOINT

Accept reasonable estimates.

Estimate using rounding.

1. 2.2 × 9.4 about 18 **2.** 26.28 × 1.71 about 52 **3.** 4.9 × 12.2 about 60

Estimate using compatible numbers.

4. 39.4 × 2.34 about 80 **5.** 12.78 × 3.39 about 39 **6.** 28.75 × 51.23 about 1500

Evaluate.

7. 5 + 4 × 6 29 **8.** 9 + 2 − 1 × 5 6 **9.** 4 + 36 ÷ 4 − 5 8

10. Choose A, B, or C. Find the total area of a rectangle that is 3 units long and 4 units wide and a rectangle that is 3 units long and 6 units wide. C

A. 25 sq units **B.** 18 sq units **C.** 30 sq units

CHAPTER 4 PROBLEM SOLVING PRACTICE

This page provides a variety of problems that can be used to reinforce and enhance the students' problem solving skills. Encourage students to read each problem carefully. Then have them refer to the list of problem solving strategies to help them decide how to solve the problems.

Point out, however, that not all questions require a strategy for solving, nor are all the strategies in the list used on this page.

Encourage students to draw a diagram for Exercises 3 and 6.

CONNECTION TO PATTERNS In Exercise 7, students continue and evaluate a pattern.

Problem Solving Practice

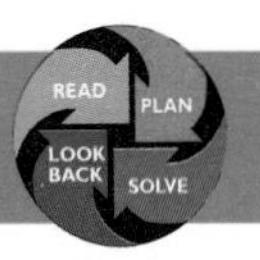

PROBLEM SOLVING STRATEGIES

Make a Table
Use Logical Reasoning
Solve a Simpler Problem
Too Much or Too Little Information
Look for a Pattern
Make a Model
Work Backward
Draw a Diagram
Guess and Test
Simulate a Problem
Use Multiple Strategies

Solve. The list at the left shows some possible strategies you can use.

1. Five friends decide that they will call each other tonight. They want to talk to each other only once. How many calls will be made in all? 10 calls

2. **Music** Paul McCartney is a singer, songwriter, and former member of the 1960's rock group, The Beatles. He earns an estimated $72/min from his recordings and composing. To the nearest million dollars about how many dollars does Paul McCartney earn in one year? about $38 million

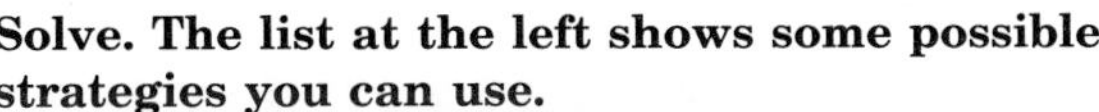

3. A passenger train has rows of 5 seats across. There are 2 seats on one side and 3 seats on the other side of the center aisle. The conductor came through and collected 76 tickets. He noted that 4 seats in every row were occupied. How many rows of seats are in the car? 19 rows

4. **Jobs** Magena has a job in a shoe store. During the last 5 weeks she sold 160 pairs of shoes. Each week she sold 7 more pairs than the previous week. How many pairs of shoes did Magena sell during each of the five weeks? 18 pairs, 25 pairs, 32 pairs, 39 pairs, 46 pairs

5. **Gardening** Rusty has a small greenhouse and waters his plants according to a schedule. He waters the zebra plants every 4 days, the coleus plants every 6 days, and the spider plants every 9 days. Rusty watered all the plants on April 1. On what date will he water all the plants again? May 7

6. A section of a large city looks like a grid. There are 12 parallel avenues running north-south. There are 22 parallel cross-streets that intersect the avenues. How many intersections are there in this section of the city? 264

7. What is the perimeter of the 100th figure in the pattern? 204

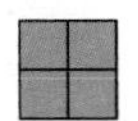
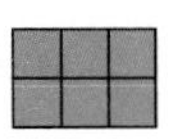
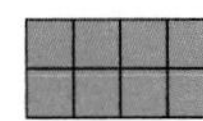

A Chinese wisteria *planted in Sierra Madre, CA in 1892 boasts branches that are 500 ft long.*

Source: *Guinness Book of Records*

4-5

Connecting to Prior Knowledge

Ask students to name times they've used or made models. Then have students describe in their own words what a model is.

THINK AND DISCUSS

CRITICAL THINKING Have students use models to test their conjectures for Question 4. Let them discuss their results.

ESL Review the vocabulary students will use in this section: *tenths, hundredths, factors, product, rows, columns.* Point out "ths" endings and check students' pronunciations.

Ongoing Assessment Have students write a description of how decimal squares model decimal products. Ask students to use their descriptions to assess their own understanding of decimal products.

KINESTHETIC LEARNERS Have ten students stand in a line facing the class. Ask them to follow your instructions as the class answers each question.

- Ask the first student to step forward. *What part of the whole group does this student represent?* **(0.1)**
- Ask the next student to step forward. *What part of the whole group do the two students represent?* **(0.2)**
- Ask two more pairs of students to step forward. *What multiplication sentence is represented now?* **($3 \times 0.2 = 0.6$)**

WORK TOGETHER

Provide each pair of students with decimal squares and colored pencils.

Error Alert! Students may shade grids incorrectly for models such as the one for Question 5. ***Remediation*** Emphasize that for Question 5 the two grids together are used to represent

> *"Responsibility educates."*
>
> —Wendell Phillips

Organizer

1. **Focus**
   Connecting to Prior Knowledge
2. **Teach**
   Think and Discuss
   Work Together
3. **Closure**
   Wrap Up

Skills Reviewed in Context of Lesson
- adding decimals

Materials and Manipulatives
- decimal squares (1 set per group)
- colored pencils (2 per group)
- graph paper (2 sheets per group)

Student Resources
Extra Practice; Practice, TR Ch. 4, p. 28
Student Study Guide; English & Spanish

Teacher Resources
Teaching Transparencies 1, 11, 12, 50
Transparency Masters, TR p. 20
Overhead Manipulatives: decimal squares
Lesson Planner, TR Ch. 4, p. 6

Prentice Hall Technology
Multimedia Math
- Math Tools, Manipulatives
- Hot Page™ 4-5

Computer Item Generator 4-5

Assignment Options

Core: 6–9, 11–16, 21, MR all	
Reinforce: 10, 17–19	**Enrich:** 20, 22

What's Ahead
- Modeling decimal products

4-5 Exploring Decimal Products

WHAT YOU'LL NEED
✓ Decimal squares 
✓ Colored pencils 
✓ Graph paper

THINK AND DISCUSS

Jared went to the amusement park with some friends. He needs two tickets to ride the loop roller coaster. Each ticket costs \$.70. How much does it cost to ride the roller coaster? You can use a sum or product to express the value of two tickets.

$$0.7 + 0.7 \text{ or } 2 \times 0.7$$

When you multiply a decimal and a whole number, you can use models to show multiplication as repeated addition.

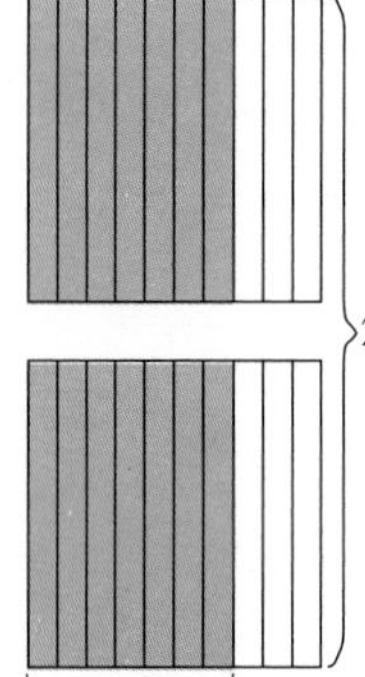

1. Use two decimal squares to model the product 2×0.7. Shade 7 columns to represent 0.7.
   a. How many tenths did you shade altogether? 14 tenths
   b. What decimal number represents the total shaded area? 1.4
2. Use 10 by 10 grids to model the product 4×0.5.
   a. How many grids do you need? four grids
   b. How much of each grid do you need to shade? five tenths
   c. How many tenths did you shade altogether? 20
   d. Write an addition sentence that describes your model. $0.5 + 0.5 + 0.5 + 0.5 = 2$

Use only one grid to model the multiplication of two decimals that are less than 1.

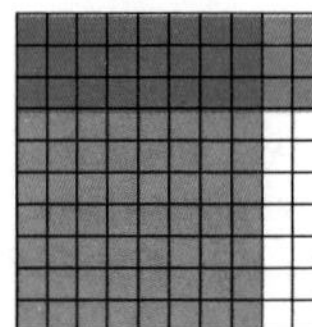

3. a. Shade 3 rows blue. What number does this represent? 0.3
   b. Shade 8 columns red. What number does this represent? 0.8
   c. The purple area where the shading overlaps represents the product. How many purple squares are shaded? 24
   d. What decimal number does this represent? 0.24
   e. Write a multiplication sentence that describes the model. $0.3 \times 0.8 = 0.24$
4. **Critical Thinking** When you multiply two decimals that are less than one, is your answer greater than or less than 1? Make a conjecture. Try several examples to test your conjecture. See Solution Key.

1.5: 1 whole grid and 0.5 of the second grid are shaded. Then, to show 1.5 × 0.5, five columns are shaded on both grids.

Wrap Up

What's the Big Idea? Ask students to explain how to model decimal products with decimal squares.

Journal Have students evaluate the usefulness of decimal squares for modeling decimal products. Ask students to list advantages and disadvantages.

Connections Have students discuss situations in which models are used to help people understand concepts or events.

- **Social Studies** (models of historic structures, dioramas)
- **Science** (models of molecules, atoms, crystals)
- **Architecture** (models of buildings, communities, blueprints)

Reteaching Activity Have students each trace a decimal square on tracing paper. Have them lightly shade five rows of the square. Then ask students to use other decimal squares to model the following products:

0.5 × 0.7 **(0.35)**
0.5 × 0.9 **(0.45)**
0.5 × 1.5 **(0.75)**

Students can place their traced 0.5 model on the squares to model each product. Point out to students that they will have to model one square at a time for the third product.

ON YOUR OWN

Students will need decimal squares for Exercises 11–21.

WRITING For Exercise 20, make sure students write clear, concise directions for drawing the model.

WORK TOGETHER

5. Work with a partner. Make a model to show the product 1.5 × 0.5. Answer the following as you work.
   a. How many grids will you use? 2
   b. How many rows and columns will you shade and what numbers will they represent? See right.
   c. What is the product? 0.75

ON YOUR OWN

Write a multiplication sentence to describe the model.

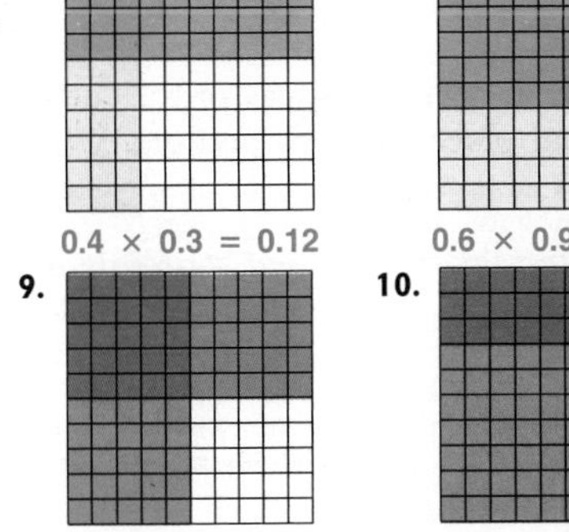

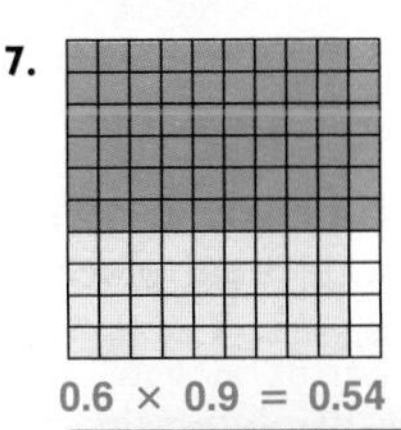

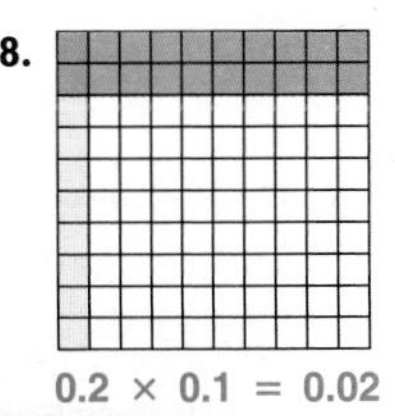

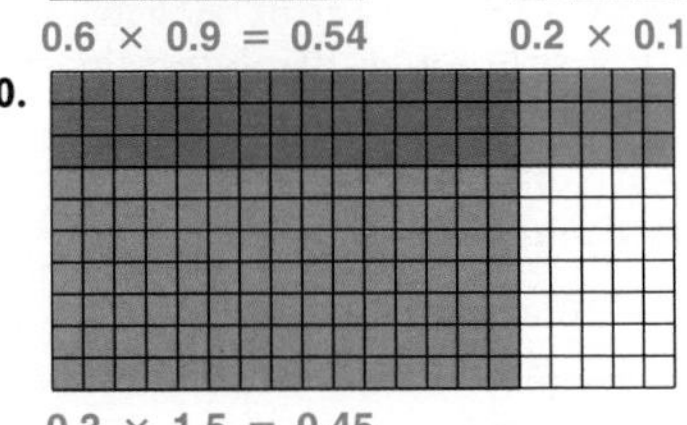

6. 0.4 × 0.3 = 0.12
7. 0.6 × 0.9 = 0.54
8. 0.2 × 0.1 = 0.02
9. 0.5 × 0.5 = 0.25
10. 0.3 × 1.5 = 0.45

Draw a model to find each product.

11. 0.2 × 3 0.6
12. 2.2 × 0.4 0.88
13. 3 × 0.6 1.8
14. 0.4 × 0.1 0.04
15. 0.7 × 0.2 0.14
16. 1.3 × 0.2 0.26
17. 2 × 0.3 0.6
18. 1.7 × 0.5 0.85
19. 0.9 × 0.8 0.72

Check students' drawings. See Solution Key.

20. **Writing** Explain how to draw a model to find the product 1.2 × 0.4. See right.
21. Draw a model to find the product 1.5 × 0.1. Write a multiplication sentence in words that describes the model. One and five-tenths times one-tenth equals fifteen hundredths.
22. You may or may not use a model to find a product. What are the advantages of using a model? Are there any disadvantages? Explain your reasoning. See Solution Key.

Mixed REVIEW

Compare. Use >, <, or =.

1. 17.34 ■ 17.051 >
2. 0.105 ■ 0.15 <
3. Draw a pair of rectangles that are not similar. See Solution Key.

Use the distributive property to find each product.

4. 24 × 5 120
5. 99 × 26 2,574
6. Find the mean of the following quiz grades: 83, 98, 64, 90, and 78. 82.6

5.b. Shade 15 columns to represent 1.5. Shade 5 rows across each grid to represent 0.5.

20. Use two grids. Shade 12 columns to represent 1.2. Shade 4 rows to represent 0.4. The 48 squares shaded by both represents the product 0.48.

Fact of the Day

Each day, half a million Americans visit an amusement park.

—*In One Day*

PH Multimedia Math Hot Page™ 4-5

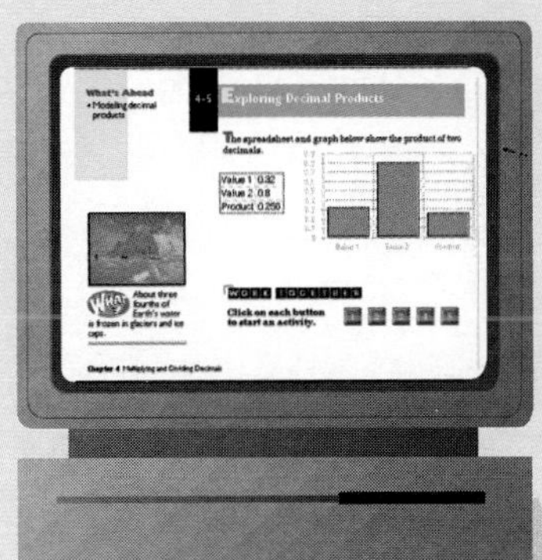

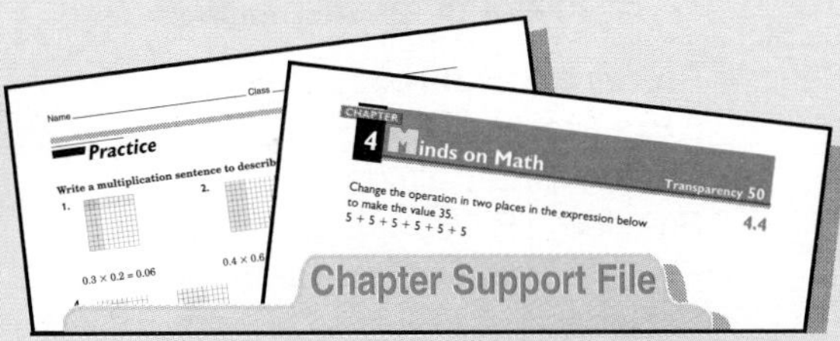

Minds on Math available in Teaching Transparencies

Math Minutes

In how many ways can you order the vowels *a, e, i, o, u?* **120**

Materials for 4-6

- graph paper
- calculator

4-6

Connecting to Prior Knowledge

Draw a line on the chalkboard that is 0.5 m long. Ask students how they could determine the combined length of six of the lines without measuring the combined total. Have students discuss how the procedure is similar to multiplying whole numbers.

WORK TOGETHER

Provide each pair of students with a calculator. Have students compare their rules when they have finished the activity.

THINK AND DISCUSS

Example 1

Point out to students the units of measurement for the factors and the product. Remind students to verify the unit of measurement in their own answers.

VISUAL LEARNERS Have students model 5 x 0.8 before answering Example 1.

AUDITORY LEARNERS After Example 1, ask students to find 0.3 × 0.06. Have students discuss what they had to do to place the decimal point in the product and why they must write zeros.

Additional Example *One m equals about 1.09 yd. About how many yd do 5 m equal?*

1.09
× 5
5.45 **5 m equals about 5.45 yd.**

Example 2

- *Why is the estimate higher than the actual product?* **(Both numbers were rounded up.)**

> *"Kindness in words creates confidence. Kindness in thinking creates profoundness. Kindness in giving creates love."*
>
> —Lao-Tzu

Organizer

1. **Focus**
   Connecting to Prior Knowledge
2. **Teach**
   Work Together
   Think and Discuss
3. **Closure**
   Try These
   Wrap Up

Skills Reviewed in Context of Lesson

- multiplying whole numbers

Materials and Manipulatives

- graph paper (1 for each group)
- calculator (1 for each group)

Student Resources

Extra Practice
Student Study Guide
Practice, TR Ch. 4, p. 29
Student Study Guide, Spanish Resources, TR
Alternate Lesson, TR Ch. 4, pp. 20–23

Teacher Resources

Teaching Transparencies 19, 50, 53
Transparency Masters, TR p. 2
Lesson Planner, TR Ch. 4, p. 7

continues next page

What's Ahead

- Multiplying decimals

4-6 Multiplying Decimals

WHAT YOU'LL NEED

✓ Graph paper 

✓ Calculator 

WORK TOGETHER

Work with a partner. Use a calculator to find each product. Then answer the questions below.

31 × 65	31 × 6.5	3.1 × 6.5	3.1 × 0.65
2,015	201.5	20.15	2.015

1. Compare the factors in each expression. How are they alike? How are they different? **The factors in all four expressions have the same digits with different place values.**
2. Compare each of the products. How are they alike? How are they different? **The products have the same digits with different place values.**
3. Now compare the number of decimal places in the factors and the number of decimal places in each product. What do you notice? **The number of decimal places in the product is the sum of the number of decimal places in the factors.**
4. Write a rule for multiplying decimals. Base your rule on the results of this Work Together activity. Use examples to test your rule. **To multiply decimals, you first write out the product as if all the factors were whole numbers. Then you place the decimal point so that the number of decimal places in the product equals the sum of the number of decimal places in the factors.**

THINK AND DISCUSS

Multiplying decimals is a lot like multiplying whole numbers.

Example 1 Today North America is moving away from Europe at the rate of 0.8 in./year. About how far will North America move in 5 years?

0.8 ← **1 decimal place**
× 5 ← **no decimal places**
4.0 ← **1 decimal place**

In 5 years, North America will move about 4.0 in. away from Europe.

5. About how far will North America move in 9 years? **about 7.2 in.**
6. Does the example above satisfy the rule you described in the Work Together? Explain. **Yes; 4.0 has one decimal place, and the sum of the decimal places in the factors is also one.**

Earth's crust continually moves, causing earthquakes, forming mountains, and separating continents.

Additional Example *How much would the same tree grow in 11.6 y at the same rate?*
Estimate: 12 × 10 = 120

$$\begin{array}{r} 11.6 \\ \times\ 10.5 \\ \hline 580 \\ 11600 \\ \hline 121.80 \end{array}$$

In 11.6 y, the tree will grow 121.80 m.

Example 3
Challenge students to find the product without using a calculator.

Error Alert! In Example 3, students may find the multiplication difficult, because they feel they cannot estimate products of factors that are less than 1. ***Remediation*** Remind students that they can determine beforehand the number of decimal places in the product. The multiplication itself is not different from multiplying whole numbers.

CRITICAL THINKING For Question 9, have students find the product without a calculator and then compare both products.

CALCULATOR Challenge students to combine their rules for Questions 10 and 11.

Example 4
Ask students if their rule from Question 10 applies in this case.

Additional Example *Find 100 × 0.0016 mentally.* **(0.16)**

Ongoing Assessment Have students predict the number of decimal places in each of the following products. Then have students find the products.

0.16 × 4.3 **(0.688)**
0.04 × 0.013 **(0.00052)**
6.2 × 2.6 **(16.12)**

Have students compare answers and then share their strategies. Make sure each student understands the strategies mentioned.

When both factors are decimal numbers, you count the decimal places in both factors to find how many places are needed in the product.

Example 2 A eucalyptus tree in New Guinea grew 10.5 m in one year. How much will this tree grow in 2.5 years if it grows at the same rate?

Estimate: 11 × 3 = 33

10.5	1 decimal place
× 2.5	1 decimal place
525	
+ 210	
26.25	2 decimal places

The eucalyptus tree will grow about 26.25 m.

The eucalyptus is the fastest growing tree in the world.

7. How can you use the estimated answer to help you place the decimal point correctly in the product? The estimated answer can help you decide how many digits are to the left of the decimal point.

When the factors are both less than 1, you may need to write zeros in the product.

Example 3 Find 0.13 × 0.02.

Press: 0.13 ⊠ 0.02 ⊟ 0.0026

The product of 0.13 and 0.02 is 0.0026.

8. Rewrite your rule for multiplying decimals to reflect any changes you notice in Example 3. See right.

9. **Critical Thinking** When you use a calculator to find 0.05 × 0.36 you get 0.018 in the display. Why do you see 3 decimal places instead of 4 places? The actual product is 0.0180; the calculator drops the last zero.

10. **Calculator** Multiply 2.5 × 10, 2.5 × 100, and 2.5 × 1,000. Compare the products. Write a rule for multiplying a decimal by 10, 100, or 1,000. 25, 250, 2,500; For each zero in the multiple of 10, the decimal point moves one place to the right.

11. **Calculator** Multiply 3 × 0.1, 3 × 0.01, and 3 × 0.001. Write a rule for multiplying by 0.1, 0.01, or 0.001. 0.3, 0.03, 0.003; For each decimal place in the multiple of 0.1, the decimal point moves one place to the left.

8. Sample: The sum of the number of decimal places in the factors equals the number of decimal places in the product. Zeros may have to be added in order to have the correct number of decimal places.

These rules can help you multiply mentally.

Example 4 Find 1,000 × 0.26 mentally.

0.260 ← 260 — Use your rule for multiplying a decimal by 1,000.

1,000 × 0.26 = 260

Organizer, continued

Prentice Hall Technology

Multimedia Math
- Math Tools, Calculation
- Math Investigations, Crisis in Hydrotown

Computer Item Generator
- 4-6

Other Available Technology
- calculator

Excel; Works by Microsoft: Questions 12–20 *(optional)*

Fact of the Day

In one day, Americans eat 815 billion calories' worth of food—about 200 billion more than they need.

—*In One Day*

TRY THESE

TECHNOLOGY OPTION For Exercises 12–20, students can use spreadsheet software to explore the concept of multiplying decimals. Have students set up a column of numbers (decimals), then have a second column of decimals that have been increased by tenths. After discussing the patterns in the products, change the second column to decimals that have been increased by hundredths. Continue the exploration and the discussion of multiplying by decimals.

MENTAL MATH For Exercises 16–19, have students check their answers by listing the steps involved in finding the products.

CONNECTION TO SCIENCE Exercise 20 has students evaluate scientific data by multiplying decimals.

Wrap Up

What's the Big Idea? Ask students to explain the steps involved in multiplying decimals.

Journal Have students compare multiplying decimals with multiplying whole numbers. Ask students if there are any cases or methods in which one is as easy as the other.

Connections Have a discussion about how multiplying decimals is used. You may want to start with these examples:

- **Business** (finding sales tax, comparing interest rates, calculating monthly rent for a year)
- **Social Science** (measuring distances on a map, computing yearly rainfall from a monthly average, comparing populations)
- **Household** (computing utility and rent bills, calculating monthly income from an hourly rate)

Assignment Options

Core: 21–34, 43, MR all	
Reinforce: 35–40, 42, 45–47	**Enrich:** 41, 44

TRY THESE

Place the decimal point in each product.

12. $0.403 \times 5 = 2015$ 2.015
13. $0.15 \times 0.31 = 00465$ 0.0465
14. $523 \times 0.5 = 2615$ 261.5
15. $8.42 \times 6.7 = 56414$ 56.414

Mental Math **Find each product.**

16. 0.1×257 25.7
17. 100×1.6 160
18. 0.47×10 4.7
19. 4.82×0.01 0.0482
20. Oceanography A dolphin swims at a rate of about 27.5 mi/h. A person can swim about 0.1 as fast. How fast can a person swim? about 2.75 mi/h

ON YOUR OWN

Place the decimal point in each product.

21. $3.2 \times 4.6 = 1472$ 14.72
22. $0.145 \times 26 = 3770$ 3.77
23. $5.05 \times 3.14 = 158570$ 15.857
24. $4.50 \times 3.8 = 17100$ 17.1

Mental Math **Find each product.**

25. 6.2×10 62
26. 7.08×0.1 0.708
27. 3.5×1000 3500
28. 26×0.01 0.26

Find each product.

29. 2.065×12 24.78
30. 0.18×0.06 0.0108
31. 3.1×0.04 0.124
32. 15.35×3.2 49.12
33. 450×0.01 4.5
34. 35.15×25 878.75
35. 0.96×0.12 0.1152
36. 7.6×0.06 0.456
37. Is $(2.3 \times 3) \times 6$ equal to $2.3 \times (3 \times 6)$? Does this seem unusual? Why or why not? Yes; answers may vary.

True or False? Give an example to support your answer.

38. The product of any number and zero is always zero. True; Sample: $2.3 \times 0 = 0$
39. If you change the order of the factors, the product will also change. False; Sample: $2 \times 3 = 6$, $3 \times 2 = 6$
40. Any number multiplied by 1 is itself. True; $1 \times 6 = 6$

Mixed REVIEW

Use the distributive property to find each product.

1. 68×8 544
2. 95×4 380
3. Draw a figure that has no line symmetry.
4. Draw a figure that has vertical and horizontal line symmetry.

3.–4. See Sol. Key.

Solve.

5. Efra drinks two juice packs a day. Each pack contains 355 mL. 1L = 1,000 mL. How many liters of juice does she drink in one week? 4.97 L
6. Mr. Garcia punched in at 7:37 A.M. and out at 4:19 P.M. He took a 15-min. lunch. How long did he work? 8 h 27 min

Reteaching Activity Present each group of problems to students.

a.

0.5	0.7	0.6	tenths
× 0.2	× 0.4	× 0.3	× tenths
(0.10)	**(0.28)**	**(0.18)**	**(hundredths)**

b.

0.03	0.08	0.17	hundredths
× 0.04	× 0.02	× 0.11	× hundredths
(0.0012)	**(0.0016)**	**(0.0187)**	**(ten-thousandths)**

Ask students to predict the number of decimal places in each product and to decide if the answer will be greater or less than either of the two factors. **(In all examples, the product is less than either of the factors.)** Then have students write rules such as are shown to the right of the multiplication operations.

ON YOUR OWN

MENTAL MATH For Exercises 25–28, encourage students to begin with an estimate.

CONNECTION TO SCIENCE Exercises 42 and 45–47 have students use multiplying decimals to evaluate scientific data.

CHAPTER INVESTIGATION In Exercise 43, get, if possible, a ream of paper (perhaps from supplies for the copy machine) to show students.

WRITING Have students compare both products side by side for Exercise 44.

41. Data File 4 (pp. 138–139) How closely does the length of your femur predict your height in centimeters? Answers may vary.

42. Astronomy The circumference of Earth is about 40,200 km at the equator. The circumference of Jupiter is 11.2 times as great. What is the circumference of Jupiter? 450,240 km

43. Investigation (p. 140) A ream consists of 500 sheets of paper. The thickness of one sheet of paper is 0.01 cm. Calculate the thickness of a ream of paper. 5 cm

44. Writing Explain how multiplying 0.3 × 0.4 is like multiplying 3 × 4. How is it different? See below.

Use the article and the chart to answer each problem.

Calorie Counter

Your body uses food to make energy, which is used for all the things you do each day. The food you eat and the energy you use are measured in calories.

Not all foods have the same number of calories and not all activities use the same number of calories. A 120 lb person would use about 80 calories by sitting for 1 h. The same person would use 336 calories playing tennis for 1 h. Your body weight is also a factor in the number of calories you use. For example, a 120 lb person would use about 216 calories in 1 h of bicycle riding, but a 60 lb person would use only about 108 calories.

The expression tells about how many calories you use for different activities.

Weight × Number of minutes of activity × Calories used per minute per pound

Activity	Calories/ min/lb
Bicycling	0.03
Playing Catch	0.03
Dancing	0.05
Jumping Rope	0.07
Roller Skating	0.05
Running	0.10
Skateboarding	0.05
Playing Soccer	0.05
Playing Softball	0.04
Standing	0.02
Walking	0.03

45. A 100-lb male jumps rope for 15 min. How many calories will he use? 105 calories

46. An 80-lb female dances for 2 h. How many calories will she use? 480 calories

47. You weigh 70-lb. How many calories will you use playing softball for 1 h 10 min? Would you use more or fewer calories if you play soccer instead? 196 calories; more

44. In both products, the numbers that are multiplied are the same, 3 and 4. But in 0.3 × 0.4, you must calculate to place the decimal point.

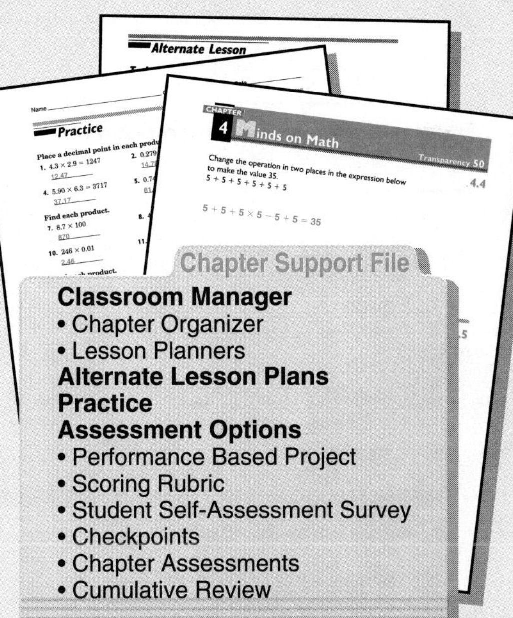

Minds on Math available in Teaching Transparencies

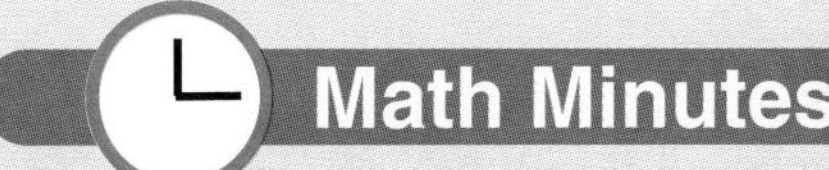

A box of 20 thank-you cards sells for $9.00. What is the price per card? **$.45**

4-7

Connecting to Prior Knowledge

Ask students if they could fly an airplane if someone just showed them the controls. Then ask students if the information they would need would include manuals for every plane built before the plane they wanted to fly. Have students think of other situations in which just the right amount of information is needed.

ESL To be sure students are familiar with the measurement terms in the problem, display a square with its length and perimeter labeled. To show the perimeter, attach a tape measure around the square.

KINESTHETIC LEARNERS Sheets of paper, centimeter rulers, scissors, and string are needed. To help students answer Question 4, have them cut out a square with sides 26.5 cm. Have them use the string to measure the perimeter of the square.

Additional Problem *Suppose you need to put a fence around a rectangular garden. The plastic fencing costs $.25 a foot, but wooden fencing costs more. The garden is 21 ft by 15 ft with an area of 315 sq. ft. How much will you pay for plastic fencing? How much more is the wooden fencing?*

To find the cost of plastic fencing, find the perimeter of the garden first.

$$P = 2l + 2w$$
$$P = (2 \times 21) + (2 \times 15)$$
$$P = 42 + 30$$
$$P = 72 \text{ ft}$$

Multiply $.25 by 72 ft: 72 × 0.25 = 18

The cost of the plastic fencing is $18. You cannot find how much more wooden fencing costs because the price is not given.

Ongoing Assessment Have students compare their strategies for the Additional Problem. Then have students write a paragraph describing what they would do differently to solve the problem more easily or more quickly.

"The impossible is often the untried."
—Jim Goodwin

Organizer

1. **Focus**
   Connecting to Prior Knowledge
2. **Teach**
3. **Closure**
   Try These
   Wrap Up

Skills Reviewed in Context of Lesson
- multiplying decimals

Materials and Manipulatives
- paper *(optional)*
- centimeter ruler *(optional)*
- scissors *(optional)*
- string *(optional)*

Student Resources
Extra Practice
Student Study Guide
Practice, TR Ch. 4, p. 30
Student Study Guide, Spanish Resources, TR

Teachers Resources
Teaching Transparency 51
Lesson Planner, TR Ch. 4, p. 8

Prentice Hall Technology
Multimedia Math
- Math Tools, Calculation

Computer Item Generator
- 4-7

PROBLEM SOLVING

4-7 Too Much, Too Little Information

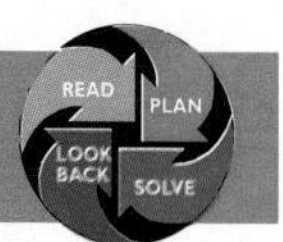

What's Ahead
- Solving problems with too much or too little information.

Sometimes you do not have enough information to solve a problem. Other times problems have more information than you need. You have to decide.

The first annual *One Sky, One World* global kite-fly was held in 1986. The focus was on global peace and the protection of the environment.

Source: *UNESCO Courier*

Pablo is making a box kite for a festival out of wood dowels and paper strips. The top and bottom of the kite are square. The sides of each square are 26.5 cm long. Pablo has $10.00 to spend on supplies. The eight dowels cost $4.50. Other supplies such as glue, string, and nails cost $4.27 altogether. Paper strips wrap around the kite. Find the total length of the paper strips he will need.

Top
Wood dowel
Paper strip
Bottom

READ — Read and understand the given information. Summarize the problem.

1. Think about the information that is given.
   a. What do you need to find out? See below.
   b. What information do you need to solve the problem? the length of each paper strip, and how many strips there are

PLAN — Decide whether there is enough information. Plan a method to solve the problem.

2. a. What is the shape of the top and bottom of the kite? square
   b. What is the length of each side? 26.5 cm
   c. How can you use this information to solve the problem? See below.
   d. How will you find the total length of paper needed? 2 × (4 × 26.5)
3. Now that you have decided what information you need, what information is given that is not needed? The amount Pablo has to spend, the cost of the dowels and the number needed, the cost of other supplies

1.a. how much paper Pablo will need for the kite
2.c. The perimeter of a square is four times the length of one side.

TRY THESE

AUDITORY LEARNERS Have students work in pairs to discuss the answers to Exercises 7 and 8.

Error Alert! Students may not recognize when problems such as Exercise 7 contain too little information. ***Remediation*** Encourage students to work backward from each problem's question. For example, if the area of a square is to be found, the length of one side must be known. Any other information in the problem may be irrelevant.

Wrap Up

What's the Big Idea? Ask students to explain how to solve problems with too little or too much information.

Journal Have students write about how they feel when they first start on a problem with a lot of information. Then ask students to brainstorm for ways they could feel more comfortable with and focused on the problem.

Connection Have a discussion about how problems with too little or too much information are used. You may want to start with these examples:

- **Household** (using manuals to fix appliances or a car, reading instructions to assemble a toy or other purchase)
- **Science** (using different methods to perform chemical analyses, trying to duplicate the results of an experiment)
- **Military** (carrying out orders, accomplishing objectives, planning strategy based on intelligence information)
- **Sports** (performing set plays, relaying play signals)

Reteaching Activity Have students work in pairs. Present the following problem and list of questions. Have partners write

4. One way to solve the problem is to find the perimeter of the square. Then double the perimeter to find the total length of paper needed for the two paper strips.
   a. What is the length of paper Pablo needs for the two strips? 212 cm
   b. What is another way to solve the problem? The kite requires 8 strips, each 26.5 cm long. $8 \times 26.5 = 212$

5. Pablo wants to know how much it will cost to make the kite.
   a. What information is given to help you find the cost of making the kite? The cost of dowels, glue, string, and nails
   b. What information is missing? The cost of the paper strips

SOLVE Use your method to find the solution.

LOOK BACK If there is too little information to solve the problem, determine what facts are needed.

TRY THESE

Solve if possible. If not, tell what information is needed.

6. Nathan bought two new bicycle tires for $21.90. The diameter of each tire is 20 in. The combined weight of the two tires is 2.9 lb.
   a. How much does each tire cost? $10.95
   b. What information did you use to solve part (a)? The total cost of two tires
   c. How much does one tire weigh? 1.45 lb
   d. What information did you use to solve part (c)? See below.
   e. What information is given that is not needed for either part (a) or part (c)? The diameter of each tire

7. **Money** Manos buys some comic books at a local store. He hands the clerk $10.00 and receives $1.45 in change. Each comic book has the same price. How much does each comic book cost?
   a. What information is given to help you find the cost of each comic book? See below.
   b. What information is missing? The number of comic books bought

8. Coretta bought a pair of curtains for $69.99. Each curtain measures 45 in. long by 98 in. wide, and the pair weighs 1.50 lbs.
   a. How much does each curtain weigh? 0.75 lb
   b. What information is given that is not needed? The length, width and cost of the curtains

6.d. The total weight of two tires
7.a. The amount of change received from $10, and the fact that all the prices are the same.

Mixed REVIEW

Find each product.

1. 1.9×0.8 1.52
2. 0.95×6 5.7
3. How many lines of symmetry does a regular octagon have? 8
4. Find two numbers whose sum is 28 and whose product is 96. 4 and 24

Arrange the numbers in increasing order.

5. 0.05 5.55 0.505 0.55
6. 9.04 90.4 900.4 9.004
7. You have two 25¢ stamps and three 30¢ stamps. How many different amounts of postage can you have? 11

5. 0.05, 0.505, 0.55, 5.55
6. 9.004, 9.04, 90.4, 900.4

Fact of the Day

There are three basic classifications of horses. A pony stands 10 to 14-2 hands (14 hands, two inches) and weighs 300 to 850 lb. A light horse stands 14-2 to 17 hands, and weighs 800 to 1,300 lb. A draft horse stands 15-2 to 19 hands, and weighs 1,500 to 2,600 lb.

—*Academic American Encyclopedia*

Assignment Options

Core: 11–13, 15, 17, MR all	
Reinforce: 9, 10, 14	**Enrich:** 16

Yes or No to tell whether or not they can answer the question. Then have the students give the answers to the questions that can be answered and tell what information is needed before the remaining questions can be answered.

It costs $3.50/h to rent a bike, and $2.50/half-hour to rent a paddle boat. Jim rents a bike at 8:00 A.M. and Cindy rents a paddle boat at the same time. Jim returns the bike at noon.

- *How long did Jim rent the bike?*
  (yes; 4 h)
- *How much must Jim pay?*
  (yes; $14)
- *How much must Cindy pay?*
  (no; need the time she returns boat)
- *How much more did Jim pay than Cindy?*
  (no; need the time she returns boat)
- *How long did Cindy rent the paddle boat?*
  (no; need the time she returns boat)

ON YOUR OWN

CONNECTION TO PATTERNS In Exercise 14, students continue and evaluate a pattern.

WRITING For Exercise 15, have students check their problems by working through the steps themselves.

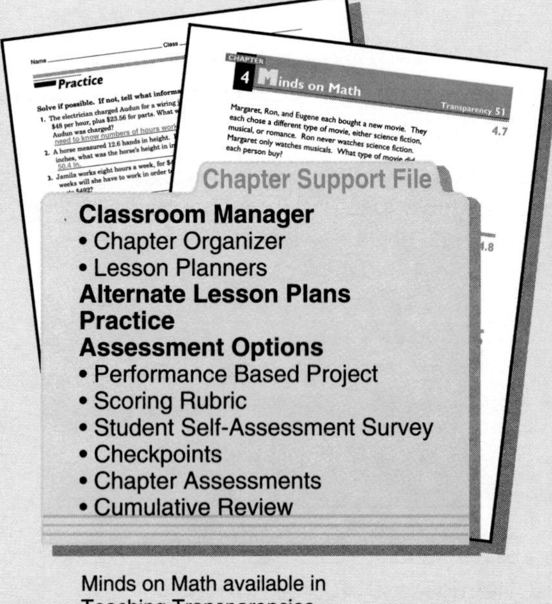

Minds on Math available in Teaching Transparencies

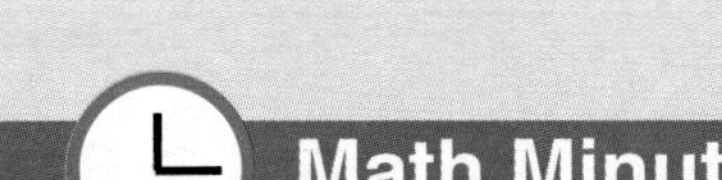

Round to the nearest hundredth.

1. 23.673 **23.67**
2. 0.798 **0.80**
3. 572.398 **572.40**

Materials for 4-8

- calculator
- graph paper
- decimal squares

A pony is a small horse that is under 14.2 hands tall. ***How many inches would that be?*** about 56.8 in.

ON YOUR OWN

Solve if possible. If not, tell what information is needed.

9. The telephone company charged Rebecca for a phone call. The rates were $2.40 for the first minute and $.60 for each additional minute. How many additional minutes was Rebecca charged for? The amount she was charged is needed to solve the problem.
10. A quilt pattern has a 5-by-5 grid of squares. The design of the grid calls for alternating blue and red squares. How many squares of each color does the grid contain? 13 blue squares and 12 red or 12 blue squares and 13 red
11. The record shoulder height for a horse is 78 in. A horse's height is measured in hands. One hand is about 4 in. What is the record shoulder height of a horse in hands? about 19.5 hands
12. Jobs Percy works at a pet store after school. At present he works Monday, Wednesday, and Friday for 2 h each day. He is saving to buy a bike that costs $245. If he earns $6 per hour, how many weeks must he work to be sure he has enough money? about 7 weeks
13. A dressmaker sent 250 dresses to several local department stores. If this dressmaker sent every store the same number of dresses, how many dresses did each store receive? The number of stores is needed to solve the problem.
14. Banking When Sasha was 7 years old her mother started a college fund. She began with $30. Every year she put a little more money into the fund as shown in the table. If she continues this pattern, how much will she put into the fund when Sasha is 16? about $1,153.35

Sasha's College Fund

Year 1	$ 30.00
Year 2	$ 45.00
Year 3	$ 67.50
Year 4	$101.25

15. a. Writing Write a word problem with too much information. Answers may vary.
    b. Write a word problem with too little information. Answers may vary.
16. Hobbies Alexis likes to collect picture postcards when she travels. On her last vacation she collected 15 postcards. Some of the cards cost $.79 and some cost $1.19. She spent a total of $14.25 for the cards. How many postcards did she buy from each price group? 9 cards costing $.79, and 6 cards costing $1.19
17. Data File 7 (pp. 272–273) Find the average water level at high tide in Bay of Fundy, Canada. Not enough information; the tidal range is 39.4. The water level at low tide is needed.

CHAPTER 4

PRACTICE

This page provides practice on the skills learned up to this point in the chapter. Daily cumulative practice can be found in the Mixed Reviews that appear in every lesson.

Practice

Round each factor to the nearest whole number. Estimate. Accept reasonable estimates.

1. 8.2 × 3.7 about 32
2. 34.5 ÷ 4.96 about 7
3. 17.8 ÷ 6.2 about 3
4. 12.79 × 9.68 about 130

Use compatible numbers to estimate. Accept reasonable estimates.

5. 14.3 ÷ 2.9 about 5
6. 19.3 × 5.1 about 100
7. 2.18 × 51.3 about 100
8. 36.1 ÷ 4.84 about 7
9. 101.5 ÷ 24.3 about 4
10. 24.1 ÷ 8.39 about 3

Use the order of operations to evaluate each expression.

11. 8 − 3 + 5 × 3 20
12. (6.4 − 1.2) × 3 15.6
13. 5 ÷ (1.6 + 3.4) 1
14. 15 ÷ 5 + 10 13
15. (15 + 12) ÷ 9 × 3 9
16. 25 ÷ 5 × (8.4 + 0.6) − 5 40

Insert operation symbols to make the equation true.

17. 24 ■ 3 ■ 3 = 5 ÷, −
18. (12 ■ 8) ■ (5 ■ 1) = 100 (+, ×, ×) or (+, ×, ÷)
19. 49 ■ 20 ■ 2 = 9 −, ×
20. 14 ■ 2 ■ 5 ■ 1 = 11 (+, −, ×) or (+, −, ÷) or (÷, +, −)

Complete.

21. 6 × (15 + 4) = (■ × 15) + (6 × ■) 6, 4
22. 22 × (10 − 3) = (22 × ■) − (■ × 3) 10, 22

Use the distributive property to evaluate each expression.

23. (3 × 7) + (3 × 4) 33
24. 8 × (70 + 3) 584
25. (7 × 4) − (7 × 2) 14
26. 6 × (4 + 10) 84
27. 5 × (20 − 8) 60
28. (12 × 7) − (12 × 3) 48

Mental Math **Use the distributive property to evaluate.**

29. 4 × 57 228
30. 7 × 203 1,421
31. 9 × 89 801
32. 3 × 312 936

Find each product.

33. 2.12 × 0.3 0.636
34. 1,000 × 0.43 430
35. 5.2 × 1.33 6.916
36. 2.3 × 0.01 0.023
37. 8.2 × 0.06 0.492
38. 3.045 × 25 76.125
39. 0.28 × 0.09 0.0252
40. 60.4 × 0.09 5.436

Resources
Extra Practice
Student Study Guide
Student Study Guide, Spanish Resources, TR

4-8

Connecting to Prior Knowledge

Ask students to recall the models used for the products of decimals. Then have students brainstorm for ways they could use the same model for quotients.

THINK AND DISCUSS

AUDITORY LEARNERS As students develop their division models, ask questions that will help them to build the concepts.

ESL Error Alert! For problems such as Question 2, students may confuse the use of a model for quotients with the procedure for finding products. ***Remediation*** Encourage students to read each expression softly to themselves. For example, for Question 2a: "In the decimal 0.8, there are how many groups of 0.4?"

DIVERSITY Students who are skilled at working problems involving division of decimals may be impatient with the time it takes to model. Encourage them to go ahead and find the answer with their calculator, and then to help other students.

Ongoing Assessment Present students with the expression 0.8 ÷ 0.05. Have each student use a model to find the quotient. **(16)** Ask students to compare models.

WORK TOGETHER

Provide each pair of students with decimal squares. You may wish to have students make their own decimal squares from graph paper.

TECHNOLOGY OPTION For Questions 6–8, students can use spreadsheet software to explore the concept of dividing decimals.

"Treat all men alike. Give them all the same laws. Give them all an even chance to live and grow."

—CHIEF JOSEPH

Organizer

1. **Focus**
   Connecting to Prior Knowledge
2. **Teach**
   Think and Discuss
   Work Together
3. **Closure**
   Wrap Up

Skills Reviewed in Context of Lesson
- dividing whole numbers

Materials and Manipulatives
- calculator (1 for each student)
- graph paper (for each student)
- decimal squares (1 set for each group)

On Your Own 14–24: graph paper

Student Resources
Extra Practice; Practice, TR Ch. 4, p. 31
Student Study Guide; English & Spanish

Teacher Resources

Teaching Transparencies 11, 12, 19, 51
Transparency Masters, TR pp. 2, 20
Lesson Planner, TR Ch. 4, p. 9

Prentice Hall Technology
Multimedia Math
- Math Tools, Calculation

Computer Item Generator 4-8

Other Available Technology
Excel; Works by Microsoft: Questions 6–8 *(optional)*

What's Ahead
- Modeling decimal quotients

4-8 Exploring Quotients of Decimals

WHAT YOU'LL NEED
✓ Calculator
✓ Graph paper

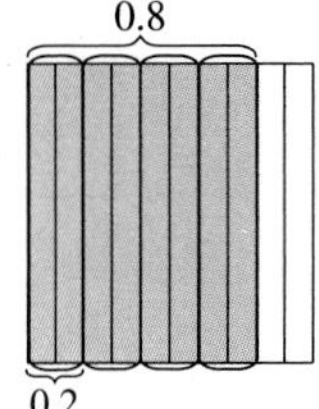

THINK AND DISCUSS

Bik is making yogurt shakes for customers at her health food restaurant. She has 0.8 lb of sliced strawberries. She uses 0.2 lb in each shake. The expression below represents the number of yogurt shakes Bik can make using the strawberries.

$$0.8 \div 0.2$$

You can use a model to divide a decimal number by tenths.

1. Use the model at the left to answer each question.
   a. How is 8 tenths, 0.8, shown in the model?
   b. How is 2 tenths, 0.2, shown in the model? See below.
   c. How many groups of 0.2 are there in 0.8? 4 groups
   d. **Calculator** Find the quotient 0.8 ÷ 0.2. How does your answer relate to the model? 4; the quotient is the number of groups.
2. Draw a model to find each quotient. See Solution Key.
   a. 0.8 ÷ 0.4 2 b. 0.9 ÷ 0.3 3 c. 1 ÷ 0.4 2.5

You can also use a model to divide a decimal number by hundredths.

3. Use the model at the left to answer each question.
   a. What number does the shaded region show? 0.4
   b. The shaded region is divided into groups. What decimal does each group represent? 0.08
   c. How many groups are in the shaded area? 5 groups
   d. Complete the sentence: 0.4 ÷ 0.08 = ■. 5
4. Draw a model to find each quotient. See Solution Key.
   a. 0.3 ÷ 0.06 5 b. 0.9 ÷ 0.15 6 c. 0.6 ÷ 0.12 5
5. **Critical Thinking** In the sentence 0.8 ÷ 0.2 = 4 the divisor, 0.2, represents the size of each group. What does the quotient, 4, represent? the number of groups

1.a. 8 shaded columns
b. 2 grouped columns

Wrap Up

What's the Big Idea? Ask students to describe how to model decimal quotients.

Journal Have students compare modeling decimal products with modeling decimal quotients.

Connections Have a discussion about how models of decimal quotients are used. You may want to start with these examples:

- **Business** (payroll and budget graphics)
- **Media** (rainfall comparisons, sports statistics)

Reteaching Activity Use the number of different coins in a dollar to connect modeling decimal quotients to something familiar to students. Have students make models showing the numbers of quarters, dimes, and nickels in a dollar.

ON YOUR OWN

Students will need graph paper for Exercises 14–22, 24.

WRITING Check students' answers for Exercise 23 to make sure their directions could be easily followed.

WORK TOGETHER

Check students' drawings. See Solution Key.

Work with a partner. Draw a model to find each quotient. First decide how many decimal squares you need. Next shade your model to show the dividend. Then circle groups of equal size. Remember, the divisor tells you the size of each group.

6. 1.8 ÷ 0.3 6 **7.** 1 ÷ 0.2 5 **8.** 2 ÷ 0.4 5

FLASHBACK

Each number in a division sentence has a special name.

24 ÷ 8 = 3

24 Dividend
8 Divisor
3 Quotient

ON YOUR OWN

Complete each sentence.

9. 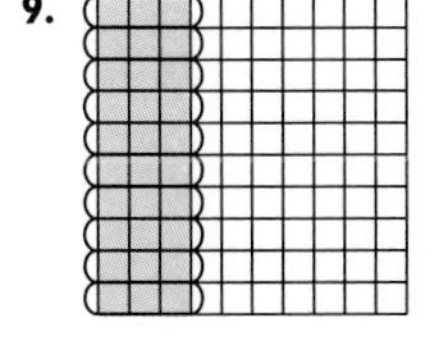 **10.** 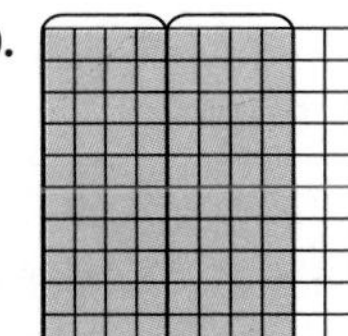 **11.** 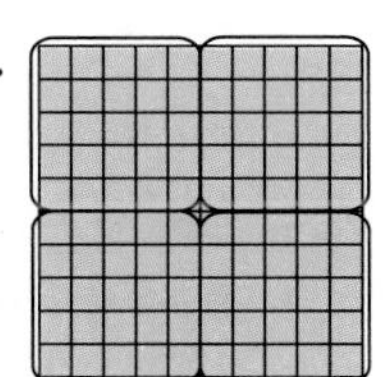

0.3 ÷ 0.03 = ■ 10 ■ ÷ 0.4 = 2 0.8 1 ÷ ■ = 4 0.25

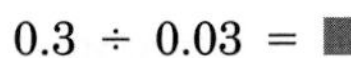

12. 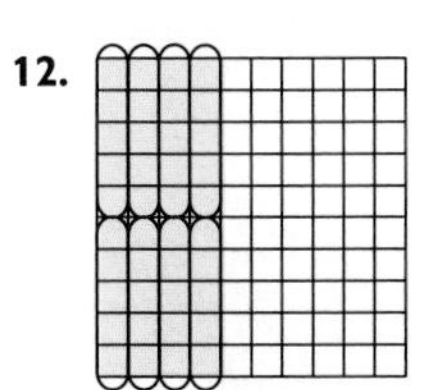 **13.** 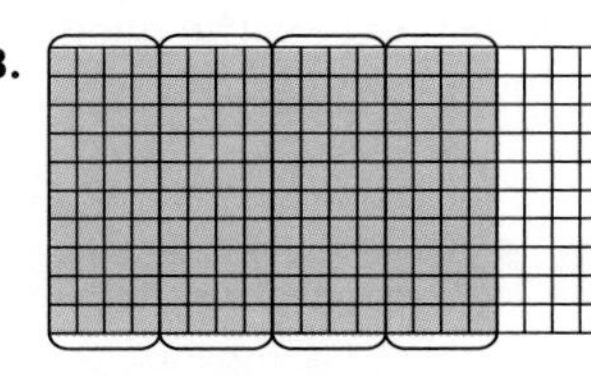

0.4 ÷ ■ = 8 0.05 ■ ÷ 0.4 = 4 1.6

Draw a model to find each quotient.

14. 0.6 ÷ 0.2 3 **15.** 0.8 ÷ 0.05 16 **16.** 1.6 ÷ 0.8 2

17. 2 ÷ 0.5 4 **18.** 1.5 ÷ 0.06 25 **19.** 0.3 ÷ 0.15 2

20. 1.2 ÷ 3 0.4 **21.** 2.4 ÷ 0.8 3 **22.** 0.36 ÷ 4 0.09

Check students' drawings. See Solution Key.

23. Writing Explain how to draw a model to find the quotient of 2.4 ÷ 0.6. use 3 squares; shade 24 columns; divide them into groups of 6; 2.4 ÷ 0.6 = 4

24. a. Draw a model to find the quotient 2.1 ÷ 7. See Solution Key.

b. In this problem, what does the divisor, 7, represent? The number of equal sized groups that 2.1 is being divided into

Mixed REVIEW

Place a decimal point in each product.

1. 5.9 × 0.46 = 2714
2. 0.08 × 0.09 = 00072
3. 0.3 × 0.2 = 0006 0.06

Solve if possible. If not, tell what information is needed.

4. Twelve-year-old Yuri swam the 100-m freestyle in 29.56 s. His best time in 1993 was 29.6 s. What time does he need to break the pool record?
5. Make four equilateral triangles using only six toothpicks.

1. 2.714
2. 0.0072
4. Pool record is needed. 5. See Solution Key.

Assignment Options

Core: 9–12, 14–17, MR all	
Reinforce: 13, 18–22	Enrich: 23, 24

Fact of the Day

Billie Jean King won a record of 20 Wimbledon titles between 1961 and 1979—6 singles, 10 women's doubles, and 4 mixed doubles.

—Guinness Book of Records

Minds on Math available in Teaching Transparencies

Math Minutes

Write five decimal numbers that round to 6.
Answers may vary; any number from 5.5 to 6.4$\overline{9}$.

Materials for 4-9

- calculator

4-9

Connecting to Prior Knowledge

Ask students to recall the situations in which it is necessary to multiply decimals. Ask students if it might also be useful to divide decimals in the situations. Challenge students to give examples such as splitting a check at a restaurant.

WORK TOGETHER

Make sure each pair of students has a calculator.

CALCULATOR For Question 3, caution students to pay attention to the placement of the decimal point.

THINK AND DISCUSS

ESL ESL Before students become involved in the lesson, give a quick review of these terms: *divisor, dividend, quotient, remainder, power, equivalent, division, mi/h.*

Example 1

Point out to students that the estimate is made by rounding to the nearest whole number.

- *Why is it useful to first estimate the quotient?* **(Estimating helps you to decide if the answer you get is reasonable.)**

Additional Example *At a walking rate of 3 mi/h, how long would it take to walk 11.49 mi?*

```
    3.83
3)11.49
 - 9
   24
 - 24
    09
   - 9
     0
```

It would take 3.83 h to walk 11.49 mi.

> *"Originality exists in every individual because each of us differs from the others. We are all primary numbers divisible only by ourselves."*
>
> —Jean Guitton

Organizer

1. **Focus**
   Connecting to Prior Knowledge
2. **Teach**
   Work Together
   Think and Discuss
3. **Closure**
   Try These
   Wrap Up

Skills Reviewed in Context of Lesson

- estimating decimals
- dividing whole numbers

Materials and Manipulatives

- calculator (1 for each group)

On Your Own Exercises 23–31: calculator

Student Resources

Extra Practice
Student Study Guide
Practice, TR Ch. 4, p. 32
Student Study Guide, Spanish Resources, TR
Checkpoint, TR Ch. 4, p. 38

Teacher Resources

Teaching Transparencies 12, 51, 53
Lesson Planner, TR Ch. 4, p. 10

continues next page

What's Ahead

- Dividing decimals

4-9 Dividing Decimals

WHAT YOU'LL NEED

✓ Calculator

WORK TOGETHER

Work with a partner. Answer the questions below.

$0.24 \div 0.06$ 4 $2.4 \div 0.6$ 4 $24 \div 6$ 4

1. Compare the numbers in each expression. How are they alike? How are they different? See left.
2. Use a calculator to find each quotient. Compare the quotients. Describe the pattern. The quotients are all the same, 4.
3. a. **Calculator** Find the quotient $2.4 \div 6$. 0.4
   b. Does this expression fit the pattern you described above? Why or why not? No; the number of decimal places in the dividend and divisor are not the same.
4. Does the expression $0.024 \div 0.006$ fit the pattern above? What would you expect the quotient to be? Check your answer using a calculator. Yes; 4.

1. Answers may vary. Sample. The numbers in the three expressions have the same digits with different place values. In each expression, the number of decimal places in the divisor and dividend are the same.

THINK AND DISCUSS

Dividing decimals is a lot like dividing whole numbers.

Example 1 The Seto Bridge is 7.64 mi long. How long would it take to cross the bridge if you walk at 4 mi/h?

Estimate: $7.64 \div 4 \approx 8 \div 4 = 2$

```
   1.91
4)7.64     Divide. Place the decimal point
 -4        in the quotient
  3 6
- 3 6
   04
  - 4
    0
```

It would take 1.91 h to walk across the bridge.

WHAT? **The Great Seto Bridge,** opened on April 10, 1988, crosses Japan's Inland Sea and is the longest road/railway suspension bridge in the world.

Source: *Guinness Book of World Records*

5. **Discussion** How is dividing decimals different than dividing whole numbers? How is it the same? See left.

Answers may vary. Sample. Dividing whole numbers and decimals uses the same process, but with decimals, you must place a decimal point correctly in your answer.

Example 2

Point out to students that both decimals (in the divisor and the dividend) have the decimal point moved the same number of spaces to the right. Then the quotient is found in the same way as in Example 1.

Additional Example *Find the quotient 0.231 ÷ 0.07.*

$$0.07\overline{)0.231} \rightarrow 7\overline{)023.1}$$

Quotient 3.3; − 21; 21; − 21; 0

0.231 ÷ 0.07 = 3.3

VISUAL LEARNERS Provide six decimal squares representing tenths, and have students work in pairs to model 5.8 ÷ 2. **(2.9)**

CRITICAL THINKING For Question 7c, have students compare what happens to both the divisor and the decimal to be divided when finding the quotient for Question 7b.

DIVERSITY At-risk students are often engaged by relevance and concreteness. In Question 11, use an actual stack of paper to help students relate to the problem.

Error Alert! Students may be confused by the wording of problems such as Question 11 and not know which numbers to use to find the answer. ***Remediation*** Point out to students that for Question 11a the group measurement of the stack of papers can be divided by the individual measurement of a single paper to find the number of papers. Show students that in both Question 10 and 11, the divisor is indicated by the word *each*.

Ongoing Assessment Give students a brief quiz to cover the concepts in the lesson. Present students with the following divisors. Have students name the number to multiply both divisor and dividend.

- *a divisor to the hundredths' place* **(100)**
- *a divisor to the tenths' place* **(10)**
- *a divisor to the thousandths' place* **(1000)**

When you divide a decimal by a decimal it helps to write the divisor as a whole number.

Example 2 Find the quotient 0.312 ÷ 0.06.

$$0.06\overline{)0.312} \rightarrow 06.\overline{)031.2}$$

Quotient 5.2; − 30; 12; − 12

Check Multiply the quotient by the divisor.
5.2 × 0.06 = 0.312 ✓

So, 0.312 ÷ 0.06 = 5.2.

LOOK BACK By what number did you multiply to write the divisor as a whole number? 100

6. a. Find the quotient 1.22 ÷ 0.4. Describe your method. a. 3.05; answers may vary.
   b. You move the decimal point in 0.4 one place to the right. This is the same as multiplying by what? 10
7. a. By what do you multiply to write 0.015 as 15? 1000
   b. Find the quotient 0.54 ÷ 0.015. 36
   c. **Critical Thinking** How does your answer in part (a) help you find the quotient in part (b)? It helps you place the decimal point correctly.

The record distance for walking on your hands is 870 mi. The record speed is 54.68 yd in 17.44 s.

You can use patterns to divide mentally. Complete the equations at the right to answer each question.

8. a. Make a conjecture. What happens to the quotient as the divisor increases? It decreases.
   b. How is the number of zeros in each divisor related to the number of places the decimal point "moves" left? See right.
   c. Find 0.8 ÷ 100 mentally. Explain what you did. See right.
   d. Write a rule for dividing a decimal by 10, by 100, or by 1,000. For each zero in the divisor, move the decimal point one place to the left.
9. a. What happens to the quotient as the divisor decreases? It increases
   b. How can you tell how many places to "move" the decimal point to the right? See below.
   c. Find 3.6 ÷ 0.01 mentally. Explain what you did. See right.
   d. Write a rule for dividing a decimal by 0.1, 0.01, or 0.001. For each decimal place in the divisor, move the decimal point one place to the right.

9.b. The decimal place moves one place to the right for each decimal place in the divisor.

8.b. The decimal point moves one place to the left for each zero in the divisor.

Divisor	Quotient
2.9 ÷ 10 =	■ 0.29
2.9 ÷ 100 =	■ 0.029
2.9 ÷ 1,000 =	■ 0.0029

8.c. 0.008; moved the decimal point two places to the left.

Divisor	Quotient
0.52 ÷ 0.1 =	■ 5.2
0.52 ÷ 0.01 =	■ 52
0.52 ÷ 0.001 =	■ 520

9.c. 360; moved the decimal point two places to the right.

Organizer, continued

Prentice Hall Technology

Multimedia Math
- Math Tools, Calculation

Computer Item Generator
- 4-9

Other Available Technology
- calculator

Excel; Works by Microsoft: Questions 12–17 *(optional)*

Fact of the Day

Susan B. Anthony (1820–1906) was an American pioneer of women's rights. She was a proponent of women's suffrage and it was partly through her efforts that the 19th amendment, which granted women the right to vote, was passed on August 26, 1920.

— ENCYCLOPEDIA AMERICANA

TRY THESE

TECHNOLOGY OPTION For Questions 12–17, students can use spreadsheet software to answer the problems. As with a calculator, it is helpful to mix problems such as Questions 12 and 13 so that students understand which number is the dividend and which number is the divisor.

MENTAL MATH Have students describe how they determined the number of places to move the decimal point for each of Exercises 18–20.

Wrap Up

What's the Big Idea? Ask students to explain how to divide decimals.

Journal Have students brainstorm for reasons why multiplying by powers of 10 is so useful in dividing decimals. Ask students to write about why they think the number 10 is so special.

Connections Have students discuss situations in which people divide decimals. You may want to start with these examples:

- **Sports** (finding average scores, speeds, or times)
- **Consumer** (finding unit cost, finding the best value)
- **Social Studies** (comparing exports and imports, land masses, and populations)

Reteaching Activity Use students' familiarity with money to review the division of decimals. Have students think of a money transaction or have them model the number of nickels in

Assignment Options

Core: 23–31, 35–38, 40, MR all, CH all	
Reinforce: 32–34, 39, 42	**Enrich:** 41, 43

10. The tallest cake ever made was 1214.5 in. high. Beth Cornell and her helpers completed the cake at the Shiwassee County Fairgrounds, MI, on Aug. 5, 1990. The cake consisted of 100 tiers of equal height. Find the height of each tier. 12.145 in.

11. Melba is given a stack of paper to pass out to her class of 25 students. The stack measures 0.9 cm thick. Each piece of paper is 0.01 cm thick.

a. How many pieces of paper does Melba have in the stack? 90 pieces

b. Does Melba have enough paper so each student in her class can have three pieces? If so, how much does she have left over? If not, how many pieces of paper does she need? Yes; she has 15 pieces left over.

TRY THESE

Find each quotient.

12. $82\overline{)155.8}$ 1.9 **13.** 29 ÷ 0.4 72.5 **14.** $0.34\overline{)0.204}$ 0.6

15. $33\overline{)237.6}$ 7.2 **16.** 51 ÷ 0.06 850 **17.** 81 ÷ 5.4 15

Mental Math **Find each quotient.**

18. 14.2 ÷ 1000 0.0142 **19.** 6.4 ÷ 0.1 64 **20.** 0.7 ÷ 10 0.07

21. On Thursday 1.4 in. of rain fell. On Friday 2.2 in. of rain fell. What was the mean rainfall for the two days? 1.8 in.

22. Discussion Would you use a model, calculator, pencil and paper, or mental math to find 0.035 ÷ 0.7? Explain. Answers may vary. Sample: Mental math 35 ÷ 7 = 5, and then place the decimal point.

Mixed REVIEW

Draw a model to find each quotient.

1. 0.9 ÷ 0.06 15
2. 1.8 ÷ 0.2 9

See Solution Key.

3. Mrs. Dunn earned $443.75 in one week. She worked 35.5 h. What was her hourly rate? $12.50/h

Find each product or quotient.

4. 0.07 × 4.8 0.336
5. 9.8 ÷ 2.8 3.5

ON YOUR OWN

Find each quotient.

23. 7.5 ÷ 3 2.5 **24.** $36\overline{)\$19.80}$ $.55 **25.** $4\overline{)0.012}$ 0.003

26. $0.5\overline{)66}$ 132 **27.** 0.3 ÷ 15 0.02 **28.** $5.6\overline{)16.24}$ 2.9

29. 0.04 ÷ 0.8 0.05 **30.** 75.03 ÷ 6.1 12.3 **31.** $8.9\overline{)0.6497}$ 0.073

each of the following dollar amounts. Then have students write a division sentence for each.

- *$2.45* **(49 nickels; 2.45 ÷ 0.05 = 49)**
- *$3.15* **(63 nickels; 3.15 ÷ 0.05 = 63)**
- *$1.70* **(34 nickels; 1.70 ÷ 0.05 = 34)**

ON YOUR OWN

CHAPTER INVESTIGATION Have students meet in groups of four to brainstorm for possible answers for Exercise 40. Then have groups compare and evaluate each other's ideas.

CRITICAL THINKING For Exercise 43, encourage students to describe what the quotient 3.5 ÷ 0.7 means, that is, what the quotient tells them.

CHECKPOINT

CONNECTION TO ALGEBRA Exercises 1 and 2 have students find a numerical value for an unknown.

Mental Math Find each quotient.

32. 0.48 ÷ 1000 0.00048
33. 3.8 ÷ 0.1 38
34. 7.3 ÷ 10 0.73
35. 64.5 ÷ 0.01 6,450
36. 11.2 ÷ 100 0.112
37. 0.32 ÷ 0.01 32

38. A pack of 15 baseball cards costs $.75. How much does one of these baseball cards cost? $.05

39. Money A stack of 300 Susan B. Anthony dollar coins is 23.7 in. thick. Find the thickness of one of these coins. 0.079 in.

40. Investigation (p. 140) Describe any methods you can think of for finding the thickness of a page in a book. See below.

41. Writing Describe how to find the quotient 12.5 ÷ 0.04. See below.

42. Choose A, B, or C. Which expression is equivalent to three and eight-tenths divided by thirty-two thousandths. B

A. 0.032 ÷ 3.8 **B.** 3.8 ÷ 0.032 **C.** 3.8 ÷ 0.32

43. a. Critical Thinking Find the quotient 3.5 ÷ 0.7. 5

b. Is the quotient greater or less than 3.5? 0.7? Does this seem reasonable? Explain. greater than both 3.5 and 0.7; Answers may vary. Sample: When the divisor is less than 1, the quotient is always greater than the dividend.

The Susan B. Anthony dollar was issued on July 2, 1979. A coin was made rather than a paper dollar to increase the circulation life of the currency, thus reducing long-term production costs.

Source: *A History of U.S. Coinage*

Problem Solving Hint

Use a decimal model to help you.

CHECKPOINT

Write the missing numbers.

1. (9 × 8) + (9 × 4) = ■ × (■ + 4) 9; 8

2. 6 × (5 − 2) = (6 × ■) − (■ × ■) 5; 6; 2

Place a decimal point in each product.

3. 5.2 × 6.3 = 3276 32.76
4. 0.239 × 8.2 = 19598 1.9598

5. Dalia earns $6.50 an hour as a cashier. For any time over 40 h, she earns $9.75 an hour. Dalia worked 45 h in a recent week. How much overtime did she earn that week? $48.75

Find each quotient.

6. 8.5 ÷ 2 4.25
7. 3.4)$48.28 $14.20
8. 0.13)2.132 16.4

40. Answers may vary. Sample: measure the thickness of 100 sheets and divide by 100.
41. Move both decimal points two places to the right, then divide as with whole numbers. 1,250 ÷ 4 = 312.5

Chapter Support File

Classroom Manager
- Chapter Organizer
- Lesson Planners

Alternate Lesson Plans

Practice

Assessment Options
- Performance Based Project
- Scoring Rubric
- Student Self-Assessment Survey
- Checkpoints
- Chapter Assessments
- Cumulative Review

Minds on Math available in Teaching Transparencies

Math Minutes

Lincoln School District has 196 sixth graders. If the students are grouped 28 to a class, how many classes are there?
7 classes

Materials for 4-10
- calculator
- ruler
- graph paper

4-10

Connecting to Prior Knowledge

Have students talk about the rise or fall in the price of any items they buy, such as a cassette or CD. Challenge students to estimate about how much the prices have changed.

THINK AND DISCUSS

Question 1: Encourage students to explain their readings of the graph for Questions 1a and b. For Question 1c, have students brainstorm for reasons that they can develop into trends for Question 1d.

Question 2: Have students support their answers for Question 2c.

DIVERSITY This lesson provides an opportunity for students from other countries to share and compare prices of items from their native countries to those in the United States.

TACTILE LEARNERS Some students will enjoy using the calculator to make comparisons in Questions 1–3.

Error Alert! Students may have difficulty in predicting the continuation of trends in problems such as Questions 2c and 3c. ***Remediation*** Encourage students to view the data in such problems as patterns. With tables of data such as in Question 3c, have students estimate the average change over each interval. Emphasize that the last intervals are the most useful for making predictions.

WORK TOGETHER

Provide each pair of students with graph paper for the activity. After the activity, have students compare graphs and evaluate any differences. In students' answers to the activity question, encourage students to offer their own assessments of the trend in price changes of bread.

"Children have more need of models than of critics."

—JOSEPH JOUBERT

Organizer

1. **Focus**
   Connecting to Prior Knowledge
2. **Teach**
   Think and Discuss
   Work Together
3. **Closure**
   Try These
   Wrap Up

Skills Reviewed in Context of Lesson
- reading graphs and tables
- estimating

Materials and Manipulatives
- calculator (1 for each group)
- ruler (1 for each group)
- graph paper (1 for each group)

On Your Own Exercises 4, 5: calculator

Student Resources
Extra Practice
Student Study Guide
Practice, TR Ch. 4, p. 33
Student Study Guide, Spanish Resources, TR

Teacher Resources
Teaching Transparencies 1, 19, 51
Transparency Masters, TR pp. 2, 3
Lesson Planner, TR Ch. 4, p. 11

continues next page

What's Ahead
- Using decimals in real-world situations.

WHAT YOU'LL NEED
✓ Calculator
✓ Ruler
✓ Graph paper

MATH AND CONSUMER ECONOMICS

4-10 Working with Data

THINK AND DISCUSS

Prices change from year to year. Some prices go up and some prices go down.

1. a. For which items in the graph did prices go up? movie ticket;candy bar
   b. For which items in the graph did prices go down? calculator; gallon of gas
   c. **Discussion** Pick an item whose price went up and one whose price went down. Give at least two reasons for each change. Answers may vary.
   d. Do you see any pattern in the way the prices changed? Answers may vary. Sample: prices on things bought for enjoyment went up

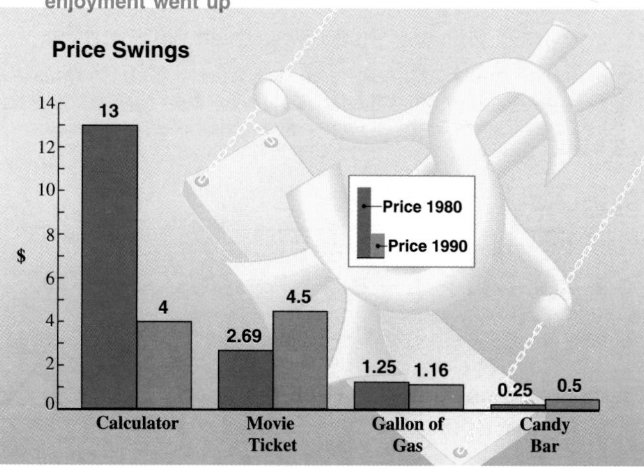

You can estimate how much prices changed over the ten year period.

2. a. Which item doubled in price from 1980 to 1990? candy bar
   b. About how many times less was the price of a calculator in 1990 than in 1980? Would you expect this kind of price reduction in calculators to continue? Why or why not? about 3 times less; Answers may vary

ESL Be sure students know what a bar graph is before they begin this activity. Also, they may need help in expressing comparative statements about the different costs of bread.

TECHNOLOGY OPTION For the problems in the Work Together section, students can use data-organizing software in order to make graphs. As with most software of this type, students can instantly choose an appropriate graph to represent their data because the software can produce line graphs, bar graphs, circle graphs, scatter plots, stem-and-leaf plots, and box-and-whisker plots with just a few keystrokes.

TRY THESE

Ongoing Assessment Have students work in groups of four. Ask students to estimate individually the unit cost of four items: a pencil, a ball-point pen, a sheet of notebook paper, and a 3″ × 5″ index card. Have group members meet and compare the calculations for their estimations based on a multi-unit package price. Then have each group member make a bar graph that displays the four estimates for one of the items. Ask students to check each other's work.

Wrap Up

What's the Big Idea? Ask students to describe how decimals are used in real-world situations.

Journal Ask students to provide reasons why every decimal is not just always rounded to the nearest whole number.

Connections Have students discuss real-world situations in which they may need to work with decimals. You may want to start with these examples:

- **Consumer** (finding total cost of purchases, comparing unit prices, comparing different packages)

c. Suppose movie tickets continued to increase by the amount in the graph. How much would you expect a movie ticket to cost in 2000? in 2005?
about $6.30; about $7.20

3. a. Look at the changes in milk prices from 1920 to 1940. Describe any patterns you see. The prices decreased.
b. Look at the changes in milk prices from 1940 to 1990. Describe any patterns you see. The prices increased.
c. **Discussion** Did the change in the price of milk remain about the same from year to year? Can you use the data in the table to predict the price of milk in five years? Why or why not? No; no; answers may vary.

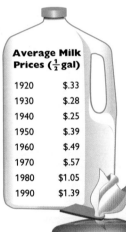

Average Milk Prices ($\frac{1}{2}$ gal)

Year	Price
1920	$.33
1930	$.28
1940	$.25
1950	$.39
1960	$.49
1970	$.57
1980	$1.05
1990	$1.39

WORK TOGETHER

Answers may vary. Sample: in 1980, bread cost more than 10 times 1930 prices.

- Work with a partner. Use the data in the table at the right to write three statements that compare bread prices.
- Make a graph showing the change in the bread prices. Explain why you chose the type of graph you used. See Solution Key.
- One student observed that the price of bread doubled every ten years. Do you agree? Explain your reasoning. Answers may vary. Sample: No, in the 1960s the price went from $.20 to $.24 in 10 years.

60 Years of Bread Prices (1 lb loaf)

Year	Price
1930	$.04
1940	$.08
1950	$.14
1960	$.20
1970	$.24
1980	$.51

TRY THESE

4. a. How much more was bread in 1980 than in 1950? $.37
b. How many times greater was the price of a loaf of bread in 1970 than in 1940? 3 times more
c. **Discussion** What factors might cause the price of bread to change? Answers may vary. Sample: grain harvest, inflation

5. In 1991 the average cost of a 16-oz jar of peanut butter was $2.04. The recommended serving size is 1 oz. What is the cost of 1 serving? Round to the nearest cent. $.13

6. When you buy items priced 2 for $1.69 or 3 for $1, the price of a single item is usually rounded up to the nearest cent.
a. Erasers are 3 for $1.00. Find the price of one eraser. $.34
b. **Discussion** Why do you think the price is rounded up? Sample: This way the store gets the extra pennies.

Organizer, continued

Prentice Hall Technology

Multimedia Math
- Hot Page 4-10

Computer Item Generator
- 4-10

Other Available Technology
- calculator

Data Insights by Sunburst: *Work Together* Questions *(optional)*

Fact of the Day

As of December 1990, there were 23,814 commercial movie theaters in the United States, 2,530 of which were in California.

—*Guinness Book of Records*

- **Banking** (balancing checkbooks, finding interest on loans)
- **Sports** (comparing distances and times in races)

Reteaching Activity Present students with the following information about two competing sporting goods stores, The Sports Place and Evalina's Sporting Goods. Tell students that The Sports Place has just opened and is having a sale. Challenge students to find who really has the better buys.

Item	Evalina's	The Sports Place
in-line skates	$59.99	2 pair for $109.99
mountain bike	$199.99	4 installments of $64.99
golf balls	box of 10 for $1.99	$2.39 a dozen

Have students answer the following questions:

- *Whose is the better price for skates? How much better is the price?*
  (The Sports Place's price is $4.99 lower.)
- *Whose is the better price for the mountain bike?*
  (Evalina's, by $59.97)
- *Write the expressions for finding the unit costs of the golf balls. Compare.*
  (Evalina's: $1.99 ÷ 10 ≈ $.20; The Sports Place: $2.39 ÷ 12 ≈ $.20; no difference)

ON YOUR OWN

ESTIMATION For Exercise 8c, have students describe their estimation strategies.

CHAPTER INVESTIGATION For Exercise 9, have students evaluate possible strategies before starting. Then have students provide step-by-step instructions for their processes.

ACTIVITY If students lack a source of information for Exercise 10, bring to class newspaper inserts for them to use.

PH Multimedia Math Hot Page™ 4-10

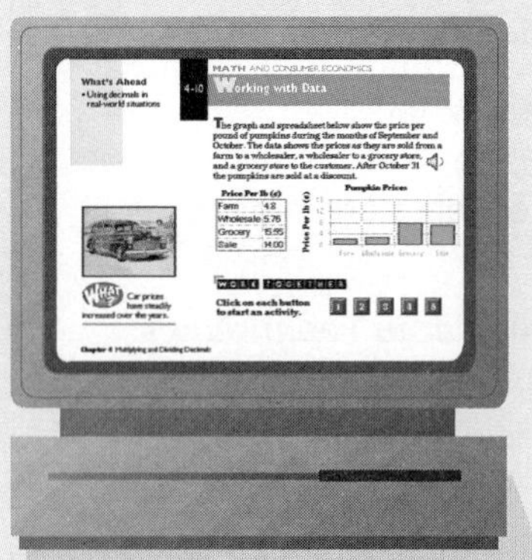

Assignment Options

Core: 4, 5, 6, 12, MR all	
Reinforce: 9–11	**Enrich:** 7, 8

Average Hourly Wage Retail Sales

1970	$2.44
1980	$4.88
1990	$6.76

ON YOUR OWN

Choose **Use a calculator, pencil and paper, estimation, or mental math.**

7. In 1992 the average cost of a movie ticket was $5.05. In 1980 the average price was $2.69.
   a. About how much did it cost to purchase 4 tickets in 1992? about $20.20
   b. How much less did 4 tickets cost in 1980 than in 1992? $9.44
8. Use the hourly wage chart at the left.
   a. The 1980 hourly wage is how many times greater than the 1970 hourly wage? two times greater
   b. Suppose Anita worked 10 h/wk in 1980. How much more would she make than working the same number of hours in 1970? $24.40
   c. Estimation About how many times greater is the 1990 hourly wage than the 1970 hourly wage? about 2.8 or 3 times greater
9. Investigation (p. 140) Find the thickness of each page in your math book. Describe the process you used. Accept reasonable estimates; about 0.007 cm or 0.003 in.

GREAT EXPECTATIONS

Pediatrician

I would like to be a pediatrician when I grow up. I want to be one because I like to help people with their medical problems. I know that they help children when they are sick. I have had experiences with pediatricians with my own health problems. Being a pediatrician ties in with math because I will have to know ratios for comparing size with how much medicine a patient should take. I will also have to know the metric system of weight measurement.

Justin Rankin

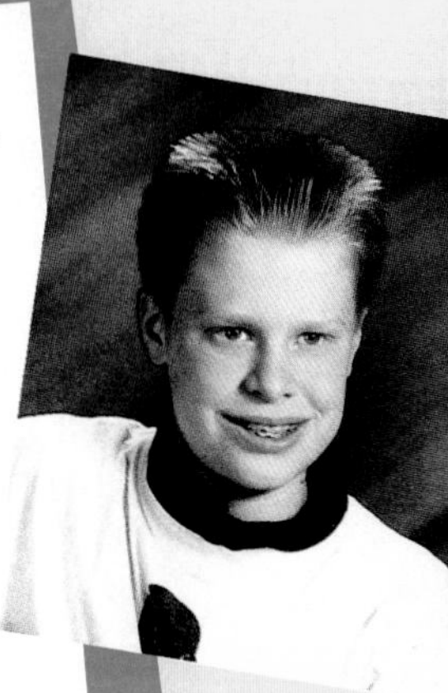

174

Great Expectations

There are many valuable resources available to the students for gathering information about pediatrics. The following list includes places to write for more information about pediatricians and publications to read.

- American Academy of Pediatrics
  141 N. W. Point Blvd., Dept. C
  Elk Grove Village, IL 60007
  (The Academy's educational department will send a catalog describing videos, books, and brochures that are available.)
- *Caring for Your Baby and Young Children* by Stephen Shelov, M. D. (American Academy of Pediatrics)
- *Pediatrics* (a journal for pediatricians)

Students can also learn from discussions with experts. Here are some possible resources.

- Invite a pediatrician to speak to the class.
- Visit a pediatrician's health clinic.

Encourage students to ask about the skills necessary for a career in pediatrics, including these topics:

- The training necessary including course work and years
- How math is used (graphs and charts with babies' weight and height statistics, calculations for dispensing medicine)

10a–b. Answers may vary. Check students' graphs.

11. Answers may vary. Sample: Multiply 12 by the difference of 27.3 and 13.2; 169.2 mi

10. **Activity** Use newspaper ads or ask an adult to help you find today's prices for each item on the list at the right.

a. Make a double bar graph comparing the 1985 prices for the items on the list at the right and the current prices.

b. Did all the prices increase? Which items increased the most? Give at least two reasons why one item might increase in price more than another.

c. What would be the total cost to buy the items on the list in the given amount today? in 1985?
Today: Answers may vary. 1985: $4.45

11. **Writing** There are at least two ways to solve the problem below. Explain two ways and solve the problem. See above.

In 1991 new cars averaged about 27.3 mi/gal of gas. In 1974, new cars averaged 13.2 mi/gal. How much farther could a 1991 car travel than a 1974 car on 12 gal of gas?

12. In 1962 the average comic book sold for a price of $.12. A comic book in 1988 cost $.75.

a. How much more did a comic book cost in 1988? $.63

b. **Estimation** About how many comic books could you get at the 1962 price for the cost of a comic book in 1988?
about 6

1985 Prices	
Ground beef (lb)	$1.68
Lettuce (1 head)	$.45
Orange Juice (qt)	$1.09
Bananas (lb)	$.32
Large eggs (doz)	$.91

Mixed REVIEW

Use mental math.

1. 3.9 ÷ 10 0.39
2. 191 ÷ 100 1.91
3. 0.82 ÷ 1000 0.00082

Complete if $\triangle RWF \cong \triangle MLK$.

4. $MK = ■$ RF
5. $\angle R \cong ■$ ∠M
6. Name the ways you could make change for $.45 with no pennies.

6. See Solution Key.

Dear Justin,

I am a pediatrician in the inner city area of Milwaukee, Wisconsin. Since I was a young boy your age, I wanted to be a doctor. Like you, I always wanted to do something that would help people. I like working with children and their families. I like helping sick kids get better. At my clinic, we take care of people from many different backgrounds. I have come to know many interesting and wonderful families.

I use math all day, every day. I use ratio just like you said. I also make graphs to show a baby's weight and height. The graph helps me decide whether a baby is growing properly. I always liked math a lot when I was in school. I am lucky I get to use math so much in my work.

David A. Waters, M.D.

Chapter Support File

Classroom Manager
- Chapter Organizer
- Lesson Planners

Alternate Lesson Plans
Practice
Assessment Options
- Performance Based Project
- Scoring Rubric
- Student Self-Assessment Survey
- Checkpoints
- Chapter Assessments
- Cumulative Review

Minds on Math available in Teaching Transparencies

Math Minutes

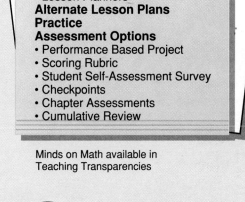

Juliet has 135 stamps. If 16 stamps fit on an album page, how many pages will she need?
9 pages

CHAPTER 4 WRAP UP

Exercises 1–4: After students have estimated the products and quotients, have them work the problems on a calculator to see how accurate their estimates are.

Ongoing Assessment Have students work with partners on Exercises 6–9. Have partners work separately and then compare results. If partners' results differ, have them work together to figure out why the results differ and which result is correct.

Exercises 15–18: Have students estimate the products and quotients before they do the calculations so that they can see whether their answers are reasonable.

Vocabulary/Symbols

area
compatible numbers
database
distributive property
field
order of operations
record
sort

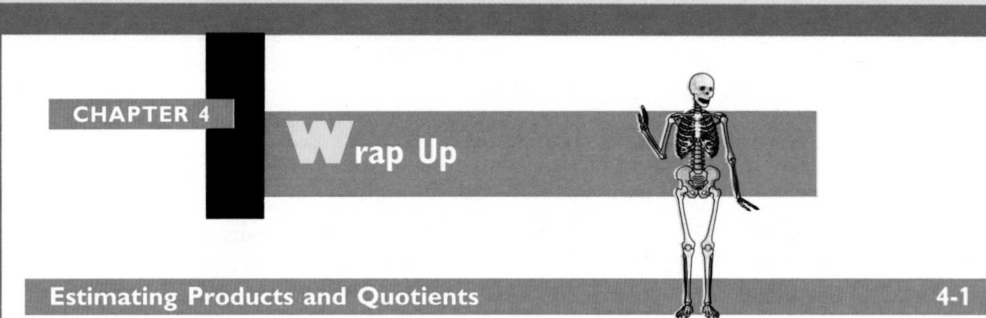

CHAPTER 4 Wrap Up

Estimating Products and Quotients 4-1

You can round to estimate decimal products. You can use compatible numbers to estimate products and quotients.

Answers may vary. Accept reasonable estimates.

Estimate using rounding or compatible numbers.

1. 23.78×5.3 about 125
2. 3.25×9.12 about 30
3. $34.1 \div 6.67$ about 5
4. 19.03×4.79 about 100

Using Databases 4-2

A ***database*** is a collection of information organized into ***records.*** A ***field*** is a category in a record.

5. Writing How would you set up a database for a class directory with information about name, address, phone number, subject, and teacher? How many records and how many fields do you need? Answers may vary.

Order of Operations and the Distributive Property 4-3, 4-4

The ***order of operations*** shows how to evaluate an expression.

You can use the ***distributive property*** to evaluate expressions involving multiplication and addition or multiplication and subtraction.

Evaluate using the order of operations and the distributive property.

6. $5 \times (4 + 12) - 8$ 72
7. $9 + 21 \div 3 - (6.3 - 2.6)$ 12.3
8. $11 \times 6 + 7 \times 6 - 3$ 105
9. $9 \times (50 - 9) - 27 \div (4.1 - 1.1)$ 360
10. **Choose A, B, C, or D.** When you insert parentheses in the expression $18 \div 6 - 3 + 2$, the greatest possible value is: A

A. 8 **B.** 3.6 **C.** 18 **D.** 36

Complete.

11. $5 \times 97 = (5 \times ■) + (5 \times 7) = ■$ 90, 485
12. $8 \times 27 = 8 \times (■ - 3) = ■$ 30, 216

Getting Ready for Chapter 5

The skills previewed will help students understand and solve problems involving variables and expressions.

Multiplying Decimals and Dividing Decimals 4-5, 4-6, 4-8, 4-9

You can use decimal squares or 10 by 10 grids to model multiplication and division of decimals.

13. Write a multiplication sentence to describe the model.
0.3 × 0.1 = 0.03

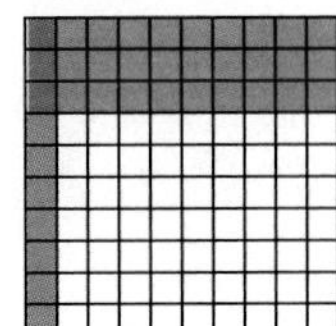

14. Write a division sentence to describe the model.
0.5 ÷ 0.1 = 5

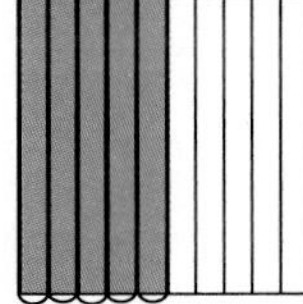

To multiply decimal numbers, count the decimal places in both factors to find how many places are needed in the product.

To divide by a decimal, move the decimal point in the divisor to make it a whole number. Then move the decimal point in the dividend the same number of places.

Find each product or quotient.

15. 3.215 × 0.04
0.1286

16. 30.72 × 1.5
46.08

17. 4.5 ÷ 6
0.75

18. $3.2\overline{)96}$
30

Draw a model for each product or quotient. 19.–22. See Solution Key.

19. 1.2 ÷ 0.4 **20.** 0.6 ÷ 0.03 **21.** 0.7 × 3 **22.** 0.8 × 0.2

Strategies and Applications 4-7, 4-10

Some problems have too little information to solve them.
Some problems have more information than you need.

Solve if possible. If not, tell what information you need.

23. Les will take a bus to a game. Tickets are $5. He plans to take about $7 for food. Students will share evenly the $125 rental fee for the bus. How much money will Les need? The number of students riding the bus is needed.

24. Sharon is 152.4 cm tall and weighs 44.5 kg. Her twin sister Karen is 1.1 cm taller and weighs 0.9 kg more. How tall is Karen? 153.5 cm tall

GETTING READY FOR CHAPTER 5

1. Writing Explain the difference between the area of a rectangle and its perimeter.

2. Critical Thinking Use the distributive property to complete the sentence: $(x \times y) + (x \times z) = \blacksquare \times (\blacksquare + \blacksquare)$.
x y z

1. Answers may vary. Sample: The perimeter is the distance around, while the area is the length times the width.

Student Resources

Practice, p. 165
Problem Solving Practice, p. 155
Extra Practice
Student Study Guide
Student Study Guide, Spanish Resources
Tools for Studying Smarter, TR
Student Self-Assessment Survey, TR Ch. 4, p. 37 *(see below)*

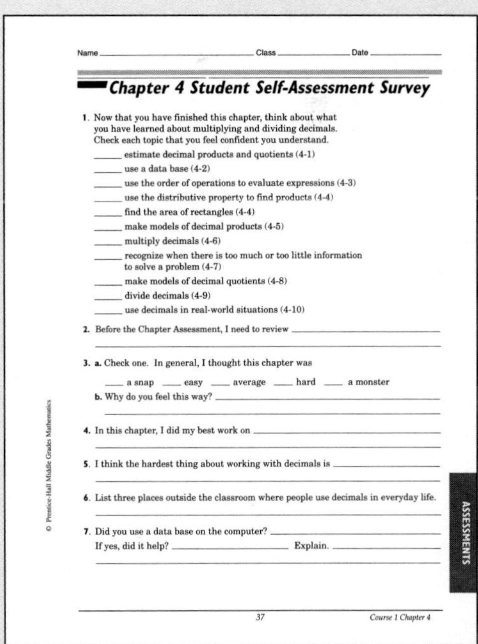

Name ________ Class ________ Date ________

Chapter 4 Student Self-Assessment Survey

1. Now that you have finished this chapter, think about what you have learned about multiplying and dividing decimals. Check each topic that you feel confident you understand.
   - ______ estimate decimal products and quotients (4-1)
   - ______ use a data base (4-2)
   - ______ use the order of operations to evaluate expressions (4-3)
   - ______ use the distributive property to find products (4-4)
   - ______ find the area of rectangles (4-4)
   - ______ make models of decimal products (4-5)
   - ______ multiply decimals (4-6)
   - ______ recognize when there is too much or too little information to solve a problem (4-7)
   - ______ make models of decimal quotients (4-8)
   - ______ divide decimals (4-9)
   - ______ use decimals in real-world situations (4-10)
2. Before the Chapter Assessment, I need to review ________
3. a. Check one. In general, I thought this chapter was
   ____ a snap ____ easy ____ average ____ hard ____ a monster
   b. Why do you feel this way? ________
4. In this chapter, I did my best work on ________
5. I think the hardest thing about working with decimals is ________
6. List three places outside the classroom where people use decimals in everyday life.
7. Did you use a data base on the computer? ________
   If yes, did it help? ________ Explain. ________

ASSESSMENTS

37 *Course 1 Chapter 4*

CHAPTER

4 PUTTING IT ALL TOGETHER

The projects on these pages can be used in a variety of ways:

- alternative assessment
- portfolio ideas
- additional assignments for gifted and talented students
- extra credit for all students

Follow Up

- The straightforward way for students to measure the thickness of a sheet of paper is to measure the thickness of a known number of sheets and divide by the number of sheets of paper.
- Other alternative approaches may be more interesting and creative than the one listed above. All methods of measuring should be encouraged.

EXCURSION Students can bring other paper samples to class that have different weights. Discuss the weights for paper used in copier machines, dot matrix printers, laser printers, and paper used in paperback novels.

The standard weight designation for paper refers to the weight of a stack of 500 (sometimes 400) sheets of paper, each measuring 2 ft by 3 ft (sometimes 17 in. by 22 in.) at a temperature of 70°F and a humidity of 50%.

Play Your Cards Right

MATERIALS AND MANIPULATIVES 3″ × 5″ Index Cards

This game may seem more advanced as the number of players increases, since students will be less likely to get one of their own problems to solve.

Materials and Manipulatives

Follow Up

- calculator (for each group)
- ruler (for each group)

Five-Minute Shopping Spree

- advertising flyers from different stores (for each group)
- calculator (for each group)

Play Your Cards Right

- index cards (for each group)

Play Ball!

- poster board (for each group)
- calculator (for each group)

Other Available Technology

Follow Up

- calculator (for each group)

Five-Minute Shopping Spree

- calculator (for each group)

Play Ball!

- calculator (for each group)

Follow Up

Take another look at the explanation you prepared at the beginning of this chapter. Revise the explanation based on your study of this chapter. The following are suggestions to help you be sure that you have chosen the most appropriate binder for your notes and daily assignments.

✓ Make a chart showing how you found the number of sheets of paper you would need for the course.

✓ Make a graph showing the number of sheets of notebook paper that will fit in each size binder.

The problems preceded by the magnifying glass (p. 161, # 43; p. 171, # 40; and p. 174, # 9) will help you complete the investigation.

Excursion: Corinne bought a ream of paper. The clerk told her that the paper was "20-pound" paper. Corinne weighed the ream at home but found that it weighed far less than 20 pounds. Find the meaning of the word **pound** as it is applied to commercially sold paper.

Who to Talk To:

- the manager of a stationery store

FIVE-MINUTE Shopping Spree

Materials: Advertising flyers from several different stores

- Three or more players
- Players have 5 minutes to "purchase" items that total less than $500. There must be at least 6 items on each player's list. The player who comes closest to spending $500 without going over that amount, is the winner.

178

Fall into Place

The mystery number is 639.725.

EXCURSION Have the students work backwards when creating their own riddle. Following the same patterns that were given in the example, students can work with place value, comparing decimals, similarities and differences of numbers, and the operations of decimals.

Play Ball!

MATERIALS AND MANIPULATIVES Students post their data on a poster, using a graph or chart. Provide poster board, markers, straightedges, pens, and pencils (and other possible art supplies) for their data presentation.

EXCURSION Have students research sports scores in the library or newspaper office.

Five-Minute Shopping Spree

COOPERATIVE GROUPS Students may have difficulty with this activity because of the type of flyers that are collected. If there is a calculator available for the group to use it may help. If the flyers list high priced items such as stereos, VCRs, and cameras, rather than low-priced items such as clothing, the time allotted to play the game may need to be altered.

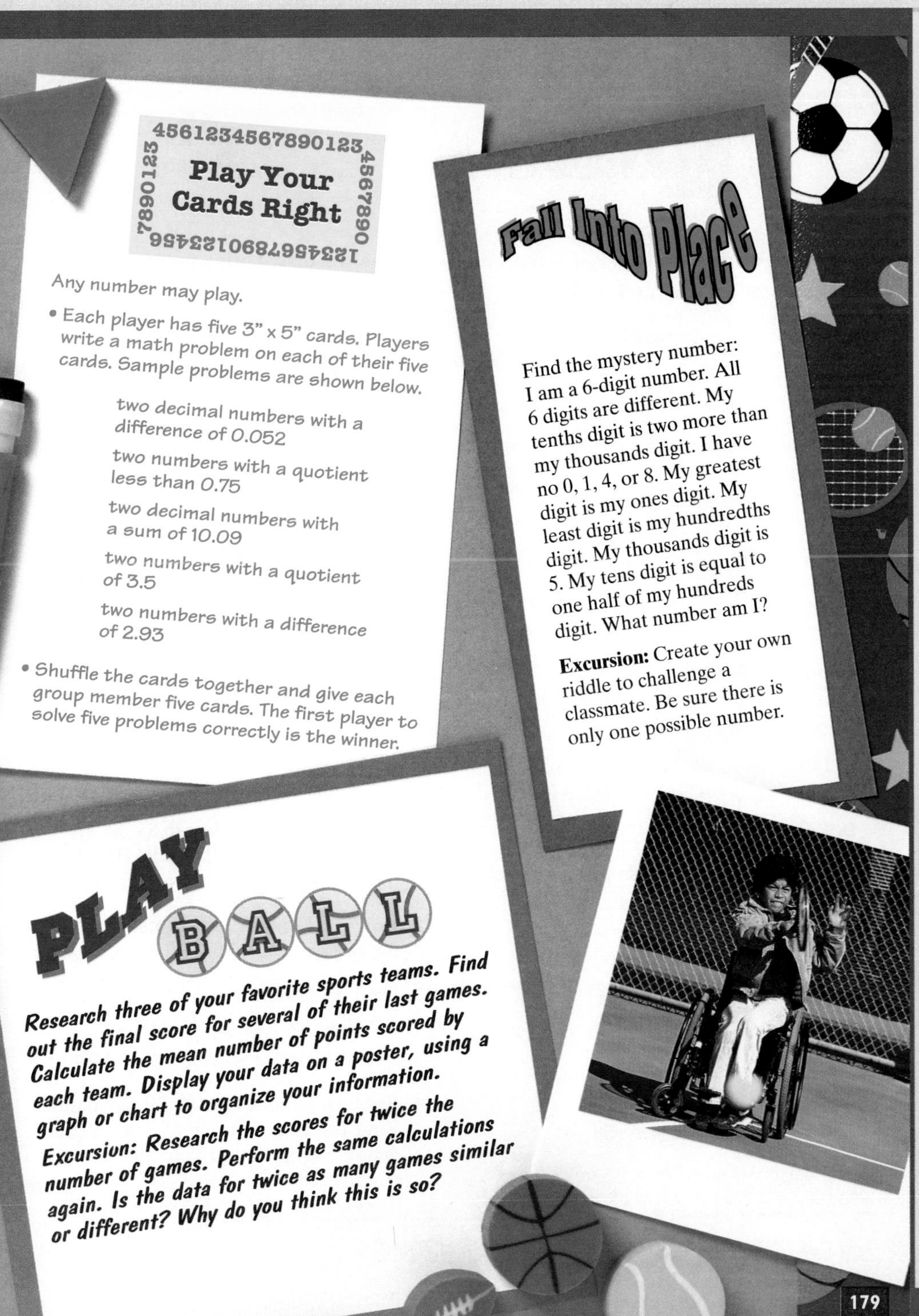

Play Your Cards Right
Any number may play.
• Each player has five 3" x 5" cards. Players write a math problem on each of their five cards. Sample problems are shown below.
two decimal numbers with a difference of 0.052
two numbers with a quotient less than 0.75
two decimal numbers with a sum of 10.09
two numbers with a quotient of 3.5
two numbers with a difference of 2.93
• Shuffle the cards together and give each group member five cards. The first player to solve five problems correctly is the winner.
Fall Into Place
Find the mystery number: I am a 6-digit number. All 6 digits are different. My tenths digit is two more than my thousands digit. I have no 0, 1, 4, or 8. My greatest digit is my ones digit. My least digit is my hundredths digit. My thousands digit is 5. My tens digit is equal to one half of my hundreds digit. What number am I?
Excursion: Create your own riddle to challenge a classmate. Be sure there is only one possible number.
PLAY BALL
Research three of your favorite sports teams. Find out the final score for several of their last games. Calculate the mean number of points scored by each team. Display your data on a poster, using a graph or chart to organize your information.
Excursion: Research the scores for twice the number of games. Perform the same calculations again. Is the data for twice as many games similar or different? Why do you think this is so?
179

CHAPTER 4

ASSESSMENT

Writing Questions allow students to describe more fully their thinking and understanding of the concepts they've learned.
Exercises 9 and 12 are writing questions.

Enhanced Multiple Choice Questions are more complex than traditional multiple choice questions, which assess only one skill. Enhanced multiple choice questions assess the processes that students use as well as the end results. They are written so that students can use more than one strategy to solve the problem. Using multiple strategies is encouraged by the National Council of Teachers of Mathematics (NCTM).
Exercise 4 is an enhanced multiple choice question.

ESTIMATION For Exercises 10, 13, and 14, have students estimate the solutions before doing the problems to see whether their answers are reasonable.

Resources

Performance Based Project, TR Ch. 4, pp. 34–36
Chapter Assessment, Forms A and B, TR Ch. 4, pp. 39–42
Spanish Chapter Assessment, Spanish Resources, TR
Computer Item Generator

CHAPTER 4

Assessment

Answers may vary. Accept reasonable estimates.

1. Estimate using rounding.
   a. 7.3 × 29.7 about 210　b. 4.63 × 50.4 about 250
2. Estimate using compatible numbers.
   a. 21.14 × 4.89 about 100　b. 17.9 ÷ 3.6 about 6
   c. 98.13 ÷ 24.27 about 4　d. 38.95 × 2.78 about 120
3. Write a multiplication expression for the model. 0.4 × 0.4 = 0.16

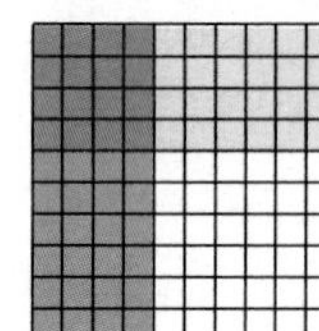

4. **Choose A, B, C, or D.** Which expression gives you a value of 18? C
   A. 26 − 5 × (2 + 2)
   B. (26 − 5) × (2 + 2)
   C. 26 − (5 × 2) + 2
   D. (26 − 5) × 2 + 2
5. Insert operation symbols to make each equation true.
   a. 9 ■ 6 ■ 3 = 27 +; ×
   b. 8 ■ 2 ■ 4 ■ 6 = 10 ÷; ×; − or ×; ÷; +
   c. (5 ■ 2) ■ (5 ■ 2) = 17
   d. 35 ■ 2 ■ 10 ■ 2 = 50 ×; −; ×
6. **Mental Math** Use the distributive property to evaluate.
   a. 5 × 112 560　b. 4 × 58 232
7. Use the distributive property to evaluate.
   a. 5 × (6 + 10) 80
   b. (7 × 6) + (7 × 5) 77
   c. 9 × (3 + 10) 117
8. Use the order of operations and the distributive property to evaluate.
   a. 3 × (6 + 5) × 4 − 3 129
   b. 8 + 7 × 3 × 4 − 6 86
   c. 2 + 3 × 9 − 1 28
   d. (4 + 3) × 2 × 5 70
9. **Writing** Explain how to make a model for the expression 0.8 × 0.7. See below.
10. Find each product.
    a. 9.063 × 24 = 217.512　b. 0.85 × 0.06 = 0.051　c. 5.2 × 0.17 = 0.884
11. Jamal bought three tickets to the movies. Each ticket cost $4.50. He paid with a $20-dollar bill. How much did it cost Jamal for the three tickets? $13.50
12. **Writing** Explain how to use a model for the quotient 0.6 ÷ 0.12. See below.
13. Find each quotient.
    a. $3.2\overline{)8.832}$ 2.76　b. $45\overline{)\$32.85}$ $.73
    c. 0.4 ÷ 0.25 1.6　d. 63.72 ÷ 0.03 2,124
14. Seedless grapes cost $1.79 per pound. Find the cost a bunch of grapes that weigh 2.2 lb. Round your answer up to the nearest cent. $3.94

5.c. ×; +; + or +; +; ×
9. Use a decimal square. Shade 8 columns and 7 rows, or 7 columns and 8 rows. The double shaded squares represent the product.

12. Use a decimal square. Shade 6 columns. Group the squares in the shaded columns into groups of 12. Count the groups.

CHAPTER 4

CUMULATIVE REVIEW

Exercise 5 is an example of an enhanced multiple choice question.

Item(s)	Review Topic	Chapter
1	estimating decimal products	4
2	metric length	3
3	congruent and similar figures	2
4	adding and subtracting decimals	3
5	order of operations	4
6	dividing decimals	4
7	tables	1
8	exploring tenths and hundredths	3
9	tessellations	2
10	comparing and ordering decimals	3

CHAPTER 4

Cumulative Review

Choose A, B, C, or D.

1. Which is the best estimate of the product 34.3 × 5.98? A

   A. 34 × 6 **B.** 35 × 6
   C. 35 × 5 **D.** 34 × 5

2. What is the best unit of measurement to use to measure the length of your driveway? C

   A. millimeters **B.** centimeters
   C. meters **D.** kilometers

3. Name two triangles in the diagram that appear to be similar but not congruent. A

   A. $\triangle ABC$, $\triangle MNC$
   B. $\triangle MNB$, $\triangle MNC$
   C. $\triangle BMC$, $\triangle AMB$
   D. $\triangle ABC$, $\triangle ADC$

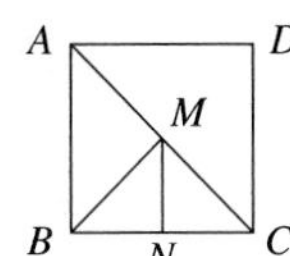

4. Kevin bought six muffins for $2.39. He paid the cashier with three one-dollar bills and some pennies. If he received no pennies in change, how many pennies did he give the cashier? D

   A. 1 **B.** 2 **C.** 3 **D.** 4

5. Where would you insert parentheses so that 6 − 2 × 9 ÷ 3 + 15 has the value 5? D

   A. (6 − 2) × 9 ÷ 3 + 15
   B. 6 − (2 × 9) ÷ 3 + 15
   C. 6 − 2 × (9 ÷ 3) + 15
   D. 6 − 2 × 9 ÷ (3 + 15)

6. Which quotient is equal to 0.317 ÷ 0.08? B

   A. 317 ÷ 8 **B.** 31.7 ÷ 8
   C. 317 ÷ 0.8 **D.** 3.17 ÷ 8

7. Kim has sixty-five cents in quarters, dimes, and nickels. (She has at least one of each of these coins.) What number of nickels can she *not* have? C

   A. 1 **B.** 2 **C.** 3 **D.** 4

8. Which number is *not* equal to 4.3? D

   A. four and thirty hundredths
   B. three and thirteen tenths
   C. two and twenty-three tenths
   D. four and three thousandths

9. Which polygon shown below cannot be used to tessellate a plane? C

   A.  **B.** 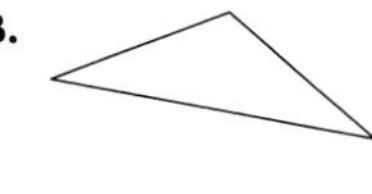

   C. 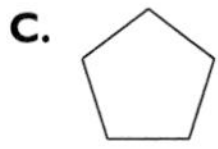 **D.** 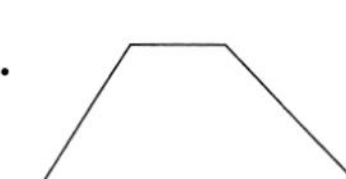

10. Which set of numbers are all between 0.5 and 1.95? C

   A. 0.504, 1.9, 1.951
   B. 0.194, 1, 1.94
   C. 0.618, 1, 1.009
   D. 0.6, 1.04, 2

Resources

Cumulative Review, TR Ch. 4, pp. 43–44
Transparency Masters, TR p. 35

CHAPTER

5 Patterns and Equations

Why Study Patterns and Equations?

If students ask this question, you may want to mention these areas in which patterns and equations are used: computer animation and graphics for television and film; voting patterns and predictions; predicting growth patterns in biology and the movement of celestial bodies in astronomy; recycling and other ecology issues; patterns of practice, scoring, and wins in various sports; and determining prices, profits, and patterns in business.

Graphic Display of Chapter Content

Below is one possible representation of the chapter's content and its applications to the world outside the classroom. Have students create their own graphic display and fill in the applications they have seen in their own lives.

- The center oval should state the main concept of the chapter: patterns and equations.
- Have students draw the ovals with the next level of concepts presented in the chapter (exponents, number and word patterns, expressions, variables, and equations). You may want students to add any other topics that they find appropriate.
- Ask students to draw as many application ovals as they can.
- Discuss all the applications that students identify.
- Have students make and present one display that includes all the students' ideas.

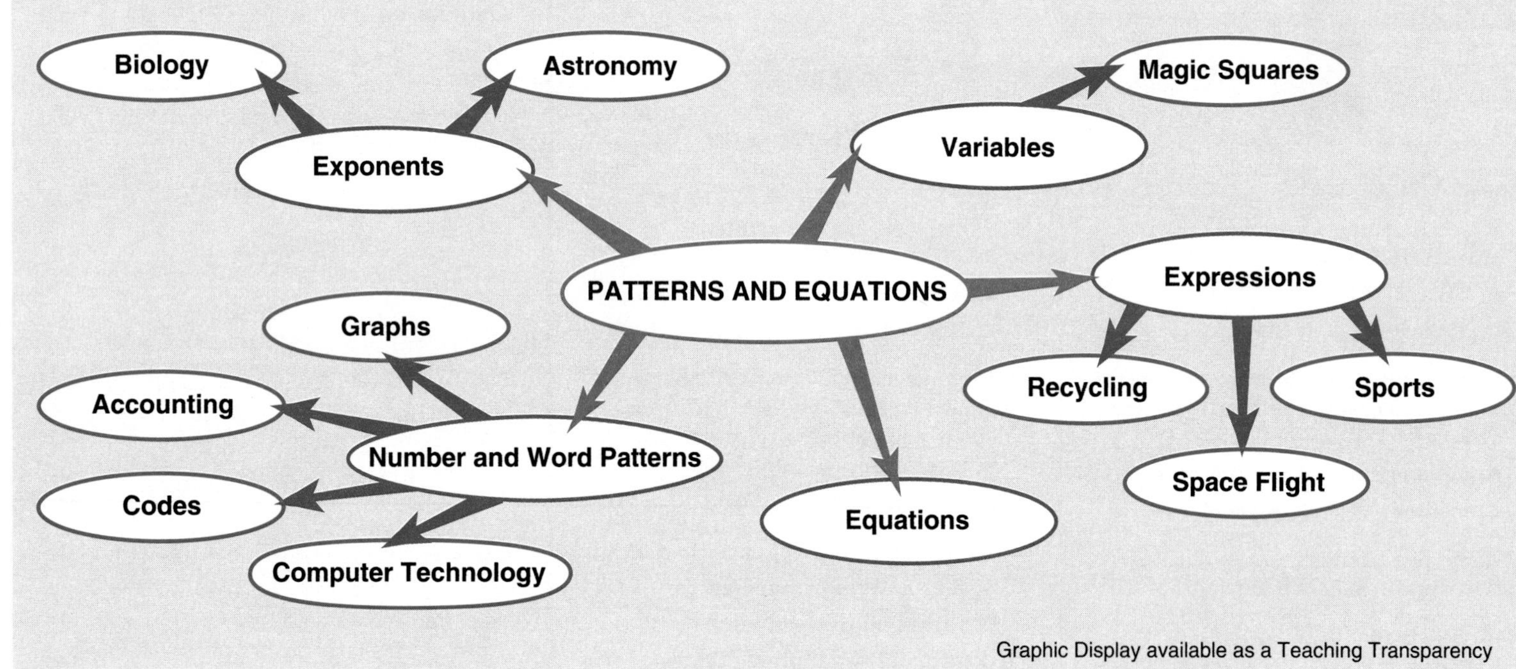

Graphic Display available as a Teaching Transparency

Vocabulary and Symbols

base	magic square
cube	numerical expression
equal sign, =	power
equation	solution
equilateral	solve
evaluate	square
exponent	term
function	variable
inverse operations	variable expression

Materials and Manipulatives

algebra tiles *(optional)*	ruled paper
computer *(optional)*	scissors
spreadsheet software *(optional)*	calculator
graph paper	

Additional Resources

Commercially Available Technology

Calculator
fraction
graphing (optional)

Software
spreadsheet software:
Excel, Works by Microsoft
ClarisWorks by Apple

graphing software:
Cricket Graph
Microsoft Graph

other software:
Algebra Expressor by William K. Bradford
Math Connections by Wings

Other Media
"Double Trouble: Exponential Growth Using Multiplication." Aims Media, 9710 DeSoto Avenue, Chatsworth, CA 91311-4409.
"Solving Pairs of Equations." Aims Media, 9710 DeSoto Avenue, Chatsworth, CA 91311-4409.

Materials at Little or No Cost

AIMS Education Foundation, P.O. Box 8120, Fresno CA 93747-8120. Sample investigations.
The Learning Team, Box 217, Armonk, NY 10504-0217. Publisher of *Mathsource*, a complimentary source book of lessons.

Bibliography

For Teachers
Immerzeel, George and Melvin Thomas. *Ideas from the Arithmetic Teacher: Grades 6-8, Middle School.* Reston, VA: NCTM, 1982.
Philips, Elizabeth. *Patterns and Functions.* Menlo Park, CA: Dale Seymour Publications, 1991.

For Students
Adler, Irving. *Mathematics.* New York: Doubleday, 1990.
Bendick, Jeanne. *Mathematics Illustrated Dictionary.* New York: Franklin Watts, Inc., 1989.
Shaw, Sheila. *Kaleidometrics: The Art of Making Beautiful Patterns from Circles.* New York: Parkwest Publications, 1986.

Prentice Hall Technology 

Multimedia Math
- Math Tools, Calculation
- Math Tools, Manipulatives
- Math Tools, Spreadsheet
- Hot Page™ 5-1
- Hot Page™ 5-4
- Hot Page™ 5-9
- Math Investigations, The Pythagorean Theorem

Computer Item Generator
- Chapter 5

Community Resources

Field Trips
- visit a computer graphics company
- visit the projection booth of a movie theater
- visit a recycling center

Guest Speakers
- a biologist who studies animal population patterns
- a cryptographer who works with codes
- a sportswriter who writes data

Backpack Take-Home Activities

Materials
- 12-month calendar
- paper
- colored pencils or pens

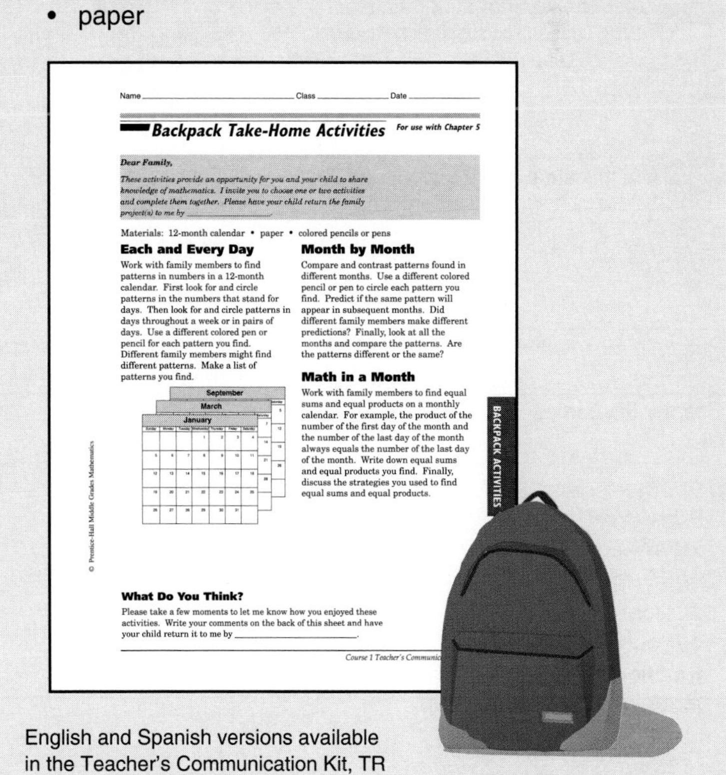

Name ________ Class ________ Date ________

Backpack Take-Home Activities *For use with Chapter 5*

Dear Family,

These activities provide an opportunity for you and your child to share knowledge of mathematics. I invite you to choose one or two activities and complete them together. Please have your child return the family project(s) to me by ________.

Materials: 12-month calendar • paper • colored pencils or pens

Each and Every Day

Work with family members to find patterns in numbers in a 12-month calendar. First look for and circle patterns in the numbers that stand for days. Then look for and circle patterns in days throughout a week or in pairs of days. Use a different colored pen or pencil for each pattern you find. Different family members might find different patterns. Make a list of patterns you find.

Month by Month

Compare and contrast patterns found in different months. Use a different colored pencil or pen to circle each pattern you find. Predict if the same pattern will appear in subsequent months. Did different family members make different predictions? Finally, look at all the months and compare the patterns. Are the patterns different or the same?

Math in a Month

Work with family members to find equal sums and equal products on a monthly calendar. For example, the product of the number of the first day of the month and the number of the last day of the month always equals the number of the last day of the month. Write down equal sums and equal products you find. Finally, discuss the strategies you used to find equal sums and equal products.

BACKPACK ACTIVITIES

What Do You Think?

Please take a few moments to let me know how you enjoyed these activities. Write your comments on the back of this sheet and have your child return it to me by ________.

© Prentice-Hall Middle Grades Mathematics

Course 1 Teacher's Communic

English and Spanish versions available in the Teacher's Communication Kit, TR

Chapter 5 Planning Guide

Objectives	Assignment Options	Critical Thinking/ Problem Solving	Writing and Reading Math	Estimation Mental Math	Materials and Manipulatives
Investigation	This chapter-long project involves open-ended questioning and data collecting and provides an additional opportunity to assess students.	p. 184 p. 184	p. 184 p. 184		
5-1 Number Patterns • Finding the next term in a number pattern • Writing a number pattern in words	**Core:** 7–9; 12–14, 17; MR all **Reinforce:** 10, 11, 15 **Enrich:** 16, 18	1c, 4b, 5d; MR: 7 p. 185; BI p. 186; MM p. 187	1c; WT: 6; 16c p. 187; JL p. 186 JL Sheet	4a; WT: 6c–d; 16b, 17 p. 186	1a, 5a; WT: 6d; 7, 8, 15, 16a pp. 185, 187; RT p. 186 TT 1, 55
5-2 Math and History: Napier's Rods • Understanding how to use patterns to multiply greater numbers	**Core:** 13–15, 21; MR all **Reinforce:** 16–20 **Enrich:** 22	1, 2; EX1, 4c, 12, 21, 22; MR: 7 pp. 188, 189; BI p. 190	11b p. 189; JL p. 189 JL Sheet		3; EX1; 5–10, 13–20 pp. 188–190 TT 55, 58
5-3 Exponents • Understanding and using exponents	**Core:** 19, 20, 22, 24–28, 32–33, 35a; MR all; CH all **Reinforce:** 21, 23, 29, 30, 34, 35b–c **Enrich:** 31, 36	4b, 5b, 7, 8, 34; MR: 5 p. 195; BI p. 194	35b, 36a p. 195; JL p. 194 JL Sheet	14–18, 24–31; MR: 1–4; CH: 5–7 MM p. 195	EX2, 3; 24–31 pp. 192, 193; RT p. 194; CH p. 195 TT 19, 55
5-4 Variables and Expressions • Understanding variables • Evaluating variable expressions	**Core:** 16–22; MR all **Reinforce:** 23–34 **Enrich:** 35, 36	5, 7, 35, 36; MR: 6 BI p. 198; MM p. 199	34–36 p. 199; JL p. 198 JL Sheet	1, 3a, 4b; EX1–2; 10–15, 19–32 pp. 196–198	EX1; 6, 19–28 p. 198 TT 56, 59
5-5 Problem Solving: Look for a Pattern • Solving problems by looking for patterns	**Core:** 13, 15, 17; MR all **Reinforce:** 19, 20 **Enrich:** 14, 16, 18, 21	All; MR: 7 pp. 200, 201; BI p. 201; RT p. 202	All p. 202; JL p. 201 JL Sheet	MR: 5, 6	p. 202 TT 56
5-6 Writing Variable Expressions • Writing variable expressions and word phrases	**Core:** 16–23; 29a, 31, 32, 35; MR all **Reinforce:** 24–28, 29b, 33a **Enrich:** 29c, 30, 33b, 34	3–5, 29–33; MR: 5 pp. 204, 206; BI p. 205	16–26; 34 p. 206; JL p. 205 JL Sheet	35; MR: 3, 4 MM p. 206	pp. 204–205 TT 56; Alt. Lesson
5-7 Technology: Graphing Functional Data • Making graphs from tables • Using computers to explore graphs	**Core:** 7; MR all **Reinforce:** None **Enrich:** 8	2a, 3c–d, 4c; WT: 5a, c; 7c–d, 8; MR:7 pp. 208, 210–211; BI p. 210	MR: 3–6 JL p. 209 JL Sheet	MR: 1, 2 MM p. 211	2b–c, 3a, 4; WT: 5b, 6b; 7e p. 208; WT p. 209; RT p. 210 TT 1, 57; Alt. Lesson
5-8 Addition and Subtraction Equations • Solving addition and subtraction equations	**Core:** 19–28, 30–32; MR all; CH all **Reinforce:** 29, 33–36, 38, 39 **Enrich:** 37, 40–44	3, 5, 10b, 14a, 16a, 18, 40, 42–44; CH: 1; MR: 5 pp. 213, 215; BI pp. 213–214	39, 43, 44 p. 215; JL p. 213 JL Sheet	6, 8, 12, 13, 19–38, 44; CH: 6–8 p. 213; CH p. 216; MM p. 216	11, 14–17, 28–38; MR: 4 p. 212; RT p. 214 TT 19, 57
5-9 Multiplication and Division Equations • Solving multiplication and division equations	**Core:** 12–20, 22; MR all **Reinforce:** 21, 23–26 **Enrich:** 27–31	WT: 1b–c; 2b, 6a, 8a, 10, 11, 28, 29; MR: 5 p. 218; WT p. 217; BI p. 218	27 p. 219; JL p. 218 JL Sheet	WT: 1a; 4, 5, 12–26; MR: 3, 4 p. 218; MM p. 219	3, 6–9, 16–26, 30, 31 pp. 217, 218; RT p. 218 TT 19, 57
Putting It All Together	These pages include a Follow-Up to the Investigation and other projects, which provide additional opportunities to assess the students.	pp. 222–223 pp. 222–223	p. 222 p. 222	p. 222 p. 222	pp. 222–223 pp. 222–223
Chapter Resources		PS Practice, CW, CA, CR PS Practice p. 207; CW pp. 220–221; CA p. 224; CR p. 225	PS Practice, CW, CA p. 182B; PS Practice p. 207; CW pp. 220–221; CA p. 224		pp. 182A, 182B Backpack Activities Manip. Kits TT 54

Student Edition (question numbers)
Teacher's Edition (page numbers)
Other Components

BI—What's the Big Idea? CA—Chapter Assessment CH—Checkpoint
CG—Computer Item Generator CR—Cumulative Review CW—Chapter Wrap Up
DM—Decision Making EP—Extra Practice EX—Example FD—Fact of the Day

Cooperative Learning Activities	Technology	Data Collection & Analysis	Interdisciplinary Connections	Applications	Assessment	Review	Strand Integration	NCTM Correlation*
p. 184 p. 184		p. 184 p. 184		recycling	p. 184 p. 184			
WT: 6 WT p. 186	15, 16a pp. 186, 187 Hot Page™ 5-1	WT: 6; 17; 18 p. 187; FD p. 186	Science pp. 186, 187	biology, astronomy pp. 186, 187	p. 185	MR: All p. 185; RT p. 186 Practice p. 23	Functions, Stat./Probability, Discrete Math, Number, Logic/Language	2, 3, 4, 5, 8
11a		12 FD p. 189		money, archaeology GE pp. 190–191	p. 188	MR: All p. 188; RT p. 190 Practice p. 24	Functions, Discrete Math, Number, Logic/Language	2, 3, 5, 7, 8, 9
Alt. Lesson	EX2, 3; 7, 8, 24–31 p. 193; CH p. 195 Alt. Lesson	36; CH: 2 FD p. 193	p. 194	entertainment, music p. 194	CH: All p. 193; CH p. 195 CH TR p. 36	MR: All p. 192; RT p. 194 Practice p. 25	Functions, Algebra, Geometry, Measurement, Number, Logic/Language	2, 3, 4, 5, 6, 8, 9, 12, 13
RT p. 198	19–28 pp. 198, 199 Hot Page™ 5-4	35, 36; MR: 1, 2 FD p. 197	pp. 198, 199	textiles pp. 196, 198, 199	p. 197	MR: All p. 196; RT p. 198 Practice p. 26	Functions, Algebra, Discrete Math, Number, Logic/Language	1, 2, 3, 4, 5, 8, 9
pp. 200, 201; RT p. 202		7, 8 FD p. 201	p. 201	computers p. 201	p. 200	MR: All p. 200; RT p. 202 Practice p. 27	Functions, Discrete Math, Number, Logic/Language	1, 2, 3, 4, 5, 8
WT: 1, 2 pp. 204–206; WT p. 204 Alt. Lesson		33, 35 p. 206; FD p. 205	p. 206	recycling, entertainment p. 206	p. 205	MR: All p. 204; RT p. 206 Practice p. 28	Functions, Algebra, Number, Logic/Language	1, 2, 3, 4, 5, 8, 9
WT: 5, 6 p. 209; WT p. 210; RT p. 210	All pp. 208–209; WT p. 210	All pp. 208–211; FD p. 209	p. 210	sports, business pp. 208–210 Alt. Lesson	p. 209	MR: All p. 208; RT p. 210 Practice p. 29	Functions, Algebra, Discrete Math, Logic/Language	1, 2, 3, 4, 5, 8, 9
WT: 1, 2 p. 213; WT p. 212; CH p. 216	14–17, 28–38 p. 214	WT: 1; MR: 3, 4 FD p. 213	Science, Language Arts pp. 212, 215	setting records p. 214	CH: All p. 213; CH pp. 215–216 CH TR p. 36	MR: All p. 212; RT p. 214 Practice p. 30	Functions, Algebra, Number, Logic/Language	1, 2, 3, 4, 5, 7, 8, 9
WT: 1 WT p. 217	6–9, 16–26, 30, 31 p. 218 Hot Page™ 5-9	WT: 1 WT p. 217; FD p. 218	Physical Education p. 217	sports p. 219	p. 218	MR: All p. 217; RT p. 218 Practice p. 31	Functions, Algebra, Number, Logic/Language	1, 2, 3, 4, 5, 7, 8, 9
pp. 222–223 pp. 222–223		pp. 222–223 pp. 222–223		recycling	pp. 222–223 pp. 222–223			
IN, PT pp. 182–184, PT pp. 222–223 Backpack Activities	p. 182B Multimedia Math, CG	Data File 5 pp. 182–183	Science, Health pp. 182F, 182–183 Interdisciplinary Units	clocks, mechanics, biology pp. 182A, 182F, 182–183 Backpack Activities, Projects, Interdisciplinary Units	IN, PT, CA pp. 182E, 184; CW pp. 220–221; PT pp. 222–223; CA p. 224 CA, Span. CA, Self Assessment, Projects	Practice, PS Practice, CW, CR, EP, SSG CW pp. 220–221 Span. SSG, CR		

GE—Great Expectations **IN—Investigation** **JL—Journal** **MM—Math Minutes**
MR—Mixed Review **PS—Problem Solving** **PT—Putting It All Together** **RT—Reteaching Activity**
SSG—Student Study Guide **TT—Teaching Transparency** **WT—Work Together**

*For a description of the NCTM Standards, see page T15.

Assessment Options

Observation Checklist

In this chapter on patterns and equations, you have opportunities to observe your students do these tasks:

✓ continue patterns of shaded squares
✓ continue number patterns and explain them in words
✓ use number patterns to multiply large numbers
✓ write and evaluate numbers with exponents
✓ apply the order of operations with exponents
✓ write variable expressions and model them with tiles
✓ solve problems by looking for a pattern
✓ describe tables with variable expressions
✓ make graphs from tables and use a calculator to explore graphs
✓ model equations with tiles
✓ solve equations

In every chapter, you are given opportunities to observe your students:

✓ work with a partner or in a group
✓ write about mathematics
✓ participate in discussions about mathematics
✓ collect and analyze data
✓ display positive attitudes about mathematics
✓ use measurement tools

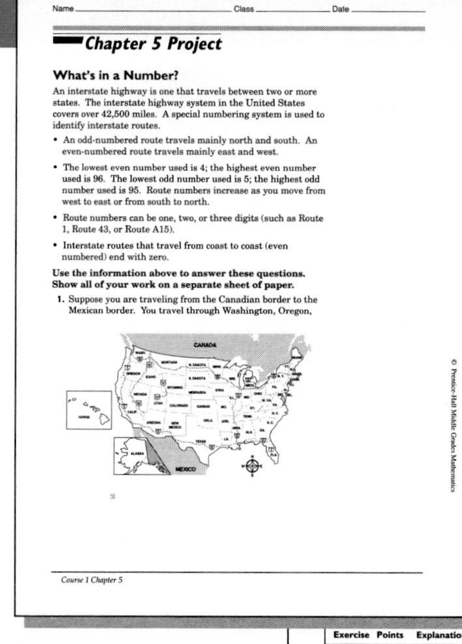

Name ____ Class ____ Date ____

Chapter 5 Project

What's in a Number?

An interstate highway is one that travels between two or more states. The interstate highway system in the United States covers over 42,500 miles. A special numbering system is used to identify interstate routes.

- An odd-numbered route travels mainly north and south. An even-numbered route travels mainly east and west.
- The lowest even number used is 4; the highest even number used is 96. The lowest odd number used is 5; the highest odd number used is 95. Route numbers increase as you move from west to east or from south to north.
- Route numbers can be one, two, or three digits (such as Route 1, Route 43, or Route A15).
- Interstate routes that travel from coast to coast (even numbered) end with zero.

Use the information above to answer these questions. Show all of your work on a separate sheet of paper.

1. Suppose you are traveling from the Canadian border to the Mexican border. You travel through Washington, Oregon,

Performance Based Project (with scoring rubric), Chapter Files, TR

? Scoring Rubric

Exercise	Points	Explanation
1.	2	Low, odd number; reasonable explanation
	1	Low number OR odd number; reasonable explanation
	0	No response OR other response
2.	2	Large or heavily-populated states, such as California, Texas, and New York; reasonable explanation.
	1	Response names states correctly with no explanation
	0	No response OR other response
3.	2	Alaska and Hawaii; neither state borders another state, both states have relatively low populations
	1	Incorrect response with explanation
	0	No response OR other response
4.	1	Both are coast-to-coast east and west routes.
	0	No response OR other response
5.	3	Addresses as many of the "rules" as possible, given the route number; addresses the issue of north and south or east and west along with at least one other element; good explanation
	2	Correct information; poorly organized explanation OR strong explanation with some inaccuracies or omissions
	1	Inaccurate information with some explanation OR weak explanation
	0	No response
Excursion	5	Creative, interesting presentation clearly-described situation; clearly-defined rules
	4	Clear presentation; clearly-defined rules
	3	Incomplete presentation; clearly-defined rules OR good presentation; vaguely-defined rules
	2	Weak presentation; some rules
	1	Response related to numbering; no rules
	0	No response OR other response

Chapter 5 Assessment • Form A

Chapter 5 Student Self-Assessment Survey

Checkpoint 1

Chapter 5 Cumulative Review

Chapter Support File

Classroom Manager
- Chapter Organizer
- Lesson Planners

Alternate Lesson Plans

Practice

Assessment Options
- Performance Based Project
- Scoring Rubric
- Student Self-Assessment Survey
- Checkpoints
- Chapter Assessments
- Cumulative Review

Spanish versions of Chapter Assessments available in Spanish Resources

Interdisciplinary Units
- **Travel and Geography**
- **Space Exploration**
- **Sports**
- **Consumer Awareness**
- **The Great Outdoors**

English & Spanish

These units include cross-curriculum connections and can be used at any time during the school year. See the Teacher's Guide for more information.

Working with Middle Grade Students

> “Mathematics are the result of mysterious powers which no one understands, and in which the unconscious recognition of beauty must play an important part. Out of an infinity of designs a mathematician chooses one pattern for beauty's sake and pulls it down to Earth.”
>
> —Marston Morse

Addressing a Variety of Learning Styles

The mathematical tasks in Chapter 5 involve various learning styles. Here are some examples.

- Visual learners continue the pattern in graphed designs (pp. 185, 186) and use magic squares (p. 196).
- Tactile learners model problems with tiles (p. 213).
- Auditory learners discuss how Napier's rods work (p. 188), and read exponents aloud (p. 192).

Alternate Lessons 5-6 and 5-7 address tactile learners by having them use manipulatives.

Cultural Connections

Leonardo Fibonacci was a thirteenth-century mathematician who brought together the mathematics of different cultures. He is famous for discovering a pattern of numbers called the Fibonacci numbers. The Fibonacci numbers occur very often in nature, especially wherever there are spirals.

Team Teaching Suggestion

Work with a language arts teacher to introduce the concept of patterns. Have the students work in groups of 2 or 3 to guess a three-letter word that one person has written. After each guess, the student responds to the group by saying, “My word comes (before/after) your guess in the dictionary.” By playing the game, the students will be able to observe the patterns that are found in vowel selection, understand the process of patterning of the alphabet, and problem solve to find the least amount of guesses in order to win.

Discrete Mathematics

Many of the number patterns in this chapter involve the use of discrete mathematics. The educational value of discrete mathematics, according to the 1991 NCTM yearbook, *Discrete Mathematics across the Curriculum, K–12,* has several components. First, it gives students an opportunity to think about elementary mathematical questions, such as number patterns; second, it provides an unfamiliar and intriguing way for students to think mathematically; and third, it has many interesting applications such as computer graphics, networks, and voting theory.

Teaching Tip

Students in the middle grades are keenly aware of their surroundings. Many choose to conform to fashion styles of their friends while others enjoy being different. As you teach this chapter on patterns, help students appreciate the patterns in their own behaviors, such as favorite clothes, accessories, slang, snacks, and activities. Encourage students to respect diverse choices and those whose patterns may differ from theirs.

Bulletin Board

Post photos or pictures from magazines that show numbers of people or objects. Label each picture with a variable that represents the objects in the picture. Have students write on an index card a word phrase and a corresponding variable expression for each picture. Have students place the cards in the envelope below each picture. Periodically post the index cards around the pictures. For example, if a photo shows hot air balloons, you might label it

b = the number of balloons.

A student's card might read:

twice the number of balloons
$2b$

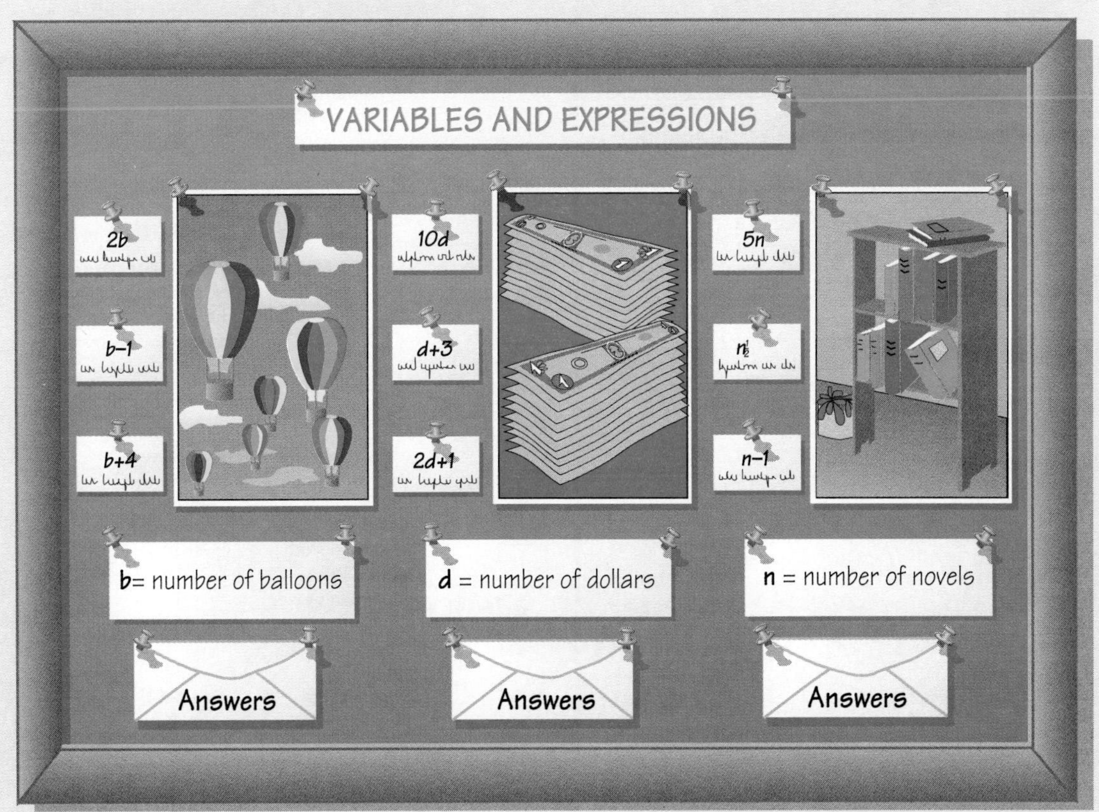

CHAPTER 5 Patterns and Functions

Cultural Connections Many people in rural areas time the planting of their crops and other farm work according to the phases of the moon. The belief that the moon influences such activities is thousands of years old, although the United States Department of Agriculture says that this view has no scientific support. For at least the last two centuries, people in the United States have used a farmer's almanac as a guide for the timing of these farming activities.

From 1792 to 1804, almanacs of astronomical tables (for the states of Pennsylvania, Delaware, Maryland, and Virginia) were published by an African American named Benjamin Banneker. Banneker used borrowed astronomy books and instruments to teach himself how to predict eclipses and how to calculate the positions of the planets. He did thousands of calculations to create data tables giving the rising times, setting times, and sky locations for the moon and other astronomical bodies. When Banneker was 22, he built a clock that struck the hours. He hand-carved the parts of his clock from wood. He had only a borrowed pocket watch to use as a model for the gears and wheels that made his clock work.

WORLD VIEW Clock making originated in Southern Germany and Switzerland. A German named Henry de Vick made the first clock around 1360. His clock rang a bell every hour. The word "clock" comes from a Latin word meaning "bell."

Digging for Data Ask students to use the graphs, diagrams, and other data to answer these questions:

- *How many complete turns of the minute wheel does it take before the gear wheel has made one complete turn?* **(30 divided by 10, or 3 turns)**

Chapter 5 Contents

Data File Questions

pages 187, 372, 494

Data File 5

CHAPTER 5 Patterns, Functions, and Equations

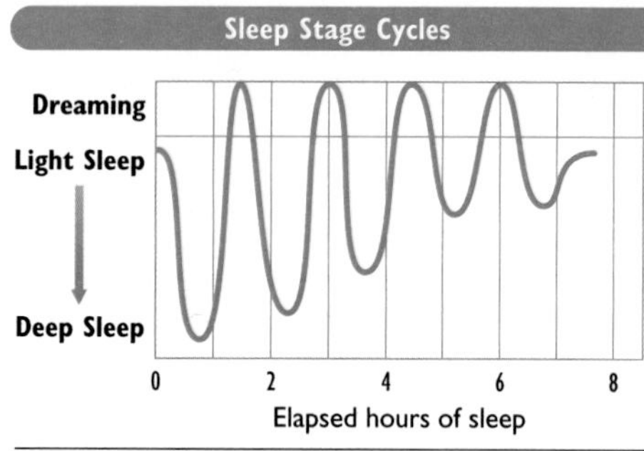

Source: *Prentice Hall Health*

Mechanical Clocks

Unwinding-springs or falling-weights power gears to keep mechanical clocks operating. The gears make sure that the minute hand and the hour hand move in the correct pattern.

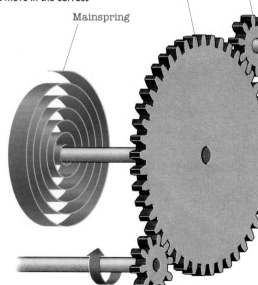

Pinion
Driving wheel
Mainspring

Sleep Time

Creature	Average hours/day
two-toed sloth	20
armadillo	19
mountain beaver	14
pig	13
jaguar	11
rabbit	10
human child	10–12
human adult	8
mole	8
cow	7
sheep	6
horse	5
giraffe	4
elephant	3
shrew	less than 1

Source: *3•2•1 Contact*

- *For one turn of the gear wheel, how many turns does the attached pinion wheel make?* **(one)**

This means that in 30 min, the hour wheel turns by just one tooth, or $\frac{1}{24}$ of a 12 h day, which is $\frac{12}{24}$ h or $\frac{1}{2}$ h.

Ask each student to survey at least 5 people and ask these questions:

- *What time do you usually get up on a weekday?*
- *What time do you usually go to sleep on a weekday?*
- *Is your age 10 years or under, under 20 but at least 11, or 20 or over?*

Collect and graph class results on the chalkboard. Discuss with the class how to design labels. Ask these questions:

- *Can you make a generalization from this graph?*
- *Can you conjecture about possible causes for these results?*

Journal Activity Have students read the objectives for the chapter under WHAT YOU WILL LEARN and ask them to write responses to these questions:

- *What do you know about writing equations?*
- *Have you ever used a computer to draw a graph?*
- *What pattern have you made use of in the last week?*

Interdisciplinary Connection [Biology] Study the chart that shows Sleep Time. Do you see a connection between the size of an animal and the average hours/day it sleeps? Do you see any connection between how active an animal is and the average hours/day it sleeps? **(No correlation is apparent from the chart.)** Most adult humans sleep 7 or 8 hours a night. Infants and adolescents need more sleep because of the growing they are doing.

WHAT YOU WILL LEARN

- how to model patterns and exponents
- how to model and write expressions and equations
- how to use technology to graph functions
- how to solve problems by looking for a pattern

SLEEP

The amount of sleep you need changes throughout your life. The chart shows some variations for people in different age groups.

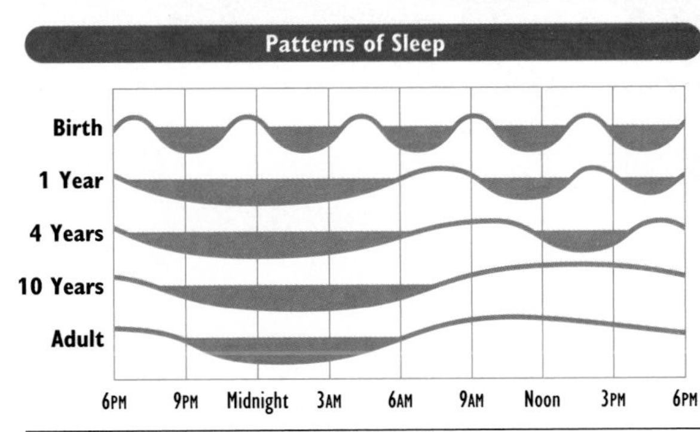

Source: *Encyclopedia Britannica*

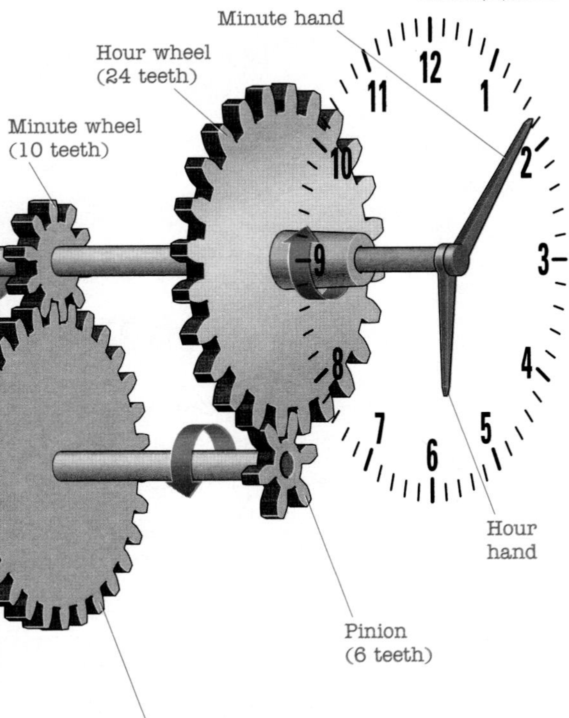

In 1955 L. Essen and J. Parry of Great Britain made the first cesium atomic clock. The 1955 clock was accurate to within one second every 300 years.

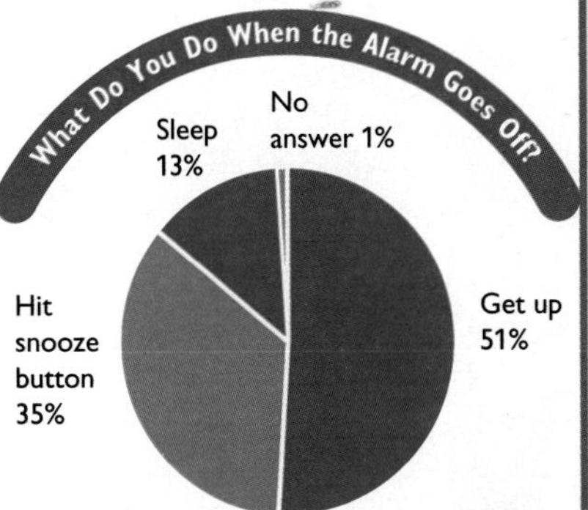

Fact of the Day

Dreams usually last longer as the night progresses, stretching from 10 or 15 minutes to 45 minutes the longer a person sleeps. On February 15, 1967, a man in a Chicago laboratory experienced the longest single dream ever recorded. It lasted more than two hours.

—*Did You Know?*

183

CHAPTER 5 INVESTIGATION

Memo

Ask students to name items that can be recycled. Solicit information from students about recycling programs in your area.

Have students name objects in the room that will be discarded eventually and are recyclable. Ask them to think of objects that could be made from discarded items.

Mission

Students should take an organized approach to tracking down school waste, beginning in their own classroom. They should identify the major sources of waste, then make lists of ways to attack the problem.

After about half the chapter has been completed, have students show you their work on the project. If they are behind schedule, you may want to give them intermediate deadlines in order to check their work.

Additional Leads to Follow

- *What are some expenses involved in recycling programs?*
- *Think about material that you throw away in a typical day at school. What could you have done without in the first place?*

Keeping a Project Notebook

Some suggestions for students' notebooks are:

- Before beginning, decide on the categories of data you will record. Possibilities: type of waste, estimate of amount, cost of removing or recycling, estimated time taken to accumulate.
- List the dates and results of all discussions about the project.
- List ideas for reducing waste amounts as they occur to you or to group members.

Project Organizer

Related Exercises
p. 187
p. 206

Follow Up
p. 222

Teacher's Notes
pp. 184, 187, 206, 222

Community Resources
- city or state environmental agencies
- city or area solid-waste department
- recycling or conservation organizations

Materials and Manipulatives
- ruler
- paper for recording data

Memo

We live in a throwaway society. Each hour, Americans throw away 2.5 million plastic bottles. Each day, we toss out half a million tons of trash. Each week, we throw away enough glass bottles and jars to fill one of the 1,350-ft towers of the World Trade Center in New York City. As much as 90% of our household trash could be recycled. But Americans recycle only about 10% of glass and 30% of paper.

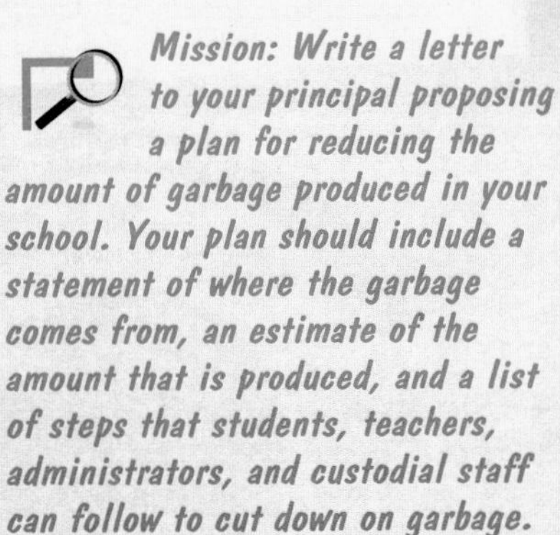

Mission: Write a letter to your principal proposing a plan for reducing the amount of garbage produced in your school. Your plan should include a statement of where the garbage comes from, an estimate of the amount that is produced, and a list of steps that students, teachers, administrators, and custodial staff can follow to cut down on garbage.

Leads to Follow

✓ What types of garbage are produced in your classroom? What could be done to reduce this trash?

✓ What other types of waste are produced in your school?

✓ What kinds of changes in behavior can you realistically expect people to be willing to make?

5-1

Connecting to Prior Knowledge

Start a discussion about number patterns with your students.

- *Name the first five odd numbers.* **(1, 3, 5, 7, 9)**
- *What is the pattern in the numbers?* **(Start with 1 and add 2 each time.)**

Have students create other number patterns and describe them. **(Students may name even numbers and then patterns of multiples.)**

THINK AND DISCUSS

DIVERSITY/ TACTILE LEARNERS Students who experience difficulty with fine motor skills could use a set of tiles instead of graph paper. For Questions 1–5, students can then lay their tiles directly on a piece of paper and create a pattern without the need to draw it.

ESL Have students review the meaning of words such as *term, pattern,* and *rule* and their mathematical contexts here.

AUDITORY LEARNERS For Question 1, it may help some students to say the number pattern and hear it, as follows: ONE, two, three, four, FIVE, six, seven, eight, NINE, ten, eleven, twelve, THIRTEEN, and so on. Emphasizing the numbers in the pattern aloud may help them understand the pattern.

Ongoing Assessment For Question 5, have students copy and label the entire pattern (from the first to the sixth designs) on graph paper. They could then write their rules for Question 5c directly under their sketches, which would allow you to check the crucial step from graphic representation to written expression of the pattern.

What's Ahead

- Finding the next term in a number pattern
- Writing a number pattern in words

WHAT YOU'LL NEED

✓ Graph paper

5-1 Number Patterns

THINK AND DISCUSS

The first three designs in a pattern made up of squares are shown below.

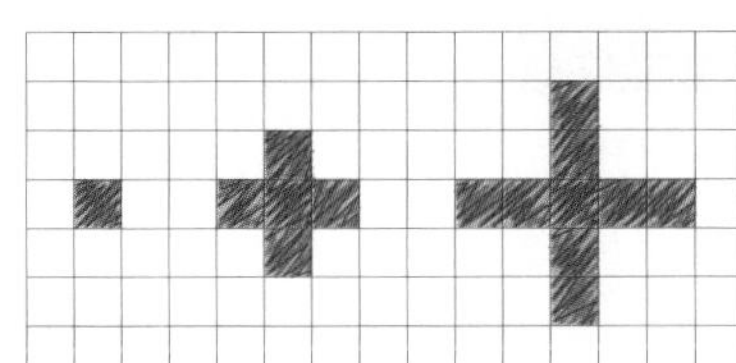

1. a. Sketch the fourth and fifth designs so that they continue the pattern. See Solution Key.
   b. How many shaded squares are in the fourth design? the fifth design? 13 squares; 17 squares
   c. **Discussion** Imagine the sixth design. Describe the design in words. See below.

You can use the pattern of designs above to form the number pattern 1, 5, 9, ... Each number in the pattern is called a **term.**

2. How are the first, second, and third terms in the number pattern related to the first, second, and third designs? The numbers in the pattern are the number of squares in each design.
3. What are the fourth and fifth terms in the number pattern? 13, 17

You can also describe the number pattern 1, 5, 9, . . . with a rule. *Start with the number 1 and add 4 repeatedly.*

4. a. Write the first five terms in the following number pattern: *Start with the number 3 and add 4 repeatedly.* 3, 7, 11, 15, 19
   b. **Discussion** Why is it important to tell what number to start with when describing a number pattern with a rule? You must know the first number in a pattern to find its terms.

FLASHBACK

The three dots, . . . , indicate that the pattern continues without end.

1. c. Answers may vary. Sample: The design is a cross with 1 square in the center and 5 squares in each of the 4 arms.

"Success is a ladder that can't be climbed with your hands in your pockets."
—Anonymous

Organizer

1. **Focus**
   Connecting to Prior Knowledge
2. **Teach**
   Think and Discuss
   Work Together
3. **Closure**
   Wrap Up

Vocabulary/Symbols
term

Skills Reviewed in Context of Lesson
- graphing lines
- ordering fractions
- ordering decimals

Materials and Manipulatives
- graph paper (for each student)

On Your Own Exercises 7–8: graph paper, Exercises 15–16: calculator

Student Resources
Extra Practice
Student Study Guide
Practice, TR Ch. 5, p. 23
Student Study Guide, Spanish Resources, TR

continues next page

WORK TOGETHER

Error Alert! In Question 6, students may try to find the relationship between the kangaroo's speed and length of hop. Although there is such a relationship (length of hop $= 0.12 \times$ speed), it might confuse students at this point. ***Remediation*** Remind students that they are looking for two number patterns, one in each column.

CONNECTION TO BIOLOGY Question 6 has students apply their knowledge of number patterns to organizing biological data.

TECHNOLOGY OPTION Have students complete Question 6d using a graphics program. Students can use a printout of the line graph to estimate distance for several speeds.

Wrap Up

What's the Big Idea? Ask students to summarize some different ways in which they can build a number pattern.

Journal Ask students: *Number patterns are involved in predicting when a full moon will appear. What are some other scientific phenomena that involve number patterns? Explain your responses.*

Reteaching Activity Have students use tiles. Tell them to make a design pattern using one, then three, and then five tiles. Have students copy their designs on the board or display them on an overhead projector.

Discuss how each design pattern develops. Ask students if the different designs all produce the same number pattern. Make sure students can connect each design pattern with the number rule, "Start with 1 and add 2 repeatedly."

Organizer, continued

Teacher Resources

Teaching Transparencies 1, 55
Transparency Masters, TR p. 1
Lesson Planner, TR Ch. 5, p. 2

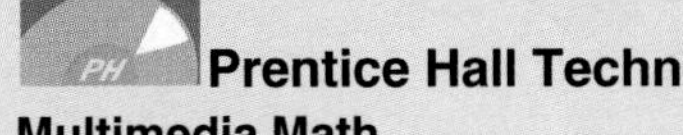

Prentice Hall Technology

Multimedia Math
- Hot Page™ 5-1

Computer Item Generator
- 5-1

Other Available Technology

Microsoft Graph: Question 6 (*optional*)

Fact of the Day

A kangaroo at birth weighs one gram and is less than 1 in. long. Blind, deaf, and hairless, it crawls through the mother's fur and into her pouch. It stays there for the next three months.

—*Kangaroos*

PH Multimedia Math Hot Page™ 5-1

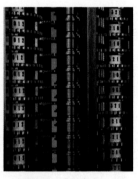

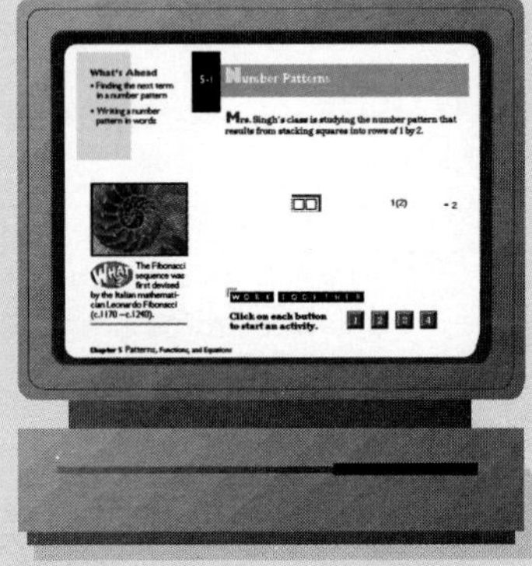

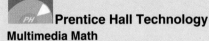

The Difference Engine is a computer designed by Charles Babbage (1791–1871), an English scientist. If you feed it a list of numbers, it will look for a pattern and continue the list. **Why do you think the computer was given this name?**

Source: *Dynamath*

Answers may vary. Sample: The computer was called the Difference Engine because it computed the differences between adjacent numbers in a list and used these differences to determine the pattern in the numbers.

5. a. Sketch the fifth and sixth designs in the pattern below.

The fifth sketch will show a column of 16 shaded squares and the sixth sketch a column of 32 shaded squares.

5. c. Start with the number 1 and multiply by 2 repeatedly.

1, 2, 4, 8, 16, 32, . . .

b. Use the pattern of designs to form a number pattern.

c. Write a rule to describe the number pattern.

d. **Discussion** Tell how this rule is different from the one that describes the number pattern 1, 5, 9, ...
Answers may vary. Sample: Here the next term is found by multiplication. In the pattern 1, 5, 9, . . . the next term is found by addition.

WORK TOGETHER

Work with a partner.

Biology Kangaroos are the only large mammals that hop. When kangaroos reach speeds between 10 km/h and 35 km/h, the distance they hop is fairly predictable.

Speed (km/h)	Length of Hop (m)
10	1.2
15	1.8
20	2.4
■ 25	■ 3.0
■ 30	■ 3.6

6. a. Copy and complete the table above.

b. Write a rule to describe each number pattern that you used to complete each column in the table.

c. About how far does a kangaroo hop when it reaches a speed of 35 km/h? **4.2 m**

d. Construct a line graph to display your data. Use the line graph to estimate how far a kangaroo hops when it reaches a speed of 27 km/h. **Accept any reasonable estimate. Sample: 3.2 m See Solution Key for graph.**

6. b. Speed: start with the number 10 and add 5 repeatedly. Length of Hop: start with the number 1.2 and add 0.6 repeatedly.

Connections Have a discussion about how number patterns and their rules are used. Here are some examples:

- **Art** (tile designs, architecture and building designs)
- **Science** (growth and decay patterns, formulas of chemical mixtures)
- **Banking** (compound interest, loan payment schedules, exchange rates)

ON YOUR OWN

Students will need graph paper for Exercises 7 and 8.

Exercises 9–14: Accept the different ways in which students might write the rules for Exercises 9–14.

CONNECTION TO ASTRONOMY Exercise 16 has students apply their understanding of number patterns to astronomical data.

CALCULATOR For Exercise 16a, you might suggest that students use the built-in constant in their calculations. They might also estimate and check by redoing the calculation.

CHAPTER INVESTIGATION Have students keep a "trash diary" to record the amount of trash they produce in one day. Compare their diaries with their lists for Exercise 17.

Answers to Problems Unique to Spanish Edition, Mixed Review
5. setenta y tres centésimas
6. trescientos ochenta y seis, y novecientas ocho milésimas

ON YOUR OWN

Use graph paper to sketch the next three designs in each pattern. See Solution Key.

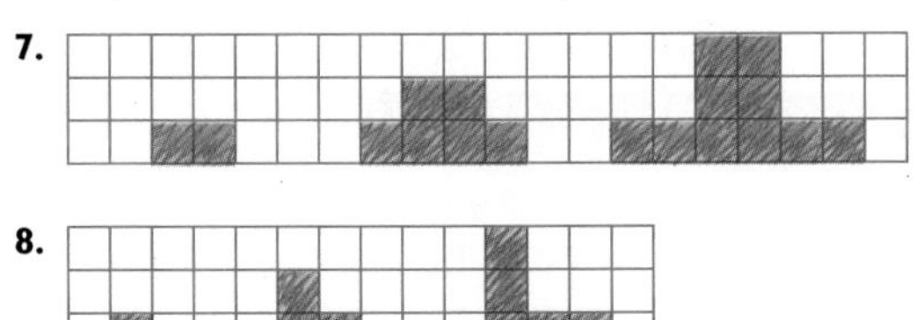

Find the next three terms in each number pattern. Write a rule to describe each number pattern. See Solution Key.

9. 7, 14, 21, 28, ■, ■, ■ — 35, 42, 49
10. 1, 3, 9, 27, ■, ■, ■ — 81, 243, 729
11. 0.25, 0.5, 0.75, ■, ■, ■ — 1, 1.25, 1.5
12. 1, 3, 5, 7, ■, ■, ■ — 9, 11, 13
13. $1, \frac{1}{2}, \frac{1}{4}, \frac{1}{8}$, ■, ■, ■ — $\frac{1}{16}, \frac{1}{32}, \frac{1}{64}$
14. 1, 0.1, 0.01, 0.001, ■, ■, ■ — 0.0001, 0.00001, 0.000001
15. **Calculator** Write the first five terms in the following number pattern: *Start with the number 1 and multiply by 1.5 repeatedly.* 1, 1.5, 2.25, 3.375, 5.0625
16. **Astronomy** Halley's comet is named for scientist Edmund Halley (1656–1742). Halley first saw the comet in 1682 and correctly predicted that it would return about every 76 years.
    a. **Calculator** Based on Halley's theory, when was the last time the comet appeared? When is the next year that the comet is expected to return? 1986; 2062
    b. About how old will you be when Halley's comet appears again? Answers may vary.
    c. **Writing** Did Edmund Halley get to see the comet appear a second time? Explain. No; the comet appeared in 1758 after Halley's death in 1742.
17. **Investigation (p. 184)** Estimate the amount of trash you produce each day. Make a list of things you can do to cut down the amount. Answers may vary. Sample: use cloth towels and napkins.
18. **Data File 5 (pp. 182–183)** Describe the sleep pattern of a newborn baby. Answers may vary. Sample: The newborn baby is awake for about 1 h and sleeps for about $2\frac{1}{2}$ h in a repeating pattern each 24 h.

Mixed REVIEW

Round to the nearest tenth.

1. 44.68 — 44.7
2. 8.146 — 8.1

Find each answer.

3. \$59.36 ÷ 7.42 — \$8
4. \$189.32 + \$33.79 — \$223.11

Write each decimal in words. See below.

5. 0.73
6. 386.908
7. Maria spent \$35 on a pair of jeans and \$18 on a shirt. She has \$24 left. How much money did she start with? \$77

5. seventy-three hundredths
6. three hundred eighty-six and nine hundred eight thousandths

Giotto, a European spacecraft, passed within 375 mi of Halley's comet the last time that it appeared. Pictures taken from the spacecraft revealed that the nucleus, or center, of the comet measured about 5 mi by 10 mi.

Source: *Reader's Digest Book of Facts*

Assignment Options

Core: 7–9, 12–14, 17, MR all	
Reinforce: 10,11,15	**Enrich:** 16, 18

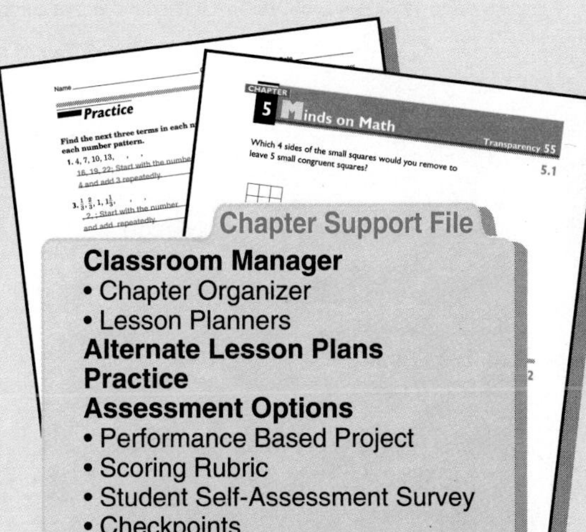

Minds on Math available in Teaching Transparencies

Math Minutes

Ask students to start with a single shaded square on a piece of graph paper. Have them add squares in such a way as to create designs that illustrate at least three terms of a pattern. Then have them write the number pattern for the designs.

Materials for 5-2

- ruled paper
- scissors

5-2

Connecting to Prior Knowledge

Ask students to recall that they probably first learned multiplication as repeated addition. Ask students to describe various ways to multiply 416 by 979. Tell them that in this lesson they will learn another procedure for multiplication.

DIVERSITY If you have students who learned to multiply in another country, invite them to show their procedures for multiplying by doing a problem of their choice on the board. You might also bring in an abacus and have a student familiar with it demonstrate how to perform multiplication.

THINK AND DISCUSS

TACTILE LEARNERS For Question 3, have students draw their Napier's rods on tag board or construction paper, or glue their paper rods to a sturdy backing to withstand extra use.

VISUAL LEARNERS Encourage students to use color coding to help them visually organize the information on their set of rods. They might write the numbers in the upper half of the box using one color and use a different color to write the numbers in the lower half of the boxes.

Ongoing Assessment Make sure students have all made a complete and correct set of Napier's rods by asking them to find matching boxes. Start with an example such as the second box of the 9 rod and the ninth box of the 2 rod. Have them explain why the boxes are the same.

Example 1

Ask students these questions to clarify the process.

- *Is it necessary to know the multiplication table to make a set of Napier's rods?*
  (no; knowing the number pattern and addition are enough)

"There is no medicine like hope, no incentive so great, and no tonic so powerful as expectation of something tomorrow."
—O. S. Marden

Organizer

1. **Focus**
   Connecting to Prior Knowledge
2. **Teach**
   Think and Discuss
3. **Closure**
   Try These
   Wrap Up

Skills Reviewed in Context of Lesson
- multiplying
- applying place value

Materials and Manipulatives
- ruled paper (one for each student)
- scissors (one for each group)

Student Resources
Extra Practice
Student Study Guide
Practice, TR Ch. 5, p. 24
Student Study Guide, Spanish Resources, TR

Teacher Resources
Teaching Transparencies 55, 58
Lesson Planner, TR Ch. 5, p. 3

continues next page

MATH AND HISTORY

5-2 Napier's Rods

What's Ahead
- Understanding how to use patterns to multiply greater numbers

WHAT YOU'LL NEED
✓ Ruled paper
✓ Scissors 

1. Answers may vary. Sample: The number in the top box is both the starting number and the number that is added repeatedly.
2a. Start with the number 1 and add 1 repeatedly.
2b. Start with the number 5 and add 5 repeatedly.
2c. Start with the number 0 and add 0 repeatedly.

THINK AND DISCUSS

John Napier (1550–1617) invented a series of ten rods that allows you to multiply two numbers by using only addition.

Napier's rods each have nine boxes. The top box contains a digit from 0 to 9. The other boxes each contain two digits separated by a diagonal line. Two of Napier's rods are shown.

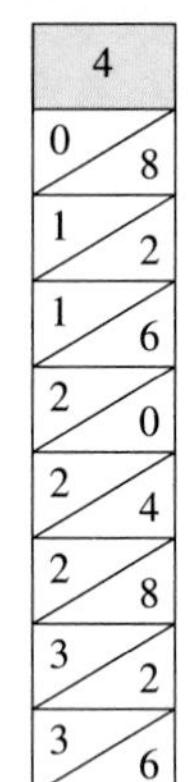

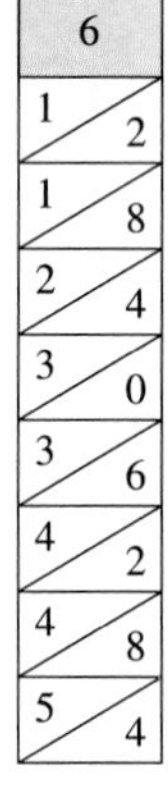

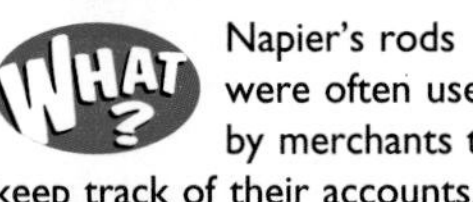
Napier's rods were often used by merchants to keep track of their accounts. They would carry a set of rods, made of ivory or wood, with them to make calculations.

Source: *The Joy of Mathematics*

1. **Discussion** For each of Napier's rods, how does the number contained in the top box of each rod relate to the numbers contained in the second through ninth boxes?
2. Name a rule to describe the number pattern that you would use to complete each rod.

a. 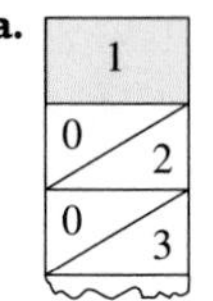

b. 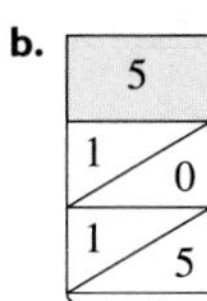

c. 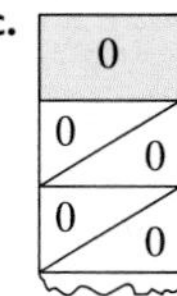

3. Draw all ten of Napier's rods on a sheet of ruled paper. Cut them out. **See Solution Key.**

- *Do you have to know the multiplication table to use Napier's rods?*
  (no; only addition is needed)

Additional Example Have students solve this problem using Napier's rods: *Class periods at Bella's school are 45 min long. There are 9 class periods/da. If Bella's school day begins at 8:30 A.M., at what time does her school day end?*
(Students should add 340 + 65 from the 4 and 5 rods to get 405, which, divided by 60, is 6.75. Bella's school day ends at 3:15 P.M.)

If your students enjoy working with Napier's rods, you may wish to further the discussion with the following questions:

- *How would you use Napier's rods to find the product 864 × 15?*
  (Sample answer: Since it is not convenient to multiply by a two-digit number with Napier's rods, think of 15 as 7 + 8. Multiply 864 × 7 and then 864 × 8 and add the products.)
- *Why might it be difficult to find the product 373 × 5?*
  (There is only one 3-rod. One way to find the product would be to make another 3-rod so that you could form 373. Another way to find the product would be to think of 373 as a sum such as 369 + 4. Then you could multiply 369 × 5 and 4 × 5 and add the products.)

Error Alert! Students may forget to count Row 1 as the row at the very top of each rod. ***Remediation*** Have students refer to the rods with the word "times." For example, the 9 rod would be the "times 9 rod." The extra word will help students remember that each box contains the product of the row number and the top number on the rod.

Journal Ask students: *If you did not have ready access to pencil and paper, a calculator, or a computer, when might you find Napier's rods useful in your daily life?*

You can use your set of Napier's rods to find a product.

Example 1 Find the product of 864 × 6.

- Pick out the 8, 6, and 4 rods. Line up the top digits in order from left to right.

8	6	4

- Count down to the sixth row, because you are multiplying by 6. Copy the digits in the upper half of each box in the sixth row, in order. Then attach a zero.

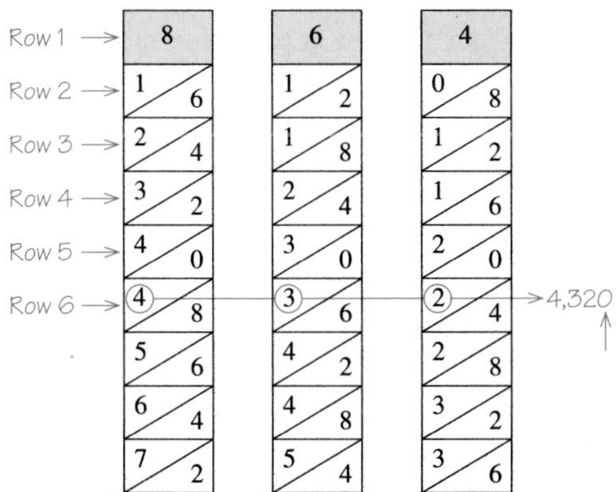

- Copy the digits in the lower half of each box in the sixth row. Do not add any extra digits.

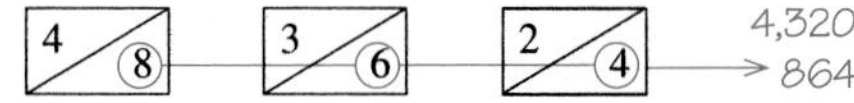

- Add these numbers 4,320 + 864 = 5,184

4. a. In terms of place value, describe the numbers found in the lower right corner of each box containing a diagonal. **The numbers represent ones.**

b. In terms of place value, describe the numbers found in the upper left corner of each box containing a diagonal. **The numbers represent tens.**

c. Discussion Why is a zero attached when working with the numbers found in the upper left corner of the boxes containing a diagonal? **The zero is attached to show that the numbers represent tens.**

WHERE? John Napier described his invention in a work entitled *Rabdologis.* This title comes from the Greek word *rabdos* meaning rods.

Source: *Historical Topics for the Mathematics Classroom*

Organizer, continued

Prentice Hall Technology
Computer Item Generator
- 5-2

Other Available Technology
calculator

Fact of the Day

In 1617, John Napier published the first book that showed the decimal point as it is used in the United States today.

—*MATHEMATICS*

TRY THESE

Exercise 7: To multiply 7 by 602, students can multiply 7 by 600 and by 2 and then add the two products. Discuss how this procedure resembles the strategy of Napier's rods.

WRITING For Exercise 11, have students name a method they could use instead of working with a partner.

Wrap Up

What's the Big Idea? Ask students: *How do Napier's rods use number patterns?*

Connections Have a discussion about inventions throughout history that were designed to make mathematical computations faster. Some examples might include the calculator, the abacus, the adding machine, and the computer.

Reteaching Activity Review the use of Napier's rods by showing students another method for reading them. Use as an example the boxes for finding the product of 864 × 6. Instead of having students read left to right, adding a zero to the top row, ask students to begin at the right and add down each diagonal.

Remind students to carry the 1 to the last step. Have students check their results by using the first method. Ask them which procedure they prefer.

ON YOUR OWN

Students will need their Napier's rods for Exercises 13–22.

Exercise 22: Students could use Napier's rods to multiply 43 × 6 and then multiply the product by 10.

Great Expectations

There are many valuable resources available to the students for gathering information about anthropology. Students can write for more information to such places as these:

Assignment Options

Core: 13–15, 21; MR all	
Reinforce: 16–20	**Enrich:** 22

Mixed REVIEW

Find each answer.

1. 19.2 ÷ 6 3.2
2. 122 ÷ 6.25 19.52

3. 256; 1,024; 4,096

Find the next three terms in each number pattern.

3. 1, 4, 16, 64, ■, ■, ■
4. 0.2, 0.5, 0.8, ■, ■, ■

1.1, 1.4, 1.7

Evaluate.

5. 8 − 2 × 3 + 5 7
6. 6 + 2(12 ÷ 4) 12

7. The sum of two numbers is 17. Their product is 60. Find the two numbers. 5, 12

TRY THESE

11. a. 15,744 11. b. Because the number 7 appears twice in 7,872 two 7 rods were needed

Use Napier's rods to find each product.

5. 39 × 8 312
6. 836 × 9 7,524
7. 602 × 7 4,214
8. 4,186 × 7 29,302
9. 16,573 × 8 132,584
10. 836,724 × 5 4,183,620
11. a. Work with a partner to find the product of 7,872 × 2.
    b. **Writing** Explain why it was helpful to work with a partner to find this product. See above.
12. **Data File 2 (pp. 38–39)** Suppose you and all of your classmates are planning to take a field trip to Kings Island. Your teacher is collecting money for admission to the amusement park. Anyone 4 ft or taller is required to pay adult admission. How much money will your teacher need to collect?
    Answers will vary.

GREAT EXPECTATIONS

Archaeologist

I am interested in becoming an archaeologist because of the history involved in the job. I love learning about how people in ancient times lived and worked. I want to know what they believed, how they raised their children, and why they fought.

If I am an archaeologist I can tell people about their past and their ancestors. I want to tell people about their ancestors' mistakes so they will never repeat them.

Katherine Shell

190

- American Anthropological Association
  1703 New Hampshire Ave NW
  Washington, DC 20009
- Smithsonian Institution
  Arts and Industries Building, Room 1163
  Washington, DC 20560
- National Geographic Society
  Educational Services
  Washington, DC 20036

Students can also learn from discussions with experts. For example:

- Invite an anthropology professor from a local college or university to speak to the class.
- Visit a museum and have the curator take the students on a guided tour.

Discuss with students the various careers associated with anthropology:

- **Ethnography** (studying cultures by living in the environment)
- **Archaeology** (learning about cultures by excavating sites)
- **Physical anthropology** (researching human artifacts)
- **Linguistics** (studying language)

ON YOUR OWN

Use Napier's rods to find each product.

13. 43 × 7 301
14. 671 × 9 6,039
15. 908 × 4 3,632
16. 7,482 × 5 37,410
17. 42,793 × 6 256,758
18. 207,416 × 8 1,659,328
19. 32,749 × 8 261,992
20. 206,831,954 × 7 1,447,823,678

21. There are 28 students in Mrs. Chin's history class. Each student must give a 5 minute speech about a favorite president. How many minutes of class time must Mrs. Chin set aside for these speeches? 140 min

22. Mr. Leonard can type 43 words each minute. About how many words can he type in one hour? (*Hint:* 1 h = 60 min) 2,580 words

Ancient Egyptians multiplied by using repeated duplications. To multiply 2,801 × 7 they did the following:

1	2,801
2	5,602
+4	+11,204
7	19,607

How would they have found the product 3,468 × 3?

Source: *Historical Topics for the Mathematics Classroom*

1	3,468
+2	+ 6,936
3	10,404

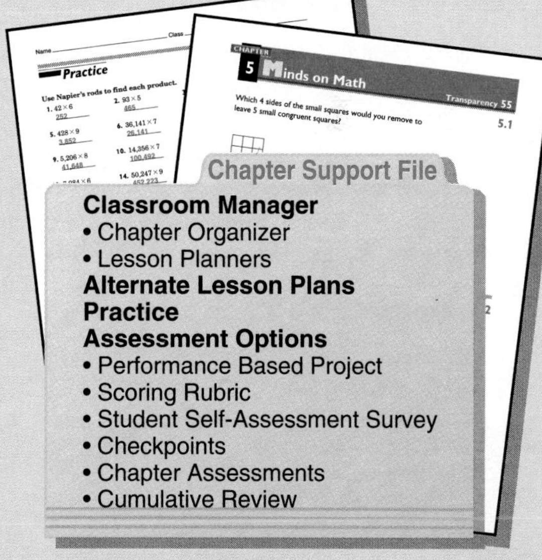

Minds on Math available in Teaching Transparencies

Dear Katherine,

I've been fascinated with archaeology since I was in the fourth grade when we studied California Indians in school. The more I learned about Native Americans, the more I thought about how badly they had been treated in this country. If we could just learn more about Native Americans, I reasoned, we could do something to help them.

And, I figured, what better way to learn than through archaeology? I'd see articles in the newspaper about archaeological digs, and the neat new finds they made. Although archaeologists were digging up stuff that was old, this kind of history was really new.

People are always surprised to hear this. Many think that archaeology is mostly ancient art, remote places, and dangerous expeditions. That part is all true, but in the everyday life of an archaeologist, we deal with science and math all the time.

David Hurst Thomas
Curator of Anthropology
American Museum of Natural History

In the 15th century, Native Americans were using baskets for grinding corn and for storage.

Math Minutes

Ask students to write a fraction that shows the ratio of prime numbers to natural numbers in the first 50 natural numbers.
$\frac{15}{50}$ or $\frac{3}{10}$

Materials for 5-3

- calculator

5-3

Connecting to Prior Knowledge

Ask students whether they choose the short or the long line when waiting to buy tickets for a movie and why. Tell students that math involves many time-saving procedures such as using multiplication for repeated addition. Demonstrate by asking them to give a concise expression of the product of $10 \times 10 \times 10 \times 10 \times 10$. **(100,000)** Tell them that just three numerals can express the same number with exponents.

THINK AND DISCUSS

ESL Some vocabulary in this lesson may need special attention. The words "base" and "power," "square" and "cube" have special mathematical meanings. Show students physical representations of squares and cubes. Using exponents, write the mathematical expression for the area of a square and the volume of a cube. Write on the board 2^2, 3^3, and 2^4. Help students read such sentences as these:

- *The area of the square is two squared.*
- *The volume of the cube is three cubed.*
- *Two multiplied by two multiplied by two multiplied by two is two to the fourth power.*

DIVERSITY Be aware that some students with visual impairments may have difficulty distinguishing an exponent from a base; for example, 10^5 may be seen as 105.

VISUAL LEARNERS The diagrams accompanying Questions 4 and 5 will be particularly appropriate for visual learners. Encourage these students to make their own diagrams.

TACTILE LEARNERS Some students may need to handle square tiles and unit cubes to build the shapes shown in Questions 4 and 5.

CONNECTION TO GEOMETRY Questions 4 and 5 review geometry by having students associate exponents with geometric figures.

"Knowledge is of two kinds. We know a subject ourselves, or we know where we can find information upon it."

—SAMUEL JOHNSON

Organizer

1. **Focus**
   Connecting to Prior Knowledge
2. **Teach**
   Think and Discuss
3. **Closure**
   Try These
   Wrap Up

Vocabulary/Symbols
exponent
base
power
square
cube
evaluate

Skills Reviewed in Context of Lesson
- factoring
- calculating area
- calculating volume

Materials and Manipulatives
- calculator (one for each student)

On Your Own Exercises 24–31: calculator (*optional*)

continues next page

What's Ahead
- Understanding and using exponents

5-3 Exponents

WHAT YOU'LL NEED
✓ Calculator 

THINK AND DISCUSS

Elis F. Stenman built a house along with the furniture in it from approximately 100,000 newspapers. You can express 100,000 as the product $10 \times 10 \times 10 \times 10 \times 10$. You can express this product using an *exponent.*

$$\underbrace{10 \times 10 \times 10 \times 10 \times 10}_{\text{5 factors}} = 10^5 \leftarrow \text{exponent}$$

(↑ base)

The **exponent** tells you how many times a number, or **base,** is used as a factor.

1. Name the base and the exponent in 3^6. 3, 6
2. Express the product $5 \times 5 \times 5 \times 5$ using an exponent. 5^4

You call a number that is expressed using an exponent a **power.** You read 10^5 as "ten to the fifth power."

3. Read each of the following powers out loud: 8^4, 3^6, 10^8. 8 to the fourth power; 3 to the sixth power; 10 to the eighth power

The exponents 2 and 3 have special names.

4. a. Complete: The area of the *square* is 3×3 or $3^{■}$. 2
   b. Why do you think the exponent 2 is read as "squared"? The model is a square.

5. a. Complete: The volume of the *cube* is $4 \times 4 \times 4$ or $4^{■}$. 3
   b. Why do you think the exponent 3 is read as "cubed"? The model is a cube.

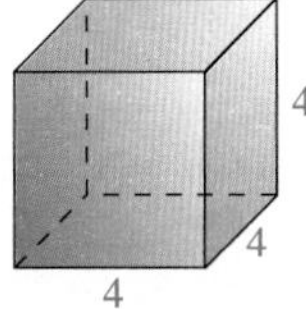

6. Read each of the following powers out loud: 6^3, 7^2, 12^3. 6 cubed; 7 squared; 12 cubed

Elis F. Stenman made the walls of his house by pasting and folding layers of newspaper. He used papers rolled into different sizes to make the furniture, which includes tables, chairs, lamps, and a grandfather clock.

Source: *The Kids' World Almanac of Records and Facts*

Example 1

AUDITORY LEARNERS Reading the problem correctly aloud (*4 to the third power, or 4 cubed*) helps students evaluate correctly.

Error Alert! Students often treat an exponent as a factor. For example, a student might evaluate 4^3 as 4 • 3, or 12, instead of 4 • 4 • 4. ***Remediation*** Emphasize to students the benefits of reading each power aloud. Reading 4^3 as "four to the third power" reminds students that the 3 tells how many times the base number is used as a factor. Students might also write the exponential expression as a product before writing the answer.

Examples 2 and 3

You may need to help students locate the [y^x] and [x^2] keys on their calculators. Some calculators may have slightly different labels on these keys.

Additional Examples *Evaluate 8^4.* **(8 [y^x] 4 [=] 4096)**
Evaluate 12^2. **(12 [x^2] 144)**

Ongoing Assessment To verify that students understand the order of operations, give them the expression $3 \times 4^2 + 5^3$ with no parentheses. Ask them to evaluate it. **(173)** Have them place parentheses to give as many different values as possible. **Solutions will include:**

$$(3 \times 4)^2 + 5^3 = 269;\ 3 \times (4^2 + 5)^3 = 27{,}783;$$
$$(3 \times 4^2) + 5^3 = 173;\ 3 \times (4^2 + 5^3) = 423$$

Encourage students to write the rules for the order of operations on an index card that they can keep on their desk and refer to as they work through operations. Using the card will help them memorize the rules correctly.

You can **evaluate,** or find the value of, a power by first writing it as a product.

Example 1 **a.** Evaluate 4^3.
$4^3 = 4 \times 4 \times 4 = 64$

b. Evaluate 1^2.
$1^2 = 1 \times 1 = 1$

A calculator is helpful when you are working with exponents. You can use the [y^x] key to evaluate *any* power.

Example 2 **a.** Evaluate 6^8.
6 [y^x] 8 [=] 1679616

b. Evaluate 25^2.
25 [y^x] 2 [=] 625

You can use the [x^2] key to square a number.

Example 3 Evaluate 26^2.
26 [x^2] 676

7. Discussion How can you use the [x^2] key to evaluate 12^4?
Enter 12, then press the [x^2] key twice.

You can extend the order of operations to include powers.

The Order of Operations

1. Do all operations within parentheses first.
2. Do all work with exponents.
3. Multiply and divide from left to right.
4. Add and subtract from left to right.

Example 4 **a.** Evaluate $2 \times (4^2 - 5)$.

$2 \times (4^2 - 5) = 2 \times (16 - 5)$ — $4^2 = 4 \times 4 = 16$; Subtract 5 from 16.
$= 2 \times 11$ — Multiply 2 and 11.
$= 22$

b. Evaluate $2^3 - 9 \div 3$.

$2^3 - 9 \div 3 = 8 - 9 \div 3$ — $2^3 = 2 \times 2 \times 2 = 8$; Divide 9 by 3.
$= 8 - 3$ — Subtract 3 from 8.
$= 5$

8. Discussion How can you use a calculator to evaluate each expression in Example 4?
Example 4a: 2 [×] [(] 4 [x^2] [−] 5 [)] [=]
Example 4b: 2 [y^x] 3 [−] 9 [÷] 3 [=]

The French mathematician René Descartes (1596–1650) introduced the use of Hindu-Arabic numerals as exponents on a given base.

Source: *Historical Topics for the Mathematics Classroom*

The phrase *Please Excuse My Dear Aunt Sally* can help you to remember the order of operations. **What does the first letter of each word in the phrase stand for?**

P - parentheses
E - exponents
M - multiply
D - divide
A - add
S - subtract

Organizer, continued

Student Resources
Extra Practice
Student Study Guide
Practice, TR Ch. 5, p. 25
Student Study Guide, Spanish Resources, TR
Alternate Lesson, TR Ch. 5, pp. 11–14
Checkpoint, TR Ch. 5, p. 36

Teacher Resources
Teaching Transparencies 19, 55
Lesson Planner, TR Ch. 5, p. 4

Prentice Hall Technology

Multimedia Math
- Math Tools, Calculation
- Math Investigations, The Pythagorean Theorem

Computer Item Generator
- 5-3

Other Available Technology
calculator

Fact of the Day

In 1991, 6.6 million tons of used newspapers were recycled—an increase of 90% since 1983. Recycling companies benefited from the increase that year as their costs for buying used newspapers dropped from $20 to $5 per ton.

—*Environmental Almanac*

TRY THESE

Error Alert! For Exercise 16, students may try to first multiply 2 and 4 instead of evaluating 4^2. ***Remediation*** Remind students of the order of operations and explain that an exponent can only have one base unless the base is within parentheses.

Wrap Up

What's the Big Idea? Ask students: *What does 7^5 mean? What is the base? the exponent?*

Journal Ask students: *You know that $10^5 = 100{,}000$, and is the same as 10 • 10 • 10 • 10 • 10. Which expression are you most comfortable using? Explain.*

Connections Have a discussion about how exponents are used. Here are some examples:

- **Measurement** (expressing area in units squared, expressing volume in units cubed)
- **Science** (finding gravitational acceleration, charting cell division, scientific notation)
- **Social Studies** (expressing the area of a state or country in square miles, population density)

Reteaching Activity Have students use graph paper to draw several squares of different sizes. Have them count the number of squares along one side. Ask students:

- *What does this number represent?* **(the base)**
- *Count the total number of squares. What does this number represent?* **(the value of the base squared)**

Have students repeat the procedure for their other squares. This activity could also be done with cube blocks.

Assignment Options

Core: 19, 20, 22, 24–28, 32–33, 35a, MR all, CH all	
Reinforce: 21, 23, 29–30, 34, 35b–c	**Enrich:** 31, 36

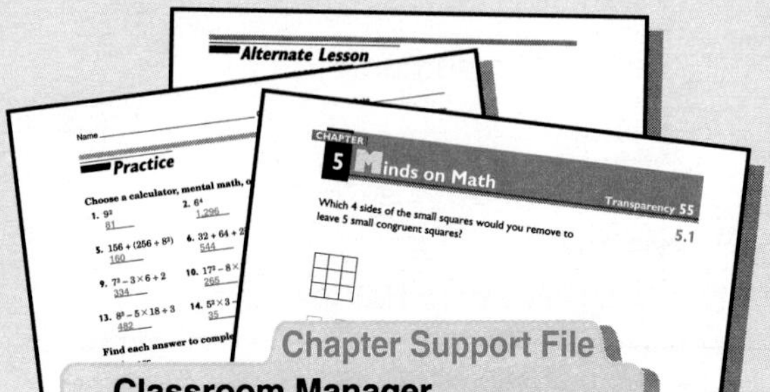

Chapter Support File

Classroom Manager
- Chapter Organizer
- Lesson Planners

Alternate Lesson Plans
Practice
Assessment Options
- Performance Based Project
- Scoring Rubric
- Student Self-Assessment Survey
- Checkpoints
- Chapter Assessments
- Cumulative Review

Minds on Math available in Teaching Transparencies

TRY THESE

Name the base and the exponent.

9. 4^5 4, 5 10. 3^2 3, 2 11. 6^3 6, 3

Write using an exponent.

12. $6 \times 6 \times 6$ 6^3 13. $3 \times 3 \times 3 \times 3 \times 3$ 3^5

Mental Math Evaluate.

14. 5^2 25 15. 2^3 8 16. $2 \times 4^2 - 32$ 0

17. $21 + (7^2 - 40)$ 30 18. $(3^2 - 1) \div 2^2$ 2

Mixed REVIEW

Estimate each product.

1. 48×195 10,000
2. 79×28 2,400

Find the next three terms in each number pattern.

3. 2, 4, 6, ■, ■, ■ 8, 10, 12
4. 6, 12, 18, ■, ■, ■ 24, 30, 36
5. The distance to your grandmother's apartment is 24 blocks. Suppose you walk 3 blocks and then take the bus 16 blocks. How much farther is it to your grandmother's? 5 blocks

ON YOUR OWN

Name the base and the exponent.

19. 7^9 7, 9 20. 8^1 8, 1 21. 10^3 10, 3

Write using an exponent.

22. $8 \times 8 \times 8 \times 8$ 8^4 23. $4 \times 4 \times 4 \times 4 \times 4 \times 4$ 4^6

Choose Use a calculator, mental math, or paper and pencil to evaluate.

24. 11^7 19,487,171 25. $5 \times 3^2 - 10$ 35 26. $7^1 \times 2^4$ 112

27. $175 + (128 \div 4^2)$ 183 28. $16 + 32 \div 2^3$ 20

29. $6^3 \div (2 \times 6) + 64$ 82 30. $674 - (14 - 6)^3$ 162

31. $498 + (2^{12} \div 2^4) \div (2^5 \times 2) - 2^1$ 500

Express each area or volume using an exponent.

32. 90^2

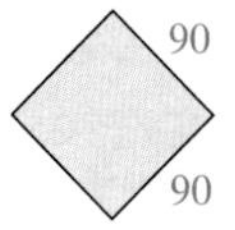

33. 2^3

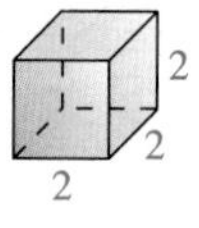

34. Critical Thinking What is the value of any number raised to the first power? What is the value of 1 raised to any power? Give an example to justify each answer.
the number itself; for example, $10^1 = 10$. 1; for example, $1^5 = 1$.

ON YOUR OWN

Exercises 22–23: You may have a student who recognizes 8 and 4 as powers of 2 and writes the answers using 2 as the base. Share these alternate answers with the rest of the class. **(The answer for both Exercise 22 and Exercise 23 is 2^{12}.)**

CRITICAL THINKING For Exercise 34, have students list many examples, or create a table, before generalizing.

WRITING For Exercise 36a, students could make a similar table with an overhead projector image.

CHECKPOINT

Exercises 3–7: Have students check their answers using calculators.

Math Minutes

Ask students to use mental math to choose the smallest fraction in each set.

$\frac{5}{7}, \frac{1}{3}, \frac{4}{6}, \frac{8}{10}$ $\mathbf{\frac{1}{3}}$

$\frac{5}{9}, \frac{4}{8}, \frac{11}{15}, \frac{3}{7}$ $\mathbf{\frac{3}{7}}$

Materials for 5-4

- algebra tiles

35. a. Copy and complete the table below.

Power	Standard Form
10^1	10
10^2	100
10^3	1,000
10^4	■ 10,000
■ 10^5	■ 100,000

FLASHBACK
A number in standard form is separated into groups of three digits by commas.

b. Writing How is the exponent related to the number of zeros that follow the numeral 1 when the power is expressed in standard form? The number of zeros is the same as the exponent.

c. Express each power in standard form: 10^8, 10^{10}, 10^{12}.
100,000,000; 10,000,000,000; 1,000,000,000,000

36. Entertainment The size of the image of a motion picture is related to the distance of the projector from the screen. Use the table at the right to answer each question.

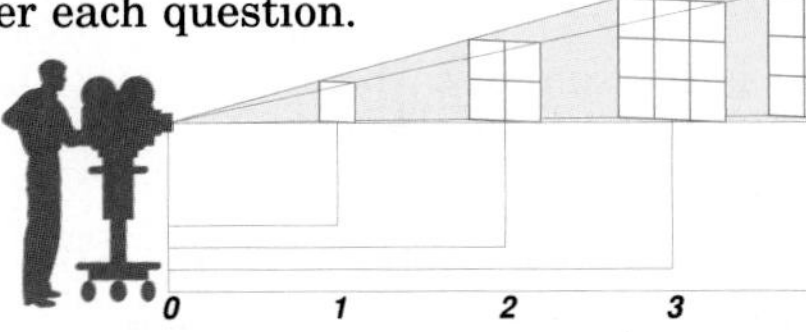

Distance from Screen (units)	Picture Size (square units)
1	1
2	4
3	9
4	16

a. Writing Describe how the size of a motion picture is related to the distance from the projector to the screen. The square of the distance from the screen is the size of the motion picture.

b. A projector is 25 ft from the screen. How big will the image of the motion picture be? 625 ft^2

CHECKPOINT

1. Write the first five terms in the following number pattern: *Start with the number 4 and multiply by 2 repeatedly.*
4, 8, 16, 32, 64

2. Music Use an exponent to express the number of singles a recording artist must sell in the U.S.A. to get a gold record. 10^6 singles

Gold Records	
Country	**Singles Sold**
Austria	100,000
Spain	100,000
Finland	10,000
U.S.A.	1,000,000
Ireland	100,000
Italy	1,000,000

Source: *The Kids' World Almanac of Records and Facts*

Evaluate.

3. 9^7 4,782,969 **4.** $7 \times 3^4 - 99$ 468 **5.** 3×2^1 6

6. $(2 \times 4^2) \div 8$ 4 **7.** $50 \div (5^2 \div 5) + 4$ 14

5-4

Connecting to Prior Knowledge

Ask students if they have ever asked someone to hold their place in a line. Point out to students that though they may have briefly left the line, their place in its order was preserved. Tell students that sometimes in math there is a number either missing or unknown in an expression. Ask students to name some ways in which the place for a number in an equation could be saved. **(Students may mention letters or some other symbol.)**

THINK AND DISCUSS

Question 1: Students who have never seen a magic square may need guidance. Point out that the diagonal running from the lower left of the square to the upper right contains no blanks and can be used to determine that each row's sum is 15. Draw arrows on the square to show the various sums.

ESL To demonstrate that a variable is a symbol that may be replaced by various numbers, remind students of formulas they have used such as $A = lw$. For any one rectangle, the l stands for just one number, the length. From problem to problem, the value of l can vary, or change. You also may want to relate the word *variable* to other, related words, like "vary, variation, variety, and various" and discuss how they contain the idea of change.

MENTAL MATH For Question 3a, have students explain how they arrived at their answers.

Error Alert! Students might mistakenly believe that the variables in Question 4 are equal. ***Remediation*** Point out to students that such placeholders are called variables because they vary in value. The fact that two or more variables are not the identical symbol indicates that it is at least possible they differ in value.

"A problem well stated is a problem half solved."

—CHARLES F. KETTERING

Organizer

1. **Focus**
   Connecting to Prior Knowledge
2. **Teach**
   Think and Discuss
3. **Closure**
   Try These
   Wrap Up

Vocabulary/Symbols
magic square
numerical expression
variable
variable expression

Skills Reviewed in Context of Lesson
- operations for whole numbers
- operations for decimals

Materials and Manipulatives
- algebra tiles (one set for each group)

On Your Own Exercises 16–18: algebra tiles, Exercises 19–28: calculator *(optional)*

Student Resources
Extra Practice
Student Study Guide
Practice, TR Ch. 5, p. 26
Student Study Guide, Spanish Resources, TR

continues next page

5-4 Variables and Expressions

What's Ahead
- Understanding variables
- Evaluating variable expressions

WHAT YOU'LL NEED
✓ Algebra tiles 

6	1	8
7	5	3
2	9	4

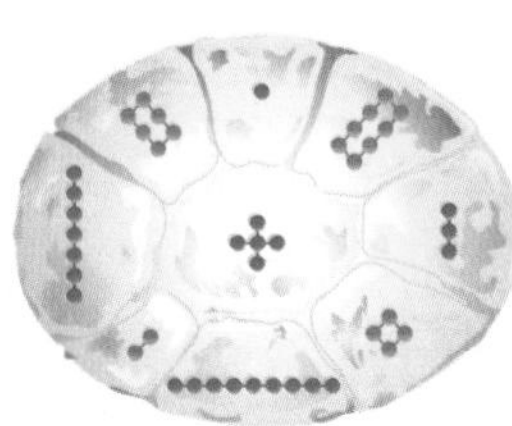

WHAT? The *lo-shu* is the oldest known magic square. It was found on the back of a tortoise shell by Emperor Yu of China about 4000 years ago. The drawing above gives you an idea of what the lo-shu may have looked like. **How would you represent this magic square?**

Source: *Math Activities for Child Involvement*

THINK AND DISCUSS

■	7	2
1	5	■
8	■	4

A **magic square** is an arrangement of numbers in a square in which the rows, columns, and diagonals each have the same sum. A magic square is shown at the right.

To find the missing values in a magic square first identify a row, column, or diagonal in which all the values appear. The sum of the completed diagonal in the magic square shown above can be represented by the *numerical expression* $8 + 5 + 2$. A **numerical expression** contains only numbers and mathematical symbols.

1. What is the sum of each row, column, and diagonal of the magic square shown above? 15

a	7	2
1	5	b
8	c	4

You can represent the missing value in each square by a *variable,* as shown at the right. A **variable** is a symbol, usually a letter, that stands for a number.

2. Name the variables in the magic square. a, b, c

The *variable expression* $a + 7 + 2$ represents the sum of the entries in the first row. A **variable expression** is an expression that contains at least one variable.

3. a. Mental Math What is the value of a? 6
   b. Name another variable expression that you could use to determine the value of a. $a + 1 + 8$ or $a + 5 + 4$
4. a. What variable expressions could you use to determine the value of b? of c? $1 + 5 + b$ or $2 + b + 4$; $8 + c + 4$ or $7 + 5 + c$
   b. Mental Math What is the value of b? of c? 9; 3

MENTAL MATH For Question 4b, have students first give the variable expressions for *b* and *c*.

VISUAL LEARNERS When looking at the models, students should be alerted not to presume that $x = 5$ simply because the green tile looks about five times the size of the yellow tile.

While looking at the expression $2y + 3$ and the accompanying model, help students see why this is not the same as 5 or as 5*y*.

Example 1

Remind students that *x* is simply a placeholder for an unknown number. Explain to students that the number 2 means two is a multiplier of the unknown number.

Example 2

In part b, alert students to the exponent.

Additional Example

Evaluate $c^3 - 5$ for $c = 2$. **(3)**

Example 3

Students may want to write the value above the variable when substituting numbers into an expression with two variables, in order to avoid mixing up the values.

Additional Examples

- *Evaluate $2c^2 + 3$ for $c = 3$.* **(21)**
- *Evaluate the expression $x(2y - 1)$ for $x = 5$ and $y = 4$.* **(35)**

Ongoing Assessment

Have students evaluate the expression $a^4 + (b - 10)^3$ when $a = 2$ and $b = 14$. **(80)** Students with the correct answer have probably successfully integrated their previous knowledge about exponents and order of operations with the new topic of variables.

Students should be able to show all the steps involved in evaluating the expression and be able to explain each step.

You can use tiles to model expressions. The yellow tiles represent ones, and the green tiles represent variables.

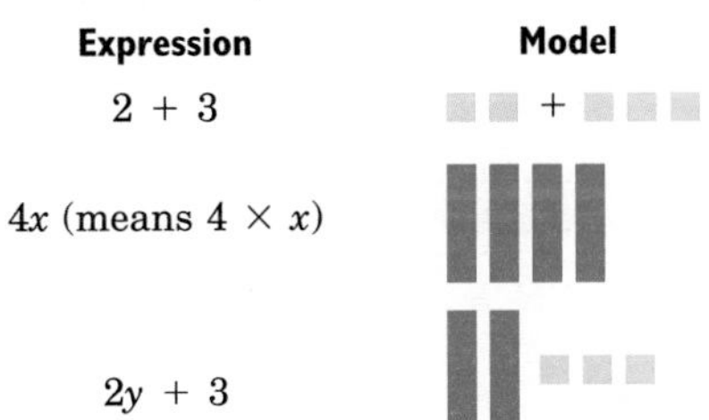

5. Discussion Why is the symbol × used to show multiplication in numerical expressions but not in variable expressions? The multiplication sign could be confused with the variable *x*.

You can evaluate a variable expression using tiles.

Example 1 Evaluate $2x + 1$ for $x = 3$.

Model the expression $2x + 1$.

Replace each green tile with 3 yellow tiles.

The value of $2x + 1$ for $x = 3$ is 7.

6. Use tiles to evaluate $6 + 3t$ for $t = 2$. 12

You can also evaluate a variable expression by replacing the variable with a number. Then follow the order of operations.

Example 2

a. Evaluate $a + 8$ for $a = 7$.

$a + 8 = 7 + 8$ Replace *a* with 7.

$= 15$ Use mental math.

b. Evaluate $b^2 - 12$ for $b = 6$.

$b^2 - 12 = 6^2 - 12$ Replace *b* with 6. Evaluate the power.

$= 36 - 12$ Subtract 12 from 36.

$= 24$

7. Discussion Will the expressions $2c^2$ and $(2c)^2$ result in the same value for $c = 4$? Explain. No. In the first expression only c is squared; in the second expression the product of 2 and c is squared; $2c^2 = 32$; $(2c)^2 = 64$

FLASHBACK

To follow the order of operations you first multiply and divide from left to right. Then add and subtract from left to right.

Organizer, continued

Teacher Resources

Teaching Transparencies 56, 59

Transparency Masters, TR p. 27

Lesson Planner, TR Ch. 5, p. 5

Prentice Hall Technology

Multimedia Math

- Hot Page™ 5-4
- Math Tools, Calculation
- Math Tools, Manipulatives

Computer Item Generator

- 5-4

Other Available Technology

calculator

Excel by Microsoft: Exercises 30–32 *(optional)*

Fact of the Day

A silkworm moth lives only two or three days. In that brief time, however, a female moth may lay between 300 and 500 eggs. These eggs hatch into silkworms, which feed and grow for about 45 days before spinning their cocoons.

—ENCYCLOPAEDIA BRITANNICA

TRY THESE

If time permits, after students complete Exercises 10–15 substituting $x = 8$, have them use calculators to evaluate each expression for $x = 3.2$. **(15.2; 25; 10.24; 6.65; 4.80; 0.4)**

MENTAL MATH Make sure students begin their solutions to Exercise 15 with a subtraction operation and then multiply.

Wrap Up

What's the Big Idea? Ask students: *What are variables and how are they used?*

Journal Have students choose a variable expression from the lesson. Then have them write a paragraph based on the expression that involves a missing item. Ask: *How does a variable expression resemble a mystery story?*

Connections Have a discussion about how variables and variable expressions are used. Here are some examples:

- **Science** (formulas, expressions of theories and laws, proofs)
- **Business** (ordering and buying at a bulk rate, determining profit, inventory)

Reteaching Activity Have students work in pairs to create a magic square that contains three variables. Have two pairs exchange and solve the square.

ON YOUR OWN

Exercises 30–32: To help students with the last blank in each exercise, you might suggest the "work backwards" strategy.

CONNECTION TO FUNCTIONS Exercises 30–32 provide a preview of function tables by introducing students to the concept of charting the different values of a variable expression.

Assignment Options

Core: 16–22, MR all	
Reinforce: 23–34	**Enrich:** 35–36

PH Multimedia Math Hot Page™ 5-4

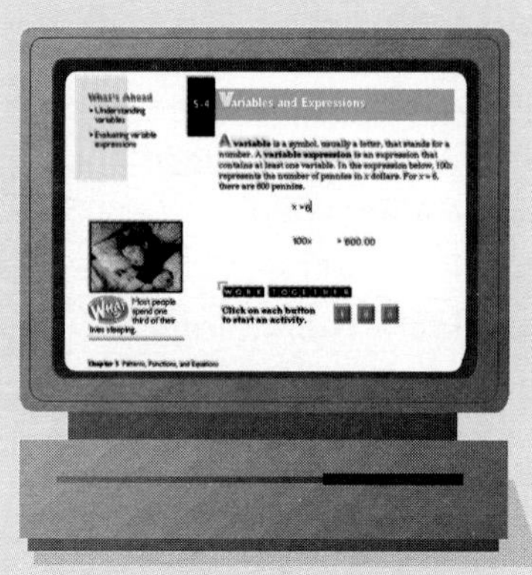

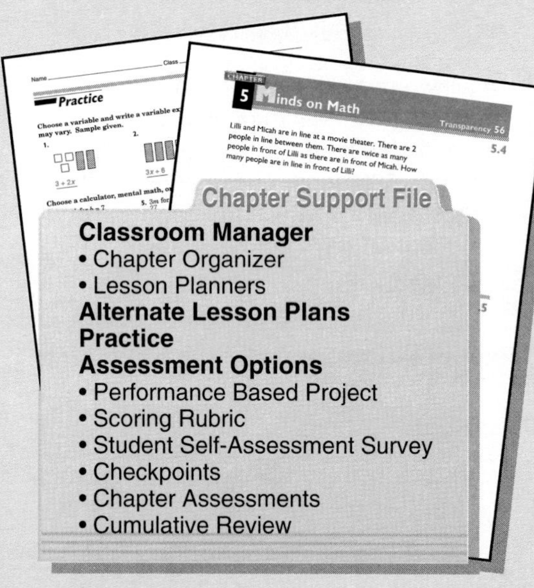

Minds on Math available in Teaching Transparencies

WHO? A counting horse named Muhamed lived in Germany in the late 1800s. His owner trained him to add, subtract, multiply, and divide. Muhamed would give an answer of 25 by tapping his left hoof twice, and his right hoof five times. **How would he give the answer to the numerical expression 97 − 12?**

Source: *The Kids' World Almanac of Animals and Pets*

He would tap his left hoof 8 times and his right hoof 5 times.

A variable expression can have more than one variable.

Example 3 Evaluate $r(36 - s)$ for $r = 0.5$ and $s = 8$.

$r(36 - s) = 0.5(36 - 8)$ Replace r with 0.5 and s with 8.

$= 0.5(28)$ Subtract 8 from 36.

$= 14$ Multiply 0.5 and 28.

TRY THESE

Choose a variable and write a variable expression for each model. Answers may vary. Samples given.

8.  $4t + 1$
9. $r + 4$

Mental Math Evaluate each expression for $x = 8$.

10. $x + 12$ 20
11. $80 \div x$ 10
12. x^2 64
13. $0.25 + 2x$ 16.25
14. $3x \div 2$ 12
15. $2(x - 3)$ 10

ON YOUR OWN

Model each variable expression. See Solution Key.

16. $3y + 5$
17. $c + 3$
18. $5b + 2$

Choose Use a calculator, mental math, or paper and pencil to evaluate.

19. $24 \div d$ for $d = 3$ 8
20. $p + 8$ for $p = 6$ 14
21. $3r - 2$ for $r = 65$ 193
22. $x^2 - 12$ for $x = 8$ 52
23. $n \div 10$ for $n = 30$ 3
24. $0.75s$ for $s = 29.98$ 22.485
25. $(2c)^3$ for $c = 3$ 216
26. $2ab$ for $a = 3.5$ and $b = 0.3$ 2.1
27. $8 - y^2$ for $y = 2$ 4
28. $2r + s$ for $r = 7$ and $s = 30$ 44
29. Copy and complete the magic square shown at the left. Find the values of r, s, and t. $r = 8, s = 11, t = 10$

4	9	r
s	7	3
6	5	t

TECHNOLOGY OPTION Have students check their answers to Exercises 30–32 by using a spreadsheet program. Enter the x values in column A and define a formula using the given expressions in column B.

WRITING For Exercise 34, ask students to write an example of both a numerical expression and an equivalent variable expression. For example, $9 + 3 - 7$ as $3x + x - 7$ for $x = 3$.

DIVERSITY The Chinese were the first to discover how to unwind the cocoon of the silkworm. China is still a leading producer of raw silk today.

Copy and complete each table by evaluating the expression for the given values of x.

30.

x	$x + 6$
1	7
4	10
7	■13
10	■16
■14	20

31.

x	$7x$
2	■14
4	■28
6	■42
8	■56
■10	70

32.

x	$100 - x$
20	■80
35	■65
50	■50
72	■28
■12	88

33. **Choose A, B, or C.** Which numerical expression has a value closest to 176? A

A. $11.5 \times 14 + 25.5$ **B.** $7.5 + 3 \times 50$

C. $(35 \times 2.5 + 300) \div 2$

34. **Writing** What is the difference between a numerical expression and a variable expression?

Use the article below to answer each question.

Smooth as Silk

Silk is the most precious fabric by weight. The silkworm spins silk to create a cocoon. Each cocoon consists of a single thread up to 1.6 km long. It takes 110 cocoons to make a man's silk tie, 630 cocoons for a blouse, and 3,000 cocoons for a kimono. It takes a silkworm about 3 days to spin the entire cocoon. During that time the worm will have shaken its head about 300,000 times.

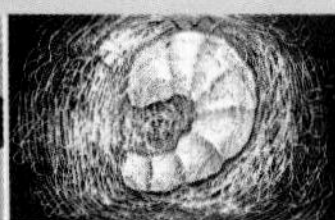

35. Write a numerical expression to represent the number of cocoons it takes to make both a tie and a blouse.
110 + 630

36. How many days would it take one silkworm to spin the silk needed to make a kimono? About how many kilometers of thread are needed to make a kimono?
9,000 days; 4,800 km

Mixed REVIEW

Use the data: 9, 16, 21, 10, 12, 17, 20.

1. Find the mean. 15
2. Find the median. 16

Write using an exponent.

3. $5 \times 5 \times 5 \times 5$ 5^4
4. $9 \times 9 \times 9$ 9^3

2, 9, 16, 23, 30
5. Write the first five terms of the following number pattern: start with 2 and add 7 repeatedly.

6. Margarite is standing in the middle of a line to buy concert tickets. There are 47 people in front of her. How many people are in the line? 95 people

34. A numerical expression contains only numbers and mathematical symbols. A variable expression contains at least one variable.

Math Minutes

Ask students to find the product of the numbers in each line:

1, 2 **2**
1, 2, 3 **6**
1, 2, 3, 4 **24**

Challenge them to find a pattern and use it to predict the product of the next line. **The product of the next line is 5 × 24, or 120. The pattern is to multiply the previous answer by the new number on the line.**

Materials for 5-5

- ruler

5-5

Connecting to Prior Knowledge

Ask students what they would do if they suddenly noticed a strange hum in the kitchen. Would they turn off all electrical appliances? Look out the window? Check the hallway? Tell students that solving a problem often involves finding a pattern. Ask students to give their own examples of problems they might solve by looking for a pattern.

ESL Ask students to restate the problem about cables in their own words. As you listen you will be able to determine whether or not the students understand that in the problem each student's computer is to be connected to all of the computers of the other students.

TACTILE/VISUAL LEARNERS The series of drawings for Questions 3–6 is appropriate for visual learners. Students can use straws and tiles to model the network of connections.

Ongoing Assessment Have volunteers share their answers and diagrams for Questions 3–6 with the class. Answering Question 7a as a class will also help you assess students' understanding of the developing pattern before they try to describe that pattern. Before having students answer Question 7b, ask them if the following statements are true: *The number of cables* = $\frac{1}{2}$ *number of computers. The number of cables = the nearest odd number to number of computers.* **(Both are false.)**

KINESTHETIC LEARNERS Have students act out the cable connections using string or rope.

Error Alert! For Question 8, students might assume that since 15 members are connected to each of the other 14 there are 15 × 14 cables. ***Remediation*** Remind students that the cable connecting the first computer to the second computer is the same cable connecting the second computer to the first. Therefore, the product of 15 and 14 must be divided by 2.

"To solve a problem, it is necessary to think. It is necessary to think even to decide what facts to collect."

—ROBERT MAYNARD HUTCHINS

Organizer

1. **Focus**
   Connecting to Prior Knowledge
2. **Teach**
3. **Closure**
   Try These
   Wrap Up

Skills Reviewed in Context of Lesson
- reading tables
- combining decimals and whole numbers

Student Resources
Extra Practice
Student Study Guide
Practice, TR Ch. 5, p. 27
Student Study Guide, Spanish Resources, TR

Teacher Resources
Teaching Transparency 56
Lesson Planner, TR Ch. 5, p. 6

continues next page

PROBLEM SOLVING

5-5 Look for a Pattern

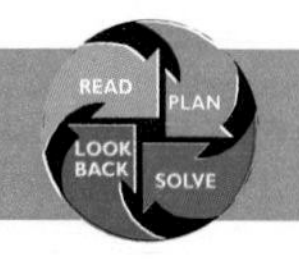

What's Ahead
- Solving problems by looking for patterns

Imagine that the Bits and Bytes Computer Club, which now has 15 members, is planning to install its own communications system. The system will connect each club member's home computer with each of the other 14. How many cables will the communications system require?

2. The problem asks you to find how many cables will be needed to connect every club member's computer with each of the other 14 members' computers.

READ Read and understand the given information. Summarize the problem.

Think about the information you are given and what you are asked to find.

1. How many members belong to the computer club? 15 members
2. What does the problem ask you to find? The number of cables required.

PLAN Decide on a strategy to solve the problem.

Draw diagrams for simpler cases. Record the number of cables needed for each case.

3. How many cables do you need to connect 2 computers? 1 cable
4. How many cables do you need to connect 3 computers? 3 cables
5. How many cables do you need to connect 4 computers? 6 cables

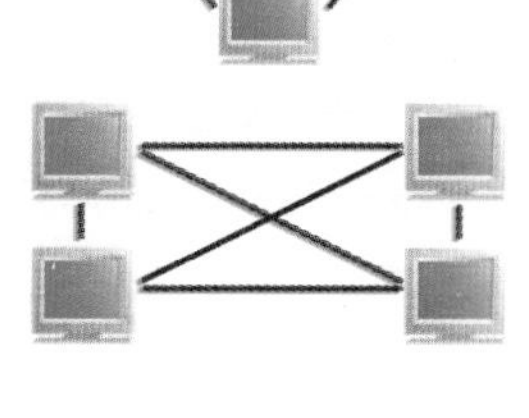

6. How many cables do you need to connect 5 computers? 10 cables

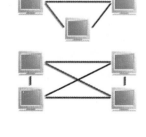

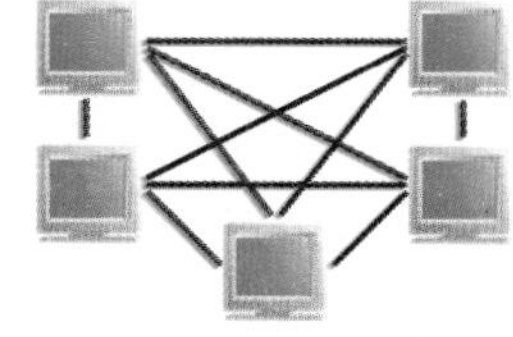

How Do Kids Use Computers?

games	84%
homework	40%
word processing	25%
graphics	12%

TRY THESE

KINESTHETIC LEARNERS For Exercise 12, acting out the handshake problem offers a meaningful way to understand what is going on.

Exercise 12: If students need help starting, tell them to imagine the people are the numbers 1–12. Ask: *If 1 shook hands with numbers 2–12, how many handshakes would that be?* **(eleven)** *If 2 shook hands with numbers 3–12 (1 and 2 have already met), how many handshakes is that?* **(ten)** Students should recognize the emerging pattern.

Additional Problem Ask students to discuss how Question 8 and Exercise 12 in the Try These are alike, and how they differ.

Wrap Up

What's the Big Idea? Ask students: *How are patterns useful in problem solving?*

Journal Ask students to name the problem solving strategies they use the most. Ask: *Do you see a pattern in your choices? Does your answer tell you something about yourself?*

Connections Discuss how patterns are used to solve problems. Here are some examples:

- **Science** (DNA patterns, behavioral responses, group hierarchies)
- **Social Studies** (patterns in the growth of cities, population growth)
- **Arts** (rhyme schemes in poetry, chord progressions in music)

Record the information in a table like the one shown below and look for a pattern in the data.

SOLVE
Try out the strategy.

Number of Home Computers	Number of Cables
2	1
3	3
4	6
5	10
6	■
7	■

+2, +3, +4, ■, ■

7. a. How many cables would you need to connect 6 computers? 7 computers? 15 cables, 21 cables
   b. Describe the pattern. Start with the number 1, Add 2, then 3, then 4, and so on.
8. Continue the pattern. Find the number of cables you need to connect all 15 members of the computer club. 105 cables

You may have wanted to draw a diagram to show the number of cables you need to connect all 15 members of the computer club.

LOOK BACK
Think about how you solved this problem.

9. Do you think this is a good strategy to use to answer the problem? Why or why not? Answers may vary. Sample: No; there are too many lines to draw.

TRY THESE

Use Look for a Pattern to solve each problem.

10. Germaine plans to save $1 the first week, $2 the second week, $4 the third week, $8 the fourth week, and $16 the fifth week. If Germaine can continue this pattern, how much money will he save the twelfth week? $2,048
11. What is the sum of the first 20 even numbers? 420
12. There are 12 people at a party. If each person shakes hands with each of the others exactly once, how many handshakes will there be altogether? 66 handshakes

President Theodore Roosevelt holds the record for the most hands shaken by a public figure at an official function. He shook 8,513 hands at a New Year's Day White House presentation in Washington, D.C., in 1907.

Source: *The Guinness Book of Records*

Organizer, continued

Prentice Hall Technology
Multimedia Math
- Math Tools, Calculation

Computer Item Generator
- 5-5

Other Available Technology
calculator

Fact of the Day

John von Neumann was one of the people who helped develop the first computers in the United States. He believed a computer should be able to do three things. One part of the computer should do arithmetic; another part should control how the computer operates; a third part should store information.

—COMPUTER LITERACY

Reteaching Activity Number students from 1 to 4. Arrange students with the same numbers into groups, and assign each group one of the following problems:

- *It's dark. You're looking for a pair of any color socks in a drawer of five red, ten white, and three blue socks. How many socks must you take from the drawer to make sure you have a matching pair?* **(four)**
- *You have seven coins that equal 53¢. Name the coins.* **(one quarter, two dimes, one nickel, and three pennies)**
- *You are introducing six friends to each other individually. How many introductions must you make?* **(15)**
- *You are buying five sandwiches. Two cost $2.50 each, two cost $3.15 each, and one costs $3.45. Four have cheese added, which is 20¢ more per sandwich. How much are you spending?* **($15.55)**

Have each group present its problem and solution to the class.

ON YOUR OWN

Exercises 13–21: Encourage students to use blocks, tiles, or any other props to model a problem. If students cannot show all of their work, have them try to explain what they did in writing.

Assignment Options

Core: 13, 15, 17, MR all	
Reinforce: 19, 20	**Enrich:** 14, 16, 18, 21

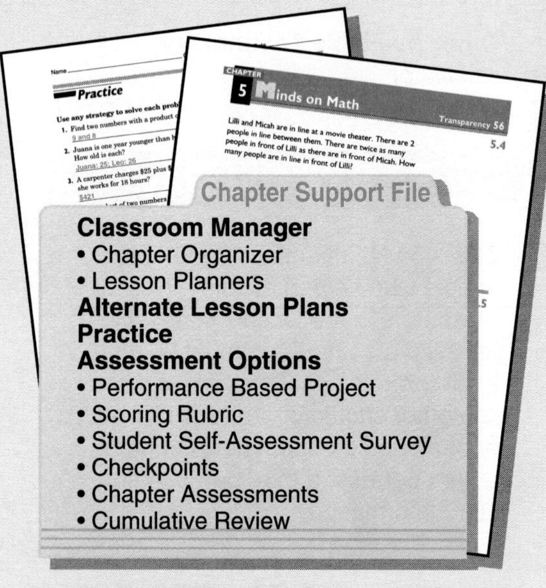

Minds on Math available in Teaching Transparencies

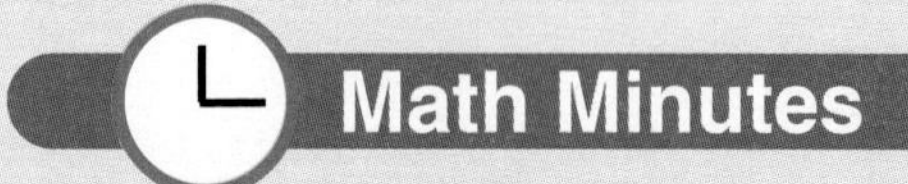

Ask students to use this data to answer the following questions:

June	13 years, 10 months
Kari	15 years, 5 months
Steve	15 years, 9 months

1. Who is oldest? **Steve**
2. How much older is Kari than June? **1 y 7 mo**

21.

	hat	coat
Anita	Althea	Beth
Cheryl	Anita	Althea
Beth	Cheryl	Anita
Althea	Beth	Cheryl

ON YOUR OWN

Use any strategy to solve each problem. Show all your work.

13. Jennifer wants to take her parents and her younger brother to the school play. Adults' tickets cost $6.00 and children's tickets cost $2.00. Jennifer earns $2.50 an hour babysitting. How many hours will she have to work in order to purchase the tickets? 7 h
14. The student council is selling carnations for a dance. They are selling white, pink, and red carnations. One of the order slips was accidentally torn. How many different combinations could have been ordered? 6 combinations
15. The bell at Lotsalearning Middle School rings at 8:20, 9:05, 9:50, and 10:35 each morning. If this pattern continues, will the bell ring at 11:20? 12:35? 2:20? yes; no; yes
16. There are 32 students in the orchestra and 44 students in the band. There are 8 students who are in both the orchestra and the band. How many students in all are enrolled in these two programs? 68 students
17. Find two numbers with a product of 63 and a sum of 16. 7 and 9
18. The lead contained in a brand new pencil could draw a line 35 mi long. About how many pencils would it take to draw a line around the circumference of Earth? (*Note:* The circumference of Earth is 24,902 mi.) 712 pencils
19. You open a book, and the product of the two facing page numbers is 600. To what pages have you opened? 24 and 25
20. Mrs. Snyder rented a car for two days. The rate was $26.50 per day and $.35 per mile. Mrs. Snyder traveled 225 mi. How much was she charged? $131.75
21. Anita, Cheryl, Beth, and Althea went to the library to work on a project. When they left the library, each of them accidentally picked up a coat belonging to someone else in the group and a hat of yet someone else. Cheryl took Anita's hat, and the girl who took Althea's hat took Beth's coat. What hat and coat did each of the girls take? See above.

Mixed REVIEW

Find each answer.

1. $48.8 + 3.47$ 52.27
2. $2.863 - 0.174$ 2.689

Name the variable in each expression.

3. $4(n - 6)$ *n*
4. $6f \div 3$ *f*

Evaluate.

5. $r^2 + 9$ for $r = 6$ 45
6. $8p - 2q$ for $p = 7$ and $q = 9$ 38
7. Karenna has a white blouse, a green blouse, a blue blouse, a plaid skirt, and a striped skirt. How many different outfits can she make? 6 outfits

CHAPTER 5

PRACTICE

This page provides practice on the skills learned up to this point in the chapter. Daily cumulative practice can be found in the Mixed Reviews that appear in every lesson.

Practice

1. Start with 2 and add 2 repeatedly.
2. Start with 1 and multiply by 2 repeatedly
3. Start with 0.2 and add 1 repeatedly.

Find the next three terms in each number pattern. Write a rule to describe each number pattern.

1. 2, 4, 6, 8, ■, ■, ■ 10, 12, 14
2. 1, 2, 4, 8, ■, ■, ■ 16, 32, 64
3. 0.2, 1.2, 2.2, ■, ■, ■ 3.2, 4.2, 5.2

Name the base and the exponent.

4. 3^2 3, 2
5. 7^4 7, 4
6. 6^3 6, 3
7. 2^8 2, 8

Express each area or volume using an exponent.

8. 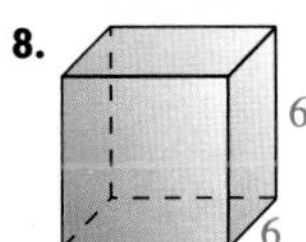

6^3

9. 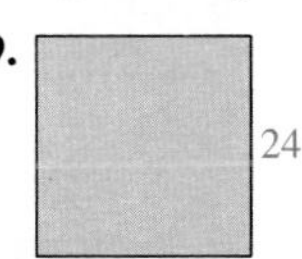

24^2

10. 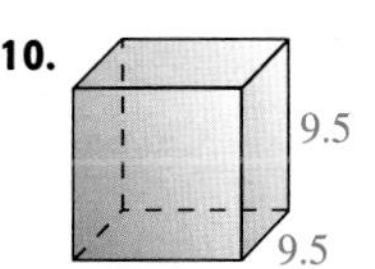

9.5^3

Choose Use a calculator, mental math, or paper and pencil to evaluate.

11. $(5^2 - 7) \div 3$ 6
12. $7 \times (4 + 7)$ 77
13. $9^8 \div 3^1$ 14,348,907
14. $6(34 + 3^4) \div 30$ 23
15. $(2 \times 4^2) \div 8$ 4
16. $135 + 64 \div 4^2$ 139
17. $7 \times 3^4 - 99$ 468
18. $50 \div (5^2 \div 5) + 4$ 14

Choose a variable and write a variable expression for each model. Answers may vary. Samples given.

19. 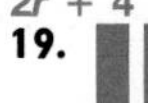  $2r + 4$
20.  $2 + 5t$
21. $2s + 3$

Mental Math Evaluate each expression for the given values of the variables.

22. $6x$ for $x = 8$ 48
23. $a + 0.75$ for $a = 4.25$ 5
24. $b^2 - 21$ for $b = 9$ 60
25. rs for $s = 7$ and $r = 3$ 21
26. $88 - 2c$ for $c = 40$ 8
27. $72 \div h$ for $h = 6$ 12
28. $5ab$ for $a = 1.5$ and $b = 6$ 45
29. $8b + 3c$ for $b = 3$ and $c = 2$ 30

Resources

Extra Practice
Student Study Guide
Student Study Guide, Spanish Resources, TR

5-6

Connecting to Prior Knowledge

Have students write an expression to match each of the following phrases:

- the product of x and y **(xy)**
- the sum of p and q **($p + q$)**
- b less than a **($a - b$)**

Ask students for the benefits of being able to use either variable expressions or their verbal equivalents. **(It helps clarify problems and ensures that you haven't changed the problem in the translation.)**

WORK TOGETHER

ESL **DIVERSITY** Students for whom English is a second language, as well as students who are hearing-impaired, may have trouble distinguishing among small changes in a word phrase that make an important difference in the variable expression, such as:

- 5 less than a number
- 5 less a number
- 5 is less than a number

Ask students for suggestions on how to avoid these problems.

THINK AND DISCUSS

Error Alert! Since students are using variables for Questions 3–5, urge them to indicate multiplication with a dot, •, instead of the × symbol. This will avoid confusing × with x, the variable.

TACTILE AND VISUAL LEARNERS For Question 5a, have partners use a rectangular object (a piece of paper, a desk top) and

“Reason means truth and those who are not governed by it take the chance that someday the sunken fact will rip the bottom out of their boat.”

—Oliver Wendell Holmes, Jr.

Organizer

1. **Focus**
   Connecting to Prior Knowledge
2. **Teach**
   Work Together
   Think and Discuss
3. **Closure**
   Try These
   Wrap Up

Skills Reviewed in Context of Lesson

- operations with whole numbers
- finding length, width, and perimeter

Student Resources

Extra Practice
Student Study Guide
Practice, TR Ch. 5, p. 28
Student Study Guide, Spanish Resources, TR
Alternate Lesson, TR Ch. 5, pp. 15–18

Teacher Resources

Teaching Transparency 56
Lesson Planner, TR Ch. 5, p. 7

continues next page

What's Ahead

- Writing variable expressions and word phrases

5-6 Writing Variable Expressions

WORK TOGETHER

1. Work with a partner to make a list of all the words or phrases you can think of that indicate each of the following operations: addition, subtraction, multiplication, and division. Answers may vary. Samples given.

   1. Answers may vary. Samples given. Addition: plus, sum, more than; Subtraction: minus, difference, less than; Multiplication: times, product; Division: quotient, divided by.

2. Use your lists to describe each numerical expression in words. Try to find as many different ways as you can.

   a. $5 + 8$ sum of 5 and 8; 5 plus 8
   b. $10 - 4$ 10 minus 4; 4 less than 10
   c. 10×3 10 times 3; product of 10 and 3
   d. $18 \div 6$ 18 divided by 6; quotient of 18 and 6

THINK AND DISCUSS

Word phrases are also used to describe variable expressions as shown in the table below.

Word Phrase	Variable Expression
the sum of m and 45	$m + 45$
22 more than a number	$n + 22$
w less than 55	$55 - w$
the product of w and 10	$10w$
the quotient of r and s	$r \div s$

3. Name two word phrases to describe each of the following variable expressions: $b + 15$, $m - n$, $10x$, and $18 \div p$.

   3. Answers may vary. Sample: b plus 15, the sum of b and 15; n less than m, m minus n; 10 times x, product of 10 and x; 18 divided by p, quotient of 18 and p

4. Write a variable expression for the word phrases *five plus a number y* and *6 times the quantity q*. $5 + y$; $6q$

5. The length of the largest lasagna was 56 ft more than its width. Let w represent the width of the lasagna.
   a. Write a variable expression for the length of the lasagna. $w + 56$
   b. **Discussion** Why is w a good variable to choose to represent the width of the lasagna? It is the first letter of the word "width."

The largest lasagna in the U.S. weighed 3,477 lb and measured 63 ft × 7 ft.

Source: *The Guinness Book of Records*

first identify the two dimensions before writing the variable expression.

Question 5b: Ask students: *What would be a good variable for length? (l)*

TRY THESE

Exercises 11–12, 14: Have students identify their variables, in addition to writing variable expressions. For example, a possible answer to Exercise 14 would be $c - 3$; $c =$ Caleb's height in inches. Do not accept $c =$ Caleb.

Ongoing Assessment Have students work in small groups. Using Exercises 6–9, have students brainstorm real-world word phrases for each variable expression. Circulate among groups to determine whether students are understanding the concept.

CONNECTION TO GEOMETRY Exercise 15 reviews geometry by having students write an expression for the perimeter of a triangle.

DIVERSITY Ask students to contribute words for counting numbers in languages other than English. Have them explain any patterns they see in the words for ten, eighteen, twenty, and one hundred as written in several different languages.

Wrap Up

What's the Big Idea? Ask students: *How do you change word phrases to variable expressions? variable expressions to word phrases?*

Journal Ask students: *Do you prefer working with variable expressions or word phrases? Explain why.*

TRY THESE

Write two word phrases for each variable expression.

6. $z + 24$ 7. $y - x$ 8. $7s$ 9. $g \div h$

Write a variable expression for each word phrase. Choose an appropriate variable to represent an unknown quantity.

10. eight less than s — $s - 8$
11. six more than a number — $n + 6$
12. 7 times the number of hats — $7h$
13. b divided by 3 — $b \div 3$
14. three inches shorter than Caleb — $c - 3$
15. Write a variable expression for the perimeter of the triangle. — $s + s + s$ or $3s$

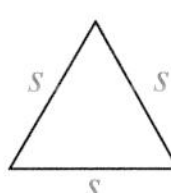

ON YOUR OWN

Write two word phrases for each variable expression.

16. $t + 6$ 17. $18 - h$ 18. ab 19. $21 \div m$

Write a variable expression for each word phrase. Choose an appropriate variable to represent an unknown quantity.

20. three more than h — $h + 3$
21. twenty-two less than k — $k - 22$
22. the sum of r and s — $r + s$
23. the product of three and m — $3m$
24. twenty students separated into some number of groups — $20 \div g$
25. three times the number of books — $3b$

Write a variable expression to describe each table.

26. $3x$

x	■
1	3
2	6
3	9
4	12

27. $a + 3$

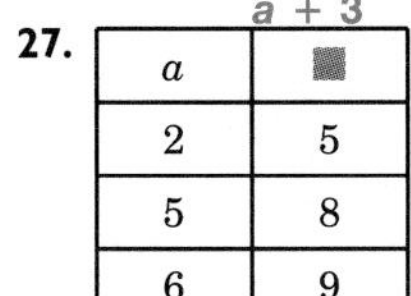

a	■
2	5
5	8
6	9
7	10

28. $m - 3$

m	■
5	2
10	7
15	12
20	17

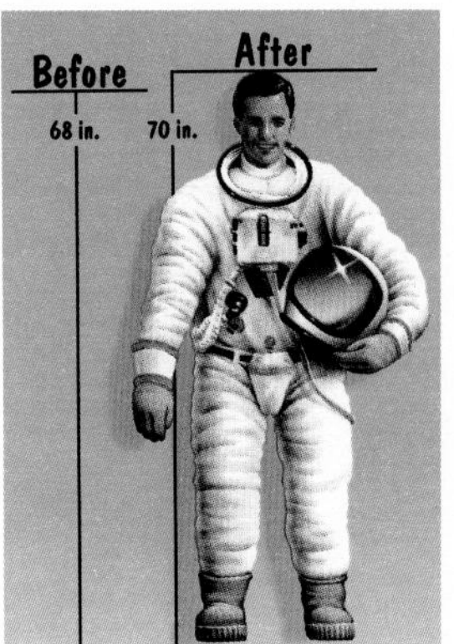

At the end of a space flight, an astronaut's height can temporarily be 2 in. greater than normal. This happens in the absence of gravity as the cartilage disks in the spine expand. Let the variable expression $h + 2$ describe this situation. **What must h represent?**

Source: *Reader's Digest Book of Facts*

h must represent the astronaut's normal height in inches.

Answers may vary. Sample given.

6. the sum of z and 24, 24 more than z
7. x less than y, difference of y and x
8. 7 times s, product of 7 and s
9. g divided by h, quotient of g and h
16. sum of t and 6, t plus 6
17. h less than 18, 18 minus h
18. a times b, product of a and b
19. quotient of 21 and m, 21 divided by m

Organizer, continued

Prentice Hall Technology
Computer Item Generator
- 5-6

Fact of the Day

Recycling all the newspapers in the United States could save 500,000 trees every week.

—*50 Simple Things Kids Can Do to Save the Earth*

Assignment Options

Core: 16–23, 29a, 31, 32, 35, MR all	
Reinforce: 24–28, 29b, 33a	**Enrich:** 29c, 30, 33b, 34

Answers to Problems Unique to Spanish Edition
12. $7s$
15. $3l$
25. $3l$

Connections Have a discussion about how word phrases are used for variable expressions. You may want to use these examples:

- **Household** (recipes often refer to a pan's area as the length "by" the width; furniture, rugs, and plywood are also labeled in this way)
- **Science** (equations or formulas may be written out instead of put in variable form: "energy is the product of mass and the speed of light squared")
- **Business** (registers often have an "at" or @ key instead of a multiplication key; products are often a quantity "for" a dollar value)

Reteaching Activity Use familiar formulas, like the area and perimeter of a rectangle, to help students see that they already know how to interchange word phrases and variable expressions.

ON YOUR OWN

CRITICAL THINKING For Exercise 33b, remind students that they must change seconds to minutes. Ask them if they can write a variable expression for the number of hours. **(Divide again by 60.)**

WRITING For Exercise 34, ask students to consider whether the word order in a word phrase is as important as the order of the numbers and variables in a variable expression. Ask them to give examples.

CHAPTER INVESTIGATION Assign groups to collect data from different areas of the school for Exercise 35. Have at least two groups work together to cover the cafeteria.

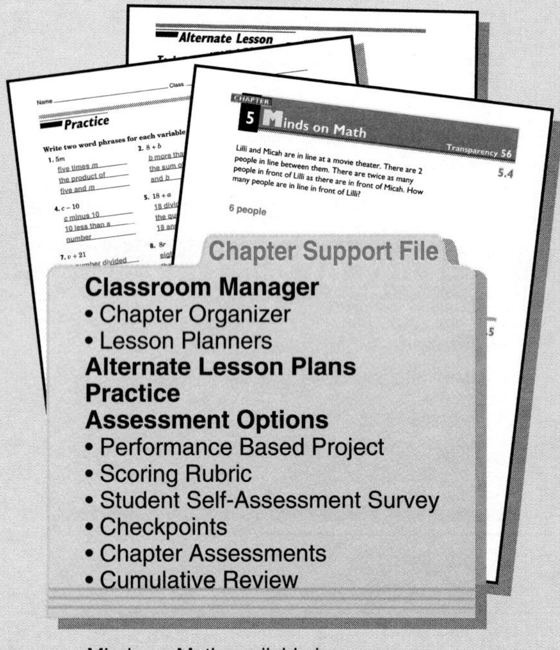

Minds on Math available in Teaching Transparencies

Math Minutes

Ask students to write the following numbers as the sum of two prime numbers.

50 **19 + 31**
36 **7 + 29**
44 **13 + 31**

Materials for 5-7

- graph paper
- ruler
- computer with spreadsheet software
- Spreadsheet Database Form

41	43	45	47	49
31	33	35	37	39
21	23	25	27	29
11	13	15	17	19
1	3	5	7	9

29. Use the sample below and the pattern at the left to find each value.

Sample Find the value of 15 ↑.

Locate the number 15 in the pattern. Then, move one unit in the direction of the arrow. The value is 25.

a. Find the values 27 ↑ and 33 ↑. 37; 43
b. If the pattern continues, what is the value of 47 ↑? 57
c. Let n represent any number in the shaded region. Write a variable expression for the values of n↑, n↓, n←, and n→. $n + 10$, $n - 10$, $n - 2$, $n + 2$

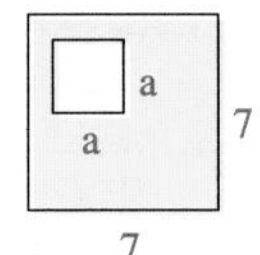

30. Choose A, B, C, or D. Which variable expression describes the area of the shaded region in the diagram at the left? D

A. $a^2 + 14$ **B.** $49 - 2a$
C. $a^2 - 49$ **D.** $49 - a^2$

31. Aaron is x years old. Write an expression for Aaron's age:

a. 3 years ago $x - 3$ b. 10 years from now $x + 10$
c. z years ago $x - z$ d. t years from now $x + t$

32. Paloma has \$3.25 in her purse. She has m dollars in her pocket. Write a variable expression for the amount of money Paloma has altogether. $m + 3.25$

33. Data File 2 (pp. 38–39) Suppose you spend the day riding the Waimea while visiting Raging Waters Park.

a. Let t represent the number of times you go on the water ride. Write a variable expression for the number of seconds you spend riding the Waimea. $15t$
b. **Critical Thinking** Write a variable expression for the number of minutes you spend riding the Waimea. $15t \div 60$

34. Writing Do the word phrases *twenty-two less than x* and *x less than twenty-two* result in the same variable expression? Explain. No; *twenty-two less than x* means $x - 22$ and *x less than 22* means $22 - x$.

35. Investigation (p. 184) Collect data on the amount of glass and paper produced in your school each day. Estimate how much glass and paper is being recycled and how much is simply being thrown away. Answers may vary.

Mixed REVIEW

Find each answer.

1. 36.18 × 4 144.72
2. 517.6 × 0.01 5.176

Compare using >, <, or =.

3. 0.630 ■ 0.63 =
4. 3.6 ■ 3.06 >
5. Suppose you cut a piece of string in half and then cut those pieces in half. If you continue this process, how many pieces of string will you have after the 5th round of cuts? 32 pieces

CHAPTER 5

PROBLEM SOLVING PRACTICE

This page provides a variety of problems that can be used to reinforce and enhance the students' problem solving skills. Encourage students to read each problem carefully. Then have them refer to the list of problem solving strategies to help them decide how to solve the problems.

Point out, however, that not all questions require a strategy for solving, nor are all the strategies in the list used on this page.

Error Alert! For Exercise 2, students may just double the time traveled. Remind students that the first floor is the starting point. Likewise, for Exercise 7, emphasize that students pay attention to the number of cuts, not to the number of pieces that result from the cuts.

DIVERSITY Students' unique problem solving strategies may reflect the diversity of their learning styles. Because students may use a variety of strategies to approach a problem, a discussion about how students choose their strategies might be helpful to you and the class. Have volunteers explain and demonstrate to the class how they approached and solved a problem.

VISUAL LEARNERS In Exercise 2, have students sketch a diagram showing floors and distance traveled. In Exercise 7, a sketch may help students relate the number of cuts to the number of pieces.

Problem Solving Practice

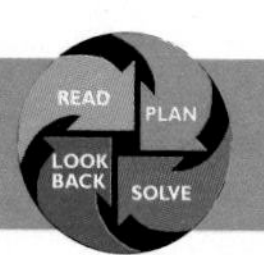

PROBLEM SOLVING STRATEGIES

Make a Table
Use Logical Reasoning
Solve a Simpler Problem
Too Much or Too Little Information
Look for a Pattern
Make a Model
Work Backward
Draw a Diagram
Guess and Test
Simulate a Problem
Use Multiple Strategies

Solve. Use an appropriate strategy or a combination of strategies.

1. Aiesha earns \$15/day babysitting, and Yvonne earns \$8/day looking after neighbors' pets. After how many days has Aiesha earned \$42 more than Yvonne? 6 days

2. An apartment building has 8 stories. It takes 6 s for the elevator to go from the first floor to the third floor. How long does it take for the elevator to go from the first floor to the sixth floor? 15 s

3. Four friends are running in a race. Harry is 0.25 km ahead of Joe. Joe is twice as far as Frank. Steve is 0.25 km behind Joe. If Harry has run 2.75 km, how far have each of the others run? Joe: 2.5 km; Frank: 1.25 km; Steve: 2.25 km

4. Sasha sold wrapping paper and greeting cards to help raise money for her school. Each roll of paper costs \$3.25 and each box of cards costs \$3.75. Sasha collected a total of \$44.75. How many of each item did Sasha sell? 8 rolls, 5 boxes

5. The art teacher uses four push pins, one in each corner, to hang a drawing on a bulletin board. If she overlaps the corners, she can hang two drawings with only six push pins. What is the minimum number of push pins the art teacher needs to hang eight drawings? 15 push pins

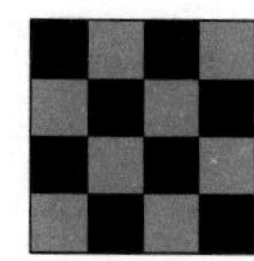

6. How many squares are there on a 4×4 checkerboard like the one shown at the left? 30 squares

7. A carpenter cuts a wooden plank into four pieces in 12 s. At the same rate, how many seconds would it take the carpenter to cut the plank into five pieces? 16 s

8. Hanukkah is a Jewish holiday that lasts eight days. Two candles are lit on the first night of Hanukkah. Every night after that the candles are replaced and one more is added. How many candles have been used by the time Hanukkah ends? 44 candles

5-7

Connecting to Prior Knowledge

Ask students to consider what happens to the perimeter of a square as the length of the side changes from 1 to 2 to 3 to 4 feet. Have them make a table that relates side and perimeter. Repeat for a circle, with a table that relates diameter and circumference. Use sketches to illustrate.

THINK AND DISCUSS

Remind students of their previous exposure to spreadsheets (Chapter 1). The terms *spreadsheet* and *cell* were introduced there.

DIVERSITY Some students may be aware that the name "football" applies not only to the American game, but to soccer and rugby as well. Have a discussion about how these games are similar to each other.

KINESTHETIC LEARNERS Use the facilities of a real football field or the nearest recreation area. Provide the students with a real football and have them kick the ball over a line that simulates a field goal. Let the students record the successful attempts in a table and then compute the points.

Error Alert! For Question 1, some students may focus on the pattern in each column. ***Remediation*** Ask them to relate the two patterns (as the first column increases by one, the second column increases by 3).

AUDITORY LEARNERS Use the discussion in Question 2 to have students verbalize the connection between the numbers in the cells of the spreadsheet and the location of the points on the graph.

Question 2: Use this exercise to review plotting points on a graph. For many of your students, this may be the first time they have plotted points on the coordinate plane. (This topic is covered in more detail in Chapter 11). Be prepared to spend some

"The office of the scholar is to cheer, to raise, and to guide men by showing them facts amidst appearances."

—RALPH WALDO EMERSON

Organizer

1. **Focus**
   Connecting to Prior Knowledge
2. **Teach**
   Think and Discuss
   Work Together
3. **Closure**
   Wrap Up

Vocabulary/Symbols
function

Skills Reviewed in Context of Lesson
- reading tables
- finding coordinate points

Materials and Manipulatives
- graph paper (for each student)
- ruler (one for each student)
- computer with spreadsheet software *(optional)*
- Spreadsheet Database Form (one for each student who does not have a computer)

On Your Own Exercise 7e: graph paper, ruler

continues next page

TECHNOLOGY

5-7 Graphing Functional Data

What's Ahead
- Making graphs from tables
- Using computers to explore graphs

WHAT YOU'LL NEED
- ✓ Graph paper
- ✓ Computer
- ✓ Software

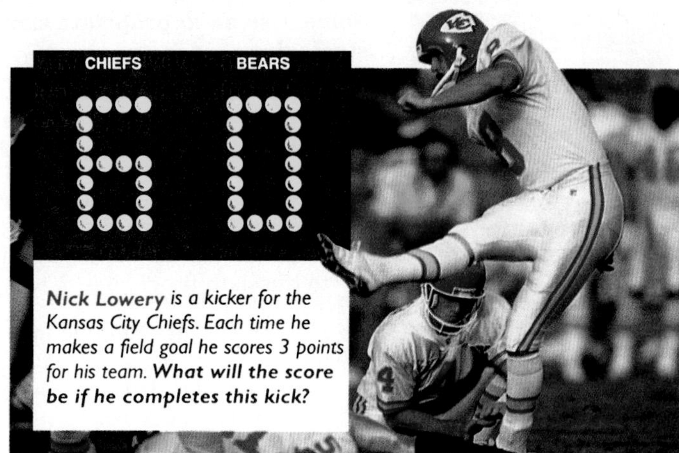

Nick Lowery is a kicker for the Kansas City Chiefs. Each time he makes a field goal he scores 3 points for his team. ***What will the score be if he completes this kick?***

THINK AND DISCUSS

In 1990 a kicker named Nick Lowery scored over 100 points in field goals. The computer spreadsheet below shows how many points you would receive for different numbers of field goals.

	A	B
1	Number of Field Goals	Points
2	1	3
3	2	6
4	3	9
5	4	12
6	5	

1. a. What number belongs in the blank cell, or box? 15
   b. How are the numbers in column B related to the numbers in column A?
   c. If f stands for the number of field goals, what variable expression represents the number of points? $3f$

1.b. B = 3A The number in column B is three times the number in column A.

extra time on this activity. You may wish to review the terms *horizontal* and *vertical axis, collinear* and *noncollinear points.*

Question 4: If you have students who are more interested in basketball, you may wish to allow them to create a spreadsheet (or make a table) to show the points scored for different numbers of foul shots, two-point throws, and three-point throws. They could then produce the corresponding graphs.

COMPUTER For Question 4a, have students construct a spreadsheet similar to the table in Question 1 and the graph in Question 2. Set column headings for Columns A and B. Beginning in cell B2, have the students enter the formulas for computing the points for touchdowns. If possible, make both scales the same for easier comparison. ***Alternate Approach*** If you are not using a computer, have students create the tables and graphs by hand.

Ongoing Assessment Have students work in pairs. Let them choose a sport and construct a two-column table on a piece of paper, displaying column headings for the name of the sport, the scoring unit, and the score (for example: Basketball, baskets, 3, 2, 1). Have the students write the formula for computing the score in the top right corner. Have classmates discuss the formulas and compute the scores for the tables.

Journal Ask students: *How is using a computer to create a spreadsheet different from constructing tables and graphs by hand? Which method do you prefer and why?*

You can create a graph to show how the two sets of numbers in the spreadsheet are related. This relationship is called a *function.* Point P represents the pair of numbers (1, 3) in the second row of the spreadsheet.

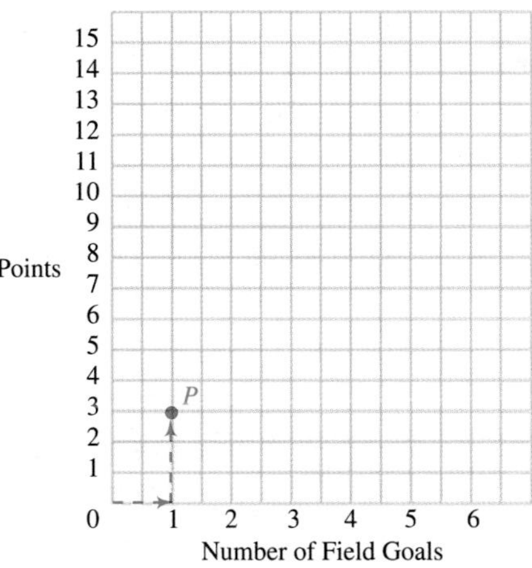

2a. Ans. may vary. Sample: move right 1 unit and up 3 units
3b. Yes; 3 × 6 = 18.
3c. Yes; in the pair of numbers representing any point on the line, the second number will always be three times the first number.

2. a. **Discussion** How is the location of point P determined?
   b. Copy the graph shown above. Plot a point for the pair of numbers (2, 6) in the third row of the spreadsheet.
   c. Plot points for the rest of the data in the spreadsheet. Are these points collinear or noncollinear? collinear
   d. Draw a line through the points on your graph.

2.b. and d. See Solution Key.

3. a. Mark the point on your line that represents 6 field goals. Draw a horizontal line through this point that intersects the vertical axis. What number do you hit? 18
   b. Does your result fit the pattern in the table? Explain.
   c. **Discussion** Do you think *every* point on the line fits the *pattern* in the table? Why or why not?
   d. **Discussion** Does *every* point on the line represent data that could appear in the table? Why or why not? No; the number of field goals and points can only be whole numbers.
4. **Computer** Create a spreadsheet and a graph to show how many points you get for each type of score in football.
   a. touchdown (6 points) b. safety (2 points)
   c. **Discussion** How are the graphs alike? different? See Solution Key.

At age 12, Kishae Swafford scored 20 touchdowns for the Marshall Minutemen, her Pop Warner football team. She was one of the league's fastest runners.

Source: *Sports Illustrated for Kids*

Organizer, continued

Student Resources
Extra Practice
Student Study Guide
Practice, TR Ch. 5, p. 29
Student Study Guide, Spanish Resources, TR
Alternate Lesson, TR Ch. 5, pp. 19–22

Teacher Resources
Teaching Transparencies 1, 57
Transparency Masters, TR p. 5
Lesson Planner, TR Ch. 5, p. 8

Prentice Hall Technology
Multimedia Math
- Math Tools, Spreadsheet

Computer Item Generator
- 5-7

Other Available Technology
graphing calculator
Excel; Works by Microsoft
Clarisworks by Apple
Microsoft Graph
Cricket Graph
(all optional)

Fact of the Day

Before 1874, American football was a modified form of soccer. Outside of the United States, soccer is usually called football. A soccer field measures 120 yd by 75 yd, or 110 m by 70 m.

—Guinness Book of World Records

WORK TOGETHER

COMPUTER For Exercise 5b, students may either use an extra column for the constant 10 (yardage from goal post to goal line) or may enter 10 into a formula on the spreadsheet and only use two columns. Some students may need to see the importance of the constant. Guide the students through labeling the column headings and the information that will be contained in each column. **(yardage to goal line and yardage from the football to the goal post)** ***Alternate Approach*** Students may create a table on paper, using a calculator or pencil, and then graph the points.

Wrap Up

What's the Big Idea? Have students discuss the steps in creating tables and graphs to solve a problem. Then ask them to indicate which of these steps can be done with the help of a computer.

Connections Have a discussion about how to graph functional data from tables. You may wish to start with the following examples:

- **Social Services** (number of Medicare recipients and cost per recipient)
- **Traveling** (miles traveled and gallons of gasoline used)
- **Florist** (number of roses bought and cost per rose)

Reteaching Activity Have students work in pairs to create two tables and two corresponding graphs. Then have pairs exchange graphs and tables with another pair. Have students determine which table corresponds to which graph.

On Your Own

Exercise 7: Students may complete one of the tables on paper. (Include the expression that represents the final tee price and the formula for computing the tee price on the spreadsheet before it is converted to the computer.)

Assignment Options

Core: 7, MR all	
Reinforce: None	**Enrich:** 8

WORK TOGETHER

Work with a partner to answer the following questions.

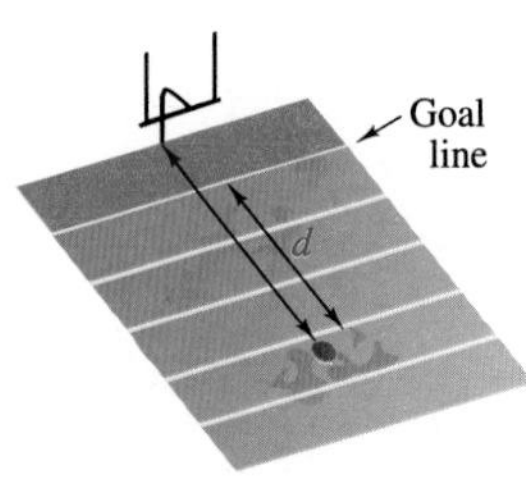

5. a. In professional football, each goalpost is 10 yd behind the goal line. If d stands for the distance in yards from the football to the goal line, what expression represents the distance from the football to the goalpost? $d + 10$

   b. **Computer** Create a spreadsheet and then a graph to show how the distance in yards from the football to the goalpost depends on d. See Solution Key.

   c. **Critical Thinking** Explain why it makes sense that the graph does not go through the point where the horizontal and vertical axes intersect. See Solution Key.

6. a. Copy and complete the table at the right.

   b. Graph the data. Connect the points with a smooth curve. How is this graph different from the other graphs you have made in this lesson? The points in this graph are noncollinear.

0	0
1	1
2	4
3	9
4	16
5	■ 25

7b. $3n + 5$; $4n - 2$
7c. Yes; the price increases at a constant rate.
7d. No; you would not order zero tees.

ON YOUR OWN

Goalposters, Inc.	
No. of Tees	**Final Price**
1	8
2	■ 11
3	■ 14
4	■ 17

The Good Sports Shop	
No. of Tees	**Final Price**
1	2
2	■ 6
3	■ 10
4	■ 14

7. Goalposters, Inc. sells kicking tees by mail for \$3 each, but adds on a shipping charge. The shipping charge is \$5 regardless of how many kicking tees you order.

   The Good Sports Shop sells tees in its store for \$4 each. Of course, there is no shipping charge. Better still, if you use a coupon, you get \$2 off of your bill.

   a. Copy and complete each table at the left. Remember to include the shipping charge and to use your coupon.

   b. Let n stand for the number of tees you order. Write expressions to represent the final price of tees from Goalposters, Inc. and The Good Sports Shop.

   c. Will the graphs be straight lines? Why or why not?

   d. Will the graphs go through the point where the horizontal and vertical axes intersect? Why or why not?

   e. Graph the data to check your predictions. See Solution Key.

Exercise 8: Have students determine which company is represented by each graph. **(A = Football Fans; B = Speedy Lettering; C = Professional Lettering; D = Sports Page.)**

You may also wish to extend this exercise with the following questions:

- *Which company would have the most expensive prices?* **(Speedy Lettering)**
- *How many extra letters would it take to change the most economical company to another?* **(7 more)**
- *How many letters does it take to reach the point where Speedy Lettering and Football Fans charge the same price?* **(10 letters)**
- *When would Sports Page and Professional Lettering charge the same for lettering?* **(for 2 letters)**

8. Choose A, B, C, or D. Your coach has received brochures from four companies who will sew your team name SAILORS on your uniforms. Professional Lettering charges $2 per letter. Football Fans charges $1 per letter plus a fee of $5. The Sports Page charges $1 per letter plus a fee of $2. Speedy Lettering charges a flat fee of $15. What graph represents the fees of the company that would be most economical for your coach to hire? (*Hint:* Only the cost for 1 to 6 letters is shown on each graph.) D

A.

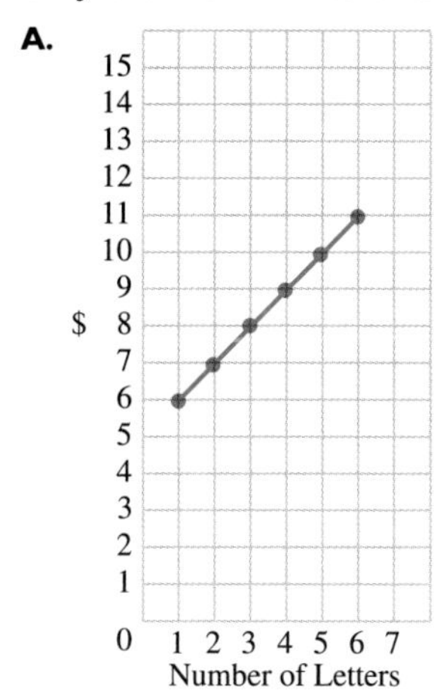

B.

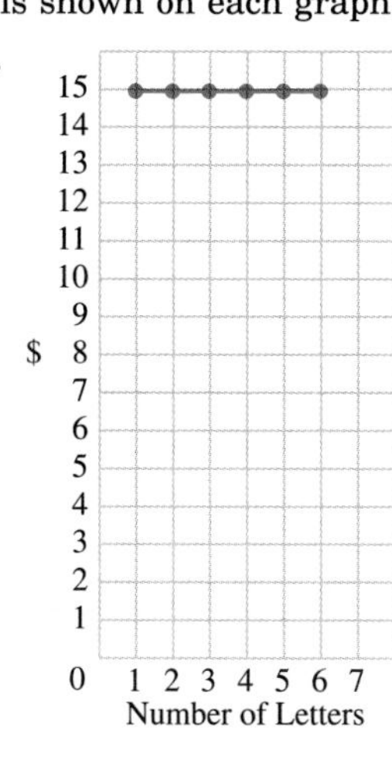

C.

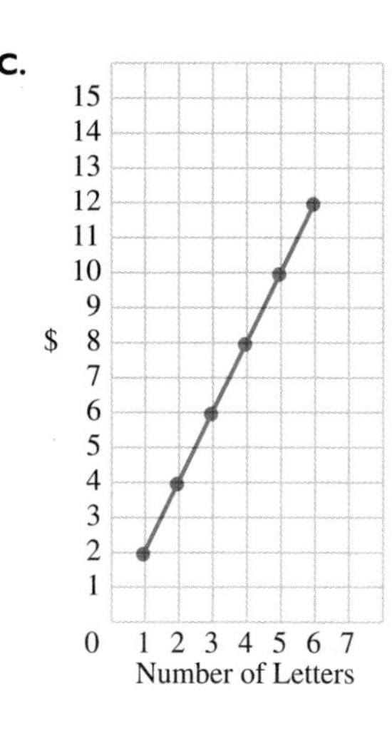

D.

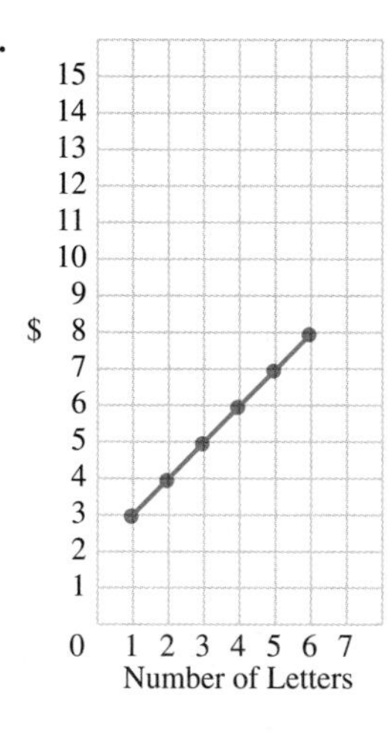

Mixed REVIEW

True or false?

1. All parallelograms are rhombuses. false
2. A trapezoid is a parallelogram. false

Write a word phrase for each variable expression.

3. $x \div 5$ See below.
4. $s + 14$

Write an expression for each word phrase.

5. 3 less than t $t - 3$
6. 8 more than a number n $n + 8$
7. Your town has 8 soccer teams. They are playing in a tournament. Each team will be out of the tournament after 1 loss. How many games will be played? 7 games

3. x divided by 5.
4. 14 more than s

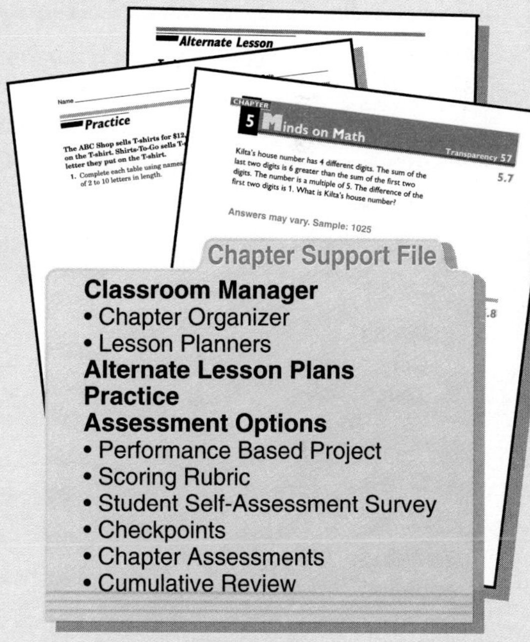

Alternate Lesson
Practice
5 Minds on Math
Transparency 57
5.7
Answers may vary. Sample: 1025
Chapter Support File
Classroom Manager
• Chapter Organizer
• Lesson Planners
Alternate Lesson Plans
Practice
Assessment Options
• Performance Based Project
• Scoring Rubric
• Student Self-Assessment Survey
• Checkpoints
• Chapter Assessments
• Cumulative Review

Minds on Math available in Teaching Transparencies

Math Minutes

Ask students to write the numbers that make these number sentences true.

$(6 \times 7) - \blacksquare = 35$ **7**
$23 - \blacksquare = 23$ **0**
$9 + \blacksquare = 21$ **12**
$8 \times \blacksquare = 56$ **7**

Materials for 5-8

- algebra tiles
- calculator

5-8

Connecting to Prior Knowledge

Give students a sentence containing "is," such as "Rex is a dog," and ask them to substitute numbers or variables for the nouns. (Students will probably suggest something like "*r* is *d*.") Replace the verb with an equal sign. Tell students that they have formed an equation. Point out that an equation is a statement such as "Rex is a dog," but with numbers and symbols instead of words.

ESL Help students distinguish between the terms "expression" and "equation" by asking them to circle the equal sign in the equations.

WORK TOGETHER

Question 2: Have students count how many operations are contained in each of the five numerical expressions they write for Question 2.

THINK AND DISCUSS

KINESTHETIC LEARNERS Let students use a balance scale to model equations like 3 + 5 = 4 + 4 using identical tiles in the pans. Seeing that the pans balance should help them understand the meaning of the equal sign. For Question 7a, you could ask students: *If you have 7 tiles in the right pan and 4 tiles in the left pan, how many do you need to add to the left pan in order to make the pans balance?* **(3)** Students might also use this method for Question 11.

ESL In Question 10b, students may not understand the meaning of "isolate." Suggest that they replace "isolate" with "get the variable alone on one side of the equation."

TACTILE LEARNERS The use of tiles in Questions 9–11 is especially appropriate for tactile learners.

"Nothing is interesting if you're not interested."

—Helen Mac Innes

Organizer

1. **Focus**
   Connecting to Prior Knowledge
2. **Teach**
   Work Together
   Think and Discuss
3. **Closure**
   Wrap Up

Vocabulary/Symbols
equation
equal sign, =
solve
solution
inverse operations
equilateral

Skills Reviewed in Context of Lesson
- writing expressions
- working with variables
- operations with whole numbers and decimals

Materials and Manipulatives
- algebra tiles (one set for each group)
- calculator (one for each student)

On Your Own Exercises 28–38: algebra tiles, calculator *(optional)*

continues next page

5-8 Addition and Subtraction Equations

What's Ahead
- Solving addition and subtraction equations

WHAT YOU'LL NEED

✓ Algebra tiles 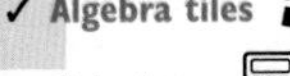

✓ Calculator 

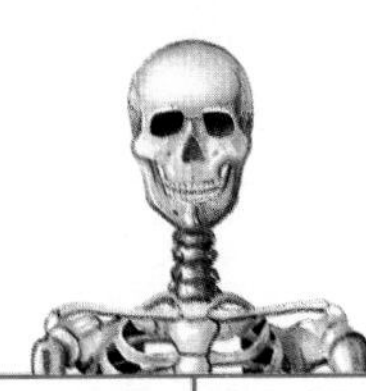

Body Part	No. of Bones
Arm	32
Leg	31
Skull	29
Spine	26
Chest	25

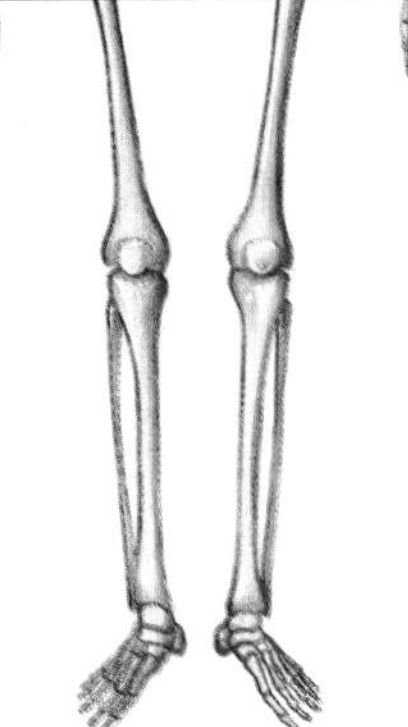

WORK TOGETHER

Work with a partner to answer each question. Use the table at the left.

1. a. Write a numerical expression to represent the total number of bones in your arm and chest. 32 + 25
   b. Write a numerical expression to represent the total number of bones in your leg and spine. 31 + 26
   c. What do you notice about the value of each of these expressions? They are equal.
2. Write five numerical expressions that have the same value as the sum of your age and your partner's age. Answers may vary.

THINK AND DISCUSS

You can say that two numerical expressions are equal when they have the same value.

3. **Discussion** Explain why the numerical expression 4 + 6 is equal to 12 − 2, but the numerical expression 3 + 6 is *not* equal to 4 + 8. 4 + 6 and 12 − 2 equal 10. 3 + 6 and 4 + 8 do not equal the same value, 3 + 6 = 9 and 4 + 8 = 12.

You can write an equation to show that two expressions are equal. An **equation** is a mathematical sentence that contains an equal sign. The symbol = is read "is equal to."

4. Read each equation out loud.
   a. 5 + 9 = 14 b. 9 + 6 = 15 c. 21 = 25 − 4
5. **Discussion** Explain why the equation 4 + 6 = 10 is true and the equation 3 + 7 = 12 is false.
6. State whether each equation is true or false.
   a. 16 = 9 + 7 true b. 3 + 11 = 15 false c. 8 + 12 = 20 true

5. The expressions 4 + 6 and 10 have the same value, but 3 + 7 and 12 have different values.

Question 10: This method of solving by isolating the variable helps avoid confusion. However, you may want to mention to students that some of their parents may have learned another way ("transposing") and might not be familiar with this method. This method is similar to that used when solving with a calculator.

Error Alert! Students may confuse operations on the two sides of an equation. For example, a student may attempt to solve the equation in Question 12b by finding 10 − 4. ***Remediation*** Remind students that they can isolate the variable, and keep the equation true, by adding the same number to both sides.

MENTAL MATH For Question 13, have students check their answers by mentally substituting their answers for the variables.

Exercise 18: Follow up Exercise 18 by asking students if they can think of other operations that undo or reverse each other.

Journal Ask students to write about what kind of learning approach they find helpful in understanding equations, such as using a balance scale or hearing the equation. Students should not limit their responses to these suggestions.

Ongoing Assessment Have each student write an addition or subtraction equation with the variable x, such as $x - 7.5 = 2.5$. Students should exchange equations with a nearby student and solve the equation given them. Then have students exchange their pages once more to check the solution given them. Work, as a class, any equations where the solutions do not match.

Wrap Up

What's the Big Idea? Ask students to explain what the equal sign means when it connects two numerical or variable

Equations can also contain variables. You **solve** an equation that contains a variable when you replace the variable with a number that makes the equation true. A number that makes the equation true is a **solution.**

7. a. Is the number 3 a solution to the equation $x + 4 = 7$? Why or not not? Yes; If you replace x with 3, the sum is 7.
   b. Is the number 5 a solution to the equation $x + 4 = 12$? Why or why not? No; If you replace x with 5, the sum is 9, not 12.
8. State whether each number is a solution to the equation.
   a. $y - 6 = 24; y = 18$ no
   b. $20 = p + 4; p = 16$ yes
   c. $150 = k - 50; k = 200$ yes
   d. $j + 30 = 70; j = 100$ no

You can use tiles to model and solve addition equations.

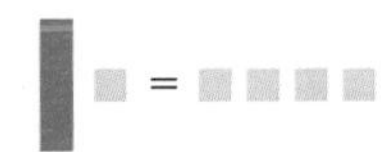

9. What equation is modeled above? $x + 1 = 4$

You can find the solution to an addition equation by isolating the variable, or getting the variable alone on one side of the equal sign.

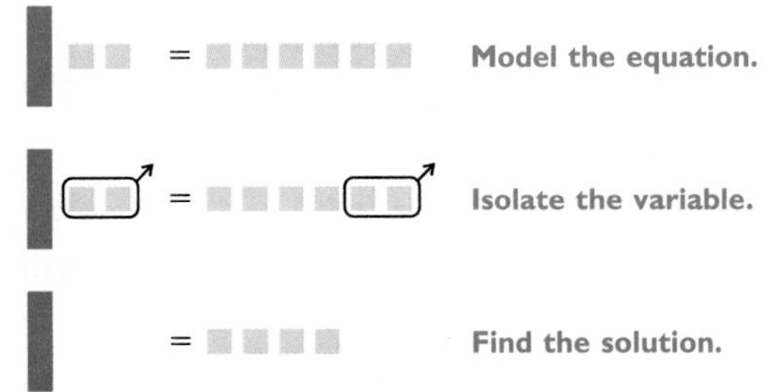
Model the equation.
Isolate the variable.
Find the solution.

10. a. What equation is modeled in the first step? $x + 2 = 6$
    b. **Discussion** What was done to isolate the variable? What operation does this action represent?
    c. What is the solution to the equation? 4
11. Use tiles to solve each addition equation.
    a. $m + 4 = 7$ 3
    b. $6 + k = 11$ 5
    c. $9 = h + 3$ 6

WHY?

Mathematicians chose the symbol = to represent equality because it was thought that nothing could be more equal than two line segments.

Source: *Historical Topics for the Mathematics Classroom*

10.b. Two tiles were removed from each side of the equation; Subtraction

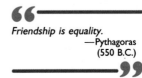

"*Friendship is equality.*
—Pythagoras (550 B.C.)"

Organizer, continued

Student Resources
Extra Practice
Student Study Guide
Practice, TR Ch. 5, p. 30
Student Study Guide, Spanish Resources, TR
Checkpoint, TR Ch. 5, p. 36

Teacher Resources
Teaching Transparencies 19, 57
Transparency Masters, TR p. 27
Lesson Planner, TR Ch. 5, p. 9

Prentice Hall Technology
Multimedia Math
- Math Tools, Manipulatives

Computer Item Generator
- 5-8

Other Available Technology
calculator
Algebra Expressor by William K. Bradford: Exercises 28–38 *(optional)*
Math Connections by Wings: Exercises 28–38 *(optional)*

Fact of the Day

Humans have 8 wrist bones in each forearm and 5 palm bones in each hand. Each finger has 3 bones, and the thumb has 2 bones.

—SKELETON

expressions. Have them summarize some ways to solve an equation containing a variable.

Reteaching Activity Have students use algebra tiles to represent an addition equation that contains a variable and whole numbers. Tell students to represent $x + 4$ by using algebra tiles on one side, and to represent 9 on the other side. Have students replace the variable tile by three number tiles. Are the results equal? Since they are not equal, 3 is not the solution of the equation. Students can continue using trial and error to find that the solution is $x = 5$. Have students analyze their results.

Connections Have a discussion about how addition and subtraction equations are used. Students can create real-world problems they might need to solve. For example:

- **Personal finances** (I had some money in my pocket this morning. At lunch time, Frank gave me the $3 he owed me and now I have $10. How much money did I have this morning?)
- **Sports** (On their second down of the game, the football team suffered a loss of 4 yards and the announcer said that, at that moment, the team's total yardage was 2 yards. How many yards did the team gain on their first down?)

ON YOUR OWN

TECHNOLOGY OPTION Have students practice solving addition and subtraction equations such as those in Exercises 28–38 using a software package that solves equations.

ESL **ESL** For Exercise 39, help ESL students connect the word *equation* with other related terms, such as *equal, equilateral triangle, equiangular, equivalent,* and non-mathematical terms like *equity.* Provide physical examples or demonstrations if possible.

Assignment Options

Core: 19–28, 30–32, MR all, CH all	
Reinforce: 29, 33–36, 38, 39	**Enrich:** 37, 40–44

You can use mental math to solve addition and subtraction equations.

12. a. In the addition equation $r + 8 = 15$, what does the value of r have to be to make the two sides of the equation equal? 7

b. In the subtraction equation $m - 4 = 10$, what does the value of m have to be to make the two sides of the equation equal? 14

13. Mental Math Solve each equation.

a. $8 = 3 + h$ 5 **b.** $a + 5 = 8$ 3
c. $m - 2.5 = 10$ 12.5 **d.** $15 = g - 5$ 20
e. $5 = n - 10$ 15 **f.** $8 = k + 7.25$ 0.75

If an equation cannot be solved using tiles or is too difficult to use mental math, you can use a calculator.

14. a. Discussion How could you use a calculator to solve the addition equation $x + 3{,}687 = 5{,}543$? Enter 5543 [−] 3687 [=]

b. When you solve an addition equation, what operation key do you use? [−]

15. Calculator Solve each addition equation.

a. $f + 1{,}478 = 3{,}652$ 2,174 **b.** $12{,}597 = h + 6{,}954$ 5,643
c. $183.35 = 119.75 + b$ 63.6 **d.** $50{,}876 + s = 877{,}942$ 827,066

16. a. Discussion How could you use a calculator to solve the subtraction equation $x - 4{,}621 = 1{,}347$? 1347 [+] 4621 [=]

b. When you solve a subtraction equation, what operation key do you use? [+]

17. Calculator Solve each subtraction equation.

a. $y - 432 = 127$ 559 **b.** $10{,}006 = k - 67{,}948$ 77,954
c. $z - 11{,}897 = 34{,}954$ 46,851 **d.** $189.622 = p - 24.752$ 214.374

18. Discussion Explain what is meant by the statement *addition and subtraction undo each other.*
Answers may vary. Example: One operation undoes the other.

Operations that undo each other, such as addition and subtraction, are called **inverse operations.**

Julia B. Robinson (1920–1985), a mathematics researcher at the University of California–Berkeley, showed that there was no automatic method of determining whether an equation had a whole number solution.

Source: *The Book of Women's Firsts*

WRITING For Exercise 39, ask students to guess what the Latin root *aequare* means. **(to make level or equal)**

CRITICAL THINKING For Exercise 40, have students write two original examples to support their findings.

CRITICAL THINKING For Exercise 44b, encourage students to think about how conditions may have differed from day to day. For example, Dwight probably didn't get very far during the storm.

To extend Exercise 44, have students write and solve other questions based on the article that involve addition or subtraction equations. For example:

- *In what year was Dwight born?* **(1956)**
- *Before Dwight's crossing, what was the previous record?* **(54 days)**

CHECKPOINT

Exercise 1 is an example of an enhanced multiple choice question.

CONNECTION TO GEOMETRY Exercise 1 reviews the parallelogram and how to find its area.

ESL Go over Checkpoint Exercises 2–5 carefully with students and provide more practice with these phrases if needed.

ON YOUR OWN

State whether each equation is true or false.

19. $5 + 10 = 15$ True
20. $9 - 3 = 2$ False
21. $24 = 6 + 18$ True

State whether the given number is a solution to the equation.

22. $h + 6 = 14; h = 7$ no
23. $k + 5 = 16; k = 11$ yes
24. $p - 10 = 20; p = 20$ no
25. $18 = m - 4; m = 22$ yes
26. $25 = 14 + y; y = 11$ yes
27. $t - 5 = 25; t = 15$ no

Choose Use tiles, mental math, or a calculator to solve each equation.

28. $x + 2 = 7$ 5
29. $152 = p + 64$ 88
30. $16 = k + 7$ 9
31. $h + 49 = 97$ 48
32. $6 + w = 9$ 3
33. $20 = m - 6.6$ 26.6
34. $62 + r = 83$ 21
35. $y - 265 = 124$ 389
36. $w - 7 = 10$ 17
37. $437.782 + y = 512.36$ 74.578
38. $18{,}943 = x - 11{,}256$ 30,199
39. **Writing** How are the words *equation* and *equilateral* related? Each word contains the prefix "equ," which means equal.
40. **Critical Thinking** Is the equality of an equation affected when you add or subtract the same value on both sides? Support your answer using examples. No; $5 - 3 = 5 - 3$ and $5 + 3 = 5 + 3$.
41. a. Continue the next three rows of the pattern of equations shown below.

    $1 + 3 = 4$ or 2^2 $1 + 3 + 5 + 7 + 9 = 25$ or 5^2

    $1 + 3 + 5 = 9$ or 3^2 $1 + 3 + 5 + 7 + 9 + 11 = 36$ or 6^2

    $1 + 3 + 5 + 7 = 16$ or 4^2 $1 + 3 + 5 + 7 + 9 + 11 + 13 = 49$ or 7^2

    b. What is the relationship between the number of addends and the base of the power? See right.

    c. How would you find the sum of the first ten odd numbers? What is their sum? See right.

    d. Find the sum of the first twenty odd numbers. 20^2 or 400
42. **Language** How is an equation like a sentence?

Mixed REVIEW

Name each polygon.

1. a polygon with 6 sides hexagon
2. a polygon with 10 sides decagon

A record club sells CDs for $10.50 each plus $1.50 shipping charge per order.

3. Make a table showing the cost of ordering 1, 2, 3, 4, and 5 CDs.
4. Graph the data in your table. See Solution Key.
5. A bus can hold 44 passengers. It starts out empty and picks up 1 passenger at the first stop, 2 at the second stop, 3 at the third stop, and so on. If no one gets off of the bus, at what stop will the bus become full?

5. ninth stop

41.b. The number of addends is equal to the base of the power.
41.c. Use 10 as the base of the power; 10^2 or 100

FLASHBACK

The *addends* in the equation $6 + 8 = 14$ are 6 and 8.

42. Answers may vary. Sample given. An equation is a statement whose verb is "is equal to."

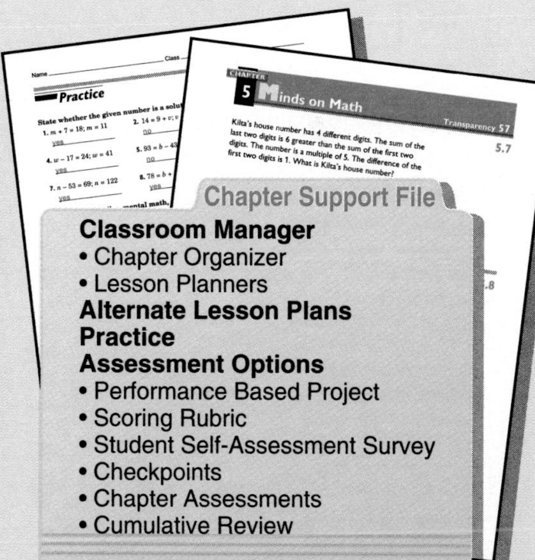

Practice
Minds on Math
Transparency 57
5.7
Chapter Support File
Classroom Manager
• Chapter Organizer
• Lesson Planners
Alternate Lesson Plans
Practice
Assessment Options
• Performance Based Project
• Scoring Rubric
• Student Self-Assessment Survey
• Checkpoints
• Chapter Assessments
• Cumulative Review

Minds on Math available in Teaching Transparencies

Exercises 2–5: If students need more practice, have them work in pairs to write similar phrases for each other and then exchange and check.

Exercises 6–8: Help students see that they can avoid careless errors by always taking the time to isolate the variable. This step is important even if they use mental math to find the solution.

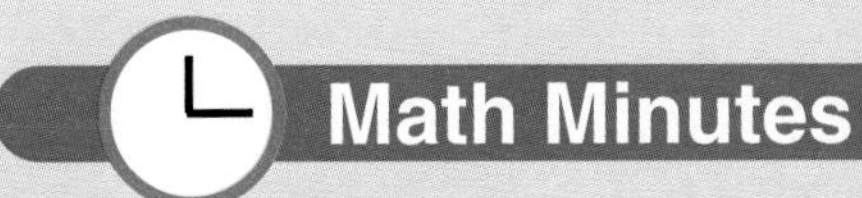

Math Minutes

Ask students to estimate the following.

19.055 − 4.41 **15**
12.89 − 5.24 **8**
4.63 + 7.71 **13**

Materials for 5-9

- algebra tiles
- calculator

Use the article below to answer each question.

A Dream Come True

Dwight Collins was ten years old when he first thought about crossing the Atlantic Ocean. Twenty-six years later, in June and July of 1992, he set out to live his dream. He set a record by pedaling his boat, *Tango,* from Newfoundland to London in just 40 days—14 days faster than the previous record. Can you imagine biking 2,250 miles across the ocean? Not even a storm with over 50 miles per hour winds could stop Dwight Collins from making his dream come true!

43. After the storm, Dwight still had about 1,200 mi of pedaling ahead of him. Let p represent the number of miles Dwight had already pedaled. Write and solve an equation to determine how many miles into the journey Dwight encountered the storm. $p + 1{,}200 = 2{,}250$; 1,050 mi

44. **a.** About how many miles did Dwight travel each day? 56 mi

b. **Critical Thinking** Do you think he traveled this distance every day? Why or why not? No; He may have traveled more on days when the weather was good and less when the weather was bad.

CHECKPOINT

1. **Choose A, B, C, or D.** Which expression has a value closest to 70 square units, the area of the parallelogram? B

A. $x^2 + 3$ when $x = 8$

B. $2(b \div 2) + 1$ when $b = 70$

C. $10^2 - 3c$ when $c = 5$

D. $2a$ when $a = 32$

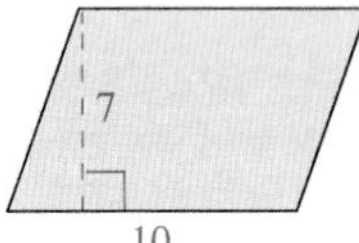

Write a variable expression for each word phrase.

2. twelve more than y — $y + 12$

3. b increased by five — $b + 5$

4. six decreased by w — $6 - w$

5. r less than twenty-two — $22 - r$

Solve each equation.

6. $b + 25 = 75$ — 50

7. $256 = m - 129$ — 385

8. $6 = 4 + y$ — 2

5-9

Connecting to Prior Knowledge

Tell students they are inviting friends over for breakfast. They don't know how many friends will be able to come, but they've made a dozen muffins. Ask them to set up a variable expression that expresses the number of muffins for each friend. **(If x = number of friends, $12 \div x$.)** If four friends arrive, how many muffins can each have? **(three)** Ask students to name the operation involved in answering the question. **(division)**

WORK TOGETHER

Have students work in groups of four. After each group has decided on its answers for Questions 1a and b, have each member answer Question 1c independently. Group members can then check each other's answers.

TACTILE LEARNERS Give students 30 tiles to represent the 30 students signed up for intramurals in Question 1 and let them act out the division to find the number of basketball or volleyball teams. They can also explore what would happen if the 30 students formed teams for baseball or soccer.

CRITICAL THINKING To extend Question 1c, ask students: *If you wanted to have a sports tournament with 30 people, which sports would you choose to play, based on the knowledge you gained in Question 1?* **(Students should answer either basketball or volleyball, since the total number of players is evenly divisible by the number of players per team for each sport.)**

THINK AND DISCUSS

ESL Help students identify the actions of adding, subtracting, multiplying, and dividing with verbs in sentences and with the word "operation," as in Question 2b.

What's Ahead

- Solving multiplication and division equations

5-9 Multiplication and Division Equations

WHAT YOU'LL NEED

✓ Algebra tiles 

✓ Calculator

Sport	Number of Players on Team
Baseball	9
Basketball	5
Soccer	11
Volleyball	6

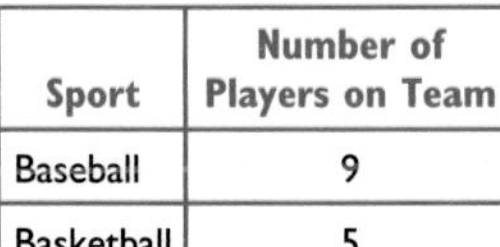

Three sports were started in the United States: basketball, volleyball, and baseball.

Source: *The Information Please Kids' Almanac*

WORK TOGETHER

The number of players on sports teams varies, as shown in the table at the left.

1. Suppose 30 students sign up for intramural sports.
   a. **Mental Math** How many volleyball teams can be formed? 5 teams
   b. **Discussion** Let t represent the number of volleyball teams that can be formed. Does the multiplication equation $6t = 30$ or $30t = 6$ represent this situation? Explain.
   c. **Critical Thinking** How would the equation change if basketball teams are being formed? $5t = 30$

1b. $6t = 30$; the number of players per team, 6, times the number of teams, t, equals the total number of players.

THINK AND DISCUSS

You can use tiles to model and solve multiplication equations.

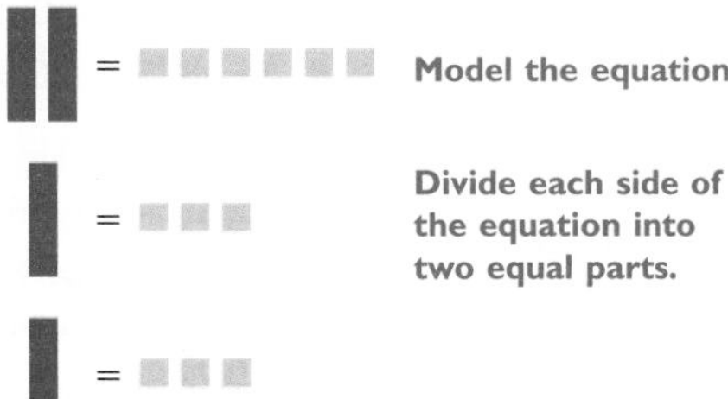

Model the equation.
Divide each side of the equation into two equal parts.

2. a. What equation is modeled in the first step? $2x = 6$
   b. **Discussion** What was done to find the value of the variable? What operation does this action represent?
   c. What is the solution to the equation? 3

2b. The variable was isolated; division.

3. Use tiles to solve each multiplication equation.
   a. $2b = 8$ 4 b. $2g = 10$ 5 c. $3x = 12$ 4

"Anyone can steer the ship when the sea is calm."
—Publilius Syrus

Organizer

1. **Focus**
   Connecting to Prior Knowledge
2. **Teach**
   Work Together
   Think and Discuss
3. **Closure**
   Wrap Up

Skills Reviewed in Context of Lesson
- multiplication and division of whole numbers and decimals

Materials and Manipulatives
- algebra tiles (one set for each group)
- calculator

On Your Own Exercises 16–26: algebra tiles, Exercises 30–31: calculator

Student Resources
Extra Practice
Student Study Guide
Practice, TR Ch. 5, p. 31
Student Study Guide, Spanish Resources, TR

Teacher Resources
Teaching Transparencies 19, 57
Transparency Masters, TR p. 27
Lesson Planner, TR Ch. 5, p. 10

continues next page

Error Alert! In an equation such as Question 5b, students may try to solve by dividing 30 by 2 and get $n = 15$.
Remediation Remind students that multiplication and division are inverse operations. Give them a quick review:

$$\frac{a}{b} = c, a = bc, \frac{a}{c} = b.$$

Ongoing Assessment Have students solve a mixed set of multiplication and division equations. Students should describe all of the steps.

MENTAL MATH Have students share the strategies they used to mentally solve Question 5.

TECHNOLOGY OPTION Have students practice solving multiplication and division equations such as those in Questions 7–9 using a software package that solves algebraic equations.

Journal Ask students to think about how problems involving multiplication and division can be based in a word problem as well as in equations using variables without labels. Have students explain which approach is easier and which is harder for them.

CALCULATOR For Questions 7 and 9, ask students to explain how they would check their answers.

CRITICAL THINKING For Question 11, encourage students to design a table that compares the four operations.

Wrap Up

What's the Big Idea? Ask students to summarize how solving multiplication and division equations differs from solving addition and subtraction equations.

Reteaching Activity Have students use algebra tiles to solve a range of multiplication equations that increase in level of difficulty. This practice with visual demonstrations will help students see what the variable represents.

Organizer, continued

Prentice Hall Technology
Multimedia Math
- Math Tools, Calculation
- Math Tools, Manipulatives
- Hot Page™ 5-9

Computer Item Generator
- 5-9

Other Available Technology
calculator
Algebra Expressor by William K. Bradford: Questions 7–9 (*optional*)
Math Connections by Wings: Questions 7–9 (*optional*)

Fact of the Day

In the United States, about 14% of the carbon dioxide released by burning fuel comes from motor vehicles.

—Environmental Almanac

PH Multimedia Math Hot Page™ 5-9

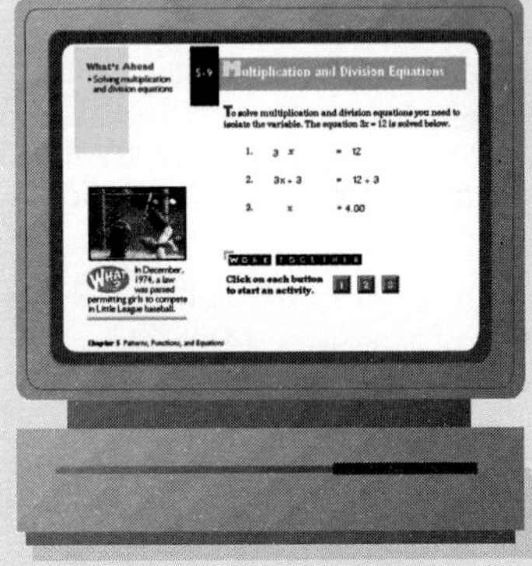

You can use mental math to solve multiplication and division equations.

4. a. In the multiplication equation $10r = 90$, what does the value of r have to be to make the two sides of the equation equal? 9
   b. In the division equation $h \div 4 = 6$, what does the value of h have to be to make the two sides of the equation equal? 24

5. **Mental Math** Solve each equation.
   a. $5c = 35$ 7
   b. $n \div 2 = 30$ 60
   c. $100 = k \div 20$ 2,000
   d. $10 = 2.5h$ 4
   e. $11m = 121$ 11
   f. $b \div 100 = 1{,}000$ 100,000

You can also solve multiplication and division equations using a calculator.

Mrs. Shakuntala Devi of India used mental math to multiply the numbers 7,686,369,774,870 and 2,465,099,745,779. She got the correct answer in an amazing 28 seconds.

Source: *The Guinness Book of Records*

6. a. **Discussion** How could you use a calculator to solve the equation $125x = 1{,}875$? 1875 ÷ 125 =
   b. When you solve a multiplication equation, what operation key do you use? ÷

7. **Calculator** Solve each multiplication equation.
   a. $125v = 2{,}750$ 22
   b. $4{,}731 = 57g$ 83
   c. $125.3p = 4{,}097.31$ 32.7
   d. $83.5375 = 25.625s$ 3.26
   e. $123{,}456n = 97{,}406{,}784$ 789

8. a. **Discussion** How could you use a calculator to solve the equation $x \div 429 = 6{,}864$? 6864 × 429 =
   b. When you solve a division equation, what operation key do you use? ×

9. **Calculator** Solve each division equation.
   a. $s \div 62{,}409 = 289$ 18,036,201
   b. $t \div 5.88 = 75.38$ 443.2344
   c. $2{,}256 = g \div 1{,}111$ 2,506,416
   d. $p \div 287 = 64{,}685$ 18,564,595

10. **Discussion** Explain what is meant by the statement *multiplication and division are inverse operations.* Answers may vary. Example: One operation undoes the other.

11. **Critical Thinking** Compare multiplication and division equations with addition and subtraction equations. How are they alike? How are they different? Answers may vary. ex: Both pairs of equations are statements of equality. Different operations are used to solve each equation.

Connections Have a discussion about how multiplication and division equations are used. Here are some examples:

- **Entertainment** (splitting a restaurant check; determining individual ticket price from a group rate)
- **Consumer skills** (buying several items at the same price, determining unit cost, calculating bulk rate)

ON YOUR OWN

WRITING Have students write the equation in Exercise 27 as a sentence: "Eight tenths of *t* equals four." Ask students if reading the sentence instead of just looking at the numbers helps them complete the exercise.

ESL For Exercise 27, make sure students understand that "multiply" does not always mean "to make bigger." Use examples to demonstrate multiplying by a fraction, such as one-half times 14.

ON YOUR OWN

State whether the given number is a solution to the equation.

12. $6h = 60$; $h = 10$ yes
13. $g \div 8 = 7$; $g = 64$ no
14. $15 = 5p$; $p = 3$ yes
15. $36 = m \div 3$; $m = 12$ no

Choose Use tiles, mental math, or a calculator to solve each equation.

16. $3m = 15$ 5
17. $g \div 5 = 25$ 125
18. $805 = 7b$ 115
19. $2.5h = 45$ 18
20. $10 = k \div 20$ 200
21. $y \div 43 = 1{,}204$ 51,772
22. $16 = 4h$ 4
23. $5.25c = 8.6625$ 1.65
24. $h \div 20 = 9$ 180
25. $204{,}425 = 1{,}258k$ 162.5
26. $d \div 1{,}000 = 100$ 100,000
27. **Writing** Without solving the equation $0.8t = 4$, state whether the value of *t* is greater than or less than 4. Explain. See right.
28. **Choose A, B, C, or D.** Leon participated in a swimathon to raise money for the local food pantry. His neighbor, Mrs. Tram, sponsored him for $.20 per lap. Leon asked Mrs. Tram for $4.40. Choose the equation that Mrs. Tram could solve to determine how many laps Leon completed.
   - **A.** $0.20(4.40) = s$
   - **B.** $0.20s = 4.40$ B
   - **C.** $0.20 \div s = 4.40$
   - **D.** $0.20 = 4.40s$
29. Gasoline is $1.28 per gallon. Laila's bill is $16.
   - **a.** To determine how many gallons of gasoline Laila received would you use the equation $1.28g = 16$ or $16g = 1.28$? $1.28g = 16$
   - **b.** How many gallons of gasoline did Laila receive? 12.5 gal

Calculator Complete each equation. Predict the fifth and sixth equations for each pattern.

30. $1 \times 8 + 1 = ■$ 9
    $12 \times 8 + 2 = ■$ 98
    $123 \times 8 + 3 = ■$ 987
    $1{,}234 \times 8 + 4 = ■$ 9,876
    $12{,}345 \times 8 + 5 = 98{,}765$
    $123{,}456 \times 8 + 6 = 987{,}654$
31. $99 \times 12 = ■$ 1,188
    $99 \times 13 = ■$ 1,287
    $99 \times 14 = ■$ 1,386
    $99 \times 15 = ■$ 1,485
    $99 \times 16 = 1{,}584$
    $99 \times 17 = 1{,}683$

Mixed REVIEW

Find the perimeter of each rectangle.

1. length 8 cm, width 5 cm 26 cm
2. length 2 m, width 56 m 116 m

Solve each equation.

3. $k + 8 = 14$ 6
4. $m - 2 = 15$ 17
5. The houses on Twelfth Avenue are numbered in order from 1 through 85. How many house numbers contain at least one digit 3?

18 house numbers

27. The value of *t* is greater than 4. $1 \times 4 = 4$, so 0.8(4) is less than 4. The solution is greater than 4.

One gallon of gasoline produces about 20 pounds of carbon dioxide. The more carbon dioxide released into the air, the more polluted the air is.

Source: *50 Simple Things You Can Do To Save The Earth*

Assignment Options

Core: 12–20, 22, MR all	
Reinforce: 21, 23–26	Enrich: 27–31

Minds on Math available in Teaching Transparencies

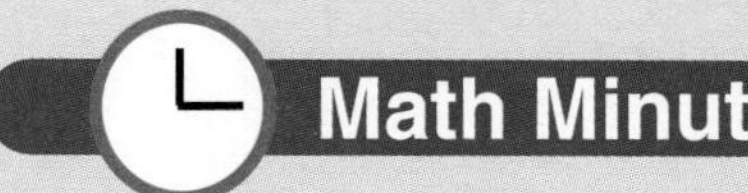

Math Minutes

Ask students to write the next 3 multiples for each.

3, 6, 9 . . . **12, 15, 18**
12, 24, 36 . . . **48, 60, 72**
14, 28, 42 . . . **56, 70, 84**

CHAPTER 5 WRAP UP

Ongoing Assessment Have students work with partners. For Exercise 1, partners could work together to solve the problem. Then have each partner make up a problem for the other partner to solve. For Exercises 2–14, one student could solve the odd-numbered exercises while the other solves the even-numbered exercises. Partners could then exchange answers and check each other's work.

VISUAL AND TACTILE LEARNERS Provide materials and manipulatives such as tiles and graph paper for students for Exercises 1 and 11–14.

TECHNOLOGY OPTION For Exercises 11–14, encourage students to use a software program for solving equations.

Exercise 15 is an example of an enhanced multiple choice question.

Vocabulary/Symbols

base
cube
equal sign, =
equation
equilateral
evaluate
exponent
function
inverse operations
magic square
numerical expression
power
solution
solve
square
term
variable
variable expression

CHAPTER 5 Wrap Up

Patterns and Napier's Rods 5-1, 5-2

Each element of a pattern is a ***term.*** You can describe a number pattern with a rule that tells the first term and what to do to get each of the following terms.

1. Find the next three terms in the number pattern 2, 6, 18, 54, ... Write a rule to describe the pattern. 162; 486; 1,458; start with the number 2 and multiply by 3 repeatedly.

Exponents 5-3

Exponents show repeated multiplication. For 2^3, the base is 2, and the exponent is 3. Two is used as a factor 3 times: $2^3 = 2 \times 2 \times 2$.

Use the order of operations to evaluate numerical expressions.

- Do operations within parentheses first.
- Do all work with exponents.
- Multiply and divide from left to right.
- Add and subtract from left to right.

Evaluate each expression.

2. 3^2 9
3. $5^2 + 4^3$ 89
4. $(6 + 2)^2 \div 4$ 16
5. $(6 + 2^2) \div 8$ 1.25

Variables and Variable Expressions 5-4, 5-6

A ***variable*** is a symbol that stands for a number. A ***variable expression,*** such as $2x - 3$, is an expression that contains at least one variable. To evaluate a variable expression, first replace each variable with a number. Then find the value of the numerical expression.

Write a variable expression for each phrase.

6. 5 less than the number x $x - 5$
7. the number y divided by p $y \div p$
8. **Choose A, B, C, or D.** Between which two numbers is the value of $(2 + x)^3$ for $x = 5$? D

   A. 1 – 99 **B.** 100 – 199 **C.** 200 – 299 **D.** 300 – 399

Getting Ready for Chapter 6

The skills previewed will help students understand how number patterns relate to formulas in measurement and geometry.

Patterns and Problem Solving 5-5, 5-7

One strategy for solving a problem is to look for a pattern. You can use a graph to show how numbers are related.

9. The cost of a 1-min call from Brookfield to the neighboring town Carnstown is \$.07. The cost of a 2-min call is \$.15 and a 3-min call is \$.23. If this pattern continues, what is the cost of a 5-min call? \$.39

10. a. Graph the data in Exercise 9. Draw a line through the points. See Solution Key.
    b. **Writing** Explain how you could use the graph to find the cost of an 8-min call. See Solution Key.

Equations 5-8, 5-9

An equation is a mathematical sentence that contains an equal sign. You solve an equation that contains a variable by finding the ***solution*** that makes the equation true. You can solve an equation by using ***inverse operations,*** operations that undo each other.

For each equation, state the inverse operation that will help find the value of the variable. Then solve.

11. $x + 7 = 12$ subtraction; 5
12. $m - 8 = 15$ addition; 23
13. $4a = 32$ division; 8
14. $t \div 4 = 32$ multiplication; 128

15. **Choose A, B, C, or D.** Ruth bought a calculator for x dollars. She gave the clerk \$20. She received \$7.54 in change. Which equation could you use to find the cost of the calculator? D

    A. $7.54x = 20$ **B.** $x - 20 = 7.54$ **C.** $x \div 7.54 = 20$ **D.** $x + 7.54 = 20$

GETTING READY FOR CHAPTER 6

1. Describe how to find the perimeter and area of a rectangle. Perimeter: add the lengths of the sides. Area: multiply the length and width.

Evaluate each variable expression.

2.

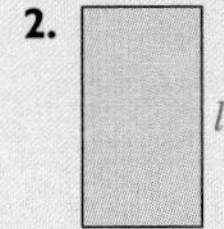

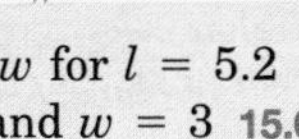

lw for $l = 5.2$ and $w = 3$ 15.6

3.

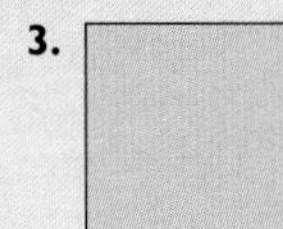

s^2 for $s = 17$ 289

4.

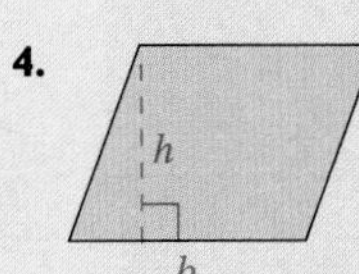

bh for $b = 12$ and $h = 10$ 120

Student Resources

Practice, p. 203
Problem Solving Practice, p. 207
Extra Practice
Student Study Guide
Student Study Guide, Spanish Resources, TR
Tools for Studying Smarter, TR
Student Self-Assessment Survey, TR Ch.5 *(see below)*

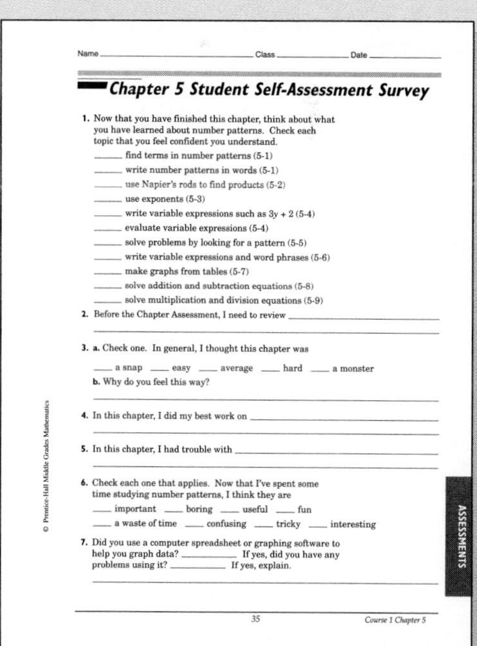

Name ________ Class ________ Date ________

Chapter 5 Student Self-Assessment Survey

1. Now that you have finished this chapter, think about what you have learned about number patterns. Check each topic that you feel confident you understand.
   ____ find terms in number patterns (5-1)
   ____ write number patterns in words (5-1)
   ____ use Napier's rods to find products (5-2)
   ____ use exponents (5-3)
   ____ write variable expressions such as $3y + 2$ (5-4)
   ____ evaluate variable expressions (5-4)
   ____ solve problems by looking for a pattern (5-5)
   ____ write variable expressions and word phrases (5-6)
   ____ make graphs from tables (5-7)
   ____ solve addition and subtraction equations (5-8)
   ____ solve multiplication and division equations (5-9)
2. Before the Chapter Assessment, I need to review ________
3. a. Check one. In general, I thought this chapter was
   ____ a snap ____ easy ____ average ____ hard ____ a monster
   b. Why do you feel this way?
4. In this chapter, I did my best work on ________
5. In this chapter, I had trouble with ________
6. Check each one that applies. Now that I've spent some time studying number patterns, I think they are
   ____ important ____ boring ____ useful ____ fun
   ____ a waste of time ____ confusing ____ tricky ____ interesting
7. Did you use a computer spreadsheet or graphing software to help you graph data? ________ If yes, did you have any problems using it? ________ If yes, explain.

ASSESSMENTS

© Prentice-Hall Middle Grades Mathematics

35 Course 1 Chapter 5

CHAPTER 5 PUTTING IT ALL TOGETHER

The projects on these pages can be used in a variety of ways.

- alternative assessment
- portfolio ideas
- additional assignments for gifted and talented students
- extra credit for all students

Follow Up

- Suggest that students list the main points concerning their investigation that they feel need to be brought out in their letter to the principal.
- Ask them to outline their letters for your review before they write them.

Students can contact school board members to obtain annual budget figures for their school. They can use these to suggest ways to spend the money that they will save the school in this project.

RESEARCH Many useful books have been published in recent years listing simple things people can do to help preserve the environment. Check the school or city library.

What's the Trick?

COOPERATIVE GROUPS Have students work in pairs and use several numbers as examples to investigate the problem. Have pairs attempt to write an expression for the problem, using x as the number. Compare the expressions in larger groups, or as a class.

Express Yourself

VISUAL LEARNERS Students might find it helpful to construct a table presenting a fictional week of work before attempting to write an expression.

Materials and Manipulatives

What's My Number?
- index cards

Follow Up
- graph paper

Prentice Hall Technology

Follow Up
Multimedia Math
- Math Tools, Spreadsheet *(optional)*

Other Available Technology

Follow Up
- *Excel* by Microsoft
- *Microsoft Graph*
- *Cricket Graph*

(all optional)

PUTTING IT ALL TOGETHER

Follow Up

Mountains of Garbage

During the time you have been studying this chapter, Americans have thrown out several million tons of trash. Before it is too late, present your proposal for school garbage reduction to the principal. Revise your plan based on your study of the chapter. The following are suggestions to help you support your proposal.

- ✓ Make a graph showing trends in school trash production.
- ✓ Make a poster.
- ✓ Conduct a survey on student/faculty willingness to follow your trash-reduction plan.

If you worked the problems preceded by the magnifying glass (p. 187, # 17; and p. 206, # 35), the data you collected will also help you support your proposal.

Your efforts to cut down on your trash production can have major results. If each of us reduces the amount of garbage we produce by only one-fourth, we can each save more than 300 pounds of raw materials annually!

Excursion: Recycling not only saves the recycled materials themselves, it saves money. Estimate the amount of money your school could save by recycling. Explain how you made your estimate. Then suggest some ways the school could use the money it saves.

Who to Talk To:
- representatives of your local or state solid-waste agency

Blink In the Eye of an Eye

Work with a partner. Count how many times each of you blink in one minute. Use a variable to represent this amount, such as b (blinks per minute) = 20. Use this variable to write a multiplication expression that would show how many times your partner would blink in an hour, a day, a week, and a year. Evaluate each expression. Share your results with your classmates. Determine the average amount of blinks per minute for the entire class.

222

What's My Number?

COOPERATIVE GROUPS Each group should consist of at least three students.

Students might also be arranged in teams of four or five. Teams could compete against each other to solve each equation as quickly as possible. Turns should rotate among team members, and a moderator might be necessary to mediate disputes.

In the Blink of an Eye

COOPERATIVE GROUPS Have students work in pairs.

Remind students that there is no "correct" number of blinks/min. You might want to discuss how blinking at an artificial rate, fast or slow, could skew the data for the class average.

Express Yourself
You and two other friends have just started your own business doing odd jobs in your neighborhood. The number of hours you work each day varies. You charge each customer the same wage per hour for the work you do. At the end of each work day, you and your two friends split your earnings evenly. Using two variables, write an expression to describe the amount of money you would earn each day.
What's the Trick?
Pick a number greater than 1.
Add 3 to your number.
Double your result.
Subtract 6.
Subtract your original number.
Record your final result.
What's the trick?
WHAT'S MY NUMBER?
Rules:
Three or more players
Each player has ten 3" x 5" index cards. Players write a division or multiplication fact with one missing number on each of their ten cards to make an equation.
Shuffle all cards together.
Players take turns drawing a card and solving the equation. When a player gives the correct answer, the product or quotient is that player's score. If the player does not give a correct answer, the player receives no score and play continues to the left.
The player with the highest score wins.
223

CHAPTER 5 ASSESSMENT

Enhanced Multiple Choice Questions are more complex than traditional multiple choice questions, which assess only one skill. Enhanced multiple choice questions assess the processes that students use as well as the end results. They are written so that students can use more than one strategy to solve the problem. Using multiple strategies is encouraged by the National Council of Teachers of Mathematics (NCTM).

Exercise 2 is an enhanced multiple choice question.

Writing Questions allow students to describe more fully their thinking and understanding of the concepts they've learned.

Exercise 3 is a writing question.

Exercise 2: You may want to extend the exercise by having students describe a rule for the patterns in answers B and C.

MENTAL MATH Have students check their answers for Exercise 11 by working backwards.

Resources

Performance Based Project, TR Ch. 5, pp. 32–33
Chapter Assessment, Forms A and B, TR Ch. 5, pp. 37–40
Spanish Chapter Assessment, Spanish Resources, TR
Computer Item Generator

CHAPTER 5

Assessment

1b. Start with the number 7 and add 9 repeatedly.

1. a. Find the next three terms in this number pattern: 7, 16, 25, 34, ... 43, 52, 61
   b. Write a rule to describe the pattern. See above.

2. **Choose A, B, or C.** Which number pattern can be described by the following rule: *Start with the number 3 and add 7 repeatedly?* A
   A. 3, 10, 17, ...
   B. 7, 10, 13, ...
   C. 1, 3, 7, ...

3. **Writing** How would you use Napier's rods to multiply 724×9? See Solution Key.

4. Evaluate each expression.
   a. $500 + (12 - 8)^3$ 564   b. $3^5 \times 2^4$ 3,888
   c. $8^2 \div 4 - 2^4$ 0   d. $8 + 4^2 \div 2$ 16

5. Compare using $<$, $>$, or $=$.
   $3 + (2)^3$ ■ $(3 + 2)^3$ $<$

6. Carol is training for a swim meet. The first week she swims 4 laps per day. The second week she swims 8 laps per day, the third week 12 laps per day, and the fourth week 16 laps per day. She continues this pattern. How many laps per day will Carol swim in the eighth week? 32 laps

7. Choose a variable. Then write an expression for each model.
   a.  $3n + 2$
   b.  $2r + 4$

8. Evaluate $2a^2 + b$ for $a = 5$ and $b = 18$. 68

a. $x + 3 = 6$; 3

9. Write and solve the equation represented by each model.
   a. 
   b. 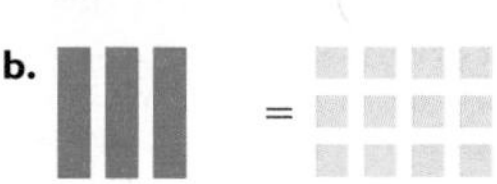
   $3y = 12$; 4

10. Write a variable expression for each word phrase.
    a. eight less than d $d - 8$
    b. twice as many as q $2q$

11. **Mental Math** Solve each equation.
    a. $14 = y - 8$ 22   b. $2m = 26$ 13

12. Solve each equation. a. 113 b. 130
    a. $25 + b = 138$ b. $n - 46 = 84$
    c. $135 = 10y$ 13.5   d. $k \div 12 = 3$ 36

13. Al made a rocket for science class. The table shows the height of the rocket after a given number of seconds.

Time (s)	Height (m)
1	1
2	3
3	6
4	10
5	■ 15
6	■ 21

   a. Copy and complete the table. Then graph the data. See Solution Key.
   b. Are the points collinear? Explain. See Solution Key.

CHAPTER 5

CUMULATIVE REVIEW

Exercises 8 and 11 are examples of enhanced multiple choice questions.

Item(s)	Review Topic	Chapter
1	place value of decimals	3
2	angles	2
3	averages	1
4	number patterns	5
5	comparing and ordering decimals	3
6	multiplying decimals	4
7	exponents	5
8	too much, too little information	4
9	special quadrilaterals	2
10	fractions and percent	pre-book
11	congruent and similar figures	2

CHAPTER 5

Cumulative Review

Choose A, B, C, or D.

1. Which number is the *best estimate* for 2.17 − 0.014? C
   A. 2 B. 2.1 C. 2.15 D. 2.2

2. Which name is *not* a name for an acute angle shown in the diagram? C

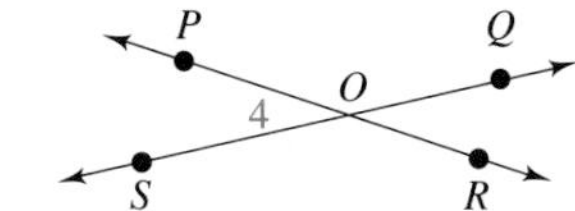

   A. ∠4 B. ∠*POS*
   C. ∠*SOR* D. ∠*ROQ*

3. In a set of data, what name is given to the number found by subtracting the smallest number from the largest? D
   A. mean B. median
   C. mode D. range

4. What rule could you use to describe the number pattern 4, 8, 12, 16, 20? A
   A. Start with 4 and add 4 repeatedly.
   B. Start with 4 and multiply by 2.
   C. Start with 4 and write the square.
   D. Write the first five powers of 4.

5. Which set of decimals below is in order from least to greatest? B
   A. 0.2, 0.02, 0.22 B. 0.15, 0.51, 1.05
   C. 0.24, 0.3, 0.05 D. 0.49, 0.4, 0.05

6. If 31.2 × ■ = 0.00312, what is the value of ■? B
   A. 10,000 B. 0.0001
   C. 1,000 D. 0.001

7. What is the value of $3 + 4 \times 2^3$? B
   A. 56 B. 35 C. 515 D. 27

8. What information do you NOT need to know in order to solve the problem?
   "At McFast Food, a cheeseburger costs 99¢; fries cost 20¢ less than a cheeseburger, and milk costs 75¢. If Jan has three dollars, can she buy two cheeseburgers and milk for lunch?" B
   A. the cost of a cheeseburger
   B. the cost of fries
   C. the cost of milk
   D. Jan has three dollars.

9. Give the name of the polygon that is *not* a quadrilateral. D
   A. trapezoid B. parallelogram
   C. rhombus D. pentagon

10. The Amazon River in South America flows through one of Earth's largest tropical rainforests and carries one sixth of Earth's water that flows into oceans. About what percent of water flowing into oceans is this? A
   A. 16% B. 10% C. 12.5% D. 6%

11. Name a pair of triangles that do *not* appear to be congruent. C
   A. △*KNO*, △*KLO*
   B. △*MON*, △*MOL*
   C. △*NKL*, △*NML*
   D. △*KMN*, △*KML*

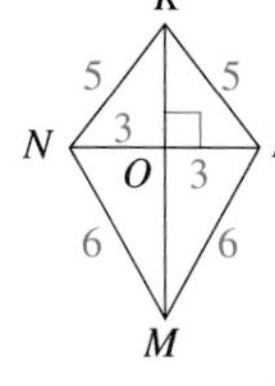

Resources

Cumulative Review, TR Ch. 5, pp. 41–42
Transparency Masters, p. 35

CHAPTER

6 Measurement

Why Study Measurement?

If students ask this question, you may want to mention these areas in which measurement is used: surveying, real estate, constructing and painting buildings, paving roads, sewing clothes, buying carpets, wrapping packages for shipping, planning driving distances for vacations, building a dog house.

Graphic Display of Chapter Content

Below is one possible representation of the chapter's content and its applications to the world outside the classroom. Have students create their own graphic display and fill in applications that they have seen in their own lives.

- The center oval should state the main concept of the chapter: measurement.
- Have students draw the ovals with the next level of concepts presented in the chapter (area, surface area, exploring π, and volume). You may want students to add other topics that they think are appropriate.
- Ask students to draw as many application ovals as they can.
- Discuss all the applications that students identify.
- Have students make and present one display that includes all the students' ideas.

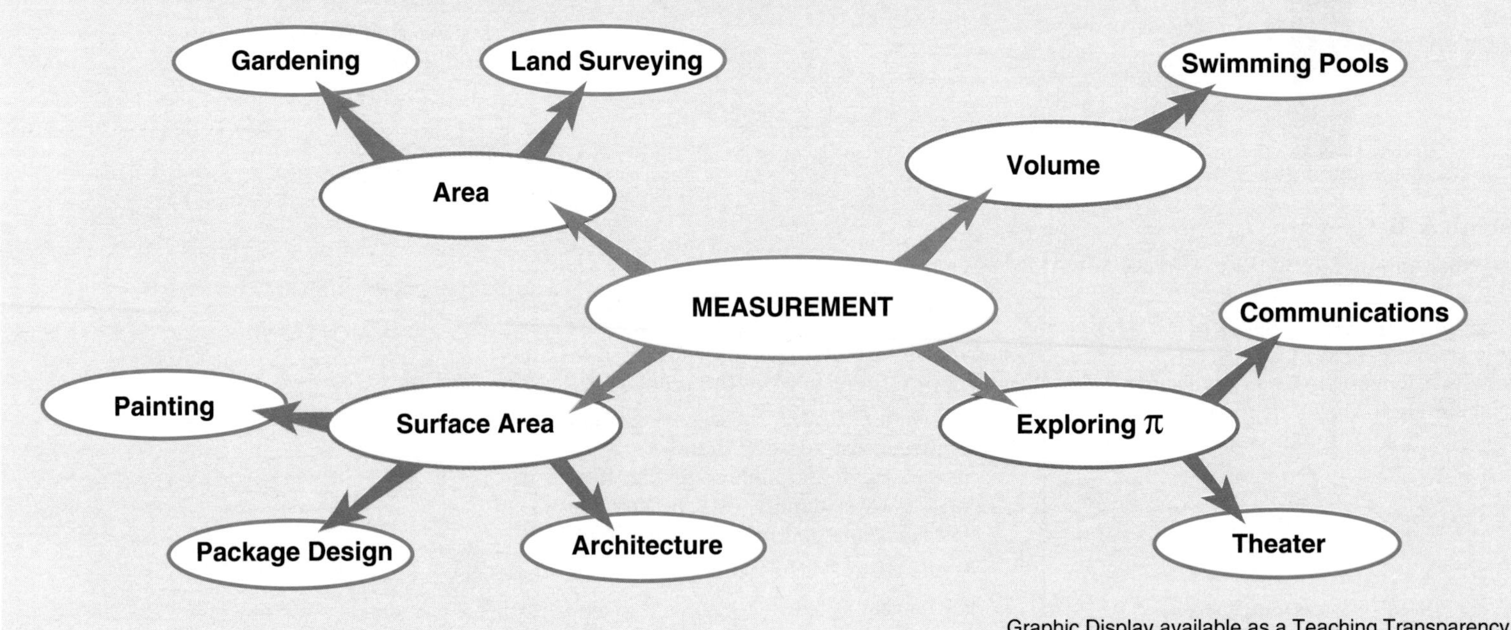

Graphic Display available as a Teaching Transparency

Vocabulary and Symbols

bases	pi, π
capacity	prism
circumference	pyramids
cone	rectangular prism
cube	sphere
cylinder	square pyramid
edge	square units
faces	surface area
height, *h*	three-dimensional figures
length, *l*	vertex
liter	volume, *V*
net	width, *w*

Materials and Manipulatives

calculator	graph paper
centimeter graph paper	pennies
centimeter ruler	scissors
compass	square tiles
computer	straightedge
geometry software	unit cubes

Additional Resources

Commercially Available Technology

Calculator

fraction

Software

geometry software

- *The Geometric Supposer* by Sunburst
- *The Geometric Super Supposer* by Sunburst
- *The Geometric Supposer: Circles* by Sunburst
- *Elastic Lines* by Sunburst

Other Media

"Architecture and Structural Engineering." PBS Video, 1320 Braddock Place, Alexandria, VA 22314-1698. (800) 344-3337.

"Manor House Mystery." Tom Snyder Productions, 80 Coolidge Hill Road, Watertown, MA 02172 (800) 342-0236.

"The Story of Pi." Tom Apostol, Reston, VA: NCTM, 1989.

Materials at Little or No Cost

National Audubon Society, 613 Riversville Rd., Greenwich, CT 06830. Publishes *Good Teaching Aids*, which include directions for making birdhouses and bird feeders.

Science-by-Mail. Museum of Science, Science Park, Boston, MA 02114. (617) 589-0437. Program that pairs students with professionals who serve as mentors.

Bibliography

For Teachers

Beaumont, Vern et al. *How to Teach Perimeter, Area, and Volume.* Reston, VA: NCTM, 1986.

Wills, Herbert. *Leonardo's Dessert: No Pi.* Reston, VA: NCTM, 1985.

For Students

Ardley, Neil. *Making Metric Measurements.* NY: Franklin Watts, 1983.

Isaacson, Philip. *A Short Walk Around the Pyramids and Through the World of Art.* NY: Knopf, 1993.

Macaulay, David. *Pyramid.* Boston: Hougton Mifflin, 1982.

Prentice Hall Technology

Multimedia Math

- Math Tools, Geometry
- Hot Page™ 6-1
- Hot Page™ 6-5
- Hot Page™ 6-6
- Math Investigations, Crisis in Hydrotown
- Math Investigations, Unidentified Flying Cubes

Computer Item Generator

- Chapter 6

Community Resources

Field Trips

- a landscaping business
- an interior decorator
- a theater set designer

Guest Speakers

- a landscaper
- a carpet layer
- a wallpaper hanger

Backpack Take-Home Activities

Materials

- tape measure
- utility bill
- paper
- pencil

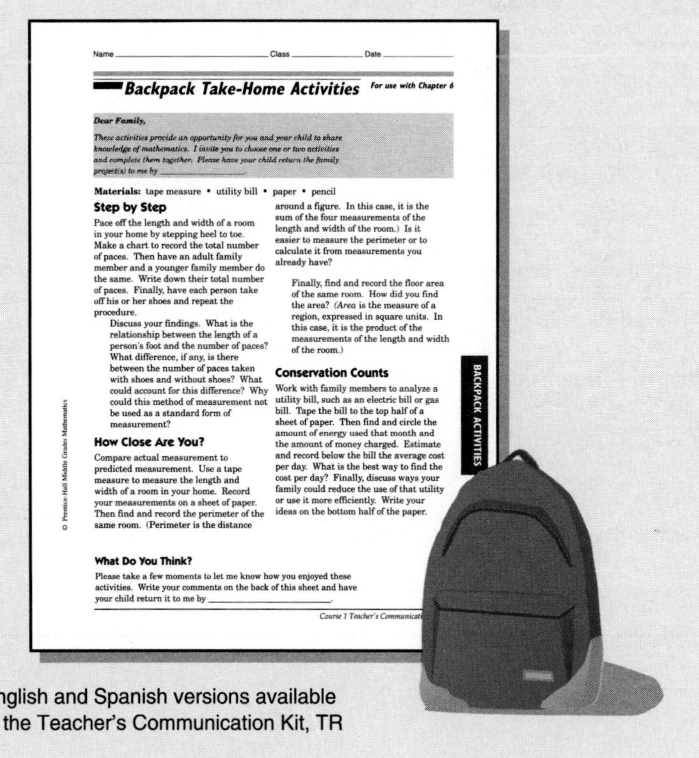

Name ________ Class ________ Date ________

Backpack Take-Home Activities *For use with Chapter 6*

Dear Family,

These activities provide an opportunity for you and your child to share knowledge of mathematics. I invite you to choose one or two activities and complete them together. Please have your child return the family project(s) to me by ________.

Materials: tape measure • utility bill • paper • pencil

Step by Step

Pace off the length and width of a room in your home by stepping heel to toe. Make a chart to record the total number of paces. Then have an adult family member and a younger family member do the same. Write down their total number of paces. Finally, have each person take off his or her shoes and repeat the procedure.

Discuss your findings. What is the relationship between the length of a person's foot and the number of paces? What difference, if any, is there between the number of paces taken with shoes and without shoes? What could account for this difference? Why could this method of measurement not be used as a standard form of measurement?

How Close Are You?

Compare actual measurement to predicted measurement. Use a tape measure to measure the length and width of a room in your home. Record your measurements on a sheet of paper. Then find and record the perimeter of the same room. (Perimeter is the distance around a figure. In this case, it is the sum of the four measurements of the length and width of the room.) Is it easier to measure the perimeter or to calculate it from measurements you already have?

Finally, find and record the floor area of the same room. How did you find the area? (*Area* is the measure of a region, expressed in square units. In this case, it is the product of the measurements of the length and width of the room.)

Conservation Counts

Work with family members to analyze a utility bill, such as an electric bill or gas bill. Tape the bill to the top half of a sheet of paper. Then find and circle the amount of energy used that month and the amount of money charged. Estimate and record below the bill the average cost per day. What is the best way to find the cost per day? Finally, discuss ways your family could reduce the use of that utility or use it more efficiently. Write your ideas on the bottom half of the paper.

What Do You Think?

Please take a few moments to let me know how you enjoyed these activities. Write your comments on the back of this sheet and have your child return it to me by ________.

BACKPACK ACTIVITIES

Course 1 Teacher's Communicati

English and Spanish versions available in the Teacher's Communication Kit, TR

Chapter 6 Planning Guide

Objectives	Assignment Options	Critical Thinking/ Problem Solving	Writing and Reading Math	Estimation Mental Math	Materials and Manipulatives
Investigation	This chapter-long project involves open-ended questioning and data collecting and provides an additional opportunity to assess students.	p. 228 p. 228	p. 228 p. 228		p. 228 p. 228
6-1 Estimating Area • Estimating area	**Core:** 6–9, 13, 17, 18; MR all **Reinforce:** 10, 11, 14, 15 **Enrich:** 12, 16, 19	1, 12b, 13, 14, 16; MR: 6 pp. 229, 231; BI p. 230; MM p. 232	13 p. 231; JL p. 230 JL Sheet	4, 5c, 8–11, 12a, 14–19; MR: 2–5 pp. 229–231; WT p. 230; BI p. 230	12, 19 pp. 229–231; WT p. 230; RT p. 231 TT 1, 16, 61
6-2 Area of Rectangles and Squares • Finding area and perimeter of rectangles and squares	**Core:** 12–20, 30; MR all **Reinforce:** 21–23, 25, 26, 28 **Enrich:** 24, 27, 29	2c, 4, 5, 22, 25, 26, 29, 30; MR: 4 pp. 233, 234; BI p. 235; MM p. 236	29 p. 236; JL p. 234 JL Sheet	3, 9–11, 15–23, 28; MR: 3	WT: 6–8; 12–23 pp. 233, 235; WT p. 234; RT p. 235 TT 1, 61, 64
6-3 Area of Parallelograms and Triangles • Developing and using area formulas for parallelograms and triangles	**Core:** 10–16; MR all; CH all **Reinforce:** 17a–c, 18 **Enrich:** 17d, 19	WT: 2; 17d, 18, 19b; CH: 2; MR: 5 pp. 238, 239; BI p. 238	19b p. 239; JL p. 238 JL Sheet	CH: 3, 4	WT: 1, 2; 12–16, 19a pp. 237–239; WT p. 237; RT p. 239 TT 1, 61, 64
6-4 Technology: Exploring π • Using π to solve circumference problems	**Core:** 10–17, 22–25, 31; MR all **Reinforce:** 18–21, 26–29, 34 **Enrich:** 32, 33	WT: 2b; 3–5, 8, 9, 30–33 pp. 243, 244; BI p. 244	WT: 1b; 34 JL p. 244 JL Sheet	WT: 2a; 3, 4c–e, 9b, 10–13; MR: 1, 2	1a, 4a, 7, 8a, 9c, 14–33 pp. 242–245; RT p. 245 TT 15, 19, 62 Alt. Lesson
6-5 Area of a Circle • Finding the area of a circle	**Core:** 11, 12, 14–17, 19–22, 25; MR all **Reinforce:** 13, 18 **Enrich:** 23, 24, 26–28	6b, 7, 19, 20, 26–28 p. 247; BI p. 248; MM p. 249	19, 26–28 p. 249; JL p. 248 JL Sheet	WT: 3, 4; EX1, 2; 16–18 pp. 246–249	WT: 1–4; 6a; EX1, 2; 8–15, 21–24 pp. 246–249; WT p. 246; RT p. 248 TT 1, 62, 64
6-6 Math and Architecture: Three-Dimensional Figures • Identifying three-dimensional figures	**Core:** 17–20, 25–28; MR all **Reinforce:** 21, 24 **Enrich:** 22, 23	3, 15, 23, 24; MR: 7 p. 252; BI p. 252; MM p. 255	23 p. 253; JL p. 252 JL Sheet	MR: 5, 6	WT pp. 251–253; WT p. 252 TT 1, 62
6-7 Exploring Surface Area • Finding the surface area of rectangular prisms	**Core:** 4–10, 13, 15, 17; MR all **Reinforce:** 11, 12 **Enrich:** 14, 16	1b, 13, 15–17; MR: 7 pp. 256, 258; BI p. 257	13 p. 257; JL p. 257 JL Sheet	2c, 3b, 4–9, 12b; MR: 1, 2, 5, 6 MM p. 258	4–12 pp. 256, 258; WT p. 256; RT p. 257 TT 63; Alt. Lesson
6-8 Volume of Rectangular Prisms • Finding the volume of rectangular prisms	**Core:** 8–15, 20; MR all; CH all **Reinforce:** 16–19, 21, 22 **Enrich:** 23, 24	4, 17b, 18–20, 23; MR: 4 p. 260; BI p. 261; MM p. 262	17b p. 261; JL p. 261 JL Sheet	CH: 3, 4; MR: 3b p. 259	WT: 1, 2; 3, 21–24; MR: 1, 2 pp. 259, 260; WT p. 259; RT p. 261 TT 63
6-9 Problem Solving: Make a Model • Solving problems by making a model	**Core:** 8, 9, 12, 13; MR all **Reinforce:** 11, 14, 16 **Enrich:** 10, 15	All; MR: 5 p. 263; BI p. 264; RT p. 264; MM p. 265	All JL p. 263 JL Sheet	9	3, 6, 7 pp. 263–265 TT 63
Putting It All Together	These pages include a Follow-Up to the Investigation and other projects, which provide additional opportunities to assess the students.	pp. 268–269 pp. 268–269	pp. 268–269		pp. 268–269 pp. 268–269
Chapter Resources		PS Practice, CW, CA, CR PS Practice p. 241; CW pp. 266–267; CA p. 270; CR p. 271	PS Practice, CW, CA p. 226B; PS Practice p. 241; CW pp. 266–267; CA p. 270		pp. 226A, 226B Backpack Activities, Manip. Kits TT 60, 65

Student Edition (question numbers)
Teacher's Edition (page numbers)
Other Components

BI—What's the Big Idea? CA—Chapter Assessment CH—Checkpoint
CG—Computer Item Generator CR—Cumulative Review CW—Chapter Wrap Up
DM—Decision Making EP—Extra Practice EX—Example FD—Fact of the Day

Cooperative Learning Activities	Technology	Data Collection & Analysis	Interdisciplinary Connections	Applications	Assessment	Review	Strand Integration	NCTM Correlation*
		p. 228 p. 228	Art	design, art	p. 228 p. 228			
WT; 12 pp. 229, p. 230	Hot Page™ 6-1	FD p. 230	Geography	geography pp. 229–231	p. 229	MR: All p. 229; RT p. 231 Practice p. 23	Geometry, Number, Logic/Language	1, 2, 3, 4, 5, 7, 8, 12, 13
WT: 6–8 pp. 233, 236; WT p. 234; RT p. 235 Alt. Lesson	15–21 p. 235 Alt. Lesson	24, 30 p. 236; FD p. 234		gardening, stamps p. 235	p. 234	MR: All p. 233; RT p. 235 Practice p. 24	Algebra, Geometry, Logic/Language	1, 2, 3, 4, 5, 7, 8, 9, 12, 13
WT: 1, 2 WT p. 237; RT p. 239	p. 238	FD p. 238		p. 239	CH: All p. 237; CH p. 240 CH TR p. 36	MR: All p. 237; RT p. 239 Practice p. 25	Algebra, Geometry, Logic/Language	1, 2, 3, 4, 5, 7, 8, 9, 12, 13
WT: 1, 2 WT pp. 242–243; RT p. 245	All pp. 242, 244	30 FD p. 243	Alt. Lesson	design, sports pp. 242, 245	p. 244	MR: All p. 242; RT p. 245 Practice p. 26	Algebra, Number, Logic/Language	1, 2, 3, 4, 6, 7, 8, 9, 12, 13
WT: 1–4 pp. 247, 249; WT p. 246; RT p. 248	6a; EX1, 2; 8–15, 21–24 pp. 246–249 Hot Page™ 6-5	25 p. 249; FD p. 247	History p. 249	radio p. 248	p. 247	MR: All p. 246; RT p. 248 Practice p. 27	Algebra, Geometry, Logic/Language	1, 2, 3, 4, 5, 7, 8, 9, 12, 13
WT pp. 251, 252; WT p. 252; RT pp. 252–253	Hot Page™ 6-6	FD p. 253	Art, Social Studies, Science	architecture, marine biology pp. 251, 253; GE pp. 253–255	p. 252	MR: All p. 251; RT pp. 252–253 Practice p. 28	Geometry, Logic/Language	1, 2, 3, 4, 8, 12
WT pp. 256, 258; WT p. 256	4–9	17 p. 258; FD p. 257		household p. 257	p. 257	MR: All p. 256; RT p. 257 Practice p. 29	Geometry, Measurement, Logic/Language	1, 2, 3, 4, 5, 7, 8, 12, 13
WT: 1, 2 WT p. 259; RT p. 261	21–24 p. 260	24 FD p. 261	p. 261	recreation p. 261	CH: All pp. 259–260; CH p. 262 CH TR p. 36	MR: All p. 259; RT p. 261 Practice p. 30	Algebra, Geometry, Logic/Language	1, 2, 3, 4, 5, 7, 8, 9, 12, 13
3 p. 264; RT p. 264		FD p. 263	pp. 263, 264	hobbies, jobs, money pp. 263, 264	p. 263	MR: All p. 263; RT p. 264 Practice p. 31	Geometry, Measurement, Logic/Language	1, 2, 3, 4, 5, 7, 8, 12, 13
pp. 268–269 pp. 268–269		pp. 268–269 pp. 268–269	Art	design, time	pp. 268–269 pp. 268–269			
IN, PT pp. 226–228; PT pp. 268–269 Backpack Activities	p. 226B Multimedia Math, CG	Data File 6 pp. 226–227	Physical Science pp. 226F, 226–227 Interdisciplinary Units	cycling, recreation pp. 226A, 226F, 226–227 Backpack Activities, Projects, Interdisciplinary Units	IN, PT, CA pp. 226E, 228; CW pp. 266–267; PT pp. 268–269; CA p. 270 CA, Span. CA, Self Assessment, Projects	Practice, PS Practice, CW, CR, EP, SSG CW pp. 266–267 Span. SSG, CR		

GE—Great Expectations IN—Investigation JL—Journal MM—Math Minutes
MR—Mixed Review PS—Problem Solving PT—Putting It All Together RT—Reteaching Activity
SSG—Student Study Guide TT—Teaching Transparency WT—Work Together

*For a description of the NCTM Standards, see page T15.

Assessment Options

Observation Checklist

In this chapter on measurement, you have opportunities to observe your students do these tasks:

✓ estimate area of irregular regions
✓ find areas and perimeters of squares, rectangles, parallelograms, and triangles
✓ find area and circumference of circles
✓ identify prisms, cylinders, pyramids, and cones
✓ find surface area and volume of rectangular prisms
✓ make models and use other strategies to solve word problems

In every chapter, you are given opportunities to observe your students:

✓ work with a partner or in a group
✓ write about mathematics
✓ participate in discussions about mathematics
✓ collect and analyze data
✓ display positive attitudes about mathematics
✓ use measurement tools

Name ____________ Class ________ Date ________

Chapter 6 Project

Park Design Contest

Jeanne Chilson is very loyal to her hometown. She is also very wealthy. She has given her town a piece of land for a park. The land is in the shape of a rectangle 2,000 ft long and 1,000 ft wide. Jeanne is also sponsoring a contest for the design of the park, with a very generous prize for the winning design. The winning design must include the following:

- A place for people to picnic
- A place for people to play games
- An area with playground equipment for young children
- Trees for shade and flowers to make things beautiful
- Paths to walk on, trash baskets to throw trash in, and water fountains to drink from

Following is a list of some of the minimum space requirements for various games and pieces of equipment:

- horseshoe court: 6 ft by 50 ft
- badminton court: 20 ft by 44 ft
- tennis court: 78 ft by 36 ft
- basketball court: 84 ft by 46 ft
- olympic swimming pool: 165 ft by 69 ft
- soccer field: 330 ft by 240 ft
- picnic table: 8 ft by 6 ft
- trash basket circle: 3 ft in diameter

1. On a separate sheet of paper, draw your design for the park. Be sure to label the objects you include in your design.
2. You need to show Ms. Chilson that your design meets each of her requirements. Complete each exercise below.
   a. How many picnic tables did you include? ____________
   b. Describe the areas that you have set aside for games.
   c. What types of playground equipment have you included for young children?

Course 1 Chapter 6

Performance Based Project (with scoring rubric), Chapter Files, TR

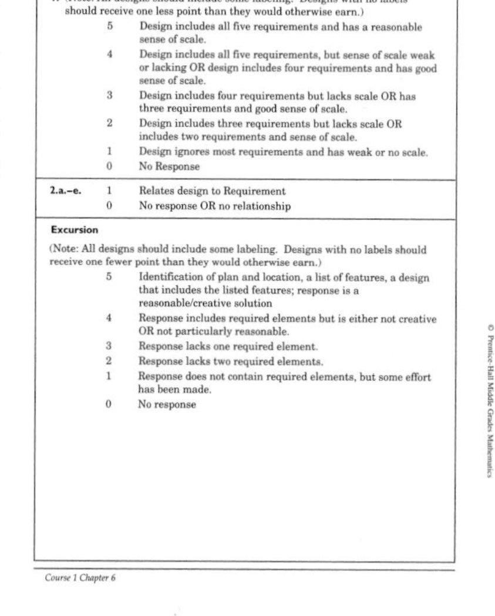

Scoring Rubric

Exercise	Points	Explanation
1.		(Note: All designs should include some labeling. Designs with no labels should receive one less point than they would otherwise earn.)
	5	Design includes all five requirements and has a reasonable sense of scale.
	4	Design includes all five requirements, but sense of scale weak or lacking OR design includes four requirements and has good sense of scale.
	3	Design includes four requirements but lacks scale OR has three requirements and good sense of scale.
	2	Design includes three requirements but lacks scale OR includes two requirements and sense of scale.
	1	Design ignores most requirements and has weak or no scale.
	0	No Response
2.a.–e.	1	Relates design to Requirement
	0	No response OR no relationship
Excursion		(Note: All designs should include some labeling. Designs with no labels should receive one fewer point than they would otherwise earn.)
	5	Identification of plan and location, a list of features, a design that includes the listed features; response is a reasonable/creative solution
	4	Response includes required elements but is either not creative OR not particularly reasonable.
	3	Response lacks one required element.
	2	Response lacks two required elements.
	1	Response does not contain required elements, but some effort has been made.
	0	No response

Course 1 Chapter 6

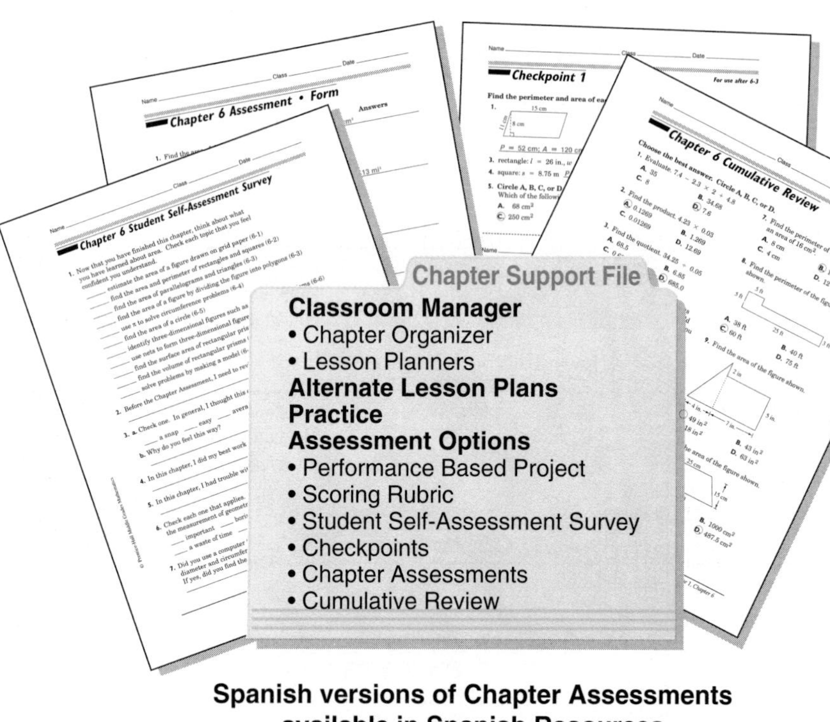

Chapter 6 Assessment • Form
Chapter 6 Student Self-Assessment Survey
Checkpoint 1
Chapter 6 Cumulative Review
Chapter Support File
Classroom Manager
• Chapter Organizer
• Lesson Planners
Alternate Lesson Plans
Practice
Assessment Options
• Performance Based Project
• Scoring Rubric
• Student Self-Assessment Survey
• Checkpoints
• Chapter Assessments
• Cumulative Review

Spanish versions of Chapter Assessments available in Spanish Resources

Interdisciplinary Units

- **Travel and Geography**
- **Space Exploration**
- **Sports**
- **Consumer Awareness**
- **The Great Outdoors**

English & Spanish

These units include cross-curriculum connections and can be used at any time during the school year. See the Teacher's Guide for more information.

Working with Middle Grade Students

> *" Measurement in grades 5–8 should be an active exploration of the real world. As students acquire the ability to use appropriate tools in measuring objects, they should extend these skills to new situations and new applications. "*
>
> —NCTM CURRICULUM AND EVALUATION STANDARDS

Addressing a Variety of Learning Styles

The mathematical tasks in Chapter 6 involve various learning styles.

- Visual learners estimate areas by using a grid (p. 230) and find the area of a drawing made of their names (p. 232).
- Tactile learners use tiles to explore area and perimeter (p. 234), use cutouts to derive a formula for the area of a circle (p. 246), and cut and rearrange triangles to form parallelograms (p. 237).
- Kinesthetic learners trace around their hands and estimate the area (p. 231).

Alternate Lessons 6-4 and 6-7 address tactile learners by having them use manipulatives.

Cultural Connections

The Fibonacci sequence is an infinite sequence of numbers that begins like this: 1, 1, 2, 3, 5, 8, 13, 21, 34, 55, . . . To get the next number, add the two previous numbers. If you look at the ratio of each Fibonacci number to the one before it, you get the sequence: $\frac{1}{1}, \frac{2}{1}, \frac{3}{2}, \frac{5}{3}, \frac{8}{5}, \frac{13}{8}$, and so on. As the Fibonacci numbers get bigger and bigger, the ratios in this sequence get closer and closer to phi, the Golden Ratio.

Team Teaching Suggestion

Work with a science teacher to show students how the volume of odd-shaped items can be measured by water displacement, allowing students the opportunity to investigate alternative forms of measurement. Use regular-shaped items first (blocks, bricks, golf balls), then irregular items that would be difficult for them to measure (rocks, marbles, bolts).

About Estimation

Students who press the wrong key on the calculator can often catch this mistake if a rough estimate is made first. They need to be able to recognize an unreasonable answer. Students need to develop methods of doing estimates quickly and of knowing what degree of accuracy is needed in a given situation. They also need to know when it is better to over-estimate (expenses when preparing a budget) or under-estimate (amount of time to stay in the sun).

Teaching Tip

Students in the middle grades are acutely aware of the wide range of differences in their sizes, so it is best to incorporate measurement exercises that do not make them self-conscious. Measurement comparisons of interesting objects are usually less sensitive. Encourage measurement of things that might especially interest girls.

Bulletin Board

Have students bring in nets of everyday items (such as tissue boxes, milk cartons, cracker or cereal boxes, and oatmeal containers) and post each net on the bulletin board. Ask students to find the surface area and volume of each net and submit their entries by the end of the week. You may wish to set aside time each day for students to record measurements. Have students concentrate on finding different shapes each week. Display students' work.

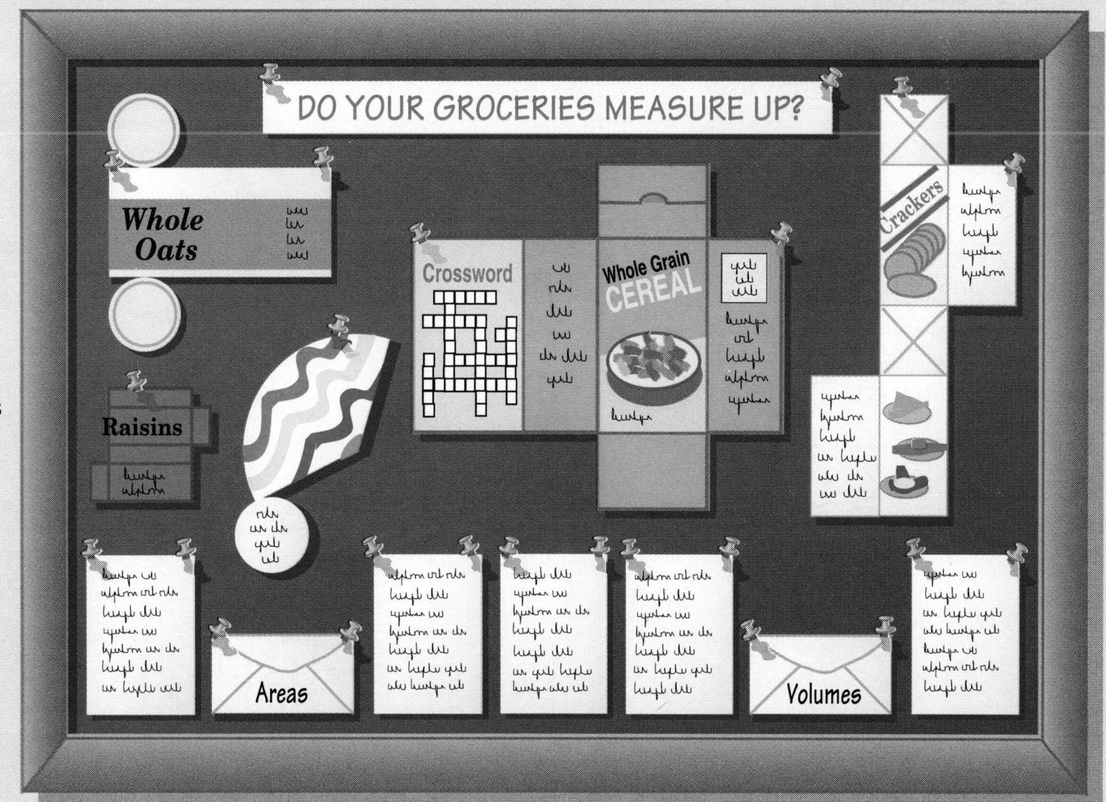

CHAPTER 6 Measurement

Cultural Connections Richard and Orville Wright opened up a bicycle shop in Dayton, Ohio, in 1892. They had always been interested in mechanical things, and after they learned about efforts made by others in attempts at flight the Wright brothers began experimenting with kites and models. In 1900, the brothers tried out their first glider that carried a person. They worked on improving their machine, especially the lift power. After several more experiments, Orville Wright piloted the world's first flight of a heavier-than-air machine on Dec. 17, 1903, at Kitty Hawk, North Carolina. The total distance flown was 120 ft and the air time was 12 s.

WORLD VIEW Wheels have been used for a long time, but they had some crude beginnings. In an effort to move heavy loads, people positioned logs under items so they could roll them along on the ground. It is believed that the original wheel came into use about 5000 years ago when a creative person cut cross sections of logs and attached them to the ends of short poles.

Digging for Data

- Different countries have various primary forms of transportation: cars and trucks, USA; bicycles, China; elephants and buffalo, Nepal.
- Have students estimate how far a 26 in. bicycle with a wheel circumference of about 82 in. will move along the ground if the wheel makes three complete revolutions. **(about 246 in.)**
- Have students talk to elderly people to see how they traveled around when they were children.

Chapter 6 Contents

Data File Questions

pp. 144, 245

CHAPTER 6 Measurement

Data File 6

Pedal POWER

USE YOUR HEAD

Wearing a properly fitting helmet while biking can reduce the risk of serious head injury by 85%. In the past five years if all the bicyclists in the United States had worn a helmet:

- a life could have been saved every day
- a head injury could have been prevented every 4 min.

7 rear-wheel sprockets plus 3 chain wheels = 21 combinations → 21 speed bike
26" diameter rim → a 26" bicycle

rear-wheel sprocket

sprung-rollers

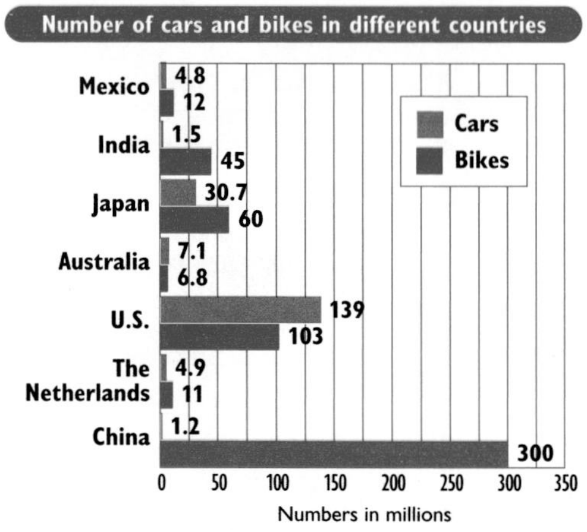

Number of cars and bikes in different countries

Country	Cars	Bikes
Mexico	4.8	12
India	1.5	45
Japan	30.7	60
Australia	7.1	6.8
U.S.	139	103
The Netherlands	4.9	11
China	1.2	300

Numbers in millions (axis 0–350)

Source: *Information Please Environmental Almanac*

Journal Activity

- Have students list what they can do to maximize their fun and safety on bicycles. **(Maintain proper inspection and maintenance; wear a helmet and protective pads; carry emergency tools and drinking water; have reflective surfaces and a light.)**
- Ask students to read the objectives under What You Will Learn. Have them draw and name as many geometric figures as they can. Ask them also to write a brief narrative about what technology they have used.

Interdisciplinary Connection

[Physical Science] Air resistance affects the speed you can attain on a bicycle. As the wind speed increases, more effort is required to ride the bicycle. Discuss how the rider can lean forward to decrease this air resistance, and how there is more surface area to cause more air resistance when the rider is in an upright position. Have pictures of bicycle racers in action.

WHAT YOU WILL LEARN

- how to estimate and find area of geometric figures
- how to use and apply measurement concepts
- how to use technology to explore PI
- how to solve problems by making a model

Source: *Arithmetic Teacher*

The Sumerians are credited with inventing the wheel in about 3,500 B.C.

seat height = 1.09 x leg length (inseam measurement)

handlebar

brake levers

seat height

chain wheel

pedal

chain

26 inches

U.S. Cycling Federation National Records for 20 km

Male		
Age	**min:s**	**km/h**
12 and under	33:33	35.77
14 and under	28:06	42.86
16 and under	25:21	47.34
18 and under	25:04	47.87
Female		
Age	**min:s**	**km/h**
12 and under	37:42	31.83
14 and under	32:22	37.08
16 and under	30:39	39.15
18 and under	29:42	40.40

Source: *U.S. Cycling Federation*

Fact of the Day

Countries that are major producers of bicycles include China, France, Great Britain, Italy, Japan, South Korea, Taiwan, and the United States.

—WORLD BOOK ENCYCLOPEDIA

CHAPTER 6 INVESTIGATION

Have students read the memo. Be sure they can identify the border of a square and that they see how to build a square from the next smaller one. As a check, ask them to build a 4-square from a 3-square and calculate the three requisite pieces of data for the new square. **(16 tiles needed in all; 12 tiles in border; 7 tiles needed to build 4-square from 3-square)**

Students can build squares from cardboard squares or some other objects of their choosing.

Encourage them to gather data about building the squares. Have the students look for patterns in the gathered data and discuss the possibilities of building a 30-square.

After about half the chapter has been completed, have students show you their work on the project. If they are behind schedule, you may want to give them intermediate deadlines in order to check their work.

Additional Leads to Follow

- *Write some simple number patterns. What rules tell you how to find the next number in each pattern?*
- *In a number pattern, how can you find the rule that tells you how to find the next number?*

Keeping a Project Notebook

Some suggestions for students' notebooks are:

- Have students draw sketches of sample squares and examples to show how to find the number of tiles, the number of tiles in each border, and the number of tiles needed to build a square from the previous square.
- Include all calculations, together with explanations for solving the problems.

Project Organizer

Related Exercises
p. 236
p. 249
p. 258

Follow Up
p. 268

Teacher's Notes
pp. 228, 236, 249, 258

Community Resources
- interior decorators or contractors who use tiles for decorating

Materials and Manipulatives
- materials for constructing squares
- graph paper

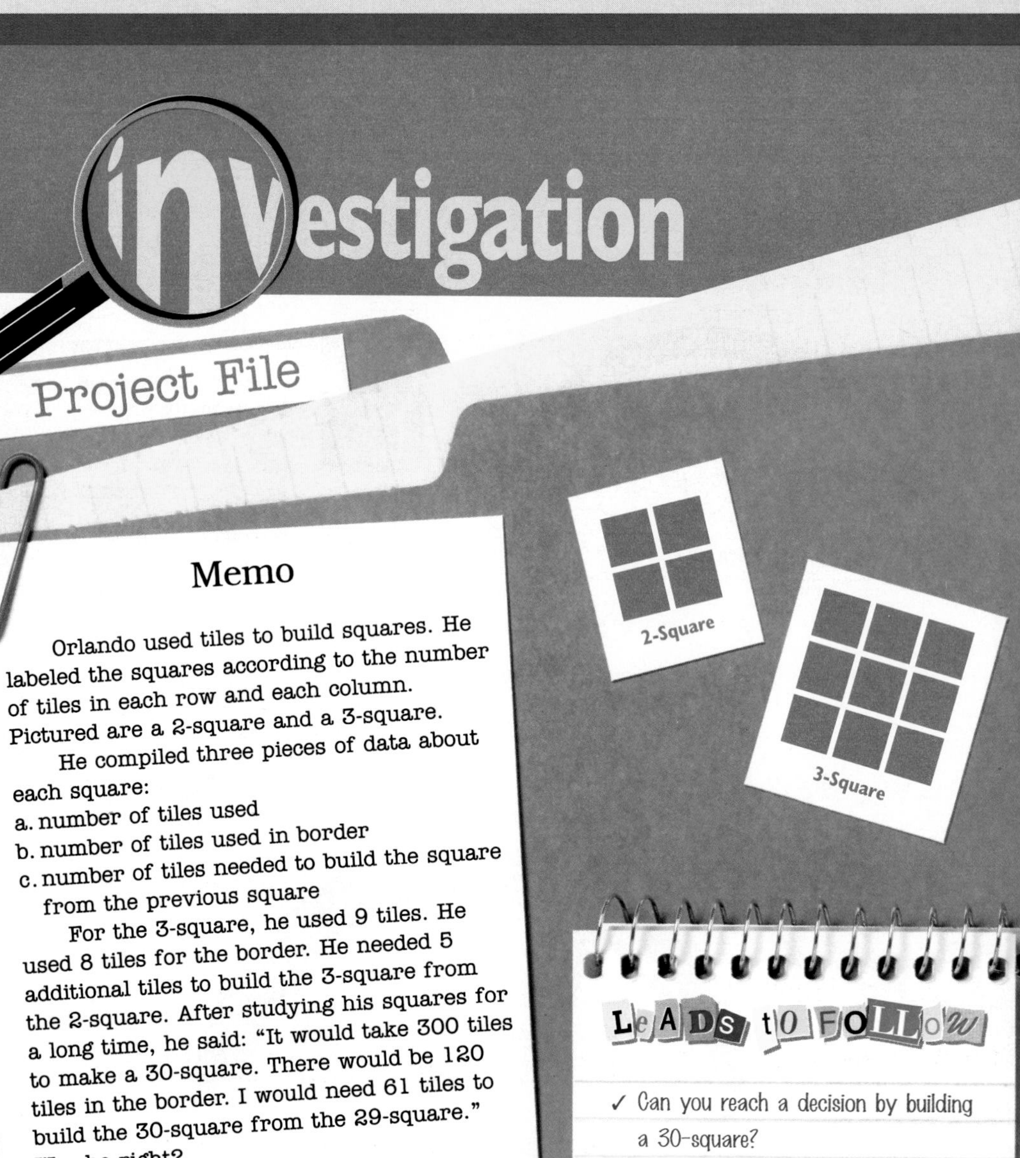

investigation
Project File
Memo
Orlando used tiles to build squares. He labeled the squares according to the number of tiles in each row and each column. Pictured are a 2-square and a 3-square.
He compiled three pieces of data about each square:
a. number of tiles used
b. number of tiles used in border
c. number of tiles needed to build the square from the previous square
For the 3-square, he used 9 tiles. He used 8 tiles for the border. He needed 5 additional tiles to build the 3-square from the 2-square. After studying his squares for a long time, he said: "It would take 300 tiles to make a 30-square. There would be 120 tiles in the border. I would need 61 tiles to build the 30-square from the 29-square." Was he right?
2-Square
3-Square
LEADS to FOLLOW
✓ Can you reach a decision by building a 30-square?
✓ How can you use patterns in your investigation?
✓ How did Orlando find the data for the 3-square?
Mission: Decide whether Orlando was right or wrong about each of his claims. Then write an explanation telling how you reached your decision.
228

6-1

Connecting to Prior Knowledge

Ask students to name measurements that are often used to describe the size of land or houses, such as square miles or square feet. Ask students what they think the word *square* refers to.

THINK AND DISCUSS

DIVERSITY Some students may try to use formulas to find the areas in Questions 1–3. Encourage them to first make an estimate by taking advantage of the grids. Then help them use any formulas they remember and want to use. Students who come to this task with no skills in finding area may be delighted to find that they can arrive empirically at a correct answer. Ask students to respect each other's thought processes, and to give everyone a chance to think through the question before anyone says the answer aloud.

Question 5: Have students discuss their estimation strategies.

Error Alert! Students may lose track of squares they have already counted for Questions 1–5. ***Remediation*** Have students use tracing paper to trace the drawings in the textbook. They can then check or number each square as it is counted.

ESL AUDITORY LEARNERS For Question 5, have students work with a partner to describe aloud a procedure for estimating the area of an irregular shape.

Ongoing Assessment Ask students to use a metric ruler to draw a 10×10 square centimeter grid. Challenge students to draw an irregular shape of their own choice that has an approximate area of 55 cm². Have students then use estimation strategies to check each other's graphs.

TACTILE LEARNERS Another strategy for Question 5 and finding areas of irregular shapes involves cutting out the irregular edges

What's Ahead

- Estimating area

6-1 Estimating Area

THINK AND DISCUSS

When you find the number of *square units* inside a figure, you are finding the area of the figure.

1. How many square units are in each figure? Describe your method for finding each area. Count squares and half squares.

a. 8 square units

b. 2 square units

c. 2 square units

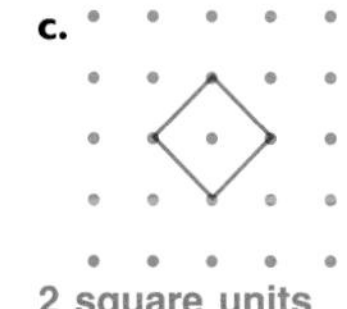

Some of the standard units we use to measure area are square centimeters (cm²), square meters (m²), square inches (in.²), square feet (ft²), and square yards (yd²).

2. Name some other units of area. Samples: square miles (mi²), square millimeters (mm²), acres (a).

This figure is shown on centimeter graph paper.

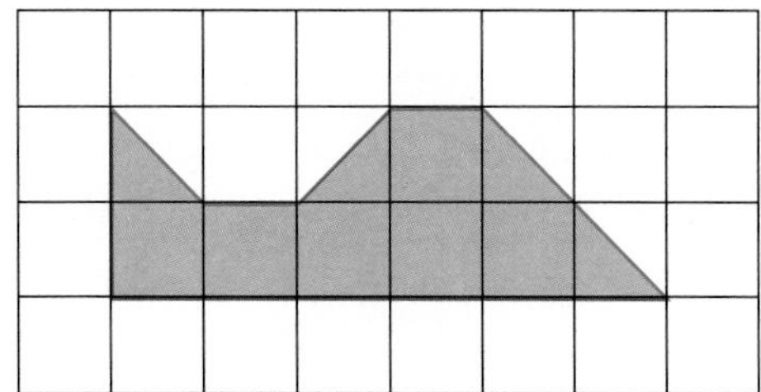

3. a. What is the area of each square of the graph paper? 1 cm²
   b. What is the area of the shaded figure? 8 cm²
   c. How did you find the area? Count 6 whole, 4 half squares.
   d. Suppose each square represents 9 m². What is the area? 72 m²

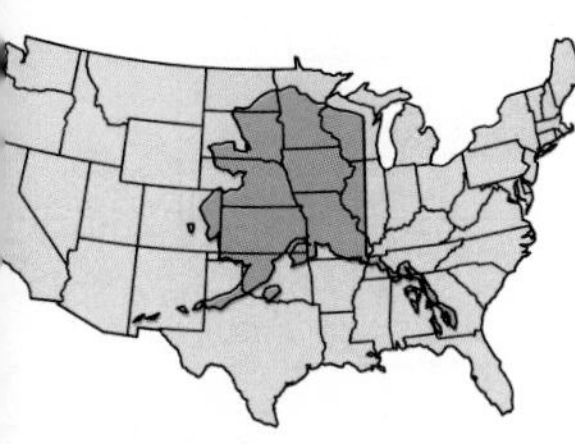

WHAT? If the United States was made up of states the size of Alaska, there would only be enough area for six states. **How many states do you think would fit if they all were the size of your state?**

Source: *Comparisons*

Answers may vary. Samples:
AZ: about 33
CA: about 23
FL: about 56

> *"The shrewd guess, the fertile hypothesis, the courageous leap to a tentative conclusion—these are the most valuable coin of the thinker at work."*
> —Jerome Bruner

Organizer

1. **Focus**
   Connecting to Prior Knowledge
2. **Teach**
   Think and Discuss
   Work Together
3. **Closure**
   Wrap Up

Vocabulary/Symbols
square units

Skills Reviewed in Context of Lesson
- identifying area

Materials and Manipulatives
On Your Own Exercises 12, 19: centimeter graph paper

Student Resources
Extra Practice
Student Study Guide
Practice, TR Ch. 6, p. 23
Student Study Guide, Spanish Resources, TR

continues next page

and filling the grid, as with puzzle pieces, to form a more nearly rectangular shape.

KINESTHETIC LEARNERS Suggest that students apply the method of Questions 4 and 5 in estimating the area of an irregular plot of ground near the school. Have them report their methods and results to the class, using a map they have drawn.

WORK TOGETHER

Encourage students to use tracing paper to copy the map of Australia. Then have students write in each square their estimation of the area of land in the square. Have the pairs of students compare their maps and strategies.

ESL AUDITORY LEARNERS Have one student in each group read the directions aloud before beginning the activity. Ask the group to discuss the task before starting the calculations.

Wrap Up

What's the Big Idea? Ask students to explain how to estimate the area of a figure.

Journal Have students think about how area is measured. Ask students: *Why is area not measured in circles or triangles? What is special about a square?*

Connections Have a discussion about how estimating area is used. You may want to start with these examples:

- **Entertainment** (adjusting size of a movie screen, picking a suitably sized room for a party)
- **Parks and Recreation** (determining a limit for the number of visitors to a park or the number of boats on a lake, choosing the right tent size for a family, setting up a football field or volleyball court at a picnic)

Organizer, continued

Teacher Resources

Teaching Transparencies 1, 16, 61
Transparency Masters, TR p. 2
Lesson Planner, TR Ch. 6, p. 2

Prentice Hall Technology

Multimedia Math

- Hot Page™ 6-1

Computer Item Generator

- 6-1

Fact of the Day

The total volume of the five Great Lakes is about 5,475 cubic mi, more than 6,000 trillion gallons.

—*Information Please Almanac*

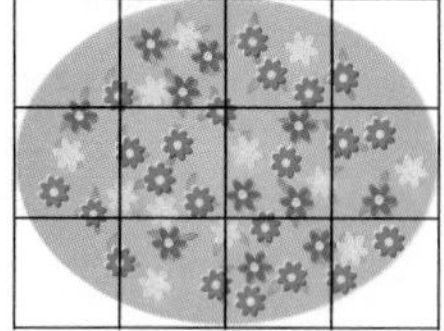

Sometimes an exact area is difficult to find but an estimate is enough. If you are using a graph, you can decide whether each square is full, almost full, about half full, or almost empty.

Accept any reasonable estimates.

4. Estimate the area of the flower bed. Each square represents 1 m^2. about 10 m^2

5. Each square below represents 4 mi^2.
   a. How many squares are filled or almost filled? 12
   b. How many squares are about half filled? 11
   c. Estimate the area of the lake. about 70 mi^2

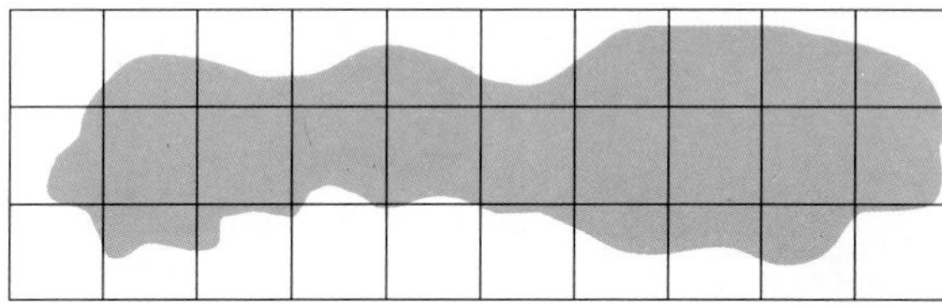

WORK TOGETHER

Work with a partner to estimate the area of Australia. Each square represents an area 240 miles by 240 miles.

about 3 million mi^2

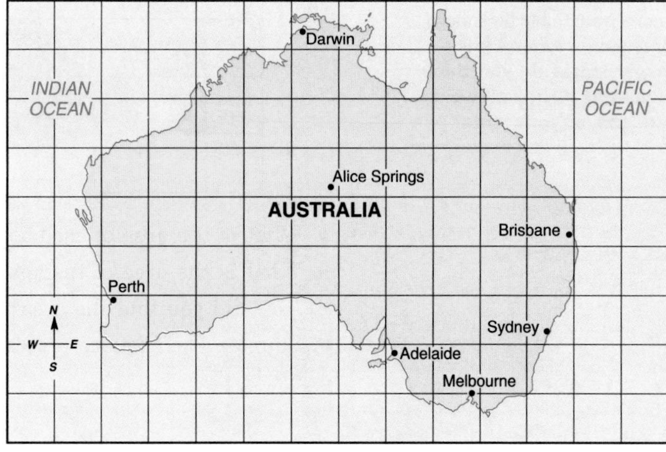

- **Technology** (using the wing area of an airplane to calculate its lift, making interchangeable tiles for the space shuttle)

Reteaching Activity Have students use blocks, tiles, or square crackers to model areas. Provide each student with about 20 of the items. Then ask students to model areas of 4, 9, 16, and 17 square units. After students have completed a model, ask for examples to share with the class. Point out that figures with the same area may have different shapes.

ON YOUR OWN

Students will need centimeter graph paper for Exercises 12 and 19.

ACTIVITY For Exercise 12, have students label their drawings with the area of each tracing.

CRITICAL THINKING Challenge students to think of several possible reasons in Exercise 12b.

WRITING For Exercise 13, encourage students to think of situations outside the classroom.

Exercise 15: Remind students that they could use a trace, cut, and fit strategy.

CRITICAL THINKING Challenge students to make an estimation before making a drawing or examining a yardstick for Exercise 16.

CONNECTION TO MEASUREMENT Exercise 16 reviews measurement by having students find the number of square inches in a square yard.

ESTIMATION In Exercises 17 and 18, encourage students to separate squares into three categories: full or almost full, half full, empty or almost empty. Remind students to round the areas by adding together incomplete squares that approximate whole squares.

ON YOUR OWN

Find the area of each figure. The area of each square is 1 cm².

6. 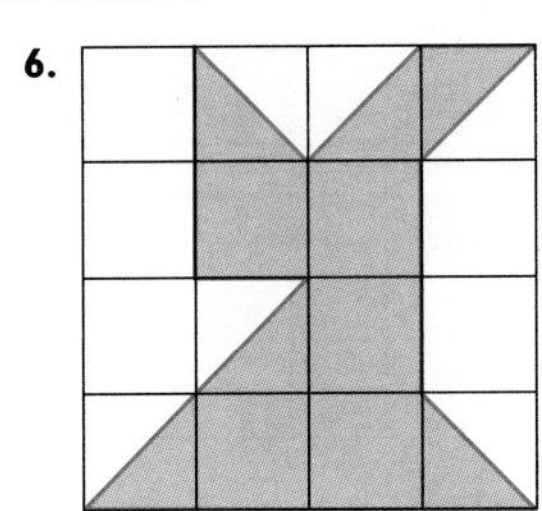

8 cm²

7.

8 cm²

Estimate the area of each figure. Assume that each square represents 1 in.². Samples given.

8. 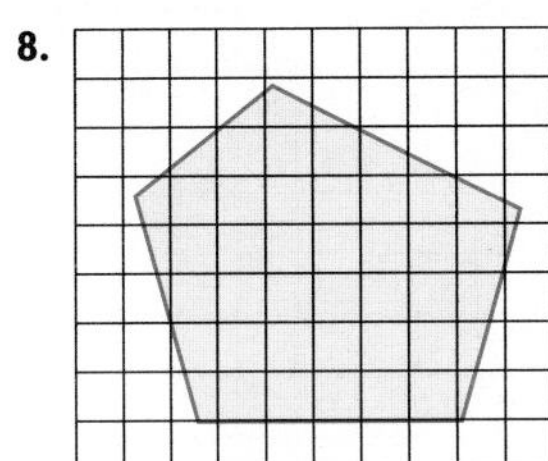

about 40 in.²

9. 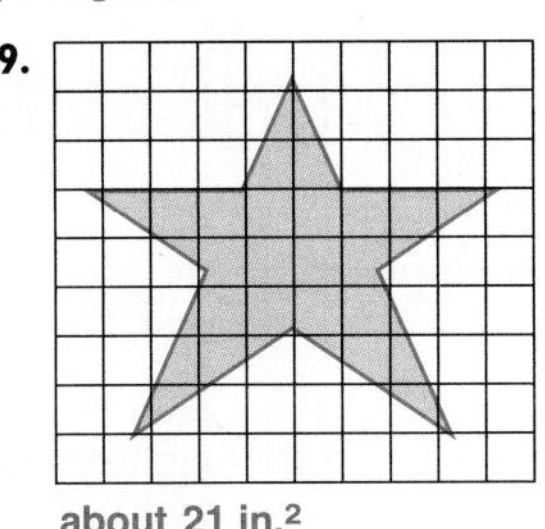

about 21 in.²

Estimate the area of each figure. Assume that each square represents 4 cm². Samples given.

10. 

about 56 cm²

11. 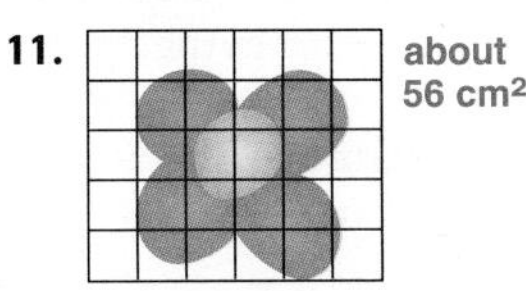

about 56 cm²

12. **Activity** Place your hand, with fingers touching, on centimeter graph paper. Trace around your hand. On a second sheet of centimeter graph paper, trace around your hand with the fingers spread apart. Try to draw a line at the same place on the wrist for both drawings.

  a. Estimate the area of each hand. Answers may vary.

  b. **Critical Thinking** What might account for any differences in your two estimates for part (a)?
  Sample: the partial squares in the second drawing are harder to count.

Mixed REVIEW

1. What is the sum of the first 20 odd numbers? 400

Solve each equation.

2. $3x = 27$ 9
3. $17 = y \div 9$ 153

Evaluate each expression.

4. 4^2 16
5. $(3 + 2)^2$ 25

6. Use the digits 1, 3, 5, 7, and 9 in any order to write a multiplication problem with the greatest product.

6. 93 × 751

PH Multimedia Math Hot Page™ 6-1

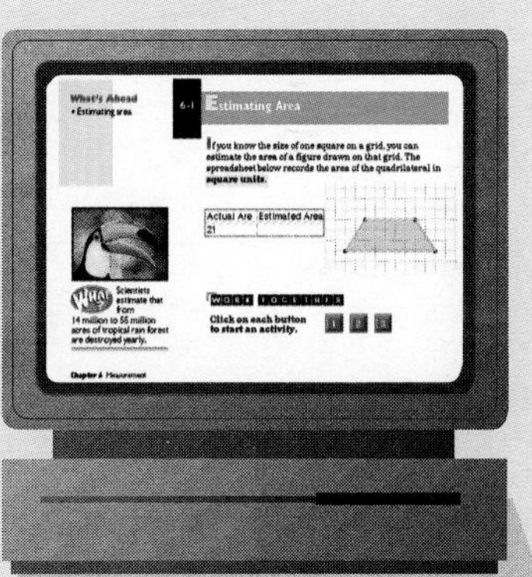

Assignment Options

Core: 6–9, 13, 17, 18, MR all	
Reinforce: 10, 11, 14, 15	**Enrich:** 12, 16, 19

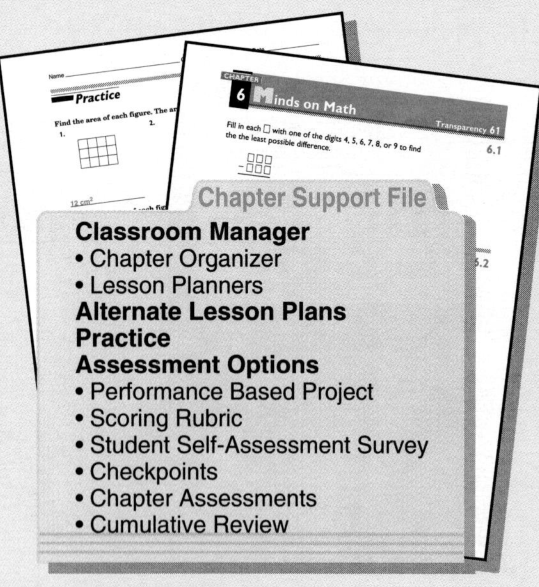

Minds on Math available in Teaching Transparencies

Math Minutes

Describe the pattern: 18, 15.25, 12.5, 9.75, . . .

Start with 18. Subtract 2.75.

Materials for 6-2

- square tiles
- graph paper

13. Sample: buying paint for a room, grass seed for a lawn

13. Writing Describe two situations where finding an estimate of an area, rather than actually measuring the area, is sufficient. See left.

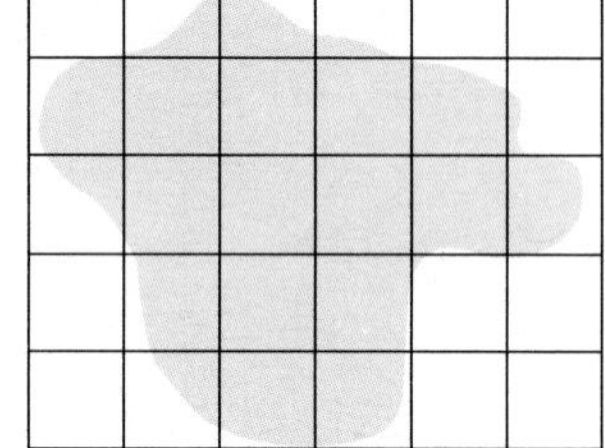

14. **Choose A, B, C, or D.** Each square represents 100 m^2. Which is the best estimate for the area of the figure? C

A. 3,000 m^2 **B.** 15.5 cm^2

C. 1,550 m^2 **D.** 15.5 m^2

15. Which region has the greatest area? Which has the least area? B;A

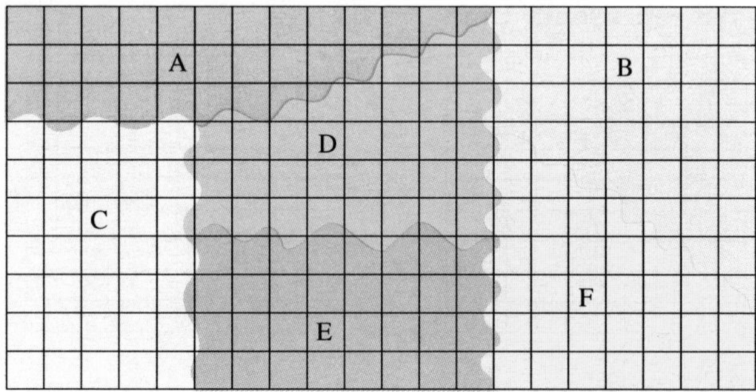

The Homestead Act provided opportunities for thousands of people. The act allowed settlers to get 160 acres of land for free. If settlers didn't want to improve the land, they could pay $1.25 per acre.

16. Critical Thinking How many square inches are in a square yard? Use a drawing to show how you found your answer. 1,296 $in.^2$; See Solution Key.

Estimate **Estimate the area of each name. Each square represents 1 $in.^2$.** Accept reasonable estimates. Samples given.

17.

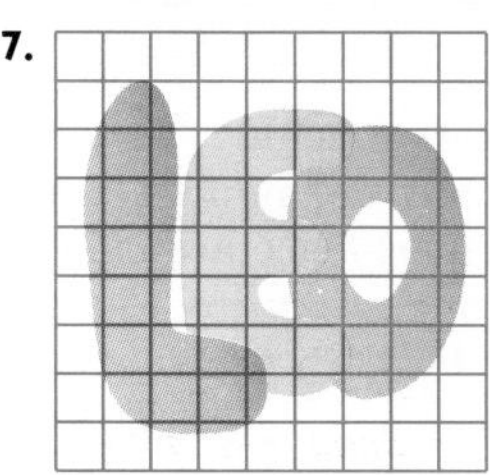

about 41 $in.^2$

18.

about 48 $in.^2$

19. Draw your name on graph paper. Estimate the area of your name in square units. Answers may vary.

6-2

Connecting to Prior Knowledge

Ask students to recall what they learned about the areas of squares. Then ask students to answer the following questions:

- *On centimeter graph paper, how long is each side of a square?* **(one centimeter)**
- *What is the area of each square?* **(one square centimeter)**

THINK AND DISCUSS

Questions 1–2: Have students test their answers by drawing the arrangements on graph paper. Some students may feel more comfortable using square tiles to solve the problem.

VISUAL LEARNERS Have students use square tiles or blocks to form different arrangements of the garden plots.

DIVERSITY Students can explore Questions 1 and 2 in a variety of ways. Some students could work in groups at the board to draw various possibilities. Others could use square floor tiles, if the classroom or hall has them. Still another group could cut squares of paper, and others could use square blocks. Ask students which method they prefer as you form the groups.

ESL **ESL** Review meanings of the terms *length* and *width.* Encourage students to use the words length and width when reading formulas containing *l* and *w.*

Example

- *Since only two sides of each part of the backyard are labeled with dimensions, how do you know the lengths of the other two sides?* **(The lengths of opposite sides of a rectangle are equal and the widths of opposite sides of a rectangle are equal.)**

What's Ahead

- Finding area and perimeter of rectangles and squares

6-2 Area of Rectangles and Squares

WHAT YOU'LL NEED

✓ Square tiles

✓ Graph paper

THINK AND DISCUSS

Moses is planning a garden. He decides to use 12 square garden plots that measure 1 m on each side. He wants to arrange them in a rectangle. After he lays out the plots, he will put a fence around the outside of the garden.

Problem Solving Hint

Drawing diagrams may help.

1. a. How could Moses arrange the plots so that he would have the least perimeter and use the least amount of fence? in a 3 m by 4 m rectangle
   b. How could Moses arrange the plots so that he would have the greatest perimeter? a 12 m by 1 m rectangle
2. a. What is the area of the arrangement with the least perimeter? 12 m^2
   b. What is the area of the arrangement with the greatest perimeter? 12 m^2
   c. Will the area change if Moses arranges the plots in a nonrectangular shape? Why or why not? No; no matter how he arranges the plots, there are 12 with area 1 m^2 each.

In the garden-plot problem you can count the square plots to find the area of the rectangular arrangement. When you do not have squares to count, you can find the area A of a rectangle by multiplying the length l and the width w. You can find the perimeter P by adding $l + w + l + w$ to get $2l + 2w$, or $2(l + w)$.

WHEN? In 600 B.C. Nebuchadnezzar had the Hanging Gardens of Babylon built. They were so beautiful and complex that they became one of the seven wonders of the ancient world.

Source: *Encyclopedia Britannica*

Area and Perimeter of a Rectangle

$$A = l \times w$$

$$P = 2(l + w)$$

A square is a rectangle in which the length and the width are equal. You can find the area A of a square by squaring the length s of a side. The perimeter P is $4s$.

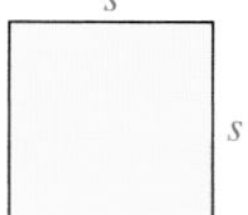

“I don't want to get to the end of my life and find that I lived just the length of it. I want to have lived the width of it as well.”

—DIANE ACKERMAN

Organizer

1. **Focus**
   Connecting to Prior Knowledge
2. **Teach**
   Think and Discuss
   Work Together
3. **Closure**
   Try These
   Wrap Up

Skills Reviewed in Context of Lesson

- using customary units

Materials and Manipulatives

- square tiles (1 set for each group)
- graph paper (for each group)

On Your Own Exercises 12–14: centimeter ruler

Student Resources

Extra Practice
Student Study Guide
Practice, TR Ch. 6, p. 24
Student Study Guide, Spanish Resources, TR
Alternate Lesson, TR Ch. 6, pp. 11–14

continues next page

- *Find the length of the house that extends beyond the backyard on both sides.*
(32 − 25 = 7; 7 ÷ 2 = $3\frac{1}{2}$; each piece is $3\frac{1}{2}$ ft long)

Additional Example *The perimeter of a square is 48 cm. Find its area.*
Since $P = 4s$, $4s = 48$ and $s = 12$.
Since $A = s^2$, $A = 12^2$, or $A = 144$ cm^2.

Journal Ask students to compare the steps for finding the area and perimeter of a square and the steps for finding the area and perimeter of a rectangle. Ask: *What accounts for the differences?*

WORK TOGETHER

Have students work in groups of three or four. Give each group 30 square tiles.

Error Alert! For Question 6, students may think that the area of a rectangle is always larger than its perimeter since area involves multiplication and perimeter involves addition. ***Remediation*** Encourage students to test the limits of possible combinations for the tiles by forming the smallest rectangle they can make and the largest rectangle they can make. Have them compare the area and perimeter for each rectangle.

Ongoing Assessment Give pairs of students 12 squares and ask them to make a table giving the perimeter and area of all the different rectangles that can be formed with these squares, along with the dimensions. Have each pair compare results with another pair.

Dimensions	Perimeter	Area
12 × 1	26 units	12 sq. units
6 × 2	16 units	12 sq. units
4 × 3	14 units	12 sq. units

Organizer, continued

Teacher Resources

Teaching Transparencies 1, 61, 64
Lesson Planner, TR Ch. 6, p. 3

Prentice Hall Technology
Computer Item Generator
- 6-2

Other Available Technology
- calculator

Elastic Lines by Sunburst: Questions 9–11 *(optional)*

Fact of the Day

The Great Wall of China is so long and broad that it is visible from the moon.

—*Information Please Kids' Almanac*

Area and Perimeter of a Square

$A = s \times s = s^2$

$P = 4s$

3. Find the perimeter and the area of a square with sides 8 cm long. **32 cm; 64 cm^2**

Example Find the area and perimeter of the backyard.

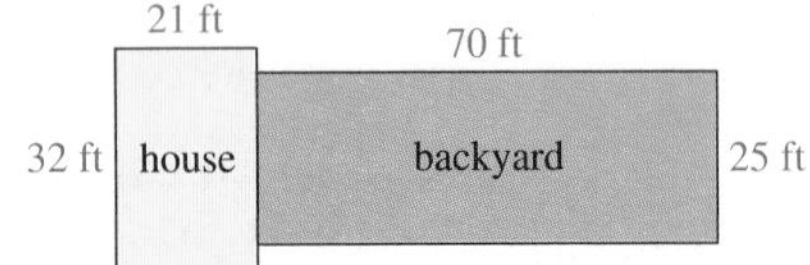

- The length of the backyard is 70 ft. The width is 25 ft. To find the area, use $A = l \times w$.
  $A = l \times w = 70 \times 25 = 1{,}750$
- To find the perimeter, use $P = 2(l + w)$.
  $P = 2(l + w) = 2(70 + 25) = 2 \times 95 = 190$

The area of the backyard is 1,750 ft^2. The perimeter is 190 ft.

***The 1,250 m^2 garden** maze at Hampton Court in England had its 300th anniversary in 1991. Every year thousands of tourists pay $2.15 to try to find their way through the 2.5 m tall hedges.*

Source: *Encyclopedia Britannica*

4. In the Example, why was the area given in square feet and the perimeter in feet? **Sample: area measures the two-dimensional space inside a plane figure.**
5. If you were to fence the backyard in the Example, would you need 190 ft of fence? Why or why not? **Sample: no; fencing would not be needed along the back wall of the house.**

WORK TOGETHER

Use square tiles to form the following rectangles. Record the results on graph paper.
See Solution Key. Sample dimensions are given.

6. Form at least two rectangles where the area (in square units) is less than the perimeter (in units). **6 by 2, 18 by 2**
7. Form at least one rectangle where the area is equal to the perimeter. **4 by 4**
8. Form at least two rectangles where the area is greater than the perimeter. **3 by 8, 5 by 5**

TRY THESE

Exercises 9–11: Make sure students use correct units in their answers.

TECHNOLOGY OPTION For Exercises 9–11, students can use geometry software.

Wrap Up

What's the Big Idea? Ask students: *How do you find the area and perimeter of a rectangle or square?*

Reteaching Activity Have students work in groups of three. Provide each group with a geoboard and a few sheets of centimeter graph paper. Ask students to form all the squares from the smallest possible to the largest possible size on the geoboard or a sheet of graph paper. Have students make a table showing the area and side of each square. Then have students draw on graph paper a rectangle with the same area as each square (except the smallest and largest). Have students compare their figures and data.

Connections Have students discuss situations in which the area and perimeter of a square or rectangle are used. You may want to begin with these.

- **Interior Design** (figuring the amount of wallpaper or floor covering needed, finding the appropriate number and size of furniture for the area)
- **Farming** (estimating acreage, crop yield, necessary water, and harvest time for different-sized fields)
- **Sports** (marking courts or fields, designing stadiums)

ON YOUR OWN

Students will need centimeter rulers for Exercises 12–14.

CONNECTION TO PATTERNS Exercises 26 and 27 have students find patterns for possible area and perimeter combinations.

Assignment Options

Core: 12–20, 30, MR all	
Reinforce: 21–23, 25, 26, 28	**Enrich:** 24, 27, 29

TRY THESE

Find the area and perimeter of each rectangle.

9.
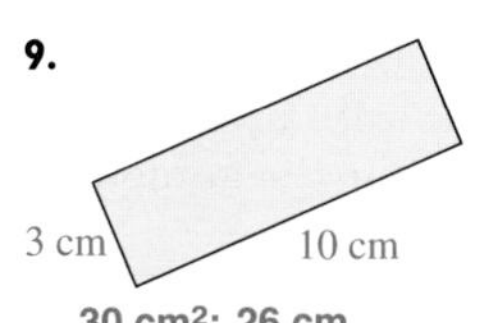

30 cm²; 26 cm

10.
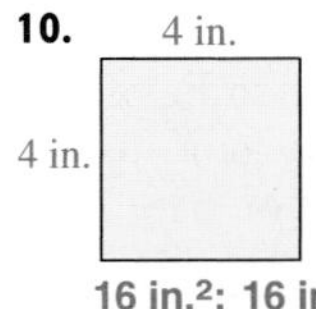

16 in.²; 16 in.

11.
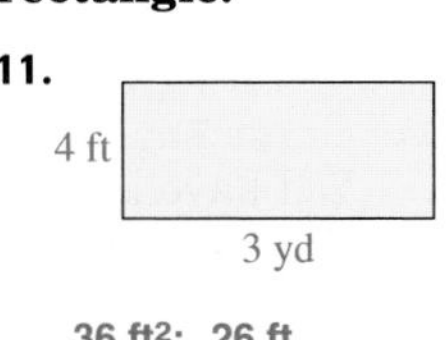

36 ft²; 26 ft

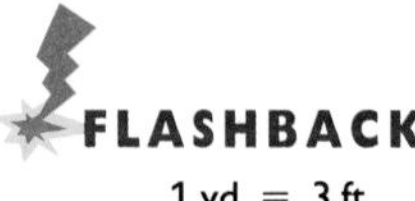

1 yd = 3 ft

ON YOUR OWN

Use a centimeter ruler to measure the length and width of each rectangle. Then find the perimeter and area.

12.

10 cm; 4 cm²

13.
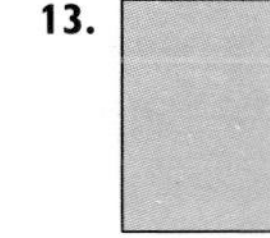
7 cm; 3 cm²

14.

9.4 cm; 5.5 cm²

Choose **Use a calculator, paper and pencil, or mental math.**

15. The length of a rectangle is 20 in. The width is 10 in.
  a. What is the area? 200 in.²
  b. What is the perimeter? 60 in.

16. The area of a rectangle is 24 in.². One dimension is 6 in. What is the perimeter? 20 in.

17. The perimeter of a square is 12 in. What is the area of the square? 9 in.²

18. The length of a rectangle is 16.5 cm. The width is 8.2 cm. What is the area of the rectangle? 135.3 cm²

19. The perimeter of a rectangle is 22 ft. The width is 4 ft. What is the length? 7 ft

20. **a.** How much fencing do you need to enclose a rectangular garden that is 9 ft by 6 ft? 30 ft
  b. If you use fence sections that are 3 ft wide, how many sections will you need? 10

Mixed REVIEW

Use Napier's rods to find each product.

1. 46 × 8 368
2. 912 × 9 8,208

Estimate the area of the circle in square units.

3.
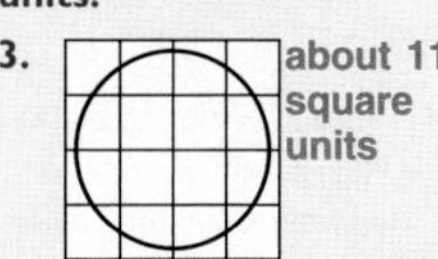
about 11 square units

4. Yuma plans to drive 1,350 mi. His car averages 25 mi/gal. The gas tank holds 15 gal. Gas costs $1.299 per gallon.
  a. How many tankfuls will he need? 3.6
  b. How much will the gas cost? $70.15

WRITING Have students write labels and captions for their illustrations for Exercise 29.

CHAPTER INVESTIGATION Have students work in groups of four for Exercise 30. One student can construct the table for part a, one can write the description for part b, and the other students can be responsible for drawing diagrams for both parts. Encourage all students to take equal roles in brainstorming for possible answers.

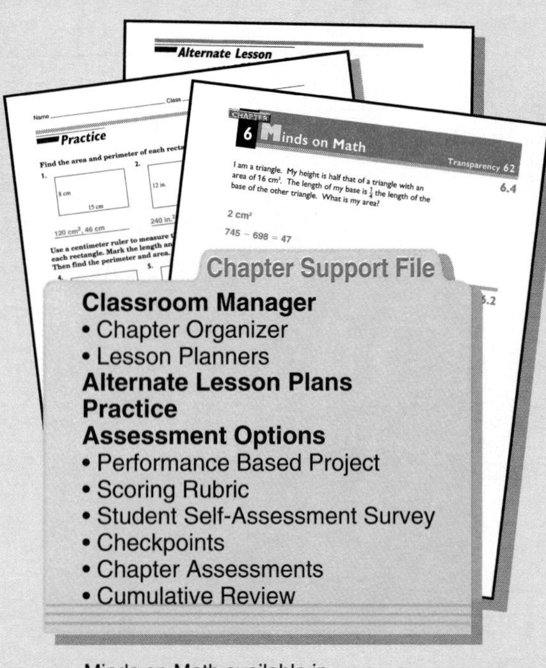

Minds on Math available in Teaching Transparencies

The length of a computer lab is 11 ft more than half of its width. What is the perimeter of the lab if it is 18 ft wide?
76 ft

Materials for 6-3

- centimeter graph paper
- scissors

The Great Wall of China spans 2,971 km along a mountain range in Northern China. The wall is 14 m high and 7 m thick in some places. **If you traveled along the wall at 10 km/h, how long would it take you to travel its length?**

Source: *A Ride Along the Great Wall*
297.1 h

21. Each side of a square is 0.5 m long.
    a. What is the perimeter? 2 m
    b. What is the area? 0.25 m^2

22. **Gardening** You'd like to have a garden with area 18 ft^2. You have a space 6 ft long in which to put the garden. How wide should it be? 3 ft

23. A rectangle is 2 m by 50 cm.
    a. What is the perimeter? 5 m
    b. What is the area? 1 m^2

24. **Data File 3 (pp. 92–93)** Find the area of the world's smallest stamp. 0.1147 in.^2

25. **Choose A, B, C, or D.** A rectangle is 15.95 m by 8.25 m. Which of the following is the best estimate for the area? D
    A. about 48 m
    B. about 48 m^2
    C. about 128 m
    D. about 128 m^2

26. The area of a rectangular parking lot is 24 yd^2. Find all the possible whole-number dimensions in yards of the parking lot. 24 by 1, 12 by 2, 8 by 3, 6 by 4

27. The perimeter of a rectangle is 10 m. Find all the possible whole-number dimensions in meters. 4 by 1, 3 by 2

28. Estimate the area of this rectangle.
    Accept any reasonable estimate; about 228 m^2.

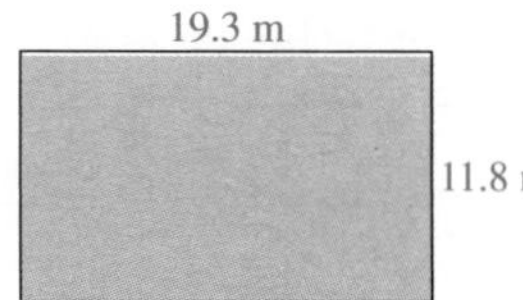

29. **Writing** Suppose you know the area of a rectangle. Can you then find its perimeter? Why or why not? Use examples to illustrate your answer. See below.

30. a. **Investigation (p. 228)** Make a table that shows the number of tiles you would need to build each tile square from a 1-square through a 10-square. See below.
    b. Describe the relationship between the number of tiles needed to build a tile square and the area of the square. They are the same.

29. No; Example: a rectangle with area 12 m^2 might have dimensions 12 m by 1 m or 2.5 m by 4.8 m.

30.a.

square	1	2	3	4	5	6	7	8	9	10
no. of tiles	1	4	9	16	25	36	49	64	81	100

6-3

Connecting to Prior Knowledge

Have students use their knowledge of the areas of squares and rectangles to guess how the area of a triangle can be found. Ask students to draw a rectangle divided by a diagonal. Ask: *What does the diagonal form?* **(two triangles)** *What is the area of one triangle?* **(one half the area of the rectangle)**

WORK TOGETHER

Have students work with a partner. Provide each pair with a sheet of graph paper and scissors.

ESL Have one student in each pair read the directions aloud before beginning the activity.

TACTILE LEARNERS Have students trace the triangle, rhombus, trapezoid, and hexagon pattern blocks. Ask students to find the area of the pieces, if the area of the triangle is 2.75 cm^2.

Ongoing Assessment Have students repeat the Work Together activity with their partners using different parallelograms. Challenge students to describe the pattern that emerges. Have the class discuss patterns for finding the area of a parallelogram and then go on to the variable expression for area on the next page. Ask students if the rule describes the pattern.

THINK AND DISCUSS

Error Alert! Students may confuse the height of a parallelogram with the length of one of its sides when finding the area of a parallelogram, as in Question 4. ***Remediation*** Remind students that the height of a parallelogram is a segment that is perpendicular to a side. This side is called the base of the parallelogram.

What's Ahead

- Developing and using area formulas for parallelograms and triangles

6-3 Area of Parallelograms and Triangles

WHAT YOU'LL NEED

✓ Graph paper 

✓ Scissors

1.b. 12 sq. units; the rectangle is formed by rearranging parts of the parallelogram.

WORK TOGETHER

- Draw a nonrectangular parallelogram on graph paper.
- Draw the perpendicular segment from one vertex to the base.
- Cut the parallelogram out and cut along the perpendicular segment.
- Rearrange the two pieces to form a rectangle.

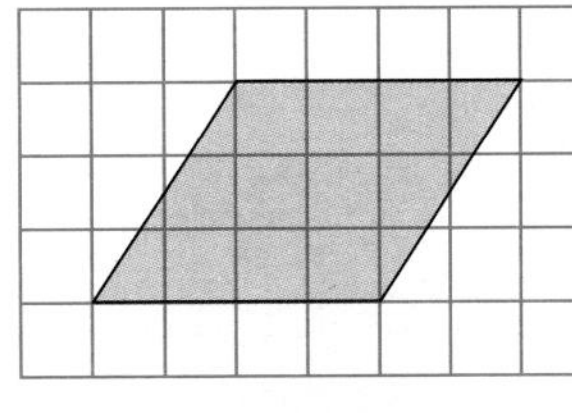

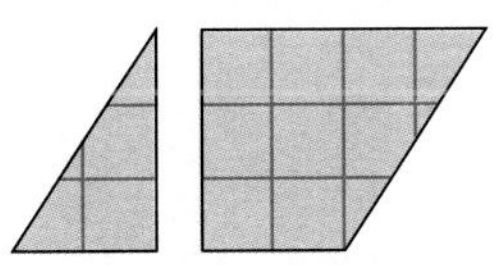

1. a. What is the area of the rectangle? 12 sq. units
   b. What was the area of the original parallelogram? Why? See left.
   c. Compare your models to those made by other groups. Are the results the same? Yes

Use centimeter graph paper to draw two congruent triangles. Cut out the triangles. Arrange them to form a parallelogram.

2. How does the area of each triangle compare to the area of the parallelogram? The area of each triangle is half that of the parallelogram.

In this pattern, the perimeter doubles each time, while the area increases slightly. If you repeat the steps, the perimeter gets gigantic but the area stays less than four times the area of the original figure.

THINK AND DISCUSS

Any side of a parallelogram or triangle can be considered the base, with length b. The *height* h of the parallelogram or triangle is the length of a perpendicular segment from a vertex to the line containing the base.

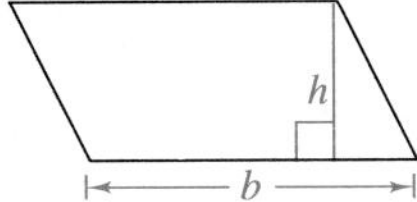

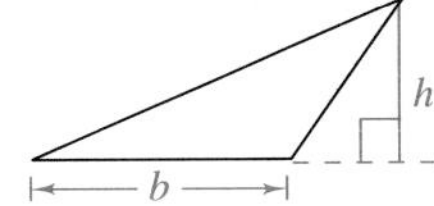

"Living is a constant process of deciding what we are going to do."
—JOSÉ ORTEGA Y GASSET

Organizer

1. **Focus**
   Connecting to Prior Knowledge
2. **Teach**
   Work Together
   Think and Discuss
3. **Closure**
   Try These
   Wrap Up

Vocabulary/Symbols
height, h

Skills Reviewed in Context of Lesson
- identifying parallelograms
- recognizing perpendicular segments and congruent triangles

Materials and Manipulatives
- centimeter graph paper (for each group)
- scissors (1 pair for each group)

On Your Own Exercises 12–15: dot paper; Exercise 16: centimeter ruler

Student Resources
Extra Practice
Student Study Guide
Practice, TR Ch. 6, p. 25
Student Study Guide, Spanish Resources, TR
Checkpoint, TR Ch. 6, p. 36

continues next page

Example

- *How can you find the lengths of the sides of the center rectangle?* **(Add the vertical segments of 2 in. and 3 in.)**

Additional Example *Find the area of the figure.*

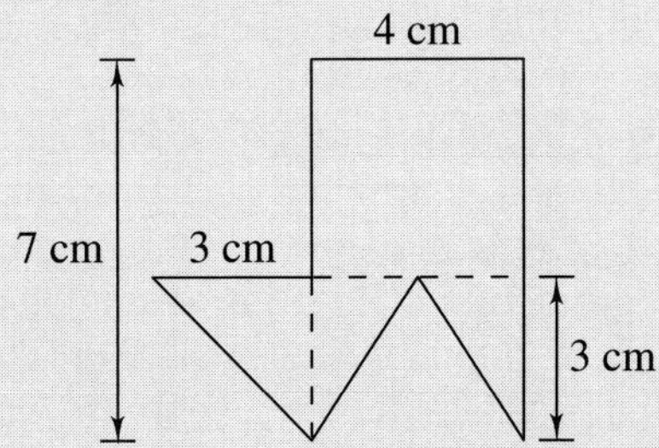

Area of larger triangle = $\frac{1}{2}(3 \times 3)$ = 4.5 cm^2

Area of smaller triangles = 2 × $\frac{1}{2}(3 \times 2)$ = 6 cm^2

Area of square = 4 × 4 = 16 cm^2

Total area = 4.5 cm^2 + 6 cm^2 + 16 cm^2 = 26.5 cm^2

TRY THESE

Exercises 6–9: Have students list all steps and discuss strategies.

TECHNOLOGY OPTION For Exercises 6–8, students can use the capabilities of a geometry software program to explore area for squares, rectangles, triangles, and parallelograms. Have the students rotate and flip the figures to show that area does not change with transformation.

Wrap Up

What's the Big Idea? Ask students to describe how to develop and use area formulas for parallelograms and triangles.

Journal Have students write whether they prefer working with pictures and figures, or with numbers and formulas. Ask them to tell why they have this preference and to give examples.

Organizer, continued

Teacher Resources

Teaching Transparencies 1, 61, 64
Transparency Masters, TR pp. 2, 19
Lesson Planner, TR Ch. 6, p. 4

Prentice Hall Technology

Multimedia Math
- Math Tools, Geometry

Computer Item Generator
- 6-3

Other Available Technology
The Geometric Supposer by Sunburst: Questions 6–8 *(optional)*

Fact of the Day

The world's first shopping center was built in 1896 at Roland Park in Baltimore, Maryland.

—Guinness Book of Records

In the Work Together activity you found that the area of a parallelogram is the same as the area of a rectangle with the same dimensions. The area of a triangle is related to the area of a parallelogram with the same base length and height.

Area of Parallelograms and Triangles
Area of a parallelogram = base length × height = bh
Area of a triangle = $\frac{1}{2}$ × base length × height = $\frac{1}{2}bh$

3. What is the area of the rectangle? **6 square units**
4. What is the area of the parallelogram that is not a rectangle? **6 square units**
5. What is the area of the triangle? **3 square units**

Sometimes it helps to divide a figure into smaller polygons. Then you can find the areas.

Example Find the area of the figure.

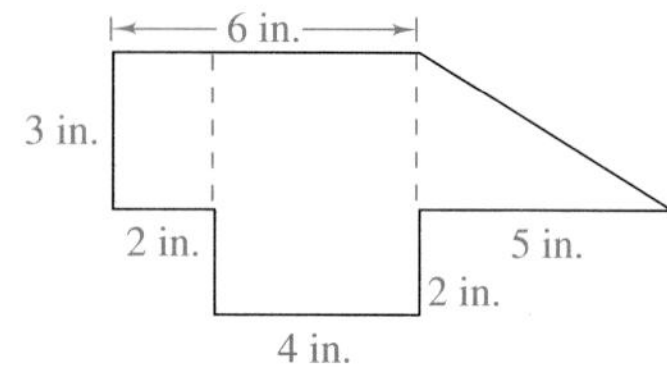

You could divide the polygon into two rectangles and a triangle, as shown by the dashed lines.

Then find the area of each of the polygons.

Area of smaller rectangle = 3 × 2 = 6 in.^{2}

Area of larger rectangle = 5 × 4 = 20 in.^{2}

Area of triangle = $\frac{1}{2}(5 \times 3) = \frac{1}{2} \times 15$ = 7.5 in.^{2}

Add the three areas to find the area of the composite figure.

6 in.^{2} + 20 in.^{2} + 7.5 in.^{2} = 33.5 in.^{2}

LOOK BACK What other ways could you divide the figure to find the area? **See Solution Key for sample answer.**

The Edmonton Mall in Alberta, Canada covers 5.2 million ft^2. The mall even has an indoor roller coaster.

Source: *Guinness Book of Records*

Connections Have a discussion about how the areas of parallelograms and triangles are used. You may want to start with these examples.

- **Media** (weather warning boxes on TV maps, using polygonal insets for graphics in newspapers or magazines)
- **Architecture** (designing buttresses or buildings with acute angles at the corners)
- **Arts and Crafts** (making sundials, using diamond patterns in fabric or quilts)

Reteaching Activity Have students form rectangles on geoboards. Then have students add two congruent triangles, one to each side of the rectangle, to form a parallelogram. Ask students to trade geoboards with a partner and find the area of each other's parallelogram. Have students repeat the activity, checking each other's answers.

ON YOUR OWN

Students will need dot paper for Exercises 12–15 and a centimeter ruler for Exercise 16.

CRITICAL THINKING For Exercise 17d, have students describe the differences among the figures.

CONNECTION TO GEOMETRY Exercise 18 reviews geometric concepts by having students compare different figures and their areas.

WRITING Have students include a diagram with their explanations for Exercise 19b.

TRY THESE

Find each area.

6. 6 square units

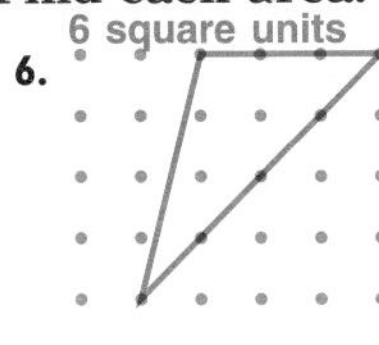

7. 8 square units

8.

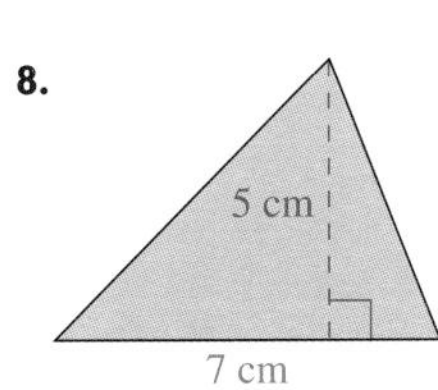

17.5 cm²

9.

38 m²

ON YOUR OWN

Find each perimeter and area.

10.

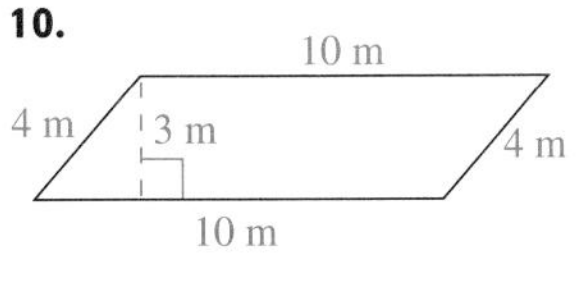

28 m; 30 m²

11.

54 cm; 90 cm²

Copy each figure on dot paper. Then find its area by dividing it into polygons for which you can find the areas. Sample divisions shown.

12. 12 square units

13. 9 square units

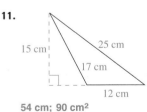

14. 13 square units

15. 16 square units

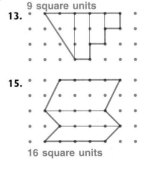

Equations are just the boring part of mathematics. I attempt to see things in terms of geometry.

—Stephen Hawking (1942–)

Assignment Options

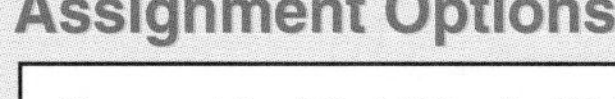

Core: 10–16, MR all, CH all	
Reinforce: 17a–c, 18	**Enrich:** 17d, 19

CHECK POINT

Exercises 1–4: Have students draw diagrams to help them find the answers.

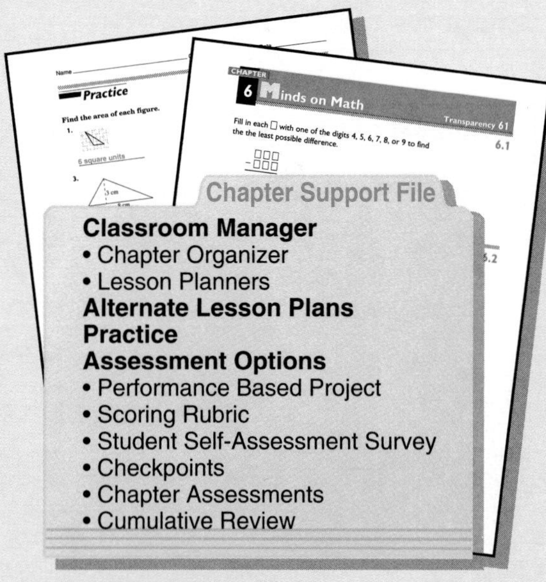

Minds on Math available in Teaching Transparencies

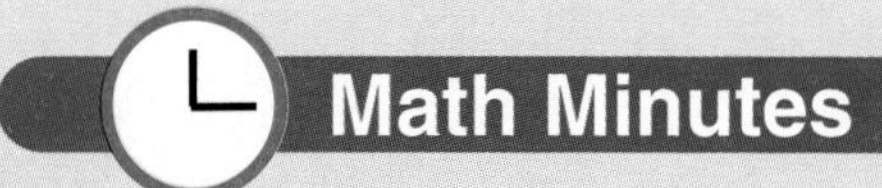

Write the decimal for two hundred six hundred-thousandths.
0.00206

Materials for 6-4

- computer *(optional)*
- geometry software *(optional)*
- calculator

Mixed REVIEW

Write *true* or *false*.

1. A butterfly's wings are symmetric. true
2. Your hand is symmetric. false

Find each area.

3. a square with sides 4 in. 16 in.^{2}
4. a rectangle with length 8 ft and width 3 ft 24 ft^2
5. A flim is worth more than a flam. A flum is worth more than a flom. If a flam is worth less than a flom, which is greater, a flum or a flam? a flum

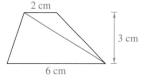

16. Use a centimeter ruler to measure the sides of the triangle. Then find its perimeter and its area. Sample: 15.3 cm; 7.9 cm^2

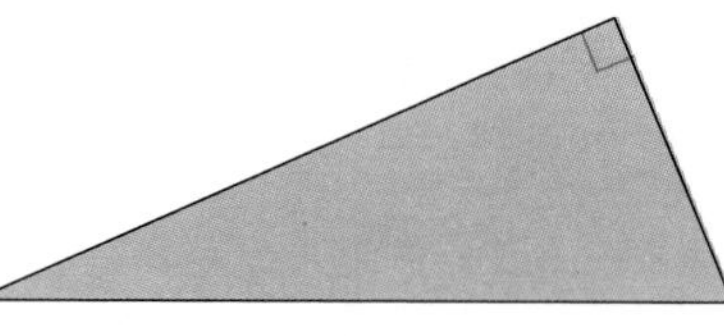

17. Find the area of each parallelogram.

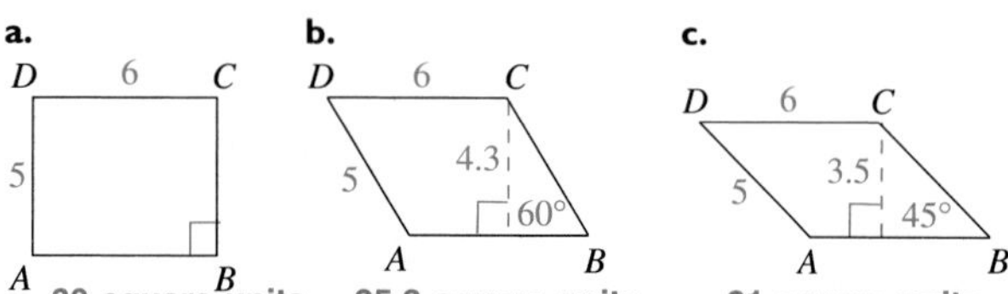

a. 30 square units b. 25.8 square units c. 21 square units

d. **Critical Thinking** How does the measure of $\angle B$ affect the area of the parallelogram? As the measure of $\angle B$ decreases, so does the area of the parallelogram.

18. **Choose A, B, C, or D.** Which statement is false? D
    - **A.** A nonrectangular parallelogram and a rectangle can have the same area.
    - **B.** A square is always a parallelogram.
    - **C.** You can divide a parallelogram into two congruent triangles.
    - **D.** Two rectangles with the same area always have the same perimeter.

2 cm

3 cm

6 cm

19. a. Copy the trapezoid on your paper. Divide it into two triangles. Then find its area. Sample division shown; 12 cm^2
    b. **Writing** Explain, using this trapezoid, how you can find the area of a trapezoid by dividing it into two triangles.
    19. b. Sample: Draw a diagonal of the trapezoid to form two triangles. Area $= \frac{1}{2} \times 2 \times 3 + \frac{1}{2} \times 6 \times 3 = 12$

CHECK POINT

1. A rectangle is 35 in. long. Its width is 5 in. What are its area and perimeter? 175 in.^{2}; 80 in.
2. How much lace do you need to trim a rectangular tablecloth that is 72 in. long and 48 in. wide? 240 in.

Find the perimeter and area of each figure.

3. rectangle: $l = 7$ in., $w = 12$ in. 38 in.; 84 in.^{2}
4. square: $s = 8.5$ cm 34 cm; 72.25 cm^2

CHAPTER 6

PROBLEM SOLVING PRACTICE

This page provides a variety of problems that can be used to reinforce and enhance the students' problem solving skills. Encourage students to read each problem carefully. Then have them refer to the list of problem solving strategies to help them decide how to solve the problems.

Point out, however, that not all questions require a strategy for solving, nor are all the strategies in the list used on this page.

USING MANIPULATIVES Provide tiles or counters for students to use to model the problem in Exercise 4.

Exercise 7: Ask students to draw a labeled diagram to support their answer.

Problem Solving Practice

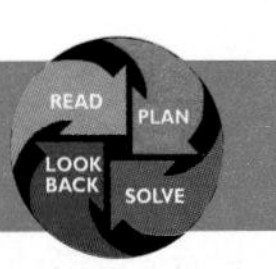

PROBLEM SOLVING STRATEGIES

Make a Table
Use Logical Reasoning
Solve a Simpler Problem
Too Much or Too Little Information
Look for a Pattern
Make a Model
Work Backward
Draw a Diagram
Guess and Test
Simulate a Problem
Use Multiple Strategies

Use any strategy to solve each problem. Show all your work.

1. Matsuda is saving his money to buy some basketball shoes that cost $78. He has $17 right now. Each week Matsuda earns $8 by mowing his neighbor's lawn. In how many weeks will he be able to buy the shoes? 8 weeks

2. Jamaica watched people walking dogs in the park. She counted a total of 17 people and dogs and a total of 54 legs. How many people did she count? How many dogs did she count? 7 people; 10 dogs

3. Rachel wants to make a fenced rectangular area in her backyard for her dog Skipper. She has 36 m of fencing for the penned region. What are the whole-number dimensions in meters of the different rectangular regions she can fence? 1 by 17, 2 by 16, 3 by 15, . . . , 8 by 10, 9 by 9

4. Todd planted 60 seeds in his garden. Not all of the seeds grew into plants. Thirty more seeds grew into plants than did not grow. How many of the 60 seeds grew into plants? 45 seeds

5. At her school carnival, Nia played a game that involved tossing four bean bags at this number board. One bean bag did not hit the board. The other three landed on different numbers. Nia's score was 34. Find the possible combinations of numbers on which the bean bags could have landed. 4, 5, 25; 9, 10, 15; 9, 12, 13

6. Rashida and her mother like to play number games. Rashida tells her mother she is thinking of a number between 50 and 125. If her mother adds 23 to the number and divides by 2, the answer is 37. What number is Rashida thinking of? 51

7. A square gameboard is 16 in. long and 16 in. wide. A square that measures 2 in. × 2 in. is cut from each corner of the board. What is the perimeter of the original figure? of the new figure? 64 in.; 64 in.

Materials and Manipulatives

- tiles or counters *(optional)*

6-4

Connecting to Prior Knowledge

Ask students to estimate the perimeter of the chalkboard as well as other objects in the classroom. Lead the discussion into the perimeter of a circle (known as *circumference*).

WORK TOGETHER

COMPUTER For Question 1a, students are given the chance to discover that the ratio of circumference to diameter is the same for all circles. Students also see that this number is slightly larger than 3. Through this example, students are exploring *pi* (without actually using the word) because the definition will make more sense after the students discover the relationship. ***Alternate Approach*** If computers are not available, do the exercise using one of the following hands-on activities to find the diameter and the circumference of several circles. Make a table showing these dimensions for each circle. Add a column in which to write the result of $C \div d$. Use a calculator to find these quotients.

- Use compasses or cans and other objects to draw circles. For each circle, cut a piece of string the length of the diameter and then measure the string. Do the same for the circumference.
- As above, draw circles, but measure the diameter with a ruler. Then use string to measure the circumference.
- Measure the circumference by marking off the distance covered by a circle when you roll it for one complete turn.

Error Alert! Students may make mistakes because they confuse the terms *diameter* and *radius* of a circle. ***Remediation*** Spend a few minutes giving students practice in naming, drawing, and identifying diameters and radii.

“Philosophy begins with wonder.”
—SOCRATES

Organizer

1. **Focus**
   Connecting to Prior Knowledge
2. **Teach**
   Work Together
   Think and Discuss
3. **Closure**
   Wrap Up

Vocabulary/Symbols
circumference
pi, π

Skills Reviewed in Context of Lesson
- identifying the diameter of a circle
- rounding decimals

Materials and Manipulatives
- computer (1 for each group)
- geometry software (for each computer)
- calculator (1 for each student)
- ruler *(optional)*

On Your Own Exercises 14–29: calculator

Student Resources
Extra Practice
Student Study Guide
Practice, TR Ch. 6, p. 26
Student Study Guide, Spanish Resources, TR
Alternate Lesson, TR Ch. 6, pp. 15–18

continues next page

TECHNOLOGY

6-4 Exploring π

What's Ahead
- Using π to solve circumference problems

WHAT YOU'LL NEED
✓ Computer
✓ Geometry software
✓ Calculator 

WORK TOGETHER

The Going in Circles band plans to live up to its name. The group will perform its next concert on a circular stage.

Imagine you are designing the circular stage. You are going to have red lights around the edge and a string of blue lights across the middle. How will the size of the stage affect the number of red lights and blue lights you will need?
The larger the stage, the more lights you will need.

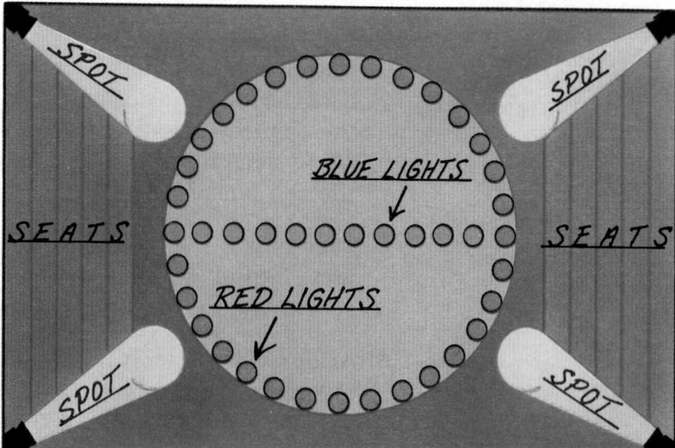

The distance around a circle is its **circumference.**

FLASHBACK
The distance across a circle (through its center) is *the diameter.*

1.a. about 3.14
b. The quotient of circumference to diameter for any circle is about 3.14.

1. a. **Computer** Use geometry software to explore the relationship between the circumference and the diameter. Make different circles and measure the circumference and diameter of each. Calculate the quotient of circumference and diameter for each circle.
   b. **Writing** Summarize your results. See left.
   c. How does the number of red lights you need compare to the number of blue lights? Does that change if the circle changes? You need about 3 times as many red lights; no.

KINESTHETIC LEARNERS Have the students form a circle inside a square, similar to the figure in Question 2. Have the students count the number of students who make the circle (circumference) and the number of students who make the square (perimeter). Have the four students who are part of both the circle and the square raise their hands.

CRITICAL THINKING From the activity just given for kinesthetic learners, have students reenact the formation of the square and the inscribed circle. Compare the number of students in the circumference of the circle with the number in the perimeter of the square.

THINK AND DISCUSS

The object of these questions is to take the developmental approach to *pi,* rather than to begin with the symbolic representation and formula evaluation.

- Use this simple approximation of "a little more than 3" to solve problems involving the ratio of circumference to diameter.
- Use a word-version of the formula $C = \pi \cdot d$ to solve problems.
- Introduce the symbol for pi and the symbolic formula $C = \pi \cdot d$

Question 3c: Students can draw a diagram to see, for example, that a 4-ft circumference would require four red bulbs, a 10-ft circumference, ten red bulbs, and a 200-ft circumference, two hundred red bulbs.

Question 4e: *Miles per hour* is used because it's familiar to students, and *feet per second* because it is easier to calculate.

Error Alert! After discussing the formulas, ask how many variables are in the formula for circumference. Students may think π is a variable because it is a symbol. ***Remediation*** Explain that π is a convenient symbol for the results of dividing the circumference of a circle by its diameter. The exact value of π is a

2.a. about 12.56 cm; 16 cm

2. a. Use your results to estimate the circumference of the circle at the right. Find the perimeter of the square.

   b. **Critical Thinking** Is the circumference of the circle less than the perimeter of the square? Does that make sense? Explain. Yes; Yes, since the diameter of the circle equals the length of a side of the square.

4 cm

4 cm

THINK AND DISCUSS

The relationship between the circumference and diameter of a circle is a powerful tool for solving problems.

3. The stage designer for the Going in Circles concert wants to know whether 200 red light bulbs will be enough. The diameter of the stage is 83 ft. The light bulbs must be 1 ft apart. Accept any reasonable estimates.

   a. Estimate the circumference of the stage. about 261 ft

   b. How did you make your estimate? Multiply 3.14 by 83.

   c. Will 200 red light bulbs be enough to go completely around the stage? How do you know? No; placing one bulb every foot along the circumference will take about 261 bulbs.

Problem Solving Hint
Drawing a diagram may help.

4. If the stage turns too quickly, the musicians may get dizzy. The guitar player plans to stand 25 ft from the center of the stage. The stage makes a complete revolution each minute. c.–e. Accept any reasonable estimates.

   a. Make a diagram. Draw a circle that shows the guitar player's path as the stage turns. See Solution Key.

   b. What is the diameter of the guitarist's path? 50 ft

   c. About how far does the guitarist move in 1 min? 157 ft

   d. About how far does the guitarist move in 1 s? 2.6 ft

   e. Write the speed as feet per second (ft/s). Will the guitar player be moving faster than 10 mi/h? 2.6 ft/s; No.

5,280 ft = 1 mi

We cannot write the quotient of the circumference and diameter of a circle exactly as a decimal or as a fraction. Mathematicians use the symbol π (read as "pi"), a letter of the Greek alphabet, to stand for this value.

5. Which point on the number line represents π? Explain.

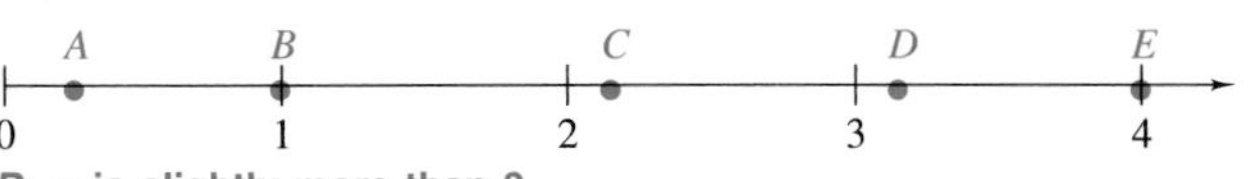

D; π is slightly more than 3.

Organizer, continued

Teacher Resources

Teaching Transparencies 15, 19, 62
Lesson Planner, TR Ch. 6, p. 5

Prentice Hall Technology

Multimedia Math
- Math Tools, Geometry

Computer Item Generator
- 6-4

Other Available Technology
- calculator

The Geometric Super Supposer by Sunburst: *(optional)*

Fact of the Day

The first practical bicycle was built in the 1860's in Paris, France.

—GUINNESS BOOK OF RECORDS

nonending, nonrepeating decimal, so it is more convenient to write the symbol, π, or an approximation of the value.

Ongoing Assessment Have the students describe the differences and similarities between these formulas: $C = 2\pi r$, $C = \pi 2r$, $C = r\pi 2$, $C = \pi d$, $C = d\pi$
(These are all the same formula, written in different forms.)

ESL **ESL** It may be helpful for each ESL student to have a set of flashcards showing symbols such as *C, d, r,* and π and their corresponding meanings.

Journal Ask students to write a paragraph describing to a friend what π is.

CALCULATOR In Question 7, make sure that students understand that, while $\pi \approx 3.14$, it is wrong to write that $\pi = 3.14$. Approximations such as 3.14 and $\frac{22}{7}$ are often used for π, but neither of these numbers is equal to π.

CALCULATOR For Question 8, ask students to compare answers with other students who have a different calculator. See if there are differences in the answers because π is rounded to a different digit.

CALCULATOR For Question 9c, students calculate the diameter knowing the circumference.

CRITICAL THINKING For Question 9d, students may want to sketch a tire and its tracks in order to complete this problem.

Wrap Up

What's the Big Idea? How do you find the circumference of a circle when you know the diameter? How do you find the diameter of a circle when you know the circumference? What is π?

Assignment Options

Core: 10–17, 22–25, 30, 31, MR all	
Reinforce: 18–21, 26–29, 34	**Enrich:** 32, 33

Mixed REVIEW

Find each sum.

1. 4.5 + 0.04 4.54
2. 0.7 + 0.12 0.82

Evaluate.

3. 17^2 4. 5.2^2 27.04
5. Find the area of a parallelogram with base 3 cm and height 7 cm.
6. Find the area of a triangle with base 2 m and height 11 m. 11 m^2
7. How many circles are in the figure? 7

3. 289
5. 21 cm^2

Problem Solving Hint

Draw a diagram. Show the tire track and the spot where the pebble makes a mark.

9.a. 82 in.; The circumference equals the distance between each pebble mark.

Because $\frac{C}{d} = \pi$, $C = \pi d$.

Circumference of a Circle

$C = \pi d$ (Circumference = pi × the diameter)

$C = 2\pi r$ (Circumference = 2 × pi × the radius)

6. Why does $C = 2\pi r$ follow from $C = \pi d$? $d = 2r$

Thanks to computers, we can write a long decimal, with thousands of digits, that is close to the actual number π. For most situations an approximation such as 3.14 is close enough. Many calculators have a π key.

7. **Calculator** Press the π key on your calculator. What is the result? The number of digits may vary; sample: 3.1415927
8. The diameter of a basketball hoop is 45 cm. A manufacturer wants to know how much metal it will take to make the rim.
   a. **Calculator** Find the circumference of the basketball hoop in the following two ways. Use 3.14 for π, and then use the π key. Compare the results. See below.
   b. How far is it around a basketball hoop? Round to the nearest centimeter. about 141 cm
9. A pebble stuck in a bicycle tire left a tell tale mark in the tire track every 82 in. How good a detective are you?
   a. What is the circumference of the tire? How do you know? See left.
   b. Estimate the diameter of the tire. about 26 in.
   c. **Calculator** Use the π key. Find the tire's diameter. Round to the nearest half inch. about 26 in.
   d. **Critical Thinking** Could a spoke that is 14 in. long belong to the bicycle that made the track? Explain. No; A spoke cannot be longer than half the diameter of the wheel.

ON YOUR OWN

Mental Math **Use 3 for π to estimate the circumference of a circle with the given radius or diameter.**

10. $d = 5$ cm about 15 cm
11. $d = 11$ m about 33 m
12. $r = 1$ in. about 6 in.
13. $r = 3$ m about 18 m

8.a. 141.3 cm; sample: 141.37167 cm; the no. using π is greater.

Connections Have a discussion about how people use π, diameter, radius, or circumference with their jobs. You may wish to start with these examples.

- **Tree Surgeon** (determine how much of a disease-fighting chemical to use on a tree)
- **Circuit Board Manufacturing** (measure diameters of holes before drilling)
- **Swimming Pool Installers** (volume of water needed to fill a round pool)

Reteaching Activity Provide several circles for students to measure the diameter and circumference, using string and then measuring the string. Have them make a table showing *C*, *d*, and $C \div d$ for each circle. Then have them add two columns showing *r* and $2\pi r$ for each circle.

ON YOUR OWN

Exercise 31: Make sure students understand that the rope spins freely around the post—the rope does not wrap around the post as the dog runs.

TACTILE LEARNERS In Exercise 32, students may need to actually draw the circle in order to answer the question.

Calculator Find the circumference of a circle with the given radius or diameter. Round to the nearest unit.

14. $d = 15$ ft 47 ft **15.** $d = 50$ m 157 m **16.** $r = 17$ in. 107 in. **17.** $r = 64$ m 402 m

18. $d = 3.9$ m 12 m **19.** $d = 17.5$ ft 55 ft **20.** $r = 9.5$ in. 60 in. **21.** $r = 0.39$ m 2 m

Calculator Find the diameter of a circle with the given circumference. Round to the nearest unit.

22. 192 ft 61 ft **23.** 85 cm 27 cm **24.** 22 in. 7 in. **25.** 56.5 m 18 m

26. 27.5 ft 9 ft **27.** 68.7 cm 22 cm **28.** 3.75 in. 1 in. **29.** 19.67 m 6 m

Use 3.14 for π or use a calculator if appropriate.

30. Data File 6 (pp. 226–227) About how many times will each wheel on the bicycle shown revolve when the bicycle travels 1,000 ft? about 147

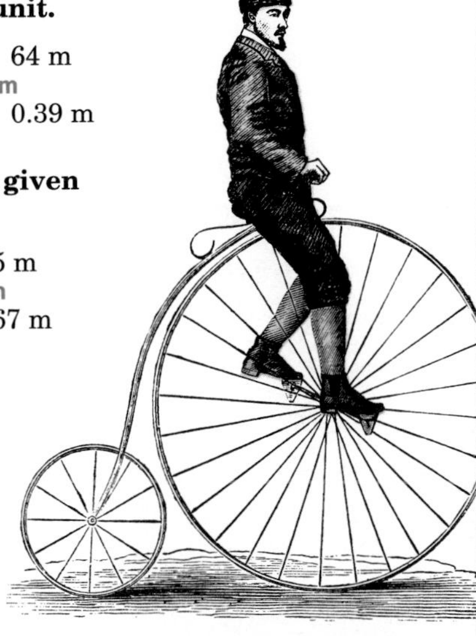

This odd looking vehicle is a penny farthing bicycle. It was named for the largest and smallest British coins of the time. The bicycle was popular in the late 1800s because it was light weight. ***Suppose the diameter of the large wheel is 3 ft. About how far will the bike travel in one full turn?*** 9.42 ft

Source: *Guinness Book of Records*

31. A dog tied to a post gets exercise by running in a circle. One day the dog ran around the post 100 times with the 10-ft rope stretched tightly. Did the dog run at least 1 mi (5,280 ft)? Yes.

32. Suppose you want to draw a circle with a circumference of 10 cm. How wide should you set your compass (to the nearest 0.1 cm)? 1.6 cm

33. On the rotating stage described in the Work Together activity, the drummer is 15 ft from the center of the stage. The keyboard player is 30 ft from the center. The stage makes a complete revolution once each minute.

a. At the end of 5 min, which musician makes more turns? Explain. See right.

b. At the end of 5 min, which musician travels farther? Explain. See right.

c. How far does the drummer travel in 1 min? Round to the nearest 0.1 ft. 94.2 ft

d. The keyboard player is twice as far from the center as the drummer. Does she travel twice as far in 1 min? Explain. Yes; $2 \times 3.14 \times 30 = 2 \times 2 \times 3.14 \times 15$

33.a. Neither; Every point on the stage turns simultaneously.
b. The keyboard player; She is on a circle with greater diameter.

34. Writing Make up a problem that you would use π to solve. Sample: How many ft of edging are needed to enclose a circular garden 6 ft in diameter?

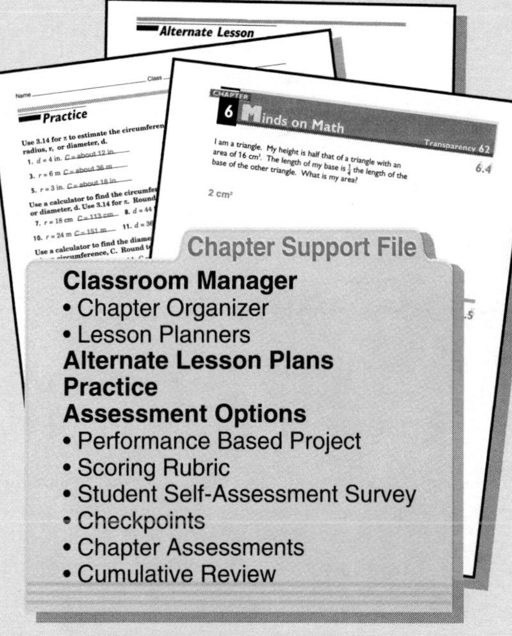

Alternate Lesson
Practice
Minds on Math
Transparency 62
6.4
I am a triangle. My height is half that of a triangle with an area of 16 cm². The length of my base is ½ the length of the base of the other triangle. What is my area?
2 cm²
Chapter Support File
Classroom Manager
• Chapter Organizer
• Lesson Planners
Alternate Lesson Plans
Practice
Assessment Options
• Performance Based Project
• Scoring Rubric
• Student Self-Assessment Survey
• Checkpoints
• Chapter Assessments
• Cumulative Review

Minds on Math available in Teaching Transparencies

Math Minutes

Write in order from least to greatest: 0.00602, 0.0062, 0.0620, 0.00600.
0.00600, 0.00602, 0.0062, 0.0620

Materials for 6-5

- centimeter graph paper
- safety compass
- straightedge
- scissors
- fraction calculator

6-5

Connecting to Prior Knowledge

Ask students to recall how to find the area of a rectangle and a square. Ask students to brainstorm for ways to estimate the area of a circle.

WORK TOGETHER

Have students work in groups of three or four. Make sure students share the work required by the activity.

TACTILE LEARNERS You may want to have students use fraction circle pieces or cut out wedges to model forming a parallelogram out of a circle.

Error Alert! Students may have difficulty visualizing the wedges in the Work Together activity as a parallelogram.

Remediation Remind students that they earlier cut parallelograms into the shape of rectangles. Emphasize that the activity is an estimation of a circle's area. Encourage students to think of the arcs of the wedges together as making a straight line.

DIVERSITY Students who have trouble learning math often lack patience and persistence in mathematics explorations such as Questions 1–4. Monitor the groups to make sure that everyone has a chance to manipulate the right regions and to provide possible responses to the questions. Suggest to the groups that they wait until each student has arranged the regions and given a response to Questions 1–3 before they discuss, as a group, their answers to Question 4. Help the student who is always first with the answer to take pride in helping another student understand, rather than solely in winning a race to the right answer.

THINK AND DISCUSS

CALCULATOR Remind students that they can use the x^2 key to find r^2 in Question 6a.

"Impatience is waiting in a hurry."
—ANONYMOUS

Organizer

1. **Focus**
   Connecting to Prior Knowledge
2. **Teach**
   Work Together
   Think and Discuss
3. **Closure**
   Try These
   Wrap Up

Skills Reviewed in Context of Lesson
- measuring with a customary ruler
- finding the circumference of a circle

Materials and Manipulatives
- centimeter graph paper (for each student)
- compass (1 for each student)
- straightedge (1 for each student)
- calculator (1 for each student)
- scissors *(optional)*

On Your Own, Exercises 8–15, 21–24: calculator

Student Resources
Extra Practice
Student Study Guide
Practice, TR Ch. 6, p. 27
Student Study Guide, Spanish Resources, TR

continues next page

What's Ahead
- Finding the area of a circle

6-5 Area of a Circle

WHAT YOU'LL NEED
- ✓ Centimeter graph paper
- ✓ Compass
- ✓ Straightedge
- ✓ Scissors
- ✓ Calculator

WORK TOGETHER

- Use a compass to draw a circle with radius 7 cm on centimeter graph paper.
- Divide the circle into eight congruent regions.
- Cut out the circle. Cut out the eight regions. Rearrange the regions as shown below.

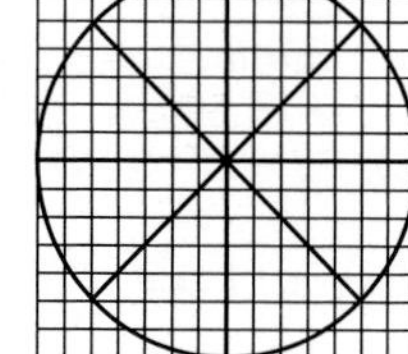

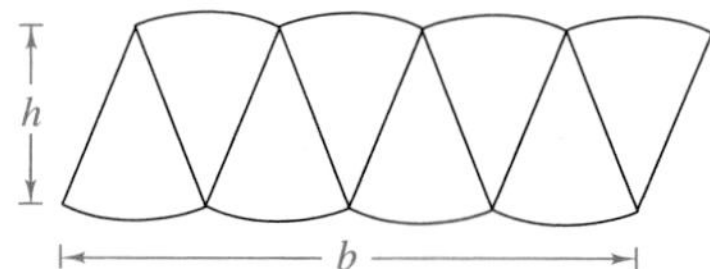

1. What was the circumference of the original circle? 43.96 cm
2. After you rearrange the eight regions, what geometric figure does the new shape remind you of? a parallelogram
3. Estimate the base length b and the height h. $b \approx 22$ cm, $h \approx 7$ cm
4. Use your answers to Questions 2 and 3 to estimate the area of the new figure. about 154 cm²

THINK AND DISCUSS

You can generalize what you did in the Work Together activity.

5. a. Suppose the radius of the circle in the Work Together activity is r. What is the height of the parallelogram? about r
   b. What would be the circumference of the circle? What would be the base length of the parallelogram?
   c. What would be the area of the parallelogram? about πr^2

5.b. $2\pi r$; about πr

Example 1

- *Would the circumference and area be larger or smaller if the radius were 4 cm?* **(Both would be smaller.)**

Additional Example *Find the circumference and area of a circle with radius 3 ft.*

Estimate: $C = 2\pi r \rightarrow C \approx 2 \cdot 3 \cdot 3 = 18$

$A = \pi r^2 \rightarrow A \approx 3 \cdot 3 \cdot 3 = 27$

2 [×] [π] [×] 3 [=] **18.849556**

[π] [×] 3 [x^2] [=] **28.274334**

C is about 19 ft and A is about 28 ft^2.

Example 2

- *How would you find the shaded region if the square were inside the circle and the part between the two were shaded?* **(Subtract the area of the square from the area of the circle.)**

Additional Example *Find the same shaded area for a circle with radius 4 cm and a square with 8 cm sides.*

Estimate: A of a square $\rightarrow 8^2 = 64$

A of a circle $\rightarrow 3 \times 4^2 = 3 \times 16 = 48$

Square area − Circle area $= 64 - 48 = 16$

π [×] 4 [x^2] [=] **50.265482**

$64 - 50 = 14$

Area of shaded region is about 14 cm^2.

Ongoing Assessment Challenge students to find a circle with a whole-number radius whose area is less than its circumference. Ask students what the radius is and to compare the area and circumference. **(radius:1; area: π; circumference: 2π)**

AUDITORY LEARNERS Have students work with a partner and take turns describing aloud the distinctions between circumference and area of a circle.

You have just found the formula for the area A of a circle.

Area of a Circle

$$A = \pi \times r \times r = \pi r^2$$

6.b. The two numbers should be close in value.

6. a. **Calculator** What is the area of a circle with radius 7 cm? **Sample: 153.93804 cm^2 (No. of decimal places may vary.)**
   b. How does the area you found in part (a) compare to the area you found in Question 4 of the Work Together?

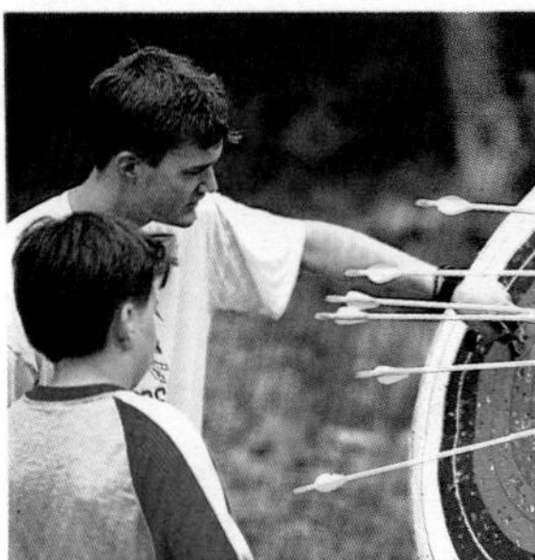

Archery targets *are made up of different color rings that are all the same width. The properties of circle areas make each succeeding ring have the area of the last ring plus two bullseyes.* ***The area of the bullseye on this target is 10 cm². What is the area of the first ring?*** **20 cm^2**

Example 1 Find the circumference and area of a circle with radius 5 cm.

Estimate: $C = 2\pi r \rightarrow C \approx 2 \times 3 \times 5 = 30$

$A = \pi r^2 \rightarrow A \approx 3 \times 5^2 = 3 \times 25 = 75$

Use a calculator.

2 [×] [π] [×] 5 [=] 31.415927 $C = 2\pi r$

[π] [×] 5 [x^2] [=] 78.539816 $A = \pi r^2$

Round to a convenient place. The circumference is about 31 cm and the area is about 79 cm^2.

You can find the area of a figure with both polygons and circles.

Example 2 Find the area of the shaded region in the figure at the right.

12 cm

6 cm

12 cm

Estimate: Area of square $\rightarrow 12^2 = 144$

Area of circle $\rightarrow 3 \times 6^2 = 3 \times 36 = 108$

Square area − Circle area $= 144 - 108 = 36$

Use a calculator.

$A = (12)^2 = 144$ $A = s^2$

[π] [×] 6 [x^2] [=] 113.09734 $A = \pi r^2$

$144 - 113 = 31$

The area of the shaded region is about 31 cm^2.

7. Compare the estimates to the calculated answers in each example. Explain the variations. **Sample: In Example 1, the estimates are less since π is rounded down to 3. In Example 2, the estimate is greater since the estimated area is less.**

Organizer, continued

Teacher Resources

Teaching Transparencies 1, 62, 64
Transparency Masters, TR p. 2
Lesson Planner, TR Ch. 6, p. 6

Prentice Hall Technology

Multimedia Math
- Math Tools, Geometry
- Hot Page™ 6-5

Computer Item Generator
- 6-5

Other Available Technology

The Geometric Supposer: Circles by Sunburst: Exercises 8–10 *(optional)*

Fact of the Day

An archery target has a bull's-eye and four different colored bands, all of which are worth different points. From the inside out, they are scored as follows: bull's-eye (gold), 9 points; red band, 7 points; blue band, 5 points; black band, 3 points; and white band, 1 point.

—ACADEMIC AMERICAN ENCYCLOPEDIA

TRY THESE

CALCULATOR Have students write an estimate for Exercises 8–10 before they do the calculations for each exercise.

TECHNOLOGY OPTION For Exercises 8–10, students can use the capabilities of a geometry software program to explore the area of circles. Some software cover a range of topics with a range of difficulty levels. Students can measure radii, diameters, and chords and can also review circumference.

Wrap Up

What's the Big Idea? Ask students: *How do you find the circumference and area of a circle?*

Journal Ask students to write their thoughts about whether it is easier to visualize and remember the calculations for finding the area of a circle or for finding the area of a rectangle. Ask them to write ways to visualize and remember each set of steps.

Connections Have students discuss situations in which the circumference and area of a circle are used:

- **Travel** (measuring mileage by a car axle's rotation, matching gears and fan belts)
- **Entertainment** (designing merry-go-rounds, Ferris wheels, carousels)
- **Art** (a potter figuring the amount of glaze needed for a circular platter, making a frame for a circular picture)

Reteaching Activity Arrange students in pairs. Have each student use a compass to draw a circle, marking the center with a dot. Ask partners to trade circles. Instruct students to use a ruler measurement of the diameter of the circle to find its circumference and area. Then have students trade circles again to check each other's work.

PH Multimedia Math Hot Page™ 6-5

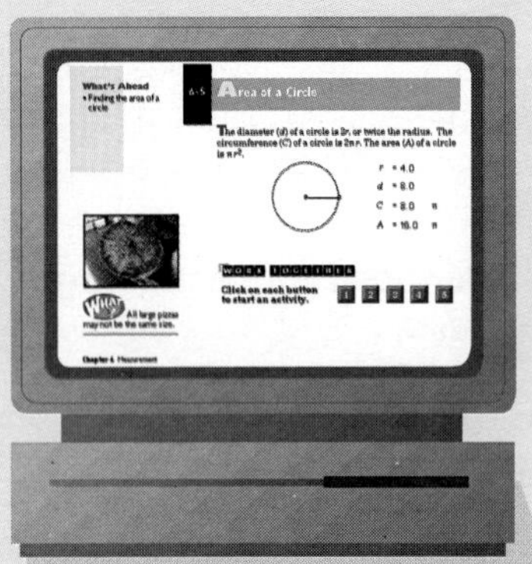

Assignment Options

Core: 11, 12, 14–17, 19–22, 25, MR all	
Reinforce: 13, 18	**Enrich:** 23, 24, 26–28

TRY THESE

Calculator **Find the circumference and the area of each circle. Round each answer to the nearest tenth of a unit.**

8. 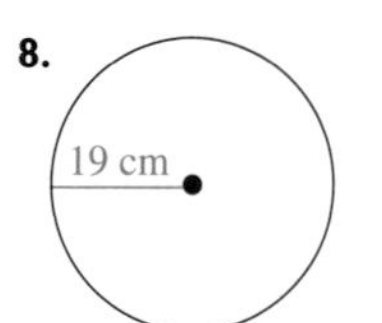

119.4 cm; 1,134.1 cm²

9.

69.1 m; 380.1 m²

10. 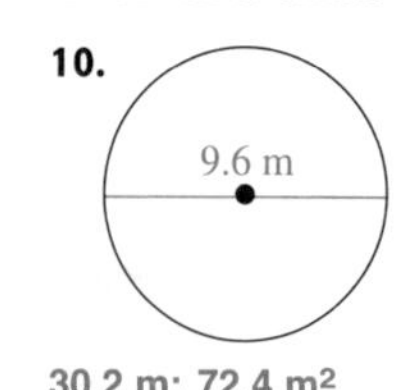

30.2 m; 72.4 m²

ON YOUR OWN

Calculator **Find the area of a circle with the given radius or diameter. Round each answer to the nearest tenth of a unit.**

11. $r = 9$ cm 254.5 cm²
12. $d = 7$ cm 38.5 cm²
13. $r = 25$ m 1,963.5 m²

Calculator **Find the area and distance around each figure. Round each answer to the nearest tenth of a unit.**

14. 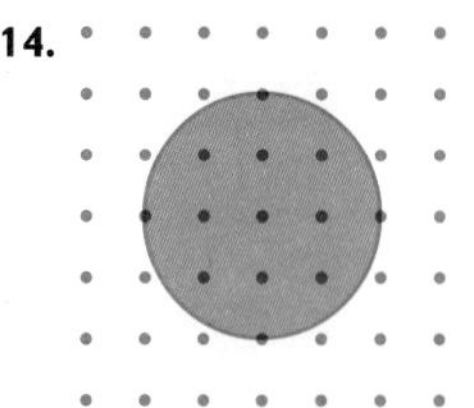
12.6 square units; 12.6 units

15. 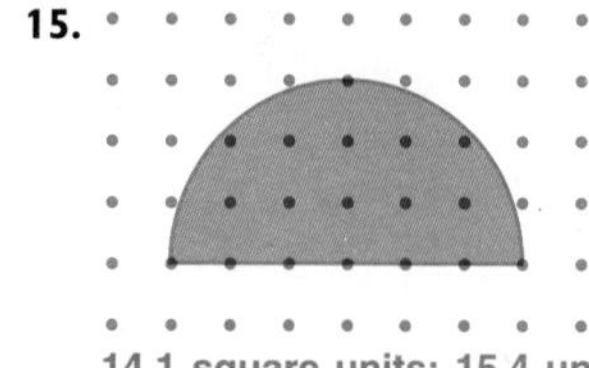
14.1 square units; 15.4 units

Mental Math **Use 3 for π to estimate the area of a circle with the given radius or diameter.**

16. $r = 2$ in. about 12 in.²
17. $d = 2$ m about 3 m²
18. $d = 10$ cm about 75 cm²

19. Writing Which is larger: a pan with a radius of 10 in. or a pan with a diameter of 18 in.? Explain. The pan with a 10 in. radius has a greater diameter.

20. You can pick up the radio signal for station WAER FM 88 in Syracuse, New York, within a 45 mi radius of the station, depending upon the hills in the surrounding region. What is the approximate area of the broadcast region? Use 3.14 for π. about 6,358.5 mi²

Mixed REVIEW

Round to the place of the underlined digit.

1. 3.957 3.96
2. 345.008 345

Find the circumference of a circle with the given radius or diameter.

3. $r = 5$ in. about 31.4 in.
4. $d = 32$ cm about 100.5 cm
5. How many triangles are in the figure shown below? 16

ON YOUR OWN

CALCULATOR For Exercises 11–13, encourage students to check their work to make sure they have rounded properly.

ESL CALCULATOR For Exercises 14 and 15, make sure students realize that "distance around" is another way to say "circumference."

MENTAL MATH Encourage students to begin their calculations for Exercises 16–18 by squaring the radius.

WRITING Have students draw a diagram to accompany their explanations for Exercise 19.

CALCULATOR Have students begin each problem by writing a plan for Exercises 21–24.

CHAPTER INVESTIGATION Have groups of students make illustrations to go with their tables for Exercise 25. Have each group express the pattern as a rule.

CONNECTION TO HISTORY Exercises 26–28 have students evaluate data about the Aztec calendar.

Calculator **Find the area of the shaded region. Round to the nearest unit.**

21. 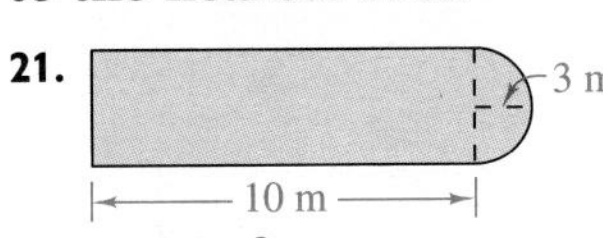

74 m²

22. 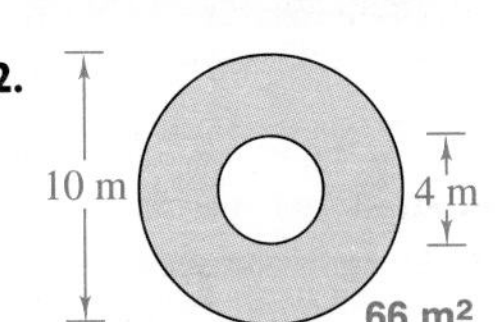

66 m²

23. 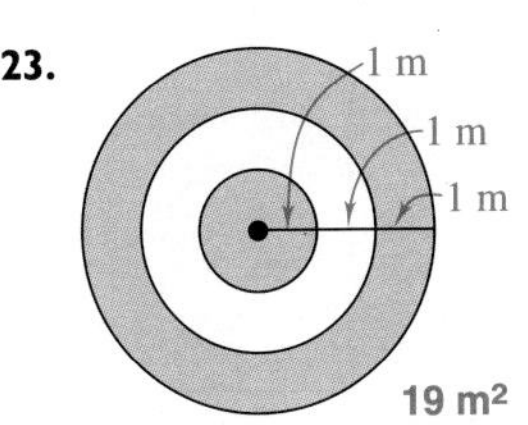

19 m²

24. 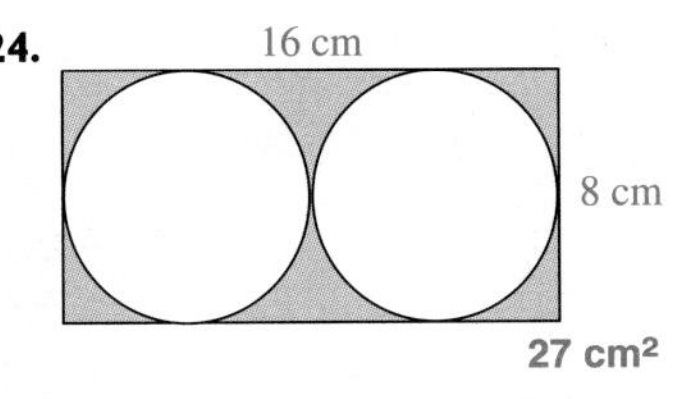

27 cm²

25. a. Investigation (p. 228) Make a table showing the number of tiles you would use in the borders of each tile square from a 2-square through a 10-square. See below.

b. Describe any patterns you see in the data in part (a). See below.

Follow the Sun

The Sun Stone or Aztec calendar is remarkable because it shows the Aztecs' accurate knowledge of astronomy and mathematics. The Aztecs carved the calendar on a circular stone 3.6 m in diameter with a mass of 24 T. They began working on the calendar in 1427 and completed the work in 1479. The center circle of the stone shows the face of Tontiuh, the Aztec sun god. There are four squares surrounding the center that are followed by 20 squares that name the days of the Aztec month. There were 18 Aztec months with 20 days each. The next circular section has eight squares with 5 dots each that seem to represent weeks that were 5 days long.

26. Find the area of the Sun Stone. Use 3.14 for π. about 10.2 m²

27. How long did it take the Aztecs to complete the calendar? 52 y

28. How many days were in the Aztec calendar? 360 days

25. a.

square	2	3	4	5	6	7	8	9	10
border tiles	4	8	12	16	20	24	28	32	36

b. Sample: Each square has 4 more border tiles than the previous square.

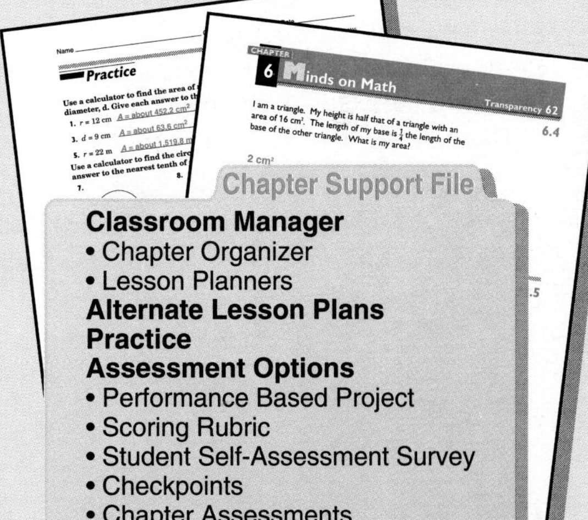

Classroom Manager
- Chapter Organizer
- Lesson Planners

Alternate Lesson Plans
Practice
Assessment Options
- Performance Based Project
- Scoring Rubric
- Student Self-Assessment Survey
- Checkpoints
- Chapter Assessments
- Cumulative Review

Minds on Math available in Teaching Transparencies

Math Minutes

Lucy and Shay were batting under 0.300. Lucy's average was 0.298 and Shay's was higher than Lucy's. What was Shay's batting average? **0.299**

Materials for 6-6

- graph paper
- scissors

CHAPTER 6

PRACTICE

This page provides practice on the skills learned up to this point in the chapter. Daily cumulative practice can be found in the Mixed Reviews that appear in every lesson.

ESL **Exercises 11–14:** Make sure students understand that π does not equal 3. Often students remember an approximation for π, but forget that it is only an approximation.

Resources

Extra Practice
Student Study Guide
Student Study Guide, Spanish Resources, TR

Practice

Estimate the area of each figure. Assume each square represents 5 cm². Accept any reasonable estimates. Samples given.

1. 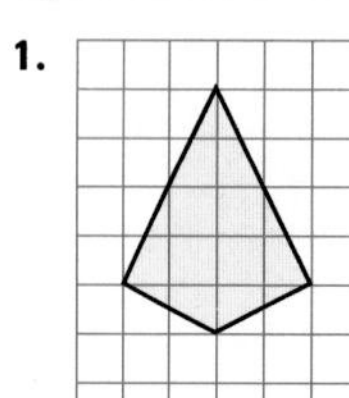 50 cm²
2. 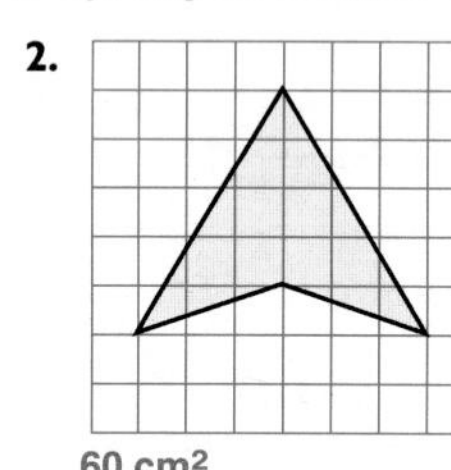 60 cm²
3. 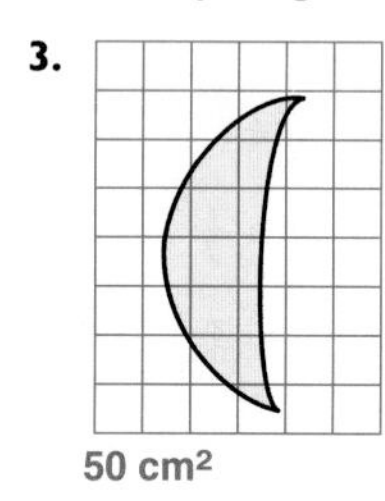 50 cm²
4. 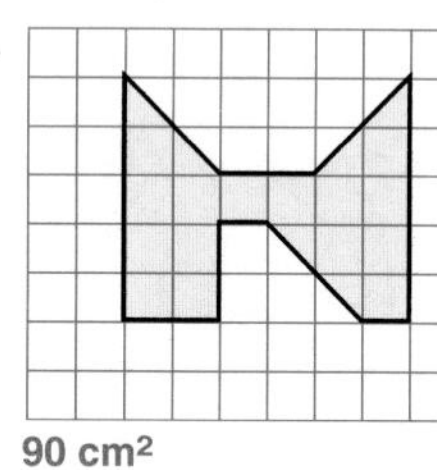 90 cm²

Find the area and perimeter of each figure.

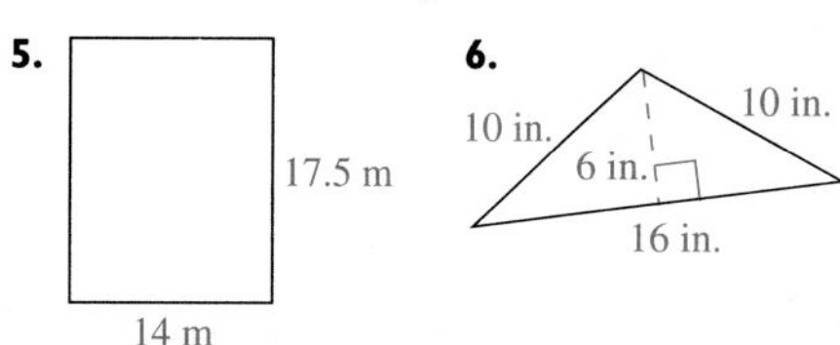

5. 245 m²; 63 m
6. 48 in.²; 36 in.
7. 24 ft²; 24 ft
8. 38.28 cm²; 25.6 cm

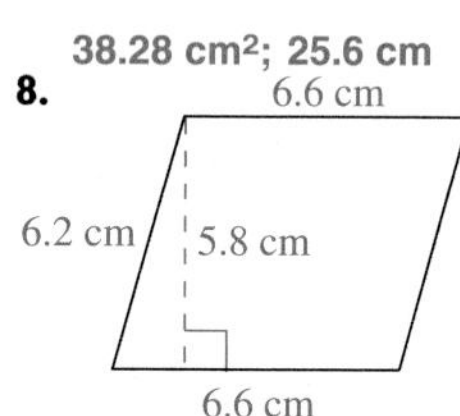

9. The area of a square is 144 in.². What is its perimeter? 48 in.
10. The area of a rectangle is 45 cm². One dimension is 5 cm. What is the other dimension? 9 cm

Use 3 for π. Estimate the circumference and area of a circle with the given radius or diameter.

11. $d = 10$ cm 30 cm; 75 cm²
12. $d = 7$ m 21 m; 36.75 m²
13. $r = 2$ cm 12 cm; 12 cm²
14. $r = 8$ m 48 m; 192 m²

Calculator **Find the circumference and area of a circle with the given radius or diameter. Round to a convenient place.**

15. $d = 21$ in. 65.97 in.; 346.36 in.²
16. $d = 17.5$ ft 54.98 ft; 240.53 ft²
17. $r = 72$ m 452.39 m; 16,286.02 m²
18. $r = 13$ in. 81.68 in.; 530.93 in.²

Find the area of each figure. Round to a convenient place.

19. 12 cm
452.16 cm²

20. 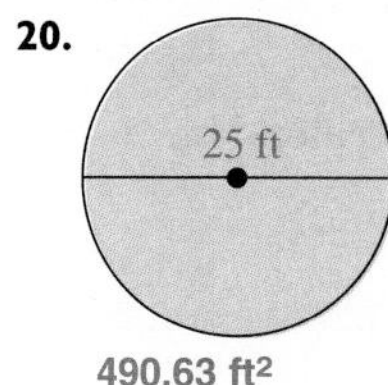

490.63 ft²

21. 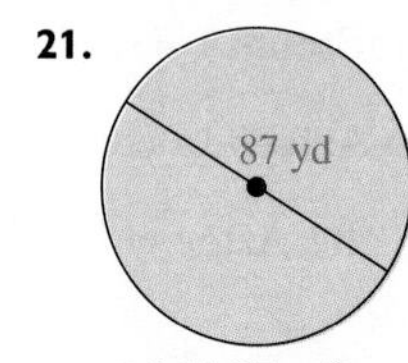

5,941.67 yd²

22. 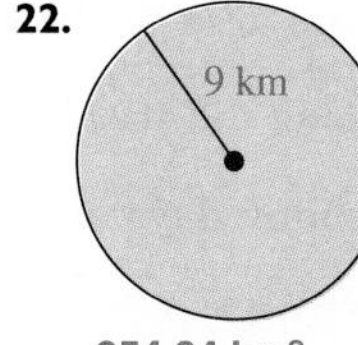

254.34 km²

6-6

Connecting to Prior Knowledge

Have students describe the shapes of different buildings they have seen in terms of squares, rectangles, triangles, and circles. Then challenge students to describe the buildings in three-dimensional terms.

THINK AND DISCUSS

Make sure students understand that a base is also a face. Thus a rectangular prism has 6 faces, 2 of which are also bases.

TACTILE LEARNERS Bring in wooden models or everyday objects that are prisms, pyramids, cylinders, cones, and spheres. Let students hold the objects so that they can understand the distinctions among the figures.

VISUAL LEARNERS Ask students who are comfortable with drawing three-dimensional figures, such as those shown in Questions 3–13, to help others learn to sketch these figures.

ESL **ESL** Have students discuss what these figures are called in their own language and make a list in both languages, so that the terms in English can be tied to more familiar terms.

Question 7: Have students explain their choices of names.

Error Alert! Students may lose track of faces, edges, and vertices they have counted for Questions 9–11. ***Remediation*** Encourage students to copy the drawings of any of the three-dimensional figures they may have problems visualizing. When counting edges and so on, students can check or number each part on their drawings.

ESL **Question 11:** Point out to students that the plural of *vertex* is *vertices.*

What's Ahead

- Identifying three-dimensional figures

WHAT YOU'LL NEED

✓ Graph paper

✓ Scissors

MATH AND ARCHITECTURE

6-6 Three-Dimensional Figures

THINK AND DISCUSS

1. What polygons do you see in the buildings shown above? Answers may vary. Sample: triangles, rectangles

Figures, such as buildings, that do not lie in a plane are *three-dimensional figures.* Some three-dimensional figures have only flat surfaces shaped like polygons, called *faces.*

Most large buildings are in the shape of *rectangular prisms.* A **prism** is a three-dimensional figure with two parallel and congruent polygonal faces, called *bases.* You name a prism by the shape of its bases.

2. What shape are the bases of a rectangular prism? rectangular

When you draw a rectangular prism, you usually draw it as if you could see three faces. You can use dashed lines to show segments that you could not see unless the prism was transparent.

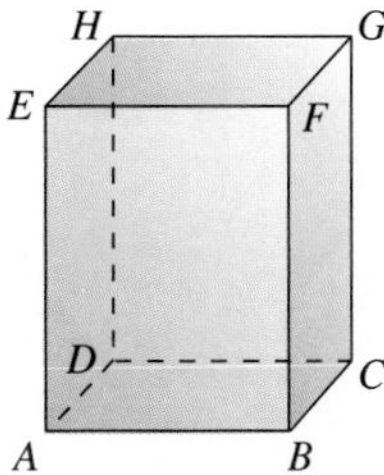

3. It would appear to be a two-dimensional rectangle.

3. Why do you think that a drawing of a rectangular prism usually does not show a view directly from the front?

4. What shape are the bases of the prism in the drawing? What shape would they be in a real 3-d figure? parallelograms; rectangles

5. Which faces are "hidden from view" in this drawing? back, bottom, and left side

" A life spent worthily should be measured by a nobler line—by deeds, not years. "

—RICHARD BRINSLEY SHERIDAN

Organizer

1. **Focus**
   Connecting to Prior Knowledge
2. **Teach**
   Think and Discuss
   Work Together
3. **Closure**
   Wrap Up

Vocabulary/Symbols

three-dimensional figures
faces
rectangular prism
prism
bases
pyramids
edge
vertex
cube
cylinder
cone
sphere
net
square pyramid

Skills Reviewed in Context of Lesson

- identifying regular geometric shapes

continues next page

Question 13: Have students compare the properties of a cube to those of a square.

AUDITORY LEARNERS Ask students to work in pairs. As one student shows a sketch or points to one in the text, the second student names the figure aloud. They then exchange roles.

Ongoing Assessment Ask students to describe what a figure with two bases and six other faces looks like. Have students draw a diagram and think of a suitable name for the figure. **(hexagonal prism)**

WORK TOGETHER

Provide each pair of students with graph paper and scissors. Have students compare results. Extend this activity by suggesting a vocabulary activity of drawing (or finding in the library) nets for other figures. Suggest that they start with a net for a cube, for which there are several different possible nets.

Wrap Up

What's the Big Idea? Ask students to describe how to identify *three-dimensional figures.*

Journal Challenge students to design a unique three-dimensional figure and to name it using some of the terms such as *prism* or *cone.* Encourage students to think of a use for their designs.

Reteaching Activity Have students meet in groups of four to make tables that organize the different types of three-dimensional figures. Indicate that the column headings on the

Organizer, continued

Materials and Manipulatives

- graph paper (for each student)
- scissors (1 pair for each group)

Student Resources

Extra Practice
Student Study Guide
Practice, TR Ch. 6, p. 28
Student Study Guide, Spanish Resources, TR

Teacher Resources

Teaching Transparencies 1, 62
Transparency Masters, TR pp. 11–17
Lesson Planner, TR Ch. 6, p. 7

Prentice Hall Technology

Multimedia Math

- Hot Page 6-6

Computer Item Generator

- 6-6

6. Match each prism with its name: choose from triangular prism, rectangular prism, pentagonal prism, or hexagonal prism.

a. 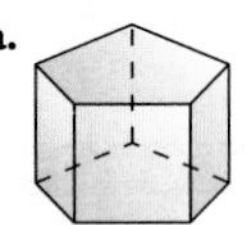 pentagonal prism

b. 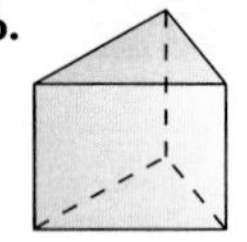 triangular prism

A **pyramid** has one polygonal base.

7. What name would you give each pyramid?

a. 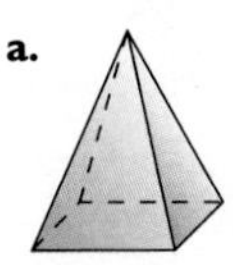 rectangular pyramid

b. 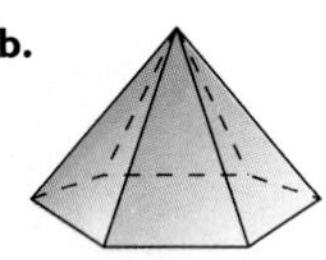 hexagonal pyramid

c. 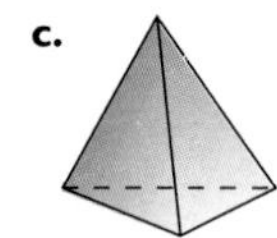 triangular pyramid

8. What shape is a face of a pyramid that is not a base? triangular

Two faces of a prism or pyramid intersect in a segment called an *edge.* Each point where edges meet is a *vertex.*

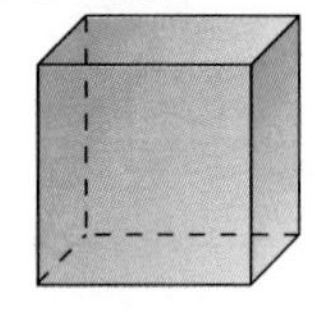

9. How many faces does this figure have? 6

10. How many edges does the figure have? 12

11. How many vertices does the figure have? 8

A **cube** is a rectangular prism with six congruent faces.

12. What shape is each face of a cube? square

13. How do the lengths of the edges of a cube compare? They are equal in length.

Some three-dimensional figures do not have polygonal faces.

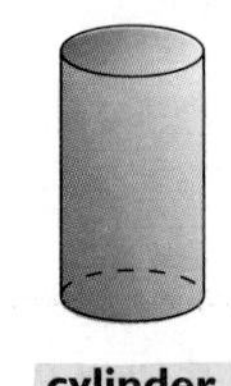

cylinder

cone

sphere

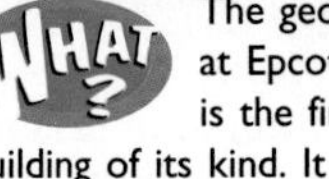

The geosphere at Epcot Center is the first building of its kind. It is a sphere with a diameter of 164 ft made up of 954 triangles of varying sizes enclosing 2,200,000 ft^3.

Source: *Fodor's Walt Disney World Guide*

table should be *No Bases*, *One Base*, and *Two Bases*, and that the rows should be labeled *No Faces*, *One Face*, *Two Faces*, and so on. Ask students to explain any blank boxes and to compare tables.

Connections Have a discussion about how three-dimensional geometric figures are used. You may want to start with these examples:

- **Manufacturing** (different boxes, cans, containers, and shapes of products to make a product eye-pleasing or interesting)
- **Markers** (construction cones, buoys, spheres on high electric or telephone lines to warn low-flying airplanes or helicopters)
- **Gardening** (cylinders or cones of fencing or mesh to protect plants, greenhouses shaped like pyramids or prisms)

ON YOUR OWN

WRITING Have students write their descriptions for Exercise 23 in the form of a set of directions for making a square pyramid.

Exercises 25–28: Have students draw diagrams of the figures formed.

Great Expectations

There are many valuable resources available to the students for gathering information about marine biology. The following list includes places to write for more information and publications to read.

- Texas A & M University at Galveston
  Marine Biology Department
  P. O. Box 1675
  Galveston, TX 77553

Fact of the Day

Ieoh Ming Pei, a Chinese-American architect, designed the new main entrance to the Louvre. The entrance is a glass pyramid, and was completed in 1988.

—ACADEMIC AMERICAN ENCYCLOPEDIA

14. Which of the figures at the bottom of page 252 have bases? What shape are the bases? cylinder and cone; circles

15. How are a cylinder and a cone alike? How are they different? Both have a circular base; a cylinder has two bases and a cone has only one.

16. What has the artist done to make the drawing of a sphere look different from a circle? The sphere is shaded to look solid and three-dimensional.

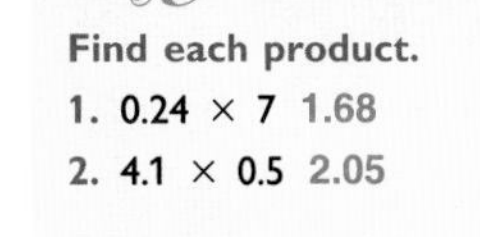

Mixed REVIEW

Find each product.

1. 0.24×7 1.68
2. 4.1×0.5 2.05

Find the area of a circle with the given radius or diameter.

3. $r = 9$ ft 254.34 ft²
4. $d = 14$ m 153.86 m²

Evaluate.

5. $5^2 + 2(6 + 4)$ 45
6. $3^2 + 6^2$ 45

7. An issue of *Teen Monthly* is $2.25. A yearly subscription costs $25.08. How much can you save by subscribing for a year?

7. $1.92

WORK TOGETHER

The pattern that you cut out and fold to form a three-dimensional figure is called a **net.**

- Suppose you cut out this net and fold it. What kind of three-dimensional figure do you think would be formed? a square pyramid
- Work with a partner to see if you are right. Draw the net on graph paper, cut it out, and fold it.

ON YOUR OWN

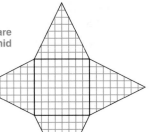

Identify each three-dimensional figure.

17.–18. See right.

17.

18.

19.

20.

17. cylinder
18. rectangular pyramid
19. cone
20. sphere

- University of Texas
  Marine Biology Department
  P. O. Box 1267
  Port Aransas, TX 78373
- *Day in a Life of a Marine Biologist* by David Paige, Troll Associates (publishers)
- Science-by-Mail
  Museum of Science
  Science Park
  Boston, MA 02114

Middle school students in the science-by-mail program are paired with professional scientists who serve as mentors. Through the mail, communications and activities travel back and forth between pairs.

Students can also learn from discussions with experts. Here are some possible sources.

- Invite a marine biologist to speak to the class.
- Write a letter to a marine biology department and ask for any educational videos that may show pictures of ocean plants and animals.
- Visit a university's marine department on the coast and see the boats and diving equipment used to explore the ocean.
- Explore computer software that is used to assist the marine biologist in analyzing data collected about marine plants and animals.

Encourage students to ask questions about the skills necessary for a career as a marine biologist, including these topics.

- The training necessary to qualify as a marine biologist, including undergraduate course work and graduate training

PH Multimedia Math Hot Page™ 6-6

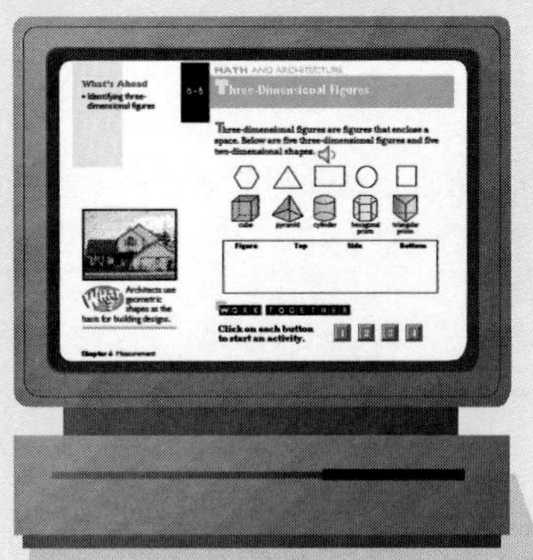

Assignment Options

Core: 17–20, 25–28, MR all	
Reinforce: 21, 24	**Enrich:** 22, 23

21. This photograph was taken at Expo 70 in Japan. What three-dimensional figures can you identify? Answers may vary. Sample: square pyramid, cylinder

22. **a.** Identify the figure. pentagonal pyramid

b. Find the number of faces, edges, and vertices the figure has. 6 faces, 10 edges, 6 vertices

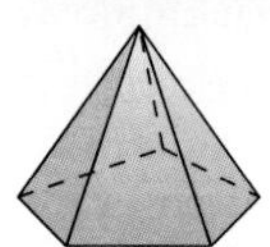

GREAT EXPECTATIONS

Marine Biologist

I would like to be a marine biologist because I think the ocean is an unknown place. I would like to learn more about animals and plants of the ocean. Then I could help them. I want to learn more because I have seen pictures and it is beautiful under water. I have always loved the beach and the ocean and have wondered about what lived there. I think the ocean is kind of like outer space in a way because it is an area unknown and an area being discovered. I would love to be part of that discovery.

Jane Broussard

- How math is used on the job (for statistical analysis, biologists rely heavily on *Biometry* by Robert Sokal and James Rohlfl, which contains text and tables for math applications in relation to the environment)
- Determining the focus of study (vertebrate or invertebrate zoology, coastal and wet lands, general biology)
- Computer applications

Marine biologists read various journals according to their area of expertise. Libraries for these scientists may include journals from:

- American Botanical Society
- Society of Coastal and Estuarine Science
- American Microbiologist

Sample: a three-dimensional figure with a square base and 4 triangular faces.

23. **Writing** Describe, in your own words, a *square pyramid.*

24. **Choose A, B, C, or D.** Which of the following is not a possible view of a cylinder? C

A. 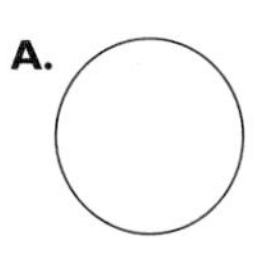 **B.** 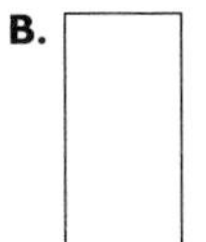 **C.** 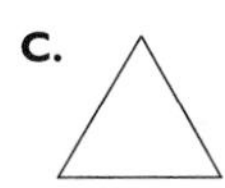 **D.** 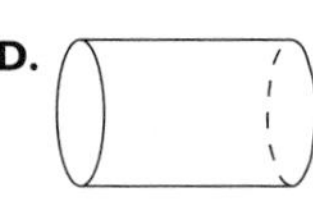

Name the figure you can form from each net.

25. 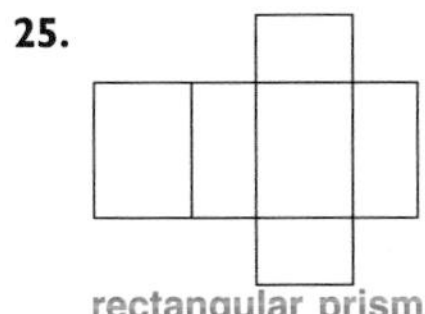
rectangular prism

26. 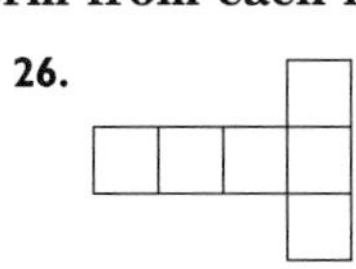
cube

27. 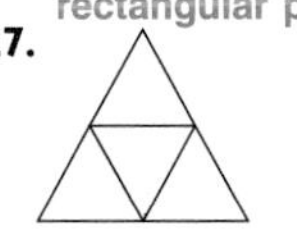
triangular prism

28. 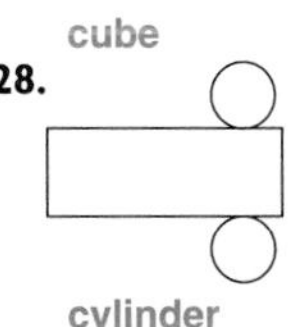
cylinder

Dear Jane,

Your letter makes several important points. Because children are our best hope for the future of our oceans, I'd like to address each point.

The oceans are indeed like outer space. Under water, an aquanaut can become weightless, gliding over coral reefs like astronauts glide among the stars in their space shuttle. Having been an underwater explorer for 13 years, I can truly say that each dive is a unique educational experience.

Although many of the world's oceans have been explored, much more exploration is needed. Why? For one reason, many scientists feel that the cure for cancer and other diseases may be found in a marine plant or animal. Sharks are a prime area of study because they can't get cancer.

I hope you pursue your interest in marine biology. I have one suggestion: also become a writer. Then you can help the marine environment and share your knowledge and enthusiasm with many others.

Rick Sammon,
President CEDAM International

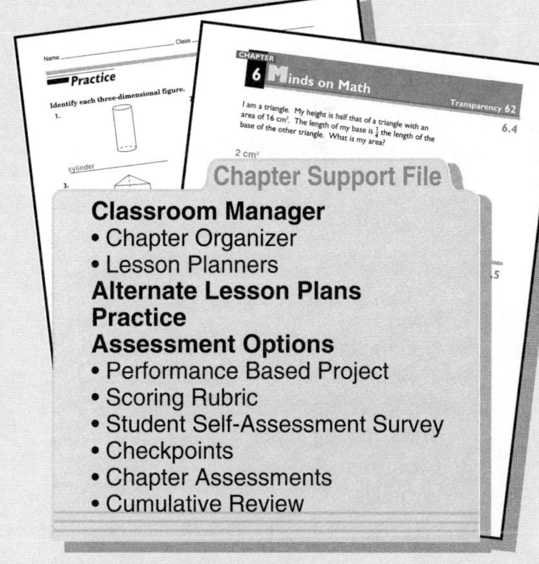

Minds on Math available in Teaching Transparencies

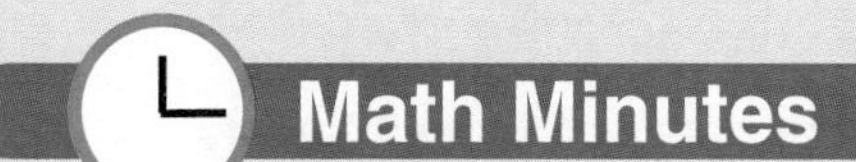

Math Minutes

Rounded to the nearest ounce, Jack's basketball weighs 22 oz. What is the least and most it could weigh, in tenths of an ounce? **21.5 oz and 22.4 oz**

Materials for 6-7

- calculator

6-7

Connecting to Prior Knowledge

Ask students to recall how to find the area of a two-dimensional figure. Then challenge them to think of ways to use the same procedures to find the surface area of a three-dimensional figure.

WORK TOGETHER

Have students work in groups of three or four. Encourage students to develop a procedural pattern for finding surface area.

VISUAL/TACTILE LEARNERS Give students a rectangular prism, such as a facial tissue box or cereal box, and have them measure to find the surface area.

THINK AND DISCUSS

Question 1: Begin the discussion by having groups share their results and the procedures they used.

CRITICAL THINKING For Question 1b, have students draw from the group discussion of the Work Together activity.

AUDITORY LEARNERS When the class has agreed on a procedure for finding surface area, have one student summarize the procedure aloud.

Error Alert! For prisms such as those in Questions 2 and 3, students may have difficulty keeping track of the dimensions for each base or figure. ***Remediation*** Encourage students first to identify the dimensions of the top and bottom of the prism and then to identify the dimensions of each of the other faces.

DIVERSITY Some students have difficulty visualizing a three-dimensional figure by looking at a two-dimensional pattern or how a two-dimensional pattern could be folded to become a three-dimensional figure. These students will benefit from being able to cut a three-dimensional object, such as a cereal or cracker box, into a two-dimensional pattern.

“Everything should be made as simple as possible, but not one bit simpler.”

—ALBERT EINSTEIN

Organizer

1. **Focus**
   Connecting to Prior Knowledge
2. **Teach**
   Work Together
   Think and Discuss
3. **Closure**
   Wrap Up

Vocabulary/Symbols
surface area

Skills Reviewed in Context of Lesson
- finding the area of rectangles and squares

Materials and Manipulatives
- calculator (1 per student)

On Your Own Exercise 16: 27 cubes *(optional)*

Student Resources
Extra Practice
Student Study Guide
Practice, TR Ch. 6, p. 29
Student Study Guide, Spanish Resources, TR
Alternate Lesson, TR Ch. 6, pp. 19–22

continues next page

What's Ahead

- Finding the surface area of rectangular prisms

6-7 Exploring Surface Area

WORK TOGETHER

If you unfold a rectangular prism, one net you might get is shown at the right.

- Find the area of the net. 112 cm²

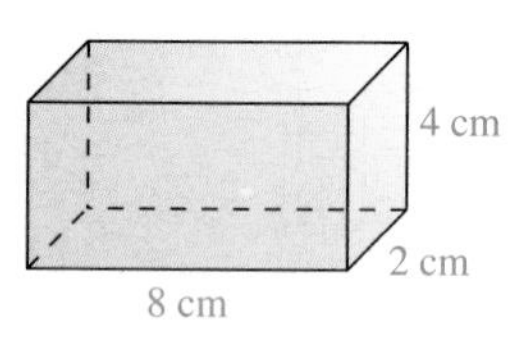

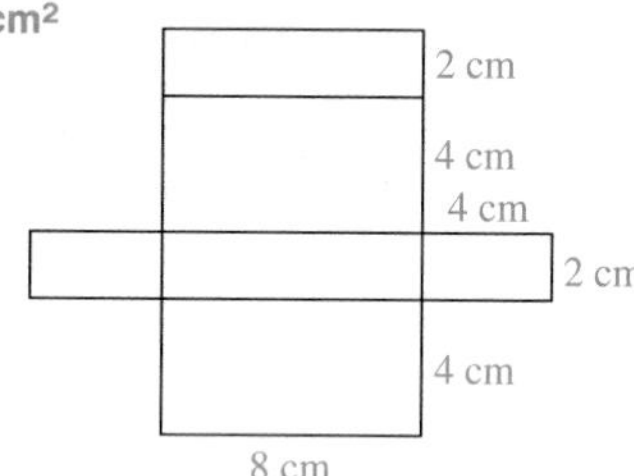

Package designers need to know the dimensions and shapes of package surfaces.

THINK AND DISCUSS

The sum of the areas of the faces of a rectangular prism is the **surface area** of the prism.

1. a. Describe the faces of the prism in the Work Together activity. Include in your description the dimensions of the faces and whether any faces are congruent. See left.
   b. **Critical Thinking** Is there more than one way to find the surface area of the rectangular prism? Explain. See left.

1.a. There are 2 pairs of congruent rectangular faces with dimensions 8 cm by 2 cm, 8 cm by 4 cm, and 4 cm by 2 cm.
b. Yes; find $(8 \times 2) + (8 \times 4) + (4 \times 2)$ and double the sum.

2. a. What is the best name for the rectangular prism? cube
   b. Describe the faces. six 4 in. squares
   c. Find the surface area. 96 in.²

3. a. Describe the faces of the rectangular prism. See left.
   b. Find the surface area. 180 m²

3.a. Two 6 m squares, four 6 m by 4.5 m rectangles

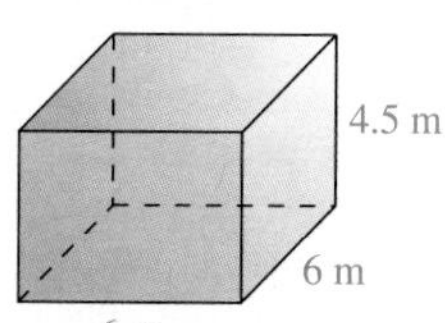

Ongoing Assessment Ask students to name the groups of sides with the same dimensions for Question 3. **(four of 4.5 m × 6 m, pair of 6 m × 6 m)** Ask students why the figure is not a cube. **(The faces are not all congruent.)**

Wrap Up

What's the Big Idea? Ask students to explain how to find the surface area of a three-dimensional figure.

Journal Ask students to name properties of rectangular prisms that make the figures so useful and common.

Connections Have a discussion about how finding the surface area of a rectangular prism is used. You may want to start with these examples:

- **Manufacturing and Business** (packaging products for shipping and for display, stacking boxes for storage)
- **Household** (painting interior or exterior of a house, insulating walls and ceilings)
- **Construction** (laying bricks, building rooms in a house)

Reteaching Activity Bring a box such as a shoe box to class. Display it for students and give students the dimensions. Ask each student to use the diagram in the Work Together activity as a guide to draw a net of the shoe box. Remind students to include six sides. Have students use their nets to determine the surface area of the box. Then measure the box and compare your calculations of the surface area with students' numbers. They should be the same.

ON YOUR OWN

Exercises 4–9: Have students show their work in finding the surface areas.

WRITING For Exercise 13, have students describe their methods step-by-step.

ON YOUR OWN

Choose **Use a calculator, paper and pencil, or mental math to find the surface area of the rectangular prism.**

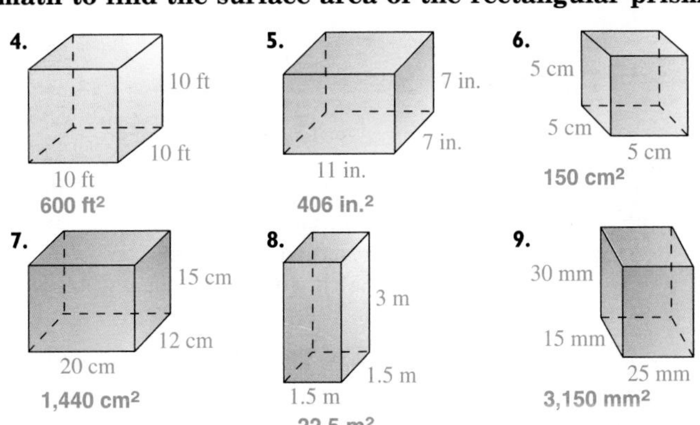

Find the surface area of the rectangular prism that has the given net.

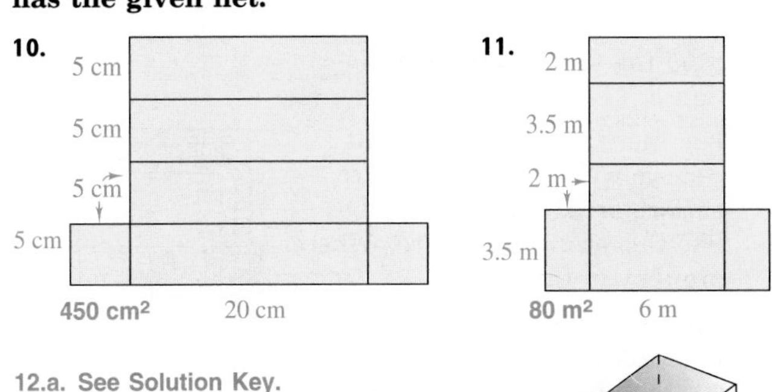

12.a. See Solution Key.

12. a. Draw a net that you could fold to form the rectangular prism.
    b. Find the surface area of the prism. 319.5 cm²

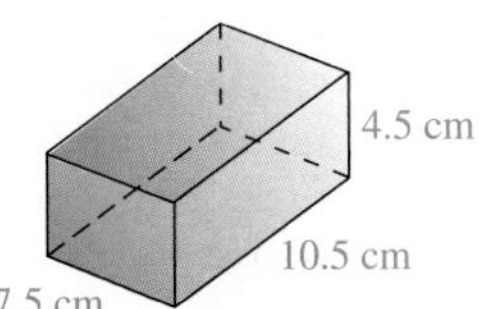

13. **Writing** Explain how you would find the surface area of a cube. Find the area of one face by squaring the length, then multiply by 6.
14. The surface area of the cube shown at the right is 24 cm². What is the length of each edge? 2 cm

Mixed REVIEW

Find each quotient.

1. 25 ÷ 0.5 50
2. 3.2 ÷ 0.8 4

Give the mathematical name for each figure.

3. a baseball sphere
4. a brick rectangular prism

Evaluate.

5. 12 × 7 × 15 1,260
6. 3.3 × 2.5 × 10.1 83.325
7. Suppose two pizzas cost the same amount. Which is a better buy: a 10-in. round pizza or a 9-in. square pizza?

7. the square pizza

Organizer, continued

Teacher Resources
Teaching Transparency 63
Transparency Masters, TR p. 11
Lesson Planner, TR Ch. 6, p. 8

Prentice Hall Technology

Multimedia Math
- Math Investigations, Unidentified Flying Cubes

Computer Item Generator
- 6-7

Other Available Technology
- calculator

Fact of the Day

Americans eat 75 acres of pizza every day—enough to cover 60 football fields.

—*In One Day*

Assignment Options

Core: 4–10, 13, 15, 17, MR all	
Reinforce: 11, 12	**Enrich:** 14, 16

CRITICAL THINKING Encourage students to model Exercise 16 by using blocks.

CHAPTER INVESTIGATION Have the groups of students display their data for Exercise 17 in tables. Challenge groups to express any patterns they find as rules.

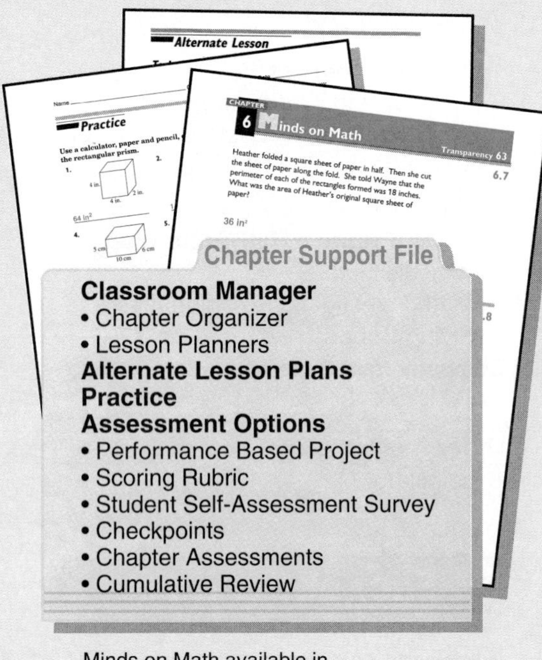

Minds on Math available in Teaching Transparencies

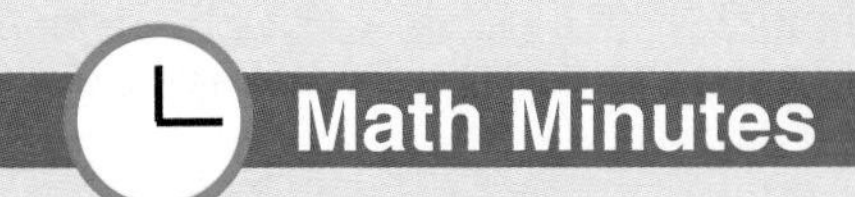

Estimate each sum or difference:

8.31 + 3.96
8 + 4 = 12

5.038 − 4.21
5 − 4 = 1

39.51 + 26.97 + 59.94
40 + 27 + 60 = 127

Materials for 6-8
- unit cubes

***Americans use three million** gallons of paint and stain every day. That would be enough to coat both sides of a 5-ft high fence 17,000 mi long.*

Source: *In One Day*

Problem Solving Hint

Building a model may help.

16.b. Yes; 9; at the corners and in the center.
c. Yes; 12; in the middle of each edge.
d. Yes; 6; the center of each face.

15. You have been hired to paint the walls in this room.

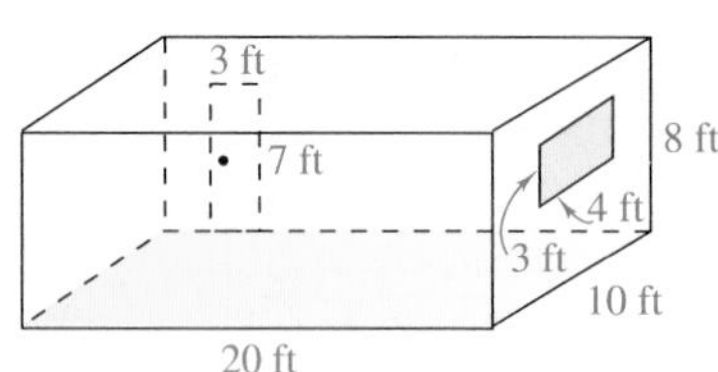

a. Find the area of the two walls that do not have doors or windows. 240 ft^2

b. Find the area of the surface you will paint on the other two walls. (Assume that you will not paint the door or the window.) 207 ft^2

c. What is the surface area of the region you will paint? 447 ft^2

d. A gallon of the paint you will use covers about 400 ft^2. How many gallons will you need? 2

16. **Critical Thinking** Each small cube in the figure below measures 1 cm on a side.

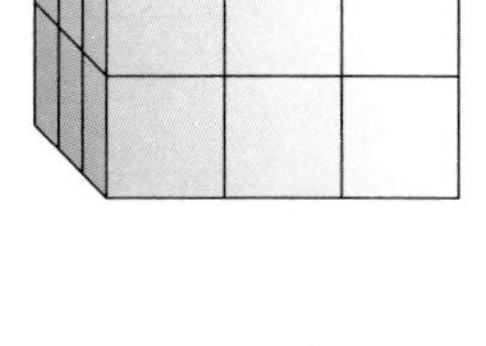

a. Find the surface area of the figure. 54 cm^2

b. Are there any cubes you can remove without changing the surface area? How many cubes like this are in the figure? Where are they in the figure? See left.

c. Are there any cubes you can remove that will increase the surface area by 2 cm^2? How many cubes like this are in the figure? Where are they in the figure? See left.

d. Are there any cubes you can remove that will increase the surface area by 4 cm^2? How many cubes like this are in the figure? Where are they in the figure? See left.

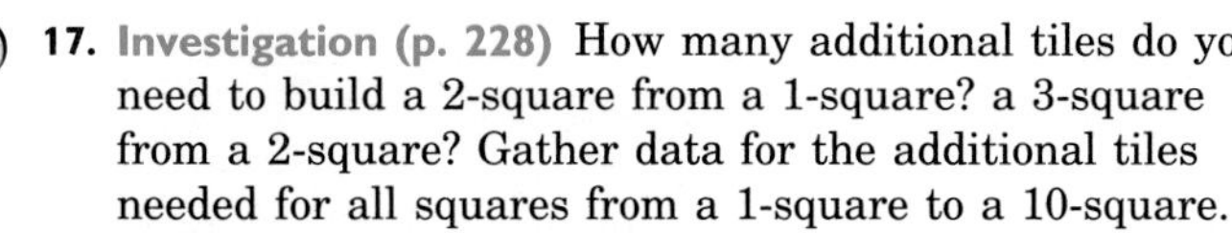

17. **Investigation (p. 228)** How many additional tiles do you need to build a 2-square from a 1-square? a 3-square from a 2-square? Gather data for the additional tiles needed for all squares from a 1-square to a 10-square. Describe any patterns you see.

square	1	2	3	4	5	6	7	8	9	10
add. tiles needed	1	3	5	7	9	11	13	15	17	19

Sample answer: The number of tiles needed are consecutive odd nos.

6-8

Connecting to Prior Knowledge

Have students define *volume*. Then ask students how volume compares to area. Challenge students to use what they know about area to brainstorm for ways to find the volume of a three-dimensional figure.

WORK TOGETHER

Have students work in groups of three or four. Give each group 50 cubes.

Question 2: Have each group draw a diagram of its prism. Encourage groups to compare prisms and volumes.

VISUAL/TACTILE LEARNERS Using the manipulatives to represent cubic units helps students better understand the concept of volume. Have students make a table showing length, width, and height of the prisms they build, as well as volume.

DIVERSITY If unit cubes are unavailable, have each group work together to create a net and make unit cubes using graph paper.

ESL Error Alert! Students may confuse volume with surface area for Questions 1 and 2 and may count the cubes that are exposed rather than the total number of cubes. ***Remediation*** Remind students that volume fills a space and that the unexposed cubes must also be counted.

THINK AND DISCUSS

ESL ESL Encourage students to write the word for "volume" in their own language and to think about its uses and connotations. This helps them learn the new term by making a connection with the familiar.

Ongoing Assessment Have students estimate how many math books could fill the classroom if it were empty. Provide students with the dimensions of the room or have them use

What's Ahead

- Finding the volume of rectangular prisms

WHAT YOU'LL NEED

✓ Unit cubes

6-8 Volume of Rectangular Prisms

WORK TOGETHER

Use unit cubes to build a rectangular prism. Use 3 rows of 6 cubes to make the bottom layer of cubes. Then add a second layer of cubes.

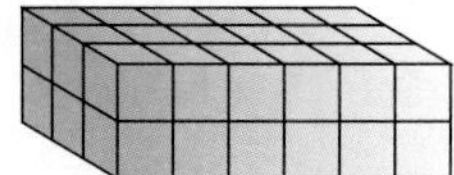

The **volume** of a three-dimensional figure is the number of cubic units needed to fill the space inside the figure.

1. a. Suppose the volume of each cube is 1 cubic unit. What is the volume of the rectangular prism? 36 cubic units
   b. How did you determine the volume? See below.
2. Build a different rectangular prism and find its volume. Sample: Make 1 layer of 4 rows of 3 cubes each, add 2 more layers; 36 cubic units.

THINK AND DISCUSS

We measure area in square units because we multiply two factors *length* and *width* to find area. We measure volume *V* in cubic units because we multiply three factors the *length l,* the *width w,* and the *height h* to find volume.

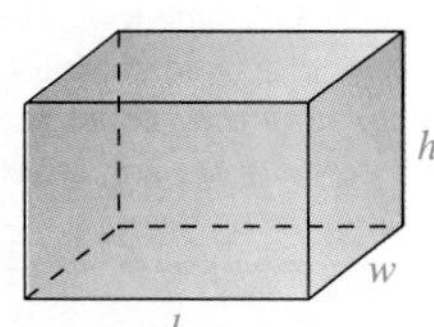

Volume of a Rectangular Prism

Volume = length × width × height

$V = lwh$

3. What are the length, width, and height of the rectangular prism you built in the Work Together activity? 6 units, 3 units, 2 units

1.b. Sample: In each layer there are 3 rows of 6 cubes each, so in 2 layers there are 36 cubes.

The familiar cereal box *measures about 7.0 cm × 10.2 cm × 4.2 cm.* ***Estimate the volume in cubic centimeters.*** about 280 cm³

"The measure of a man's real character is what he would do if he knew he never would be found out."

—Thomas Macaulay

Organizer

1. **Focus**
   Connecting to Prior Knowledge
2. **Teach**
   Work Together
   Think and Discuss
3. **Closure**
   Try These
   Wrap Up

Vocabulary/Symbols

volume
length
width
height
volume, *V*
length, *l*
width, *w*
capacity
liter

Skills Reviewed in Context of Lesson

- identifying length and width

Materials and Manipulatives

- unit cubes (36 per group)

continues next page

yardsticks to measure it themselves. Tell students to use one cubic foot as the measurement of a stack of ten math books.

Example 1

Remind students to pay close attention to the unit of measurement in a problem. In the example, the sides are measured in cm and the volume in cm³.

Additional Example *Find the volume of a rectangular prism measuring 6 m × 5 m × 8 m.*

$V = 6 \times 5 \times 8 = 240$

The volume is 240m³.

CRITICAL THINKING Challenge students to name the relevant property of multiplication for answering Question 4. **(commutative)**

Example 2

- *If you know the volume and one dimension of a prism, can you find the other two dimensions?* **(no, unless the prism is a cube)**
- *Name a rectangular prism with equal length, width, and height measurements.* **(cube)**

Additional Example *The volume of a rectangular prism is 250 cm³. The length is 5 cm. The width is 10 cm. What is the height of the prism?*

$$250 = 5 \times 10 \times h$$
$$250 = 50h$$
$$\frac{250}{50} = \frac{50h}{50}$$
$$5 = h$$

Check $5 \times 10 \times 5 = 250$

The height is 5 cm.

TRY THESE

Exercises 6–7: Have students list the steps in their calculations.

TECHNOLOGY OPTION For Exercises 6 and 7, students can use geometry software to find the volume of a rectangular prism.

Organizer, continued

Student Resources
Extra Practice
Student Study Guide
Practice, TR Ch. 6, p. 30
Student Study Guide, Spanish Resources, TR
Checkpoint, TR Ch. 6, p. 36

Teacher Resources
Teaching Transparency 63
Lesson Planner, TR Ch. 6, p. 9

Prentice Hall Technology

Multimedia Math
- Math Investigations, Unidentified Flying Cubes
- Math Investigations, Crisis in Hydrotown

Computer Item Generator
- 6-8

Other Available Technology
The Geometric Supposer by Sunburst: Questions 6, 7, Exercises 8–10, 17 *(optional)*

The gram is the basic unit of mass in the metric system. One gram is officially equal to the weight of one cubic centimeter of distilled water at 4°C.

Source: *Webster's New World Dictionary*

We measure volume in units such as cubic centimeters (cm³), cubic meters (m³), and cubic inches (in.³).

Example 1 Find the volume of the rectangular prism.

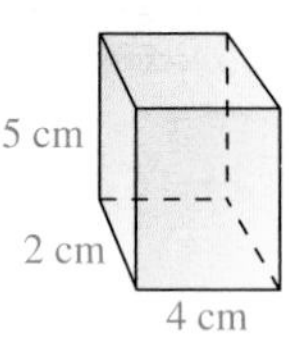

Use $V = lwh$.

$V = 4 \times 2 \times 5 = 40$

The volume is 40 cm³.

4. Critical Thinking Suppose you turn the prism in Example 1 so that the base is 2 cm by 5 cm and the height is 4 cm. Is the volume the same? Why or why not? **Yes; the dimensions of the prism are still 4 cm by 2 cm by 5 cm.**

If you know the volume and two of the dimensions of a rectangular prism, you can find the third dimension.

Example 2 The volume of a rectangular prism is 105 in.³. The height of the prism is 5 in. The length is 7 in. What is the width of the prism?

Use $V = lwh$.

$105 = 7 \times w \times 5$ Substitute.

$105 = 35w$

$\frac{105}{35} = \frac{35w}{35}$ Divide each side by 35.

$w = 3$

Check $7 \times 3 \times 5 = 105$ ✓

The width is 3 in.

In 1978, millions of cube puzzles were sold. Despite the trillions of possible combinations, some people practiced solving the cubes until they could restore the colors from any random position in under 45 s.

Source: *The Simple Solution to Rubik's Cube*

5. The volume of a rectangular prism is 36 m³. The area of the base is 9 m². What is the height of the prism? **4 m**

TRY THESE

Find the volume of each rectangular prism.

6.

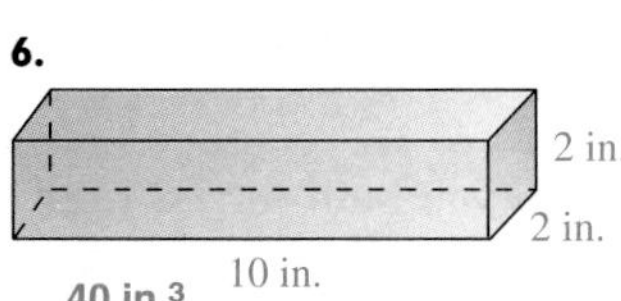

40 in.³

7.

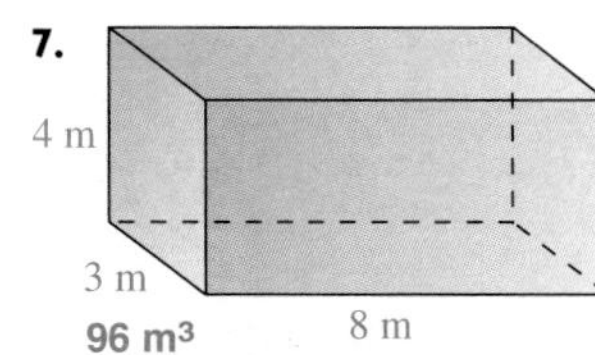

96 m³

Wrap Up

What's the Big Idea? Ask students to list the steps involved in finding the volume of a rectangular prism.

Journal Ask students to think of a shape of rectangular prism that holds more volume for the same surface area as prisms with lesser volumes. Then ask students if the shape is a common one. Have students give explanations for their answers.

Reteaching Activity Group students in pairs and provide each pair with 20 cubes. Have students take turns constructing prisms and measuring the volume of the prisms. Ask students to make two different prisms with 8, 12, 16, and then all 20 cubes. Have students determine the relationship between the volumes of prisms made of the same number of cubes.

Connections Have a discussion about how volume is used. You may want to start with these examples:

- **Engineering** (building dams, canals, drainage ditches, aqueducts, and sewer systems; making hydraulic machinery)
- **Food Processing** (packaging beverages or sauces in cans, bottles, and jars; finding a package that uses surface area efficiently)
- **Science** (mixing precise amounts of solutions, calculating rate of evaporation)

ON YOUR OWN

CONNECTION TO ALGEBRA Exercises 14–16 review algebraic concepts by having students use variable expressions.

WRITING For Exercise 17b, have students use the formula for the area of a square, $A = s \times s$, as a guide.

ON YOUR OWN

Find the volume of each rectangular prism.

8.

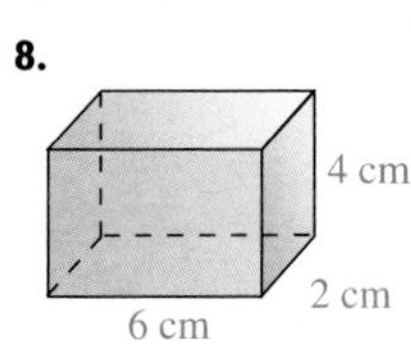

48 cm³

9. 15 in., 4 in., 10 in.

600 in.³

10.

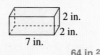

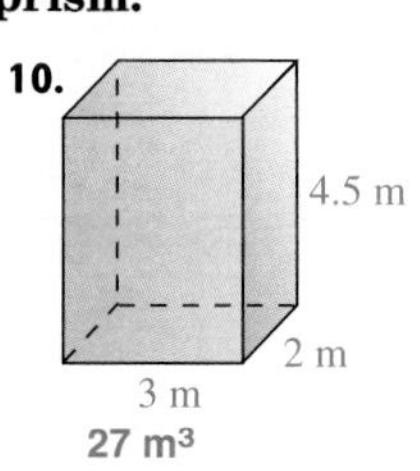

27 m³

11. $l = 5$ mm, $w = 4$ mm, $h = 9$ mm 180 mm³

12. $l = 14$ cm, $w = 7$ cm, $h = 2.5$ cm 245 cm³

13. $l = 6$ ft, $w = 1$ ft, $h = 7$ ft 42 ft³

The volume and two dimensions of a rectangular prism are given. Find the third dimension.

14. $V = 154\text{ yd}^3$, $h = 11$ yd, $w = 2$ yd $l = 7$ yd

15. $V = 120\text{ cm}^3$, $w = 4$ cm, $h = 6$ cm $l = 5$ cm

16. $V = 108\text{ ft}^3$, $l = 6$ ft, $w = 2$ ft $h = 9$ ft

17. a. Find the volume of the cube. 125 cm³

b. **Writing** How could you write the formula for the volume of a cube in a different way than $V = lwh$? Explain.

Sample: $V = s^3$ where s is the length of a side.

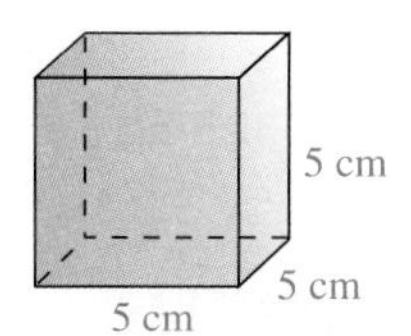

18. Choose A, B, C, or D. This rectangular prism is made of cubes measuring 1 cm on each side. If the top level of cubes is removed, what is the volume of the remaining prism? A

A. 45 cm³ **B.** 60 cm³

C. 48 cm³ **D.** 40 cm³

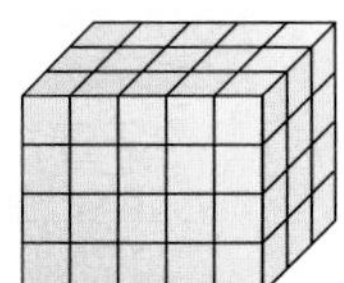

19. Choose A, B, C, or D. A rectangular prism is 2 m long, 50 cm wide, and 1 m high. What is its volume? C

A. 100 m³ **B.** 100 cm³ **C.** 1 m³ **D.** 10,000 cm³

Mixed REVIEW

1. Draw a figure that will tessellate. See Sol. Key.
2. Draw a figure that will not tessellate.
3. a. Name the figure.
   b. Find the surface area.

   2 in., 2 in., 7 in.

   64 in.²
4. Melanie has 19 nickels. Jerry has 11 dimes. Who has more money? How much more? Jerry; 15¢

2. See Sol. Key.
3. rectangular prism

Fact of the Day

The largest swimming pool in the world is the seawater Orthlieb Pool in Casablanca, Morocco, which is 1,574 ft long and 246 ft wide.

—*Guinness Book of Records*

Assignment Options

Core: 8–15, 20, MR all, CH all	
Reinforce: 16–19, 21, 22	**Enrich:** 23, 24

Exercises 21 and 22: Have students display the possible dimensions for each exercise in a table.

CHECKPOINT

Exercises 3 and 4: Remind students to label the surface areas with the correct unit of measure.

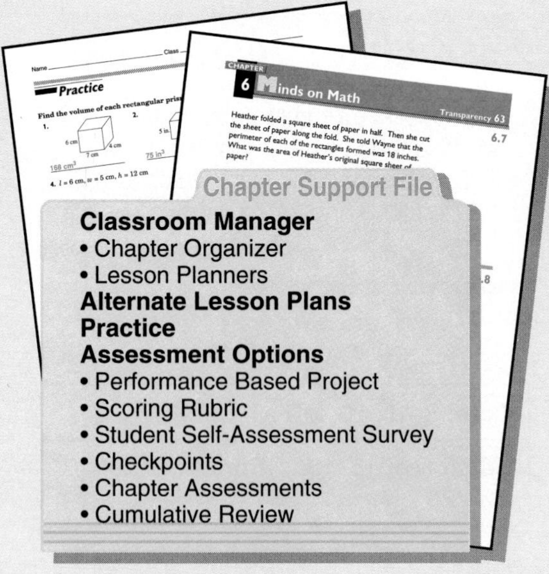

Chapter Support File

Classroom Manager
- Chapter Organizer
- Lesson Planners

Alternate Lesson Plans

Practice

Assessment Options
- Performance Based Project
- Scoring Rubric
- Student Self-Assessment Survey
- Checkpoints
- Chapter Assessments
- Cumulative Review

Minds on Math available in Teaching Transparencies

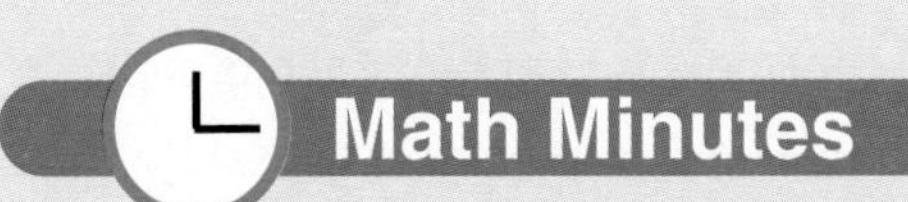

Math Minutes

Nikki is twice as old as her sister Kelly. The sum of their ages is 24. How old are the sisters? **Nikki is 16; Kelly is 8.**

Materials for 6-9

- pennies
- centimeter ruler

20. The volumes are equal; the prism on the left has the greater surface area.

20. How do the volumes of these rectangular prisms compare? How do the surface areas compare? See left.

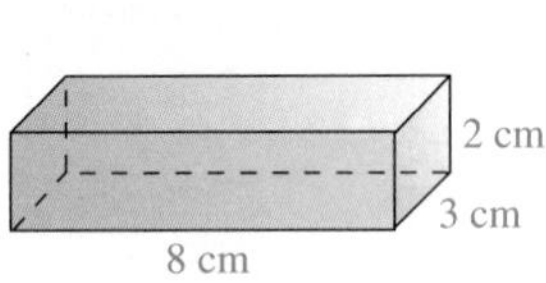

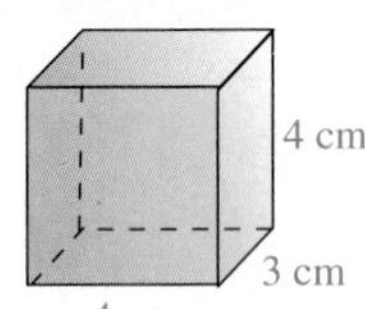

Problem Solving Hint

A 2 cm × 3 cm × 5 cm prism is the same as a 3 cm × 5 cm × 2 cm prism.

Find the whole-number dimensions of all possible rectangular prisms that have the given volume.

21. $V = 32\text{ cm}^3$ **22.** $V = 48\text{ cm}^3$

21.–22. See left.

21. 1 by 1 by 32, 2 by 1 by 16, 2 by 2 by 8, 2 by 4 by 4, 4 by 1 by 8.

22. 1 by 1 by 48, 1 by 2 by 24, 1 by 3 by 16, 1 by 4 by 12, 1 by 6 by 8, 2 by 2 by 12, 2 by 3 by 8, 2 by 4 by 6, 3 by 4 by 4.

23. A rectangular municipal swimming pool is 24 m long and 16 m wide. The average depth of the water is 2.5 m.

a. What is the volume of the water? about 960 m³

b. We use units of *capacity,* like the *liter,* to measure liquids. A volume of 1 m³ is equivalent to 1,000 L of capacity. What is the capacity, in liters, of the swimming pool? about 960,000 L

c. What would be the dimensions of a cover large enough to cover the surface of the water? at least 24 m by 16 m

24. Data File 9 (pp. 360–361) What is the volume of a finishing post at a track meet? 1,952 cm³

CHECKPOINT

Name each space figure. Give the number of faces, edges, and vertices.

1.

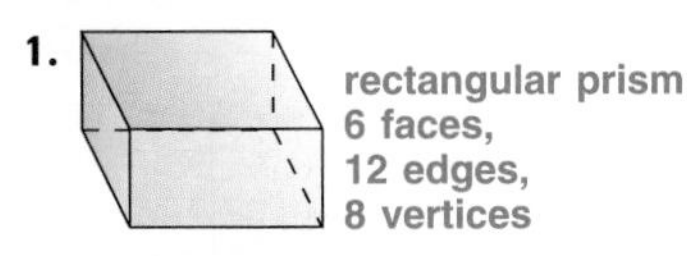

rectangular prism; 6 faces, 12 edges, 8 vertices

2.

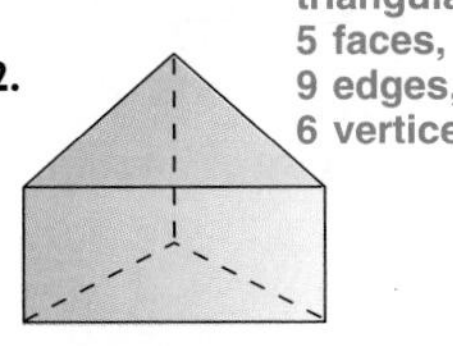

triangular prism; 5 faces, 9 edges, 6 vertices

Find the surface area of each figure.

3.

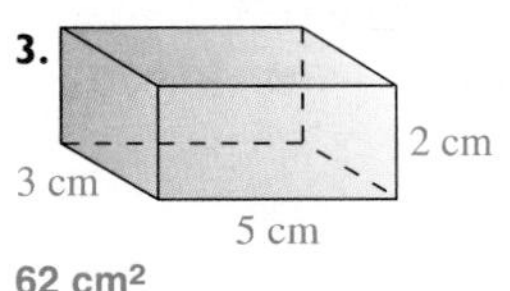

62 cm²

4.

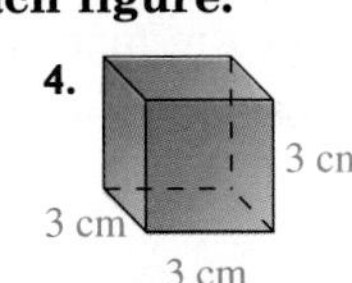

54 cm²

6-9

Connecting to Prior Knowledge

Ask students to recall times when people have used a physical model to explain something. For example, a coach might draw lines in the dirt to model a passing route in a football game. Challenge students to think of models they have used in classes, such as art or science.

TACTILE LEARNERS Encourage the use of real pennies to help students think of various ways to model the problem.

ESL **Error Alert!** Students may misunderstand the problem and think that they should look at surface area instead of volume. ***Remediation*** Encourage students to make a habit of rephrasing a problem's question in their own words. Tell students that after rephrasing a problem, a good first step is to determine exactly what the form of the solution should be. For the example problem, the word "hold" indicates that the volume of the box, not its surface area, will be used to find the number of pennies in the box.

Additional Problem *A prism has two rectangular faces that measure 2 cm by 3 cm, two rectangular faces that measure 2 cm by 8 cm, and two rectangular faces that measure 3 cm by 8 cm. What type of prism is it, what are its dimensions, and what is its volume?* **(rectangular; 2 cm × 3 cm × 8 cm; 48 cm³)**

Ongoing Assessment Ask students to share their strategies for the Additional Problem. Have students compare the strategies and determine whether one is better than another or if there is more than one good way of solving the problem.

Journal Ask students to name as many materials as they can that can be used to make models. Then have them explain why making a model makes a problem easier and how they can use models to solve problems.

What's Ahead

- Solving problems by making a model

PROBLEM SOLVING

6-9 Make a Model

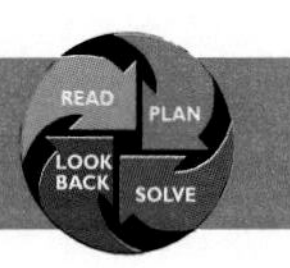

WHAT YOU'LL NEED

✓ Pennies

✓ Centimeter ruler

Sometimes a physical model can help you solve a problem.

> Danny collects pennies. He keeps his pennies in a box with interior dimensions 21 cm by 21 cm by 21 cm. How many pennies will the box hold?

READ Read and understand the given information. Summarize the problem.

1. Think about the information you are given and what you are asked to find.
   a. What does the problem ask you to find? **How many pennies will fit in a box that is 21 cm by 21 cm by 21 cm**
   b. Are you given all the information you need? What else do you need to know? **No; the dimensions of a penny**

PLAN Decide on a strategy to solve the problem.

Making a model will help you solve the problem. If you have enough pennies, you can find out how many are needed to form one layer that fits inside a square 21 cm by 21 cm. However, it will be enough to find out how many pennies you can fit in a row no longer than 21 cm.

2. Do you need to have a stack of pennies 21 cm high in order to find out how many layers will fit in the box? Why or why not? **No; Sample: You could see how many pennies fit in a stack 1 cm high and multiply by 21.**

SOLVE Try out the strategy.

3. Work with your group to make models you can measure.
   a. How many pennies can you fit in a row 21 cm long? **11**
   b. How many pennies will fit in a stack of pennies 21 cm high? **147**
4. a. How many pennies will fit in one layer? **121**
   b. How many pennies will fit in the box? **17,787**

LOOK BACK Think about how you solved this problem.

5. Suppose you measure the diameter and height of only one penny. How could you use the information to get the same result? **Sample: Divide 21 by the diameter (in cm) to estimate how many pennies fit in one row. Divide 21 by the height (in cm) to estimate how many pennies fit in a stack 21 cm high.**

"One must learn by doing the thing; for though you think you know it, you have no certainty until you try."

—SOPHOCLES

Organizer

1. **Focus**
   Connecting to Prior Knowledge
2. **Teach**
3. **Closure**
   Try These
   Wrap Up

Skills Reviewed in Context of Lesson
- calculating volume

Materials and Manipulatives
- pennies (20 for each group)
- centimeter ruler (1 for each group)

Student Resources
Extra Practice
Student Study Guide
Practice, TR Ch. 6, p. 31
Student Study Guide, Spanish Resources, TR

Teacher Resources
Teaching Transparency 63
Lesson Planner, TR Ch. 6, p. 10

Prentice Hall Technology
Computer Item Generator
- 6-9

TRY THESE

Exercises 6–7: Have students discuss their models in groups of three or four.

Wrap Up

What's the Big Idea? Ask students to describe how making a model can help solve a problem.

Journal Ask students to explain why making a model makes a problem easier and how they can use models to solve problems.

Connections Have students discuss occupations in which people use models to solve problems:

- **Architecture** (making a model of a building before constructing the building)
- **Science** (making a model of a real-life situation to examine variables)
- **Inventions** (making a model to examine different factors in the product)

Reteaching Activity Have students review their models for the problems and for the Try These exercises. Then have students meet in groups of four to create a set of steps that will help to solve any problem.

ON YOUR OWN

CONNECTION TO GEOMETRY Exercise 11 reviews geometry by having students measure a triangle.

CONNECTION TO PATTERNS Exercise 9 has students find and continue a pattern.

Exercise 12: Suggest that students make a sketch to accompany their answer.

Fact of the Day

In a scale model of our galaxy, if the Earth were a ball one inch in diameter, the nearest star outside our solar system, Alpha Centauri, would have to be placed almost 51,000 mi away.

—*The Great Big Super Giant Book of Trivia*

Assignment Options

Core: 8, 9, 12, 13, MR all	
Reinforce: 11, 14, 16	**Enrich:** 10, 15

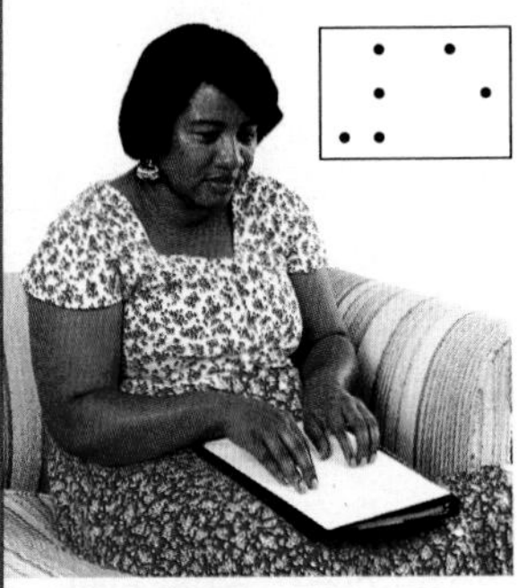

***Blind people** can use the Braille system to read books. Letters and numbers are indicated by combinations of six raised dots. The number 5 is shown above.*

TRY THESE

Make a model to solve each problem.

6. Lincoln's head is right-side-up on the penny on the left. If you roll the penny halfway around the other penny, will Lincoln's head be right-side-up, upside-down, or neither? right-side-up
7. It takes Clarence 12 min to cut a log into 4 pieces. How long will it take him to cut a log that is the same size into 5 pieces? 16 min

ON YOUR OWN

Use any strategy to solve each problem. Show all your work.

8. The numbered pages in the book *Why Do Clocks Run Clockwise?* go from 1 to 251. How many of these page numbers contain at least one 2? 90

   Answers may vary.
9. a. Find three numbers that continue the pattern.

   Samples given. 1, 2, 4, ■, ■, ■ 8, 16, 32

   b. Find another three numbers that continue the pattern in a different way. 7, 11, 16 or 7, 12, 20
10. Which of the following nets could you fold to form a box without a top? c, e, f, g, h, j, k, l

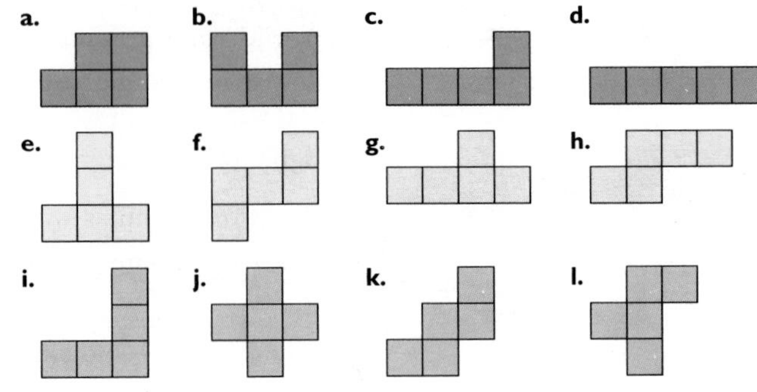

Exercise 13: Remind students that there are ways to organize their search for a solution.

Exercise 16: Ask students to design and solve a similar problem in miniature using a matchbox.

11. What is the area of the triangle? 9.5 square units

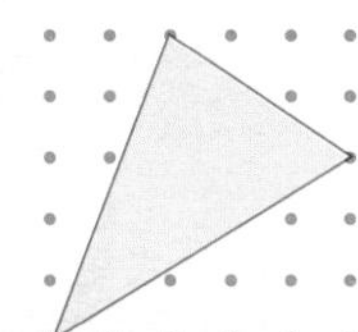

12. Mosi works in a grocery store after school. He stacked grapefruit in the shape of a square pyramid. There was one grapefruit on the top level, four on the next level, and nine on the next level. If there were eight levels in all, how many grapefruit did Mosi stack? 204 grapefruit

13. What are the whole-number dimensions of the rectangular prism with a volume of 12 cubic units and the greatest possible surface area for such a prism? 1 by 1 by 12

14. Kevin went to the grocery store with exactly 90¢ in change. He did not have any pennies.

a. What is the least number of coins he could have? 4

b. What is the greatest number of coins he could have? 18

15. Pilar's birthday cake is in the shape of a cube, with icing on the top and four sides. She cut it as shown.

a. How many cuts did Pilar make? 6

b. How many pieces did she cut the cake into? 27

c. How many of the pieces don't have any icing? 1

16. **Choose A, B, or C.** Which piece of wrapping paper shown below can you *not* use to wrap the box shown without cutting? C

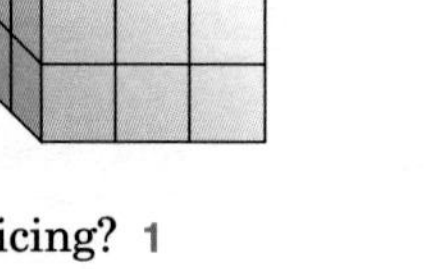

A.

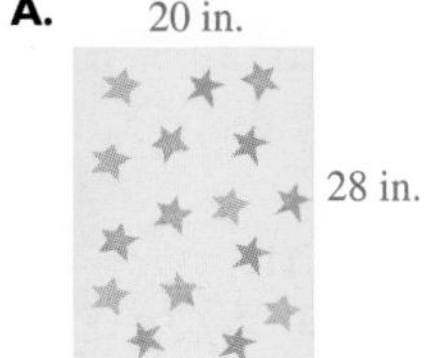

B.

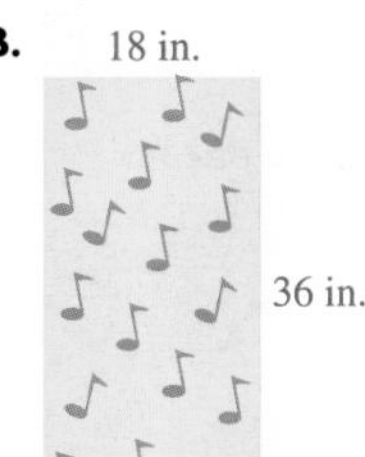

C.

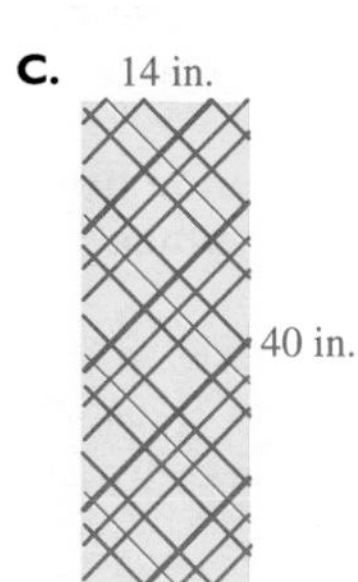

Mixed REVIEW

Write using an exponent.

1. $6 \times 6 \times 6 \times 6$ 6^4

2. $22 \times 22 \times 22$ 22^3

Find the volume of each rectangular prism.

3. $l = 7$ cm, $w = 2$ cm, and $h = 4$ cm 56 cm³

4. $l = 5$ ft, $w = 3$ ft, and $h = 7$ ft 105 ft³

5. A collector buys a stamp for \$25, sells it for \$30, buys it back for \$33, and finally sells it for \$35. How much money did he make or lose in buying and selling this stamp?

5. makes \$7

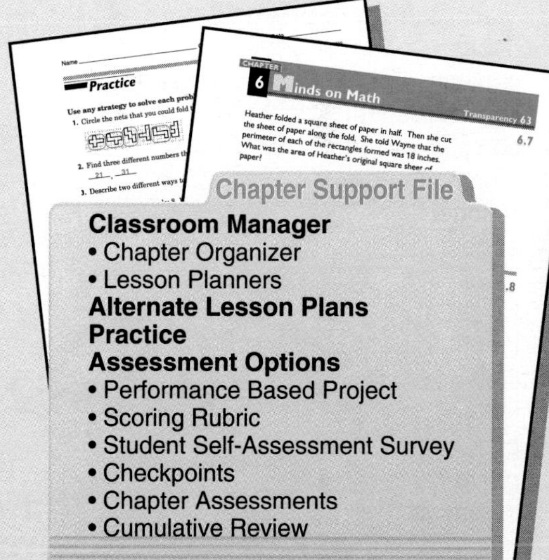

Chapter Support File

Classroom Manager
- Chapter Organizer
- Lesson Planners

Alternate Lesson Plans

Practice

Assessment Options
- Performance Based Project
- Scoring Rubric
- Student Self-Assessment Survey
- Checkpoints
- Chapter Assessments
- Cumulative Review

Minds on Math available in Teaching Transparencies

Math Minutes

Summer has \$1.00 in change in her pocket. She has 9 coins and her largest coin is a quarter. What coins does she have?

1 quarter, 7 dimes, 1 nickel *or* 2 quarters, 3 dimes, 4 nickels

CHAPTER 6 WRAP UP

Exercise 1: You may need to remind students that the area of the figure is the number of squares enclosed by the figure, including parts of squares.

Exercises 5–8: You may need to remind students, or have them remind each other, how to find the circumference and area of a circle, given its radius or diameter. Point out that in Exercises 7 and 8, the diameter, rather than the radius, is given.

Exercises 9–11: Have students estimate the circumference and area before computing them by calculator.

Ongoing Assessment Have students work with partners or in groups on Exercises 16 and 17.

Exercise 16 can be done by drawing pictures, but it might be more interesting to have students move squares of construction paper into different arrangements.

For Exercise 17, it might be helpful for students to work with cubical building blocks. (These need not actually be 4 in. on each side.) Students can experiment with making boxes out of construction paper and tape to enclose four blocks. Encourage students to try as many shapes as possible for their boxes. Then have them compare the amount of construction paper used for each box, and find the box shape that uses the least amount of paper. Some students may be daunted by the idea of building boxes or unsure how to begin. Circulate and help these students. Have the class discuss the problem and compare results. Come to a consensus on the shape of the box that uses the least amount of material (paper) to enclose four blocks.

Vocabulary/Symbols

bases
capacity
circumference
cone
cube
cylinder
edge
faces
height, h
length, l
liter
net
pi, π
prism
pyramids
rectangular prism
sphere
square pyramid
square units
surface area
three-dimensional figures
vertex
volume, V
width, w

Materials and Manipulatives

- construction paper or manila folders
- scissors

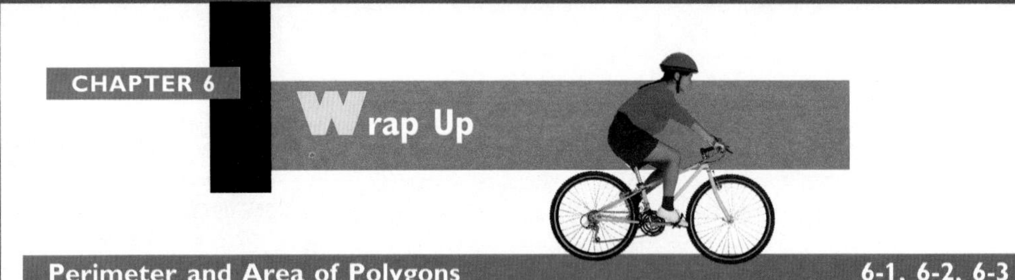

Perimeter and Area of Polygons 6-1, 6-2, 6-3

Perimeter is the distance around a figure.

Area is the number of square units inside a figure.

1. Estimate the area of the figure. Assume each square stands for 1 m^2. about 18 m^2

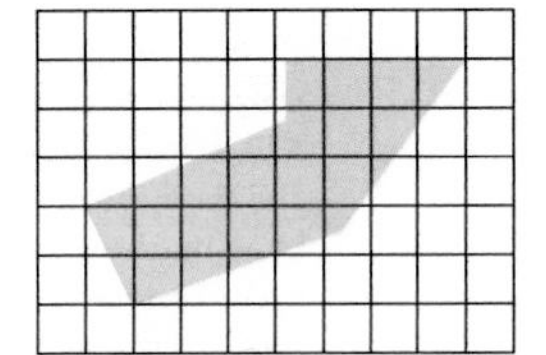

2. Find the area and perimeter of the figure. 13.5 cm^2; 22 cm

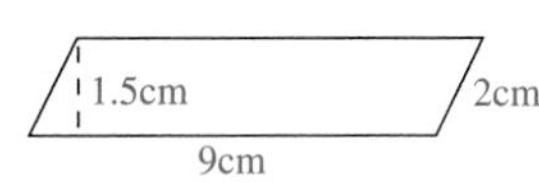

3. A rectangular yard has an area of 72 m^2. One side is 8 m long. How much fence do you need to enclose the entire yard? 34 m

4. Find the area of a triangle with a base 12 cm and height 7.6 cm. 45.6 cm^2

Circumference and Area of Circles 6-4, 6-5

We use the symbol π to stand for the quotient of the circumference and diameter of a circle. The formula for area of a circle is $A = \pi r^2$.

Find the circumference and area of a circle with the given radius or diameter. Use 3.14 for π. Round to a convenient place.

5. $r = 6$ in. 37.7 in.; 113.0 in.^2
6. $r = 3.8$ m 23.9 m; 45.3 m^2
7. $d = 24.5$ cm 76.9 cm; 471.2 cm^2
8. $d = 37.6$ ft 118.1 ft; 1,109.8 ft^2

Calculator **Find the circumference and area of each circle. Round to a convenient place.**

9. 5 in

31.4 in.; 78.5 in.^2

10. 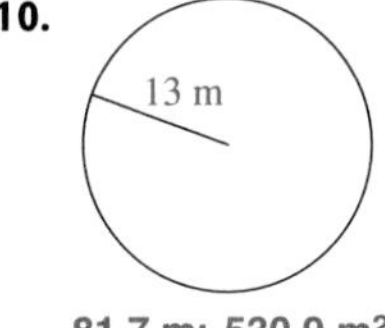

81.7 m; 530.9 m^2

11. 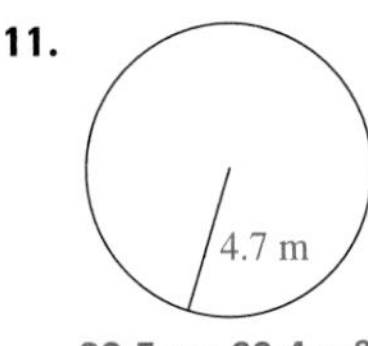

29.5 m; 69.4 m^2

Getting Ready for Chapter 7

The skills previewed will help students understand and solve problems involving divisibility and factorization.

Three-Dimensional Figures 6-6

Three dimensional figures are figures such as boxes, cans, and baseballs that do not lie in a plane. Some three-dimensional figures have flat, polygonal surfaces called ***faces.*** When two faces intersect, the resulting segment is called an ***edge.*** Each point where edges meet is a ***vertex.***

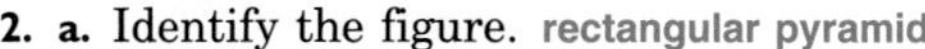

12. a. Identify the figure. rectangular pyramid

b. Find the number of faces, edges, and vertices. 5, 8, 5

13. Writing Give a description of a sphere. Sample answer: A sphere is a three-dimensional figure with no faces, edges, or vertices.

Surface Area and Volume 6-7, 6-8

The sum of the areas of the faces of a three-dimensional prism or pyramid is the ***surface area*** of the figure.

The ***volume*** of a three-dimensional figure is the number of cubic units needed to fill the space inside the figure. The volume of a rectangular prism is $V = lwh$.

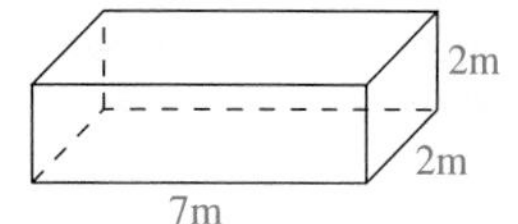

14. Find the surface area and the volume of the rectangular prism. $64\ m^2$; $28\ m^3$

15. Choose A, B, C, or D. Which could not be dimensions for a rectangular prism with a volume of $60\ m^3$? B

A. 1 m by 1 m by 60 m **B.** 4 m by 15 m by 2 m

C. 3 m by 4 m by 5 m **D.** 1 m by 6 m by 10 m

Strategies and Applications 2-7

Sometimes a physical model can help you solve a problem.

16. You have 12 square tables. One person can sit on each side. You need to arrange the tables so that at least one side is touching another table. How many people can you seat? 36

17. Design a box to hold 4 cube-shaped candles. Use the least possible amount of material. Each candle has 4 in. sides. The dimensions of the box are 8 in. by 8 in. by 4 in.

GETTING READY FOR CHAPTER 7

Tell whether each number is divisible by 2, 5, or 10.

1. 72 2 **2.** 40 2, 5, 10 **3.** 47 no **4.** 55 5 **5.** 1,000 2, 5, 10 **6.** 129 no

Student Resources

Practice, p. 250
Problem Solving Practice, p. 241
Extra Practice
Student Study Guide
Student Study Guide, Spanish Resources
Tools for Studying Smarter, TR
Student Self-Assessment Survey, TR Ch 6, p. 35 *(see below)*

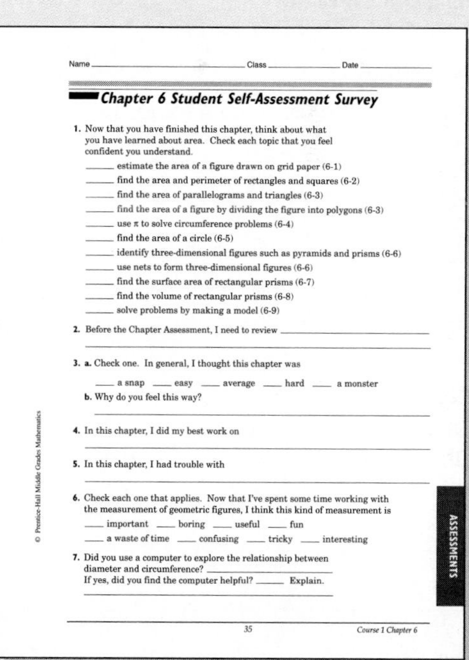

Name ____________ Class ____________ Date ____________

Chapter 6 Student Self-Assessment Survey

1. Now that you have finished this chapter, think about what you have learned about area. Check each topic that you feel confident you understand.

_____ estimate the area of a figure drawn on grid paper (6-1)
_____ find the area and perimeter of rectangles and squares (6-2)
_____ find the area of parallelograms and triangles (6-3)
_____ find the area of a figure by dividing the figure into polygons (6-3)
_____ use π to solve circumference problems (6-4)
_____ find the area of a circle (6-5)
_____ identify three-dimensional figures such as pyramids and prisms (6-6)
_____ use nets to form three-dimensional figures (6-6)
_____ find the surface area of rectangular prisms (6-7)
_____ find the volume of rectangular prisms (6-8)
_____ solve problems by making a model (6-9)

2. Before the Chapter Assessment, I need to review ____________

3. a. Check one. In general, I thought this chapter was

___ a snap ___ easy ___ average ___ hard ___ a monster

b. Why do you feel this way?

4. In this chapter, I did my best work on

5. In this chapter, I had trouble with

6. Check each one that applies. Now that I've spent some time working with the measurement of geometric figures, I think this kind of measurement is

___ important ___ boring ___ useful ___ fun
___ a waste of time ___ confusing ___ tricky ___ interesting

7. Did you use a computer to explore the relationship between diameter and circumference? ____________
If yes, did you find the computer helpful? _____ Explain.

ASSESSMENTS

35 Course 1 Chapter 6

CHAPTER 6

PUTTING IT ALL TOGETHER

The projects on these pages can be used in a variety of ways.

- alternative assessment
- portfolio ideas
- additional assignments for gifted and talented students
- extra credit for all students

Follow Up

After students have completed their work, ask them to conjecture how Orlando might have made his mistaken calculations. Then ask them to identify the square, if any, with the properties Orlando found: 300 total **(none);** 120 tiles in the border **(31-square);** 61 tiles needed to build the square **(31-square from a 30-square).**

EXCURSION Fifteen tiles are needed to build an 8-triangle from a 7-triangle.

One of These Days!

MATERIALS AND MANIPULATIVES Along with a protractor and a compass, students will also need plain paper for their circle graphs.

Practice this activity with the whole class before groups divide to work on the circle graphs. Begin with a simple activity that has four parts, then continually change the instructions so that the students can round the time, divide the circle into fractions, and eventually determine what relationship there is between the measurement of a circle and a fraction that represents a part of the school day.

3-D Concentration

Students may want to color or decorate the space figures so provide crayons or colored markers to do this.

COOPERATIVE GROUPS Have students work in groups of three or more players. Make sure the surface area where the students

Materials and Manipulatives

Follow Up

- triangular algebra tiles

One of These Days!

- protractor
- compass
- straightedge
- plain paper

3-D Concentration

- 24 3″ × 5″ index cards

Boxed In

- graph paper or manila folders

PUTTING IT ALL TOGETHER

Follow Up

Patterns and Squares

In this chapter you have learned about areas and perimeters of figures. You have learned to solve problems by making models. Have you learned anything to change your mind about Orlando's claims about tile squares? Take another look at the decision you reached regarding his claims. If necessary, revise your decision. Then write a short paper explaining how you reached your decision. The following are suggestions to help you support your reasoning.

✓ Use patterns.
✓ Make a model.
✓ Draw a graph.

The problems preceded by the magnifying glass (p. 236, # 30; p. 249, # 25; and p. 258, # 17) will help you complete the investigation.

Excursion: Suppose Orlando had investigated triangles instead of squares.

How many tiles would he need to build an 8-triangle from a 7-triangle?

Do this with your group. You will need a protractor and compass.

Prepare a circle graph that represents how your time is spent during a typical school day. You should round your time to the nearest quarter hour. Divide your circle into fractions that represent the time spent on each activity.

Some things to think about: How many hours are represented by the circle graph? How can you use the measurement of a circle (360 degrees) to determine what fraction is needed to represent a part of the school day?

268

are playing is level and wide enough to accommodate all the players who need to see the cards.

Boxed In

Students may want to extend the activity by actually building the box. Provide students with tag board or used manila folders that can be cut and folded.

Encourage the students to explore the possibilities for designing the boxes. Cylinders, trapezoids, or unusual shapes may intrigue the students' curiosity and provide an excellent educational activity for the creative students.

RESEARCH There is an interesting book of net designs for all the packaging designs used in industry. The book may be found at a large city library or a university library: *The Packaging Designer's Book of Patterns* by Laszlo Roth and George L. Wybenga (New York: Van Nostrand Reinhold, 1991). The book also contains the history of paper making and box construction.

What's On Your Mind

Ask a representative from each group to choose their best space figure and have them play against the class. Record the amount of guesses needed to determine the space figure for each group. The group with the least amount of points wins.

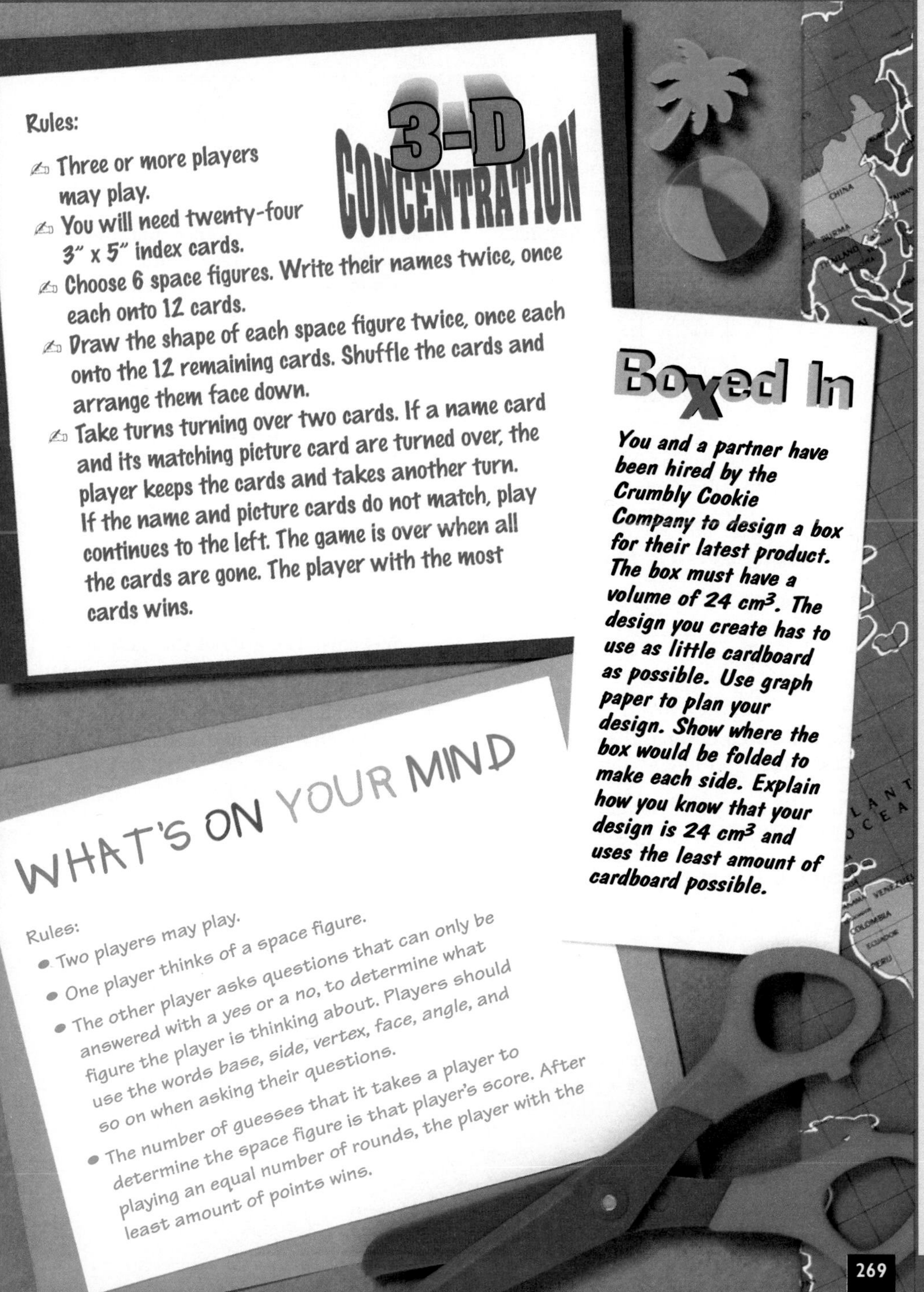
3-D CONCENTRATION
Rules:
Three or more players may play.
You will need twenty-four 3" x 5" index cards.
Choose 6 space figures. Write their names twice, once each onto 12 cards.
Draw the shape of each space figure twice, once each onto the 12 remaining cards. Shuffle the cards and arrange them face down.
Take turns turning over two cards. If a name card and its matching picture card are turned over, the player keeps the cards and takes another turn. If the name and picture cards do not match, play continues to the left. The game is over when all the cards are gone. The player with the most cards wins.
Boxed In
You and a partner have been hired by the Crumbly Cookie Company to design a box for their latest product. The box must have a volume of 24 cm³. The design you create has to use as little cardboard as possible. Use graph paper to plan your design. Show where the box would be folded to make each side. Explain how you know that your design is 24 cm³ and uses the least amount of cardboard possible.
WHAT'S ON YOUR MIND
Rules:
Two players may play.
One player thinks of a space figure.
The other player asks questions that can only be answered with a yes or a no, to determine what figure the player is thinking about. Players should use the words base, side, vertex, face, angle, and so on when asking their questions.
The number of guesses that it takes a player to determine the space figure is that player's score. After playing an equal number of rounds, the player with the least amount of points wins.
CHINA
BURMA
THAILAND
VENEZUELA
COLOMBIA
ECUADOR
PERU
269

CHAPTER 6 ASSESSMENT

Writing Questions allow students to describe more fully their thinking and understanding of the concepts they've learned.

Exercise 8 is a writing question.

Enhanced Multiple Choice Questions are more complex than traditional multiple choice questions, which assess only one skill. Enhanced multiple choice questions assess the processes that students use as well as the end results. They are written so that students can use more than one strategy to solve the problem. Using multiple strategies is encouraged by the National Council of Teachers of Mathematics (NCTM).

Exercise 15 is an enhanced multiple choice question. It might be helpful to allow students to copy all four drawings. Then they should try to cut out and fold each drawing into the shape of a rectangular prism. Folding is allowed only where there are lines in the drawings.

Resources

Performance Based Project, TR Ch. 6, pp. 32–34
Chapter Assessment, Forms A and B, TR Ch. 6, pp. 37–40
Spanish Chapter Assessment, Spanish Resources, TR
Computer Item Generator

CHAPTER 6

Assessment

10.a. 62.8 km; 314.0 km² b. 37.7 cm; 113.0 cm² c. 23.2 yd; 43.0 yd² d. 169.6 m; 2,289.1 m²

1. Find the area of the figure. Assume each square represents 1 cm². 16 cm²

2. Find the area and perimeter of a square with sides 6 m. 36 m²; 24 m
3. The perimeter of a rectangle is 32 ft. One dimension is 9 ft. Find the area. 63 ft²
4. Find the area of the figure below. 126 m²

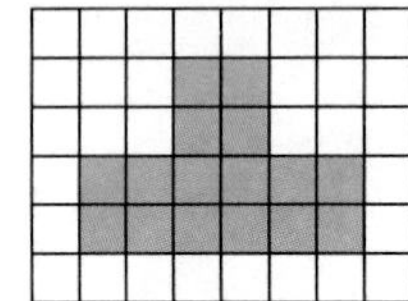

5. Find the area of a parallelogram with base 12 cm and height 7 cm. 84 cm²
6. Find the area of a triangle with base 9.2 m and height 19.3 m. 88.78 m²
7. Find the area of the triangle below. 12 yd²

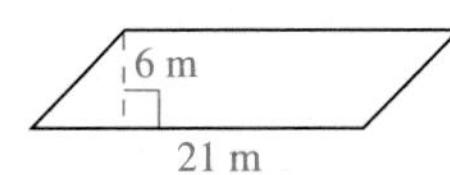

8. **Writing** Which is larger: a pie plate with a radius of 5 in. or a pie plate with a diameter of 9 in.? Explain. The plate with radius 5 in.; its diameter is 10 in.
9. What is the surface area of a box with length 8 ft, width 5 ft, and height 4 ft? 184 ft²
10. Find the circumference and area of a circle with the given radius or diameter. Round to the nearest tenth.
    a. $r = 10$ km b. $d = 12$ cm
    c. $d = 7.4$ yd d. $r = 27$ m
11. a. Identify the figure. triangular prism
    b. Find the number of faces, edges, and vertices. 5, 9, 6

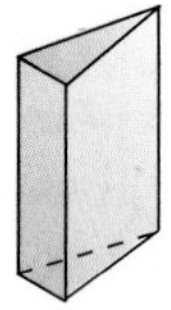

12. A rectangular prism is 17 m long, 3 m wide, and 5 m high. Find its volume. 255 m³
13. The volume of a rectangular prism is 504 cm³. The area of the base is 72 cm². Find the height of the prism. 7 cm
14. The volume and two dimensions of a rectangular prism are given. Find the third dimension. a. 9 cm b. 12 in.
    a. $V = 189$ cm³, $h = 7$ cm, $w = 3$ cm
    b. $V = 1{,}080$ in.³, $h = 15$ in., $w = 6$ in.
    c. $V = 360$ ft³, $h = 9$ ft, $w = 4$ ft 10 ft
15. **Choose A, B, C, or D.** Which could be a net for a rectangular prism? B

A.
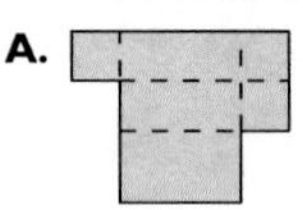

B.
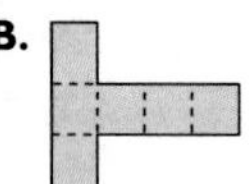

C.
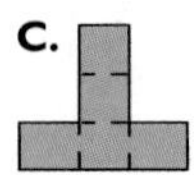

D.
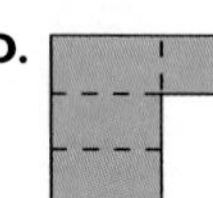

CHAPTER 6 CUMULATIVE REVIEW

Exercises 4, 5, 7, and 9 are enhanced multiple choice questions.

Exercise 4: Some students may find it helpful to draw a picture. Others may need or want to copy, cut out, and fold the figure. Encourage students to do whatever helps them visualize the situation.

Exercise 7: You may want to remind students what the distributive property is.

Exercise 9: Encourage students to draw pictures. Before they do this exercise, ask students to explain how to find the perimeters of a triangle and a rectangle.

Item(s)	Review Topic	Chapter
1	area of circles	6
2	measures of central tendency	1
3	evaluating expressions	4
4	volume of rectangular prisms	6
5	patterns	5
6	dividing decimals	4
7	distributive property	4
8	representation of data	1
9	perimeter	6

CHAPTER 6 Cumulative Review

Choose A, B, C, or D.

1. What is the area of a circle whose diameter is 6 cm? C

A. 36 cm^2 **B.** 6 cm^2

C. 28 cm^2 **D.** 12 cm^2

2. What is the median cost of peanut butter per serving? C

A. 20 cents **B.** 20.5 cents

C. 21 cents **D.** 22 cents

Peanut Butter Prices (3 tbsp serving)

Sticky Stuff	22¢	Grandma's Choice	20¢
Shop Along	19¢	All Natural	22¢
Cityside	14¢	Nutty Taste	22¢

3. What do you do first to evaluate the expression $3.9 + 4.1 \times 16 - 6 \div 4.8$? B

A. Add 3.9 and 4.1.

B. Multiply 4.1 by 16.

C. Subtract 6 from 16.

D. Divide 6 by 4.8.

4. Find the volume of the open box made by folding the sides of the net shown. A

A. 90 in.^{3} **B.** 66 in.^{3}

C. 165 in.^{3} **D.** 14 in.^{3}

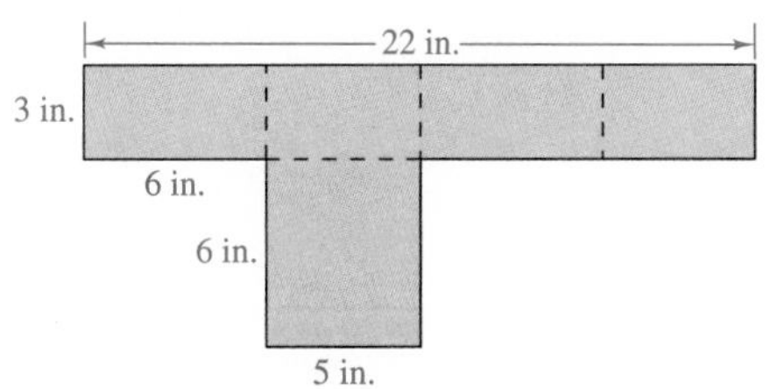

5. If you continue the pattern which figure will have 51 blocks? A

A. the 26th **B.** the 25th

C. the 50th **D.** the 100th

6. A 13.5 mi high speed train will cost \$622 million. About how much is that per mile? C

A. \$460,000 **B.** \$4.6 million

C. \$46 million **D.** \$460 million

7. Which equation is *not* an example of the distributive property? D

A. $12(6.2) + 12(3.8) = 12(6.2 + 3.8)$

B. $0.75(8.869) + 0.25(8.869) = 8.869$

C. $19.1(80) = 19.1(100) - 19.1(20)$

D. $8.1(1.9 + 3.5) = (8.1 + 1.9)(3.5)$

8. Which display would you use to show your height for each year since birth? C

A. line plot **B.** bar graph

C. line graph **D.** circle graph

9. A triangle and a rectangle have equal bases and equal heights. How do their perimeters compare? B

A. The perimeter of the triangle is greater.

B. The perimeter of the rectangle is greater.

C. The perimeters are equal.

D. It is impossible to tell.

Resources

Cumulative Review, TR Ch. 6, pp. 41–42
Transparency Masters, TR p. 35

CHAPTER

7 Fraction Concepts

Why Study Fraction Concepts?

If students ask this question, you may want to mention the following people who use fraction concepts: bank teller, engineer, cook, musician, athletic coach, carpenter, auto mechanic, sales clerk, dietitian, nurse, pharmacist, scientist, and architect.

Graphic Display of Chapter Content

Below is one possible representation of the chapter's content and its applications to the world outside the classroom. Have students create their own graphic display and fill in applications that they have seen in their own lives.

- The center oval should state the main concept of the chapter: fractions.
- Have students draw the ovals with the next level of concepts presented in the chapter (greatest common factor and least common multiple, equivalent fractions, mixed numbers and improper fractions, comparing and ordering, and fractions and decimals). You may want students to add other topics that they think are appropriate.
- Ask students to draw as many application ovals as they can.
- Discuss all the applications that students identify.
- Have students make and present one display that includes all the students' ideas.

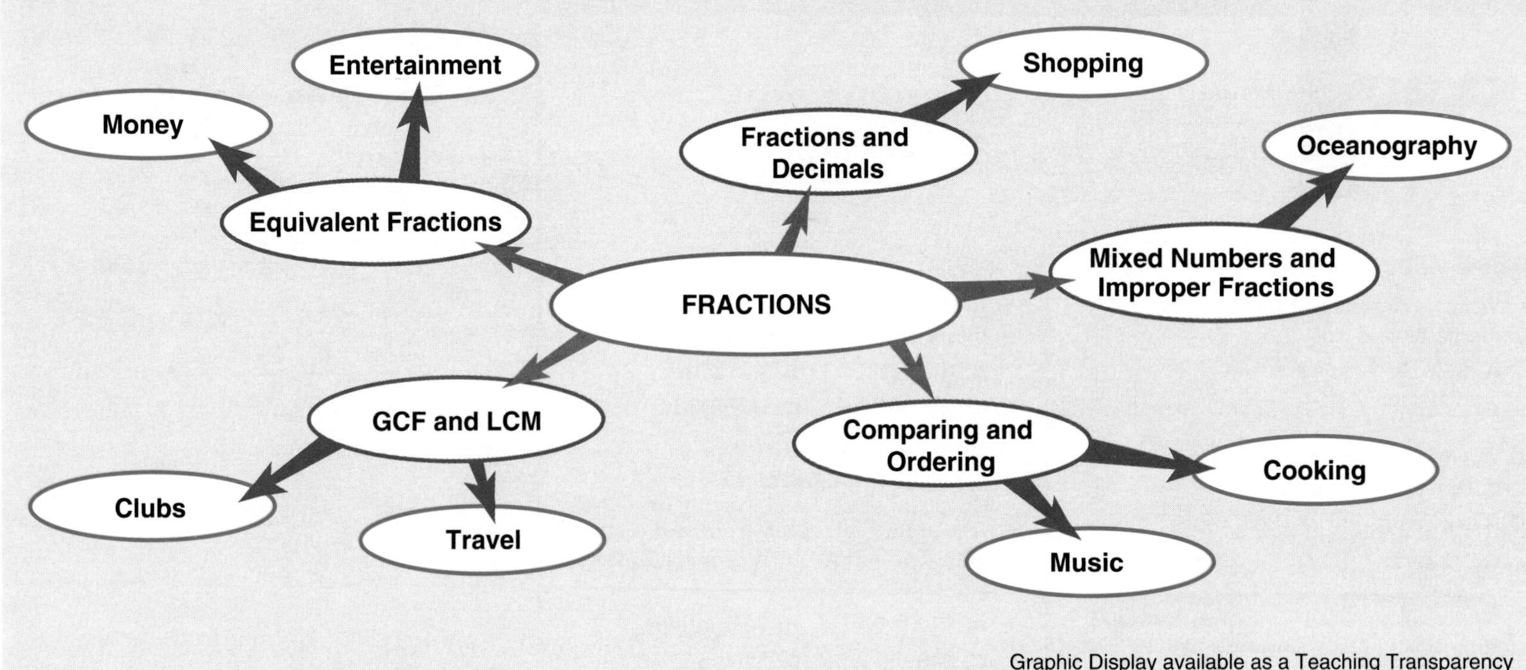

Graphic Display available as a Teaching Transparency

Vocabulary and Symbols

common denominator
common factors
common multiples
composite number
divisibility
equivalent fractions
factor
factor tree
fraction bars
greatest common factor, GCF
improper fraction
least common denominator, LCD
least common multiple, LCM
mixed number
multiple
prime factorization
prime number
repeating decimal
sieve
simplest form
terminating decimal
twin primes

Materials and Manipulatives

calculator	graph paper
decimal squares	square tiles
fraction bars	

Additional Resources

Commercially Available Technology

Calculator
fraction

Software
fraction software
The Fraction Machine by Computer Software
Fraction Practice Unlimited by Computer Software
spreadsheet software
Excel; Works by Microsoft

Other Media
"Conquering Fractions." Minnesota Educational Computing Corp. 3490 Lexington Ave. N. St. Paul, MN 55216. (800) 685-6322.
"Math Football." Gamco Industries, P.O. Box 1911A7, Big Spring, TX 79721. (800) 351-1404.
"Whole Numbers, Decimals, and Fractions." Gamco Industries, P.O. Box 1911A7, Big Spring, TX 79721. (800) 351-1404.

Materials at Little or No Cost

Math/Science Network, 2727 College Avenue, Berkeley, CA 94705. (415) 841-6284. Activites, resources, and newsletter.
Operation Smart, Girls Club of America, Inc., 205 Lexington Ave., New York, NY; 10016. Hands-on activities to encourage adolescent girls in the fields of math and science.

Bibliography

For Teachers
Easterday, Kenneth, et al. *Activities for Junior High School and Middle School Mathematics.* Reston, VA: NCTM, 1981.
Webb, Norman L. *Assessment in the Mathematics Classroom.* Reston, VA: NCTM, 1993.

For Students
Anderson, Norman D. and Walter R. Brown. *Ferris Wheels.* NY: Pantheon, 1983.
Blum, Raymond. *Mathemagic.* NY: Sterling, 1991.
Fekete, Irene and Jamine Deyer. *Mathematics.* NY: Facts on File, 1990.

Prentice Hall Technology 

Multimedia Math
- Math Tools, Fraction Strips
- Math Tools, Manipulatives
- Hot Page™ 7-4
- Hot Page™ 7-7
- Hot Page™ 7-9
- Math Investigations, Hazard City Messengers

Computer Item Generator
- Chapter 7

Community Resources

Field Trips
- a greenhouse
- a computer repair shop
- a machine shop

Guest Speakers
- a botanist (on Fibonacci numbers in nature)
- a police dispatcher

Backpack Take-Home Activities

Materials
- cookbook
- recipe that serves six people
- paper
- pencil

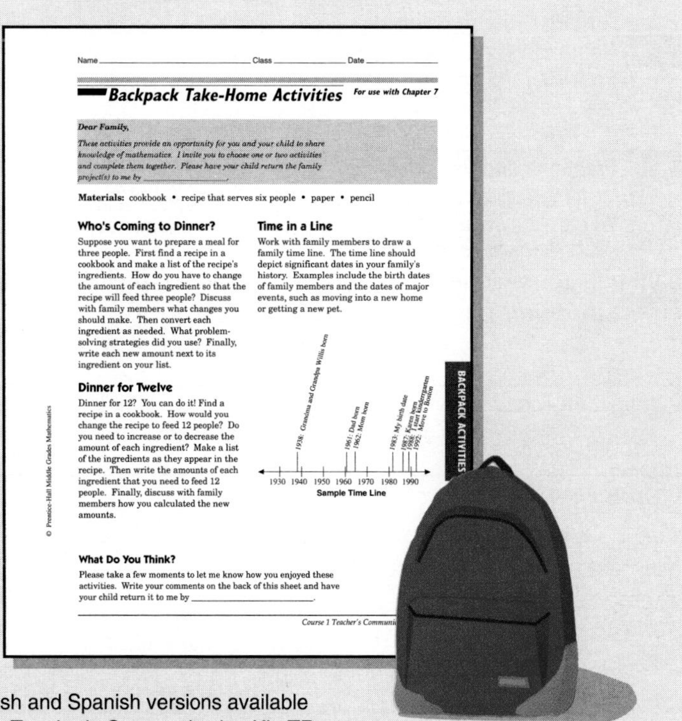

Name ______ Class ______ Date ______

Backpack Take-Home Activities *For use with Chapter 7*

Dear Family,

These activities provide an opportunity for you and your child to share knowledge of mathematics. I invite you to choose one or two activities and complete them together. Please have your child return the family project(s) to me by ______.

Materials: cookbook • recipe that serves six people • paper • pencil

Who's Coming to Dinner?
Suppose you want to prepare a meal for three people. First find a recipe in a cookbook and make a list of the recipe's ingredients. How do you have to change the amount of each ingredient so that the recipe will feed three people? Discuss with family members what changes you should make. Then convert each ingredient as needed. What problem-solving strategies did you use? Finally, write each new amount next to its ingredient on your list.

Dinner for Twelve
Dinner for 12? You can do it! Find a recipe in a cookbook. How would you change the recipe to feed 12 people? Do you need to increase or to decrease the amount of each ingredient? Make a list of the ingredients as they appear in the recipe. Then write the amounts of each ingredient that you need to feed 12 people. Finally, discuss with family members how you calculated the new amounts.

Time in a Line
Work with family members to draw a family time line. The time line should depict significant dates in your family's history. Examples include the birth dates of family members and the dates of major events, such as moving into a new home or getting a new pet.

What Do You Think?
Please take a few moments to let me know how you enjoyed these activities. Write your comments on the back of this sheet and have your child return it to me by ______.

Course 1 Teacher's Communi

© Prentice-Hall Middle Grades Mathematics

English and Spanish versions available in the Teacher's Communication Kit, TR

Chapter 7 Planning Guide

Objectives	Assignment Options	Critical Thinking/ Problem Solving	Writing and Reading Math	Estimation Mental Math	Materials and Manipulatives
Investigation	This chapter-long project involves open-ended questioning and data collecting and provides an additional opportunity to assess students.	p. 274 p. 274	p. 274		p. 274
7-1 Mental Math: Divisibility • Exploring divisibility using mental math	**Core:** 11–14, 19, 20, 23, 26, 30; MR all **Reinforce:** 15–18, 21, 22, 24, 25, 27 **Enrich:** 28, 29	1b, 1e, 2e, 26–28, 29c, 30; MR: 1–3 pp. 275, 277; BI p. 276; MM p. 277	28 p. 277; JL p. 277 JL Sheet	1c, 1d, 2a, 2c; EX2; 3–18; MR: 4–7 pp. 275, 277	29b p. 276; RT p. 277 TT 1, 67; Alt. Lesson
7-2 Prime Factorization • Recognizing prime and composite numbers • Finding the prime factorization of a composite number	**Core:** 26, 27, 30–35, 42, 45–48, 55, 56; MR all **Reinforce:** 28, 29, 36–41, 43, 44, 49–52 **Enrich:** 25, 53, 54	1, 3, 7, 8a, 9, 25; MR: 7 p. 278; BI p. 280	25 p. 281; JL p. 280 JL Sheet	EX2; 42–44; MR: 1–4 p. 279	4; WT: 10–14; 25–29, 53–55 pp. 278–281; WT p. 280; RT p. 281 TT 1, 14, 67
7-3 Greatest Common Factor • Finding the greatest common factor of two or more numbers	**Core:** 13–15, 19–21; MR all; CH all **Reinforce:** 16–18, 22–24, 26 **Enrich:** 25	WT: 1–4; 5, 6c, 12, 25; MR: 7 p. 283; BI p. 284	25 p. 284; JL p. 284 JL Sheet	7–10, 13–18; CH: 1–4 pp. 282, 283; RT p. 284; CH p. 284	WT p. 282 TT 67
7-4 Exploring Fractions • Exploring fractions and equivalent fractions using models • Estimating fractions	**Core:** 11–14, 17; MR all **Reinforce:** 15, 16, 18 **Enrich:** 19	4, 17, 19; MR: 7 p. 287; BI p. 287	17 p. 287; JL p. 287 JL Sheet	WT: 7–10; 18 p. 287	3, 5c, 6, 13–16 p. 286; RT p. 287 TT 22–29, 68
7-5 Equivalent Fractions • Finding equivalent fractions • Expressing fractions in simplest form	**Core:** 14–17, 25–32; MR all **Reinforce:** 18–24, 33, 34 **Enrich:** 35, 36	2, 3c, 4c, 33, 35; MR: 6 pp. 288, 290; BI p. 289	33 p. 290; JL p. 289 JL Sheet	3a, 3d, 4a, 4d, 6–13, 18–32 p. 288	1b, 2, 5 pp. 288–290 TT 23–26, 29, 68
7-6 Technology: Simplifying Fractions • Using a calculator to simplify fractions	**Core:** 12–17; MR all **Reinforce:** 18, 19 **Enrich:** 20	2, 20b; MR: 7 p. 292; BI p. 293	20b JL p. 293 JL Sheet	WT: 3–7; 12–19; MR: 3–6 p. 292; MM p. 293	EX; WT: 3–7; 8–20 pp. 292, 293; RT p. 293 TT 19, 68 Alt. Lesson
7-7 Mixed Numbers and Improper Fractions • Writing mixed numbers and improper fractions using models and computation	**Core:** 14, 16–18, 21, 22, 26; CH all; MR all **Reinforce:** 15, 19, 20, 23, 24 **Enrich:** 25	4d, 26; MR: 3, 4 p. 294; BI p. 295	14, 27 JL p. 295 JL Sheet	10–13, 21–24; CH: 1–14; MR: 1, 2 p. 295; MM p. 296	6 WT p. 294; RT p. 296 TT 68
7-8 Math and Planning: Least Common Multiple • Finding the least common multiple of two or three numbers	**Core:** 4–9; MR all **Reinforce:** 10, 11, 13 **Enrich:** 12	3, 10, 11, 13; MR: 7 pp. 297, 298; BI p. 298; MM p. 299	2c, 12d p. 298; JL p. 297 JL Sheet	MR: 1–4, 6 p. 297	p. 297 TT 69
7-9 Comparing and Ordering Fractions • Comparing and ordering fractions	**Core:** 13–20; MR all **Reinforce:** 21, 23 **Enrich:** 22	2c, 2d, 12, 17, 22e, 23 pp. 300, 301; BI p. 302; MM p. 302	22e p. 302; JL p. 301 JL Sheet	WT: 1; 3; 4–11, 13–16 pp. 300, 301	WT: 1; 2a, b p. 302; WT p. 300 TT 23–29, 69
7-10 Fractions and Decimals • Modeling fractions and decimals • Writing decimals as fractions • Writing fractions as decimals	**Core:** 17–24, 31, 32, 34, 35a; MR all; CH all **Reinforce:** 25–29 **Enrich:** 30, 33, 35b	3a; CH: 12; MR: 6 p. 303; BI p. 305; MM p. 306	35 p. 306; JL p. 305 JL Sheet	4; MR: 1–5	2a; EX4; 8a, 33a pp. 303–306 TT 11, 12, 19, 69
7-11 Problem Solving: Work Backward • Solving problems by working backward	**Core:** 12–14, 18, 20, 21, 23; MR all **Reinforce:** 11, 15, 16, 22, 24 **Enrich:** 17, 19	All; MR: 7 pp. 307–309; BI p. 308; MM p. 309	All p. 309; JL p. 308 JL Sheet	MR: 3–5	p. 307 TT 69
Putting It All Together	These pages include a Follow-Up to the Investigation and other projects, which provide additional opportunities to assess the students.	pp. 312–313 pp. 312–313	p. 313 p. 313		p. 313 pp. 312–313
Chapter Resources		PS Practice, CW, CA, CR PS Practice p. 285; CW pp. 310–311; CA p. 314; CR p. 315	PS Practice, CW, CA p. 272B; PS Practice p. 285; CW pp. 310–311; CA p. 314		pp. 272A, 272B Backpack Activities, Manip. Kits TT 66, 70, 71

Student Edition (question numbers)
Teacher's Edition (page numbers)
Other Components

BI—What's the Big Idea? CA—Chapter Assessment CH—Checkpoint
CG—Computer Item Generator CR—Cumulative Review CW—Chapter Wrap Up
DM—Decision Making EP—Extra Practice EX—Example FD—Fact of the Day

Cooperative Learning Activities	Technology	Data Collection & Analysis	Interdisciplinary Connections	Applications	Assessment	Review	Strand Integration	NCTM Correlation*
		p. 274	Social Studies, Science	art, architecture, chemistry	p. 274 p. 274			
p. 276; RT p. 277	29b p. 276 Alt. Lesson	FD p. 276		architecture, money pp. 275, 277	p. 276	MR: All p. 275; RT p. 277 Practice p. 25	Number, Logic/Language	1, 2, 3, 4, 6, 7, 8, 9
WT: 10–15 p. 278; WT p. 280; RT p. 281	53–55 p. 281	FD p. 279	Art p. 280	art p. 280	p. 279	MR: All p. 278; RT p. 281 Practice p. 26	Geometry, Number, Logic/Language	1, 2, 3, 4, 6, 7, 8
WT: 1–4 WT p. 282; RT p. 284		FD p. 283	p. 284	hobbies p. 284	CH: All p. 283; CH p. 284 CH TR p. 40	MR: All p. 282; RT p. 284 Practice p. 27	Discrete Math, Number, Logic/Language	1, 2, 3, 4, 6, 7, 8, 9
WT: 7–10 p. 286; WT p. 287	p. 286 Hot Page™ 7-4	FD p. 287	p. 287	pp. 286, 287	p. 287	MR: All RT p. 287 Practice p. 28	Number, Logic/Language	2, 3, 4, 5, 6, 7, 8
p. 289; RT p. 290	p. 289	36 FD p. 289	Science p. 289	money, entertainment p. 289	p. 289	MR: All p. 288; RT p. 290 Practice p. 29	Algebra, Number, Logic/Language	2, 3, 4, 5, 6, 7, 8, 9
WT: 3–7 pp. 292, 293; WT p. 292; RT p. 293 Alt. Lesson	All p. 293	WT: 3–7 FD p. 293	p. 293	p. 293	p. 293	MR: All p. 292; RT p. 293 Practice p. 30	Number, Logic/Language	2, 3, 4, 5, 7, 8
WT: 1–3 p. 294; WT p. 294; RT p. 296	Hot Page™ 7-7	25, 26 p. 296; FD p. 295	Science pp. 295, 296	oceanography pp. 294–296	CH: All WT p. 294; CH p. 296	MR: All RT p. 296 Practice p. 31	Number, Logic/Language	2, 3, 4, 5, 7, 8, 13
Alt. Lesson		12d FD p. 298		planning, travel pp. 297, 298; GE p. 299 Alt. Lesson	p. 297	MR: All p. 297; RT p. 298 Practice p. 32	Number, Logic/Language	1, 2, 3, 4, 6, 7, 8, 13
WT: 1 p. 301; WT p. 300; RT p. 302	p. 302 Hot Page™ 7-9	21 FD p. 301	Home Economics p. 302	cooking, sports p. 302	p. 301	MR: All p. 300; RT p. 302 Practice p. 33	Number, Logic/Language	2, 3, 4, 6, 7, 8
WT: 1–3 p. 303; WT p. 303; RT p. 305	EX4; 9–28, 33a pp. 305, 306	30 FD p. 304	Science	shopping pp. 303, 305	CH: All p. 304; CH p. 306 CH TR p. 40	MR: All p. 303; RT p. 305 Practice p. 34	Number, Logic/Language	2, 3, 4, 6, 7, 8
RT p. 308		21 p. 309; FD p. 308	Science	money, hobbies, sports, music p. 308	p. 308	MR: All p. 307; RT p. 308 Practice p. 35	Functions, Number, Logic/Language	1, 2, 3, 4, 5, 7, 8, 13
pp. 312–313 pp. 312–313		pp. 312–313 pp. 312–313	Social Studies, Science	art, architecture, sports	pp. 312–313 pp. 312–313			
IN, PT pp. 272–274; PT pp. 312–313 Backpack Activities	p. 272B Multimedia Math, CG	Data File 7 pp. 272–273	Science, Social Studies pp. 272F, 272–273 Interdisciplinary Units	oceanography pp. 272A, 272–273 Backpack Act., Interdisciplinary Units, Projects	IN, PT, CA pp. 272E, 274, 310–314 CA, Span. CA, Self Assessment, Projects	Practice, PS Practice, CW, CR, EP, SSG CW pp. 310–311 Span. SSG, CR		

GE—Great Expectations IN—Investigation JL—Journal MM—Math Minutes
MR—Mixed Review PS—Problem Solving PT—Putting It All Together RT—Reteaching Activity
SSG—Student Study Guide TT—Teaching Transparency WT—Work Together

*For a description of the NCTM Standards, see page T15.

Assessment Options

Observation Checklist

In this chapter on fraction concepts, you have opportunities to observe your students do these tasks:

- ✓ use rules of divisibility to factor numbers mentally
- ✓ find the prime factorization of a number
- ✓ find the greatest common factor and least common multiple of a set of numbers
- ✓ model fractions using fraction bars
- ✓ estimate fractions
- ✓ write fractions in simplest form
- ✓ convert mixed numbers to improper fractions and vice versa
- ✓ compare and order fractions
- ✓ convert fractions to decimals and vice versa
- ✓ solve word problems by working backward

In every chapter, you are given opportunities to observe your students:

- ✓ work with a partner or in a group
- ✓ write about mathematics
- ✓ participate in discussions about mathematics
- ✓ collect and analyze data
- ✓ display positive attitudes about mathematics
- ✓ use measurement tools

Name ______ Class ______ Date ______

Chapter 7 Project

The Perfect Birdhouse

Did you know that birds will not move into just any birdhouse? A bird wants a house that fits; most prefer houses that are just big enough for them to squeeze into.

The picture below shows an entrance hole that is just the right size for a Downy woodpecker. The table beside it lists the right size of hole for some other kinds of birds.

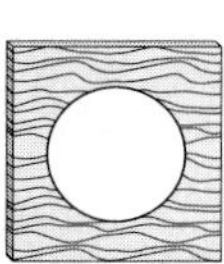

Bird	Diameter of Entrance Hole
Chickadee	$1\frac{1}{8}$ in.
House wren	$1\frac{1}{8}$ in.
Downy woodpecker	$1\frac{1}{4}$ in.
Hairy woodpecker	$1\frac{1}{2}$ in.
Red-headed woodpecker	2 in.
Crested flycatcher	2 in.
Bluebird	$1\frac{1}{2}$ in.
Tree swallow	$1\frac{1}{2}$ in.
Purple martin	$2\frac{1}{2}$ in.
Screech owl	$3\frac{1}{4}$ in.

1. Why do you suppose a bird is so particular about the size of its entrance hole?
2. Make a circle that shows the size of the entrance hole you would need to make in a birdhouse for a Chickadee. You can use a ruler and a compass to help you.
3. Three woodpeckers are pictured on page 37. One is a Red-headed woodpecker, one is a Downy woodpecker, and one is a Hairy woodpecker. Below each outline is the bird's length. Use the information in the table to help you identify each.

Course 1 Chapter 7

Performance Based Project (with scoring rubric), Chapter Files, TR

...se Scoring Rubric

Exercise	Points	Explanation
1.	1	Logical answer related to predators OR keeping larger birds out
	0	No response OR illogical answer
2.	2	Correct diameter ($1\frac{1}{8}$ in.) and reasonably round circle
	1	Correct diameter; poor circle OR incorrect diameter; good circle
	0	No response OR incorrect diameter with poor circle
3.	3	All birds correctly labeled (Red-headed = 10 in., Hairy = 9 in., Downy = 6 in.); reasoning: largest bird requires largest entrance-hole size, and so on.
	2	All birds correctly labeled with poor or no explanation OR good explanation with one reversal of names
	1	One bird correct with poor or no explanation
	0	No response
4.	2	Both smaller and larger birds listed correctly (smaller birds: chickadee, House wren and Downy woodpecker; larger birds: all others)
	1	Either smaller OR larger correct
	0	No response OR neither correct
5.	2	All three conversions correct
	1	Two conversions correct
	0	No response OR only one conversion correct
Excursion	5	Clear drawing showing all six pieces with dimensions marked; reasonable mounting site
	4	Clear drawing of six pieces but some dimensions missing; reasonable mounting site
	3	Clear drawing of six pieces but all dimensions missing; reasonable mounting site
	2	Weak drawing but reasonable mounting site OR adequate drawing with no mounting site
	1	Weak drawing and no mounting site
	0	No response OR other response

Course 1 Chapter 7

Chapter 7 Assessment • Form A

Chapter 7 Student Self-Assessment Survey

Checkpoint 1

Chapter 7 Cumulative Review

Chapter Support File

Classroom Manager
- Chapter Organizer
- Lesson Planners

Alternate Lesson Plans

Practice

Assessment Options
- Performance Based Project
- Scoring Rubric
- Student Self-Assessment Survey
- Checkpoints
- Chapter Assessments
- Cumulative Review

Spanish versions of Chapter Assessments available in Spanish Resources

Interdisciplinary Units
- **Travel and Geography**
- **Space Exploration**
- **Sports**
- **Consumer Awareness**
- **The Great Outdoors**

English & Spanish

These units include cross-curriculum connections and can be used at any time during the school year. See the Teacher's Guide for more information.

Working with Middle Grade Students

> *"The objective of discourse is to build on students' strengths, to listen to students and to have them explore mathematics in a group setting. The vignettes in the professional teaching standards illustrate this process as it occurs.*
> *Discourse makes mathematics much more of an interactive discipline by helping children construct their own knowledge through guiding, probing, and listening. It's a classroom that's not entirely filled with lectures."*
>
> —Dr. Mary M. Lindquist

Addressing a Variety of Learning Styles

The mathematical tasks in Chapter 7 involve various learning styles. Here are some examples.

- Visual learners sketch rectangles using square tiles (p. 281) and make lists to find common factors (p. 282).
- Tactile learners model fractions using fraction bars (p. 286) and use a calculator to simplify fractions (p. 292).
- Auditory learners discuss the relationship between the dimensions of rectangles and factors of numbers (p. 278) and discuss the greatest common factors and prime factorization (p. 283).
- Kinesthetic learners work with a partner to find prime numbers (p. 280).

Alternate Lesson 7-1 addresses tactile learners by having them use manipulatives.

Cultural Connections

Much of what we know about early Egyptian mathematics is from the Rhind papyrus. This papyrus was written by a scribe named Ah'mose around 1500 B.C. and says that it is a copy of another papyrus written around 1800 B.C.

The Egyptians used fractions, with denominators from 2 to at least 101. But as far as we know, the Egyptians only used what are called aliquot fractions—fractions with a numerator of 1. Have students find out how the ancient Egyptians multiplied numbers and fractions. Discuss any odd tricks or calculating methods that students or their friends or relatives may know.

Team Teaching Suggestion

Work with a music teacher to introduce the concept of fractions as note values and as time signatures in musical compositions. Provide examples of taped music, and have students participate by comparing note values and counting beats per measure.

Talking About Mathematics

Mathematics is essentially an active discipline. Have students work problems at the blackboard and explain them to other students. Encourage students to work in groups to perform experiments and solve problems. Have them check each other's answers. They will enjoy the feeling of competence and independence that comes of doing mathematics themselves.

Teaching Tip

There is a tendency to round off portions and say "close enough" for giving exact measurements. Point out several examples of when it really makes a difference to include the fraction involved.

Bulletin Board

Distribute a card to each team. Each card should have a fraction on it equivalent to one of the fractions on the board. Choose a spokesperson to identify the equivalent fraction on the board. If the response is correct, this student flips the taped card up and picks a question from either the "A" or the "B" envelope (as indicated under the card). These envelopes contain questions from the chapter that vary in difficulty and points (worth 1–3 points). If the group answers correctly, their marker moves that many spaces forward on the gameboard. Continue the game until one group finishes.

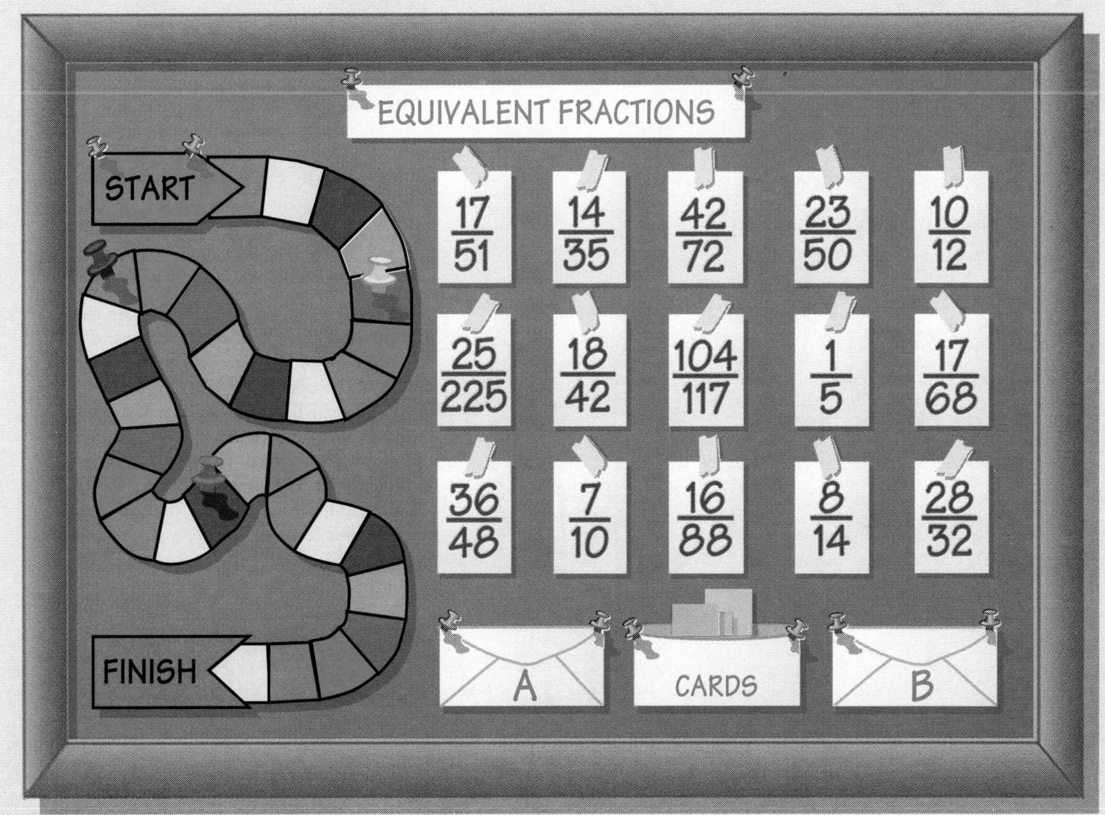

CHAPTER 7

Fraction Concepts

Cultural Connections A very personal account of a tsunami was given by Francis P. Shepard, a distinguished marine geologist. Shepard and his wife were staying in a cottage in northern Oahu, Hawaii, when a tsunami hit the bay on April 1, 1946. The huge wave was caused by an earthquake in the Aleutian Trench of the Pacific Ocean, at a depth of about 10,000 ft. There was a 100-ft wave which demolished a lighthouse (and killed five men) about 70 mi away from where the Shepards were staying. When the tsunami hit Hawaii four hours later, it was a 56-ft-high wave. Francis got his camera and stayed on high ground, ahead of the third and larger wave. There were about six more smaller waves yet to come, taking a total of 173 lives and causing $25 million in damages. After this, the United States Coast Guard and Geodetic Survey established the Seismic Sea Wave Warning System to help warn people of approaching tsunamis.

WORLD VIEW In 1896, an underwater earthquake which occurred 93 mi east of Honshu, Japan, sent 100-ft waves onto the beach at Sanriku. Tide gauges in San Francisco recorded waves 10.5 h later. In 1933, the beach at Sanriku was again surged by a tsunami caused by an underwater earthquake, this time killing 3,000 people, destroying 9,000 houses, and upsetting 8,000 boats.

Digging for Data

- Have students ask family members and friends if they have ever been in earthquakes, tornadoes, hurricanes, or typhoons. List the survey results and the number of responses for each (including "none of the above").
- Have students find out the height of the tallest building in the community and compare that to how high tsunamis can be.

Chapter 7 Contents

Data File Questions

pp. 164, 290, 306, 329

CHAPTER 7 Fraction Concepts

Data File 7

WORLD VIEW The highest tsunami was about 278 ft. It appeared off Ishigaki Island, Japan on April 24, 1771. The tsunami tossed an 826.7–T block of coral more than 1.3 mi.

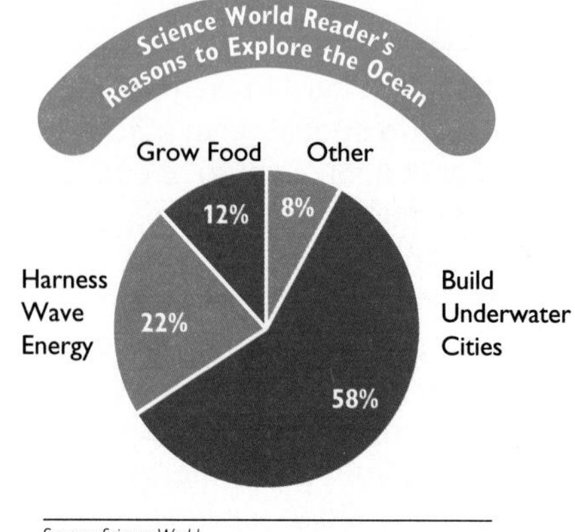

Source: *Science World*

A *tsunami* is an unusually large wave caused by a volcanic eruption on the ocean floor. The speed of a tsunami and the distance between crests relate to the depth of the ocean. The diagram shows that a wave in 18,000 ft of water will travel up to 519 mi/h. More shallow water slows the bottom of a wave. The top continues to push forward. This causes the wave to grow higher and higher until it hits the shore with tremendous force.

sea level

speed (mi/h)	519
depth (feet)	18,000

Journal Activity

- Have students read the objectives for the chapter and explain what they know about the importance of fractions in measuring things.
- Have students list as many energy sources as they can think of and make drawings of them.
- Have students write stories about building an underwater city and illustrate the different phases involved in its construction.

Interdisciplinary Connection [Science and Social Studies] In 1981, the United States imported 98% of its cobalt, 96% of its manganese, and 70% of its nickel from politically unstable areas in Africa and South America. In the 1970s, a presidential inventory resulted in a report called *Global 2000,* which estimated that land-based reserves of copper, cobalt, nickel, and manganese would be used up in about 40 y. These four strategic metals have been found scattered across the ocean floors, waiting to be mined (no easy task at such depths in water).The seas near the coastlines of nations are easily identifiable, but the oceans are a different matter for mining rights, so the world's nations have to come to some agreement about who can do the mining at sea. Scientists have worked out methods for doing the mining, but politicians have to work out legal rights and negotiate agreements. Planet Earth is shared by all countries, and all countries have to come together to make decisions on the shared waters. Discuss with students some of the possibilities of mining the oceans.

WHAT YOU WILL LEARN

- how to model, compare, and order fractions
- how to use technology to simplify fractions
- how to solve problems by working backward

The *tidal range* measures the difference between water level at high tide and low tide.

Tidal Ranges

Location	Average tidal range (ft)
Bay of Fundy, Canada	39.4
Boston, MA, USA	9.5
Galveston, TX USA	1.0
Rio de Janeiro, Brazil	2.5
Sunrise, Cook Inlet, AK USA	30.3
Darwin, Australia	14.4
Rangoon, Burma	12.8
Hamburg, Germany	7.3

Source: *Collier's Encyclopedia*

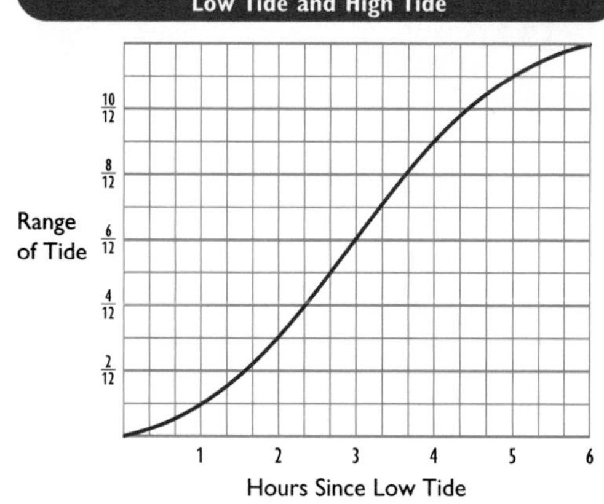

When a tsunami gets closer to land where the water is shallower, the wavelength becomes narrower. The tsunami may hit the coast with a wall of water up to 125 ft high.

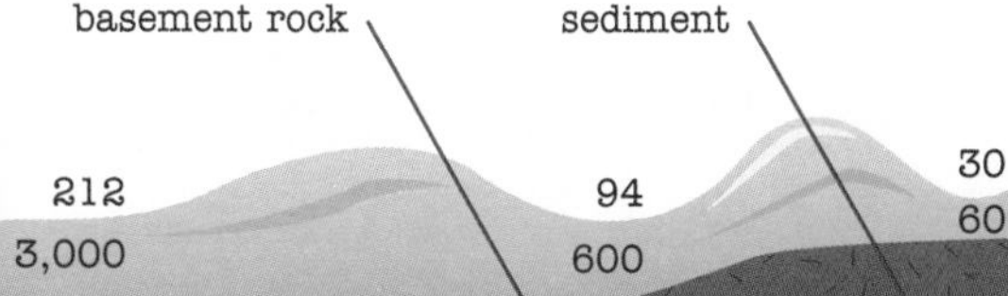

Fact of the Day

It is estimated that as much as 60 million kilowatts of electric power could be generated worldwide by damming tidal currents. This output would be about 5% of present world generating capacity.

—ACADEMIC AMERICAN ENCYCLOPEDIA

CHAPTER 7

INVESTIGATION

Memo

Have students read the memo. Ask them to explain how each figure in the illustration represents the number 6. Then ask them what changes could be made to each figure to represent 7.

Mission

Emphasize that the goal of the project is to acquire a collection of objects that can represent numbers. Ask students to aim for the numbers 1–10 but to go as high as possible. Through brainstorming, students can probably get ideas for a few simple numbers. For more difficult numbers, they may have to undertake a search.

After about half the chapter has been completed, have students show you their work on the project. If they are behind schedule, you may want to give them intermediate deadlines in order to check their work.

Additional Leads to Follow

- *How might looking at an object from a different angle help you in your search?*
- *Think about other properties of objects besides shape. How might the color or texture of an object, for example, help you in your search?*

Keeping a Project Notebook

Some suggestions for students' notebooks are these.

- Record all ideas for objects that might represent numbers. Some ideas may need modification.
- List the dates and results of all discussions about the project.
- Keep samples or sketches of the objects you have considered and the ones you finally choose.

Project Organizer

Related Exercises
p. 296
p. 306
p. 309

Follow Up
p. 312

Teacher's Notes
pp. 274, 296, 305, 309, 312

Community Resources
- university or museum anthropologist

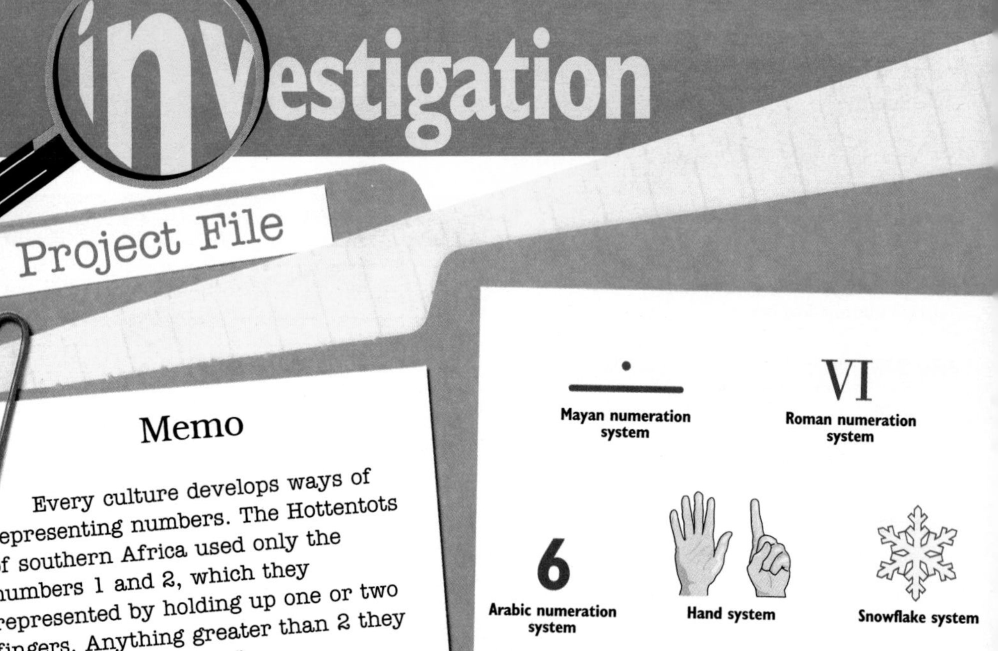

Memo

Every culture develops ways of representing numbers. The Hottentots of southern Africa used only the numbers 1 and 2, which they represented by holding up one or two fingers. Anything greater than 2 they referred to as "many."

There are many ways to represent numbers visually. The illustration shows five ways to represent the number 6.

What other objects besides a snowflake can you think of that you could use to represent the number 6?

***Mission:** Make a list of objects you could use to represent whole numbers 0 through 9. Anyone looking at an object should easily understand the number it represents. Decide how to use the objects to represent the numbers 10 through 20. Make a poster displaying your own personalized numeration system.*

LEADS TO FOLLOW

✓ Would a snowflake be an appropriate choice for representing the number 6 in your system? Why or why not?

✓ Suppose you can think of several objects to represent a number. How can you decide which object is best?

7-1

Connecting to Prior Knowledge

Ask students to describe situations in which they have had to share fairly an even number of items among an odd number of people (for example, a dozen cookies among seven friends), or an odd number of items among an even number of people (such as sharing nine peaches among six friends). Have students name problems they have encountered and strategies they have used to share fairly.

THINK AND DISCUSS

Error Alert! Students may not recognize the patterns for divisibility for Question 1. Students may understand the divisibility rule for 2 in terms of even and odd numbers. Make sure that students understand an even number is divisible by 2 and an odd number is not divisible by 2. ***Remediation*** Have students make a table for each part of Question 1. For parts 1b and 1e, encourage students to describe the relevant tables. Emphasize that it is important to organize information in order to recognize patterns.

ESL Make sure students understand that the word *remainder* is another way of saying "left over." Perhaps using the word *remain* in context will help to reinforce the meaning of the word *remainder.* For example, you might say that if seven friends fairly shared one dz cookies (12 cookies), each friend would get 1 cookie, but 5 cookies would remain on the plate. Help students understand that the 5 cookies on the plate are the "remainder."

Examples

Encourage students to copy the table of divisibility rules and add the rules for 3 and 9 to the table.

- *Is 4,716 divisible by 3? by 9?*

  4 + 7 + 1 + 6 = 18

  18 ÷ 3 = 6 4,716 is divisible by 3

  18 ÷ 9 = 2 4,716 is divisible by 9

What's Ahead

- Exploring divisibility using mental math

7-1 Mental Math: Divisibility

THINK AND DISCUSS

What's so important about *divisibility*? Is it the ability to completely disappear? No, that's *invisibility.* **Divisibility** is the ability of one number to divide into another with no remainder. You'll use divisibility many times working with and understanding fractions.

1. Look at the numbers in the table below.

Divisible by 2	Not divisible by 2
10 14 202 5,756 798 80 120	9 13 467 4,005 99 42,975

Answers may vary. Sample: 20 and 100; 15 and 25.

a. Give two more numbers that are divisible by 2. Give two more numbers that are not divisible by 2.

b. **Discussion** Give a rule for divisibility by 2. See left.

1. b. Any even number is divisible by 2.

c. Which of the numbers in the table that are divisible by 2 are also divisible by 5? divisible by 10? 10, 80, 120; 10, 80, 120

d. Which of the numbers in the table that are not divisible by 2 are divisible by 5? divisible by 10? 4,005 and 42,975; none

e. **Discussion** Give rules for divisibility by 5 and divisibility by 10. Any number ending with a 5 or a 0 is divisible by 5. Any number ending with a 0 is divisible by 10.

The rules for divisibility can help you save time finding the divisibility of a number. One of the fun things about mathematics is that there are a lot of patterns that lead to great shortcuts. The chart below shows some facts about divisibility.

Divisible By	Rule
1	All numbers are divisible by 1.
2	All even numbers are divisible by 2.
5	Numbers ending in 5 or 0 are divisible by 5.
10	Numbers ending in 0 are divisible by 10.

Enjoying an ear of corn *can be a mathematical experience! An ear of corn always has an even number of rows.* ***By what number is the number of rows divisible?*** 2

"The reward of a thing well done is to have done it."

—Ralph Waldo Emerson

Organizer

1. **Focus**
   Connecting to Prior Knowledge
2. **Teach**
   Think and Discuss
3. **Closure**
   Try These
   Wrap Up

Vocabulary/Symbols
divisibility

Skills Reviewed in Context of Lesson
- dividing whole numbers

Materials and Manipulatives
On Your Own Exercise 29: calculator

Student Resources
Extra Practice
Student Study Guide
Practice, TR Ch. 7, p. 25
Student Study Guide, Spanish Resources, TR
Alternate Lesson, TR Ch. 7, pp. 13–16

continues next page

Additional Example *Is 5,730 divisible by 1? by 2? by 3? by 5? by 9? by 10?*
5,730 is divisible by 1, 2, 3, 5, and 10. It is not divisible by 9 since 5 + 7 + 3 = 15, and 15 is not divisible by 9.

Ongoing Assessment Divide the class into two teams. Take turns presenting each team with a number and have the team name numbers by which it is divisible. Encourage the other team to make a list also. Give each team a point for a correct answer and three points for providing an answer missed by the other team. Have students take turns being their team's spokesperson.

TRY THESE

TACTILE LEARNERS Divide the class into pairs or groups of four and have them predict the divisibility in Exercises 3–10 using the divisibility rules. Then have the groups check their predictions by using calculators.

TECHNOLOGY OPTION For Questions 3–10, students can use spreadsheet software to set up a table for reviewing divisibility. They can list the divisors (1, 2, 3, 5, 9, 10) in Column A . In Column B they can list the divisibility rule for each divisor in Column A. In Column C they can list the number to be checked for divisibility. They can use Column D for calculations. Have students suggest other ways they can use a spreadsheet to explore divisibility rules and check numbers for divisibility.

MENTAL MATH Encourage students to refer to their tables of divisibility rules if they have any problems with Exercises 3–10.

Wrap Up

What's the Big Idea? Ask students to list ways they can use mental math to determine divisibility.

Organizer, continued

Teacher Resources

Teaching Transparencies 1, 67
Lesson Planner, TR Ch. 7, p. 2

Prentice Hall Technology
Computer Item Generator
- 7-1

Other Available Technology
- calculator

Excel; Works by Microsoft: Questions 3–10 *(optional)*

Fact of the Day

Plato was born in Athens in 428 B.C. His writings, all of which have apparently survived, consist of 26 dramatic dialogues on philosophical and related themes. His reputation as one of the most important and creative thinkers of the ancient world is based on these works.

—ACADEMIC AMERICAN ENCYCLOPEDIA

Assignment Options

Core: 11–14, 19, 20, 23, 26, 30, MR all	
Reinforce: 15–18, 21, 22, 24, 25, 27	**Enrich:** 28, 29

You can determine whether a number is divisible by 3 by adding up the digits. Then determine whether the sum is divisible by 3.

Example 1 Is 2,571 divisible by 3?
- Find the sum of the digits.
  2 + 5 + 7 + 1 = 15
  Determine whether the sum is divisible by 3.
  15 ÷ 3 = 5

The sum of the digits is divisible by 3, so 2,571 is divisible by 3.

A Greek mathematician named Plato (427?–348 B.C.) wrote about the number 5,040 in his work *The Laws.* He stated that 5,040 is divisible by 60 numbers, including 1 through 10.

Source: *Number Theory*

The divisibility rule for 9 is like the divisibility rule for 3.

2. a. **Mental Math** Is 99 divisible by 9? yes
   b. What is the sum of the digits of the number 99? Is this sum divisible by 9? 18; yes
   c. **Mental Math** Is 66 divisible by 9? no
   d. What is the sum of the digits of the number 66? Is this sum divisible by 9? 12; no
   e. **Discussion** Give a rule for divisibility by 9. A number is divisible by 9 when the sum of its digits is divisible by 9.

Example 2 Is 27,216 divisible by 1, 2, 3, 5, 9, or 10?

1	Yes, all numbers are divisible by 1.
2	Yes, it is an even number.
3	Yes, the sum of the digits is divisible by 3.
5	No, it does not end in 5 or 0.
9	Yes, the sum of the digits is divisible by 9.
10	No, it does not end in zero.

TRY THESE

Mental Math Determine whether the first number is divisible by the second.

3. 525; 5 yes
4. 848,960; 10 yes
5. 2,385; 10 no
6. 36,928; 1 yes
7. 60,714; 3 yes
8. 757,503; 9 yes
9. 4,673; 2 no
10. 333,335; 3 no

Journal Have students compare the divisibility rules. Ask students to determine if any of the rules are more difficult to perform mentally than others. Challenge students to think of ways to remember the rules.

Connections Have a discussion about how divisibility is used. You may want to start with these examples:

- **Household** (determining the number or amount of portions per person from a recipe, dividing chores evenly)
- **Consumer** (estimating the number of items that may be bought with a certain amount of money)
- **Business** (sharing extra profit among employees as a bonus)

Reteaching Activity Group students in pairs. Provide each pair with about 50 blocks or other counters. Have each student choose a number of blocks and determine numbers by which the group is divisible. Students can take turns modeling each other's numbers by arranging the number of blocks in equal groups.

ON YOUR OWN

MENTAL MATH Have students make a brief note of each rule they used for Exercises 11–18.

CONNECTION TO ALGEBRA Exercises 19–22 have students solve for an unknown value.

CRITICAL THINKING Encourage students to use the rules of divisibility for 5 and 2 to provide two examples for Exercise 26.

WRITING Have students organize their answers to Exercise 28 by the rules of divisibility for each number.

ON YOUR OWN

Mental Math State whether each number is divisible by 1, 2, 3, 5, 9, or 10.

11. 105 1, 3, 5
12. 15,345 1, 3, 5, 9
13. 40,020 1, 2, 3, 5, 10
14. 8,516 1, 2
15. 356,002 1, 2
16. 12,345 1, 3, 5
17. 2,021,112 1, 2, 3, 9
18. 70,641 1, 3, 9

Find the digit to make each number divisible by 9.

19. 34,76■ 7
20. ■7,302 6
21. 2■6,555 4
22. 19,76■,228 1

Find a number that satisfies the given conditions.

23. a three-digit number divisible by 1, 2, 3, and 5
Answers may vary. Sample: 330.

24. a four-digit number divisible by 1, 2, 3, 5, 9, and 10
Answers may vary. Sample: 9,900.

25. a number greater than 1 billion divisible by 1, 2, and 3
Answers may vary. Sample: 1,200,000,000.

26. Critical Thinking If a number is divisible by 5, must it be divisible by 10? Use an example to support your answer. See right.

27. Choose A, B, C, or D. The five sides of the Pentagon are congruent. The perimeter of the building is divisible by 5 and 10. What is the length of each side? C

A. 351 ft **B.** 353 ft **C.** 352 ft **D.** 357 ft

28. Writing Describe how you can use your calculator to tell if one number is divisible by another. To determine divisibility by 1, 2, 3, 5, 9, or 10, do you think it is easier to use mental math or a calculator? Explain. See right.

29. Use the numbers at the right.

a. Use the divisibility rules to tell which numbers are divisible by both 2 and 3. 78; 8,010; 21,822

b. Calculator Which numbers are divisible by 6? 78; 8,010; 21,822

c. Use your results to write a divisibility rule for 6. A number is divisible by 6 if it is divisible by both 2 and 3.

30. Elissa and eight of her friends went to lunch at a Thai restaurant. The total amount of the check was $56.61.

a. Can the group split the check into equal parts? yes

b. Do you think divisibility rules hold for decimal numbers? Use examples to support your answer. See right.

Mixed REVIEW

Suppose it takes 27 number cubes to fill a clear cubical box.

1. How many number cubes will be touching the bottom of the box? 9

2. How many number cubes will be touching the box? 26

3. How many number cubes will not be visible? 1

Solve.

4. $a - 7 = 23$ 30

5. $35 = 19 + c$ 16

6. $54 = 3t$ 18

7. $\frac{y}{9} = 30$ 270

26. Answers may vary. Sample: No, 25 is divisible by 5, but not by 10.

28. Answers may vary. Sample: Use the calculator by inputting one number, pressing the divide key, inputting the second number, and pressing the equal key. Mental math is easier because it's faster.

78 154 237
8,010 21,822

30. Answers may vary. Sample: Yes, $.90 is divisible by 1, 2, 3, 6, 9, and 10 following the same divisibility rules as dividing 90 by those numbers.

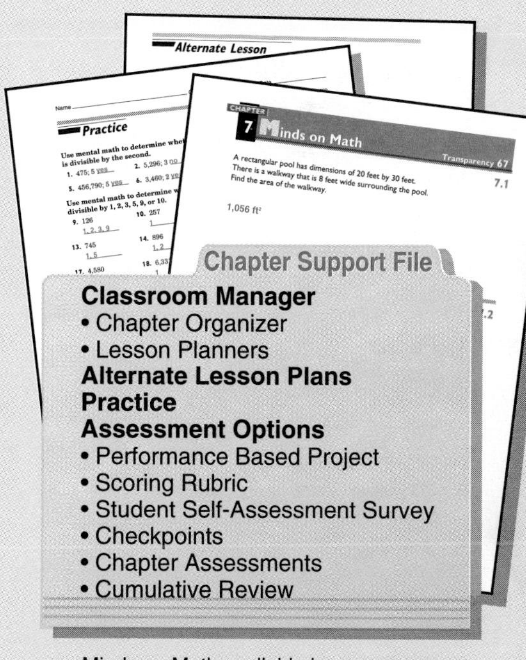

Minds on Math available in Teaching Transparencies

A six-pound bag of dog food sells for $2.70. Kay has three dogs. She bought three bags. What is the price per pound for the dog food?
45¢ per pound

Materials for 7-2

- graph paper
- square tiles

7-2

Connecting to Prior Knowledge

Have students recall the rules they used in determining divisibility. Ask students to describe how many numbers could divide a given number. **(Some numbers are divisible by many numbers, some by only a few.)** Ask students if every number is divisible by at least one number. **(Yes; by at least two, 1 and itself, except for the numbers 1 and 0.)**

THINK AND DISCUSS

Questions 1–2: Encourage students to model the rectangles with blocks, tiles, or on graph paper.

Questions 5–6: Have students compare examples of models for each type of number.

ESL Students may have difficulty with the vocabulary in this section. Make sure students understand what *factors* are and that prime and composite numbers are defined by the number of factors they have. Encourage students to give simple examples of both types of numbers and to give the factors of dictated numbers. Ask students to write their ages and their street addresses on paper. Have them determine if their numbers are prime or composite.

TACTILE LEARNERS Have students use square tiles for Questions 1–7. The students may work in groups if there are not enough tiles for everyone.

Example 1

Encourage students to describe how the factors of 9 are illustrated by the models. Students can replace the word *dimensions* with "rows" or "groups" and so on. Have students check the example with their own models.

*"Diamonds are only chunks of coal,
That stuck to their jobs, you see."*
—Minnie Richard Smith

Organizer

1. **Focus**
   Connecting to Prior Knowledge
2. **Teach**
   Think and Discuss
   Work Together
3. **Closure**
   Try These
   Wrap Up

Vocabulary/Symbols

factor
prime number
composite number
factor tree
prime factorization
sieve
twin primes

Skills Reviewed in Context of Lesson

- multiplying whole numbers
- reviewing properties of rectangles
- dividing whole numbers

Materials and Manipulatives

- square tiles (16 for each group)
- graph paper (for each student)

On Your Own Exercises 53–54: calculator

continues next page

7-2 Prime Factorization

What's Ahead

- Recognizing prime and composite numbers
- Finding the prime factorization of a composite number

WHAT YOU'LL NEED

✓ Square tiles

✓ Graph paper

THINK AND DISCUSS

You can build all the rectangles shown at the right using exactly 12 square tiles.

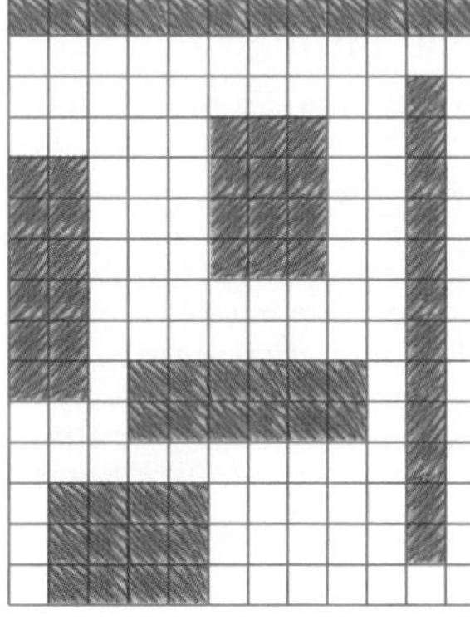

1. **Discussion** Does a 4 by 3 rectangle have the same shape as a 3 by 4 rectangle? Explain. See left.
2. How many rectangles with different shapes can you build using exactly 12 square tiles? What are their dimensions? 3 rectangles; 1×12, 2×6, and 3×4

1. Answers may vary. Sample: Yes, both rectangles have a side measuring 3 units and a side measuring 4 units. So, they have the same shape but they are positioned differently.

The numbers 1, 2, 3, 4, 6, and 12 are *factors* of 12. One number is a **factor** of another if it divides that number with no remainder.

3. **Discussion** How are the dimensions of the rectangles built using exactly 12 tiles related to the factors of 12? The dimensions of the rectangles are all factors of 12.
4. Use square tiles to find all the factors of 17 and of 20. 17: 1 and 17   20: 1, 2, 4, 5, 10, and 20

You call a number that has exactly two factors, 1 and itself, a **prime number.** A number that has more than two factors is called a **composite number.**

5. How many rectangles with different shapes can you build using a prime number of square tiles? 1 rectangle
6. Describe the number of rectangles with different shapes you can build using a composite number of tiles. more than 1 rectangle
7. **Discussion** Why is the number 1 considered to be neither prime nor composite? See left.

WHAT ? A perfect number is a number that is the sum of all its factors except itself. The smallest perfect number is 6, since $6 = 1 + 2 + 3$. **What is the next smallest perfect number?** 28

Source: *More Joy of Mathematics*

7. Answers may vary. Sample: By definition, a prime number has exactly two factors and a composite number has more than two factors. Since 1 has only one factor, it is not considered to be prime or composite.

Additional Example *Use a rectangular model to tell whether 11 is prime or composite.*
(The only rectange that can be modeled is 1 by 11, so 11 is prime.)

Error Alert! In using a factor tree for problems such as in Question 8, students may make a careless error in finding prime factors. ***Remediation*** Encourage students to check their factor trees in three steps:

1. Check to make sure each bottom factor is prime.
2. Multiply the branches together to find each larger branch.
3. Multiply the prime factors together to find the beginning number.

Example 2
Have students use mental math to determine that 75 is divisible by 3. **(The sum of the digits, 12, is divisible by 3.)** Encourage students to check the example tree.

Additional Example *Find the prime factorization of 42.*

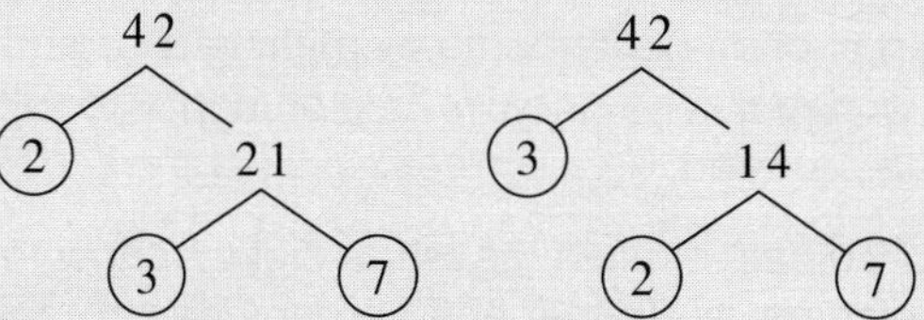

The prime factorization of 42 is $2 \times 3 \times 7$.

Ongoing Assessment Give students the number 60 and have them suggest different factor trees for finding the prime factorization of the number. **(There are five starts: 2 and 30, 3 and 20, 4 and 15, 5 and 12, and 6 and 10.)** Have volunteers write the factor trees on the chalkboard and verify that the prime factors are the same in each case. **($2 \times 2 \times 3 \times 5$)**

Example 1 Tell whether 9 is prime or composite.

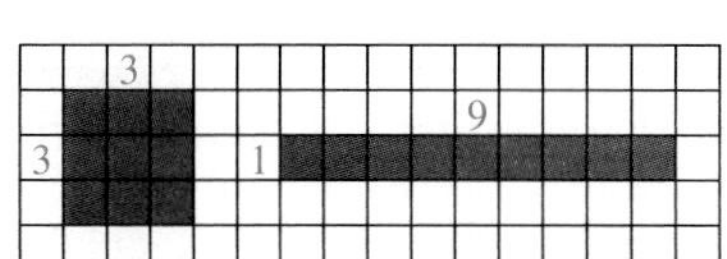

The dimensions of the rectangles show that the factors of 9 are 1, 3, and 9. So, 9 is composite.

A composite number is divisible by its prime factors. You can find these prime factors using a **factor tree.** Two factor trees for the number 36 are shown below.

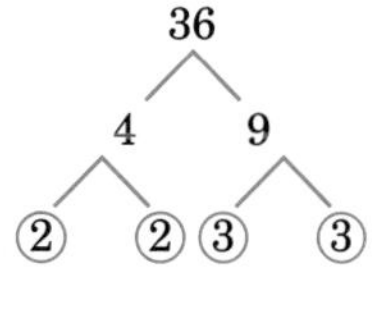

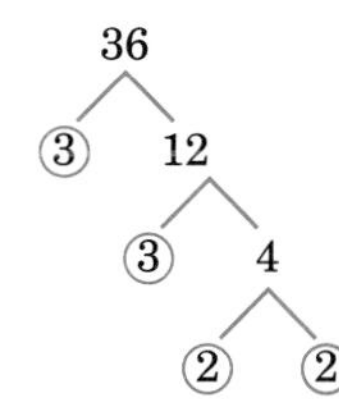

8. a. **Discussion** How are the two factor trees alike? How are they different? See right.
   b. Name the prime factors of 36. 2 and 3

9. **Discussion** How can you use divisibility rules to begin a factor tree? Divisibility rules can help find a factor for the number.

You can write a composite number as a product of its prime factors. This product is the **prime factorization** of the number.

Example 2 Find the prime factorization of 75 using a factor tree.

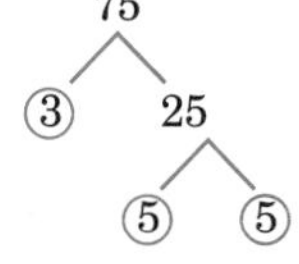

Choose a pair of factors that multiply to 75.

The prime factorization of 75 is $3 \times 5 \times 5$.

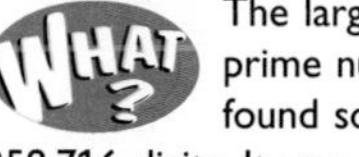

The largest prime number found so far has 258,716 digits. It was discovered in 1994 by a group of computer scientists.

8. a. The trees are alike in that they both have the same end result. They differ in the initial factors chosen to start the process.

Problem Solving Hint
It is helpful to circle each prime factor as soon as it appears in your factor tree.

Organizer, continued

Student Resources
Extra Practice
Student Study Guide
Practice, TR Ch. 7, p. 26
Student Study Guide, Spanish Resources, TR

Teacher Resources
Teaching Transparencies 1, 14, 67
Transparency Masters, TR p. 2
Lesson Planner, TR Ch. 7, p. 3

Prentice Hall Technology
Computer Item Generator
- 7-2

Other Available Technology
- calculator

Fact of the Day

Eratosthenes of Cyrene was a Greek geographer who is best known for his accurate calculation of the Earth's circumference. He also originated Eratosthenes' sieve and determined the inclination of the ecliptic to the celestial equator.

—*Academic American Encyclopedia*

WORK TOGETHER

Have each pair of students begin by making a large 6 × 9 grid on a sheet of paper. The grid will help students keep their sieves neat and easy to read.

ESL To help explain the word "sieve," show the students a kitchen colander or strainer and perhaps demonstrate its use by separating sand and beans.

Question 15: Make sure each pair of students has arrived at the same conclusion and listed all the prime numbers. Students may need to review the steps for checking prime numbers.

TRY THESE

Exercises 17–18: Encourage students to use either a model or a factor tree to find the factors of these two numbers.

Wrap Up

What's the Big Idea? Ask students: *What are prime and composite numbers? How do you find the prime factorization of a composite number?*

Journal Encourage students to evaluate the factor tree method of prime factorization. Ask students to describe the advantages of the strategy and why the strategy works.

Connections Have a discussion about prime factorization. You may want to start with the following examples.

- **Art** (making patterns with tiles or pieces of fabric)
- **Business** (determining ways to arrange items in a display or organizing departments in a store by aisles)
- **School** (arranging squads of cheerleaders or band members at a school rally)

Assignment Options

Core: 26, 27, 30–35, 42, 45–48, 55, 56, MR all	
Reinforce: 28, 29, 36–41, 43, 44, 49–52	**Enrich:** 25, 53, 54

WORK TOGETHER

Work with a partner to find prime numbers using a method called a *sieve.* List the numbers 1 to 50 as shown at the left.

1	2	3	4	5	6
7	8	9	10	11	12
13	14	15	16	17	18
19	20	21	22	23	24
25	26	27	28	29	30
31	32	33	34	35	36
37	38	39	40	41	42
43	44	45	46	47	48
49	50				

10. Mark out 1, since it's not prime. Circle 2, since it is prime. Mark out every multiple of 2. What pattern do you notice for the multiples of 2? They form three columns, with every number except 2 marked out.

11. Circle the first number after 2 that is unmarked. This is the next prime number. Mark out all of its multiples. What pattern do you notice for these multiples? They form two columns, with every number except 3 marked out.

12. The next prime number is 5. Circle it and mark out all of its multiples. Describe the pattern formed by the multiples of 5. They form two diagonals, with every number except 5 marked out.

13. What is the next prime number? Circle it and mark out all of its multiples. 7

20. 1, 2, 4, 5, 10, 20, 25, 50, 100; C

14. Circle 11 because it is prime. Why have you already marked out all of the multiples of 11 in the table? They are all divisible by 2 or 3.

15. What do you notice about the rest of the unmarked numbers? List the prime numbers less than 50. They are prime. The prime numbers less than 50 are 2, 3, 5, 7, 11, 13, 17, 19, 23, 29, 31, 37, 41, 43, and 47.

The Sieve of Eratosthenes allows you to determine all prime numbers less than a given value. This procedure was established by Eratosthenes (c. 276–195 B.C.), a Greek mathematician.

Source: *The Joy of Mathematics*

TRY THESE

16. The rectangles that can be formed using exactly 16 square tiles are shown below. List all the factors of 16. 1, 2, 4, 8, 16

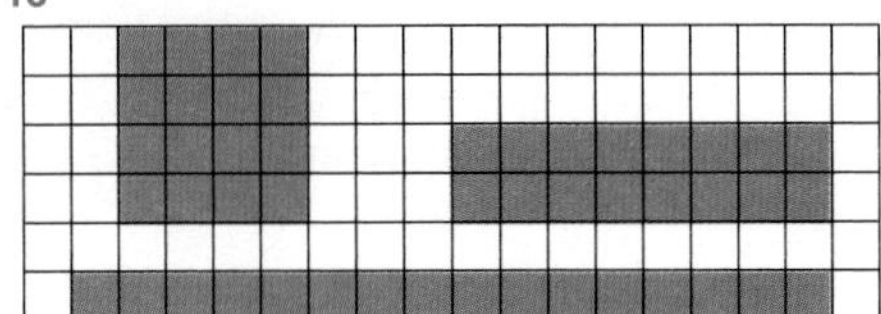

List all the factors of each number. Tell whether each number is prime or composite. P: prime, C: composite

17. 55 1, 5, 11, 55; C
18. 51 1, 3, 17, 51; C
19. 103 1, 103; P
20. 100 See left.

Find the prime factorization using a factor tree.

21. 30 2 × 3 × 5
22. 63 3 × 3 × 7
23. 120 2 × 2 × 2 × 3 × 5
24. 275 5 × 5 × 11

Reteaching Activity Group students in pairs. Give students the numbers 32 and 21. Have one student in each pair make a rectangular model for the first number and a factor tree for the other. The other student can make a factor tree for the first and a rectangular model for the second. Have each pair of students compare models and factor trees.

ON YOUR OWN

Students will need graph paper for Exercises 25–29.

WRITING Have students make specific references to their diagrams as they give their explanations for Exercise 25.

CALCULATOR Have students check their answers for Exercises 53–54 to make sure they do not forget a number or enter a number too many times.

ON YOUR OWN

25. Writing Sketch all the rectangles with different shapes that can be formed using exactly 8 square tiles. Explain how to use your diagram to find the factors of 8 and to tell if 8 is a prime or composite number. See Solution Key.

Sketch all the rectangles with different shapes that can be formed using exactly the given number of square tiles. List all the factors of each number. Tell whether each number is prime or composite.

26. 15 1, 3, 5, 15; C
27. 3 1, 3; P
28. 28 1, 2, 4, 7, 14, 28; C
29. 21 1, 3, 7, 21; C

Tell whether each number is prime or composite.

30. 36 C	**31.** 19 P	**32.** 72 C	**33.** 90 C
34. 44 C	**35.** 7 P	**36.** 80 C	**37.** 86 C
38. 93 C	**39.** 71 P	**40.** 150 C	**41.** 56 C

Copy and complete each factor tree.

42. 27
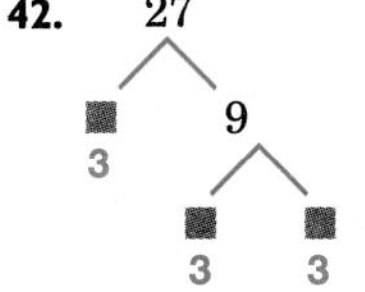

43. 68
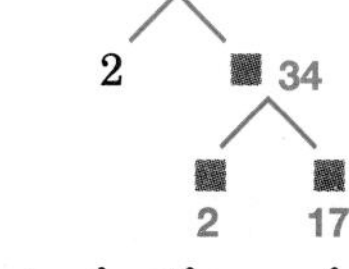

44. 150
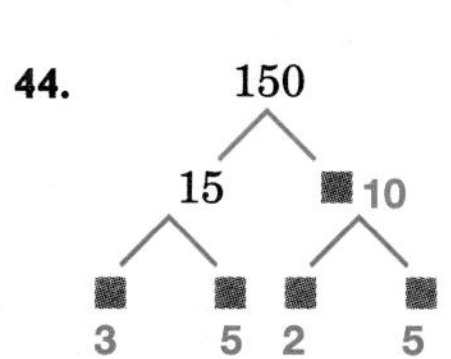

Find the prime factorization using a factor tree. See right.

45. 50	**46.** 32	**47.** 45	**48.** 90
49. 143	**50.** 160	**51.** 108	**52.** 531

Calculator **Find the number with the given prime factorization.**

53. $3 \times 17 \times 17 \times 17 \times 47$ 692,733

54. $7 \times 7 \times 17 \times 23 \times 23$ 440,657

55. Two prime numbers that differ by 2, such as 3 and 5, are called *twin primes*. Find all twin primes that are less than 100. 3, 5; 5, 7; 11, 13; 17, 19; 29, 31; 41, 43; 59, 61; 71, 73

56. How can you use exponents to write the prime factorization $2 \times 2 \times 2 \times 3 \times 3 \times 5$? $2^3 \cdot 3^2 \cdot 5$

Christian Goldbach (1690–1764) believed that every even number could be written as the sum of two prime numbers. His belief has never been proven or disproven. **How can you write the number 24 as the sum of two primes?**

Source: *The I Hate Mathematics Book*

11 + 13, 19 + 5, or 17 + 7

45. $2 \times 5 \times 5$
46. $2 \times 2 \times 2 \times 2 \times 2$
47. $3 \times 3 \times 5$
48. $2 \times 3 \times 3 \times 5$
49. 11×13
50. $2 \times 2 \times 2 \times 2 \times 2 \times 5$
51. $2 \times 2 \times 3 \times 3 \times 3$
52. $3 \times 3 \times 59$

Mixed REVIEW

Determine whether each number is divisible by 3, 5, or 9.

1. 378 3, 9 **2.** 6,480 3, 5, 9

3. 4,095 3, 5, 9 **4.** 3,003 3

Find the area.

5. 24 m² (right triangle: 8 m, 6 m, 10 m) **6.** 5.76 cm² (rectangle: 1.2 cm, 4.8 cm)

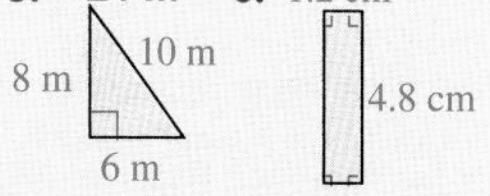

7. Find the sum of the whole numbers from 25 through 50. 975

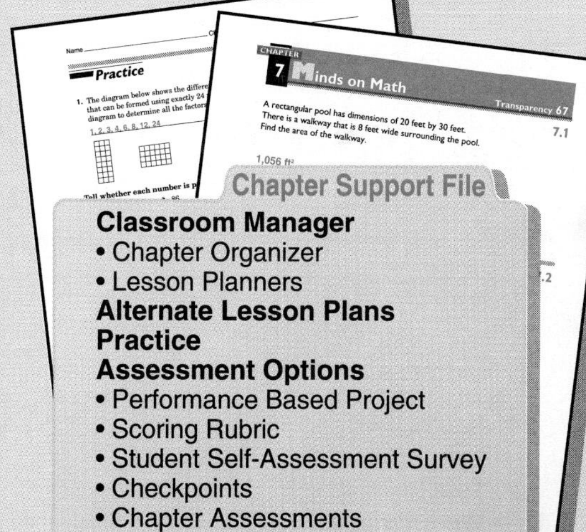

Minds on Math available in Teaching Transparencies

Math Minutes

The largest crater on the moon is called Bailly. It covers an area of about 26,000 square miles. Write this area in scientific notation.

2.6×10^4 mi²

7-3

Connecting to Prior Knowledge

Discuss with students whether it is possible for two different numbers to have some or all factors in common. Challenge students to provide examples in the form of factor trees.

WORK TOGETHER

Have students meet in groups of four. Each student can be responsible for organizing the group's answer to one question. Encourage each group to model the problem with blocks.

TACTILE LEARNERS Provide tiles in two colors representing the stamps for students to use for Questions 1–4.

THINK AND DISCUSS

ESL To help students understand "common" in GCF, use the analogy of two students having a common hobby.

Example 1

Have students use a special mark such as a double circle to distinguish between the GCF and other common factors.

Additional Example *Find the GCF of 64 and 48.*

64: 1, 2, 4, 8, (16), 32, 64
48: 1, 2, 3, 4, 6, 8, 12, (16), 24, 48
The GCF of 64 and 48 is 16.

Error Alert! Students may have difficulty finding common factors by making a list of all factors, instead of just listing the prime factors, as in Example 1. ***Remediation*** Remind students that they know how to use mental math to find the divisibility of a number by using divisibility rules for the numbers 1–10. Point out that if a number is less than 100, they can first list its factors that are between 1 and 10. Then they can list the multiples for each of the factors to complete the set.

> *"I find that a great part of the information I have acquired was by looking up something and finding something else on the way."*
>
> —Franklin P. Adams

Organizer

1. **Focus**
   Connecting to Prior Knowledge
2. **Teach**
   Work Together
   Think and Discuss
3. **Closure**
   Try These
   Wrap Up

Vocabulary/Symbols
common factors
greatest common factor, GCF

Skills Reviewed in Context of Lesson
- multiplying and dividing whole numbers
- creating factor trees

Student Resources
Extra Practice
Student Study Guide
Practice, TR Ch. 7, p. 27
Student Study Guide, Spanish Resources, TR
Checkpoint, TR Ch. 7, p. 40

continues next page

What's Ahead
- Finding the greatest common factor of two or more numbers

7-3 Greatest Common Factor

WORK TOGETHER

At a Collectors Club meeting, the sponsor announces that two sets of stamps have been donated. The sponsor is planning to distribute each set equally among the members present at the meeting. Suppose one set contains 18 stamps and the other set contains 24 stamps. Let's find the greatest number of members that can be present at the meeting.

1. Is it possible only five members are present? Explain. No, neither set of stamps could be divided evenly among five members.
2. Is it possible only three members are present? Explain. Yes, each member could receive 6 stamps from one set and 8 stamps from the other.
3. What must be true about the number of members present? The number must be a factor of both 18 and 24.
4. List all the possible numbers of members that can be present at the meeting. What is the largest number of members that can be present? 1 member, 2 members, 3 members, 6 members; 6 members

The stamps above are a sample of those that have been printed to honor mathematicians.

THINK AND DISCUSS

The factors that are the same for two or more numbers are their **common factors.** The **greatest common factor** (GCF) of two or more numbers is the greatest number that is a factor of each number. You can find the GCF of two numbers by making a list.

Example 1 Find the GCF of 18 and 30.

- Make a list of factors for each number. Then circle the factors the numbers have in common.

18: (1), (2), (3), (6), 9, 18
30: (1), (2), (3), 5, (6), 10, 15, 30

The GCF of 18 and 30 is 6, since it is the greatest of their common factors.

5. **Discussion** Explain how you can find the GCF of three or more numbers. See left.

5. Answers may vary. Sample: Find the GCF by making a list of factors for each of the three numbers, circling the common factors, and then determining which is the greatest common factor.

Example 2

Emphasize to students that the GCF and the greatest common prime factor are not the same. Point out to students that common prime factors are multiplied together to find the GCF.

Additional Example *Find the GCF of 24 and 96.*

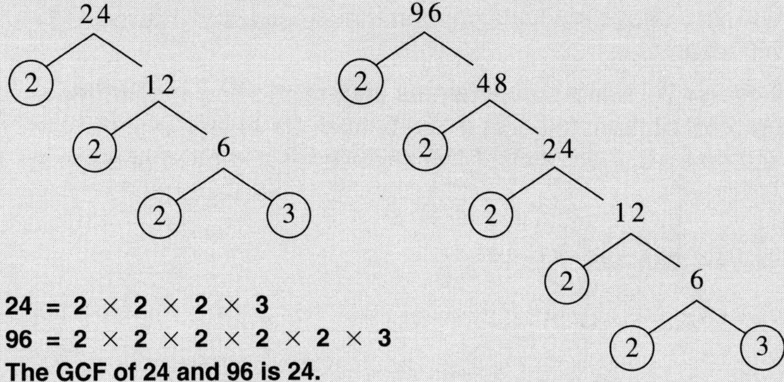

24 = 2 × 2 × 2 × 3
96 = 2 × 2 × 2 × 2 × 2 × 3
The GCF of 24 and 96 is 24.

TRY THESE

MENTAL MATH Encourage students to make a note of their observations and strategies for Exercises 7–10.

CRITICAL THINKING Have students list the factors for each possible value for Exercise 12.

VISUAL LEARNERS Make sure students write down all of the factors for the numbers in Exercises 7–12 so they can easily see the GCF. They may find it easiest to write the prime factorization, arranged from least to greatest, for each number; then circle the matching pairs, and, finally, multiply one of each of these matched prime factors.

Ongoing Assessment Have students discuss their answers to Exercise 12. Make sure students are comfortable finding common factors using mental math and do not always need to use a factor tree or list.

You can also use prime factorization to find the GCF of a set of numbers.

Example 2 Find the GCF of 42 and 90.

- Make a factor tree for each number.

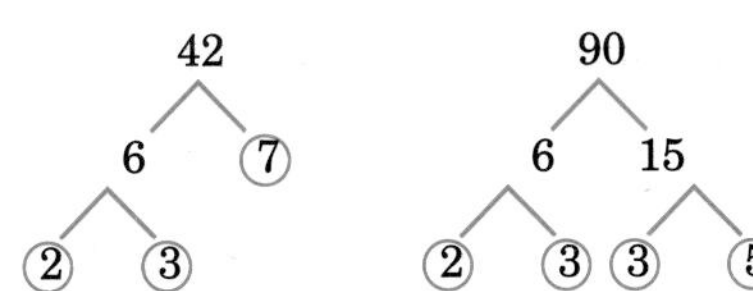

- Write the prime factorization for each number. Then identify common factors.

  42 = 2 × 3 × 7
  90 = 2 × 3 × 3 × 5

- Multiply the common factors together.

  2 × 3 = 6

The GCF of 42 and 90 is 6.

6. a. Make a list to find the GCF of 28 and 33. See right.

b. Use prime factorization to find the GCF of 28 and 33. Explain why the GCF is not easily recognized using this method. See right.

c. Discussion How will you know that the GCF of a set of numbers is 1 when you use prime factorization? The GCF of a set of numbers is 1 when there is no common factor for all the numbers other than 1.

6. a. 28: 1, 2, 4, 7, 14, 28; 33: 1, 3, 11, 33; The GCF is 1.
6. b. 28 = 2 × 2 × 7; 33 = 3 × 11; The GCF is not easily recognized because 1 is not listed as part of the prime factorization.

I think the one lesson I have learned is that there is no substitute for paying attention.

—Diane Sawyer (1945–)

TRY THESE

Mental Math **Find the GCF of each set of numbers.**

7. 14, 21 7
8. 6, 18 6
9. 10, 15, 20 5
10. 13, 17 1

11. a. Name all the factors of 36 and of 56. See right.

b. Name all the common factors of 36 and 56. 1, 2, 4

c. Find the GCF of 36 and 56. 4

12. Critical Thinking The GCF of 18 and some number is 6. What are three possible values for the number? Answers may vary. Sample: 6, 12, and 24.

11. a. 36: 1, 2, 3, 4, 6, 9, 12, 18, 36; 56: 1, 2, 4, 7, 8, 14, 28, 56.

Organizer, continued

Teacher Resources

Teaching Transparency 67
Lesson Planner, TR Ch. 7, p. 4

Prentice Hall Technology
Computer Item Generator
- 7-3

Fact of the Day

The earliest adhesive stamps were those used for local delivery by the *City Dispatch Post,* which was established in New York City on February 15, 1842.

—GUINNESS BOOK OF RECORDS

Assignment Options

Core: 13–15, 19–21, MR all, CH all	
Reinforce: 16–18, 22–24, 26	**Enrich:** 25

Wrap Up

What's the Big Idea? Ask students: *How do you find the GCF of two or more numbers?*

Journal Ask students: *Do you prefer the listing method or the prime factorization method for finding GCF? Does the size of the numbers affect your choice? Explain.*

Connections Have a discussion about how greatest common factor is used. You may want to start with these:

- **Household** (comparing different dimensions of rugs or other items to fit a certain area)
- **Chemistry** (comparing the number of atoms and molecules in two solutions)

Reteaching Activity Group students in pairs. Have each student use mental math to find the GCF of the numbers 30 and 72. **(6)** Then have students check their own answers with factor trees and a listing. They can then compare results.

ON YOUR OWN

WRITING Have students support their answers to Exercise 25 with examples.

Exercise 26: Make sure students understand how to read the graph. Ask them to begin at the bottom, for example, with 14, and go up to the dot at 2. This shows the GCF of 14 and 4 is 2.

CHECKPOINT

MENTAL MATH Have students check their answers to Questions 1–4 by listing and following the divisibility rule for each number.

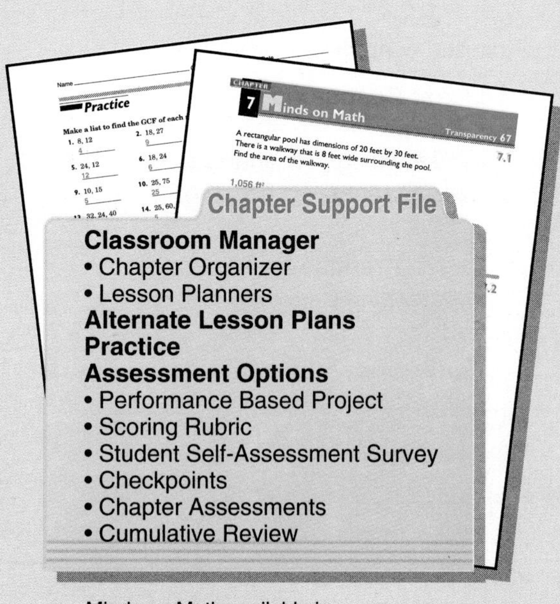

Minds on Math available in Teaching Transparencies

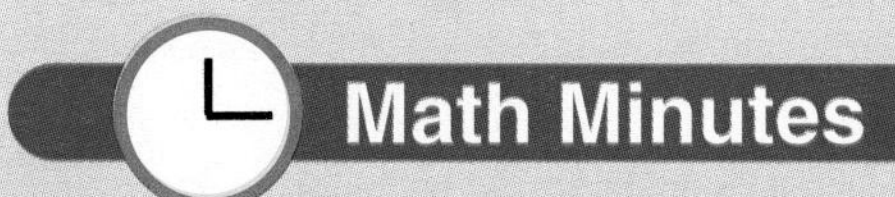

Write the next number in the sequence: 0.214, 0.234, 0.254, 0.274, ▒ .
0.294

Materials for 7-4

- fraction bars

Mixed REVIEW

Write the prime factorization. See below.

1. 324 **2.** 600

Use graph paper to model each decimal.

3. 0.75 **4.** 0.7
See Solution Key.

Find the area of each circle. Use 3.14 for π.

5. radius = 7 m 153.86 m²

6. diameter = 16 in. 200.96 in.²

7. The bus from Montreal to Chicago is scheduled to leave at 5:43 A.M. and arrive at 4:54 P.M. How long is the trip if the bus passes through one time zone, gaining an hour?

12 h 11 min
1. 2 × 2 × 3 × 3 × 3 × 3
2. 2 × 2 × 2 × 3 × 5 × 5

25. By definition, a prime number has no factors other than 1 and itself. So, the only common factor of two prime numbers is 1.

5. 2 × 2 × 2 × 2 × 2 × 2 × 3 × 5
6. 3 × 3 × 3 × 3 × 3
7. 2 × 3 × 5 × 7 × 11
8. 2 × 3 × 5 × 13 × 13

ON YOUR OWN

Make a list to find the GCF of each set of numbers.

13. 14, 35 7 **14.** 24, 25 1 **15.** 12, 15, 21 3

16. 26, 34 2 **17.** 11, 23 1 **18.** 6, 8, 12 2

Use prime factorization to find the GCF of each set of numbers.

19. 22, 104 2 **20.** 64, 125 1 **21.** 6, 57, 102 3

22. 13, 120 1 **23.** 17, 85 17 **24.** 150, 240 30

25. Writing What is the GCF of any two prime numbers? Explain why this is true. See left.

26. The graph shows the GCF of a number x and 4.

a. Describe the pattern in the graph. The numbers 1, 2, 1, 4 repeat.

b. What is the GCF of 8 and 4? 4

c. Use the graph to predict the GCF of 18 and 4. 2

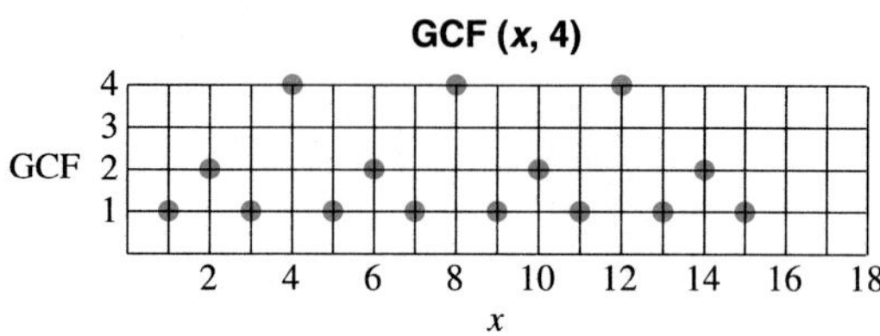

CHECKPOINT

Mental Math **State whether each number is divisible by 1, 2, 3, 5, 9, or 10.**

1. 960 1, 2, 3, 5, 10 **2.** 243 1, 3, 9 **3.** 2,310 1, 2, 3, 5, 10 **4.** 5,070 1, 2, 3, 5, 10

Find the prime factorization using a factor tree. See left.

5. 960 **6.** 243 **7.** 2,310 **8.** 5,070

Find the GCF of each set of numbers.

9. 48, 56 8 **10.** 24, 42, 72 6 **11.** 300, 450 150

CHAPTER 7 PROBLEM SOLVING PRACTICE

This page provides a variety of problems that can be used to reinforce and enhance the students' problem solving skills. Encourage students to read each problem carefully. Then have them refer to the list of problem solving strategies to help them decide how to solve the problems.

Point out, however, that not all questions require a strategy for solving, nor are all the strategies in the list used on this page.

Exercise 3: Suggest that students use a Venn diagram to model the problem.

USING MANIPULATIVES Encourage students to use blocks or tiles to model Exercises 2, 3, and 6.

Problem Solving Practice

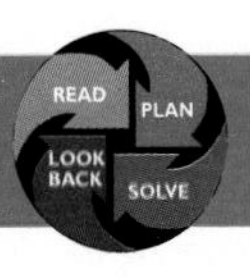

PROBLEM SOLVING STRATEGIES

- Make a Table
- Use Logical Reasoning
- Solve a Simpler Problem
- Too Much or Too Little Information
- Look for a Pattern
- Make a Model
- Work Backward
- Draw a Diagram
- Guess and Test
- Simulate a Problem
- Use Multiple Strategies

Solve. The list at the left shows some possible strategies you can use.

1. Alicia and Brad are at the library today. Alicia goes to the library every 6 days and Brad goes to the library every 8 days. How many times in the next 12 weeks will Alicia and Brad be at the library on the same day? 3 times

2. In how many different ways can Latosha, Pang-Ni, and Charles stand in line at the bookstore? 6 different ways

3. **Health** After a health screening in her homeroom, Ms. Kato reported the results. Of the 25 students in the class, a total of 11 needed a dental check-up, 17 needed an eye exam, and 5 students needed neither a dental check-up nor an eye exam. How many students needed both? 8 students

4. **Money** Taesha has $1.35 in nickels and dimes. She has a total of 15 coins. How many of each coin does she have? 3 nickels and 12 dimes

5. Each time Aretha's grandmother visits, she doubles the amount of money Aretha has saved and gives her $3 extra to spend. After her grandmother's first visit, Aretha had a total of $19. How much had Aretha saved before her grandmother's visit? $8

6. Box A has 9 green balls and 4 red balls. Box B has 12 green balls and 5 red balls. You want the fraction of green balls in Box A to equal the fraction of red balls in Box B. How many green balls must move from Box A to Box B? 8 green balls

7. How many days old are you? Check student's work.

8. **Entertainment** At the grand opening of the Plex Cinema, every 15th person to buy a ticket got a free ticket for a future feature. Every 10th person got a coupon for a free box of popcorn. Of the 418 ticket buyers, how many received both prizes? 13 ticket buyers

9. Alaina is watching a football game at school. Alaina's piano recital begins at 7:00 P.M. It takes her 15 min to get home, 20 min to eat supper, 25 min to change, and 10 min to get there. What time should she leave the game? 5:50 P.M.

WHO? Shigechiyo Izumi holds the record for the longest living person. Shigechiyo lived 120 years, 237 days. **About how many minutes is that?**

Source: *Guinness Book of World Records*

63 million

7-4

Connecting to Prior Knowledge

Have students describe fractions in concrete terms, such as pizza slices. Ask students: *If you slice a pizza into eight equal parts and eat three of them, what portion of the pizza did you eat?* ($\frac{3}{8}$)

DIVERSITY Students who have lived in countries that use the metric system may not be familiar with the use of fractions in everyday living. Some students will easily learn about fractions from the formal mathematical definitions. Others will need concrete examples. Have students share real-world examples of fractions as you work through the lesson. Have volunteers share how the use of fractions in the United States compares with the use of measures in the metric system in other countries. For example, students might purchase 0.5 kg of cheese rather than a "half pound" of cheese.

THINK AND DISCUSS

TACTILE LEARNERS Students can use fraction bars to help them with Questions 1–6. If necessary, have the students make them out of strips of paper. In fact, making the fraction bars is a good exercise as well.

ESL **AUDITORY LEARNERS** Since "four" and "fourth" differ by only the "th" sound, explain to students that most fractions are read by using the ordinal number pronunciation, such as sixth, seventh, eighth, and so on. Note the exceptions for two, three, and five: "half," "third," and "fifth." You may wish to remind students that calendar dates are read using the ordinal numbers.

TECHNOLOGY OPTION For Questions 5 and 6, students can explore equivalent fractions by using fraction software programs. Have students work in pairs and challenge each other by naming fractions for which equivalent fractions should be found. Have pairs share their strategies and findings with the class.

"Never, never, never, never give up."

—Winston Churchill

Organizer

1. **Focus**
   Connecting to Prior Knowledge
2. **Teach**
   Think and Discuss
   Work Together
3. **Closure**
   Wrap Up

Vocabulary/Symbols
fraction bars   equivalent fractions

Materials and Manipulatives
- fraction bars (1 set per group)

Student Resources
Extra Practice; Practice, TR Ch. 7, p. 28
Student Study Guide; English & Spanish

Teacher Resources
Teaching Transparencies 22–29, 68
Transparency Masters, TR pp. 21–24
Lesson Planner, TR Ch. 7, p. 5

Prentice Hall Technology
Multimedia Math
- Math Tools, Fraction Strips
- Hot Page™ 7-4

Computer Item Generator 7-4

Assignment Options

Core: 11–14, 17, MR all	
Reinforce: 15, 16, 18	**Enrich:** 19

286

What's Ahead
- Exploring fractions and equivalent fractions using models
- Estimating fractions

WHAT YOU'LL NEED
✓ Fraction bars 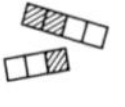

1. The numerator is represented by the number of shaded parts. The denominator is represented by the number of parts making up the fraction bar.

5d. Answers will vary. Sample: $\frac{2}{4}$, $\frac{3}{6}$, and $\frac{4}{8}$.

***A flash of lightning** lasts for about $\frac{3}{100}$ of a second. That's quicker than the blink of an eye!*

7-4 Exploring Fractions

THINK AND DISCUSS

You can model fractions using *fraction bars.* **Fraction bars** represent fractions as shaded parts of a region.

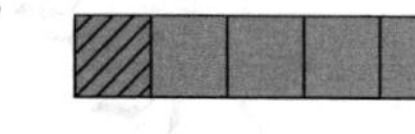

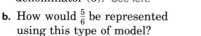

1. a. How does the model represent the numerator (1) and denominator (6)? See left.
   b. How would $\frac{5}{6}$ be represented using this type of model? Five of the six parts would contain slanted lines.
2. Name the fraction modeled by each fraction bar.
   a.  $\frac{4}{6}$
   b. 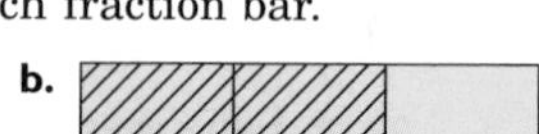 $\frac{2}{3}$
3. Find a fraction bar that models each fraction.
   a. $\frac{2}{6}$ $\frac{1}{3}$ or $\frac{4}{12}$ b. $\frac{3}{4}$ $\frac{6}{8}$ or $\frac{9}{12}$ c. $\frac{6}{10}$ $\frac{3}{5}$ d. $\frac{2}{5}$ $\frac{4}{10}$
4. **Discussion** What number is represented when all the regions are shaded in a fraction bar? Explain. 1; The numerator and denominator of the modeled fraction are equal.

The fraction bars at the right show equivalent fractions. **Equivalent fractions** are fractions that represent the same part of a whole.

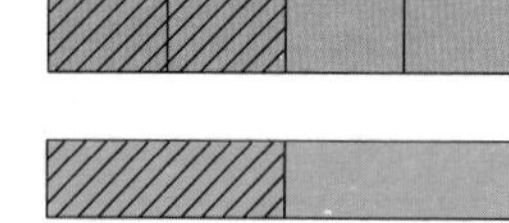

5. a. What fraction is modeled by the blue fraction bar? the green fraction bar? $\frac{2}{4}$; $\frac{1}{2}$
   b. Compare the area shaded in the blue fraction bar with the area shaded in the green fraction bar. $\frac{2}{4} = \frac{1}{2}$
   c. Find two other fraction bars that show the same shaded area as the fraction bars shown above. $\frac{3}{6}$, $\frac{4}{8}$, $\frac{5}{10}$, or $\frac{6}{12}$
   d. Name three fractions that are equivalent to $\frac{1}{2}$. See left.
6. Find a fraction bar that models $\frac{4}{6}$. Name two other fraction bars that show an equivalent fraction. $\frac{2}{3}$ and $\frac{8}{12}$

WORK TOGETHER

Error Alert! For problems such as Question 8, students may have difficulty recognizing approximate values for fractions.

Ongoing Assessment Have students verbalize the rules they used for finding the fractions asked for in Question 10.

Journal Have students describe the mental pictures they use to help them to visualize simplifying fractions.

Wrap Up

What's the Big Idea? Ask students: *What does a fraction like $\frac{3}{4}$ mean? How can fraction strips be used to model fractions and equivalent fractions?*

Reteaching Activity Bring empty egg cartons to class and use the 12 spaces to model fractions. Ask students to represent $\frac{1}{2}$, $\frac{1}{3}$, $\frac{1}{4}$, $\frac{1}{6}$, $\frac{1}{12}$, $\frac{2}{3}$, $\frac{3}{4}$, $\frac{5}{6}$, and so on, as parts of the whole.

Connections Have a discussion about how fractions are used. You may want to start with these examples:

- **Music** (naming notes, describing ranges and pitches)
- **Economics** (stock market prices, describing changes in rates)

ON YOUR OWN

WRITING For Exercise 17, have students estimate the difference between $\frac{2}{4}$ and $\frac{1}{3}$.

CRITICAL THINKING Encourage students to draw models to help them with Exercise 19.

WORK TOGETHER

Work with a partner to write rules for estimating fractions.

7. The fractions at the right are close to 0. Write a rule to tell when a fraction is close to 0. See right. $\frac{1}{14}$ $\frac{3}{17}$ $\frac{2}{25}$ $\frac{7}{125}$

8. The fractions at the right are close to $\frac{1}{2}$. Write a rule to tell when a fraction is close to $\frac{1}{2}$. See right. $\frac{3}{8}$ $\frac{8}{14}$ $\frac{11}{23}$ $\frac{55}{100}$

9. The fractions at the right are close to 1. Write a rule to tell when a fraction is close to 1. See right. $\frac{99}{100}$ $\frac{3}{4}$ $\frac{45}{50}$ $\frac{79}{91}$

10. Use your rules to write three fractions that are close to 0, three fractions that are close to $\frac{1}{2}$, and three fractions that are close to 1. Then exchange with your partner to see if he or she can estimate each fraction. Check student's work.

ON YOUR OWN

Name the fraction modeled by each fraction bar.

11. 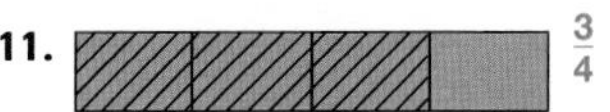 $\frac{3}{4}$

12. 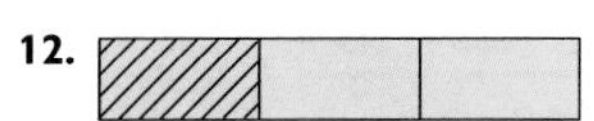 $\frac{1}{3}$

Find a fraction bar that models each fraction. Name other fraction bars that show an equivalent fraction.

13. $\frac{1}{2}$ $\frac{2}{4}$, $\frac{3}{6}$, $\frac{5}{10}$, $\frac{6}{12}$ **14.** $\frac{9}{12}$ $\frac{3}{4}$ **15.** $\frac{2}{3}$ $\frac{4}{6}$, $\frac{6}{9}$, $\frac{8}{12}$ **16.** $\frac{2}{6}$ $\frac{1}{3}$, $\frac{4}{12}$

17. Writing Use the models at the right to explain why the fractions $\frac{2}{4}$ and $\frac{1}{3}$ are not equivalent. See right.

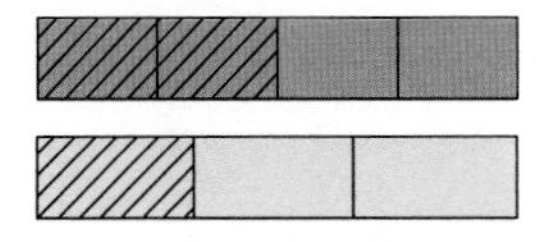

18. Estimation Tell whether each fraction at the right is close to 0, close to $\frac{1}{2}$, or close to 1. 0: $\frac{3}{30}$, $\frac{1}{10}$, $\frac{5}{99}$; $\frac{1}{2}$: $\frac{17}{40}$, $\frac{45}{100}$, $\frac{35}{80}$; 1: $\frac{7}{9}$, $\frac{38}{45}$, $\frac{75}{80}$

$\frac{3}{30}$	$\frac{7}{9}$	$\frac{1}{10}$
$\frac{38}{45}$	$\frac{17}{40}$	$\frac{45}{100}$
$\frac{35}{80}$	$\frac{5}{99}$	$\frac{75}{80}$

19. Critical Thinking Write three fractions that are close to 0, three fractions that are close to $\frac{1}{2}$, and three fractions that are close to 1. Check student's work.

Mixed REVIEW

Find the GCF.

1. 18, 24 6
2. 30, 45 15
3. 36, 56, 72 4

Write a variable expression. $n - 10$

4. 10 less than a number
5. the sum of twice a number and 5 $2n + 5$
6. the product of a number and 6 $6n$
7. Find the length and width of a rectangle whose area is 48 m^2 and whose perimeter is 32 m.

12 m by 4 m

7. A fraction is close to 0 when the numerator is much less than half the denominator.
8. A fraction is close to $\frac{1}{2}$ when the numerator is about half the denominator.
9. A fraction is close to 1 when the numerator is about equal to the denominator.
17. The shaded area in the fraction bar for $\frac{2}{4}$ is not equal to the shaded area in the fraction bar for $\frac{1}{3}$.

Fact of the Day

Every year, 625 people in the United States are struck by lightning.

—*In One Day*

PH Multimedia Math Hot Page™ 7-4

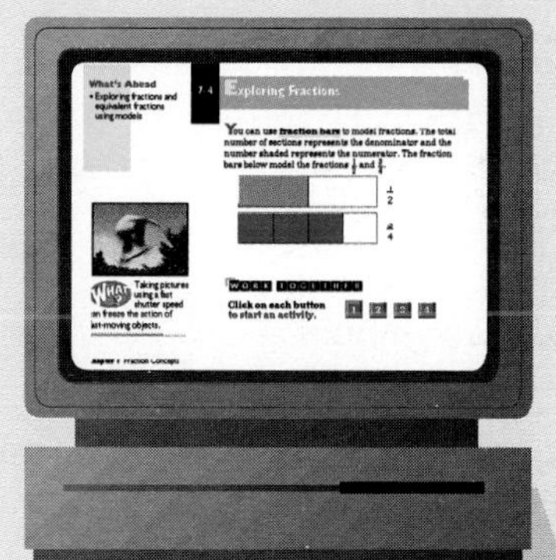

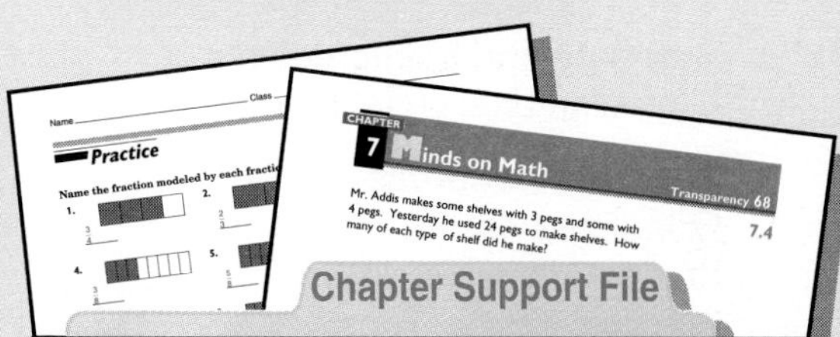

Minds on Math available in Teaching Transparencies

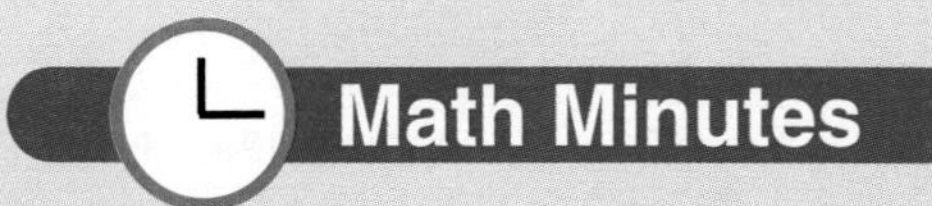

Math Minutes

What is the value of the *6* in 2.0346?

6 ten-thousandths

Materials for 7-5

- fraction bars

7-5

Connecting to Prior Knowledge

Ask students to brainstorm in one minute as many equivalent fractions as they can for the fraction $\frac{1}{2}$. ($\frac{2}{4}$; $\frac{3}{6}$; $\frac{4}{8}$) Have a volunteer list the fractions on the chalkboard. Have students find other words besides *equivalent* to describe the relationship between equivalent fractions.

THINK AND DISCUSS

ESL **AUDITORY LEARNERS** Make sure that students understand the relationship between *equivalent* and *equal.*

VISUAL LEARNERS Have students use fraction bars in Questions 1–4 so they can see the equivalence of fractions by comparing the shaded areas. Use fraction bars on the overhead projector or draw models on the chalkboard as you explain the answers.

Error Alert! Students may misunderstand equivalent fractions in problems such as in Question 3. They may think, in error, that $\frac{3}{4} \times 3$ is equivalent to $\frac{3 \times 3}{4 \times 3}$. ***Remediation*** Have students model $\frac{3}{3}$ and 3 and note the difference between the two. Point out that multiplying a fraction by $\frac{3}{3}$ does not change the value of the fraction, but multiplying by 3 does.

Example

Point out that both numerator and denominator are divided by the same number, and this results in an equivalent fraction.

Additional Example *Write $\frac{16}{40}$ in simplest form.*

16: 1, 2, 4, (8), 16

40: 1, 2, 4, 5, (8), 10, 20, 40

$\frac{16}{40} \div \frac{8}{8} = \frac{2}{5}$ **The fraction $\frac{16}{40}$ in simplest form is $\frac{2}{5}$.**

> *"There is nothing either good or bad, but thinking makes it so."*
>
> —William Shakespeare

Organizer

1. **Focus**
   Connecting to Prior Knowledge
2. **Teach**
   Think and Discuss
3. **Closure**
   Try These
   Wrap Up

Vocabulary/Symbols
simplest form

Skills Reviewed in Context of Lesson
- multiplying and dividing whole numbers
- finding GCF

Materials and Manipulatives
- fraction bars (1 set for each group)

Student Resources
Extra Practice
Student Study Guide
Practice, TR Ch. 7, p. 29
Student Study Guide, Spanish Resources, TR

Teacher Resources
Teaching Transparencies 23–26, 29, 68
Transparency Masters, TR pp. 21–24
Overhead Manipulatives: fraction bars
Lesson Planner, TR Ch. 7, p. 6

continues next page

What's Ahead
- Finding equivalent fractions
- Expressing fractions in simplest form

WHAT YOU'LL NEED
✓ Fraction bars 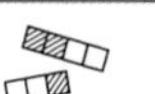

3. b. Answers may vary. Sample: There are 3 times as many total regions and 3 times as many shaded regions.

7-5 Equivalent Fractions

THINK AND DISCUSS

The area shaded in the red fraction bar is equal to the area shaded in the yellow fraction bar. Therefore, the models represent equivalent fractions.

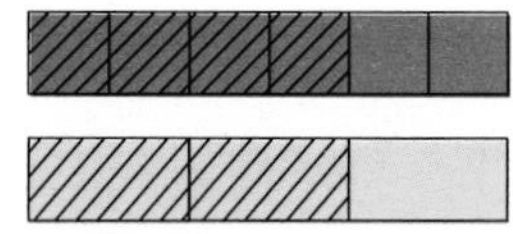

1. a. Name the pair of equivalent fractions that are modeled. $\frac{4}{6}, \frac{2}{3}$
   b. Find another fraction bar that represents a fraction equivalent to those modeled above. What fraction is represented? $\frac{6}{9}$ or $\frac{8}{12}$
2. **Discussion** Model the fractions $\frac{3}{5}$ and $\frac{3}{4}$ using fraction bars. Use the model to explain why the fractions are not equivalent. The shaded area in the fraction bar for $\frac{3}{5}$ is not equal to the shaded area in the fraction bar for $\frac{3}{4}$.

You can form equivalent fractions by multiplying or dividing the numerator and denominator by the same nonzero number.

3. The fractions $\frac{3}{4}$ and $\frac{9}{12}$ are modeled below.

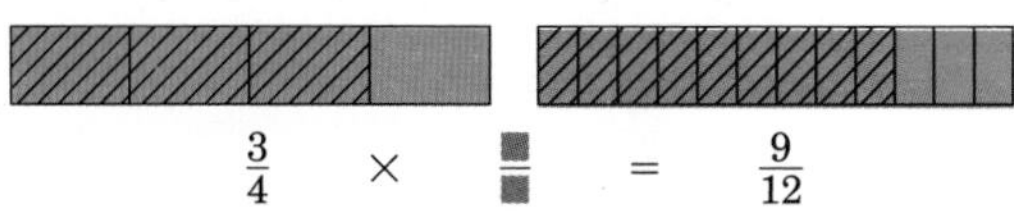

$\frac{3}{4} \times \frac{■}{■} = \frac{9}{12}$

   a. What number can you multiply both the numerator and denominator of $\frac{3}{4}$ by to get $\frac{9}{12}$? 3
   b. Explain how multiplication by this number is shown in the models. See left.
   c. **Discussion** What whole number are you actually multiplying $\frac{3}{4}$ by to get $\frac{9}{12}$? Explain. 1
   d. Use multiplication to find two other fractions equivalent to $\frac{3}{4}$. Answers may vary. Sample: $\frac{6}{8}, \frac{12}{16}$

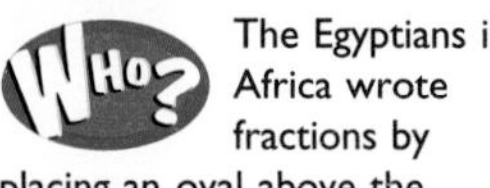

WHO? The Egyptians in Africa wrote fractions by placing an oval above the symbols for their numbers.

Source: *The History of Mathematics*

TRY THESE

TECHNOLOGY OPTION For Exercises 6–9, students can use fraction software programs to review fraction concepts. Have students work in pairs and share their methods with other pairs.

MENTAL MATH Have students share with the class the methods they used to determine the simplest form of each fraction. Have them identify the GCF they used for Exercises 10–13. Some students may have determined the simplest form without using a GCF. Have them share their strategies with the class.

Ongoing Assessment Give students the fractions $\frac{4}{20}$ and $\frac{3}{15}$. Ask them to use models to determine if the fractions are equivalent. Then have students express each in simplest form. **(They are equivalent; both are $\frac{1}{5}$.)** Have students discuss their procedures.

Wrap Up

What's the Big Idea? Ask students: *What are equivalent fractions? How do you express fractions in simplest form?*

Journal Ask students to compare finding an equivalent fraction to expressing a fraction in simplest form. Have students describe similarities and differences in the procedures.

Connections Have a discussion about how equivalent fractions are used. You may want to start with these examples:

- **Construction** (matching equivalent sizes of pipes and tools)
- **Business** (describing inventory by replacing specific numbers with equivalent simplified fractions)

4. The fractions $\frac{6}{12}$ and $\frac{2}{4}$ are modeled below.

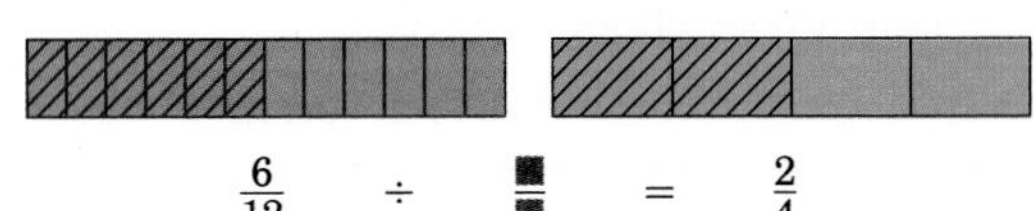

$\frac{6}{12} \div \frac{■}{■} = \frac{2}{4}$

a. What number can you divide both the numerator and denominator of $\frac{6}{12}$ by to get $\frac{2}{4}$? 3

b. Explain how division by this number is modeled. See right.

c. **Discussion** What whole number are you actually dividing $\frac{6}{12}$ by to get $\frac{2}{4}$? Explain. 1

d. Use division to find two other fractions equivalent to $\frac{6}{12}$. $\frac{3}{6}$, $\frac{1}{2}$

When you divide both the numerator and denominator of a fraction by the greatest common factor (GCF), the fraction is **in simplest form.**

Example 1 Write $\frac{20}{28}$ in simplest form.

- Make a list of factors for the numerator and denominator. Circle the common factors and identify the GCF.

  20: (1), (2), (4), 5, 10, 20

  28: (1), (2), (4), 7, 14, 28 ← The GCF is 4

- Divide both the numerator and denominator of $\frac{20}{28}$ by their GCF of 4.

$$\frac{20}{28} \div \frac{4}{4} = \frac{5}{7}$$

The fraction $\frac{20}{28}$ written in simplest form is $\frac{5}{7}$.

Can you imagine stacking up one billion dollars worth of $100 bills? You would build a tower $\frac{6}{10}$ of a mile high! **What is the height in simplest form?** $\frac{3}{5}$ mi

Source: *Junior Fact Finder*

4. b. Answers may vary. Sample: The number of total regions and the number of shaded regions are both divided by 3.

TRY THESE

5. Model equivalent fractions $\frac{3}{5}$ and $\frac{6}{10}$ using fraction bars. Check student's work. Answers will vary. Sample given.

Write two fractions equivalent to each fraction.

6. $\frac{1}{4}$ $\frac{2}{8}$, $\frac{3}{12}$
7. $\frac{10}{20}$ $\frac{1}{2}$, $\frac{2}{4}$
8. $\frac{4}{5}$ $\frac{8}{10}$, $\frac{12}{15}$
9. $\frac{15}{45}$ $\frac{1}{3}$, $\frac{3}{9}$

Mental Math Write each fraction in simplest form.

10. $\frac{16}{18}$ $\frac{8}{9}$
11. $\frac{12}{16}$ $\frac{3}{4}$
12. $\frac{21}{24}$ $\frac{7}{8}$
13. $\frac{120}{150}$ $\frac{4}{5}$

Organizer, continued

Prentice Hall Technology

Multimedia Math
- Math Tools, Fraction Strips

Computer Item Generator
- 7-5

Other Available Technology

The Fraction Machine by Computer Software: Questions 6–9 *(optional)*

Fact of the Day

Maximum tides, called spring tides, occur when the sun, moon, and earth all lie approximately in a straight line, so that the tidal forces of the sun and moon reinforce each other. Minimum tides, called neap tides, occur when the sun and moon are about 90 degrees apart as viewed from the earth, so that their gravitational attractions partially cancel each other.

—Academic American Encyclopedia

Assignment Options

Core: 14–17, 25–32, MR all	
Reinforce: 18–24, 33, 34	**Enrich:** 35, 36

Reteaching Activity Group students in pairs and provide each pair with four fraction bars. Have students in each pair name three equivalent fractions for each bar and name the simplest form for each. Have partners compare results.

ON YOUR OWN

CONNECTION TO ALGEBRA Exercises 18–20 have students solve for unknown values.

WRITING For Exercise 33, have students provide examples to support their answers.

CRITICAL THINKING Encourage students to consider all possibilities for Exercise 35.

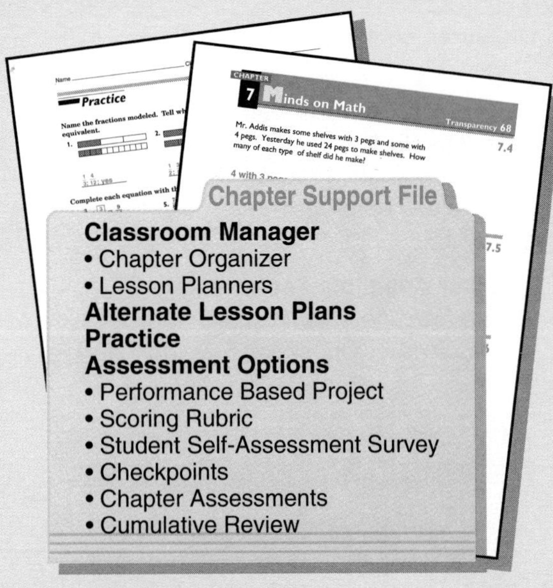

Minds on Math available in Teaching Transparencies

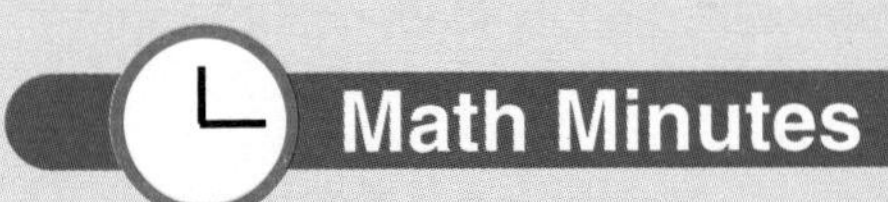

Write the number eight billion. **8,000,000,000**

Materials for 7-6

- calculator

Marlee Matlin, who is hearing impaired, won an Oscar award for Best Actress for her role in the movie "Children of a Lesser God."

Mixed REVIEW

Tell whether each fraction is close to 0, $\frac{1}{2}$, or 1.

1. $\frac{23}{25}$ 1
2. $\frac{3}{40}$ 0
3. $\frac{37}{80}$ $\frac{1}{2}$

Find the surface area.

4. a cube with a side of 10 cm 600 cm^2
5. a rectangular prism with a height of 4 in., a length of 6 in., and a width of 5 in. 148 in.^{2}
6. A swim team can line up in 6 lanes with an equal number of swimmers in each lane. If only 5 lanes are used, two lanes have an extra person. What is the least number of people on the swim team? 12 people

ON YOUR OWN

Write a fraction for each sentence.

14. **Money** It costs the United States government about four-fifths of a cent to make one penny. $\frac{4}{5}$
15. **Entertainment** Best Director and Best Picture Oscars have gone to the same film 47 out of 64 times. $\frac{47}{64}$

Name the fractions modeled. Tell whether they are equivalent.

16. $\frac{8}{12}$, $\frac{3}{5}$; no
17. $\frac{2}{6}$, $\frac{1}{3}$; yes

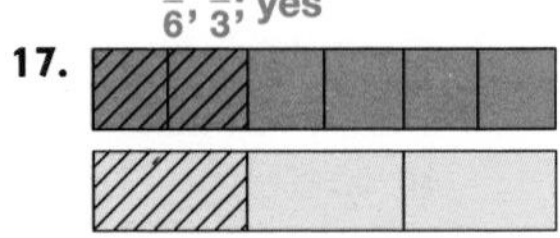

Replace each ■ with the appropriate number.

18. $\frac{2}{5} \times \frac{■}{■} = \frac{8}{20}$ $\frac{4}{4}$
19. $\frac{40}{50} \div \frac{■}{■} = \frac{8}{10}$ $\frac{5}{5}$
20. $\frac{4}{16} \div \frac{4}{4} = \frac{■}{■}$ $\frac{1}{4}$

Write two fractions equivalent to each fraction. Answers will vary Sample given.

21. $\frac{4}{8}$ $\frac{1}{2}$, $\frac{2}{4}$
22. $\frac{1}{6}$ $\frac{2}{12}$, $\frac{3}{18}$
23. $\frac{6}{18}$ $\frac{1}{3}$, $\frac{2}{6}$
24. $\frac{7}{21}$ $\frac{1}{3}$, 14

State whether each fraction is in simplest form. If not, write it in simplest form.

25. $\frac{24}{56}$ no; $\frac{3}{7}$
26. $\frac{21}{77}$ no; $\frac{3}{11}$
27. $\frac{25}{150}$ no; $\frac{1}{6}$
28. $\frac{3}{50}$ yes
29. $\frac{45}{135}$ no; $\frac{1}{3}$
30. $\frac{17}{51}$ no; $\frac{1}{3}$
31. $\frac{10}{65}$ no; $\frac{2}{13}$
32. $\frac{126}{153}$ no;

33. **Writing** Can you write a fraction in simplest form if you divide the numerator and denominator by a number other than the GCF? Explain. See Solution Key.
34. What is the only common factor of the numerator and denominator when a fraction is written in simplest form? 1
35. **Critical Thinking** Use the numbers 2, 6, 4, and 12 to write two pairs of equivalent fractions. $\frac{2}{6}$, $\frac{4}{12}$; $\frac{2}{4}$, $\frac{6}{12}$
36. **Data File 7 (pp. 272–273)** Four hours after low tide, what part of the tidal range will be covered? Express your answer in simplest form. $\frac{3}{4}$

CHAPTER 7 PRACTICE

This page provides practice on the skills learned up to this point in the chapter. Daily cumulative practice can be found in the Mixed Reviews that appear in every lesson.

Practice

Mental Math **Decide whether each number is divisible by 1, 2, 3, 5, 9, or 10.**

1. 124 1, 2
2. 365 1, 5
3. 480 1, 2, 3, 5, 10
4. 7,083 1, 3, 9
5. 3,498 1, 2, 3

Tell whether each number is prime or composite.

6. 2 P
7. 24 C
8. 31 P
9. 51 C
10. 17 P

Find the prime factorization using a factor tree.

11. 35 5×7
12. 148 $2 \times 2 \times 37$
13. 273 $3 \times 7 \times 13$
14. 75 $3 \times 5 \times 5$
15. 144 $2 \times 2 \times 2 \times 2 \times 3 \times 3$

Find the GCF of each set of numbers.

16. 18, 24 6
17. 25, 35 5
18. 13, 19 1
19. 56, 63 7
20. 14, 8, 24 2

Name the fraction modeled by each fraction bar.

21. 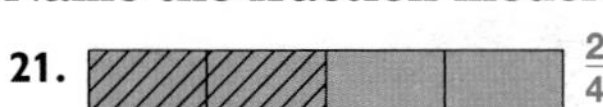 $\frac{2}{4}$
22. 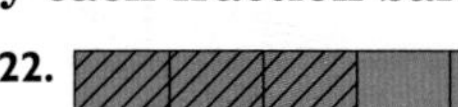 $\frac{3}{5}$
23.  $\frac{1}{3}$

Find a fraction bar that models each fraction. Name other fraction bars that show an equivalent fraction.

24. $\frac{2}{3}$ $\frac{4}{6}, \frac{6}{9}, \frac{8}{12}$
25. $\frac{3}{4}$ $\frac{6}{8}, \frac{9}{12}$
26. $\frac{1}{2}$ $\frac{2}{4}, \frac{3}{6}, \frac{4}{8}, \frac{5}{10}, \frac{6}{12}$
27. $\frac{2}{5}$ $\frac{4}{10}$
28. $\frac{1}{4}$ $\frac{2}{8}, \frac{3}{12}$

Write two fractions equivalent to each fraction. Answers may vary. Sample given.

29. $\frac{1}{6}$ $\frac{2}{12}, \frac{3}{18}$
30. $\frac{9}{16}$ $\frac{18}{32}, \frac{27}{48}$
31. $\frac{2}{8}$ $\frac{1}{4}, \frac{6}{24}$
32. $\frac{3}{5}$ $\frac{6}{10}, \frac{9}{15}$
33. $\frac{11}{12}$ $\frac{22}{24}, \frac{33}{36}$

Name the fractions modeled. Tell whether they are equivalent.

34. 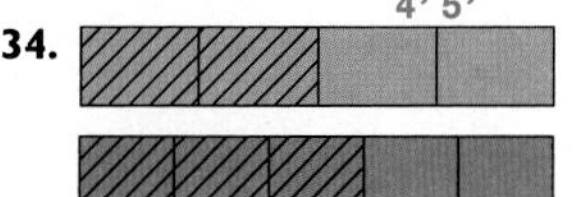 $\frac{2}{4}, \frac{3}{5}$; no
35. 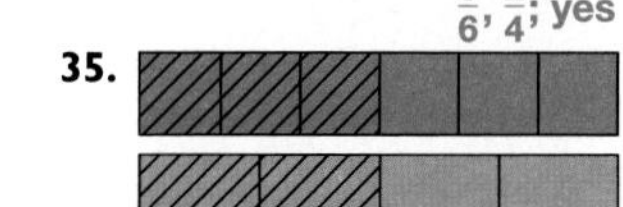 $\frac{3}{6}, \frac{2}{4}$; yes
36. 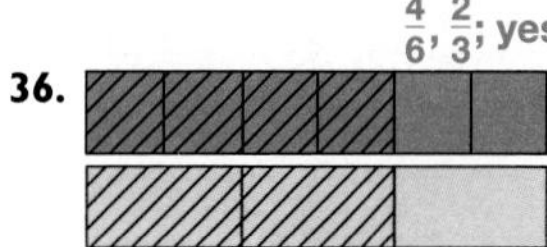 $\frac{4}{6}, \frac{2}{3}$; yes

Write each fraction in simplest form.

37. $\frac{12}{18}$ $\frac{2}{3}$
38. $\frac{24}{60}$ $\frac{2}{5}$
39. $\frac{15}{90}$ $\frac{1}{6}$
40. $\frac{14}{35}$ $\frac{2}{5}$
41. $\frac{33}{77}$ $\frac{3}{7}$

Resources

Extra Practice
Student Study Guide
Student Study Guide, Spanish Resources, TR

Materials and Manipulatives

- fraction bars

7-6

Connecting to Prior Knowledge

Ask students to explain what it means to "simplify a fraction" and how they can simplify fractions. Ask how they can tell when a fraction is in simplest form.

THINK AND DISCUSS

If a fraction calculator is available, demonstrate how to use the fraction keys and the simplification function. Students' calculators may have different methods for simplifying fractions.

Alternate Approach If a fraction calculator is not available, have groups of students choose one of the fractions and then use a calculator to find out if that fraction can be simplified. To check, try dividing the numerator and denominator by all factors to see if the only common factor is 1.

CRITICAL THINKING For Question 2, ask students to discuss the importance of the capital and lower-case letters in the sample.

DIVERSITY In discussing capital and lower-case letters in the English alphabet, keep in mind that some students may be part of a culture whose language does not make a distinction between letters and/or symbols that is in any way akin to what we know as "capital" and "small" letters. Invite students to share their alphabets/symbols with the class.

Error Alert! Some students may attempt to divide the numerator and denominator beginning with the number 2 and then increase the divisor (by one) after each guess. ***Remediation*** It may help to review divisibility rules to help the students better estimate their guesses for the problems in Questions 3–7.

WORK TOGETHER

AUDITORY LEARNERS Have the student who is not operating the calculator read the steps of the game aloud while the other student enters the data.

"A man's life is interesting primarily when he has failed—I well know. For it's a sign that he tried to surpass himself."

—Georges Clemenceau

Organizer

1. **Focus**
   Connecting to Prior Knowledge
2. **Teach**
   Think and Discuss
   Work Together
3. **Closure**
   Try These
   Wrap Up

Skills Reviewed in Context of Lesson
- estimating GCF

Materials and Manipulatives
- calculator (1 for each student)

On Your Own Exercises 12–20: calculator

Student Resources
Extra Practice; Practice, TR Ch. 7, p. 30
Student Study Guide; English & Spanish
Alternate Lesson, TR Ch. 7, pp. 17–20

Teacher Resources
Teaching Transparencies 19, 68
Lesson Planner, TR Ch. 7, p. 7

Prentice Hall Technology
Computer Item Generator
- 7-6

Other Available Technology
- calculator

What's Ahead
- Using a calculator to simplify fractions

WHAT YOU'LL NEED
✓ Calculator

TECHNOLOGY

7-6 Simplifying Fractions

THINK AND DISCUSS

You can use a fraction calculator to simplify a fraction. The fraction calculator divides the numerator and denominator by a common factor and rewrites the fraction. You repeat the process until the fraction is in simplest form.

Example Use a fraction calculator to simplify $\frac{9}{27}$.

Press	Display	
9 [/] 27	9/27	Enter the fraction.
[Simp]	SIMP N/D→n/d 9/27	
[=]	N/D→n/d 3/9	The fraction is simplified once.
[Simp]	SIMP N/D→n/d 3/9	
[=]	1/3	The fraction is in simplest form.

1. By what common factor were the numerator, 9, and the denominator, 27, first divided? 3

2. **Critical Thinking** The display N/D→n/d could be written $\frac{N}{D} \rightarrow \frac{n}{d}$. What do the n's and the d's represent? Sample: the n's represent the numerators, the d's represent the denominators; $\frac{n}{d}$ shows a reduced fraction.

A fruit salad *with 10 c of fruit contains 2 c of strawberries. So $\frac{2}{10}$ or $\frac{1}{5}$ of the salad is strawberries.*

WORK TOGETHER

Work with a partner to simplify fractions using a calculator. Each person should copy the table that appears on the following page. You may work with your partner to simplify the first fraction, $\frac{12}{20}$. Then, work separately on the remaining fractions. The person with the most points wins.

Step 1 Guess the GCF of the numerator and denominator of the fraction. Record your guess in your table.

Step 2 Enter the fraction into the calculator using the [/] key.

TRY THESE

CALCULATOR Students may use any calculator and work in pairs to divide the task. ***Alternate approach*** If a calculator is not available, have students simplify the fractions by using pencil and paper. Have the students name the GCF as part of the exercise.

Ongoing Assessment For Questions 8, 10, and 11, the simplified fraction is the same. Ask students to name five other fractions that would have $\frac{1}{3}$ as the answer if they were simplified.

Wrap Up

What's the Big Idea? Ask Students: *Why are Greatest Common Factors useful in simplifying fractions?*

Connections Have a discussion about the purpose of simplifying fractions. You may wish to start with this example:

- **Cooking** (for reducing the amount of ingredients in a recipe so that there are fewer servings)

Reteaching Activity While playing the Work Together guessing game with a partner, have the students use fraction bars or other fraction manipulatives.

Journal Ask students to explain why it is easier to work with fractions when they are in simplest form. Have them describe the method they prefer for writing fractions in simplest form.

ON YOUR OWN

CALCULATOR For Exercise 20a, students are introduced to a function key that students may or may not have on their calculators. Check students' calculators prior to this exercise.

Step 3 Press [Simp]. Enter your guess for the GCF of the numerator and denominator of the fraction. Press [=].

Step 4 If N/D→n/d is not displayed, you chose the GCF of the numerator and denominator of the fraction. Give yourself 3 points and go on to the next fraction.

If N/D→n/d is displayed, the factor you chose is not the GCF of the numerator and denominator of the fraction. Re-enter the fraction and try again. After three tries, you do not receive any points.

	Fraction	First Guess (3 points)	Second Guess (2 points)	Third Guess (1 point)	Points	Simplified Form
3.	$\frac{12}{20}$	■ GCF = 4	■	■	■	$\frac{3}{5}$ ■
4.	$\frac{15}{25}$	■ GCF = 5	■	■	■	$\frac{3}{5}$ ■
5.	$\frac{21}{24}$	■ GCF = 3	■	■	■	$\frac{7}{8}$ ■
6.	$\frac{5}{40}$	■ GCF = 5	■	■	■	$\frac{1}{8}$ ■
7.	$\frac{27}{81}$	■ GCF = 27	■	■	■	$\frac{1}{3}$ ■

TRY THESE

Calculator Use a calculator to simplify each fraction.

8. $\frac{4}{12}$ $\frac{1}{3}$
9. $\frac{30}{45}$ $\frac{2}{3}$
10. $\frac{18}{54}$ $\frac{1}{3}$
11. $\frac{16}{48}$ $\frac{1}{3}$

ON YOUR OWN

Choose Use a calculator, paper and pencil, or mental math to simplify each fraction.

12. $\frac{8}{24}$ $\frac{1}{3}$
13. $\frac{20}{65}$ $\frac{4}{13}$
14. $\frac{17}{68}$ $\frac{1}{4}$
15. $\frac{14}{35}$ $\frac{2}{5}$
16. $\frac{105}{180}$ $\frac{7}{12}$
17. $\frac{35}{56}$ $\frac{5}{8}$
18. $\frac{24}{64}$ $\frac{3}{8}$
19. $\frac{39}{117}$ $\frac{1}{3}$

20. a. **Calculator** Simplify $\frac{19}{57}$. $\frac{1}{3}$
    b. **Writing** Press the [x⇄y] key. What number appears in the display? Why?
    19; the numerator and denominator have been divided by 19 to simplify the fraction.

Mixed REVIEW

Replace each ■ with = or ≠.

1. $\frac{7}{10}$ ■ $\frac{2}{3}$ ≠
2. $\frac{5}{15}$ ■ $\frac{24}{72}$ =

Simplify using the order of operations.

3. $5 + 2 \times 8 - 1$ 20
4. $16 \div 2 \times 3 - 20$ 4
5. $3^2 - 2^3$ 1
6. $6 \times (8 - 3)^2 - 10^2$ 50
7. A mischievous child got off the elevator at the 9th floor. She had already gone down 5, up 6, and down 3 floors. On what floor did she first enter the elevator? 11th floor

Assignment Options

Core: 12–17, MR all	
Reinforce: 18, 19	Enrich: 20

Fact of the Day

In 1852, Elisha Graves Otis designed the first safety device for elevators. In 1857, Otis installed the first passenger elevator (a steam-powered one) in a New York City store.

—Academic American Encyclopedia

Minds on Math available in Teaching Transparencies

Math Minutes

Suppose the letter a = \$1, b = \$2, c = \$3, . . . z = \$26. What is the value of your name?

Answers will vary.

7-7

Connecting to Prior Knowledge

Point out to students that so far they have been learning about fractions that are less than 1. Challenge students to name other types of fractions **("improper" fractions; fractions greater than 1; mixed numbers)** and to name situations in which they are used **(highway signs such as "Construction $1\frac{1}{4}$ mi ahead").**

ESL **KINESTHETIC LEARNERS** Choose two groups of four students to come to the front of the room to help demonstrate improper fractions. Explain to the class that each group of four students makes up one whole group. Next, pull one student out of one of the groups and ask the class what fraction of one whole he or she represents. ($\frac{1}{4}$) Then have this student join the group that still has four in it and ask the class what fraction of the whole group the group of five now represents. ($\frac{5}{4}$)

WORK TOGETHER

Ongoing Assessment Encourage each pair of students to display their results from Questions 1–3 in an organized table. Have students use the categories "Fractions Less Than 1," "Fractions Equal to 1," and "Fractions Greater than 1" with examples, models, and descriptions of each type. Have groups compare tables.

THINK AND DISCUSS

Example 1

Make sure students understand how the improper fraction and mixed number both refer to the same model and value. Ask students to recall that $\frac{4}{4} = 1$.

"I'll follow them into their own minds and fraternize there. . . . "

—Sylvia Ashton-Warner

Organizer

1. **Focus**
   Connecting to Prior Knowledge
2. **Teach**
   Work Together
   Think and Discuss
3. **Closure**
   Try These
   Wrap Up

Vocabulary/Symbols
improper fraction
mixed number

Student Resources
Extra Practice
Student Study Guide
Practice, TR Ch. 7, p. 31
Student Study Guide, Spanish Resources, TR
Checkpoint, TR Ch. 7, p. 40

Teacher Resources
Teaching Transparency 68
Transparency Masters, TR p. 10
Lesson Planner, TR Ch. 7, p. 8

Prentice Hall Technology

Multimedia Math
- Hot Page 7-7

Computer Item Generator
- 7-7

7-7 Mixed Numbers and Improper Fractions

What's Ahead
- Writing mixed numbers and improper fractions using models and computation

WORK TOGETHER

Work with a partner to explore the fractions modeled below.

$\frac{4}{4}$ 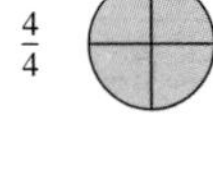 $\frac{5}{2}$ 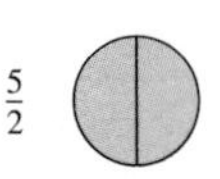 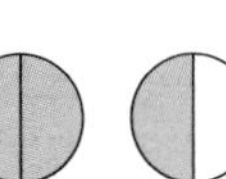 $\frac{1}{6}$ 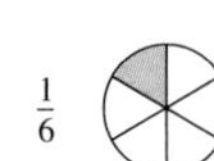

$\frac{1}{2}$  $\frac{11}{8}$ 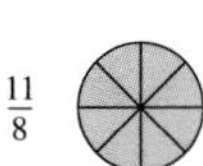 $\frac{3}{3}$ 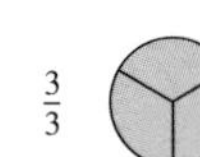

1. a. What fractions name a number equal to 1? $\frac{4}{4}, \frac{3}{3}$
   b. Compare the numerator and denominator of a fraction that is equal to 1. (*Hint:* Use >, <, or =.) numerator = denominator
2. a. What fractions name a number less than 1? $\frac{1}{6}, \frac{1}{2}$
   b. Compare the numerator and denominator of a fraction that is less than 1. numerator < denominator
3. a. What fractions name a number greater than 1? $\frac{5}{2}, \frac{11}{8}$
   b. Compare the numerator and denominator of a fraction that is greater than 1. numerator > denominator

The next time** you're in a car, watch for mixed numbers! They are often on signs indicating distances to various destinations.* ***What mixed numbers appear on the road signs above?
$1\frac{1}{2}$, $2\frac{1}{2}$, and $3\frac{1}{4}$

THINK AND DISCUSS

A fraction whose numerator is greater than or equal to its denominator is called an **improper fraction.** You can write an improper fraction greater than 1 as a *mixed number.* A **mixed number** shows the sum of a whole number and a fraction.

4. a. What improper fraction is modeled at the left? $\frac{5}{4}$
   b. How many whole circles are shaded? 1
   c. What additional fraction of a circle is shaded? $\frac{1}{4}$
   d. **Discussion** The mixed number $1\frac{1}{4}$ describes the shaded portion. How does this number show the sum of a whole number and a fraction? Answers may vary. Sample: The model shows $\frac{4}{4} + \frac{1}{4} = \frac{5}{4}$. Since $\frac{4}{4} = 1$, the model also shows $1 + \frac{1}{4} = 1\frac{1}{4}$.

Additional Example *Write $2\frac{1}{3}$ as an improper fraction.*
The mixed number $2\frac{1}{3}$ can be written as $\frac{7}{3}$.

Example 2
Have students check the division in Example 2. Point out that the remainder is the numerator of the new fraction.

ESL DIVERSITY Students may mistakenly assume that an "improper" fraction is somehow a wrong answer. Discuss the use of the word *improper* in this context and how it differs from "improper behavior." You might have students share what is proper behavior in different cultures, for example, at meals.

Error Alert! For problems such as Example 2, students may mistakenly change the denominator of the new fraction. ***Remediation*** Point out to students that because an improper fraction and its mixed number form are equivalent, they have the same denominator. Remind students to check their answers.

TRY THESE

Exercise 6: Have students compare their models and answers. Elicit the fact that an "improper" fraction can also be described as "a fraction greater than 1."

Exercises 7–9: Be sure students understand that they are combining the shaded regions from all five squares.

Wrap Up

What's the Big Idea? Ask students: *How do you represent mixed numbers and improper fractions? How do you change from one form to the other?*

Journal Have students compare mixed numbers and improper fractions. Ask students which are easier to estimate, and why.

5. Describe the shaded region at the right using an improper fraction and using a mixed number. $\frac{11}{4}$; $2\frac{3}{4}$

You can use a model to help you write a mixed number as an improper fraction.

Example 1 Write $2\frac{1}{4}$ as an improper fraction.

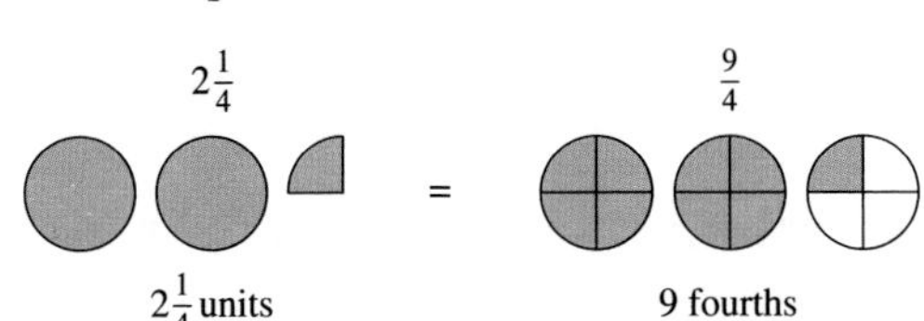

The mixed number $2\frac{1}{4}$ can be written as $\frac{9}{4}$.

Problem Solving Hint
To write a mixed number as an improper fraction, you can multiply the whole number by the denominator and add the numerator. Then write the result over the denominator.

You can use division to write an improper fraction as a mixed number.

Example 2 Write $\frac{11}{5}$ as a mixed number.

$5\overline{)11}$ = 2 R1 — Divide 11 by 5.

$2\frac{1}{5}$ — Express the remainder as a fraction.

The fraction $\frac{11}{5}$ can be written as $2\frac{1}{5}$.

TRY THESE

6. Is an improper fraction greater than, less than, or equal to one? Use a model to support your answer. > one

Five 2 × 2 squares are shown at the right. Each 2 × 2 square represents 1 unit. Describe each shaded region using an improper fraction and a mixed number.

7.  $\frac{6}{4}$; $1\frac{2}{4}$ **8.** $\frac{9}{4}$; $2\frac{1}{4}$ **9.** $\frac{5}{4}$; $1\frac{1}{4}$

Write each improper fraction as a mixed number. Write each mixed number as an improper fraction.

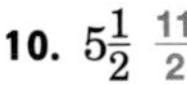
10. $5\frac{1}{2}$ $\frac{11}{2}$ **11.** $\frac{9}{4}$ $2\frac{1}{4}$ **12.** $\frac{17}{7}$ $2\frac{3}{7}$ **13.** $4\frac{3}{5}$ $\frac{23}{5}$

Fact of the Day

The pearl is produced as an abnormal growth within the shells of some oysters, mussels, clams, and abalones. These mollusks have an inner layer of shell made of mother-of-pearl, or nacre. When a particle of foreign matter enters the shell, the mollusk coats it with nacre, turning it into a pearl. It may take three years or more to make a commercially valuable pearl.

—*Academic American Encyclopedia*

PH Multimedia Math Hot Page™ 7-7

Assignment Options

Core: 14, 16–18, 21, 22, 26, CH all, MR all	
Reinforce: 15, 19, 20, 23, 24	**Enrich:** 25

Reteaching Activity Have students construct a number line from 0 to 3, divided into fourths. Have students change the improper fractions $\frac{5}{4}$, $\frac{7}{4}$, and $\frac{11}{4}$ into mixed numbers and mark the numbers on the line. Have students meet in groups of four to compare answers.

Connections Have a discussion about how improper fractions and mixed numbers are used. You may want to start with these examples:

- **Household** (recipe measures, measurements for sewing or carpentry projects)
- **Travel** (mileage markers, measurements on maps)
- **Art** (mixtures for colors of paint, dimensions of canvases)

ON YOUR OWN

CONNECTION TO SCIENCE Exercise 14 has students identify mixed numbers in a scientific article. (Lao-tze is pronounced lou-dzuh.)

CONNECTION TO MEASUREMENT Exercise 25 has students use improper fractions to compare Celsius and Fahrenheit scales.

CHAPTER INVESTIGATION For Exercise 26, remind students to make sure their representations are equivalent.

CHECKPOINT

Exercises 11–14: Students are so used to giving answers as mixed numbers that they sometimes object to reversing the process. Tell them that the improper fraction form is more useful than the mixed number form if further calculations are to be done. For this reason, improper fractions are often used in algebra.

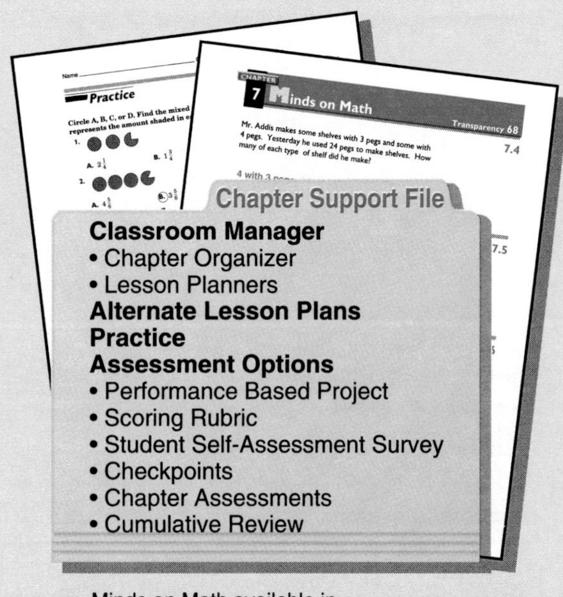

Practice
Minds on Math
Transparency 68
Chapter Support File
Classroom Manager
• Chapter Organizer
• Lesson Planners
Alternate Lesson Plans
Practice
Assessment Options
• Performance Based Project
• Scoring Rubric
• Student Self-Assessment Survey
• Checkpoints
• Chapter Assessments
• Cumulative Review

Minds on Math available in Teaching Transparencies

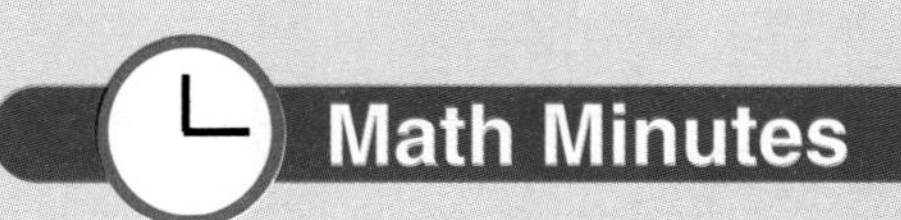

Evaluate: 48 ÷ (2 × 4) = ■
6

Gifts from the Sea

Pearls are the only gems that come from the sea. They are also the only gem that is made by a living thing—a clam. The largest pearl was found in the Philippines in 1934 in the shell of a giant clam. It was $9\frac{1}{2}$ in. long by $5\frac{1}{2}$ in. in diameter and weighed 14 lb 1 oz. This pearl is called The Pearl of Lao-tze and is valued at about $42 million.

ON YOUR OWN

14. Identify the mixed numbers in the article at the left. Write each mixed number as an improper fraction. $9\frac{1}{2}$, $5\frac{1}{2}$; $\frac{19}{2}$, $\frac{11}{2}$

15. Choose A, B, C, or D. What mixed number represents the amount shaded? B

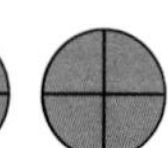

A. $4\frac{3}{4}$ B. $3\frac{3}{4}$

C. $3\frac{15}{16}$ D. $3\frac{1}{4}$

Write each improper fraction as a mixed number.

16. $\frac{17}{5}$ $3\frac{2}{5}$ 17. $\frac{13}{7}$ $1\frac{6}{7}$ 18. $\frac{27}{5}$ $5\frac{2}{5}$ 19. $\frac{37}{12}$ $3\frac{1}{12}$ 20. $\frac{53}{23}$ $2\frac{7}{23}$

Write each mixed number as an improper fraction.

21. $6\frac{3}{5}$ $\frac{33}{5}$ 22. $2\frac{7}{8}$ $\frac{23}{8}$ 23. $4\frac{1}{2}$ $\frac{9}{2}$ 24. $3\frac{1}{4}$ $\frac{13}{4}$

25. Data File 11 (pp. 446–447) What improper fraction is in the formula used to change from degrees Celsius to degrees Fahrenheit? Write the improper fraction as a mixed number. $\frac{9}{5}$; $1\frac{4}{5}$

26. Investigation (p. 274) The illustration shows five ways to represent visually the number 6. Choose any whole number other than 6 and list at least five ways to represent visually that number. Check student's work.

27. Writing Describe two situations in which you have used mixed numbers. Answers will vary.

3. 1,728 cm^3

Mixed REVIEW

Write in simplest form.

1. $\frac{45}{60}$ $\frac{3}{4}$ 2. $\frac{36}{64}$ $\frac{9}{16}$

Find the volume.

3. a cube with a side length equal to 12 cm See above.

4. a rectangular prism with a height of 10 cm and a base with an area of 18 cm^2 180 cm^3

5. Replace each ■ with +, −, ×, or ÷.
4 ■ 4 ■ 4 = 20
× + or + ×

CHECKPOINT

Write each fraction in simplest form.

1. $\frac{12}{16}$ $\frac{3}{4}$ 2. $\frac{64}{96}$ $\frac{2}{3}$ 3. $\frac{21}{27}$ $\frac{7}{9}$ 4. $\frac{9}{54}$ $\frac{1}{6}$ 5. $\frac{18}{36}$ $\frac{1}{2}$

Write each improper fraction as a mixed number.

6. $\frac{49}{5}$ $9\frac{4}{5}$ 7. $\frac{21}{8}$ $2\frac{5}{8}$ 8. $\frac{49}{6}$ $8\frac{1}{6}$ 9. $\frac{17}{4}$ $4\frac{1}{4}$ 10. $\frac{5}{2}$ $2\frac{1}{2}$

Write each mixed number as an improper fraction.

11. $5\frac{2}{3}$ $\frac{17}{3}$ 12. $12\frac{3}{4}$ $\frac{51}{4}$ 13. $8\frac{5}{6}$ $\frac{53}{6}$ 14. $10\frac{1}{2}$ $\frac{21}{2}$

7-8

Connecting to Prior Knowledge

Ask students to imagine that they are doctors who have prescribed two medicines for a patient to take: one every 4 h and one every 6 h. Ask students: *If the patient starts taking the medicines at midnight, when will she take both at the same time?* **(noon)** Have students share strategies.

THINK AND DISCUSS

ESL VISUAL LEARNERS Use a calendar when discussing the haircut problem to help students visualize the different periods of time between haircuts.

Error Alert! Students may confuse LCM with GCF for problems such as in the Example. ***Remediation*** Alert students to the danger of confusing the two acronyms, especially as both involve prime factorization. Have students use the full names instead of just saying the letters.

Example

Explain to students that the LCM contains every prime factor in the list (2, 3, and 5).

Additional Example *Find the LCM of 3, 10, and 25 .*
The LCM is 150.

Ongoing Assessment Give students the numbers 3, 6, and 10 and have them use a list of the multiples and prime factorization to find the LCM. Have students verify that each method results in the same answer. **(30)**

Journal Have students compare both methods for finding the LCM and tell which method they prefer and why they prefer that method.

MATH AND PLANNING

7-8 Least Common Multiple

What's Ahead

- Finding the least common multiple of two or three numbers

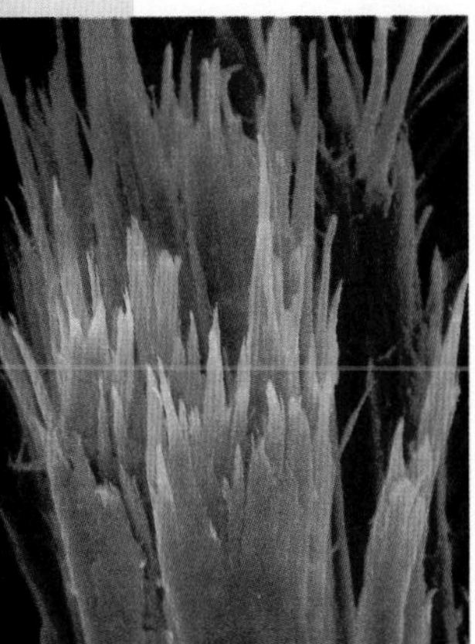

Under magnification, you can see the "split ends" of a human hair. Regular haircuts can prevent this from happening.

THINK AND DISCUSS

Pam and Teresa get their hair cut at the same place on Saturdays. Pam gets a haircut every six weeks, and Teresa gets a haircut every four weeks. One Saturday Pam sees Teresa getting a haircut.

Here's a list of Pam and Teresa's haircut schedules.

Pam, every 6 weeks: 6, 12, 18, 24, 30, 36, 42, 48, 54, ... weeks
Teresa, every 4 weeks: 4, 8, 12, 16, 20, 24, 28, 32, 36, ... weeks

In 18 weeks Pam will have had 3 haircuts. The number 18 is a *multiple* of 6. A **multiple** of a number is the product of that number and a nonzero whole number.

1. List the weeks that Pam and Teresa will get haircuts on the same day. 12, 24, 36

These numbers are multiples of both 6 and 4, so they are **common multiples.** The smallest common multiple of two or more numbers is the **least common multiple (LCM).** The LCM of 6 and 4 is 12.

You can also use the prime factorization of each number to find the LCM of the numbers.

Example Find the LCM of 15, 18, and 20.

- Write the prime factorizations.

$15 = 3 \times \textcircled{5}$
$18 = 2 \times \textcircled{3 \times 3}$
$20 = \textcircled{2 \times 2} \times 5$

Circle all the different factors where they appear the greatest number of times.

- Multiply the circled factors.

$2 \times 2 \times 3 \times 3 \times 5 = 180$

The LCM is 180.

> *"Brevity is the soul of wit."*
> —WILLIAM SHAKESPEARE

Organizer

1. **Focus**
   Connecting to Prior Knowledge
2. **Teach**
   Think and Discuss
3. **Closure**
   Try These
   Wrap Up

Vocabulary/Symbols
multiple
common multiples
least common multiple, LCM

Skills Reviewed in Context of Lesson
- finding multiples
- using prime factorization

Student Resources
Extra Practice
Student Study Guide
Practice, TR Ch. 7, p. 32
Student Study Guide, Spanish Resources, TR
Alternate Lesson, TR Ch. 7, pp. 21–24

continues next page

TRY THESE

WRITING Have students describe both methods in their answers to Exercise 2c.

Wrap Up

What's the Big Idea? Ask students: *How do you find the least common multiple of two or more numbers?*

Connections Have a discussion about how least common multiples are used. You may want to start with these examples:

- **Travel** (coordinating bus, train, or ferry departures and arrivals)
- **Business** (making schedules for part-time employees)

Reteaching Activity Have students draw a line on the chalkboard showing 0 to 50. Tell them to imagine that three frogs with different sized leaps but the same speed are racing down a track. One leaps 3 ft at a time, one 4 ft, and the other 6 ft. Have students mark the number line where all three frogs will land together. **(12 ft, 24 ft, 36 ft, 48 ft)** Have students check their answers by listing multiples and using prime factorization.

ON YOUR OWN

CRITICAL THINKING For Exercise 10, have students show all steps in their solutions.

WRITING For Exercise 12d, have students write their descriptions as rules.

CONNECTION TO PATTERNS Exercise 12 has students evaluate a pattern to find a relationship between two numbers' LCM and GCF.

Organizer, continued

Teacher Resources

 Teaching Transparency 69
Lesson Planner, TR Ch. 7, p. 9

Prentice Hall Technology
Computer Item Generator
- 7-8

Other Available Technology
- calculator

Fact of the Day

The tallest roller coaster in the world is the *Moonsault Scramble* at the Fujikyu Highland Park near Kawaguchi Lake, Japan. It is 206.7 ft tall.

—GUINNESS BOOK OF RECORDS

Assignment Options

Core: 4–9, MR all	
Reinforce: 10, 11, 13	**Enrich:** 12

Mixed REVIEW

Change to a whole or a mixed number.

1. $\frac{15}{6}$ $2\frac{1}{2}$
2. $\frac{63}{8}$ $7\frac{7}{8}$
3. $\frac{27}{4}$ $6\frac{3}{4}$
4. $\frac{42}{3}$ 14

Find the area and perimeter. See below.

5. 4.8 cm by 2.4 cm rectangle
6. 15 m by 15 m square — A = 225 m^2, P = 60 m

7. Mugsy is tied with a 20-ft-long rope to a stake in the ground. Draw a diagram and find the approximate area of the dog's play space.

about 1,256 ft^2

5. A = 11.52 cm^2 P = 14.4 cm

TRY THESE

a. and b. See Solution Key. The LCM is 600.

2. a. List the multiples of each number to find the LCM of 30, 40, and 50.
   b. Use prime factorization to find the LCM of 30, 40, and 50.
   c. Writing Which method do you think is more efficient? Explain your choice. Sample: use prime factorization because there are fewer calculations to make.
3. I lift weights every third day and swim every fourth day. I did both this morning. When will be the next time I do both exercise activities? in 12 days

ON YOUR OWN

Find the LCM of each set of numbers.

4. 75, 100 300
5. 22, 55, 60 660
6. 4, 12 12
7. 12, 20 60
8. 5, 6, 10 30
9. 14, 33 462

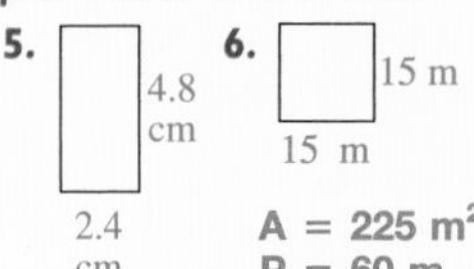

GREAT EXPECTATIONS

Amusement Park Designer

I want to be an amusement park designer. This career interests me because I like to make things and I have good ideas to make things. I want to learn more about this because it uses math and I'm good at math. If I do become an amusement park designer it would be fun. My interest started in this when I first rode on a roller coaster and tried to find another ride I would like. I couldn't find one, so I said to myself that if I become someone who makes rides, I can make rides that I like. There was one time when I went to a park and I wanted a ride that was fast and would get me wet. I got wet on it, but it wasn't fast enough. I make models, which would help me learn how to build models of the parks before they were made.

Stephen Horel

298

Great Expectations

DIVERSITY In the Great Expectations section, both the student and engineer are male. Be aware that there is a subtle cultural assignment of gender roles in the United States that has traditionally tended to exclude females from careers involving math and science. Avoid expecting females, minority, or disadvantaged students to have lower math abilities than males.

There are many valuable resources available to students for gathering information about amusement park design. The following lists places to write for more information.

- Paramount Parks
  Design and Entertainment
  8720 Red Oak Blvd. Suite 315
  Charlotte, NC 28217
- International Association of Amusement Parks and Attractions (IAAPA)
  1448 Duke Street
  Alexandria, VA 22314
  1-703-836-4800

Students can also learn from discussions with experts. Here are some possible sources.

- Invite any of the 3,500 members of IAAPA to speak in class.
- Visit the administrative offices of an amusement park to see the "behind the scenes" designers and their computers.

Encourage students to ask questions about the skills necessary for a career as an amusement park designer, including these topics.

- The training necessary to qualify as an amusement park designer, including course work and college degrees associated with design
- How math is used on the job (waiting time of rides, speed of roller coasters, stress design)

10. Critical Thinking A number has both 8 and 10 as factors.

a. What is the smallest the number could be? 40

b. Name four other factors of the number.
Sample: 1, 2, 4, 5, 20, or 40.

11. Travel Two ships sail back and forth between Boston and London. One ship makes a round trip in 12 days. The other ship makes a round trip in 16 days. They are both in London today. In how many days will both ships be in London again? in 48 days

In the early 1500s a sea voyage from North America to Europe took an average of three to four months.

12. For each pair of numbers, find the GCF, the LCM, the product of the two numbers, and the product of the GCF and LCM.

a. 12 and 18 6; 36; 216; 216
b. 20 and 25 5; 100; 500; 500
c. 24 and 28 4; 168; 672; 672

d. Writing Look over your results. Describe the pattern.
The product of the two numbers equals the product of GCF and LCM.

13. **Choose A, B, C, or D.** The LCM of a number and 15 is 120. What is the number? D

A. 20 B. 12 C. 6 D. 24

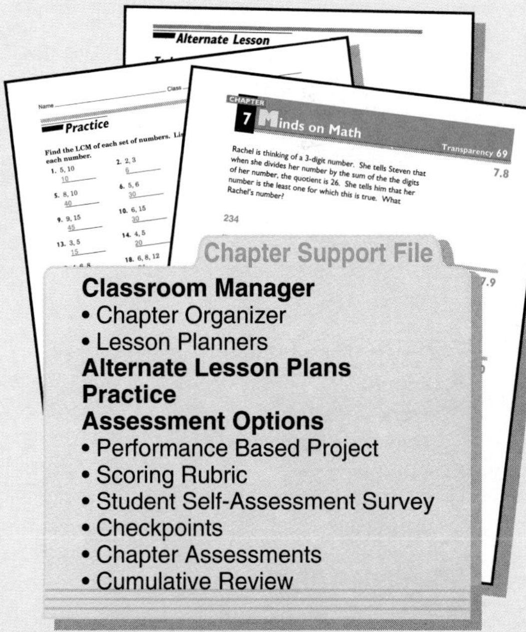

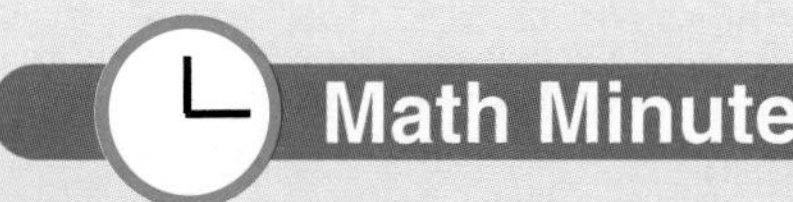

Chapter Support File

Classroom Manager
- Chapter Organizer
- Lesson Planners

Alternate Lesson Plans
Practice
Assessment Options
- Performance Based Project
- Scoring Rubric
- Student Self-Assessment Survey
- Checkpoints
- Chapter Assessments
- Cumulative Review

Minds on Math available in Teaching Transparencies

Dear Stephen,

Yes, it certainly is fun developing theme park attractions. When I help design a new ride, it is surprising how much math and physics I use. I think of ratio and capacity when I try to figure out how fast the ride will go and how many people should be on it at one time. Most roller coaster attractions run two trains with an average of 32 seats on each train. Each ride takes approximately two minutes. We allow one minute to load guests and one minute to unload them. We call this a cycle of four minutes. If thirty-two guests ride every cycle, in one hour with two trains leaving the station every two minutes, there are thirty cycles. Now we see that our roller coaster has a capacity of 960 guests per hour.

Hugh Darley
Design and Entertainment, Paramount Parks

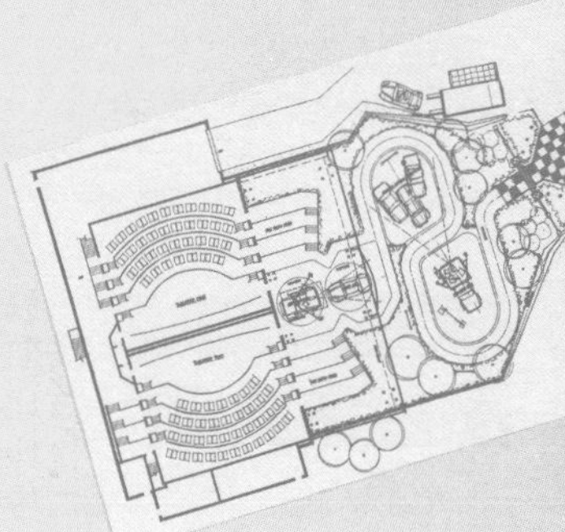

Math Minutes

Find three numbers whose sum is 14 and whose product is 54.
2, 3, 9

Materials for 7-9

- fraction bars

7-9

Connecting to Prior Knowledge

Have students recall how to determine whether a fraction is close to 0, $\frac{1}{2}$, or 1. Ask students how they can compare the values of the fractions so they order a set of fractions.

WORK TOGETHER

Have students work in groups of three or four. Students in each group can take turns lining up the fraction bars for comparison.

VISUAL LEARNERS Make sure students use fraction bars in Question 1 to compare the fractions, because the difference between the fractions, when seen on the bars, is striking.

ESL **AUDITORY LEARNERS** Have students state the answers to Question 1 in terms of greater than, less than, or equal to, so that they properly associate the symbols (>, <, =) with their corresponding meanings.

THINK AND DISCUSS

Example 1

Point out that when you compare fractions, sometimes it is necessary to find equivalent fractions with a common denominator.

Additional Example *Compare $\frac{3}{4}$ and $\frac{5}{6}$.*

$$\frac{3}{4} = \frac{3}{4} \times \frac{3}{3} = \frac{9}{12} \qquad \frac{5}{6} = \frac{5}{6} \times \frac{2}{2} = \frac{10}{12}$$

Compare the numerators.

$$9 < 10$$

Since $\frac{9}{12} < \frac{10}{12}$, then $\frac{3}{4} < \frac{5}{6}$.

" . . . we will be victorious if we have not forgotten how to learn. "

—Rosa Luxemburg

Organizer

1. **Focus**
   Connecting to Prior Knowledge
2. **Teach**
   Work Together
   Think and Discuss
3. **Closure**
   Try These
   Wrap Up

Vocabulary/Symbols
common denominator
least common denominator, LCD

Skills Reviewed in Context of Lesson
- using equivalent fractions
- using LCM

Materials and Manipulatives
- fraction bars (1 set for each group)

Student Resources
Extra Practice
Student Study Guide
Practice, TR Ch. 7, p. 33
Student Study Guide, Spanish Resources, TR

Teacher Resources
Teaching Transparencies 23–29, 69
Transparency Masters, TR, pp. 21–24
Overhead Manipulatives: fraction bars
Lesson Planner, TR Ch. 7, p. 10

continues next page

What's Ahead
- Comparing and ordering fractions

7-9 Comparing and Ordering Fractions

WHAT YOU'LL NEED
✓ Fraction bars 

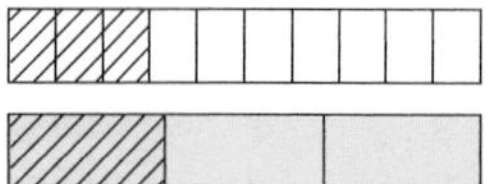

WORK TOGETHER

Work in groups. Use fraction bars to compare each pair of fractions. First, find the appropriate bars. Then, line up the left edges of the two fraction bars and compare the shaded regions. The fraction bars at the left show that $\frac{3}{10} < \frac{1}{3}$.

1. Compare using $<$, $>$, or $=$.

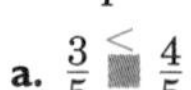

a. $\frac{3}{5}$ ■ $\frac{4}{5}$ $<$ b. $\frac{3}{4}$ ■ $\frac{3}{5}$ $>$ c. $\frac{3}{12}$ ■ $\frac{1}{4}$ $=$
d. $\frac{9}{10}$ ■ $\frac{7}{10}$ $>$ e. $\frac{1}{4}$ ■ $\frac{2}{5}$ $<$ f. $\frac{2}{3}$ ■ $\frac{8}{12}$ $=$
g. $\frac{2}{6}$ ■ $\frac{4}{12}$ $=$ h. $\frac{7}{10}$ ■ $\frac{3}{5}$ $>$ i. $\frac{1}{3}$ ■ $\frac{2}{5}$ $<$

THINK AND DISCUSS

You used fraction bars to *compare* fractions. You can also use fraction bars to *order* fractions.

2. Use fraction bars to order each set of fractions from least to greatest.

a. $\frac{7}{10}, \frac{1}{10}, \frac{3}{10}$ $\frac{1}{10}, \frac{3}{10}, \frac{7}{10}$ b. $\frac{3}{4}, \frac{3}{5}, \frac{3}{10}, \frac{3}{12}$ $\frac{3}{12}, \frac{3}{10}, \frac{3}{5}, \frac{3}{4}$

c. How are the fractions in part (a) alike? Without using fraction bars, how can you tell which fraction is the greatest? See left.

d. How are the fractions in part (b) alike? Without using fraction bars, how can you tell which fraction is the greatest? They all have the same numerator. The one with the smallest denominator is greatest.

2c. They all have the same denominator; the fraction with the greatest numerator is greatest.

It is easy to compare fractions with the same denominator. The parts of the whole are the same size, so the fraction with the larger numerator is greater. For example, $\frac{5}{6} > \frac{4}{6}$ because the numerator $5 > 4$. The fraction bars at the left confirm this result.

Ongoing Assessment Make sure students understand the procedure for comparing fractions. Divide the class into groups of four students to draw up a list of steps for the procedure. Emphasize clarity and thoroughness of the directions. Have the groups compare and evaluate each other's lists.

Example 2

Emphasize to students that the procedure for ordering fractions is really no different from that for comparing fractions. Only the last step of ordering is added.

- *How would the answer appear if the example directions indicated to order the fractions from greatest to least?* ($\frac{2}{5} > \frac{3}{8} > \frac{7}{20}$)

Journal Have students evaluate different cases of ordering fractions. Ask students if ordering improper fractions and mixed numbers, for example, is more difficult than ordering fractions. Have students describe ways they overcome their difficulties.

Additional Example *Order from least to greatest:* $\frac{2}{7}, \frac{1}{5}, \frac{3}{10}$.

The LCM of 7, 5, and 10 is 70. The LCD is 70.

Write the fractions using the LCD.

$\frac{2}{7} = \frac{20}{70}$ $\quad \frac{1}{5} = \frac{14}{70}$ $\quad \frac{3}{10} = \frac{21}{70}$

Put the numerators in order: 14 < 20 < 21

Since $\frac{14}{70} < \frac{20}{70} < \frac{21}{70}$, **then** $\frac{1}{5} < \frac{2}{7} < \frac{3}{10}$.

Error Alert! For a problem such as Question 4, students may make a mental error and write something incorrect such as $\frac{4}{14} = \frac{16}{42}$. ***Remediation*** Encourage students to list each step in a solution. If students do use mental math, advise them to make notes such as jotting down the multiplier next to both denominator and numerator when finding an equivalent fraction.

Suppose you want to compare two fractions with different denominators. You can use equivalent fractions to find a *common denominator* of the two fractions. A common denominator must be a multiple of each of the original denominators. The **least common denominator (LCD)** is the least common multiple (LCM) of the original denominators.

FLASHBACK

To write equivalent fractions, multiply the numerator and the denominator by the same nonzero factor.

Example 1 Compare $\frac{7}{24}$ and $\frac{5}{18}$. Use <, >, or =.

- The LCM of 24 and 18 is 72. So the LCD is 72.
- Write equivalent fractions using the LCD.

  $\frac{7}{24} = \frac{7}{24} \times \frac{3}{3} = \frac{21}{72}$ $\quad \frac{5}{18} = \frac{5}{18} \times \frac{4}{4} = \frac{20}{72}$
- Compare the numerators.

  $21 > 20$

  Since $\frac{21}{72} > \frac{20}{72}$, then $\frac{7}{24} > \frac{5}{18}$.

When comparing mixed numbers, first compare the quantity of each whole number. Decide which number is greater. If the whole number part of each mixed number is the same, then compare the fraction part of each number as in Example 1.

3. Compare using <, >, or =.

a. $3\frac{2}{5}$ ■ $2\frac{4}{5}$ > **b.** $1\frac{2}{3}$ ■ $1\frac{5}{9}$ > **c.** $5\frac{7}{8}$ ■ $6\frac{5}{6}$ <

d. $2\frac{4}{7}$ ■ $2\frac{12}{21}$ = **e.** $4\frac{2}{5}$ ■ $4\frac{3}{7}$ < **f.** $3\frac{8}{12}$ ■ $3\frac{3}{4}$ <

To order three or more fractions, find the LCD. Use the LCD to write equivalent fractions. Then order the numerators.

Example 2 Order from least to greatest: $\frac{3}{8}, \frac{2}{5}, \frac{7}{20}$.

- The LCM of 8, 5, and 20 is 40. So the LCD is 40.
- Write equivalent fractions using the LCD.

  $\frac{3}{8} = \frac{15}{40}$ $\quad \frac{2}{5} = \frac{16}{40}$ $\quad \frac{7}{20} = \frac{14}{40}$
- Put the numerators in order.

  $14 < 15 < 16$

  Since $\frac{14}{40} < \frac{15}{40} < \frac{16}{40}$, then $\frac{7}{20} < \frac{3}{8} < \frac{2}{5}$.

4. Order from least to greatest: $\frac{2}{6}, \frac{8}{21}, \frac{4}{14}$.
$\frac{4}{14}, \frac{2}{6}, \frac{8}{21}$

***Musical notes** are based on fractions of a whole note.* **Order these notes from least to greatest.**
$\frac{1}{16}, \frac{1}{8}, \frac{1}{4}, \frac{1}{2}$

Organizer, continued

Prentice Hall Technology

Multimedia Math
- Math Tools, Fraction Strips
- Hot Page™ 7-9
- Math Investigations, Hazard City Messengers

Computer Item Generator
- 7-9

Other Available Technology

Fraction Practice Unlimited by Computer Software: Questions 5–11 *(optional)*

Fact of the Day

Our present system of musical notation dates from the 17th century. It is based on the duple division of each successive note—one whole note equals two half notes which equals four quarter notes, and so on.

—*Academic American Encyclopedia*

PH Multimedia Math Hot Page™ 7-9

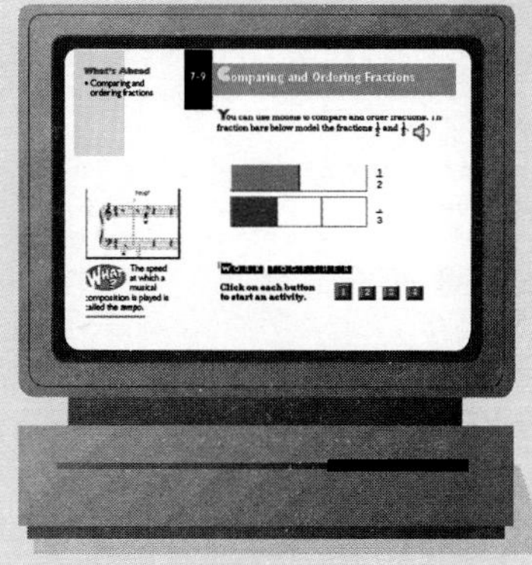

TRY THESE

TECHNOLOGY OPTION For Exercises 5–11, students can review ordering and comparing of fractions by using fraction software programs.

Exercise 12: Encourage students to list the ingredients from least to greatest before answering the questions.

Wrap Up

What's the Big Idea? Ask students: *How do you compare and order fractions?*

Connections Have a discussion about how ordering fractions is used. You may want to start with the following example:

- **Geography** (comparing distances on a map)

Reteaching Activity Bring a map to class. Have students measure distances between cities with a ruler and describe the distances by using fractions and improper fractions to describe the ruler measurements. Then challenge the students to order the fractions from least to greatest. Have students compare answers and compare the distances.

ON YOUR OWN

WRITING Have students support their answers to Exercise 22b with descriptions of each procedure.

Assignment Options

Core: 13–20, MR all	
Reinforce: 21, 23	**Enrich:** 22

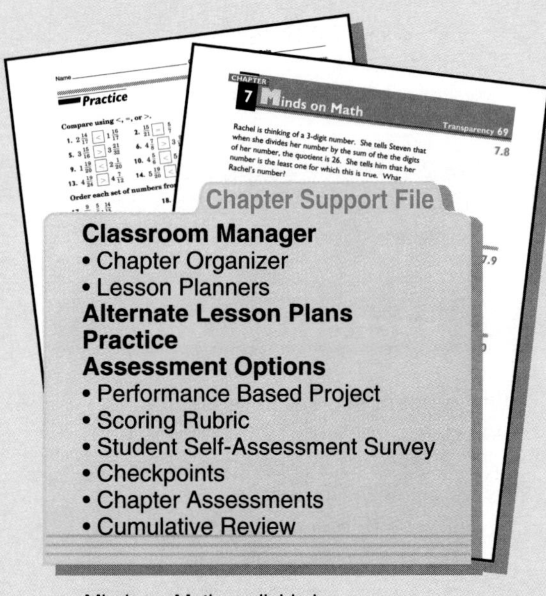

Minds on Math available in Teaching Transparencies

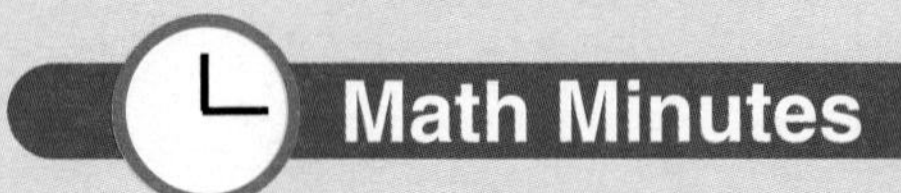

What will be in the 23rd position in this pattern?

■●▲+▲■●▲+▲■

Answer: ▲

Materials for 7-10

- calculator
- decimal squares

TRY THESE

Compare using <, >, or =.

5. $2\frac{11}{19}$ ■ $1\frac{13}{19}$ >
6. $\frac{13}{20}$ ■ $\frac{1}{4}$ >
7. $\frac{9}{24}$ ■ $\frac{3}{8}$ =
8. $\frac{15}{17}$ ■ $\frac{9}{10}$ <

Order each set of fractions from least to greatest.

9. $\frac{11}{24}, \frac{5}{8}, \frac{5}{12}$ $\frac{5}{12}, \frac{11}{24}, \frac{5}{8}$
10. $\frac{11}{15}, \frac{2}{3}, \frac{7}{12}$ $\frac{7}{12}, \frac{2}{3}, \frac{11}{15}$
11. $\frac{5}{7}, \frac{11}{14}, \frac{3}{4}$ $\frac{5}{7}, \frac{3}{4}, \frac{1}{1}$

Torta Garfagnana
1/2 cup sweet almonds
2 2/3 cups flour
1 teaspoon baking soda
3/4 cup butter
1 tablespoon aniseed
2/3 cup milk

12. **Cooking** Compare the recipe amounts for sweet almonds, butter, and milk. Which is the greatest? the least? butter; sweet almonds

ON YOUR OWN

Compare using <, >, or =.

13. $5\frac{4}{7}$ ■ $5\frac{5}{7}$ <
14. $\frac{3}{11}$ ■ $\frac{1}{4}$ >
15. $3\frac{1}{4}$ ■ $3\frac{1}{5}$ >
16. $\frac{2}{9}$ ■ $\frac{4}{15}$ <

17. Timothy ran $1\frac{3}{4}$ mi. Wenona ran $1\frac{7}{10}$ mi. Who ran farther? Timothy

Order each set of numbers from least to greatest. See left.

18. $\frac{1}{5}, \frac{1}{8}, \frac{7}{40}, \frac{3}{10}$
19. $\frac{7}{12}, \frac{23}{40}, \frac{8}{15}, \frac{19}{30}$
20. $1\frac{8}{11}, 2\frac{1}{4}, 1\frac{3}{4}$

18. $\frac{1}{8}, \frac{7}{40}, \frac{1}{5}, \frac{3}{10}$
19. $\frac{8}{15}, \frac{23}{40}, \frac{7}{12}, \frac{19}{30}$
20. $1\frac{8}{11}, 1\frac{3}{4}, 2\frac{1}{4}$

21. **Data File 8 (pp. 316–317)** Order the Women's Olympic Long Jump Winners from least to greatest distance. See Solution Key.
22. Tell whether each fraction is greater than, less than, or equal to $\frac{1}{2}$.

    a. $\frac{3}{5}$ > b. $\frac{5}{12}$ < c. $\frac{5}{8}$ > d. $\frac{2}{3}$ >

    e. **Writing** How can you use your results to compare $\frac{3}{5}$ and $\frac{5}{12}$? Is it possible to use the results above to compare $\frac{3}{5}$ and $\frac{5}{8}$? Why or why not? See Solution Key.
23. **Choose A, B, C, or D.** To compare $\frac{9}{24}$ and $\frac{5}{15}$, which would you do first and why? B; smaller numbers are easier to work with.

    A. Find the LCM of 24 and 15.

    B. Simplify each fraction.

    C. Find the prime factorization of 24 and 15.

    D. Multiply 24 × 15 to find a common denominator.

Mixed REVIEW

Find the LCM of each set of numbers.

1. 8, 12, 6 24
2. 5, 6, 15 30
3. 9, 15, 18 90
4. 36, 40 360

Use the distributive property to simplify.

5. 7(100 − 2) 686
6. 8(50 + 3) 424
7. What is the quotient of the circumference of a circle divided by its diameter? π

7-10

Connecting to Prior Knowledge

Ask students if they know of any other ways of expressing numbers less than 1. Have students consider their experience with money. Ask students to describe ways in which 50 cents can be written as part of a dollar. **($.50)** Ask students to express the decimal as a fraction. **($\frac{1}{2}$ or "half dollar")**

WORK TOGETHER

Provide each pair of students with decimal squares. Have students compare their answers to Question 3.

KINESTHETIC LEARNERS Read a decimal aloud to the class and select a student to go to the chalkboard to write it as a fraction. Then select another student to go to the chalkboard to write it as a decimal.

THINK AND DISCUSS

ESL **AUDITORY LEARNERS** Have the students read decimals aloud so that they understand 0.25 is "twenty-five hundredths" as well as "point two five." Have students work with partners and take turns dictating, writing, and reading decimals.

Example 1

Have students explain how to find the GCF of 225 and 1,000. **(list the factors or use a factor tree)**

Additional Example *Write 0.55 as a fraction in simplest form.*

$$0.55 = \frac{55}{100}$$
$$= \frac{55 \div 5}{100 \div 5} = \frac{11}{20}$$
$$0.55 = \frac{11}{20}$$

What's Ahead

- Modeling fractions and decimals
- Writing decimals as fractions
- Writing fractions as decimals

WHAT YOU'LL NEED

✓ Calculator

✓ Decimal squares

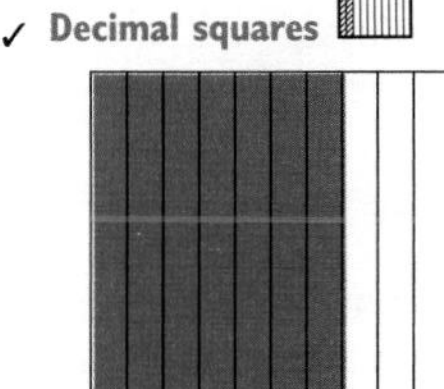

3a. Answers may vary. Sample:
1. Say the decimal.
2. Write the fraction from what you said.
3. Reduce.

7-10 Fractions and Decimals

WORK TOGETHER

Work with a partner.

1. a. What decimal does the model at the left represent? 0.7
   b. Say the decimal out loud. "seven tenths"
   c. Have your partner write the decimal as a fraction. $\frac{7}{10}$
   d. Complete this statement using the decimal and the fraction: ■ = ■. $0.7 = \frac{7}{10}$
2. a. Find a decimal square that models 0.05.
   b. Have your partner read the decimal out loud. "five hundredths"
   c. Write the decimal as a fraction. $\frac{5}{100}$
   d. Simplify the fraction. Complete this statement using the fraction and the decimal: ■ = ■. $\frac{1}{20}$; $0.05 = \frac{1}{20}$
3. a. **Discussion** List the steps you need to follow to write a decimal as a fraction. See left.
   b. Do you need to use a model? Give an example to support your answer. No; write the fraction as you would say the decimal. Example: 0.25 is said, "twenty-five hundredths" so write $\frac{25}{100}$ which equals $\frac{1}{4}$.

THINK AND DISCUSS

To express a decimal as a fraction, write the fraction as you would say the decimal. Then simplify the fraction.

FLASHBACK
You read 0.225 as "two hundred twenty-five thousandths."

Example 1 Write 0.225 as a fraction in simplest form.

$$0.225 = \frac{225}{1000}$$
$$= \frac{225 \div 25}{1000 \div 25}$$ Simplify. The GCF of 225 and 1000 is 25.
$$0.225 = \frac{9}{40}$$

4. Write each decimal as a fraction in simplest form.
   a. 0.6 $\frac{3}{5}$ b. 0.35 $\frac{7}{20}$ c. 0.130 $\frac{13}{100}$

"Many little leaks may sink a ship."
—THOMAS FULLER

Organizer

1. **Focus**
   Connecting to Prior Knowledge
2. **Teach**
   Work Together
   Think and Discuss
3. **Closure**
   Try These
   Wrap Up

Vocabulary/Symbols
terminating decimal
repeating decimal

Skills Reviewed in Context of Lesson
- modeling decimals
- dividing whole numbers and decimals

Materials and Manipulatives
- calculator (1 for each group)
- decimal squares (1 set for each group)

On Your Own Exercise 33: calculator

Student Resources
Extra Practice
Student Study Guide
Practice, TR Ch. 7, p. 34
Student Study Guide, Spanish Resources, TR
Checkpoint, TR Ch. 7, p. 40

continues next page

Error Alert! For problems such as the one in Example 1, students may have difficulty expressing a decimal as a fraction. ***Remediation*** Point out to students that decimals are easily converted into fractions. One needs only to set the number as a numerator over its place value. For example, 0.35 is 35 placed over $\frac{1}{100}$, or $\frac{35}{100}$. Encourage students to read each decimal aloud ("thirty-five hundredths") to help them convert the decimals into fractions.

Ongoing Assessment Make sure students are correctly reading decimals. Have each student read a decimal aloud and then convert it to a fraction. Write the decimals on the chalkboard for students to read.

Example 2

Have students note that the whole number is kept unchanged while the fraction part is simplified.

Additional Example *Write 2.8 as a mixed number in simplest form.*

$2.8 = 2\frac{8}{10} = 2\frac{8 \div 2}{10 \div 2} = 2\frac{4}{5}$

Example 3

Point out to students the position of the decimal point in the dividend and in the quotient. Be sure students understand why zeros can be annexed to the dividend without changing values.

Additional Example *Write the fraction $\frac{1}{6}$ as a decimal.*

$\frac{1}{6} \rightarrow 6\overline{)1.000}$ with quotient .166. The digit 6 repeats. $\frac{1}{6} = 0.1\overline{6}$

TRY THESE

Exercise 8: Have students draw their decimal squares on graph paper and label the amount shown.

Organizer, continued

Teacher Resources

Teaching Transparencies 11, 12, 19, 69
Transparency Masters, TR p. 20
Overhead Manipulatives: decimal squares,
Lesson Planner, TR Ch. 7, p. 11

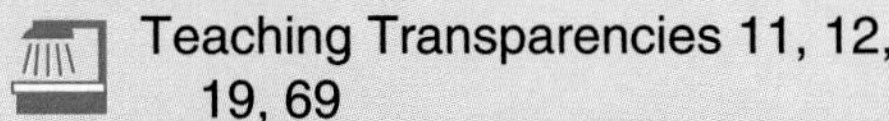

Prentice Hall Technology

Multimedia Math
- Math Tools, Manipulatives

Computer Item Generator
- 7-10

Other Available Technology

Excel; Works by Microsoft: Questions 9–16 *(optional)*

Fact of the Day

The three main components of the Space Shuttle are the orbiter, the external tank, and the solid rocket boosters. The Shuttle weighs 4.5 million lb (2.0 million kg) at launch, and is 184.2 ft (56.1 m) tall. It can carry up to 65,000 lb (29,500 kg) of cargo on one mission.

—*Academic American Encyclopedia*

If a decimal is greater than one, it can be written as a mixed number.

Example 2 Write 1.32 as a fraction in simplest form.

$1.32 = 1\frac{32}{100}$ — Keep the whole number 1.

$= 1\frac{32 \div 4}{100 \div 4}$ — Simplify. The GCF of 32 and 100 is 4.

$1.32 = 1\frac{8}{25}$

One way to express a fraction as a decimal is to divide the numerator by the denominator. The fraction symbol itself means division. For example, here's how to write $\frac{3}{4}$ as a decimal using a calculator.

3 ÷ 4 = 0.75 ← $\frac{3}{4} = 0.75$

If there is no remainder, the quotient is a **terminating decimal.** Sometimes the quotient does have a remainder. A quotient that repeats digits and does not end is a **repeating decimal.** The number 0.4444 . . . is an example of a repeating decimal. You write the decimal as $0.\overline{4}$. The bar over the 4 means that the digit 4 repeats.

FLASHBACK Annex zeros to the dividend.

Example 3 Write the fraction $\frac{4}{15}$ as a decimal.

$$\frac{4}{15} \rightarrow \begin{array}{r} 0.266 \\ 15\overline{)4.000} \\ -\ 3\,0 \\ \hline 100 \\ -\ 90 \\ \hline 100 \\ -\ 90 \\ \hline 1 \end{array}$$

The digit 6 repeats.

$\frac{4}{15} = 0.2\overline{6}$

You can show repeating decimals using a calculator.

Example 4 Write the fraction $\frac{8}{11}$ as a decimal.

- Divide the numerator by the denominator.

  8 ÷ 11 = 0.72727727

- Notice which digits repeat: 72.
- Write the decimal using a bar over these digits.

  $\frac{8}{11} = 0.\overline{72}$

TECHNOLOGY OPTION For Exercises 9–16, students can use spreadsheet software to rewrite fractions as decimals. Using separate columns for the numerator and the denominator, students will be able to divide one cell (numerator) by another cell (denominator).

Wrap Up

What's the Big Idea? Ask students to describe how to model fractions and decimals. Then have students explain how decimals are written as fractions and how fractions are written as decimals.

Journal Ask students which form they use most often outside the classroom, fractions or decimals. Have them support their choice with examples.

Connections Have a discussion about how fractions and decimals are used. You may want to start with these examples:

- **Graphs** (expressing a fraction of a budget circle graph as a precise amount of money)
- **Construction** (using different sizes of lumber at different prices)

Reteaching Activity Group students in pairs or in small groups. Have one student in each pair or group use decimal squares and one student use fraction bars to model the following amounts: 0.3, 0.25, and 0.6. Have students in each pair compare models and describe the similarities and the differences. Discuss the results with the class.

ON YOUR OWN

CHAPTER INVESTIGATION For Exercise 32, ask students whether it is necessary to represent the number in two different ways.

Assignment Options

Core: 17–24, 31, 32, 34, 35a, MR all, CH all	
Reinforce: 25–29	**Enrich:** 30, 33, 35b

5. Write each fraction as a decimal. Use a bar to show repeating decimals.
   a. $\frac{5}{9}$ $0.\overline{5}$ b. $\frac{2}{3}$ $0.\overline{6}$ c. $\frac{5}{11}$ $0.\overline{45}$
6. a. How would you write $\frac{1}{3}$ as a decimal? $0.\overline{3}$
   b. How would you write 2 as a decimal? 2.0
   c. How can you use your results from parts (a) and (b) to write $2\frac{1}{3}$ as a decimal? Explain. Add them, $2.\overline{3}$; $2 + \frac{1}{3} = 2\frac{1}{3}$ so, $2 + 0.\overline{3} = 2.\overline{3}$.

TRY THESE

7. a. What decimal does the model at the right represent? 0.80 or 0.8
   b. Write this number as a fraction in simplest form. $\frac{4}{5}$
8. a. Draw a decimal square to show 0.68. See Solution Key.
   b. Write 0.68 as a fraction in simplest form. $\frac{17}{25}$

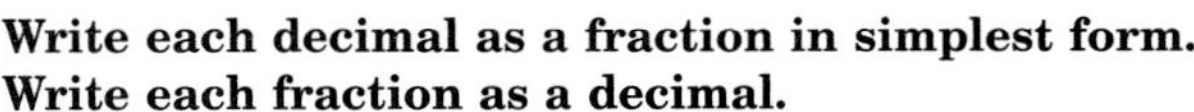

Write each decimal as a fraction in simplest form. Write each fraction as a decimal.

9. 0.3 $\frac{3}{10}$ 10. $\frac{9}{20}$ 0.45 11. $\frac{11}{8}$ 1.375 12. 0.004 $\frac{1}{250}$
13. 2.625 $2\frac{5}{8}$ 14. $\frac{5}{6}$ $0.8\overline{3}$ 15. 0.075 $\frac{3}{40}$ 16. $\frac{5}{12}$ $0.41\overline{6}$

ON YOUR OWN

Write each decimal as a fraction in simplest form. Write each fraction as a decimal.

17. 0.565 $\frac{113}{200}$ 18. 1.62 $1\frac{31}{50}$ 19. 0.07 $\frac{7}{100}$ 20. 0.064 $\frac{8}{125}$
21. $1\frac{1}{9}$ $1.\overline{1}$ 22. $\frac{14}{25}$ 0.56 23. $\frac{7}{15}$ $0.4\overline{6}$ 24. $4\frac{7}{10}$ 4.7
25. $\frac{5}{24}$ $0.208\overline{3}$ 26. $\frac{7}{16}$ 0.4375 27. $3\frac{4}{11}$ $3.\overline{36}$ 28. $\frac{7}{20}$ 0.35

29. **Shopping** Pallaton took the bus to the grocery store to buy sliced turkey to make sandwiches for his school lunches. He orders a quarter pound ($\frac{1}{4}$ lb) of turkey at the delicatessen. What decimal should Pallaton see on the digital scale? 0.25

In the space shuttle a typical lunch is corned beef with asparagus, strawberries, and an almond crunch bar.

Source: *How in the World?*

CALCULATOR Encourage students to check their calculations for Exercise 33.

WRITING For Exercises 35a and 35b, encourage students to number the steps as they explain how they would simplify the fraction and write the fraction as a decimal.

CHECKPOINT

Exercise 12 is an example of an enhanced multiple choice question.

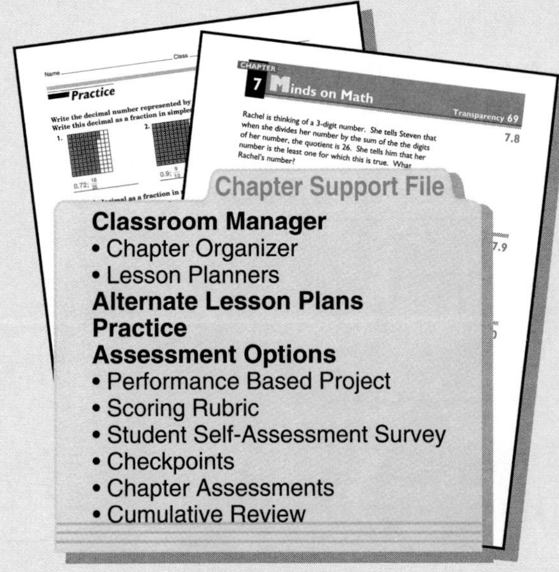

Chapter Support File

Classroom Manager
- Chapter Organizer
- Lesson Planners

Alternate Lesson Plans
Practice
Assessment Options
- Performance Based Project
- Scoring Rubric
- Student Self-Assessment Survey
- Checkpoints
- Chapter Assessments
- Cumulative Review

Minds on Math available in Teaching Transparencies

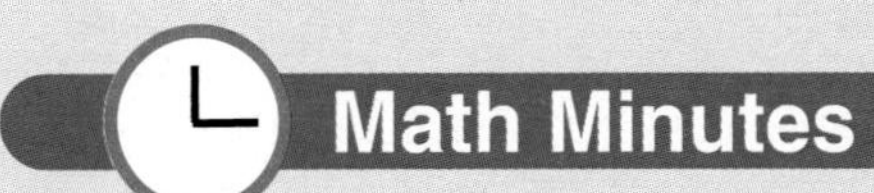

Math Minutes

The sum of two whole numbers each rounded to the nearest ten is 100. One number rounds to 80. What are the two largest whole numbers that will meet these conditions?

84, 24

30. $\frac{9}{12} = \frac{3}{4}$, 0.75

31. $\frac{55}{100} = \frac{11}{20}$

30. Data File 7 (pp. 272–273) It's been four hours since low tide. Find the range of tide as a fraction and a decimal.

31. Channa has \$1 to spend. She buys a package of sunflower seeds for \$.55. What fraction of her money did she spend?

32. Investigation (p. 274) Use your personal numeration system to write a number as a fraction and a decimal. Answers may vary.

33. a. Calculator Write each fraction as a decimal: $\frac{17}{50}$, $\frac{1}{3}$, $\frac{8}{25}$, $\frac{26}{75}$. 0.34, $0.\overline{3}$, 0.32, $0.34\overline{6}$

b. Arrange the fractions in order from least to greatest. See below.

c. Would you prefer to use equivalent fractions with a common denominator to order the numbers in part (a)? Why or why not? Sample: No; it would involve more computation to use equivalent fractions.

34. Order each set of numbers from least to greatest.

a. $\frac{7}{8}$, 0.8, $\frac{9}{11}$, 0.87 0.8, $\frac{9}{11}$, 0.87, $\frac{7}{8}$

b. 1.65, $1\frac{2}{3}$, $1\frac{3}{5}$, 1.7 See below.

35. a. Writing Explain the steps you would use to write 0.8 as a fraction in simplest form. See below.

b. Writing Explain the steps you would use to write $\frac{2}{9}$ as a decimal. Divide 2 by 9; the digit 2 repeats so put a bar over it, so $\frac{2}{9} = 0.\overline{2}$.

33b. $\frac{8}{25}$, $\frac{1}{3}$, $\frac{17}{50}$, $\frac{26}{75}$ 34b. $1\frac{3}{5}$, 1.65, $1\frac{2}{3}$, 1.7
35a. 0.8 is "eight-tenths" and $\frac{8}{10}$ reduces to

Mixed REVIEW

Order from least to greatest.

1. $\frac{3}{4}$, $\frac{2}{3}$, $\frac{7}{10}$ $\frac{2}{3}$, $\frac{7}{10}$, $\frac{3}{4}$
2. $\frac{1}{5}$, $\frac{1}{6}$, $\frac{3}{10}$ $\frac{1}{6}$, $\frac{1}{5}$, $\frac{3}{10}$
3. $3\frac{3}{8}$, $\frac{32}{10}$, $\frac{7}{2}$ $\frac{32}{10}$, $3\frac{3}{8}$, $\frac{7}{2}$

Write three equivalent fractions for each.

4. $\frac{9}{10}$ 5. $\frac{3}{4}$ See below.

6. Jan and Leah both earn money running errands for elderly neighbors. Leah earns \$1.25 more an hour than Jan. If together they earned \$15.75 for 3 hours of work, how much did each earn per hour?

Jan \$2.00
Leah \$3.25

4. Sample: $\frac{18}{20}$, $\frac{27}{30}$, $\frac{36}{40}$

5. Sample: $\frac{6}{8}$, $\frac{9}{12}$, $\frac{12}{16}$

CHECKPOINT

Find the LCM of each set of numbers.

1. 16, 24, 32 96
2. 28, 56, 63 504
3. 40, 36, 18 360

Write each fraction as a decimal.

4. $\frac{2}{5}$ 0.4
5. $\frac{7}{100}$ 0.07
6. $\frac{3}{8}$ 0.375
7. $\frac{1}{6}$ $0.1\overline{6}$

Write each decimal as a fraction in simplest form.

8. 0.52 $\frac{13}{25}$
9. 0.04 $\frac{1}{25}$
10. 0.75 $\frac{3}{4}$
11. 15.025 15

12. Choose A, B, C, or D. Which set of numbers is in order from greatest to least? D

A. 0.56, 0.055, 0.53, 0.52

B. 1.75, $\frac{3}{2}$, 1.25, 2.0

C. 3.47, $3\frac{1}{2}$, 3.6, $\frac{8}{3}$

D. $\frac{7}{8}$, 0.8, 0.75, $\frac{8}{11}$

7-11

Connecting to Prior Knowledge

Ask students: *I'm thinking of a number. If I multiply my number by 2 and then add 3, I get 15. What's my number?* Most students can figure out that the number is 6 by working backward. Discuss this process.

KINESTHETIC LEARNERS Have the students perform the actions described to help them solve the problems. Give the students pencils so they can simulate the actions of the teacher to determine how many pencils she had.

ESL DIVERSITY Understanding the problems in this lesson requires reading skills. If a student is having difficulty solving word problems, try to determine whether it is because of reading difficulties or math or problem-solving skills.

Error Alert! Students may forget that, when working backward, you do the inverse operation at each step. ***Remediation*** Encourage students to list the steps in a problem before beginning to work backward through them. Remind them that addition and multiplication in the problem become subtraction and division in the solution process.

Additional Problem *Pedro and Gabriella burned the first dozen cookies they baked, but the rest of the batch turned out fine. They gave half of the unburned cookies to Gabriella's mother and put the remaining cookies in the freezer. The next day they ate half of the frozen batch and decided to save the remaining eight cookies for their school lunches. How many cookies did Pedro and Gabriella bake?*

8 cookies saved; 8 cookies eaten; 16 cookies to Gabriella's mother; 12 cookies burned.

They baked 44 cookies.

What's Ahead

- Solving problems by working backward

PROBLEM SOLVING

7-11 Work Backward

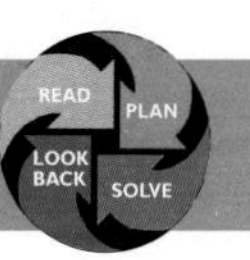

Sometimes you need to work backward from a known result to find a fact at the beginning.

> A teacher lends pencils to students. At the end of one day she has 16 pencils. She remembers giving out 7 pencils in the morning, collecting 5 before lunch, and giving out 3 after lunch. How many pencils did the teacher have at the start of the day?

READ Read and understand the given information. Summarize the problem.

1. How many pencils does the teacher have at the end of the day? **16 pencils**
2. How many times did the teacher give out pencils? collect pencils? **twice; once**
3. Do you think she had *more than* or *fewer than* 16 pencils at the start of the day? Why? **More, because she gave out more than the number returned.**

PLAN Decide on a strategy to solve the problem.

In this problem you know that there were 16 pencils at the *end* of the day. Work backward to find out how many pencils the teacher had at the *start* of the day. Add or subtract each time the teacher gave out or collected pencils.

SOLVE Try out the strategy.

4. What was the teacher's last action with pencils before the end of the day? How many pencils did she have just before that action? **She gave out 3 pencils; 19 pencils.**
5. Continue working backward to find the number of pencils the teacher had at the start of the day. **21 pencils**

LOOK BACK Think about how you solved this problem.

6. Check by starting with your answer and working *forward.* Did you get 16 pencils for the end of the day? **Sample: Check: 21 − 7 = 14, 14 + 5 = 19, 19 − 3 = 16; yes.**
7. **Writing** Some people might prefer to solve using the strategy "guess and check." Solve the problem using 18 as your guess. Which strategy do you prefer? Why? **Answers may vary. Sample: the strategy work backward is preferable because it is more efficient.**

> *"Few things are harder to put up with than the annoyance of a good example."*
>
> —Mark Twain

Organizer

1. **Focus**
   Connecting to Prior Knowledge
2. **Teach**
3. **Closure**
   Try These
   Wrap Up

Skills Reviewed in Context of Lesson

- adding, subtracting, multiplying and dividing whole numbers

Student Resources

Extra Practice
Student Study Guide
Practice, TR Ch. 7, p. 35
Student Study Guide, Spanish Resources, TR

Teacher Resources

Teaching Transparency 69
Lesson Planner, TR Ch. 7, p. 12

Prentice Hall Technology

Computer Item Generator

- 7-11

VISUAL LEARNERS The preceding problem can also be conveniently solved using a diagram, in which the whole set of unburned cookies is represented by a large unit rectangle, subdivided at each step. At the end, just add the burned cookies.

TRY THESE

Ongoing Assessment Make sure students list the steps or draw diagrams for Exercises 8–10. If a student looks discouraged at the start, suggest thinking by writing: listing the steps, drawing a picture, or keeping a tally.

Wrap Up

What's the Big Idea? Ask students: *How can you solve problems by working backward?*

Reteaching Activity Have students compare the ways they worked backward to solve the problems in Exercises 8–10. Demonstrate various ways to use the strategy on the chalkboard. Encourage students to evaluate the strategies.

Journal Have students pretend they are tutoring a younger neighbor and have to explain how to solve problems by working backward. Have them outline a lesson they would use to help the neighbor understand how to use this strategy.

Connections Have a discussion about how working backward is used to solve problems. You may want to use these examples:

- **Law Enforcement** (recreating crime based on collected evidence)
- **Household** (finding lost items by retracing one's steps)
- **Games** (evaluating strategies after a result)
- **Inventions** (creating devices for a specific purpose)

Fact of the Day

The "lead" for pencils is made by blending powdered graphite, clay, and water together, drawing the mixture out into thin rods and letting it dry, then kiln-firing the rods at 1,900°F (1,000°C). The porous rods are then impregnated with wax to impart smoothness.

—ACADEMIC AMERICAN ENCYCLOPEDIA

Assignment Options

Core: 12–14, 18, 20, 21, 23, MR all	
Reinforce: 11, 15, 16, 22, 24	**Enrich:** 17, 19

Leroy "Satchel" Paige was the first African American pitcher to enter major league baseball when he played for the Cleveland Indians. A 1953 *Topps* baseball card of Paige costs over $100.

Source: *The Book of Lists*

TRY THESE

Work backward to solve each problem.

8. **Money** At the first store in the mall, I spent half my money. At a second store, I spent half my remaining money and $6 more. Then I had just $2. How much money did I have when I arrived at the mall? $32

9. I'm thinking of a number. If I multiply by 3 and then add 5, the result is 38. What is the number? 11

10. **Hobbies** Horace decided to sell all the cards in his baseball card collection to some friends. He sold Juanita half his cards plus 1 card. Next he sold Ethan half the remaining cards. Then he sold Erica 13 cards. Finally, he sold the remaining 9 cards to Cleon. How many cards were in Horace's collection at the start? 90 baseball cards

ON YOUR OWN

Use any strategy to solve each problem. Show your work.

11. **Sports** Olivia won a chess tournament by winning three games. At each round the loser is eliminated and the winner advances to the next round. How many players were in the tournament? 8

12. I'm thinking of two numbers. Their greatest common factor is 6, and their least common multiple is 18. What are the two numbers? 6 and 18

13. Kathy and Bill baked some muffins. They put half of them away for the next day and divided the remaining muffins among their 3 sisters, each of whom received 3 muffins. How many muffins did Kathy and Bill bake? 18 muffins

14. **Sports** In a box of sporting equipment there are twice as many bats as softballs and two more golf clubs than bats. Six items are either golf clubs or golf balls. There are two golf balls. How many softballs are in the box? 1 softball

15. The last Thursday of a certain month is the 27th day of that month. What day of the week is the first day of the month? Saturday

ON YOUR OWN

CRITICAL THINKING For Exercise 17, encourage students to draw diagrams to keep track of possibilities.

WRITING Have students support their answers to Exercise 19 with examples.

CHAPTER INVESTIGATION Ask students if there is any relationship between their representation for 10 and that for 7. Is 10, in some sense, larger?

16. Aaron has a track meet at 4:00 P.M. It takes him 5 min to change his clothes and 10 min to get to the track. Before the start of the race, Aaron needs to meet with his coach for 10 min and stretch for 15 min. When school is over, he plans to spend some time in the library.

a. When should Aaron leave the library? 3:20 P.M.

b. If school lets out at 2:50 P.M., how much time can Aaron spend in the library? 30 min

17. Critical Thinking Suppose you are stranded on a desert island with only a 3-qt container and a 5-qt container. Without marking the odd-shaped containers, explain how you can measure exactly 1 qt of water. See Solution Key.

18. Music I owned some CDs. I received a shipment of 12 more, but my sister borrowed 4 of them. Later she returned 2 CDs. Now I have 30 CDs. How many did I have before the shipment arrived? 20 CDs

19. Writing Why is it sometimes necessary to use inverse operations when working backward? Explain. Sample: to reverse the action taken in the first place.

20. Find a number between 1 and 100 that satisfies these conditions. If it is divided by 3 or 5, the remainder is 1. If it is divided by 7, the remainder is 4. 46

21. Investigation (p. 274) Use your personalized numeration system to write the number 10. What would the number 7 look like? Answers may vary.

22. What is the greatest number of 3 in. by 5 in. index cards that can be cut from a rectangular sheet of construction paper that measures 2 ft by $2\frac{1}{2}$ ft? 48 index cards

23. A bacterial population grows rapidly, doubling in size every 6 min. A teaspoon of bacteria is placed in a jar, and in 2 h the jar is filled. How long did it take for the jar to be half full? 1 h 54 min

24. On January 27th, Eldridge's aunt and grandmother came to visit. His aunt visits every four days, and his grandmother visits every six days. What was the first date in January that both visited Eldridge on the same day? Jan 3

Over 632,487 units of Stevie Wonder's "Jungle Fever" have been sold. A Gold Award is given for sales of 500,000 units. Units include tapes, CDs, and albums.

Mixed REVIEW

Write each fraction as a decimal.

1. $\frac{17}{20}$ 0.85 2. $\frac{3}{25}$ 0.12

Write each decimal as a fraction in simplest form.

3. 0.48 $\frac{12}{25}$ 4. 0.06 $\frac{3}{50}$

5. 0.95 $\frac{19}{20}$ 6. 0.152 $\frac{19}{125}$

7. Kale counted 12 wheels on the cycles in the Annual Homecoming Parade. His sister Leilani counted 7 cycles in all. The only cycles allowed were unicycles, bicycles, and tricycles. How many cycles of each type were in the parade?

Sample: 1 tricycle, 3 bicycles, 3 unicycles

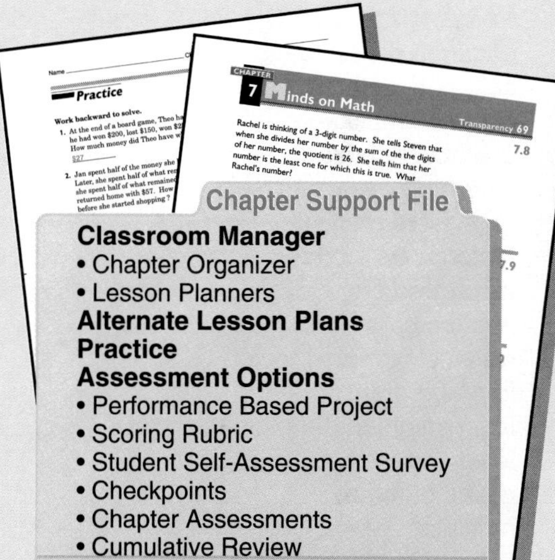

Practice
Minds on Math
Transparency 69
Chapter Support File
Classroom Manager
• Chapter Organizer
• Lesson Planners
Alternate Lesson Plans
Practice
Assessment Options
• Performance Based Project
• Scoring Rubric
• Student Self-Assessment Survey
• Checkpoints
• Chapter Assessments
• Cumulative Review

Minds on Math available in Teaching Transparencies

Math Minutes

If you take a number, multiply it by 3 and then subtract 7, you get 11. What is the number?

6

CHAPTER 7 WRAP UP

Exercises 1–6: Students should be able to do these exercises mentally. You may want to review the divisibility rules for 3 and 9 before students begin to work.

Exercise 7: Students should be able to determine easily that 525 and 530 are not prime. (Both are divisible by 5; 530 is divisible by 10 and 2.) If they recall the rule of divisibility for 3 (sum of digits is divisible by 3), they will realize that 519 is not prime. This leaves 523 as the prime number.

Ongoing Assessment You may wish to have students work with partners on Exercises 8–13. Have each student work the problems individually. Then have partners exchange papers and check each other's work.

Exercises 14–19: You may want to review the difference between GCF and LCM before students begin to work these exercises.

Exercises 39–44: You may want to remind students that the bar in a fraction means "divided by."

Vocabulary/Symbols

common denominator
common factors
common multiples
composite number
divisibility
equivalent fractions
factor
factor tree
fraction bars
greatest common factor, GCF
improper fraction
least common denominator, LCD
least common multiple, LCM
mixed number
multiple
prime factorization
prime number
repeating decimal
sieve
simplest form
terminating decimal
twin primes

Materials and Manipulatives

- calculator

Divisibility and Prime Factorization 7-1, 7-2

The rules for divisibility can help you find factors. A ***prime number*** has exactly two factors, 1 and itself, while a ***composite number*** has more than two factors.

When a composite number is written as a product of its prime factors, it is called the ***prime factorization.***

State whether each number is divisible by 1, 2, 3, 5, 9, or 10.

1. 69 1, 3 **2.** 146 1, 2 **3.** 837 1, 3, 9 **4.** 405 1, 3, 5, 9 **5.** 628 1, 2 **6.** 32,870 1, 2, 5, 10

7. Choose A, B, C, or D. Which number is a prime number? B

A. 519 **B.** 523 **C.** 525 **D.** 530

Find the prime factorization using a factor tree.

8. 72 $2 \times 2 \times 2 \times 3 \times 3$ **9.** 120 $2 \times 2 \times 2 \times 3 \times 5$ **10.** 33 3×11 **11.** 80 $2 \times 2 \times 2 \times 2 \times 5$ **12.** 234 $2 \times 3 \times 3 \times 13$ **13.** 345 $3 \times 5 \times 23$

GCF, LCM, and Simplifying Fractions 7-3, 7-6, 7-8

The ***greatest common factor*** (GCF) of two or more numbers is the greatest number that is a factor of each number.

To simplify a fraction, divide both the numerator and the denominator of the fraction by the GCF. You can also use a fraction calculator to simplify fractions.

The ***least common multiple*** (LCM) of two or more numbers is the smallest number that is a multiple of each number.

Find the GCF and the LCM of each set of numbers.

14. 40, 140 20; 280 **15.** 28, 33 1; 924 **16.** 24, 9 3; 72 **17.** 15, 25 5; 75 **18.** 18, 42, 60 6; 1,260 **19.** 10, 12, 16 2; 240

Write each fraction in simplest form.

20. $\frac{16}{18}$ $\frac{8}{9}$ **21.** $\frac{24}{60}$ $\frac{2}{5}$ **22.** $\frac{15}{50}$ $\frac{3}{10}$ **23.** $\frac{27}{72}$ $\frac{3}{8}$ **24.** $\frac{16}{44}$ $\frac{4}{11}$ **25.** $\frac{6}{21}$ $\frac{2}{7}$

Getting Ready for Chapter 8

The skills previewed will help students understand and solve problems involving estimation and fractions.

Equivalent Fractions — 7-4, 7-5

You form ***equivalent fractions*** by multiplying or dividing the numerator and denominator by the same nonzero number.

Answers may vary. Sample given.

Write two fractions equivalent to each fraction.

26. $\frac{1}{8}$ $\frac{2}{16}$, $\frac{3}{24}$ **27.** $\frac{2}{10}$ $\frac{1}{5}$, $\frac{4}{20}$ **28.** $\frac{5}{25}$ $\frac{1}{5}$, $\frac{10}{50}$ **29.** $\frac{3}{5}$ $\frac{6}{10}$, $\frac{9}{15}$ **30.** $\frac{14}{28}$ $\frac{1}{2}$, $\frac{2}{4}$ **31.** $\frac{30}{50}$ $\frac{3}{5}$, $\frac{6}{10}$

Comparing and Ordering Fractions and Mixed Numbers — 7-7, 7-9

An ***improper fraction*** has a numerator greater than its denominator. A ***mixed number*** shows the sum of a whole number and a fraction. Compare fractions by finding a common denominator.

Write each improper fraction as a mixed number. Write each mixed number as an improper fraction.

32. $4\frac{3}{4}$ $\frac{19}{4}$ **33.** $\frac{22}{5}$ $4\frac{2}{5}$ **34.** $\frac{57}{7}$ $8\frac{1}{7}$ **35.** $2\frac{3}{7}$ $\frac{17}{7}$ **36.** $\frac{30}{14}$ $2\frac{2}{14}$ or $2\frac{1}{7}$ **37.** $5\frac{2}{11}$ $\frac{57}{11}$

38. Order from least to greatest: $1\frac{5}{6}$, $1\frac{7}{9}$, $\frac{35}{36}$, $1\frac{3}{4}$. $\frac{35}{36}$, $1\frac{3}{4}$, $1\frac{7}{9}$, $1\frac{5}{6}$

Fractions and Decimals; Strategies — 7-10, 7-11

To express a decimal as a fraction, write the fraction as you would say the decimal. Then simplify the fraction. To write a decimal as a fraction, divide the numerator by the denominator. Write a bar over the digit or digits that repeat.

Write each decimal as a fraction in simplest form. Write each fraction as a decimal.

39. 0.04 $\frac{1}{25}$ **40.** 3.875 $3\frac{7}{8}$ **41.** 2.14 $2\frac{7}{50}$ **42.** $\frac{17}{40}$ 0.425 **43.** $\frac{8}{9}$ $0.\overline{8}$ **44.** $\frac{6}{11}$ $0.\overline{54}$

45. At the first store Tina spent $7. At the next store she spent half of her remaining money. At the last store she spent half of her remaining money and $3 more. Tina had $5 left. How much money did she have before shopping? $39

GETTING READY FOR CHAPTER 8

Tell whether each fraction is close to 0, to $\frac{1}{2}$, or to 1.

1. $\frac{54}{98}$ $\frac{1}{2}$ **2.** $\frac{11}{12}$ 1 **3.** $\frac{1}{6}$ 0 **4.** $\frac{2}{9}$ 0 **5.** $\frac{19}{40}$ $\frac{1}{2}$ **6.** $\frac{5}{11}$ $\frac{1}{2}$

Student Resources

Practice, p. 291
Problem Solving Practice, p. 285
Extra Practice
Student Study Guide
Student Study Guide, Spanish Resources
Tools for Studying Smarter, TR
Student Self-Assessment Survey, TR Ch. 7, p. 39 (see below)

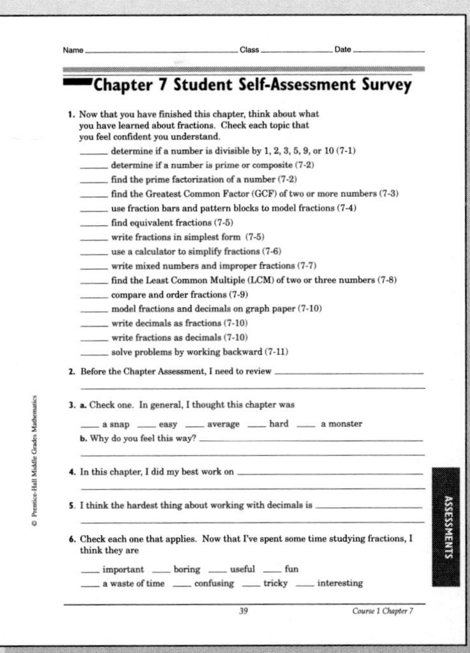

Name ______ Class ______ Date ______

Chapter 7 Student Self-Assessment Survey

1. Now that you have finished this chapter, think about what you have learned about fractions. Check each topic that you feel confident you understand.
   - ______ determine if a number is divisible by 1, 2, 3, 5, 9, or 10 (7-1)
   - ______ determine if a number is prime or composite (7-2)
   - ______ find the prime factorization of a number (7-2)
   - ______ find the Greatest Common Factor (GCF) of two or more numbers (7-3)
   - ______ use fraction bars and pattern blocks to model fractions (7-4)
   - ______ find equivalent fractions (7-5)
   - ______ write fractions in simplest form (7-5)
   - ______ use a calculator to simplify fractions (7-6)
   - ______ write mixed numbers and improper fractions (7-7)
   - ______ find the Least Common Multiple (LCM) of two or three numbers (7-8)
   - ______ compare and order fractions (7-9)
   - ______ model fractions and decimals on graph paper (7-10)
   - ______ write decimals as fractions (7-10)
   - ______ write fractions as decimals (7-10)
   - ______ solve problems by working backward (7-11)
2. Before the Chapter Assessment, I need to review ______
3. a. Check one. In general, I thought this chapter was
   ____ a snap ____ easy ____ average ____ hard ____ a monster
   b. Why do you feel this way? ______
4. In this chapter, I did my best work on ______
5. I think the hardest thing about working with decimals is ______
6. Check each one that applies. Now that I've spent some time studying fractions, I think they are
   ____ important ____ boring ____ useful ____ fun
   ____ a waste of time ____ confusing ____ tricky ____ interesting

ASSESSMENTS

39 Course 1 Chapter 7

CHAPTER 7

PUTTING IT ALL TOGETHER

The projects on these pages can be used in a variety of ways:

- alternative assessment
- portfolio ideas
- additional assignments for gifted and talented students
- extra credit for all students

Follow Up

Have a number "show and tell" for the class. Have students show objects from their number systems. Other students can try to guess the numbers represented.

To extend their personalized numeration system, students might represent $\frac{2}{3}$ by placing the object for 2 over that for 3. A more sophisticated method would be to mark or otherwise indicate two thirds of the object for 1. Other methods are possible.

Discuss with students the difference between $\frac{2}{3}$ (a number between 0 and 1) and $\frac{2}{3}$ of 6 (the number 4).

EXCURSION The triangular numbers that follow 6 are 10, 15, 21, 28, 36, 45, 55, and 66. Two evident patterns are that the difference between succeeding pairs of numbers increases by 1 and that pairs of odd numbers and even numbers alternate.

Prime Puzzler

COOPERATIVE GROUPS Have students work with a partner or in groups of four. Have students explore and discuss the sample problem for answers. Then each student can create a puzzle to challenge a partner or the other group members.

EXCURSION Elicit the fact that answers can fall between a range of numbers. So it is possible to have more than one answer to the given Prime Puzzler. For example, 468 and 312 are both solutions to the given problem.

Materials and Manipulatives

Two of a Kind

- 30 index cards or cut paper cards

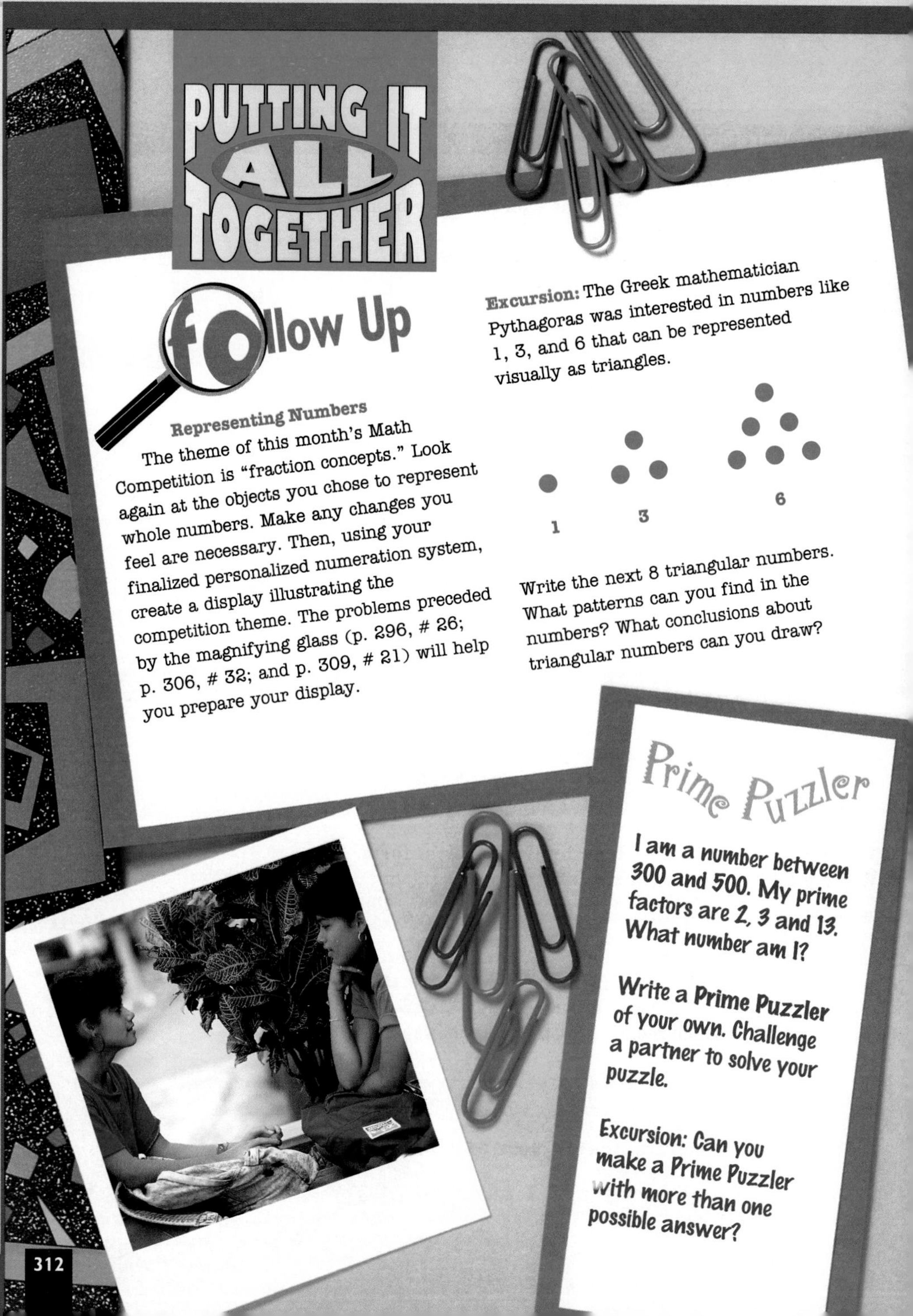

PUTTING IT ALL TOGETHER

Follow Up

Representing Numbers

The theme of this month's Math Competition is "fraction concepts." Look again at the objects you chose to represent whole numbers. Make any changes you feel are necessary. Then, using your finalized personalized numeration system, create a display illustrating the competition theme. The problems preceded by the magnifying glass (p. 296, # 26; p. 306, # 32; and p. 309, # 21) will help you prepare your display.

Excursion: The Greek mathematician Pythagoras was interested in numbers like 1, 3, and 6 that can be represented visually as triangles.

1 3 6

Write the next 8 triangular numbers. What patterns can you find in the numbers? What conclusions about triangular numbers can you draw?

Prime Puzzler

I am a number between 300 and 500. My prime factors are 2, 3 and 13. What number am I?

Write a Prime Puzzler of your own. Challenge a partner to solve your puzzle.

Excursion: Can you make a Prime Puzzler with more than one possible answer?

312

Two of a Kind

COOPERATIVE GROUPS Have students work in groups of three or four. You may wish to begin by reviewing equivalent fractions and equivalent decimals.

EXCURSION By using familiar fractions, students can pay close attention when comparing the fraction and decimal equivalents. Some students may need to separate cards into fraction and decimal categories so that they can first be studied separately for order, and then combined later for further review.

The Write Stuff

Make sure the students understand that the word problem must make sense. However, allow students to be creative. For example, they may want to rewrite 0.64 as money or use 5 halves instead of $2\frac{1}{2}$.

To Be or Not to Be

COOPERATIVE GROUPS Have students brainstorm the possible and impossible fraction situations. Have one student record the suggestions. Students may feel comfortable listing possible situations because of their familiarity with fractions. Ask students to reword, modify, or change reasonable situations into impossible situations.

EXCURSION As a whole class, decide on the criteria for judging the best situations. Then, as an assessment, have each group present to the class their best choices for possible and impossible situations.

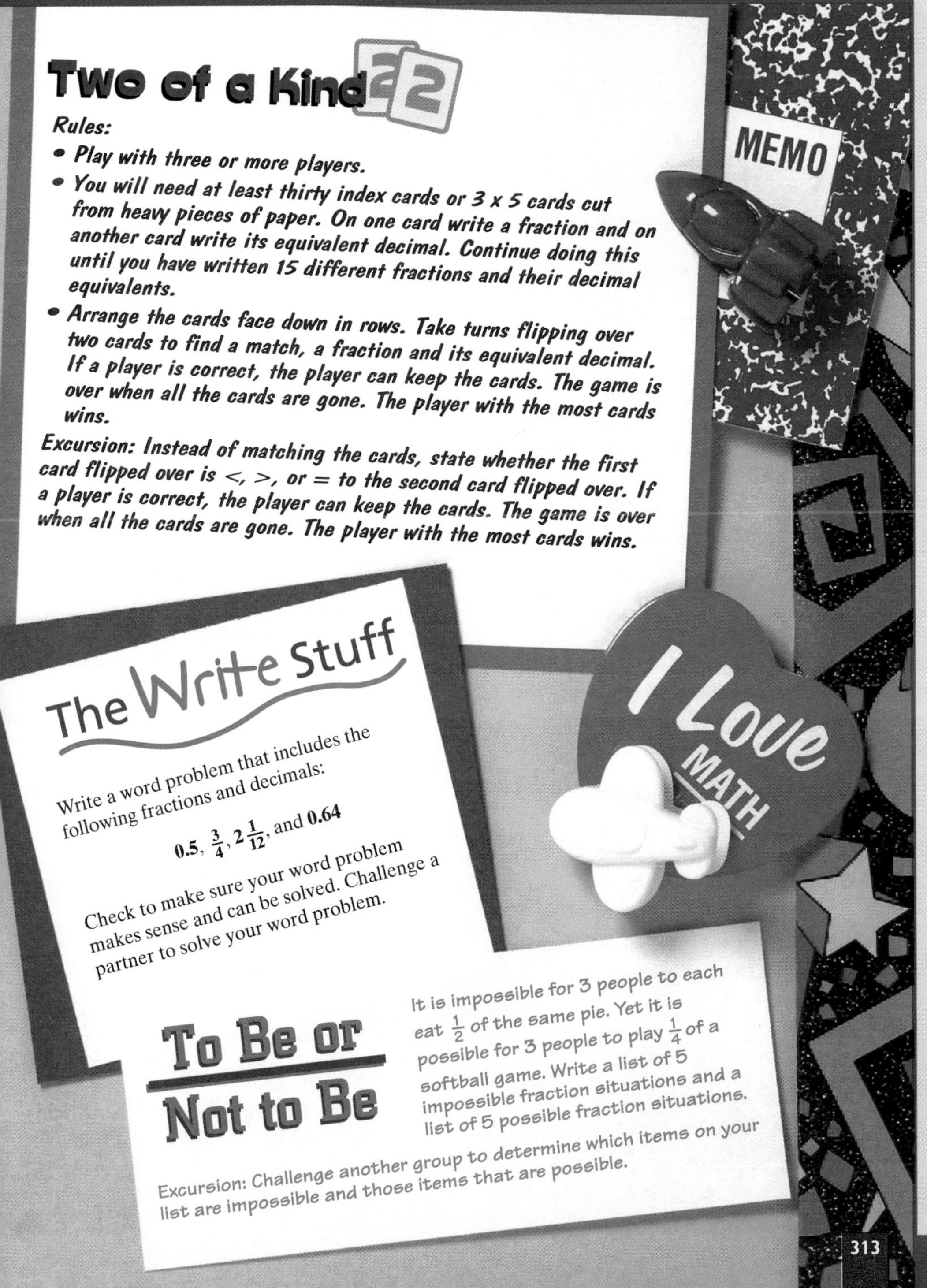

Two of a Kind
Rules:
• Play with three or more players.
• You will need at least thirty index cards or 3 x 5 cards cut from heavy pieces of paper. On one card write a fraction and on another card write its equivalent decimal. Continue doing this until you have written 15 different fractions and their decimal equivalents.
• Arrange the cards face down in rows. Take turns flipping over two cards to find a match, a fraction and its equivalent decimal. If a player is correct, the player can keep the cards. The game is over when all the cards are gone. The player with the most cards wins.
Excursion: Instead of matching the cards, state whether the first card flipped over is <, >, or = to the second card flipped over. If a player is correct, the player can keep the cards. The game is over when all the cards are gone. The player with the most cards wins.
MEMO
The Write Stuff
Write a word problem that includes the following fractions and decimals:
0.5, 3/4, 2 1/12, and 0.64
Check to make sure your word problem makes sense and can be solved. Challenge a partner to solve your word problem.
I Love MATH
To Be or Not to Be
It is impossible for 3 people to each eat 1/2 of the same pie. Yet it is possible for 3 people to play 1/4 of a softball game. Write a list of 5 impossible fraction situations and a list of 5 possible fraction situations.
Excursion: Challenge another group to determine which items on your list are impossible and those items that are possible.
313

CHAPTER 7

ASSESSMENT

For Exercise 16, students will need to work backward, guess and test, or use some other problem-solving strategy. Encourage students not to give up after one or two unsuccessful tries.

Writing Questions allow students to describe more fully their thinking and understanding of the concepts they've learned.

Exercise 1 is a writing question.

Enhanced Multiple Choice Questions are more complex than traditional multiple choice questions, which assess only one skill. Enhanced multiple choice questions assess the processes that students use as well as the end results. They are written so that students can use more than one strategy to solve the problem. Using multiple strategies is encouraged by the National Council of Teachers of Mathematics (NCTM).

Exercises 2 and 12 are enhanced multiple choice questions.

For Exercises 4 and 10, before students begin work, you may wish to have volunteers explain and demonstrate for the class the difference between a GCF (greatest common factor) and an LCM (least common multiple) of a set of numbers.

Resources

Performance Based Project, TR Ch. 7, pp. 36–38

Chapter Assessment, Forms A and B, TR Ch. 7, pp. 41–44

Spanish Chapter Assessment, Spanish Resources, TR

Computer Item Generator

CHAPTER 7

Assessment

3.b. 1, 2, 3, 6, 9, 18, 27, 54: C
3.d. 1, 2, 3, 6, 17, 34, 51, 102: C

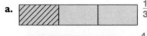

1. **Writing** Is 24,357 divisible by 9? Explain your answer. No, the sum of the digits is not divisible by 9.
2. **Choose A, B, C, or D.** Which number is divisible by 2, 3, and 10? D

   A. 375 **B.** 430 **C.** 2,328 **D.** 5,430
3. List all the factors of each number. Tell whether each number is prime or composite.

   a. 33 1, 3, 11, 33: C **b.** 54 See above. **c.** 19 1, 19: P **d.** 102 See above.
4. Find the GCF of each set of numbers.

   a. 24, 36 12 **b.** 20, 25, 30 5 **c.** 45, 105 15 **d.** 7, 19 1
5. Find the prime factorization of each number.

   a. 132 $2 \times 2 \times 3 \times 11$ **b.** 360 $2 \times 2 \times 2 \times 3 \times 3 \times 5$
6. Name the fraction modeled.

   a. $\frac{1}{3}$
   b. $\frac{4}{5}$
7. **Estimation** Classify each fraction as close to 0, close to $\frac{1}{2}$, or close to 1.

   a. $\frac{15}{16}$ 1 **b.** $\frac{2}{20}$ 0 **c.** $\frac{24}{50}$ $\frac{1}{2}$ **d.** $\frac{40}{75}$ $\frac{1}{2}$
8. Name two fractions that are equivalent to $\frac{6}{18}$. Answers may vary. Sample: $\frac{1}{3}, \frac{12}{36}$.
9. Write each fraction in simplest form.

   a. $\frac{5}{45}$ $\frac{1}{9}$ **b.** $\frac{34}{51}$ $\frac{2}{3}$ **c.** $\frac{56}{128}$ $\frac{7}{16}$ **d.** $\frac{120}{180}$ $\frac{2}{3}$
10. Find the LCM of each set of numbers.

    a. 4, 8 8 **b.** 6, 11 66 **c.** 18, 45 90 **d.** 10, 12, 15 60
11. Compare. Fill in the ■ with <, >, or =.

    a. $1\frac{2}{5}$ ■ $1\frac{1}{5}$ > **b.** $\frac{15}{4}$ ■ $\frac{17}{5}$ > **c.** $\frac{7}{14}$ ■ $\frac{1}{2}$ = **d.** $2\frac{3}{5}$ ■ $2\frac{7}{11}$ <
12. **Choose A, B, or C.** Lee jogged $\frac{1}{2}$ mi, Mary jogged $\frac{2}{3}$ mi, and Rosalinda jogged $\frac{3}{8}$ mi. Who jogged the longest distance? B

    A. Lee **B.** Mary **C.** Rosalinda
13. Order each set of numbers from least to greatest. See below.

    a. $5\frac{3}{4}, 5\frac{1}{8}, 5\frac{2}{4}$ **b.** $4\frac{4}{5}, 3\frac{7}{10}, 3\frac{3}{5}$ **c.** $2\frac{1}{4}, 1\frac{3}{4}, 3\frac{2}{4}$ **d.** $\frac{2}{9}, \frac{7}{63}, \frac{5}{18}, \frac{1}{2}$
14. Write each decimal as a fraction in simplest form.

    a. 0.4 $\frac{2}{5}$ **b.** 0.82 $\frac{41}{50}$ **c.** 0.025 $\frac{1}{40}$
15. Write each fraction as a decimal. Use a bar to show repeating decimals.

    a. $\frac{5}{8}$ 0.625 **b.** $\frac{6}{11}$ $0.\overline{54}$ **c.** $\frac{15}{45}$ $0.\overline{3}$
16. Solve the following puzzle. When I add 2 to a number, subtract 5, and then multiply by 3, my result is 24. What is my number? 11

13. a. $5\frac{1}{8}, 5\frac{2}{4}, 5\frac{3}{4}$
13. b. $3\frac{3}{5}, 3\frac{7}{10}, 4\frac{4}{5}$
13. c. $1\frac{3}{4}, 2\frac{1}{4}, 3\frac{2}{4}$
13. d. $\frac{7}{63}, \frac{2}{9}, \frac{5}{18}, \frac{1}{2}$

CHAPTER 7 CUMULATIVE REVIEW

Exercises 1, 2, 5, 9, and 10 are enhanced multiple choice questions.

For Exercise 1, students may interpret "three" to mean "three or more," and choose C. If this happens, ask whether there are any other possible answers.

Item(s)	Review Topic	Chapter
1	exploring polygons	2
2	number patterns	5
3	classifying angles	2
4, 7	variables and expressions	5
5	congruent and similar figures	2
6, 11	fractions and decimals	7
8	greatest common factor	7
9	exploring fractions	7
10	special quadrilaterals	2

CHAPTER 7 Cumulative Review

Choose A, B, C, or D.

1. In which polygon can three diagonals be drawn from one vertex? B

A. quadrilateral **B.** hexagon
C. 7-sided polygon **D.** pentagon

2. Which number pattern can be described by the following rule: *Start with the number 12 and subtract 4 repeatedly?* A

A. 12, 8, 4, . . . **B.** 12, 8, 10, . . .
C. 12, 16, 24, . . . **D.** 12, 24, 20, . . .

3. Which angle does not appear to be a right angle? Classify the angle as acute, obtuse, or straight. B; acute

A. $\angle COD$
B. $\angle DOE$
C. $\angle AOB$
D. $\angle CEO$

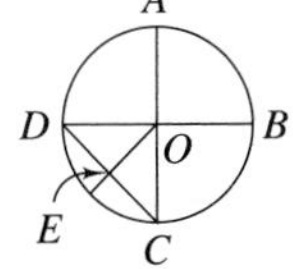

4. Which expression has a value of 13? C

A. $3 + (2)^2$ **B.** $(3 + 2)^2$
C. $3^2 + 2^2$ **D.** $3^3 + 2^2$

5. Which of the pairs of triangles appear to be similar but *not* congruent? B

A. 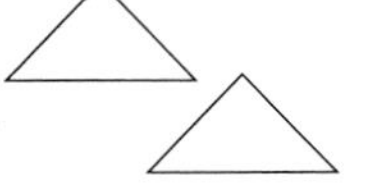 **B.** 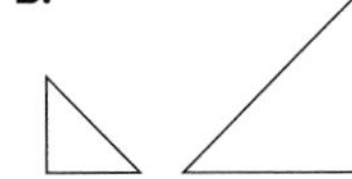

C. 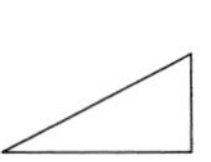 **D.**  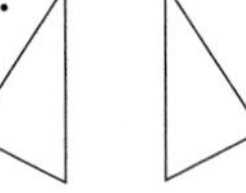

6. Which decimal is equivalent to $\frac{3}{8}$? C

A. 0.037 **B.** 0.38 **C.** 0.375 **D.** 3.75

7. Which word phrase describes the variable expression $2b - 8$? D

A. eight minus two times b
B. two times b
C. two minus eight times b
D. two times b minus eight

8. Which set of numbers has a GCF of 8? C

A. 24, 36, 48 **B.** 56, 63, 42
C. 64, 24, 56 **D.** 56, 36, 28

9. Which fraction model does *not* equal $\frac{2}{3}$? C

A. 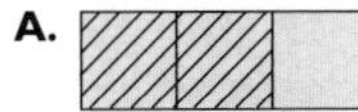 **B.** 

C.  **D.**

10. Which name best describes the quadrilateral? A

A. parallelogram
B. square
C. rhombus
D. rectangle

11. Which fraction is *not* equivalent to 0.125? D

A. $\frac{5}{40}$ **B.** $\frac{125}{1000}$ **C.** $\frac{1}{8}$ **D.** $\frac{15}{200}$

Resources

Cumulative Review, TR Ch. 7, pp. 45–46
Transparency Masters, TR p. 35

CHAPTER

8 Fraction Operations

Why Study Fraction Operations?

If students ask this question, you may want to mention the following people who use fractions: sales clerks, computer programmers, stockbrokers, insurance agents, cooks, architects, contractors, designers, and surveyors.

Graphic Display of Chapter Content

Below is one possible representation of the chapter's content and its applications to the world outside the classroom. Have students create their own graphic display and fill in applications that they have seen in their own lives.

- The center oval should state the main concept of the chapter: fraction operations.
- Have students draw the ovals with the next level of concepts presented in the chapter (estimation, addition and subtraction, multiplication and division, and measurement). You may want students to add other topics that they think are appropriate.
- Ask students to draw as many application ovals as they can.
- Discuss all the applications that students identify.
- Have students make and present one display that includes all the students' ideas.

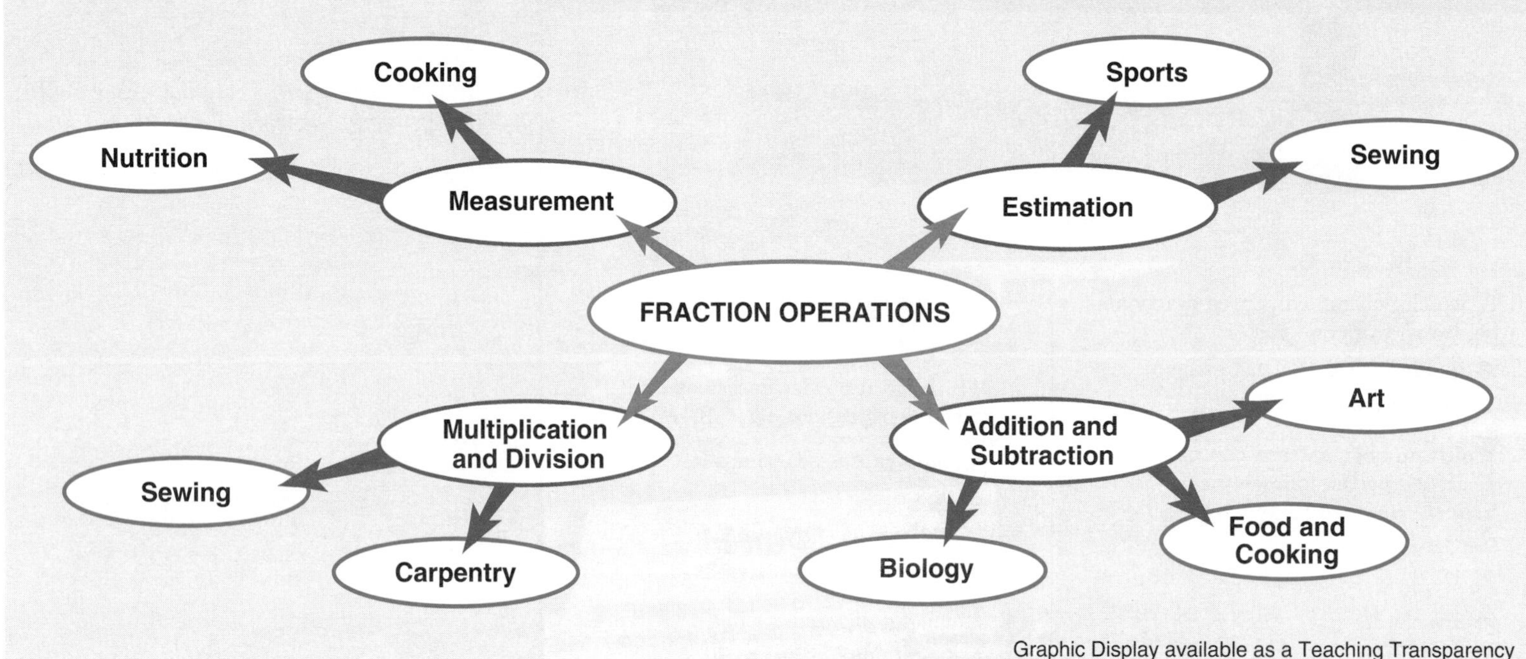

Graphic Display available as a Teaching Transparency

Vocabulary and Symbols

reciprocals
whole numbers

Materials and Manipulatives

calculator	computer
fraction bars	graph paper
ruler	spreadsheet software
scissors	string

Additional Resources

Commercially Available Technology

Calculator
fraction

Software
algebra software
- *Math Blaster Plus* by Davidson and Associates
- *Fast Track Fractions* by Computer Software

spreadsheet software
- *Excel; Works* by Microsoft
- *1-2-3* by Lotus
- *ClarisWorks* by Apple

Other Media
- "Addition with Mixed Numerals." Aims Media, 9710 DeSoto Avenue, Chatsworth, CA 91311.
- "Equivalent Fractions." Aims Media, 9710 DeSoto Avenue, Chatsworth, CA 91311.
- "Multiplying with Fractions." Aims Media, 9710 DeSoto Avenue, Chatsworth, CA 91311.

Materials at Little or No Cost

Mathematical Association of America, 1529 18th St., NW, Washington, DC 20036. Activities.

Pieces and Patterns: A Patchwork in Math and Science. AIMS Education Foundation, Box 8120, Fresno, CA 93747-8120.

Bibliography

For Teachers

Fennell, Francis. *Number Sense Now.* Reston, VA: NCTM, 1993.

Stevenson, Frederick. *Exploratory Problems in Mathematics.* Reston, VA: NCTM, 1992.

For Students

Dennis, Richard. *Fractions Are Parts of Things.* NY: Crowell, 1983.

Simon, Seymour. *How to Be an Ocean Scientist in Your Own Home.* NY: Lippincott, 1988.

Zubrowski, Bernie. *Messing Around with Drinking Straw Construction.* Boston: Little, Brown, 1981.

Prentice Hall Technology 

Multimedia Math
- Math Tools, Fraction Strips
- Math Tools, Spreadsheet
- Hot Page™ 8-2
- Hot Page™ 8-7
- Hot Page™ 8-9
- Math Investigations, Unidentified Flying Cubes

Computer Item Generator
- Chapter 8

Community Resources

Field Trips
- a construction site
- a kitchen at a local restaurant
- a packaging plant

Guest Speakers
- a land surveyor
- a cook or caterer
- a stockbroker

Backpack Take-Home Activities

Materials
- pencil
- paper
- scissors
- bowl
- teacup
- coffee mug
- drinking glass
- straightedge
- measuring cup marked in oz
- 3 kitchen storage containers: tall, round, rectangular
- construction paper: 1 white sheet, 5 colored

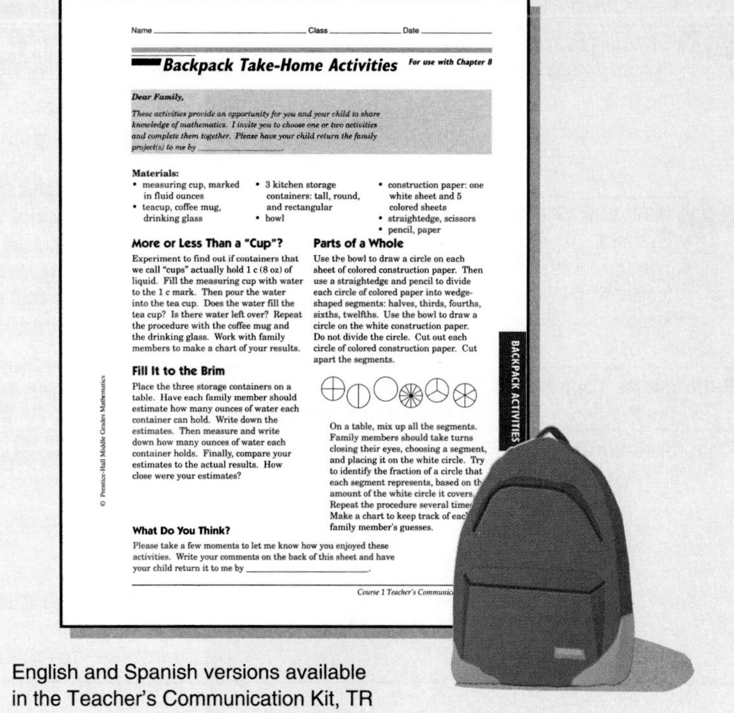

Name ______ Class ______ Date ______

Backpack Take-Home Activities *For use with Chapter 8*

Dear Family,

These activities provide an opportunity for you and your child to share knowledge of mathematics. I invite you to choose one or two activities and complete them together. Please have your child return the family project(s) to me by ______.

Materials:
- measuring cup, marked in fluid ounces
- teacup, coffee mug, drinking glass
- 3 kitchen storage containers: tall, round, and rectangular
- bowl
- construction paper: one white sheet and 5 colored sheets
- straightedge, scissors
- pencil, paper

More or Less Than a "Cup"?

Experiment to find out if containers that we call "cups" actually hold 1 c (8 oz) of liquid. Fill the measuring cup with water to the 1 c mark. Then pour the water into the tea cup. Does the water fill the tea cup? Is there water left over? Repeat the procedure with the coffee mug and the drinking glass. Work with family members to make a chart of your results.

Fill It to the Brim

Place the three storage containers on a table. Have each family member should estimate how many ounces of water each container can hold. Write down the estimates. Then measure and write down how many ounces of water each container holds. Finally, compare your estimates to the actual results. How close were your estimates?

Parts of a Whole

Use the bowl to draw a circle on each sheet of colored construction paper. Then use a straightedge and pencil to divide each circle of colored paper into wedge-shaped segments: halves, thirds, fourths, sixths, twelfths. Use the bowl to draw a circle on the white construction paper. Do not divide the circle. Cut out each circle of colored construction paper. Cut apart the segments.

On a table, mix up all the segments. Family members should take turns closing their eyes, choosing a segment, and placing it on the white circle. Try to identify the fraction of a circle that each segment represents, based on th[e] amount of the white circle it covers. Repeat the procedure several time[s]. Make a chart to keep track of eac[h] family member's guesses.

What Do You Think?

Please take a few moments to let me know how you enjoyed these activities. Write your comments on the back of this sheet and have your child return it to me by ______.

BACKPACK ACTIVITIES

Course 1 Teacher's Communic[ation Kit]

English and Spanish versions available in the Teacher's Communication Kit, TR

Chapter 8 Planning Guide

Objectives	Assignment Options	Critical Thinking/ Problem Solving	Writing and Reading Math	Estimation Mental Math	Materials and Manipulatives
Investigation	This chapter-long project involves open-ended questioning and data collecting and provides an additional opportunity to assess students.	p. 318 p. 318	p. 318		p. 318 p. 318
8-1 Estimating Sums and Differences • Rounding fractions and mixed numbers • Estimating sums and differences of fractions and mixed numbers	**Core:** 12–17, 19, 20, 26–28, 29, 32, 34; MR all **Reinforce:** 18, 21–25, 33 **Enrich:** 30, 31	2, 3, 11, 18, 31, 32, 34; MR: 3–5 pp. 319–321; BI p. 320; MM p. 321	32 p. 321; JL p. 320 JL Sheet	7–10, 17, 21–30, 33, 34 pp. 319, 321; RT p. 321	6 p. 319; WT p. 319; RT p. 321 TT 73; Alt. Lesson
8-2 Adding and Subtracting Fractions • Modeling addition and subtraction of fractions with like denominators • Adding and subtracting fractions with like denominators	**Core:** 16–21, 26–28, 38–40, 45; MR all **Reinforce:** 22–25, 29–34, 41–44 **Enrich:** 35–37	9, 12–15, 25, 44; MR: 5 pp. 322–323; BI p. 324; MM p. 325	10, 35–37 p. 325; JL p. 323 JL Sheet	26–34, 38–43; MR: 3, 4 p. 325	4, 8, 45 p. 322; WT p. 324 TT 73, 76
8-3 Unlike Denominators • Using a variety of methods to add and subtract fractions with unlike denominators	**Core:** 26–33, 38–41, 44; MR all **Reinforce:** 34–37, 43 **Enrich:** 42	WT: 1, 2; 3, 4, 9; EX5; 10, 25 p. 328; BI p. 329; WT p. 326; MM p. 329	WT: 2; 37 p. 329; WT p. 326; JL p. 329 JL Sheet	EX3–5; 22–24, 31–36, MR: 1–4 p. 328	WT: 1; EX1, 2, 4; 5, 19–21, 31–36, 44 pp. 327–329; WT p. 326; RT p. 329 TT 17–19, 22–29, 73
8-4 Technology: Exploring Patterns in Fraction Sums • Exploring series • Using spreadsheets to list and graph fraction sums	**Core:** 20, 21, 26; MR all; CH all **Reinforce:** 24, 25 **Enrich:** 22, 23	1–5, 7, 8, 13; WT: 18, 19; 24–26 pp. 331–333; BI p. 332; MM p. 333	WT: 19; 22; CH: 11c p. 333; JL p. 333; CH p. 333 JL Sheet	CH: 3–6	6, 9–12, 14, 16, 17, 21, 23 pp. 331, 333; WT p. 332; RT p. 333 TT 17, 19, 74
8-5 Adding & Subtracting Mixed Numbers • Solving problems that involve adding and subtracting mixed numbers	**Core:** 18–24, 28–31, 37, 39, 42; MR all **Reinforce:** 25–27, 32–36, 40 **Enrich:** 38, 41	1, 2; EX2; 4, 5, 16–20, 37–42; MR: 5 pp. 334, 335, 337; BI p. 336; MM p. 337	16, 38 p. 337; JL p. 337; MM p. 337 JL Sheet	EX5; 7–12, 21–24, 27, 36	EX5; 28–35, 42 pp. 334–336; WT p. 336; RT p. 337 TT 74
8-6 Problem Solving: Draw a Diagram • Solving a problem by drawing a diagram	**Core:** 14, 18–20; MR all **Reinforce:** 15, 17, 21 **Enrich:** 16	All; MR: 5 pp. 338, 339; BI p. 339	All JL p. 340 JL Sheet	MR: 1, 2	1, 2, 6, 7 pp. 338–340; TT 74
8-7 Multiplying Fractions & Mixed Numbers • Multiplying fractions and mixed numbers	**Core:** 27–29, 33–36, 41–44; MR all **Reinforce:** 24–26, 32, 37–40 **Enrich:** 30, 31	WT: 1; 4, 5; EX1; 7, 11, 20–24, 29–32, 41–44; MR: 3–5 pp. 342, 343; BI p. 344	31, 41–44 p. 345; JL p. 344 JL Sheet	EX2; 16–23, 25–28; MR: 1, 2 pp. 343, 344; MM p. 345	WT: 1; 2–6 p. 345 TT 17, 19, 22–29, 75
8-8 Dividing Fractions & Mixed Numbers • Dividing fractions and mixed numbers	**Core:** 27, 29–36, 41, 42, 47, 48, 51–54, 59; MR all; CH all **Reinforce:** 37–40, 43, 44, 46, 49, 50, 55–58 **Enrich:** 28, 45	5; EX1–2; 10; 18, 27, 28, 46–50; CH: 11 pp. 346–348; BI p. 348	45 p. 349; JL p. 347 JL Sheet	7, 11–16, 41–44, CH: 2 p. 349; MM p. 349	WT: 1 pp. 346, 348 TT 17, 19, 22–29, 75
8-9 Math and Measurement: The Customary System • Solving problems that involve changing units of length, weight, and capacity in the customary system	**Core:** 14–16, 20–24, 30, 31; MR all **Reinforce:** 17–19, 25, 27, 28, 32 **Enrich:** 26, 29	1, 3; EX1, 2; 4, 12, 13, 20–22, 27–29; MR: 5 pp. 350, 351, 353; BI p. 352; MM p. 353	26 JL p. 352 JL Sheet	2, 8 pp. 350, 351	p. 350; RT pp. 352–353 TT 75, 77
Putting It All Together	These pages include a Follow-Up to the Investigation and other projects, which provide additional opportunities to assess the students.	pp. 356–357 pp. 356–357	p. 356		pp. 356–357 p. 357
Chapter Resources		PS Practice, CW, CA, CR PS Practice p. 330; CW pp. 354–355; CA p. 358; CR p. 359	PS Practice, CW, CA p. 316B; PS Practice p. 330; CW pp. 354–355; CA p. 358		pp. 316A, 316B Backpack Activities, Manip. Kits TT 72

Student Edition (question numbers)
Teacher's Edition (page numbers)
Other Components

BI—What's the Big Idea? CA—Chapter Assessment CH—Checkpoint
CG—Computer Item Generator CR—Cumulative Review CW—Chapter Wrap Up
DM—Decision Making EP—Extra Practice EX—Example FD—Fact of the Day

Cooperative Learning Activities	Technology	Data Collection & Analysis	Interdisciplinary Connections	Applications	Assessment	Review	Strand Integration	NCTM Correlation*
				design	p. 318			
	p. 318				p. 318			
WT		9, 10, 17	Health	sports, sewing		MR: All	Measurement, Number, Logic/Language	1, 2, 3, 4, 5, 7, 8, 10, 12, 13
pp. 319, 320; WT p. 319 Alt. Lesson		FD p. 320	p. 321	pp. 319, 321	p. 320	p. 319; RT p. 321 Practice p. 23		
WT			Social Studies	food, cooking, sports		MR: All	Algebra, Number, Logic/Language	1, 2, 3, 4, 5, 7, 8, 9, 12, 13
pp. 322, 323; WT p. 324	Hot Page™ 8-2	FD p. 323	p. 324	p. 324	p. 323	p. 322; RT p. 324 Practice p. 24		
WT: 1, 2	EX4; 19–21, 31–36	28, 29, 42	Science, Art, Social Studies	geology, food		MR: All	Algebra, Number, Logic/Language	1, 2, 3, 4, 5, 7, 8, 9, 13
p. 326; WT p. 326	pp. 328, 329	FD p. 327	p. 329	pp. 326, 329	p. 328	p. 326; RT p. 329 Practice p. 25		
WT: 15–19	All	7, 8, 14, 15, 19, 20, 22; CH: 11c; MR: 5		rewards	CH: All	MR: All	Discrete Math, Number, Logic/Language	1, 2, 3, 4, 5, 7, 8, 9, 13
p. 332; WT p. 332 Alt. Lesson	pp. 331, 333; WT p. 332	FD p. 332	p. 333 Alt. Lesson	p. 333	p. 332; CH p. 333 CH TR p. 36	p. 331; RT p. 333 Practice p. 26		
WT	EX5; 28–35	39	Science, Home Economics	biology, cooking, gardening, sports		MR: All	Algebra, Number, Logic/Language	1, 2, 3, 4, 5, 7, 8, 9, 10, 12, 13
WT p. 336; RT p. 337	p. 336	FD p. 335	pp. 336, 337	pp. 336, 337	p. 336	p. 334; RT p. 337 Practice p. 27		
		MR: 3, 4	Art	carpentry, gar-dening, pets		MR: All	Geometry, Number, Logic/Language	1, 2, 3, 4, 5, 7, 8, 12, 13
p. 339		FD p. 339	p. 340	pp. 338, 340	p. 339	p. 338; RT p. 340 Practice p. 28		
WT: 1	WT: 1		Social Studies	community, recre-ation, carpentry, sewing		MR: All	Number, Logic/Language	1, 2, 3, 4, 5, 7, 8, 12, 13
p. 344; WT p. 342; RT p. 345	p. 345 Hot Page™ 8-7	FD p. 343	p. 345	pp. 344, 345	p. 344	p. 342; RT p. 345 Practice p. 29		
WT: 1	WT: 1	29–32	Geography, Home Economics	food, crafts, cook-ing	CH: All	MR: All	Number, Logic/Language	1, 2, 3, 4, 5, 7, 8, 10, 12, 13
pp. 346, 348; WT p. 346; RT p. 348 Alt. Lesson	p. 348	FD p. 347		pp. 346, 349	p. 348; CH p. 349 CH TR p. 36	p. 346; RT p. 348 Practice p. 30		
			Social Studies	measurement, cooking, nutrition, engineering		MR: All	Measurement, Logic/Language	1, 2, 3, 4, 5, 7, 8, 13
p. 350	Hot Page™ 8-9	FD p. 351	p. 352	p. 352; GE p. 353	p. 351	p. 350; RT p. 352 Practice p. 31		
pp. 356–357		pp. 356–357	Science	engineering, travel	pp. 356–357			
p. 357	pp. 356–357	pp. 356–357			pp. 356–357			
IN, PT		Data File 8	History, Physical Education	sports, design	IN, PT, CA	Practice, PS Practice, CW, CR, EP, SSG		
pp. 316–318; PT pp. 356–357 Backpack Activities	p. 316B Multimedia Math, CG	pp. 316–317	pp. 316F, 316–317 Interdisciplinary Units	pp. 316A, 316F, 316–317 Backpack Activities, Projects, Interdisciplinary Units	pp. 316E, 318; pp. 354–358 CA, Span. CA, Self Assessment, Projects	CW pp. 354–355 Span. SSG, CR		

GE—Great Expectations IN—Investigation JL—Journal MM—Math Minutes
MR—Mixed Review PS—Problem Solving PT—Putting It All Together RT—Reteaching Activity
SSG—Student Study Guide TT—Teaching Transparency WT—Work Together

*For a description of the NCTM Standards, see page T15.

Assessment Options

Observation Checklist

In this chapter on fraction operations, you have opportunities to observe your students do these tasks:

- ✓ round fractions and mixed numbers
- ✓ estimate sums, differences, products, and quotients of fractions and mixed numbers
- ✓ add and subtract fractions and mixed numbers using technology and other methods
- ✓ draw diagrams to solve word problems
- ✓ multiply and divide fractions and mixed numbers
- ✓ convert between units of measure in the customary system

In every chapter, you are given opportunities to observe your students:

- ✓ work with a partner or in a group
- ✓ write about mathematics
- ✓ participate in discussions about mathematics
- ✓ collect and analyze data
- ✓ display positive attitudes about mathematics
- ✓ use measurement tools

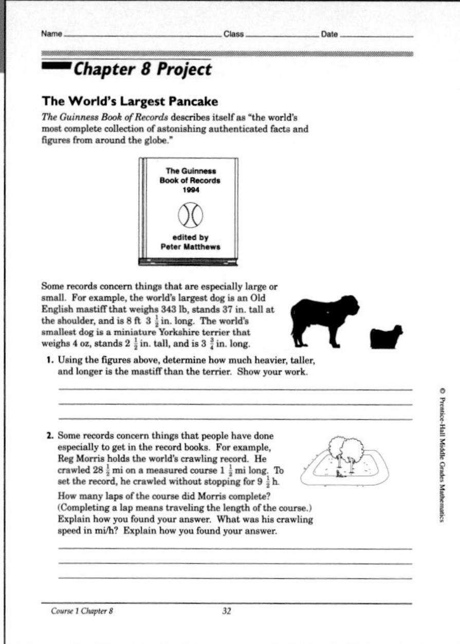

Name ______ Class ______ Date ______

Chapter 8 Project

The World's Largest Pancake

The Guinness Book of Records describes itself as "the world's most complete collection of astonishing authenticated facts and figures from around the globe."

Some records concern things that are especially large or small. For example, the world's largest dog is an Old English mastiff that weighs 343 lb, stands 37 in. tall at the shoulder, and is 8 ft $3\frac{1}{2}$ in. long. The world's smallest dog is a miniature Yorkshire terrier that weighs 4 oz, stands $2\frac{1}{2}$ in. tall, and is $3\frac{3}{4}$ in. long.

1. Using the figures above, determine how much heavier, taller, and longer is the mastiff than the terrier. Show your work.

2. Some records concern things that people have done especially to get in the record books. For example, Reg Morris holds the world's crawling record. He crawled $28\frac{1}{2}$ mi on a measured course $1\frac{1}{2}$ mi long. To set the record, he crawled without stopping for $9\frac{1}{2}$ h. How many laps of the course did Morris complete? (Completing a lap means traveling the length of the course.) Explain how you found your answer. What was his crawling speed in mi/h? Explain how you found your answer.

Course 1 Chapter 8 32

Performance Based Project (with scoring rubric), Chapter Files, TR

Pancake Scoring Rubric

Exercise	Points	Explanation
1.	3	The mastiff is $342\frac{3}{4}$ lbs heavier, $34\frac{1}{2}$ in. taller, and 7 ft $11\frac{3}{4}$in. longer.
	2	Two of the above values correct
	1	One value correct
	0	No response OR other incorrect response
2.	3	19 laps; 3 mi/h; both explanations correct
	2	Both values correct, but explanations weak or missing OR correct explanations for both, but value(s) incorrect due to computational errors
	1	One correct explanation OR one correct value
	0	No response OR other incorrect response
3.	4	Method clear; suitable multiplier chosen; correct calculations
	3	Method clear; suitable multiplier chosen; minor computational error
	2	Method clear, but application weak
	1	Method unclear or inaccurate; attempt at calculation
	0	No response
Excursion	5	Letter with clear plan including goal, method of measurement, and judges
	4	Letter with clear plan including goal, but inadequate measurement OR unacceptable judges
	3	Answer not in letter form, but goal, measurement and judges listed OR letter with vague goal or violation of one of the rules
	2	Answer not in letter form and lacking one of the three major elements
	1	Answer not in letter form and lacking two of the three major elements
	0	No response OR other incorrect response

Course 1 Chapter 8 34

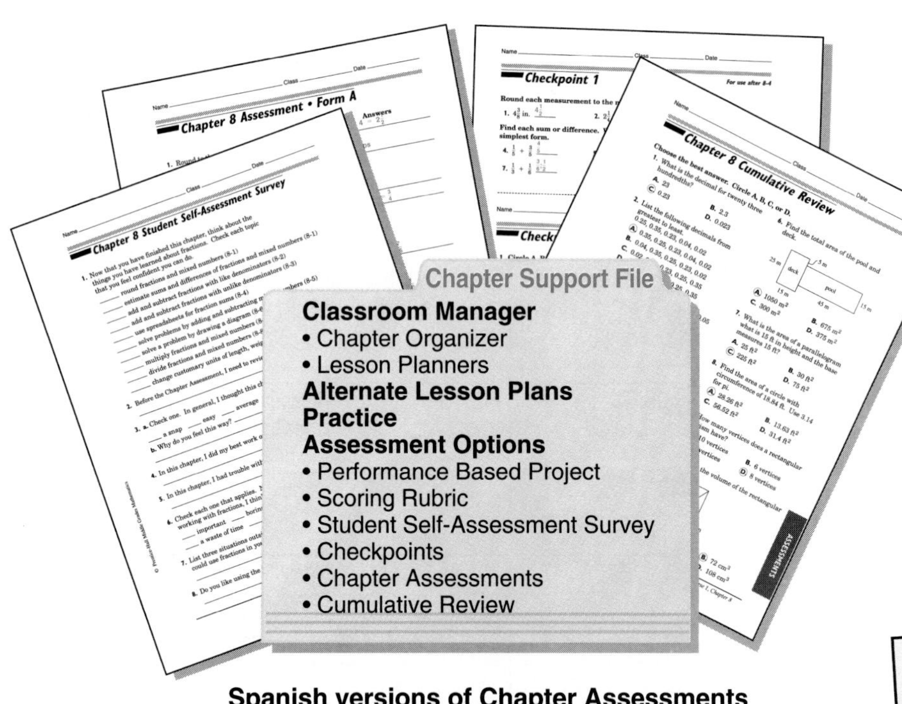

Chapter 8 Assessment • Form A
Chapter 8 Student Self-Assessment Survey
Checkpoint 1
Chapter 8 Cumulative Review
Chapter Support File
Classroom Manager
• Chapter Organizer
• Lesson Planners
Alternate Lesson Plans
Practice
Assessment Options
• Performance Based Project
• Scoring Rubric
• Student Self-Assessment Survey
• Checkpoints
• Chapter Assessments
• Cumulative Review

Spanish versions of Chapter Assessments available in Spanish Resources

Interdisciplinary Units

- **Travel and Geography**
- **Space Exploration**
- **Sports**
- **Consumer Awareness**
- **The Great Outdoors**

English & Spanish

These units include cross-curriculum connections and can be used at any time during the school year. See the Teacher's Guide for more information.

Working with Middle Grade Students

> *"In the middle school years, students come to recognize that numbers have multiple representations, so the development of concepts for fractions, ratios, decimals, and percents and the idea of multiple representations of these numbers need special attention and emphasis. The ability to generate, read, use, and appreciate multiple representations of the same quantity is a critical step in learning to understand and do mathematics. . . ."*
>
> —NCTM CURRICULUM AND EVALUATION STANDARDS

Addressing a Variety of Learning Styles

The mathematical tasks in Chapter 8 involve various learning styles. Here are some examples.

- Visual learners write fractions from visual models (p. 319) and write addition sentences from visual models (p. 322).
- Tactile learners use fraction bars to model the addition of fractions with unlike denominators (p. 326) and use a fraction calculator to compute differences in fractions (p. 327).
- Auditory learners discuss which type of model they prefer to use (p. 323) and discuss rewards involving fractions (p. 331).
- Kinesthetic learners measure hand spans (p. 319) and use string to add and subtract mixed numbers (p. 336).

Alternate Lesson 8-1 addresses tactile learners by having them use manipulatives.

Cultural Connections

Before 200 B.C., units of measure in China were based on parts of the body. Measures of length included tshun (fingers) and chih (hands). Sometimes there were eight tshun in one chih and sometimes there were ten, because "chih" meant both "woman's hand" (8 tshun) and "man's hand" (10 tshun). These old units of measure were replaced by a system of units based on powers of ten.

Team Teaching Suggestion

Work with a social studies teacher to have students compare statistical information in terms of fractions. Students can be given numbers for areas and populations. Possible comparisons would be land areas, geographic features, and census figures.

Form Follows Function

Many students have been taught that it is incorrect to write a fraction in any way other than simplest form. This approach discourages students, and also ignores the fact that the simplest form is not the most useful form in every situation. For example, on checks, it is customary to write fractions with denominators of 100.

Teaching Tip

Middle school students have a tendency to become distracted by their increasing activities and involvements. Sometimes they forget basic concepts they have learned, such as operations with fractions. Have posters to remind them of the steps for adding and subtracting, and for multiplying and dividing fractions.

Bulletin Board

Post large pictures of items on the bulletin board. Have students write a word problem (that involves fractions) for each picture. Ask students to include a solution. Have them exchange word problems (without solutions) with a partner, solve, and check each other's work. You may want to change the pictures periodically. Encourage students to write problems using various operations.

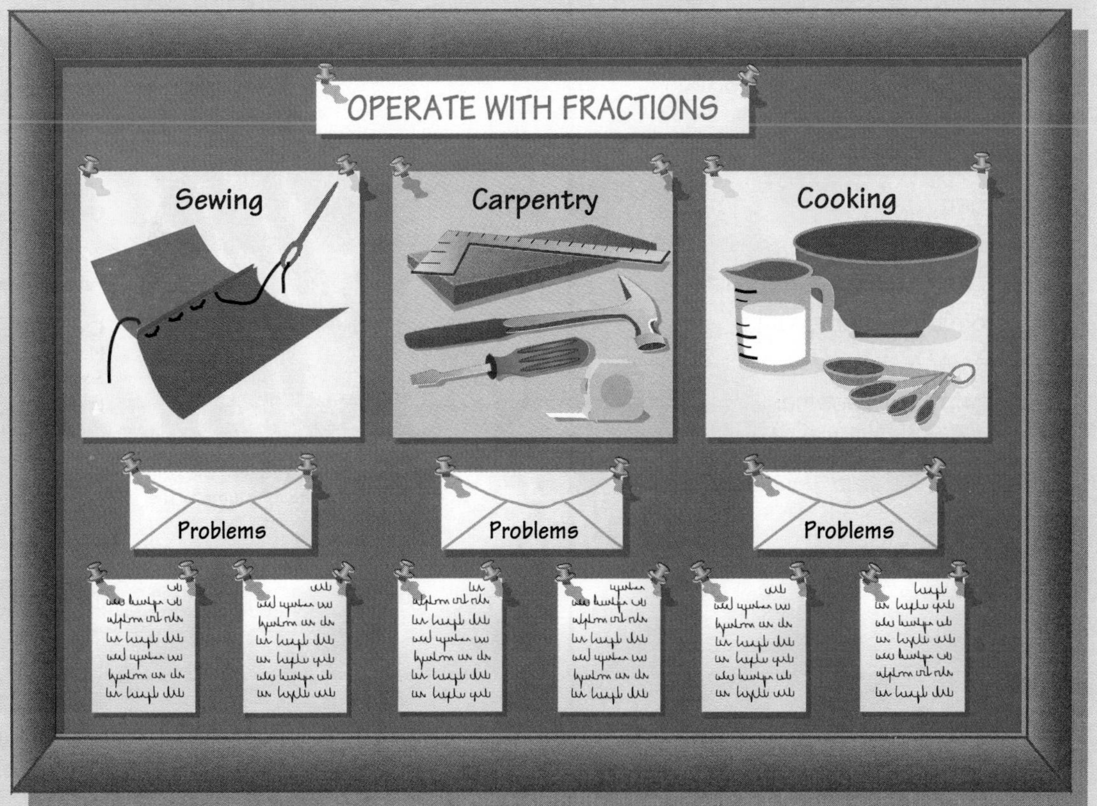

CHAPTER 8 Fraction Operations

Cultural Connections Many world-class athletes have overcome medical problems. Doctors work closely with athletes to help them face their health problems and learn how to deal with them. In spite of asthma, Jackie Joyner-Kersee is a record-breaking track star (entering seven different events). She advises others to find out what their limitations are and then work out a plan to overcome them. Joyner-Kersee reminds us that we can accomplish great things by working on them a little bit at a time.

WORLD VIEW The Summer Olympics for 1972 were held in Munich, Germany, with 7,150 competitors. Compare this with the 311 competitors for the first modern Olympics, held in Athens in 1896. The outstanding competitor of the 1972 Summer Olympics was the American swimmer Mark Spitz, who created an all-time record by winning seven gold medals.

Digging for Data Have students do the following:

- Ask athletic coaches if there are any training programs in the local area for sending athletes to Olympic competition and what the requirements are for potential competitors.
- Ask a librarian to help them find out how many of the 1992 Summer Olympic medals were won by men for each of the ranks (gold, silver, and bronze).

Journal Activity

- Have students read the four objectives for the chapter and explain what they want to learn in this chapter.
- Have students write the rules and a list of equipment needed to play their favorite sport.
- Have students write a story about an Olympic event.

Chapter 8 Contents

Data File Questions

pp. 147, 302, 337, 486

CHAPTER 8 Fraction Operations

Data File 8

Barcelona, Spain, hosted the 1992 Summer Olympics. More than 14,000 athletes represented 172 nations. The athletes competed for medals in 257 events.

Carl Lewis received the gold medal for the long jump at the 1992 Summer Olympics.

Top Medal Winners in the 1992 Summer Olympics

Country	Number of Gold	Number of Silver	Number of Bronze	Total Medals
Unified Team	45	38	29	112
United States of America	37	34	37	108
Germany	33	21	28	82
People's Republic of China	16	22	16	54
Cuba	14	6	11	31
Hungary	11	12	7	30
South Korea	12	5	12	29
France	8	5	16	29
Australia	7	9	11	27
Spain	13	7	2	22
Japan	3	8	11	22
Great Britain	5	3	12	20

Source: *United States Olympic Committee*

Nations Participating in Summer Olympic Games, 1956–1992

Source: *Runner's World*

316

Interdisciplinary Connection [History and Physical Education] The original Olympic Games were held in ancient Greece every four years, from before 776 B.C. to A.D. 396. When the Greeks started the original Olympics, footraces were the only events, but later they added boxing, wrestling, and chariot and horse races. The modern Olympic Games have been held every four years since 1896 (except in wartime). Beginning in the winter of 1994, the Olympic Games will be held every two years, alternating between the summer and winter games.

The Olympic Games are supervised by the International Olympic Committee (IOC). There are about 257 events for competitors.

WHAT YOU WILL LEARN

- how to estimate with fractions
- how to model fraction concepts and operations
- how to use technology to explore patterns
- how to solve problems by drawing a diagram

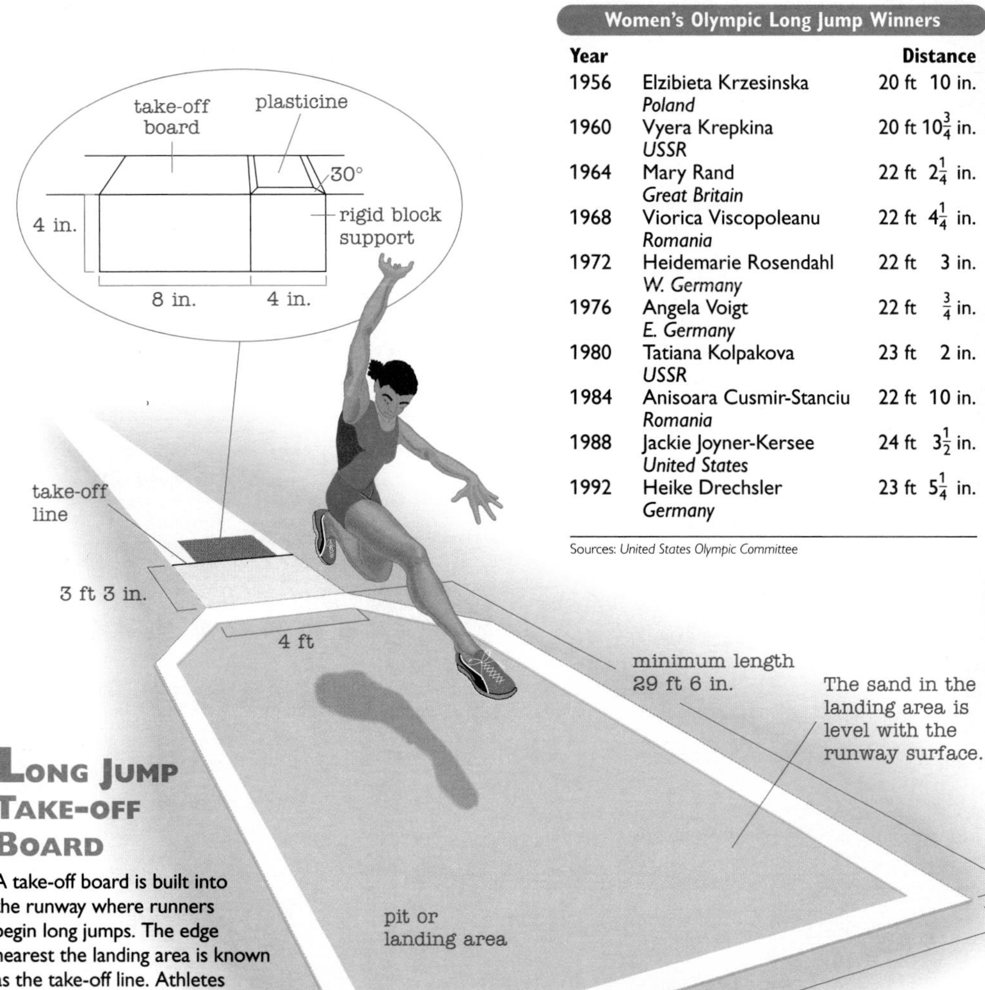

Women's Olympic Long Jump Winners

Year		Distance
1956	Elzibieta Krzesinska *Poland*	20 ft 10 in.
1960	Vyera Krepkina *USSR*	20 ft $10\frac{3}{4}$ in.
1964	Mary Rand *Great Britain*	22 ft $2\frac{1}{4}$ in.
1968	Viorica Viscopoleanu *Romania*	22 ft $4\frac{1}{4}$ in.
1972	Heidemarie Rosendahl *W. Germany*	22 ft 3 in.
1976	Angela Voigt *E. Germany*	22 ft $\frac{3}{4}$ in.
1980	Tatiana Kolpakova *USSR*	23 ft 2 in.
1984	Anisoara Cusmir-Stanciu *Romania*	22 ft 10 in.
1988	Jackie Joyner-Kersee *United States*	24 ft $3\frac{1}{2}$ in.
1992	Heike Drechsler *Germany*	23 ft $5\frac{1}{4}$ in.

Sources: *United States Olympic Committee*

Long Jump Take-off Board

A take-off board is built into the runway where runners begin long jumps. The edge nearest the landing area is known as the take-off line. Athletes cannot step past this line. A clay-like substance is on the edge of the board. If athletes step past the line, their footprint can be seen in the clay.

Source: *Rules of the Game*

Fact of the Day

The oldest person to compete in the Olympics was Oscar Gomer Swahn of Sweden (1847–1927), who won a silver medal for shooting at the 1920 Olympic Games at Antwerp. He also qualified for the 1924 Games, but could not participate due to illness.

—*The Guinness Book of Records*

CHAPTER 8 INVESTIGATION

Memo

Ask students to describe common operations they perform on their calculators. Then ask them to list operations that are difficult or impossible to perform. **(geometry problems, making choices, seeing patterns)**

Some students may have calculators that add fractions. Ask them to describe how to use a calculator to add fractions. Tell the class that in this project students will construct a simple device for adding fractions.

Mission

Have students describe how the nomograph works. Encourage them to construct a simple nomograph (for example, adding halves and fourths) before they take on the assigned instrument. Tell them that the larger the nomograph they construct, the more accuracy they can expect to achieve.

After about half the chapter has been completed, have students show you their work on the project. If they are behind schedule, you may want to give them intermediate deadlines in order to check their work.

Additional Leads to Follow

- *How could you use the nomograph you are making to add fractions with denominators of 32?*

Keeping a Project Notebook

Some suggestions for students' notebooks are these:

- What did you learn when you made a simple nomograph? Write notes about mistakes, successes, and what you would do differently.
- Describe how you can apply what you learned in the preliminary project to the large nomograph you will make.
- List the dates and results of all discussions about the project.

Project Organizer

Related Exercises
p. 325
p. 329
p. 337

Follow Up
p. 356

Teacher's Notes
pp. 318, 325, 329, 337, 356

Materials and Manipulatives
- materials for constructing nomographs

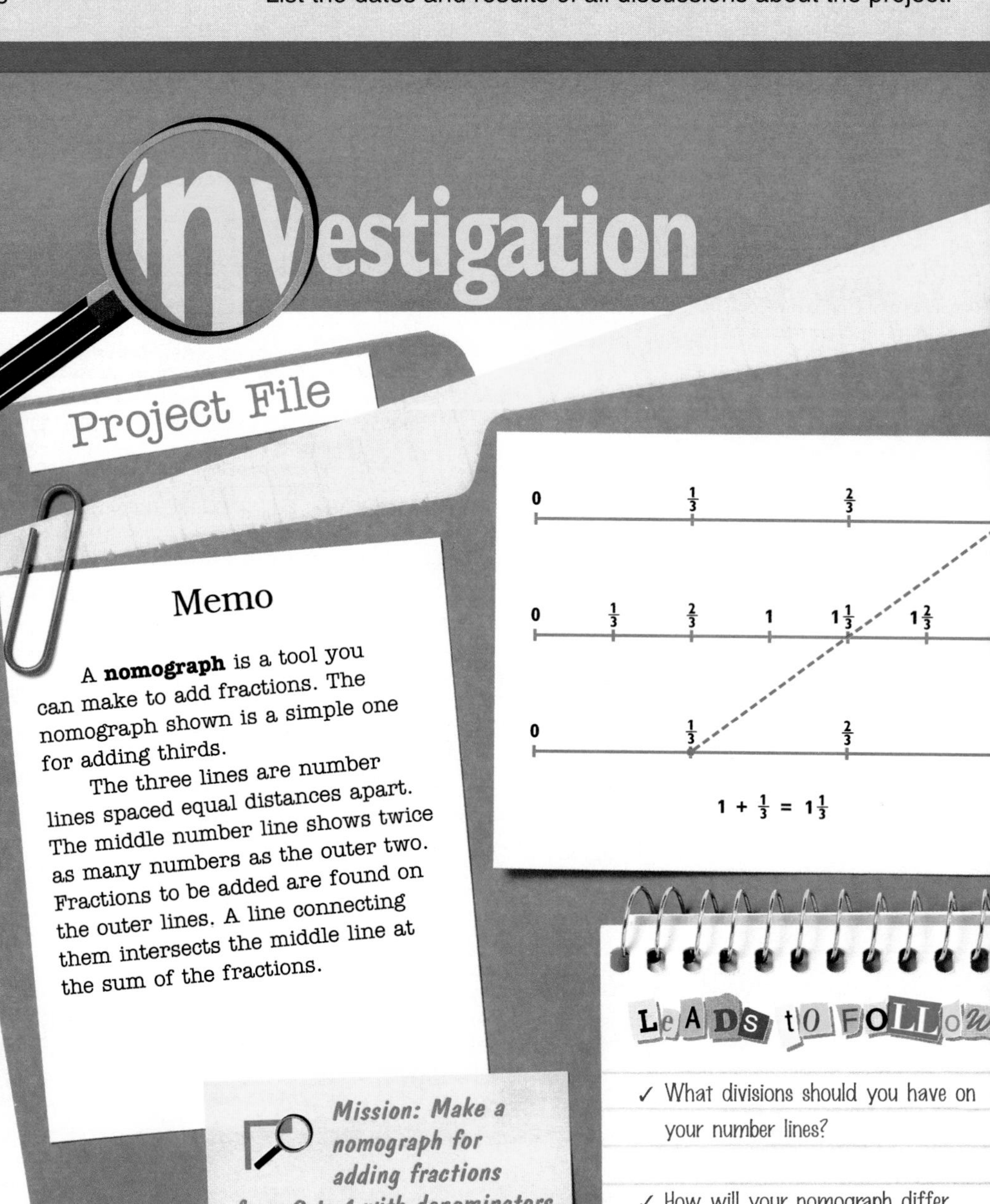

investigation
Project File
Memo
A **nomograph** is a tool you can make to add fractions. The nomograph shown is a simple one for adding thirds.
The three lines are number lines spaced equal distances apart. The middle number line shows twice as many numbers as the outer two. Fractions to be added are found on the outer lines. A line connecting them intersects the middle line at the sum of the fractions.
0
1/3
2/3
0
1/3
2/3
1
1 1/3
1 2/3
0
1/3
2/3
1 + 1/3 = 1 1/3
Mission: Make a nomograph for adding fractions from 0 to 1 with denominators of 2, 4, 8, or 16. Use any materials you wish. Demonstrate how to use the nomograph.
LEADS TO FOLLOW
✓ What divisions should you have on your number lines?
✓ How will your nomograph differ from the nomograph for adding thirds?

318

8-1

Connecting to Prior Knowledge

Have students list as many facts as they can where they might estimate sums or differences of fractions or mixed numbers. For example, they can compare the heights, weights, and ages of people or pets, or the distances they live from school.

ESL **DIVERSITY** Some students may not be familiar with the customary system of measurement because they are from a country where the metric system is used. Review abbreviations of customary units. Have students work in groups with others who are familiar with the customary system until all are confident with its use. Also have students who are acquainted with the metric system explain it to the class and demonstrate its use.

WORK TOGETHER

Have students work in groups of four. Students should measure the hand span of each member of their group. When they have completed measuring, students should compare measurements to see if any remeasuring is necessary. After they have found the range, you may wish to have students identify the median and mode of the set of measurements while other groups complete their work.

KINESTHETIC LEARNERS Have students measure their wrists and compare this measurement to their hand spans.

THINK AND DISCUSS

VISUAL LEARNERS Have students use fraction bars, yardsticks, or rulers to aid in visualizing the fractions in Questions 1–4.

Question 2: Share some general rules about rounding fractions. For instance, if the numerator is much smaller than the denominator, use 0. If the numerator is about half the denominator, use $\frac{1}{2}$. If the numerator is nearly equal to the denominator, use 1.

Question 3: Remind students to round to the nearest half inch.

What's Ahead

- Rounding fractions and mixed numbers
- Estimating sums and differences of fractions and mixed numbers

WHAT YOU'LL NEED

✓ Ruler

8-1 Estimating Sums and Differences

WORK TOGETHER

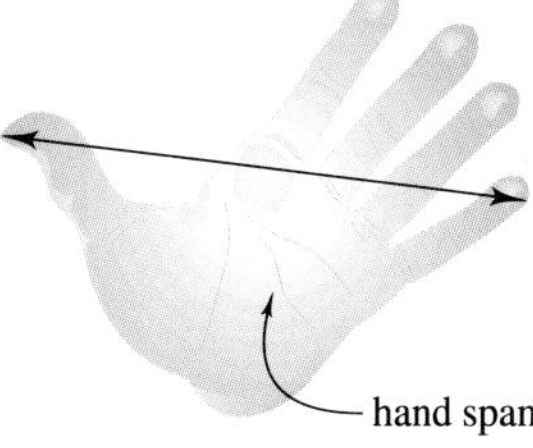

Use a ruler to measure the hand span of each member of your group. Record each measurement to the nearest half inch. What is the range of hand spans within your group? Check student's work.

THINK AND DISCUSS

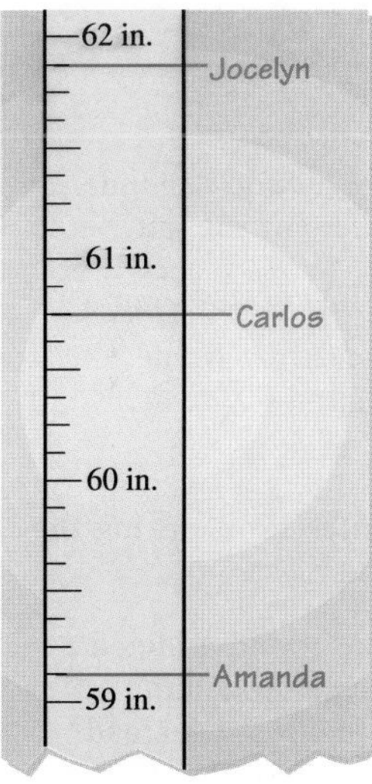

At the beginning of the summer, Jocelyn, Carlos, and Amanda measured their heights. See the growth chart at the left.

1. Round each height to the nearest half inch.
   a. Jocelyn: $61\frac{7}{8}$ in. 62 in. b. Carlos: $60\frac{3}{4}$ in. 61 in. c. Amanda: $59\frac{1}{8}$ in. 59 in.
2. **Discussion** How do you round to the nearest half inch? Did you round when measuring your hand spans? See left.

When you round a measurement to the nearest half inch, you decide if the fraction is closest to 0, $\frac{1}{2}$, or 1.

3. Is each fraction closest to 0, $\frac{1}{2}$, or 1?
   a. $\frac{1}{10}$ 0 b. $\frac{7}{9}$ 1 c. $\frac{5}{12}$ $\frac{1}{2}$ d. $\frac{1}{4}$ the same distance from 0 and $\frac{1}{2}$
4. **Discussion** Does $\frac{1}{4}$ round to 0 or $\frac{1}{2}$? Why? $\frac{1}{2}$; Answers may vary. Sample: When a fraction is halfway, round up.

You can use models to round a fraction.

5. Write the fraction represented by the model. Then round to the nearest $\frac{1}{2}$.

a. 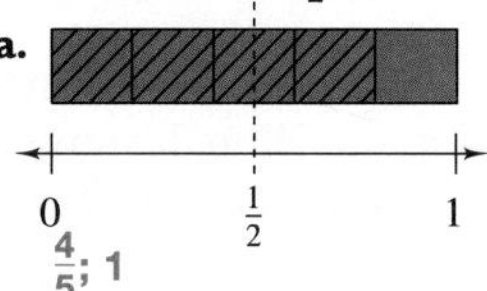

$\frac{4}{5}$; 1

b. 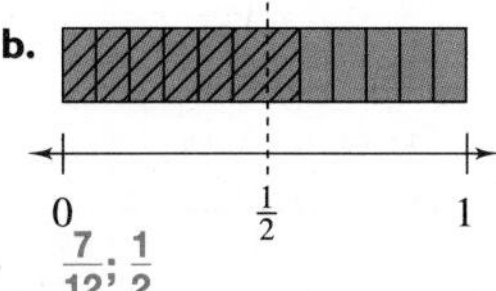

$\frac{7}{12}$; $\frac{1}{2}$

2. Answers may vary. Sample: You see whether the fraction part is closer to 0, $\frac{1}{2}$, or 1.; yes

“We should all be concerned about the future because we will have to spend the rest of our lives there.”
—Charles F. Kettering

Organizer

1. **Focus**
   Connecting to Prior Knowledge
2. **Teach**
   Work Together
   Think and Discuss
3. **Closure**
   Wrap Up

Vocabulary/Symbols
whole numbers

Skills Reviewed in Context of Lesson
- rounding fractions

Materials and Manipulatives
- ruler (1 per group)

Student Resources
Extra Practice
Student Study Guide
Practice, TR Ch. 8, p. 23
Student Study Guide, Spanish Resources, TR
Alternate Lesson, TR Ch. 8, pp. 11–14

Teacher Resources
Teaching Transparency 73
Transparency Masters, TR p. 3
Lesson Planner, TR Ch. 8, p. 2

continues next page

Error Alert! Students may incorrectly round mixed numbers. For example, to round $59\frac{1}{8}$ they may round to 60. ***Remediation*** To round to the nearest whole number, have students decide whether $59\frac{1}{8}$ is closer to 59 or to 60. **(59)** Similarly, have them ask themselves whether $60\frac{5}{8}$ is closer to 60 or 61. **(61)**

Question 11: This is a good time to point out again that rounding gives an *approximate* answer using numbers that are easier to work with. To round to one-half may be more accurate, but it may also be more difficult to use in quick estimations.

Ongoing Assessment Have students work in pairs to round each fraction to the nearest $\frac{1}{2}$.

a. $\frac{3}{5}$ **($\frac{1}{2}$)** b. $\frac{2}{9}$ **(0)** c. $\frac{3}{16}$ **(0)** d. $\frac{5}{8}$ **($\frac{1}{2}$)** e. $\frac{9}{16}$ **($\frac{1}{2}$)**

f. $\frac{4}{10}$ **($\frac{1}{2}$)** g. $\frac{5}{6}$ **(1)** h. $\frac{1}{4}$ **($\frac{1}{2}$)** i. $\frac{3}{15}$ **(0)** j. $\frac{15}{17}$ **(1)**

As you monitor students' performance, notice whether or not they have a sense of how large or small a fraction is, and observe how they reason as they decide how to round.

Wrap Up

What's the Big Idea? Ask students the following questions: *When you round a mixed number, how do you decide whether to round up or down? How does rounding help you estimate a sum or difference containing fractions or mixed numbers?*

Journal Ask students to write a few sentences to answer these questions: *How are estimating sums and differences of fractions and estimating sums and differences of mixed numbers alike? How are they different? Who might be interested in estimating with these numbers?*

Organizer, continued

Prentice Hall Technology

Computer Item Generator

- 8-1

Fact of the Day

Kudzu, a member of the pea family, is native to China and Japan, where it is cultivated for its edible roots and for its stem fibers, known as ko-hemp. It was introduced into the southern United States as an ornamental plant under its Japanese name during the 1870's.

—ACADEMIC AMERICAN ENCYCLOPEDIA

Assignment Options

Core: 12–17, 19, 20, 26–28, 29, 32, 34, MR all	
Reinforce: 18, 21–25, 33	**Enrich:** 30, 31

6. Represent each fraction or mixed number with a model. Use fraction bars, rulers, number lines, or decimal squares. Then round to the nearest $\frac{1}{2}$.

a. $\frac{6}{10}$ $\frac{1}{2}$ **b.** $1\frac{1}{3}$ $1\frac{1}{2}$ **c.** $2\frac{3}{4}$ 3 **d.** $\frac{1}{100}$ 0

To estimate a sum or difference of fractions, you can round each fraction to the nearest $\frac{1}{2}$. Then add or subtract.

7. Estimate the sum $\frac{7}{12} + \frac{4}{5}$.

a. Round each fraction to the nearest $\frac{1}{2}$. So round $\frac{7}{12}$ to ■, and round $\frac{4}{5}$ to ■. $\frac{1}{2}$; 1

b. Add the rounded fractions: ■ + ■ = ■. $\frac{1}{2}$; 1; $1\frac{1}{2}$

8. Estimate the difference $\frac{9}{10} - \frac{3}{7}$. about $\frac{1}{2}$

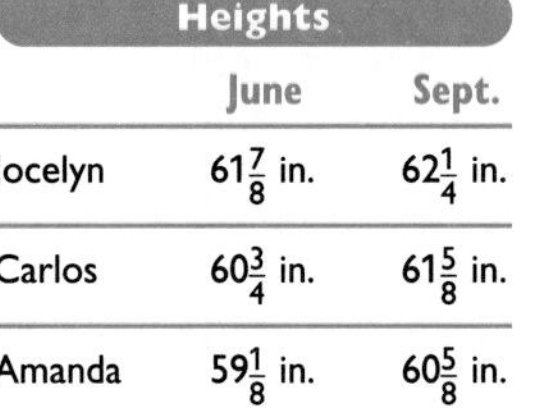

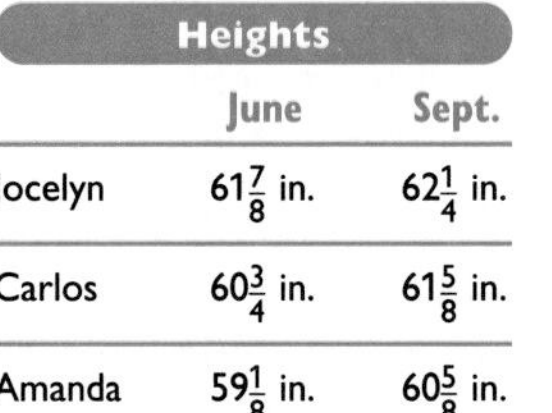

Heights	June	Sept.
Jocelyn	$61\frac{7}{8}$ in.	$62\frac{1}{4}$ in.
Carlos	$60\frac{3}{4}$ in.	$61\frac{5}{8}$ in.
Amanda	$59\frac{1}{8}$ in.	$60\frac{5}{8}$ in.

At the end of the summer, Carlos, Jocelyn, and Amanda measured their heights again. See the table at the left.

9. About how much did Amanda grow during the summer? about 2 in.

a. Round each mixed number to the nearest whole number. So round $59\frac{1}{8}$ to ■, and round $60\frac{5}{8}$ to ■. 59; 61

b. Subtract the whole numbers: ■ − ■ = ■. 61; 59; 2

10. About how much did Carlos and Jocelyn grow during the summer? Which of the three grew the most?
Carlos: 1 in., Jocelyn: 0 in.; Amanda

11. **Discussion** Why does it make sense to round a mixed number to the nearest *whole number* before adding or subtracting? Could you round to the nearest $\frac{1}{2}$ instead?
Answers may vary. Sample: Rounding to the nearest whole number allows you to add or subtract mentally.; yes

David Wells 1992 World Series						
Game	1	2	3	4	5	6
Innings Pitched	1	$1\frac{2}{3}$	–	–	$1\frac{1}{3}$	$\frac{1}{3}$

ON YOUR OWN

Round each measurement to the nearest half inch.

12. $6\frac{5}{8}$ in. $6\frac{1}{2}$ **13.** $10\frac{3}{16}$ in. 10 **14.** $1\frac{7}{8}$ in. 2 **15.** $100\frac{1}{4}$ in. 100

16. Round each measurement in Exercises 12–15 to the nearest inch. 7; 10; 2; 100

17. **Estimation** About how many innings did David Wells of the Toronto Blue Jays pitch in the 1992 World Series? Use the information at the left. about 4 innings

Connections Have students discuss when they might estimate sums and differences in other subject areas.

- **Social Studies** (estimating combined distances on maps)
- **Physical Education** (estimating differences in distances run or jumped)
- **Industrial Arts** (estimating total lengths of framing or woodworking materials)

Reteaching Activity Students will need rulers. Have students measure the length and width of their desks to the nearest $\frac{1}{2}$ in. Have them use the measurements to estimate the perimeter of their desks and the difference between the length and width. Have students discuss how they arrived at each answer.

Exercises 23–28: Suggest that students check to see if they used the correct operation for each exercise.

CRITICAL THINKING Exercise 31 helps students see the shortcomings of estimation.

WRITING Exercise 32 helps students see the shortcomings of estimating by comparing numbers that all round to eight.

ESTIMATION For Exercise 33, students need to write the final answer as a whole number to answer the question.

CONNECTION TO GEOMETRY In Exercise 33, students estimate perimeter.

ON YOUR OWN

ESTIMATION For Exercise 21, tell students to estimate to the nearest foot.

18. **Choose A, B, C, or D.** Which number is closest to 5? C

 A. $4\frac{3}{4}$ B. $4\frac{2}{6}$ C. $4\frac{7}{8}$ D. $4\frac{1}{3}$

Write the fraction modeled by the fraction bar. Then round to the nearest $\frac{1}{2}$.

19. 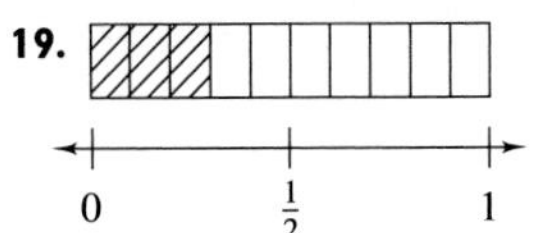 $\frac{3}{10}$; $\frac{1}{2}$

20. 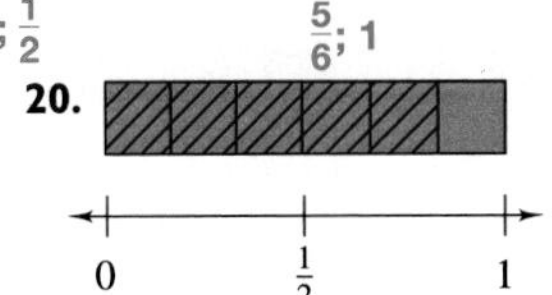 $\frac{5}{6}$; 1

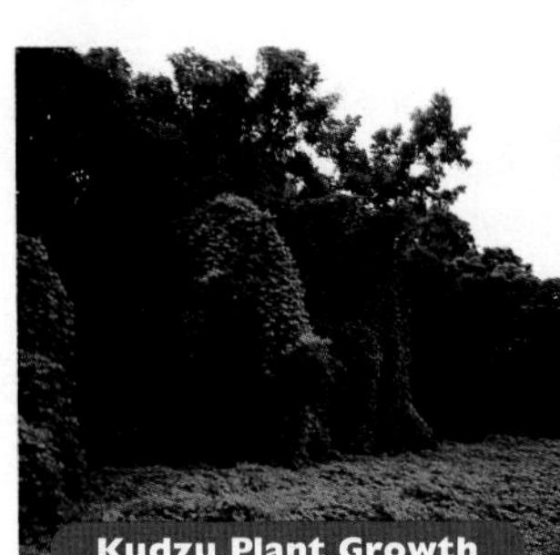

Kudzu Plant Growth

Day	1	2	3	4	5
Height (ft)	$1\frac{1}{12}$	$1\frac{7}{8}$	$2\frac{3}{4}$	$3\frac{5}{8}$	$4\frac{7}{12}$

Use the information at the right.

21. **Estimation** About how much did the Kudzu plant grow from Day 1 to Day 2? about 1 ft

22. Estimate the average growth per day for the Kudzu plant. about 1 ft

Estimate each sum or difference. Estimates may vary.

23. $\frac{7}{8} + \frac{5}{12}$ $1\frac{1}{2}$
24. $\frac{9}{10} - \frac{3}{8}$ $\frac{1}{2}$
25. $3\frac{3}{4} - 1\frac{2}{5}$ 3
26. $\frac{9}{16} + \frac{5}{8}$ 1
27. $7\frac{8}{12} + 4\frac{10}{12}$ 13
28. $4\frac{8}{12} - \frac{5}{6}$ 4

29. Think of three fractions with a sum of about 1. Answers will vary. Sample: $\frac{1}{10}, \frac{2}{10}, \frac{8}{10}$.

30. Think of two mixed numbers with a difference of about 5. Answers will vary. Sample: $7\frac{1}{4}$, $1\frac{3}{4}$

31. **Critical Thinking** Will the sum of many fractions less than $\frac{1}{4}$ ever be greater than 1? Support your answer. See Solution Key.

32. **Writing** Suppose you are a finalist in a contest to build the tallest tower of recycled cans. Your tower is $7\frac{7}{8}$ ft. The other towers are $7\frac{3}{4}$ ft and $7\frac{15}{16}$ ft. If you round each height, will you be able to tell who wins? Explain. See right.

32. No. When the heights are rounded to the nearest half or whole number, they are the same.

33. **Estimation** You plan to put a fence around your garden, shown at the right. About how much fence will you need? about 24 ft

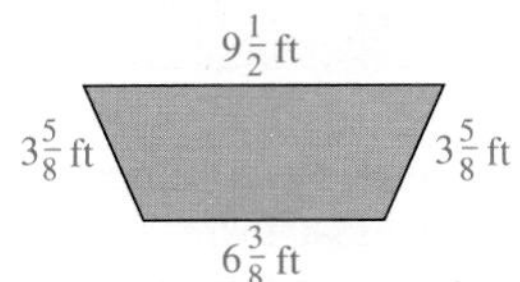

34. **Sewing** Bonita is making a quilt. Material costs $4.96 per yard. She needs $1\frac{5}{8}$ yd of a solid material and $\frac{3}{4}$ of a print material. About how much will the material cost? about $15

Mixed REVIEW

Round to the place of the underlined digit.

1. 0.093 0.1
2. 5.6184 5.618
3. The last Friday of a certain month is the 28th day of the month. What day of the week is the first day of the month? Saturday
4. When I divide a number by 8, add 6, and then multiply by 2, my result is 18. What is my number? 24
5. Find the information needed to answer: Ajayi bought 3 juices. How much did he pay for them?

The cost of each juice.

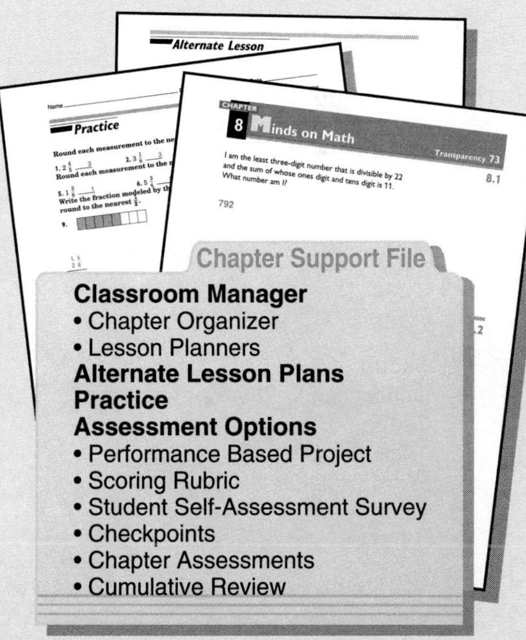

Minds on Math available in Teaching Transparencies

Math Minutes

Daylight Donuts charges $2.00 for 7 doughnuts. How many doughnuts can you buy for $24.00?
84

Materials for 8-2
- fraction bars

8-2

Connecting to Prior Knowledge

Have students recall how they used models to add and subtract decimals. Ask what kinds of models they could use to represent fractions. Choose one of the models discussed and ask them how they think they could use the model to add and subtract fractions.

THINK AND DISCUSS

ESL **AUDITORY LEARNERS** For Questions 3, 6, and 10, have the students work with partners and read aloud their addition or subtraction sentences.

TACTILE LEARNERS Have the students make their own fraction bars, in addition to the ones you provide, and then have them use the fraction bars to solve problems whenever they need to do so.

DIVERSITY Students with disabilities may not be able to draw or use their own fraction bars. Have them work with others who will help them use the fraction bars to solve the problems.

Question 4: Remind students to divide the numerator and denominator by the greatest common factor.

Error Alert! Students may add denominators as well as numerators. They might incorrectly write the result of $\frac{3}{9} + \frac{4}{9}$ as $\frac{7}{18}$. ***Remediation*** Use concrete models to reinforce the idea that denominators tell the size of the parts, so the denominators

“I think self-awareness is probably the most important thing towards being a champion.”

—Billie Jean King

Organizer

1. **Focus**
   Connecting to Prior Knowledge
2. **Teach**
   Think and Discuss
   Work Together
3. **Closure**
   Wrap Up

Skills Reviewed in Context of Lesson
- simplifying fractions

Materials and Manipulatives
- fraction bars (1 set per group)

Student Resources
Extra Practice
Student Study Guide
Practice, TR Ch. 8, p. 24
Student Study Guide, Spanish Resources, TR

Teacher Resources
Teaching Transparencies 73, 76
Transparency Masters, TR pp. 21–24
Overhead Manipulatives: fraction bars
Lesson Planner, TR Ch. 8, p. 3

continues next page

What's Ahead
- Modeling addition and subtraction of fractions with like denominators
- Adding and subtracting fractions with like denominators

WHAT YOU'LL NEED

✓ Fraction bars 

8-2 Adding and Subtracting Fractions

THINK AND DISCUSS

Suppose you and a friend order a pizza for dinner. The pizza is cut into eight equal pieces. You eat two pieces, and your friend eats three pieces. What portion of the pizza is eaten? What portion of the pizza is left? You can model this problem.

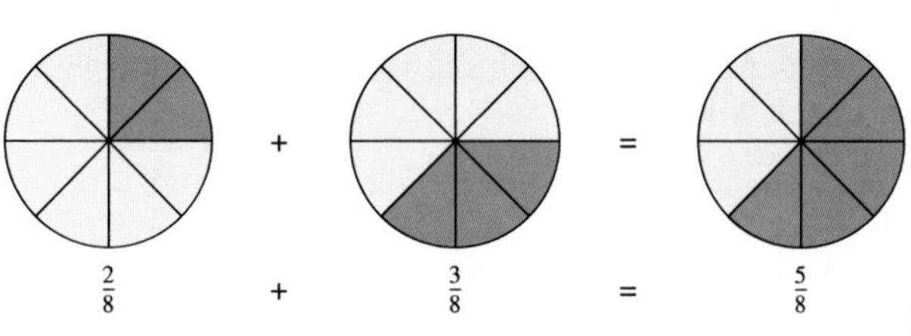

$\frac{2}{8}, \frac{3}{8}, \frac{5}{8}$

1. What fraction represents the amount of pizza you have eaten? What fraction represents the amount of pizza your friend has eaten? What portion of the pizza is eaten?
2. What fraction represents the whole pizza? What portion of the pizza is left? $\frac{8}{8}, \frac{3}{8}$

You can use fraction bars to model addition problems.

3. Write the addition sentence for each model.

a. 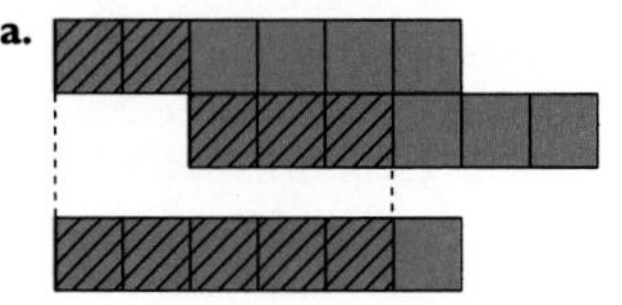

b. 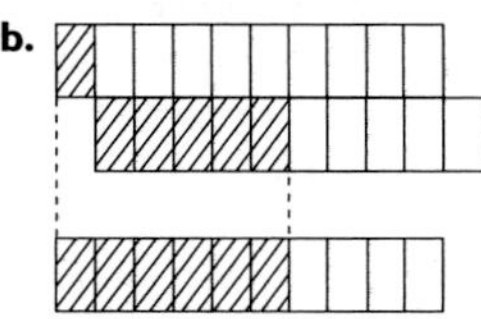

3a. $\frac{2}{6} + \frac{3}{6} = \frac{5}{6}$
3b. $\frac{1}{10} + \frac{5}{10} = \frac{6}{10}$

FLASHBACK
To write a fraction in simplest form, divide the numerator and the denominator by the GCF. Or, use a fraction calculator to simplify.

4. In Exercise 3b. the sum $\frac{6}{10}$ is not in simplest form. Write $\frac{6}{10}$ in simplest form. Use fraction bars to show that the two fractions are equivalent. $\frac{3}{5}$
5. Draw a model and write the sum in simplest form.

   a. $\frac{2}{5} + \frac{1}{5}$ $\frac{3}{5}$ b. $\frac{1}{6} + \frac{1}{6}$ $\frac{1}{3}$ c. $\frac{3}{10} + \frac{7}{10}$ 1 do not change. Then suggest that students write the denominators before they add the numerators.

Question 8: Remind students to simplify their answer.

Question 9: Students have an opportunity to express their opinion on the type of model used. Use this information when choosing models for class examples in future lessons.

Question 14: Have students simplify the right side of the equation before they subtract.

Question 15: Ask students how their other methods are similar to solving the equation. *Did you subtract the same amounts?*

Ongoing Assessment Have students work in pairs. Tell each pair to make models of the fractions $\frac{3}{8}$, $\frac{1}{8}$, $\frac{4}{8}$, and $\frac{7}{8}$ and use them to complete this activity. Monitor students' performance to see that they understand the relationship among the fractions.

- *Write an addition sentence that must be simplified.*
  (Possible answer: $\frac{3}{8} + \frac{1}{8} = \frac{4}{8} = \frac{1}{2}$)
- *Write a subtraction sentence that must be simplified.*
  (Possible answer: $\frac{7}{8} - \frac{3}{8} = \frac{4}{8} = \frac{1}{2}$)
- *Write an addition sentence and a related subtraction sentence using one variable.*
  (Possible answers: $\frac{4}{8} + x = \frac{7}{8}$; $\frac{7}{8} - x = \frac{4}{8}$ or $\frac{7}{8} - \frac{4}{8} = x$)

Journal Imagine that a new student enters your class. He has been educated in a country that uses the metric system and has not worked with fractions. Describe how you would go about helping him learn how to add and subtract fractions.

The sum of fractions is sometimes greater than 1.

6. Write the addition sentence for the model shown below. Write the sum as a mixed number in lowest terms. $\frac{3}{4} + \frac{3}{4} = \frac{6}{4}$; $1\frac{1}{2}$

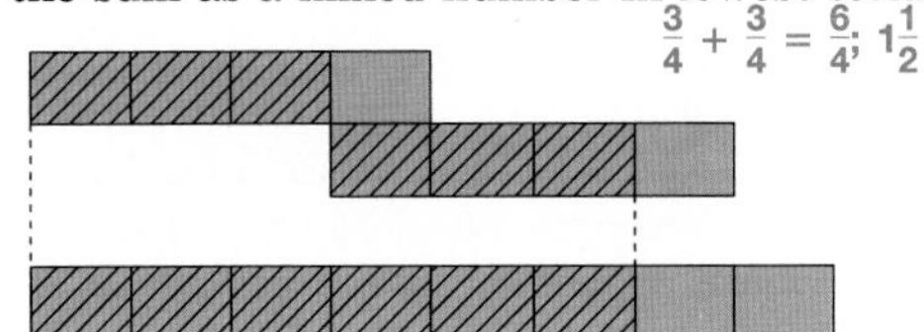

7. Draw a model to represent $\frac{4}{5} + \frac{3}{5} = \frac{7}{5}$. Write $\frac{7}{5}$ as a mixed number. Does the result match your model? See Solution Key.

FLASHBACK

To write an improper fraction as a mixed number, divide the numerator by the denominator.

You can model subtraction problems. Suppose there are 3 pieces of a pizza. You eat 1 piece. The circles show what's left.

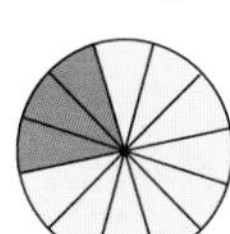 − 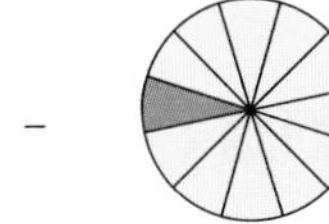 = 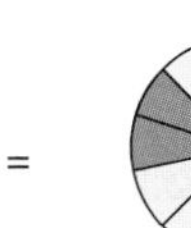 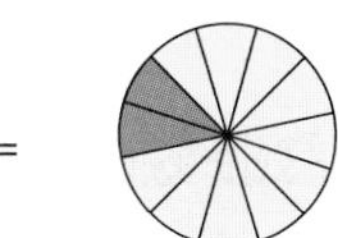

8. Use the model to write a subtraction sentence for the problem. What portion of the pizza is left? $\frac{3}{12} - \frac{1}{12} = \frac{2}{12}$; $\frac{1}{6}$

9. **Discussion** You can also use fraction bars to model this problem. Do you prefer circles or fraction bars? Why? Answers will vary. Check student's work

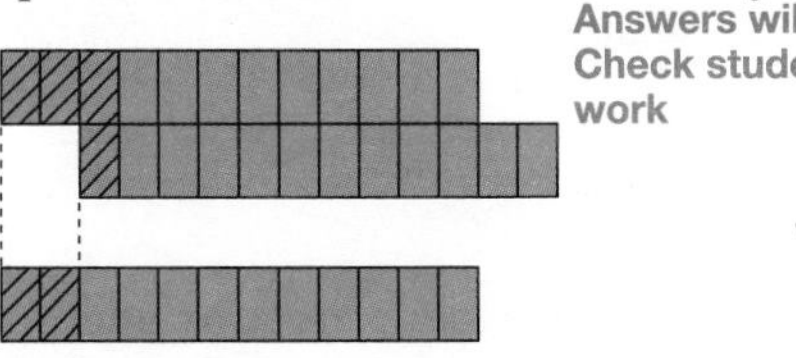

Pizza originated in Naples, Italy. The first pizza restaurant in the United States opened in 1905 in New York City.

10. Write the subtraction sentence for each model.

a. $\frac{3}{4} - \frac{2}{4} = \frac{1}{4}$

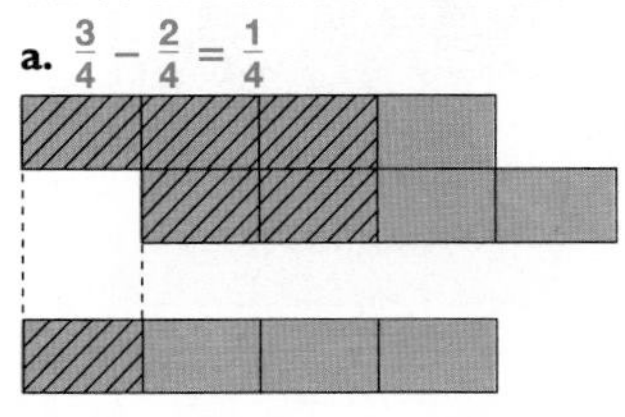

b. $\frac{7}{10} - \frac{3}{10} = \frac{4}{10}$ or $\frac{2}{5}$

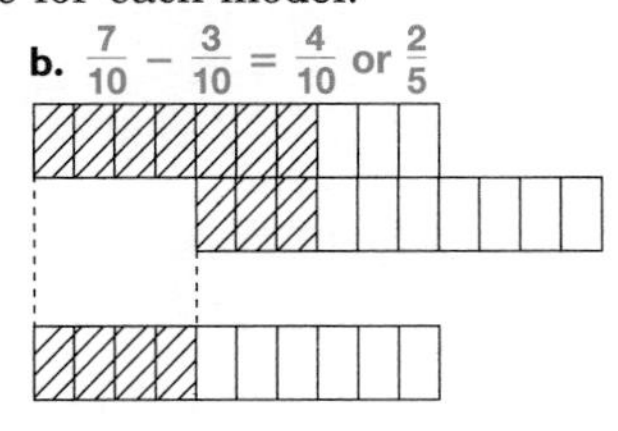

11. Draw a model and write the difference in simplest form.

a. $\frac{5}{6} - \frac{1}{6}$ $\frac{2}{3}$ b. $\frac{3}{8} - \frac{1}{8}$ $\frac{1}{4}$ c. $\frac{9}{10} - \frac{7}{10}$ $\frac{1}{5}$

Organizer, continued

Prentice Hall Technology

Multimedia Math
- Hot Page™ 8-2
- Math Tools, Fraction Strips

Computer Item Generator
- 8-2

Fact of the Day

The peanut is native to South America. It was introduced to Africa by European explorers and later was brought to North America from there. It is now cultivated in more than 40 countries on six continents.

—ACADEMIC AMERICAN ENCYCLOPEDIA

WORK TOGETHER

Have markers available for students who wish to decorate their pizza with various toppings. Tell students to use separate sheets of paper for their problem and solution. When groups have finished their work have them trade problems with another group. Students may later exchange papers to check solutions with their "solution key."

Wrap Up

What's the Big Idea? Ask students: *How do you add and subtract fractions with like denominators?*

Connections Have students discuss real-life situations where addition and subtraction of fractions are used.

- **Consumer** (determining the total amount of fabric or ingredients needed)
- **Music** (writing or reading music)
- **Industrial Arts** (finding the total amount of material needed for a project)

Reteaching Activity Display this number line on the chalkboard:

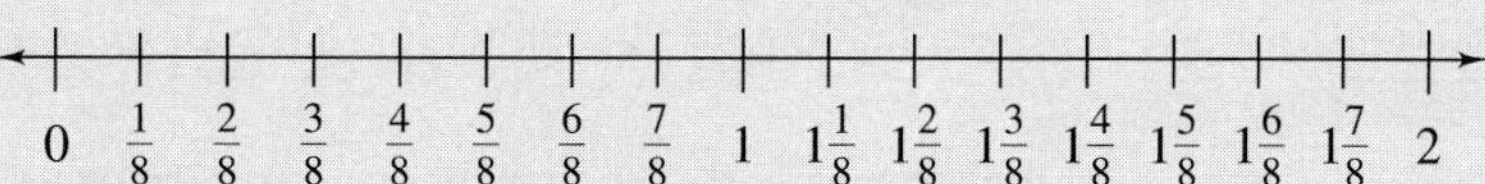

Demonstrate how to use the number line to find the result for each expression below.

a. $\frac{2}{8} + \frac{3}{8}$ **($\frac{5}{8}$)** b. $\frac{6}{8} + \frac{4}{8}$ **($1\frac{2}{8}$ or $1\frac{1}{4}$)** c. $\frac{6}{8} - \frac{4}{8}$ **($\frac{2}{8}$ or $\frac{1}{4}$)**

Then have students draw a number line from 0 to 2 with intervals of $\frac{1}{5}$. Have students use the number line to find each result below.

d. $\frac{1}{5} + \frac{3}{5}$ **($\frac{4}{5}$)** e. $\frac{3}{5} + \frac{4}{5}$ **($1\frac{2}{5}$)** f. $\frac{5}{5} - \frac{3}{5}$ **($\frac{2}{5}$)**

PH Multimedia Math Hot Page™ 8-2

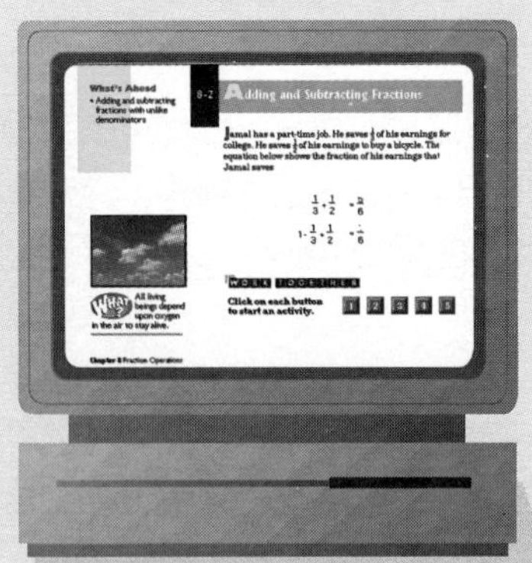

Assignment Options

Core: 16–21, 26–28, 38–40, 45, MR all	
Reinforce: 22–25, 29–34, 41–44	**Enrich:** 35–37

12. **Discussion** How can you add or subtract fractions without using a model? Develop a rule for adding and subtracting fractions with like denominators. **Add or subtract the numerators and keep the denominator the same.**

You can use an equation to solve some fraction problems. Suppose you and a friend order a pizza with eight equal pieces. Your friend eats three pieces and asks how many you have eaten. You do not remember! You both look at the pizza and see that two pieces are left. What portion of the pizza did you eat?

13. To solve this problem, write the equation $\frac{3}{8} + x = \frac{8}{8} - \frac{2}{8}$. What does each part of the equation represent? **See left.**

14. Solve for x. What portion of the pizza did you eat? $\frac{3}{8}$

15. **Discussion** Think of another way to solve this problem. $\frac{8}{8} - \frac{3}{8} - \frac{2}{8} = \frac{3}{8}$

13. $\frac{3}{8}$ = the portion your friend ate; x = the portion you ate; $\frac{8}{8}$ = whole pizza; $\frac{2}{8}$ = portion uneaten

WORK TOGETHER

Check student's work.

Work with a partner. Draw a diagram of a pizza. Make your pizza rectangular or circular. Divide the pizza into as many equal pieces as you wish. Write a problem about yourselves and your pizza. Make sure the problem uses addition or subtraction of fractions. Write a complete solution to your problem. Draw a model or a diagram to show the problem and your solution.

Mixed REVIEW

Name each space figure. Give the number of faces, edges, and vertices. See below.

1. 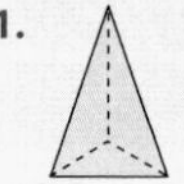 2. 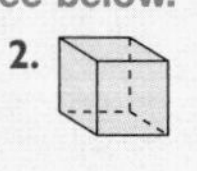

Estimate each sum or difference.

3. $\frac{9}{10} + \frac{3}{4}$ about 2

4. $6\frac{7}{12} - 2\frac{11}{12}$ about 4

5. Akira spent one third of his money, then spent $6, then spent half the money he had left to leave him with exactly $4. How much money did he start with? $21

1. triangular pyramid; 4; 6; 4
2. cube; 6; 12; 8

ON YOUR OWN

Write an addition sentence for each model.

16. $\frac{5}{12} + \frac{2}{12} = \frac{7}{12}$ 17. $\frac{1}{5} + \frac{3}{5} = \frac{4}{5}$

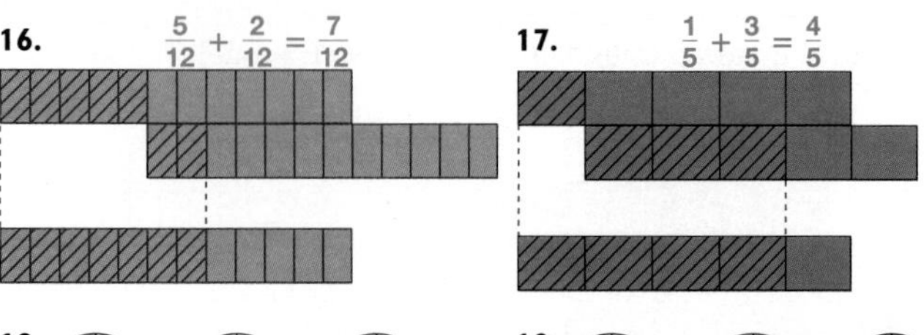

18. 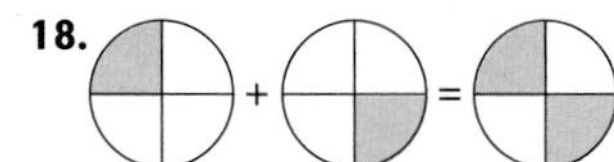 $\frac{1}{4} + \frac{1}{4} = \frac{2}{4}$ or $\frac{1}{2}$

19. 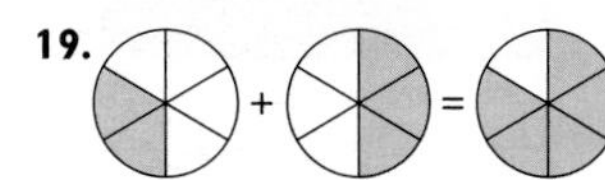 $\frac{2}{6} + \frac{3}{6} = \frac{5}{6}$

ON YOUR OWN

Exercise 24: Students' models must show that the solution is greater than one.

Exercise 25b: Students may need to draw or use a fraction model to divide $\frac{1}{2}$ in half.

MENTAL MATH For Exercises 26–31, emphasize that students check whether they are to add or subtract before solving.

Exercises 28 and 30: Students must add mentally and then change an improper fraction to a mixed number.

WRITING Exercises 35–37 require students to match correctly the colors of the flag to fractions used in the problems.

MENTAL MATH In Exercises 38–43, students undo addition and subtraction in equations with fractions.

CHAPTER INVESTIGATION You may wish to discuss nomographs before you assign Exercise 45.

Write a subtraction sentence for each model.

20. 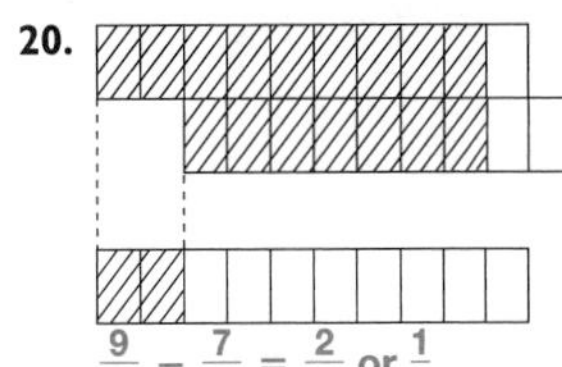

$\frac{9}{10} - \frac{7}{10} = \frac{2}{10}$ or $\frac{1}{5}$

21. 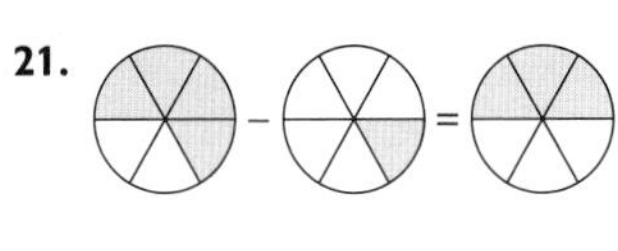

$\frac{4}{6} - \frac{1}{6} = \frac{3}{6}$ or $\frac{1}{2}$

Draw a model and find each sum or difference.

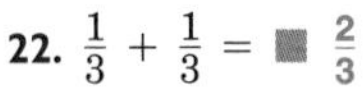

22. $\frac{1}{3} + \frac{1}{3} = ■$ $\frac{2}{3}$

23. $\frac{9}{10} - \frac{1}{10} = ■$ $\frac{8}{10}$ or $\frac{4}{5}$

24. $\frac{4}{7} + \frac{6}{7} = ■$ $\frac{10}{7}$ or $1\frac{3}{7}$ See right.

25. **Cooking** Peanut sauce is commonly used as a base for stews and soups in Nigeria, Ghana, and Sierra Leone.
    a. To make the sauce spicier, you decide to double the amount of cayenne. How much cayenne will you use?
    b. You decide to use an equal amount of apple and apricot juices. How much of each type of juice will you use?

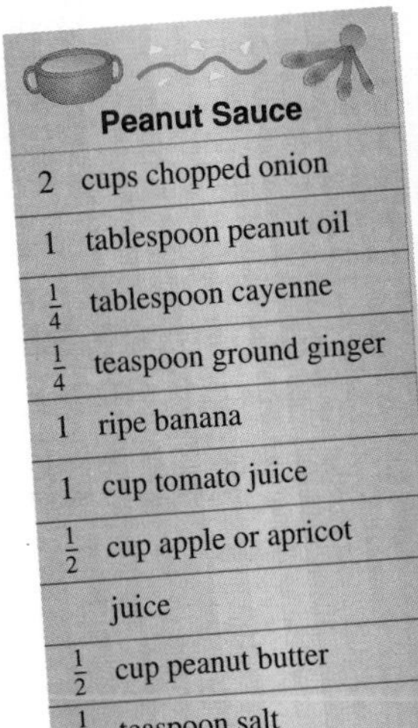

Peanut Sauce
2 cups chopped onion
1 tablespoon peanut oil
1/4 tablespoon cayenne
1/4 teaspoon ground ginger
1 ripe banana
1 cup tomato juice
1/2 cup apple or apricot juice
1/2 cup peanut butter
1/2 teaspoon salt

25. a. $\frac{1}{2}$ tablespoon

25. a. $\frac{1}{4}$ cup

Mental Math **Decide if the answer will be greater than 1. Write *yes* or *no*. Then add or subtract.**

26. $\frac{4}{7} + \frac{2}{7}$ no; $\frac{6}{7}$

27. $\frac{4}{5} - \frac{2}{5}$ no; $\frac{2}{5}$

28. $\frac{7}{10} + \frac{4}{10}$ yes; $\frac{11}{10}$ or $1\frac{1}{10}$

29. $\frac{8}{9} - \frac{4}{9}$ no; $\frac{4}{9}$

30. $\frac{5}{6} + \frac{4}{6}$ yes; $\frac{9}{6}$ or $1\frac{1}{2}$

31. $\frac{3}{3} - \frac{1}{3}$ no; $\frac{2}{3}$

Is each answer correct? Write *yes* or *no*. If *no*, write the correct answer. Write answers in simplest form.

32. $\frac{3}{10} + \frac{3}{10} = \frac{4}{5}$ no; $\frac{3}{5}$

33. $\frac{7}{12} - \frac{3}{12} = \frac{4}{12}$ yes; $\frac{1}{3}$

34. $\frac{5}{6} + \frac{4}{6} = 1\frac{1}{2}$ yes

Writing **The flag of Thailand is at the right. Describe what each equation can represent in the flag.** See Sol. Key.

35. $\frac{1}{6} + \frac{1}{6} = \frac{2}{6}$

36. $\frac{6}{6} - \frac{4}{6} = \frac{2}{6}$

37. $\frac{1}{3} + \frac{1}{3} = \frac{2}{3}$

Mental Math **Find *x*. Do not write in simplest form.**

38. $\frac{5}{6} - \frac{1}{6} = x$ $\frac{4}{6}$

39. $\frac{3}{10} + x = \frac{8}{10}$ $\frac{5}{10}$

40. $x + \frac{2}{5} = \frac{4}{5}$ $\frac{2}{5}$

41. $x = \frac{2}{8} + \frac{5}{8}$ $\frac{7}{8}$

42. $\frac{6}{7} - x = \frac{4}{7}$ $\frac{2}{7}$

43. $x - \frac{1}{3} = \frac{1}{3}$ $\frac{2}{3}$

44. **Sports** In an archery tournament, Zwena hit the target 9 times out of 12. What portion of Zwena's arrows did not hit the target? Draw a model to show your solution. $\frac{3}{12}$ or $\frac{1}{4}$

45. **Investigation (p. 318)** Make a nomograph to add $\frac{2}{6}$ and $\frac{3}{6}$. $\frac{5}{6}$; See Solution Key for diagram.

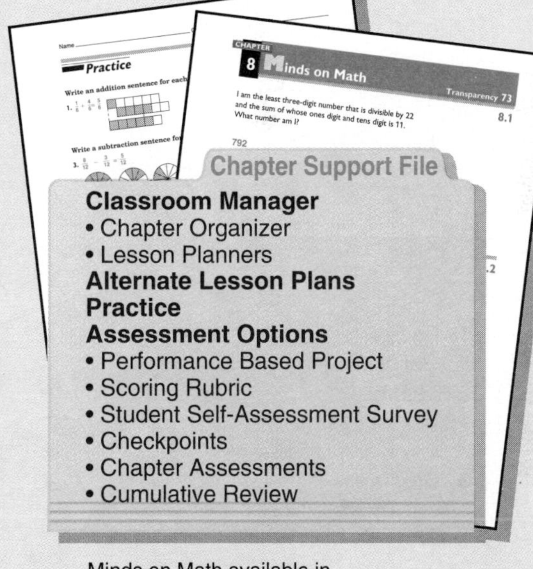

Minds on Math available in Teaching Transparencies

Erica had a piece of red licorice 15 in. long. If she cut it into 10 equal pieces, how long would each piece be?
$1\frac{1}{2}$ in.

Materials for 8-3

- fraction bars
- calculator

8-3

Connecting to Prior Knowledge

Tell students that you have seven nickels and four pennies in your pocket. Ask them to find the total amount of money you have in your pocket. **(39 cents)** Have students describe how they arrived at their answer.

KINESTHETIC LEARNERS Students will need measuring cups with fourths and halves marked, plastic containers, and water. Have students measure $\frac{1}{4}$ c of water and pour it into the plastic container. Then measure $\frac{1}{2}$ c of water and pour it into the container. Finally pour back the combined water into the measuring cup. Challenge students to write an addition sentence to show what they did. **($\frac{1}{4} + \frac{1}{2} = \frac{3}{4}$)**

WORK TOGETHER

Have one student record the steps taken to solve the problem. Be sure they include which models they tried and exactly how they used the models. If students become frustrated because of the unlike denominators, make suggestions about which models they could use to solve the problem.

WRITING For Question 2, have each group turn in one explanation. As a class, discuss the different approaches students used to solve the problems and which approaches seemed to be most effective.

THINK AND DISCUSS

ESL **ESL** Make sure students are familiar with terms such as *numerator* and *denominator.* A poster illustrating these terms may be a helpful reference for students.

ESL **AUDITORY LEARNERS** Have students work with a partner and explain to each other what the LCD is, and how they can use the LCD to find equivalent fractions for Example 1.

"A man without knowledge, and I have read, may well be compared to one that is dead."

—THOMAS INGELEND

Organizer

1. **Focus**
   Connecting to Prior Knowledge
2. **Teach**
   Work Together
   Think and Discuss
3. **Closure**
   Try These
   Wrap Up

Skills Reviewed in Context of Lesson
- adding and subtracting simple fractions

Materials and Manipulatives
- fraction bars (1 set per pair)
- calculator (1 per group)

Student Resources
Extra Practice
Student Study Guide
Practice, TR Ch. 8, p. 25
Student Study Guide, Spanish Resources, TR

Teacher Resources
Teaching Transparencies 17–19, 22–29, 73
Transparency Masters, TR pp. 21–24
Overhead Manipulatives: fraction bars
Lesson Planner, TR Ch. 8, p. 4

continues next page

What's Ahead
- Using a variety of methods to add and subtract fractions with unlike denominators

WHAT YOU'LL NEED
✓ Fraction bars
✓ Calculator

8-3 Unlike Denominators

WORK TOGETHER

Work with a partner to solve the problem below. Try to think of several different ways to solve it. Use fraction bars, circle models, number lines, rulers, or any other materials.

1. Shika is preparing a display of crystals and rocks for the science fair. She needs $\frac{1}{4}$ yd of black velvet for the crystals and $\frac{5}{12}$ yd for the rocks. How many yards of black velvet does Shika need for the display? $\frac{8}{12}$ or $\frac{2}{3}$ yd

2. **Writing** Explain how you solved the problem. How is this problem different from problems in the previous lesson? Answers may vary. Sample: Change $\frac{1}{4}$ to $\frac{3}{12}$. Then add $\frac{3}{12}$ and $\frac{5}{12}$; The denominators are different.

THINK AND DISCUSS

There are many different ways to solve problems like the one above. You can use fraction bars even when the denominators are not the same.

Example 1 Find the sum $\frac{1}{4} + \frac{2}{3}$.

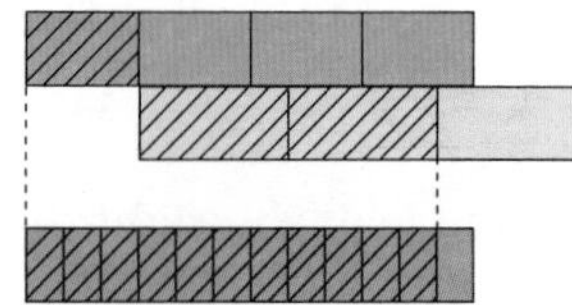

Use the fraction bar for $\frac{1}{4}$.
Use the fraction bar for $\frac{2}{3}$.
Find a fraction bar with an area equal to the sum.

$\frac{1}{4} + \frac{2}{3} = \frac{11}{12}$

WHY? Quartz crystals are used in clocks. Because of the electric current that passes through the crystal, quartz clocks keep time within 1 second each year.

Source: *Did You Know?*

3. **Discussion** Why does the sum of $\frac{1}{4}$ and $\frac{2}{3}$ not have a denominator of 4 or 3? Neither 4 nor 3 is a common denominator.

4. **Discussion** Draw circle models for $\frac{1}{4}$ and $\frac{2}{3}$. How can you use the models to find the sum $\frac{1}{4} + \frac{2}{3}$? See Solution Key.

5. Use models to find each sum or difference.
   a. $\frac{1}{2} + \frac{1}{3}$ $\frac{5}{6}$
   b. $\frac{4}{5} - \frac{1}{2}$ $\frac{3}{10}$
   c. $\frac{5}{6} + \frac{1}{9}$ $\frac{17}{18}$
   d. $\frac{1}{2} - \frac{1}{4}$ $\frac{1}{4}$

Example 1

Have students carefully line up the three fraction bars used so they can see that twelfths are necessary. Some students may need to try other fraction bars so they can see why they do not work for this problem.

Additional Example *Find the sum $\frac{1}{3} + \frac{5}{12}$.*

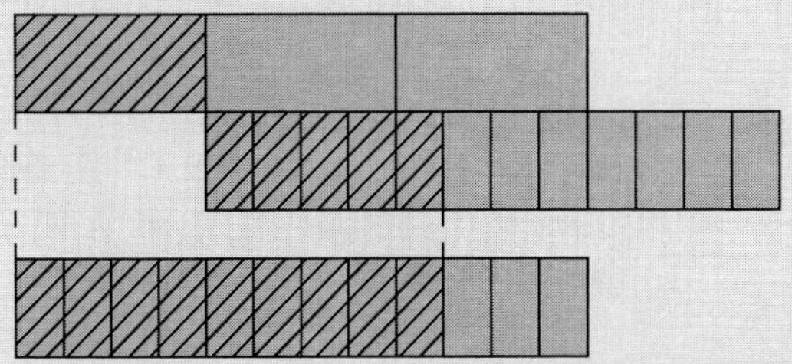

$\frac{1}{3} + \frac{5}{12} = \frac{9}{12} = \frac{3}{4}$

Question 3: Have students line up the fraction bars marked in fourths and thirds to see that no lines match up.

Example 2

Have students tell why bars are placed differently for subtraction.

Additional Example *Find the difference $\frac{1}{3} - \frac{1}{4}$.*

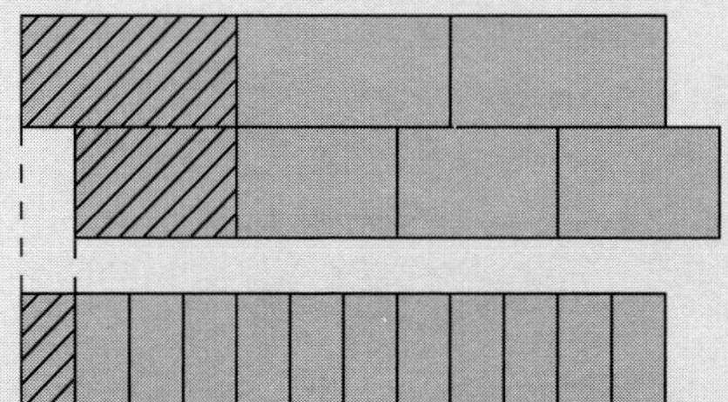

$\frac{1}{3} - \frac{1}{4} = \frac{1}{12}$

Error Alert! Students may have trouble finding the LCD for fractions whose denominators are not multiples or may find a common denominator that is not the least. ***Remediation*** Have students list the multiples of the greater denominator and identify the first number that is a multiple of the lesser denominator.

You can use fraction bars another way. Find equivalent fractions with the same denominator, then add or subtract.

Example 2 Find the difference $\frac{1}{2} - \frac{1}{3}$.

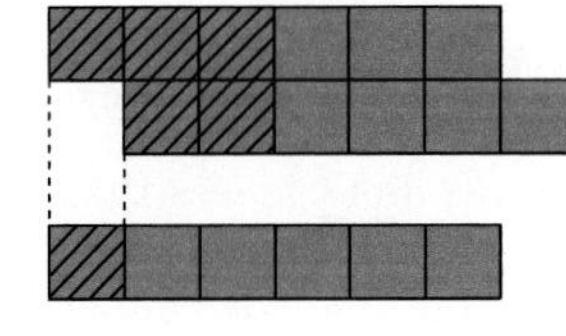

Use the $\frac{3}{6}$ fraction bar for $\frac{1}{2}$.

Use the $\frac{2}{6}$ fraction bar for $\frac{1}{3}$.

Subtract: $\frac{3}{6} - \frac{2}{6}$.

$\frac{1}{2} - \frac{1}{3} = \frac{3}{6} - \frac{2}{6} = \frac{1}{6}$

6. What is the least common denominator (LCD) of $\frac{1}{2}$ and $\frac{1}{3}$? 6
7. Draw circle models for $\frac{1}{2}$ and $\frac{1}{3}$. Then divide each circle into six equal parts. Use the models to find the difference. $\frac{1}{6}$
8. Add or subtract. Use models and equivalent fractions.
   a. $\frac{3}{5} + \frac{1}{10}$ $\frac{7}{10}$ b. $\frac{5}{6} - \frac{2}{3}$ $\frac{1}{6}$ c. $\frac{1}{3} + \frac{1}{4}$ $\frac{7}{12}$ d. $\frac{5}{12} - \frac{1}{4}$ $\frac{2}{12}$ or $\frac{1}{6}$

You can use equivalent fractions without models.

Example 3 Find the sum $\frac{7}{8} + \frac{1}{6}$.

Estimate: $1 + 0 = 1$ — Round to the nearest $\frac{1}{2}$.

The LCD is 24. — Find the LCD of 8 and 6.

$\frac{7}{8} = \frac{21}{24}$ $\frac{1}{6} = \frac{4}{24}$ — Write equivalent fractions.

$\frac{7}{8} + \frac{1}{6} = \frac{21}{24} + \frac{4}{24} = \frac{25}{24} = 1\frac{1}{24}$ — Add. Write a mixed number.

You can use a fraction calculator to compute.

Example 4 Find the difference $\frac{13}{16} - \frac{5}{8}$.

Estimate: $1 - \frac{1}{2} = \frac{1}{2}$

Press 13 [/] 16 [−] 5 [/] 8 [=] 3/16

$\frac{13}{16} - \frac{5}{8} = \frac{3}{16}$

9. **Discussion** Suppose you have a calculator that does not compute fractions. How can you use the calculator to find a sum or difference of fractions? To find the numerator, enter the problem and multiply by the LCD. The denominator is the LCD.

FLASHBACK
The least common denominator (LCD) is the least common multiple (LCM) of the denominators.

FLASHBACK
To write equivalent fractions, multiply the numerator and the denominator by the same non-zero factor.

Organizer, continued

Prentice Hall Technology

Multimedia Math
- Math Tools, Fraction Strips

Computer Item Generator
- 8-3

Other Available Technology

calculator

Math Blaster Plus by Davidson & Associates: Exercises 16–24 *(optional)*

Fact of the Day

Quartz is the most abundant silica mineral; it is made almost solely of silicon dioxide. The name quartz is believed to have originated in the early 1500's from the Saxon word *querklufterz* (cross-vein ore).

—*Academic American Encyclopedia*

Example 3
Some students may benefit from a review of equivalent fractions.

Example 4
Take the time to explain the function of each key used.

Additional Example *Find the difference $\frac{5}{6} - \frac{2}{3}$.*

Estimate: 1 − 1 = 0

5 [/] 6 [−] 2 [/] 3 [=] $\frac{1}{6}$

Example 5
Students should note that estimation does not always work in similar problems. Try $\frac{7}{12}$ and $\frac{4}{11}$ as an example.

Additional Example *John wants to be at school in fifteen minutes. First he has to mail some letters, and the mailbox is $\frac{3}{8}$ of a mile away. Then it is a $\frac{1}{2}$ mi walk from the mailbox to school. John knows he can walk a mile in fifteen minutes. Can he make it to school in time?*

Since $\frac{3}{8}$ is less than $\frac{1}{2}$, the sum $\frac{3}{8} + \frac{1}{2}$ must be less than 1. So, John can make it to school in fifteen minutes.

VISUAL LEARNERS For Example 5, have students show that $\frac{1}{4}$ and $\frac{1}{3}$ are both less than $\frac{1}{2}$ on a number line by estimating where both fractions are located.

TRY THESE

Ongoing Assessment Walk around the room and observe student work on Exercises 11–25. Check to see that they correctly find the least common denominator for Exercises 16–18. Also carefully check the denominators in their answers to make sure they are not incorrectly adding them.

TECHNOLOGY OPTION For Exercises 16–24, students can use fraction software to practice adding and subtracting fractions.

Assignment Options

Core: 26–33, 38–41, 44, MR all	
Reinforce: 34–37, 43	**Enrich:** 42

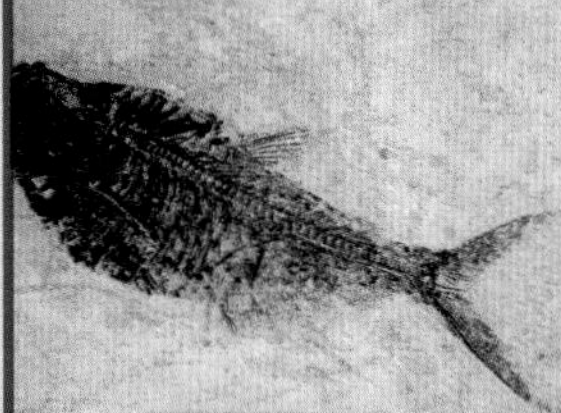

WHAT? A fossil is a rock that contains the preserved remains of a plant or animal. Scientists often date rocks by finding the age of the remains in the rock.

Source: *Rocks and Minerals*

Sometimes you can use estimation to solve a fraction problem.

Example 5 Two students explore a fossil rock ledge along an old road. One student explores $\frac{1}{3}$ mi of the ledge, while the other explores $\frac{1}{4}$ mi of the ledge. Do they explore at least 1 mi of the ledge altogether?

Since $\frac{1}{3}$ is less than $\frac{1}{2}$, and $\frac{1}{4}$ is less than $\frac{1}{2}$, the sum $\frac{1}{3} + \frac{1}{4}$ must be less than 1. So the students do *not* explore at least 1 mi of the ledge altogether.

10. Discussion Describe all the different ways you can solve problems that involve adding or subtracting fractions. Which methods do you prefer? Why? estimation, fraction bars, circles, finding the LCD, using a calculator; Answers will vary. Check student's work.

TRY THESE

Write a number sentence for each model shown.

11. **12.**

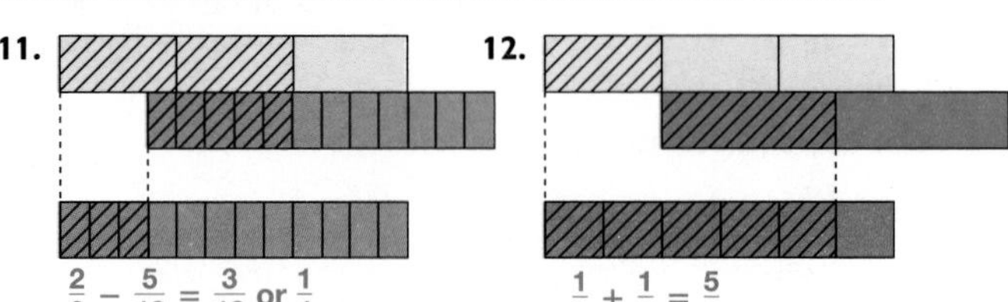

$\frac{2}{3} - \frac{5}{12} = \frac{3}{12}$ or $\frac{1}{4}$ $\frac{1}{3} + \frac{1}{2} = \frac{5}{6}$

Draw a model for each equation. See Solution Key.

13. $\frac{5}{6} - \frac{1}{3} = \frac{3}{6}$ **14.** $\frac{3}{8} + \frac{1}{2} = \frac{7}{8}$ **15.** $\frac{3}{4} + \frac{1}{3} = 1\frac{1}{12}$

Write the LCD. Then add or subtract.

16. $\frac{1}{3} + \frac{5}{8}$ 24; $\frac{23}{24}$ **17.** $\frac{9}{10} - \frac{2}{5}$ 10; $\frac{5}{10}$ or $\frac{1}{2}$ **18.** $\frac{5}{6} - \frac{1}{10}$ 30; $\frac{22}{30}$ or $\frac{11}{15}$

Calculator **Add or subtract. Write in simplest form.**

19. $\frac{7}{10} - \frac{1}{8}$ $\frac{23}{40}$ **20.** $\frac{9}{16} + \frac{3}{4}$ $1\frac{5}{16}$ **21.** $\frac{1}{2} + \frac{1}{3} + \frac{1}{4}$ $1\frac{1}{12}$

Estimation **Is the answer greater or less than 1?**

22. $\frac{1}{8} + \frac{1}{4}$ less **23.** $\frac{4}{5} - \frac{1}{2}$ less **24.** $\frac{1}{2} + \frac{3}{4}$ greater

25. Art Suppose you use $\frac{3}{4}$ yd of felt on the top of a bulletin board display. Then you use another $\frac{2}{3}$ yd on the bottom of the display. How much felt do you use altogether? $1\frac{5}{12}$ yd

5. Wahkuna—pharmacist; Alma—stock broker; Yuji—teacher

Mixed REVIEW

Solve. Write the answer in simplest form.

1. $\frac{4}{9} + \frac{2}{9}$ $\frac{2}{3}$ **2.** $\frac{13}{18} - \frac{11}{18}$ $\frac{1}{9}$

Solve. Use models if they help you.

3. 2.6 + 0.4 = 3 **4.** 3.17 − 1.26 = 1.91

5. Wahkuna, Alma, and Yuji are a pharmacist, a teacher, and a stock broker. Wahkuna met the teacher and the stock broker at a fund-raiser. The teacher went to college with Alma. Match each person with the correct occupation.

See above.

CALCULATOR For Exercises 19–21, use a calculator that can compute fraction sums and differences.

Wrap Up

What's the Big Idea? Ask students: *Why must you first change fractions to equivalent fractions with a like denominator before you add or subtract?*

Journal Read students the following situation and have them write a response. *Your little brother writes $\frac{1}{2} + \frac{2}{3} = \frac{3}{5}$. How would you explain to him why this is incorrect?*

Connections Have students discuss where addition and subtraction of fractions are used:

- **Archeology** (recording the locations and sizes of artifacts)
- **Music** (determining the correct combination of different notes per measure based on the number of beats per note)

Reteaching Activity Have students make and cut apart models to show sums and differences. Have them describe and record each step in the addition and subtraction process.

ON YOUR OWN

CONNECTION TO SOCIAL STUDIES Exercises 28–30 use fractional data about the population in Central America.

WRITING Some students may have difficulties finding four ways to complete the additions for Exercise 37. Encourage them to find as many as they can.

CHAPTER INVESTIGATION For Exercise 44, you may wish to first discuss nomographs in class.

ON YOUR OWN

Write a number sentence for each model.

26. $\frac{2}{5} + \frac{1}{2} = \frac{9}{10}$

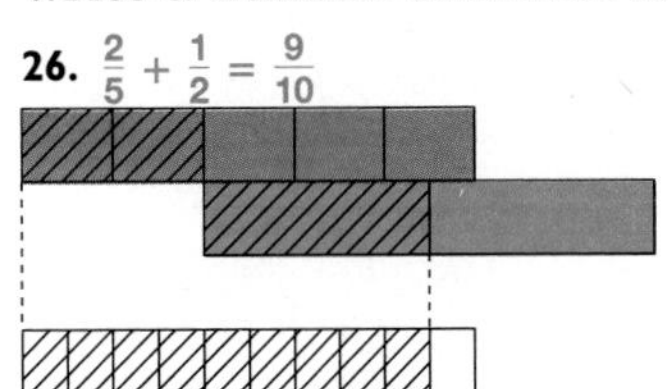

27. $\frac{1}{3} - \frac{1}{6} = \frac{1}{6}$

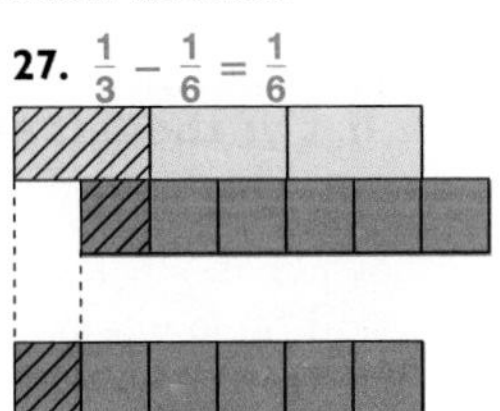

Social Studies **Use the data at the right.**

28. Order the countries from least to greatest population. See right.

29. Is the population of Costa Rica and Nicaragua together greater than or less than the population of Honduras? >

30. Do the fractions add to 1? Why or why not? No; the fractions are estimates. The actual fractions would not be easy to work with.

Choose **Use any method to add or subtract.**

31. $\frac{5}{8} + \frac{9}{12}$ $1\frac{9}{24}$ or $1\frac{3}{8}$

32. $\frac{11}{30} - \frac{1}{5}$ $\frac{5}{30}$ or $\frac{1}{6}$

33. $\frac{2}{5} + \frac{1}{2}$ $\frac{9}{10}$

34. $\frac{3}{4} - \frac{1}{3}$ $\frac{5}{12}$

35. $\frac{1}{3} + \frac{1}{2}$ $\frac{5}{6}$

36. $\frac{9}{10} - \frac{7}{8}$ $\frac{1}{40}$

37. Writing Explain four different ways to find the sum $\frac{1}{2} + \frac{3}{4}$. See right.

Find x. Write the answer in simplest form.

38. $x = \frac{1}{6} + \frac{1}{2}$ $\frac{2}{3}$

39. $\frac{2}{5} - \frac{3}{10} = x$ $\frac{1}{10}$

40. $x = \frac{2}{3} + \frac{7}{12}$ $1\frac{1}{4}$

41. You and a friend order a pizza with eight equal pieces. You eat half the pizza and take the rest home. The next day you eat one piece. What portion of the pizza is left? Draw a model that shows the problem and your solution. $\frac{3}{8}$

42. Data File 7 (pp. 272–273) Compute the fraction of the tide covered between hours 1 and 2, 2 and 3, 3 and 4, 4 and 5, and 5 and 6. Describe any patterns you see. See right.

43. A package of sliced ham weighs $\frac{1}{2}$ lb. Another package of sliced ham weighs $\frac{3}{4}$ lb. You buy both packages. Do you have enough ham for each of four persons to get $\frac{1}{3}$ lb? no

44. Investigation (p. 318) Make a nomograph to add $\frac{2}{3}$ and $\frac{1}{6}$. $\frac{5}{6}$; See Solution Key.

28. Belize, Panama, Costa Rica, Nicaragua, Honduras, El Salvador, Guatemala

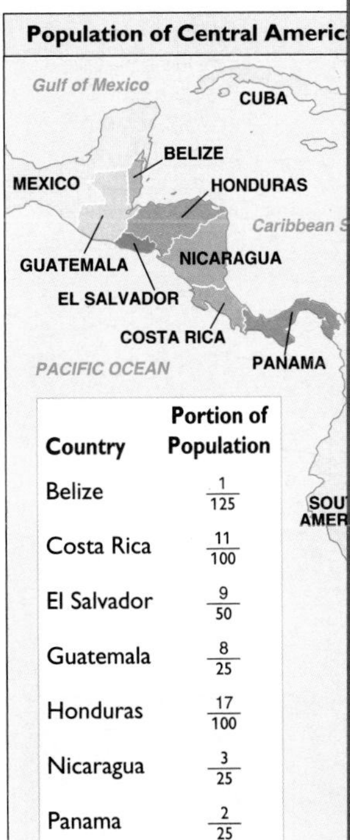

Country	Portion of Population
Belize	$\frac{1}{125}$
Costa Rica	$\frac{11}{100}$
El Salvador	$\frac{9}{50}$
Guatemala	$\frac{8}{25}$
Honduras	$\frac{17}{100}$
Nicaragua	$\frac{3}{25}$
Panama	$\frac{2}{25}$

37. Answers may vary. Sample: estimation, fraction bars, circles, finding the LCD, using a calculator

42. $\frac{2}{12}, \frac{3}{12}, \frac{3}{12}, \frac{2}{12}, \frac{1}{12}$; the fraction of the tide starts small, becomes large for a while, and gets small again.

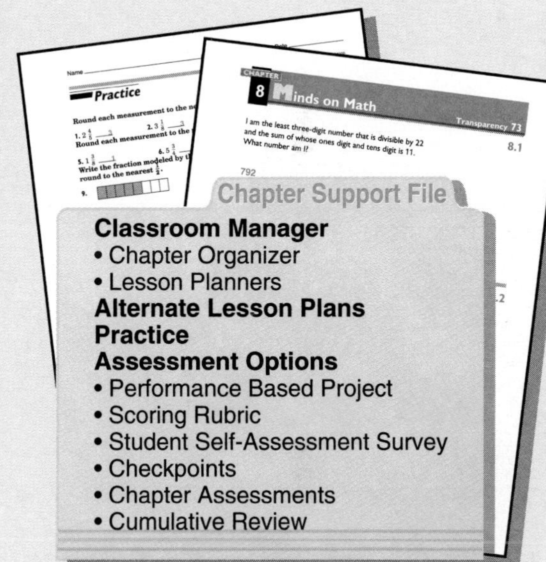

Minds on Math available in Teaching Transparencies

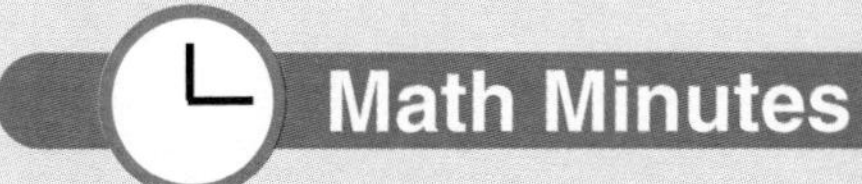

In Ms. Nicolay's class of 6 students, each person shakes hands once with each of the other people in the class. How many handshakes are exchanged?
15

Materials for 8-4

- computer *(optional)*
- spreadsheet *(optional)*
- calculator

CHAPTER 8 PROBLEM SOLVING PRACTICE

This page provides a variety of problems that can be used to reinforce and enhance the students' problem solving skills. Encourage students to read each problem carefully. Then have them refer to the list of problem solving strategies to help them decide how to solve the problems.

Point out, however, that not all questions require a strategy for solving, nor are all the strategies in the list used on this page.

Exercise 2: Some students may need to use a model to solve this problem.

Exercise 5: Students can work backward from 9:30 A.M. to solve this problem.

Problem Solving Practice

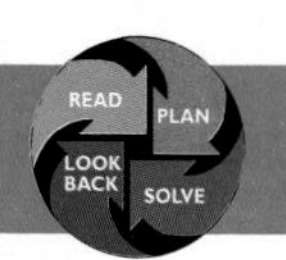

PROBLEM SOLVING STRATEGIES

- Make a Table
- Use Logical Reasoning
- Solve a Simpler Problem
- Too Much or Too Little Information
- Look for a Pattern
- Make a Model
- Work Backward
- Draw a Diagram
- Guess and Test
- Simulate a Problem
- Use Multiple Strategies

Solve. The list at the left shows some possible strategies you can use.

1. A store owner is stacking boxes for a window display. The top row will have one box. The second row will have three boxes. The third row will have five boxes. If this pattern continues, how many boxes will the tenth row have? 19 boxes
2. Kyle is sewing a square pillow. He cut out thirteen pieces of material. Then he forgot how to place the pieces to make the pillow! There are eight isosceles right triangles and five squares. All the triangles are the same size, and all the squares are the same size. The area of two triangles equals the area of one square. Think of at least one way Kyle can place all the pieces to make the square pillow. See Solution Key.
3. William drives about 24 mi total to and from work each day. He works five days each week and takes two weeks of vacation each year. About how many miles does William drive to and from work in one year? 6,000 mi
4. Three cousins shared a relative's inheritance. Amina got $\frac{1}{2}$ of the money. Kareem got $\frac{1}{5}$ of the money. Ahmed got \$3,000. How much money was the total inheritance? \$10,000
5. Britta needs to get to work by 9:30 A.M. She must drive her son to school, which takes 12 min. She will also drop off some dry cleaning. From school to the dry cleaners takes about 15 min. From the dry cleaners to work takes about 18 min. By what time should Britta leave home? 8:45 A.M.
6. Juan is making sandwiches for a party. Each sandwich has one type of bread, one type of cheese, and one type of meat. There are two choices for bread, for cheese, and for meat. How many different sandwiches can Juan make? 8
7. **Sports** A basketball team sold 496 raffle tickets and collected \$396.80. Expenses totaled \$75.98. How much did each ticket cost? \$.80

The National Wheelchair Athletic Association was founded in 1957 and has about 1,500 members.

8-4

Connecting to Prior Knowledge

Have students recall the classic puzzle in which you choose between getting a lump sum of $1 million or 1 cent the first day, 2 cents the second day, 4 cents the third day, and so on for a month. This lesson includes similar puzzles in which the amounts get progressively smaller instead of larger.

THINK AND DISCUSS

Question 1: Some students may choose A because it's simpler. Some may choose B because you keep getting gold. Allow students to give reasons without much debate. Students do not need to see the better choice now, because the next few exercises will lead them through a mathematical analysis.

Question 4: Use this exercise to make sure students understand the table before going further.

Question 5: Discuss the hint so students see how to save time and effort by using calculations they have already done. Instead of adding all the fractions in the expression, students can simply add the new fraction to the previous sum.

COMPUTER Use Question 9 to review how to use formulas in spreadsheets. For simplicity, use a fixed number of decimal places for column D. Four places is enough to show the pattern. In Question 12, note that the spreadsheet will need 11 rows to list 10 pieces because the first row is used for headings. You may need to create a separate spreadsheet to make the line graph called for in Question 14. ***Alternate Approach*** Use calculators to fill in hand-made tables. Some students can work on column C, some on column B, and the rest on column D for Question 12.

Question 14: After the graph is completed, ask whether the point (0, 0) belongs on the curve. Refer to the context—after 0 pieces, you have received a total of 0 oz. Then extend the graph through the origin to give a more dramatic picture of how quickly the total rises and levels off.

TECHNOLOGY

8-4 Exploring Patterns in Fraction Sums

What's Ahead

- Exploring series
- Using spreadsheets to list and graph fraction sums

WHAT YOU'LL NEED

✓ Computer

✓ Spreadsheet software

✓ Calculator

THINK AND DISCUSS

Alarms scream out from a jewelry store. A car screeches away. You see the license plate and memorize the number. Thanks to your memory and a computer search, the stolen jewels are returned. The jeweler offers you a choice between the two rewards described at the left. Which reward will you choose?

Reward B

A piece of gold every minute for the rest of your life in the pattern described below.

1st piece: $\frac{1}{2}$ oz

2nd piece: $\frac{1}{4}$ oz

3rd piece: $\frac{1}{8}$ oz

1. **Discussion** Which reward seems to be the better choice? Answers will vary. Sample: Reward B
2. With reward B, how much will the 4th piece of gold weigh? How much will the 5th piece of gold weigh? $\frac{1}{16}$ oz; $\frac{1}{32}$ oz
3. With reward B, how many ounces of gold will you have after you receive the second piece? $\frac{3}{4}$ oz

You can use a table to analyze reward B.

Piece	Ounces	Total Ounces: Expression	Total Ounces: Sum
1	$\frac{1}{2}$	$\frac{1}{2}$	$\frac{1}{2}$
2	$\frac{1}{4}$	$\frac{1}{2}+\frac{1}{4}$	■ $\frac{3}{4}$
3	$\frac{1}{8}$	$\frac{1}{2}+\frac{1}{4}+\frac{1}{8}$	■ $\frac{7}{8}$

4. **Discussion** What does each column in the table show? piece; weight of each piece; cumulative weights; sum of weights
5. **Discussion** Describe the pattern in the "Ounces" column. Each successive weight is halved.
6. **Calculator** Copy and complete the table above. Add another row. 4; $\frac{1}{16}$; $\frac{1}{2}+\frac{1}{4}+\frac{1}{8}+\frac{1}{16}$; $\frac{15}{16}$
7. **Discussion** Analyze the fractions in the "Sum" column. Describe any patterns you see in the numerators or denominators of the fractions. See left.
8. How much gold will you have after you get piece 5? First use the pattern to make a prediction, then calculate. about 1 oz; $\frac{31}{32}$ oz

7. Each successive numerator is the sum of the previous numerator and denominator. Each successive denominator is twice the previous denominator.

> *"If I can teach you something, it may mean that I can count at least somewhere."*
>
> —Hannah Green

Organizer

1. **Focus**
   Connecting to Prior Knowledge
2. **Teach**
   Think and Discuss
   Work Together
3. **Closure**
   Wrap Up

Skills Reviewed in Context of Lesson

- adding fractions

Materials and Manipulatives

- computer (1 per group; *optional*)
- spreadsheet software (per computer; *optional*)
- calculator

On Your Own Exercise 21: calculator; Exercise 23: computer and spreadsheet software *(optional)*

Student Resources

Extra Practice
Student Study Guide
Practice, TR Ch. 8, p. 26
Student Study Guide, Spanish Resources, TR
Checkpoint, TR Ch. 8, p. 36
Alternate Lesson, TR Ch. 8, pp. 15–18

continues next page

TACTILE LEARNERS Students can model reward B by folding and cutting paper strips to represent the fractions for each addition.

DIVERSITY Some students may fail to see that adding fractions in some patterns, such as the ones in this lesson, will never reach a certain sum. What they probably do not realize is that as the numbers in the denominators in these fractions increase, the size of the fraction decreases. Show students how much smaller $\frac{1}{16}$ is than $\frac{1}{8}$, and how much smaller $\frac{1}{32}$ is than $\frac{1}{16}$.

Error Alert!

Students may have trouble identifying the patterns in the Sum columns of the spreadsheets. ***Remediation*** Have students work with a partner to discuss possible patterns and then decide upon a pattern that best represents the data.

WORK TOGETHER

Have students work together in groups of three or four. Try to have at least one person in each group who is familiar with computers and, if possible, spreadsheets.

COMPUTER For Question 16, set the spreadsheet to display the decimal equivalents with at least five, and preferably six, decimal places. Four decimal places is not sufficient to show the continuing pattern.

CRITICAL THINKING Question 18 introduces students to the concept of limits.

Ongoing Assessment

Observe students' work in the Work Together section to determine whether or not reteaching is necessary.

Wrap Up

What's the Big Idea? Ask students: *How did finding patterns help save you time and effort in computing sums of fractions in this lesson?*

Organizer, continued

Teacher Resources

Teaching Transparencies 17, 19, 74

Transparency Masters, TR p. 5

Lesson Planner, TR Ch. 8, p. 5

Prentice Hall Technology

Multimedia Math

- Math Tools, Spreadsheet

Computer Item Generator

- 8-4

Other Available Technology

calculator

Excel; Works by Microsoft

1-2-3 by Lotus *(optional)*

ClarisWorks by Apple *(optional)*

Fact of the Day

When used in jewelry, gold is usually combined with another metal, such as platinum, silver, or palladium, to increase its hardness. The proportion of gold to the other metal is measured in karats. Pure gold is designated as 24 karat (24K). A 14K mixture is 14 parts gold and 10 parts of the other metal.

—World Book Encyclopedia

Assignment Options

Core: 20, 21, 26, MR all, CH all	
Reinforce: 24, 25	**Enrich:** 22, 23

332

Mixed REVIEW

Solve. Write the answer in simplest form.

1. $\frac{5}{6} + \frac{9}{10}$ $1\frac{11}{15}$
2. $\frac{9}{16} - \frac{2}{6}$ $\frac{11}{48}$

Name each of the following for circle O.

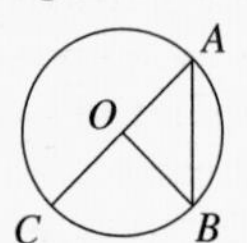

3. a diameter
4. two radii See below.
5. Data File 2 (pp. 38–39) Find the total time you would expect to spend at Space Mountain in Walt Disney World. 47 min 50 s

3. $\overline{CA}$
4. $\overline{OB}$, $\overline{OA}$, or $\overline{OC}$

◇◇◇ **Reward C** ◇◇◇

A piece of gold every minute for the rest of your life in the pattern described below.

1st piece: $\frac{1}{3}$ oz

2nd piece: $\frac{1}{9}$ oz

3rd piece: $\frac{1}{27}$ oz

You can use a spreadsheet to see what happens as you continue to get more pieces of gold with reward B.

9. **Computer** Set up a spreadsheet like the one below. Which columns of the table you made will you use? piece number column, sum column

	A	B	C	D
1	Piece	Numerator of the Sum	Denominator of the Sum	Sum as a Decimal
2	1	1	2	0.500
3	2	3	4	0.750

10. Use the patterns you described in Exercise 7 to write formulas for columns B and C. Sample: B3: =B2+C2; C3: =2*C2
11. Use columns B and C to write a formula for column D. Sample: D2: =B2/C2
12. **Computer** Fill in the spreadsheet for the first 10 pieces of gold. What do you notice about the values in column D? The values get closer to 1.
13. **Discussion** Now that you have analyzed reward B, which reward is the better choice? Are you surprised? Reward A
14. **Computer** Draw a line graph of the values in columns A and D. How does the graph show the pattern of reward B? See Solution Key for graph. As the value of A increases, the graph increases and gets closer to 1.

WORK TOGETHER

Suppose you are offered a third choice. Reward C is described at the left. Work in small groups to analyze reward C.

15. Complete a table that shows at least four pieces of gold. See Solution Key.
16. **Computer** Use a spreadsheet to see what happens as you get more and more pieces of gold. Check student's work.; the sum approaches $\frac{1}{2}$
17. Draw a graph that shows the pattern of reward C. See Solution Key.
18. **Critical Thinking** Do you think there is a limit to how much gold you will get with reward C? Support your answer. Yes; The graph indicates the total amount will not exceed $\frac{1}{2}$.
19. **Writing** How are rewards B and C similar? How are they different? Which is the better choice between the two? Answers may vary. Sample: Both rewards increase over time.; Reward B approaches 1 and Reward C approaches $\frac{1}{2}$.; B

Journal In mythology, people are sometimes assigned an impossible task. One such task involves rolling a large boulder halfway up a hill, then half of the remaining distance, then half of the next remaining distance. Have students create a similar imaginary situation and write a short description of it.

Connections Have students discuss situations similar to the example in the text that would give similar results.

- **Science** (bouncing a ball)
- **Finance** (increasing debt by paying only a fraction of the interest charge)

Reteaching Activity Have students complete a spreadsheet using the expressions $\frac{1}{2}$, $\frac{1}{2} + \frac{1}{3}$, $\frac{1}{2} + \frac{1}{3} + \frac{1}{4}$, and so on. Ask questions like: *How could you find the sum by adding only two fractions? What would the next expression be?*

ON YOUR OWN

WRITING For Exercise 22, students should express each sum as a decimal to six or seven decimal places to see a pattern.

COMPUTER For Exercise 23, set the spreadsheet to display the decimal equivalents with eight decimal places.

CHECKPOINT

WRITING Exercise 11c will help students recognize patterns.

ON YOUR OWN

Use the pattern of fraction sums at the right.

20. Analyze the "Expression" column. Write the next expression in the pattern. $\frac{1}{4} + \frac{1}{16} + \frac{1}{64} + \frac{1}{256}$
21. **Calculator** Copy and complete the table. Add another row. See table at right.
22. **Writing** Add more rows to the table until you see a pattern in the sum. Describe the pattern. Check student's work. The sum approaches $\frac{1}{3}$.
23. **Computer** Make a spreadsheet like the one on the previous page. Fill in values for the first ten sums. Then draw a line graph of the sums. See Solution Key.
24. **Critical Thinking** If this pattern continues forever, do you think the sum will ever reach $\frac{3}{8}$? Why or why not? No; the sum approaches $\frac{1}{3}$ and $\frac{3}{8}$ is greater than $\frac{1}{3}$.
25. Reward D is described at the right. Which of the rewards A, B, C, or D is the best choice? Explain. D; In the eleventh minute, you would receive more than $1\frac{1}{2}$ oz.
26. Suppose you start at your school and walk 1 mi north, then $\frac{1}{2}$ mi south, then $\frac{1}{4}$ mi north, $\frac{1}{8}$ mi south, and so on. About how far from your school will you end up? $\frac{2}{3}$ mi

Expression	Sum
$\frac{1}{4}$	$\frac{1}{4}$
$\frac{1}{4} + \frac{1}{16}$	$\frac{5}{16}$
$\frac{1}{4} + \frac{1}{16} + \frac{1}{64}$	$\frac{21}{64}$
$\frac{1}{4} + \frac{1}{16} + \frac{1}{64} + \frac{1}{256}$	$\frac{85}{256}$

Reward D

A piece of gold every minute for the rest of your life in the pattern described below.

1st piece: $\frac{1}{2}$ oz

2nd piece: $\frac{1}{4}$ oz

3rd piece: $\frac{1}{6}$ oz

CHECKPOINT

Write the fraction modeled by the fraction bar. Then round to the nearest $\frac{1}{2}$.

1. 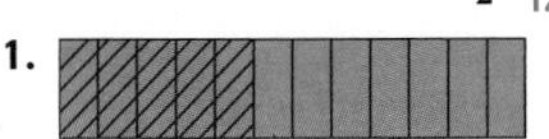 $\frac{5}{12}$; $\frac{1}{2}$
2. 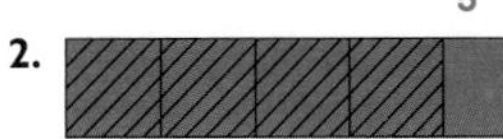 $\frac{4}{5}$; 1

Find each sum or difference. Then write the answer in simplest form.

3. $\frac{2}{7} + \frac{4}{7}$ $\frac{6}{7}$
4. $\frac{3}{8} + \frac{1}{8}$ $\frac{4}{8}$; $\frac{1}{2}$
5. $\frac{5}{9} - \frac{2}{9}$ $\frac{3}{9}$; $\frac{1}{3}$
6. $\frac{7}{12} - \frac{6}{12}$ $\frac{1}{12}$
7. $\frac{4}{9} + \frac{2}{5}$ $\frac{38}{45}$
8. $\frac{3}{8} + \frac{3}{4}$ $\frac{9}{8}$; $1\frac{1}{8}$
9. $\frac{7}{10} - \frac{1}{4}$ $\frac{9}{20}$
10. $\frac{2}{3} - \frac{6}{13}$ $\frac{8}{39}$
11. Use the pattern of fraction sums at the right.
    a. Copy and complete the table. See table.
    b. Add another row. $\frac{1}{5} + \frac{1}{25} + \frac{1}{125} + \frac{1}{625}$; $\frac{156}{625}$
    c. **Writing** Describe the pattern in the sum. The sum approaches $\frac{1}{4}$.

Expression	Sum
$\frac{1}{5}$	$\frac{1}{5}$
$\frac{1}{5} + \frac{1}{25}$	$\frac{6}{25}$
$\frac{1}{5} + \frac{1}{25} + \frac{1}{125}$	$\frac{31}{125}$

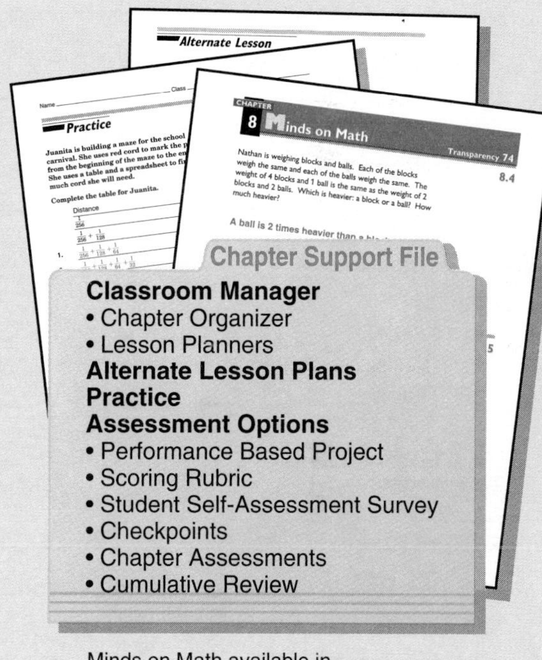

Minds on Math available in Teaching Transparencies

Math Minutes

An adult's brain weighs about 0.03 times his or her body weight. Mr. Martinez weighs 165.5 lb. What is the weight of his brain?
about 5 lb

Materials for 8-5

- ruler
- scissors
- string

8-5

Connecting to Prior Knowledge

Ask students to think of examples of mixed numbers. **(possible student responses: 5 ft 2 in.; 3 dollars 15 cents; $5\frac{1}{4}$)** Then ask students to predict how adding and subtracting mixed numbers is related to adding and subtracting fractions.

THINK AND DISCUSS

You may wish to share pictures of a giant tortoise, an antelope, and a cheetah with your class before beginning the examples.

TACTILE LEARNERS Have students use fraction bars to help them model the examples involving mixed numbers.

KINESTHETIC LEARNERS Have students use yardsticks to measure and mark the distance the turtle traveled in Example 1. Have them measure both distances traveled, consecutively, and then measure the total distance.

ESL Make sure students know the difference between a whole number, a fraction, and a mixed number.

Example 1

Point out to students that the last equation combines the solutions to the first two equations (the whole number part and fraction part).

Additional Example *A photographer watched a gorilla walk $6\frac{1}{3}$ yd to a river for a drink and then run $2\frac{1}{6}$ yd into the bush. How far did the gorilla travel?*

Calculate $6\frac{1}{3} + 2\frac{1}{6}$ to find the distance the gorilla traveled.

$6 + 2 = 8$	**Add whole numbers.**
$\frac{1}{3} + \frac{1}{6} = \frac{2}{6} + \frac{1}{6} = \frac{3}{6} = \frac{1}{2}$	**Add fractions.**
$8 + \frac{1}{2} = 8\frac{1}{2}$	**Combine.**

The gorilla traveled $8\frac{1}{2}$ yd.

“Knowledge is a treasure but practice is the key to it.”

—PROVERB

Organizer

1. **Focus**
   Connecting to Prior Knowledge
2. **Teach**
   Think and Discuss
   Work Together
3. **Closure**
   Try These
   Wrap Up

Skills Reviewed in Context of Lesson
- adding and subtracting simple fractions
- estimating fractions

Materials and Manipulatives
- ruler (1 per group)
- scissors (1 pair per group)
- string ($14\frac{1}{2}$ in. for each group)

Student Resources
Extra Practice
Student Study Guide
Practice, TR Ch. 8, p. 27
Student Study Guide, Spanish Resources, TR

Teacher Resources
Teaching Transparency 74
Transparency Masters, TR p. 3
Lesson Planner, TR Ch. 8, p. 6

continues next page

What's Ahead
- Solving problems that involve adding and subtracting mixed numbers

8-5 Adding & Subtracting Mixed Numbers

WHAT YOU'LL NEED
✓ Ruler

✓ Scissors
✓ String

THINK AND DISCUSS

The giant tortoise is one of the slowest moving animals. Suppose a giant tortoise travels $8\frac{1}{4}$ yd in one minute, and $7\frac{1}{2}$ yd the next minute. How far did the giant tortoise travel during these two minutes?

1. Solve the problem above. Explain your solution. $15\frac{3}{4}$ yd
2. **Discussion** Think of several different ways to find $8\frac{1}{4} + 7\frac{1}{2}$. **Answers will vary. Sample: Add the whole numbers and use a model to add the fractions, use a calculator.**

WHAT? The slowest giant male tortoise ever recorded crawled only 15 feet in 43.5 seconds!

Source: *Guinness Book of World Records*

One way to add or subtract mixed numbers is to compute the whole number and fraction parts separately.

Example 1 Calculate $8\frac{1}{4}$ yd $+ 7\frac{1}{2}$ yd to find the distance the giant tortoise traveled.

$8 + 7 = 15$	**Add whole numbers.**
$\frac{1}{4} + \frac{1}{2} = \frac{3}{4}$	**Add fractions.**
$15 + \frac{3}{4} = 15\frac{3}{4}$	**Combine whole number and fraction parts.**

The giant tortoise traveled $15\frac{3}{4}$ yd.

3. Use the method in Example 1 to find the sum $10\frac{1}{8} + 6\frac{3}{16}$. $16\frac{5}{16}$

Sometimes the sum of the fraction part is improper. So rename it as a mixed number.

FLASHBACK Divide to rename an improper fraction as a mixed number.

Example 2 After traveling $15\frac{3}{4}$ yd, the giant tortoise traveled another $3\frac{1}{2}$ yd. How far did the tortoise travel?

$15 + 3 = 18$	**Add whole numbers.**
$\frac{3}{4} + \frac{1}{2} = \frac{3}{4} + \frac{2}{4} = \frac{5}{4}$	**Add fractions.**
$18 + \frac{5}{4} = 18 + 1\frac{1}{4} = 19\frac{1}{4}$	**Rename the improper fraction as a mixed number and combine.**

The giant tortoise traveled $19\frac{1}{4}$ yd.

Example 2

Have students create a list of steps for adding mixed numbers.

Additional Example *A gorilla spent $2\frac{3}{4}$ h grooming and playing with two younger gorillas. Then she searched for food and ate for $1\frac{1}{3}$ h. How much time was spent on these activities?*

Add $1\frac{1}{3} + 2\frac{3}{4}$.

$1 + 2 = 3$ **Add whole numbers.**

$\frac{1}{3} + \frac{3}{4} = \frac{4}{12} + \frac{9}{12} = \frac{13}{12}$ **Add fractions.**

$3 + \frac{13}{12} = 3 + 1\frac{1}{12} = 4\frac{1}{12}$ **Rename and combine.**

$4\frac{1}{12}$ hours were spent.

Example 3

Ask students to explain why $6\frac{1}{4}$ must be renamed.

Error Alert! When renaming a mixed number, students often forget to decrease the whole number part by 1, or they incorrectly rename the mixed number. ***Remediation*** Suggest that students write the numbers as a vertical subtraction problem. Show students that the 1 that they "borrow" can be written as $\frac{4}{4}$ which they add to the $\frac{1}{4}$ already present.

Example 4

Ask students how they would solve the equation $4 + x = 6$. Point out that the same process is used to solve $4\frac{1}{2} + x = 6\frac{1}{4}$.

Example 5

Discuss the function of the unit key with students. Some students may have calculators that do not have unit keys. Modify the instructions as needed.

Sometimes you need to rename before you subtract.

4. An antelope ran $4\frac{1}{2}$ yd while a cheetah ran $6\frac{1}{4}$ yd. Write a subtraction expression to show how much farther the cheetah ran than the antelope. Can you subtract $\frac{1}{2}$ from $\frac{1}{4}$?
$6\frac{1}{4} - 4\frac{1}{2}$; no

Example 3 Calculate $6\frac{1}{4}$ yd $-$ $4\frac{1}{2}$ yd to find how much farther the cheetah ran than the antelope.

Since you cannot subtract $\frac{1}{4} - \frac{1}{2}$, rename $6\frac{1}{4}$.

$6\frac{1}{4} = 5 + 1\frac{1}{4} = 5 + \frac{5}{4} = 5\frac{5}{4}$ Rename the mixed number.

$5 - 4 = 1$ Subtract whole numbers.

$\frac{5}{4} - \frac{1}{2} = \frac{5}{4} - \frac{2}{4} = \frac{3}{4}$ Subtract fractions.

$5\frac{5}{4} - 4\frac{1}{2} = 1\frac{3}{4}$ Combine.

The cheetah ran $1\frac{3}{4}$ yd farther than the antelope.

***The cheetah** is the fastest animal on land for distances up to 350 yd. The prong-horned antelope is faster than the cheetah after 350 yd.*

5. Look at the addition equation $4\frac{1}{2} + x = 6\frac{1}{4}$. Can you use this equation to solve the problem above? If so, how?
Yes; Subtract $4\frac{1}{2}$ from each side of the equation to solve for x.

Example 4 Solve the equation $4\frac{1}{2} + x = 6\frac{1}{4}$.

Think: What must you add to $4\frac{1}{2}$ to get $6\frac{1}{4}$?

$4\frac{1}{2} + \frac{1}{2} + 1 + \frac{1}{4} = 6\frac{1}{4}$

So $x = \frac{1}{2} + 1 + \frac{1}{4} = 1\frac{3}{4}$.

6. Use the method in Example 4 to find the difference between $5\frac{3}{8}$ yd and $2\frac{3}{4}$ yd. Then subtract to compare.
$2\frac{5}{8}$ yd

You can use a fraction calculator with mixed numbers. First estimate the answer. Write the answer in simplest form.

FLASHBACK

To estimate, round each mixed number to the nearest whole number. Then add or subtract.

Example 5 Find the sum $8\frac{11}{16} + 5\frac{3}{8}$.

Estimate: $9 + 5 = 14$

Press: 8 [Unit] 11 [/] 16 [+] 5 [Unit] 3 [/] 8 [=]

Display: 13 U 17 / 16

$8\frac{11}{16} + 5\frac{3}{8} = 13\frac{17}{16} = 14\frac{1}{16}$

Organizer, continued

Prentice Hall Technology

Multimedia Math
- Math Tools, Fraction Strips

Computer Item Generator
- 8-5

Other Available Technology

Math Blaster Plus by Davidson & Associates: Exercises 13–15 *(optional)*

Fact of the Day

The three-toed sloth of South America has an average ground speed of 6–8 ft/min (0.068–0.098 mi/h). Compare this to the average speed of the garden snail (0.03 mi/h) and the giant tortoise (0.17 mi/h).

—Guinness Book of Records

WORK TOGETHER

Each group will need a ruler and a piece of string *at least* $14\frac{3}{8}$ in. long. Use 18–20 in. per group, if possible, to allow for errors during the measuring and cutting process. There are ten possible addition problems using two strings. Challenge groups to find as many addition problems as they can.

TRY THESE

Ongoing Assessment Have students tell which of the following expressions require them to rename, and what is the result of that renaming. Then have students find the value of the expression.

- $3\frac{1}{2} - 2\frac{1}{2}$ **(no renaming; 1)**
- $6\frac{2}{5} - 4\frac{3}{5}$ **($5\frac{7}{5}$; $1\frac{4}{5}$)**
- $1\frac{3}{8} + 2\frac{1}{4}$ **($2\frac{2}{8}$; $3\frac{5}{8}$)**
- $5\frac{7}{10} - 2\frac{3}{10}$ **(no renaming; $3\frac{2}{5}$)**

TECHNOLOGY OPTION For Exercises 13–15, students can use fraction software to practice adding and subtracting fractions and mixed numbers.

Wrap Up

What's the Big Idea? Ask students: *What are mixed numbers and how do you add and subtract them?*

Connections Have students discuss where addition and subtraction of mixed numbers are used in real-world situations:

- **Stock Market** (determining the difference between high and low stock prices)
- **Sports** (comparing distances and speed)
- **Science** (comparing units of mass, length, or capacity)

Assignment Options

Core: 18–24, 28–31, 37, 39, 42, MR all	
Reinforce: 25–27, 32–36, 40	Enrich: 38, 41

WORK TOGETHER

Check student's work.

Work with a partner. Cut a piece of string each length: $1\frac{3}{8}$ in., $2\frac{1}{4}$ in., $1\frac{7}{8}$ in., $3\frac{1}{8}$ in., $5\frac{3}{4}$ in. Select two pieces of string.

- Make a line with the two pieces and measure its length.
- Write an addition equation for the two pieces and the length.
- Find the sum and compare it to the measured length.

Repeat several times by selecting two other pieces of string.

TRY THESE

Complete to rename each mixed number.

7. $3\frac{1}{10} = 2\frac{■}{10}$ 11 **8.** $5\frac{5}{6} = 4\frac{■}{6}$ 11 **9.** $1\frac{3}{4} = \frac{■}{4}$ 7

Estimate each sum or difference. Estimates may vary.

10. $6\frac{1}{4} + 2\frac{3}{5}$ 9 **11.** $2\frac{5}{16} + 1\frac{1}{4}$ 3 **12.** $8\frac{1}{5} - 3\frac{3}{4}$ 4

Find each sum or difference.

13. $1\frac{1}{4} + 6\frac{1}{2}$ $7\frac{3}{4}$ **14.** $3\frac{1}{3} + 1\frac{5}{6}$ $5\frac{1}{6}$ **15.** $9\frac{1}{2} - 4\frac{7}{8}$ $4\frac{5}{8}$

16. Explain how you can mentally find $9\frac{1}{4} + 6\frac{3}{4}$. Add the sum of the whole numbers, 15, and the sum of the fractions, 1.

17. Cooking A recipe lists $1\frac{3}{4}$ c milk, and another recipe lists $1\frac{1}{2}$ c milk. You measure the milk in your refrigerator. You have about 3 c. Do you have enough milk for both recipes? No

ON YOUR OWN

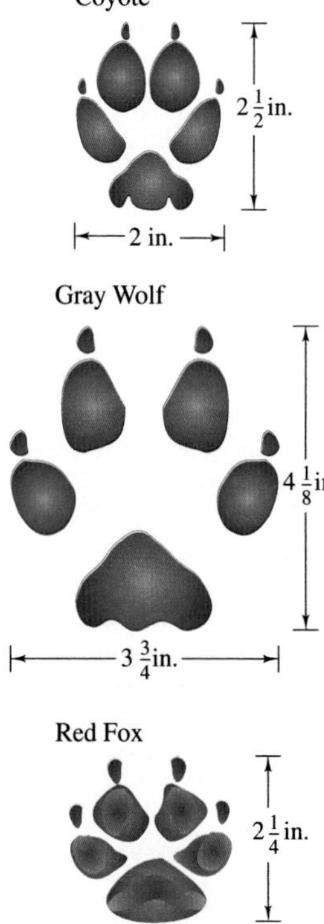

Biology **Use the scale drawings of animal tracks.**

18. How much wider is the gray wolf's track than the red fox's track? $1\frac{5}{8}$ in.

19. Which is longer, the coyote's track or the red fox's track? How much longer? coyote; $\frac{1}{4}$ in.

20. Is the length or the width of the gray wolf's track larger? by how much? length; $\frac{3}{8}$ in.

Journal Ask students to think about what they have learned in this lesson and write themselves a list of what they feel is most difficult to remember.

Reteaching Activity Have students make circle models to illustrate addition and subtraction of mixed numbers. Have each student cut out eight 6-in. circles. Then have them fold and cut one circle to show halves, one to show fourths, and one to show eighths. Have students work in pairs to write problems and model and complete them.

ON YOUR OWN

CONNECTION TO BIOLOGY Exercises 18–20 use animal tracks to demonstrate fractional lengths.

CONNECTION TO GEOMETRY Exercise 36 requires students to estimate perimeter.

WRITING For Exercise 38, students can use the commutative property of addition to find the sum mentally.

CRITICAL THINKING For Exercise 41, students should first find the difference to complete the pattern.

CHAPTER INVESTIGATION You may wish to discuss nomographs before assigning Exercise 42.

Mental Math **Add or subtract mentally.**

21. $9\frac{2}{3} - 5\frac{2}{3}$ 4 22. $1 - \frac{1}{6}$ $\frac{5}{6}$ 23. $3 + 1\frac{2}{3}$ $4\frac{2}{3}$ 24. $4\frac{1}{2} + 4\frac{1}{2}$ 9

Biology **Use the data at the right.**

25. Rewrite the table showing the lengths of the cones from shortest to longest. Black, Red, White, Norway

26. Find the difference in length between the shortest cone and the longest cone. $4\frac{5}{8}$ in.

27. Estimation Which two cones differ in length by about $\frac{1}{2}$ in.? White and Red; Red and Black

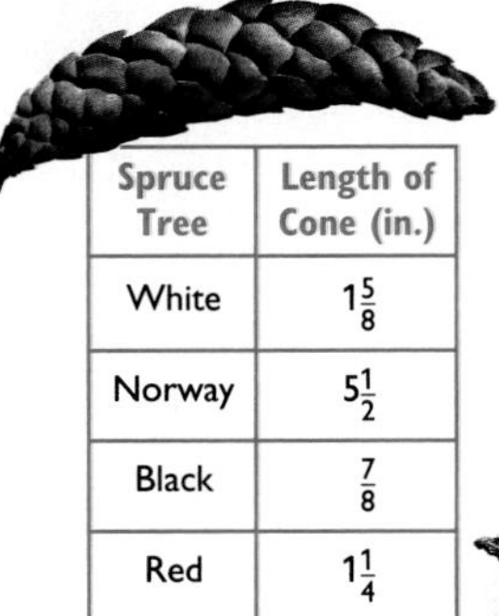
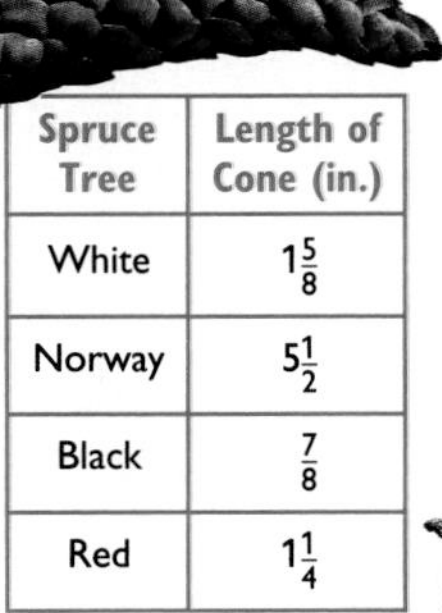

Spruce Tree	Length of Cone (in.)
White	$1\frac{5}{8}$
Norway	$5\frac{1}{2}$
Black	$\frac{7}{8}$
Red	$1\frac{1}{4}$

Choose **Use any method to add or subtract.**

28. $7\frac{1}{10} + 3\frac{2}{5}$ $10\frac{1}{2}$ 29. $1\frac{7}{8} + 1\frac{1}{4}$ $3\frac{1}{8}$ 30. $4\frac{5}{12} - 1\frac{1}{2}$ $2\frac{11}{12}$ 31. $6\frac{4}{5} - 2\frac{1}{3}$ $4\frac{7}{15}$

32. $8 - 1\frac{2}{3}$ $6\frac{1}{3}$ 33. $4\frac{5}{8} - 1\frac{3}{8}$ $3\frac{1}{4}$ 34. $3\frac{1}{6} - 2$ $1\frac{1}{6}$ 35. $10\frac{1}{4} + 3\frac{1}{3}$ $13\frac{7}{12}$

36. Estimation The sides of a triangle have lengths $5\frac{1}{2}$ in., $3\frac{7}{8}$ in., and $2\frac{1}{4}$ in. Is a 12-in. piece of string long enough to go around the triangle? Yes

37. Gardening Paul plans to fence a rectangular flower garden that measures $4\frac{1}{2}$ ft by $3\frac{1}{4}$ ft. Fencing costs $5/ft. How much will the fence for the flower garden cost? $77.50

38. Writing Explain how you can mentally find the sum $5\frac{1}{3} + 3\frac{4}{5} + 2\frac{2}{3} + 6\frac{1}{5}$. Add $5\frac{1}{3}$ and $2\frac{2}{3}$, to get 8. Add $3\frac{4}{5}$ and $6\frac{1}{5}$ to get 10. Add 8 and 10 to get 18.

39. Data File 8 (pp. 316–317) How much farther did Jackie Joyner-Kersee jump than Heike Drechsler? $10\frac{1}{4}$ in.

40. **Choose A, B, C, or D.** Which two mixed numbers are equivalent to $3\frac{1}{5}$? B

A. $3\frac{1}{10}$ and $2\frac{6}{5}$ **B.** $3\frac{2}{10}$ and $2\frac{6}{5}$

C. $3\frac{2}{10}$ and $3\frac{6}{5}$ **D.** $3\frac{3}{5}$ and $2\frac{5}{5}$

41. Critical Thinking Write the next two numbers in the pattern: $9\frac{1}{3}$, $8\frac{1}{6}$, 7, $5\frac{5}{6}$, $4\frac{2}{3}$, ■, ■. $3\frac{1}{2}$; $2\frac{1}{3}$

42. Investigation (p. 318) Explain how you can use a nomograph to add any two mixed numbers. Make a nomograph to add $2\frac{5}{6}$ and $1\frac{1}{3}$. $4\frac{1}{6}$; See Solution Key.

1. $\frac{7}{5}; \frac{9}{5}; \frac{11}{5}$

2. $\frac{7}{10}; \frac{3}{5}; \frac{1}{2}$

Mixed REVIEW

Look for a pattern. Then write the next three numbers. See above.

1. $\frac{1}{5}$, $\frac{3}{5}$, 1, ■, ■, ■

2. 1, $\frac{9}{10}$, $\frac{4}{5}$, ■, ■, ■

Classify each triangle as scalene, isosceles, or equilateral. equilateral

3. side lengths of 7, 7, 7

4. side lengths of 3, 5, 3 isosceles

5. The rotary club has $140 in savings. The dues from 8 new members raised the amount to $198. Find the dues from each member. $7.25

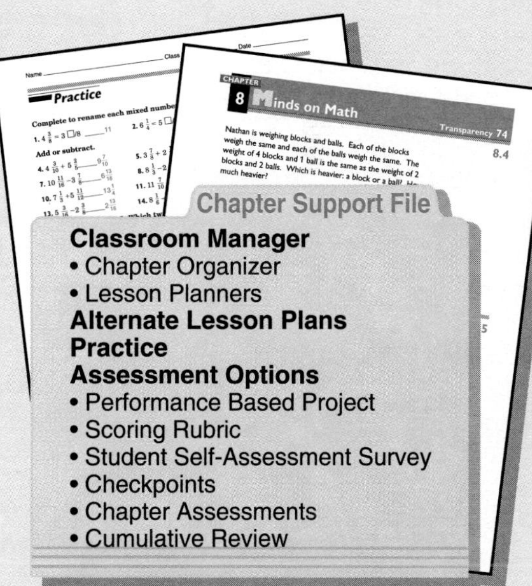

Minds on Math available in Teaching Transparencies

Math Minutes

Leah's scores on her math tests were 84, 64, 72, 86, 69, 85, and 87. Her teacher says that Leah's average score on the tests is about 78. Leah calculated an 84 average. What did each person mean? Whose interpretation of the data describes it most accurately? Why?

Her teacher gave the mean; Leah gave the median. The teacher's interpretation was more accurate because the scores dropped quite far below the median.

Materials for 8-6

- graph paper

8-6

Connecting to Prior Knowledge

If possible, bring in samples of the instructions that come with different appliances. Share the diagrams with the class. Have students discuss experiences they have had with diagrams that have come with items such as computers, toys, and bikes. Guide students to realize that diagrams usually clarify verbal directions for assembling an item.

DIVERSITY The initial problem involves Native American art. Ask your students to describe what type of art might be displayed on the wall. If you have any Native American students, see if they can bring examples or lend insight into the type of art or picture writing that might be displayed.

TACTILE LEARNERS Have students use square tiles to model the wall used in Questions 1–10.

Additional Problem *A rectangular garden measures 7 ft × 13 ft. Suppose you divide the garden into two new sections. You want one section to be square.*

- *What are the dimensions of the two new sections?*
- *How much fencing is needed for the garden so that it is completely enclosed and the two sections are separated?*

Draw a diagram of the original rectangle. Divide and label it.
Square: 7 ft on a side
Other rectangle: 6 ft × 7 ft
Find the perimeter of the original rectangle.

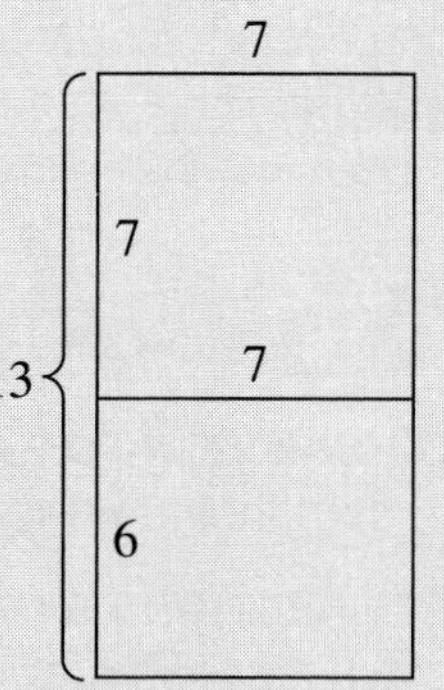

$P = 2l + 2w$

$P = 2(13) + 2(7)$

$P = 26 + 14$

$P = 40$ ft

Add the 7-ft section that separates the two sections.

Since 40 ft + 7 ft = 47 ft, 47 ft of fencing is needed.

> *“Be ashamed to die until you have won some victory for humanity.”*
>
> —Horace Mann

Organizer

1. **Focus**
   Connecting to Prior Knowledge
2. **Teach**
3. **Closure**
   Try These
   Wrap Up

Skills Reviewed in Context of Lesson
- adding and subtracting fractions

Materials and Manipulatives
- graph paper (for each student)

Student Resources
Extra Practice
Student Study Guide
Practice, TR Ch. 8, p. 28
Student Study Guide, Spanish Resources, TR

Teacher Resources
Teaching Transparency 74
Transparency Masters, TR p. 1
Lesson Planner, TR Ch. 8, p. 7

Prentice Hall Technology
Multimedia Math
- Math Investigations, Unidentified Flying Cubes

Computer Item Generator
- 8-6

PROBLEM SOLVING

8-6 Draw a Diagram

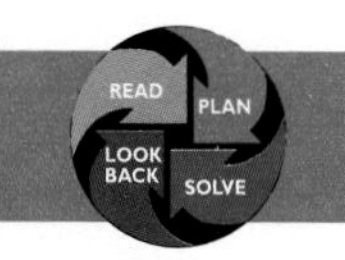

What's Ahead
- Solving a problem by drawing a diagram

Drawing a diagram is a strategy you can use to solve many problems. A diagram helps you to see a problem and its solution more clearly.

Prehistoric Zuni design of a turkey

An artist is creating a tiled wall for the Native American wing of a museum. The wall will display scenes of Native American life in the past and present. The border will be tiles containing Native American picture writing. Each border tile will have a different symbol. Each tile is a square that measures $\frac{1}{2}$ ft on a side. The tiled wall, including the border, will be 6 ft high by 10 ft wide. How many border tiles does the artist need to make?

READ
Read and understand the given information. Summarize the problem.

Identify the information you need to use to solve the problem.

1. What size and shape are the border tiles? Sketch one tile. **$\frac{1}{2}$ ft squares**
2. What size and shape is the tiled wall? Sketch the wall. Do the dimensions include the border? **a 6 ft by 10 ft rectangle; Yes.**
3. Is the problem asking you to find the total number of tiles the artist needs to make for the tiled wall? **No**

PLAN
Decide on a strategy to solve the problem.

If you draw a diagram of the tiled wall, you can then draw in the border. You may want to use grid paper, then count the number of border tiles needed.

4. Suppose you let one unit on the grid paper represent 1 ft. How many tiles will fit across the top of the wall? **20 tiles**
5. Instead you let one square on the grid paper represent one tile. How many tiles will fit across the top of the wall? **20 tiles**
6. Experiment with the two methods described in Exercises 4 and 5. Which do you prefer? Why? **Answers will vary.**

Questions 8 and 9: These will help students understand the value of drawing a diagram.

Question 10: This will help students see the pitfalls of quickly completing a problem without a diagram. You may wish to point out that if the tiles are expensive, the artist would have bought four tiles unnecessarily and wasted money.

TRY THESE

ESL VISUAL LEARNERS Have the students use graph paper to draw the diagrams for the problems in this lesson.

Error Alert! For Exercise 11, students may forget to add the height of the four shelves when calculating the total height of the bookcase. ***Remediation*** Remind students that the thickness of the wood will also add to the height of the bookcase and that this thickness should be accounted for in their diagrams.

Ongoing Assessment Have students work in small groups. Have each group do the following:

- Draw a diagram of any item typically found in school, including at least one measure other than length and width.
- Write a description of your diagram that includes geometric terms.
- Exchange written descriptions with other groups and draw the other group's diagram based on their description.

Monitor students' performance to see that their written descriptions correspond to their diagrams before they exchange with other groups.

Wrap Up

What's the Big Idea? Ask students: *Explain how and when to use the problem solving strategy of drawing a diagram.*

Draw a diagram to "see" the problem and its solution.

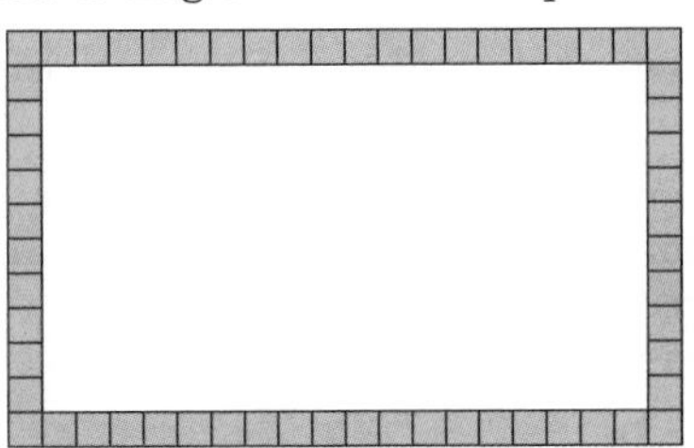

1 square = 1 tile

SOLVE
Try out the strategy.

7. Use the diagram to find the number of border tiles the artist needs to make. Explain why your answer is correct. 60 tiles
8. **Discussion** As soon as the diagram was drawn, was this problem easy to solve? Answers may vary.
9. **Discussion** Do you think this problem would be difficult to solve without drawing a diagram? Answers may vary.
10. **Discussion** Instead of drawing a diagram, one student did the following. Find the number of border tiles needed for each side of the wall: top, 20; bottom, 20; left side, 12; right side, 12. Then add: 20 + 20 + 12 + 12 = 64 border tiles. What is wrong with this solution? The four corner tiles were counted twice.

LOOK BACK
Think about how you solved this problem.

TRY THESE

Draw a diagram to solve each problem.

11. **Carpentry** Barbara is making a bookcase with wood that is $\frac{3}{4}$ in. thick. The bookcase has four shelves. One shelf is used for the top of the bookcase, and one is used for the bottom. The space between shelves is 12 in. Find the total height of the bookcase. 39 in.
12. **Gardening** Hahnee is planting flowers along the edge of a circular flower bed. He will place the plants 6 in. apart. The diameter of the circle measures about 7 ft. How many plants will Hahnee need? about 44 plants
13. **Pets** Joseph has 24 ft of fence for a rectangular dog kennel. Each side will be a whole number of feet (no fractions). List all possible dimensions for the kennel. Which will give Joseph's dog the greatest area? 6 ft by 6 ft

"A picture shows me at a glance what it takes dozens of pages of a book to expound."
—Ivan Sergeyevich Turgenev (1818–1883)

Fact of the Day

Native American farmers started selectively breeding wild corn for size about 5,000 years ago. The cultivation of corn then spread from Central Mexico south to Peru and north to what is now the United States.

—Information Please Almanac

Assignment Options

Core: 14, 18–20, MR all	
Reinforce: 15, 17, 21	**Enrich:** 16

Journal Discuss with students the value of a diagram. Have students write a short paragraph answering the question: *What is one task you find difficult at school that you wish you had a diagram to help you understand? Why?*

Connections Have students discuss where diagrams can be used in other subject areas.

- **Science** (diagrams of a microscope, molecules, or a human body)
- **Social Studies** (diagrams of machines used in the past, exploration routes)
- **Physical Education** (diagrams showing how to exercise)

Reteaching Activity Have students cut out square pieces of paper (or use algebra tiles) to model the figure in this problem: *A rectangular picture frame is made of 1-in. square ceramic tiles. The corner tiles are black and the rest of the tiles are yellow. The outer dimensions of the frame are 12 in. by 16 in. How many black and how many yellow tiles are needed?*

First, have students model the border of tiles using the square pieces of paper. Have them label the four corner tiles "black." Then have students draw a diagram of the model. If possible allow students to use graph paper. Students should label the dimensions and the four corner tiles. Finally, have students record the number of tiles needed. **(4 black, 48 yellow)**

ON YOUR OWN

CONNECTION TO GEOMETRY All these exercises except Exercises 15 and 20 require knowledge of perimeter, area, or circumference.

VISUAL LEARNERS For Exercises 15 and 20, students can make tables of the given information.

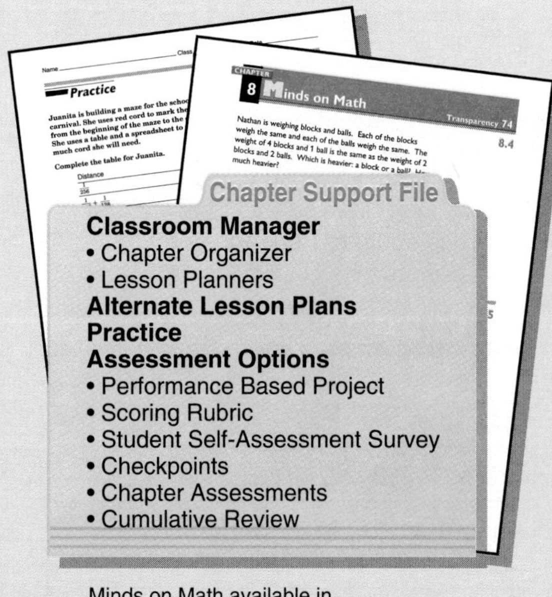

Minds on Math available in Teaching Transparencies

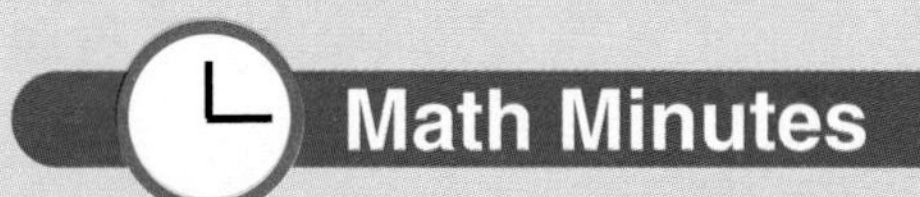

What kind of graph represents a whole broken into its parts?
circle graph

Materials for 8-7
- fraction bars
- calculator

ON YOUR OWN

Use any strategy to solve each problem. Show all your work.

14. Elisheba has a rug that is 12 ft by 18 ft in her living room. She wants to cut it into two smaller rectangular rugs that can be placed in other rooms. Show how she can make one cut and end up with two rugs the same size and shape. She can make two 9 ft by 12 ft rugs or two 6 ft by 18 ft rugs.

15. To celebrate its opening day, a store is offering a free gift to every 15th customer. The store manager expects about 100 customers each hour. About how many gifts will the store offer by the end of its 12-h opening day? about 80 gifts

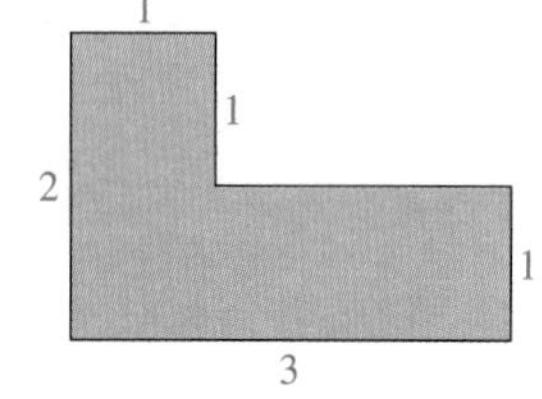

16. **Writing** Write a problem that can be solved using the diagram at the left. Solve your problem. Answers will vary. Check student's work.

17. An artist created four rectangular wooden panels for a gallery floor. Each panel measures $5\frac{1}{2}$ ft by 4 ft. The panels will be placed end-to-end along the 4-ft side. There will be 3 ft of space between the center two panels. Will the panels fit on the gallery floor, which is 25 ft long? Yes

18. Suppose your class is setting up the Recycling Relay Race for your school's celebration of Earth Day. You are using a rectangular area that is 15 ft by 40 ft. You will hammer a pole into the ground every 5 ft along the perimeter of the rectangular area. How many poles will you need? 22 poles

19. Six flags are evenly spaced around a circular track. LaWanda times herself as she runs around the track. It takes her 10 s to run from the first flag to the third flag. At this pace, how long will it take LaWanda to run around the entire track? 30 s

20. There are four containers on a shelf. The shapes of the containers are circular, square, oval, and rectangular. The colors are blue, white, green, and red. The blue container is neither square nor rectangular. The containers with a curved surface are blue or green. The green container is neither square nor round. The square container is not red. What color is each container? circle—blue, square—white, oval—green, rectangle—red

21. A rectangle has an area of 3,000 sq. ft. One side is 40 ft. Find the perimeter of the rectangle. 230 ft

Mixed REVIEW

Find each sum or difference.

1. $2\frac{3}{7} + 4\frac{3}{14}$ $6\frac{9}{14}$

2. $6\frac{2}{3} - 4\frac{1}{6}$ $2\frac{1}{2}$

Use the data. Math Test Grades: A, C, B, B, C, F, A, A, C, D. See Solution Key.

3. Make a line plot.

4. How many students received a grade of C or better? 8 students

5. Eight people are attending a meeting. Each person shakes hands with each of the others exactly once. What is the total number of handshakes exchanged?

28 handshakes

CHAPTER 8 PRACTICE

This page provides practice on the skills learned up to this point in the chapter. Daily cumulative practice can be found in the Mixed Reviews that appear in every lesson.

Exercise 17: Students may have difficulty finding the lowest common denominator for three fractions. Ask them to review possible strategies.

Exercise 32: Students can draw a diagram, marking off twenty feet, to help them solve the problem.

Practice

Estimate each sum or difference. Estimates may vary.

1. $\frac{5}{7} + \frac{6}{11}$ $1\frac{1}{2}$
2. $4\frac{1}{4} - 2\frac{6}{7}$ 1
3. $\frac{7}{16} + \frac{5}{32}$ $\frac{1}{2}$
4. $\frac{7}{10} - \frac{2}{5}$ $\frac{1}{2}$

Round each measurement to the nearest half inch.

5. $7\frac{3}{4}$ in. 8 in.
6. $1\frac{6}{7}$ in. 2 in.
7. $3\frac{1}{3}$ in. $3\frac{1}{2}$ in.
8. $99\frac{2}{5}$ in. $99\frac{1}{2}$ in.
9. $10\frac{2}{15}$ in. 10 in.

Draw a model and find each sum or difference.

10. $\frac{1}{7} + \frac{1}{7}$ $\frac{2}{7}$
11. $\frac{7}{8} - \frac{3}{8}$ $\frac{4}{8}; \frac{1}{2}$
12. $\frac{1}{10} + \frac{3}{10}$ $\frac{4}{10}; \frac{2}{5}$
13. $\frac{3}{4} - \frac{1}{4}$ $\frac{2}{4}; \frac{1}{2}$

Use any method to add or subtract.

14. $\frac{1}{4} + \frac{1}{3}$ $\frac{7}{12}$
15. $\frac{1}{5} - \frac{1}{10}$ $\frac{1}{10}$
16. $\frac{7}{8} - \frac{3}{4}$ $\frac{1}{8}$
17. $\frac{1}{6} + \frac{1}{7} + \frac{1}{8}$ $\frac{73}{168}$
18. $\frac{5}{6} - \frac{5}{8}$ $\frac{5}{24}$
19. $\frac{7}{12} - \frac{3}{10}$ $\frac{17}{60}$
20. $\frac{3}{4} + \frac{1}{3}$ $1\frac{1}{12}$
21. $\frac{3}{10} + \frac{4}{5}$ $1\frac{1}{10}$

22. Analyze the "Expression" column. Fill in the sums, then write the next expression in the pattern. See table at right. The next expression would be $\frac{1}{1} + \frac{1}{4} + \frac{1}{9} + \frac{1}{16}$.

Expression	Sum	
$\frac{1}{1}$	$\frac{1}{1}$	
$\frac{1}{1} + \frac{1}{4}$	■	$1\frac{1}{4}$
$\frac{1}{1} + \frac{1}{4} + \frac{1}{9}$	■	$1\frac{13}{36}$

Find each sum or difference.

23. $5\frac{2}{3} + 2\frac{1}{2}$ $8\frac{1}{6}$
24. $4\frac{1}{2} - 3\frac{3}{4}$ $\frac{3}{4}$
25. $1\frac{2}{3} + 1\frac{1}{4}$ $2\frac{11}{12}$
26. $7\frac{3}{5} - 3\frac{2}{3}$ $3\frac{14}{15}$
27. $2\frac{3}{4} + 6\frac{5}{16}$ $9\frac{1}{16}$
28. $9\frac{4}{7} - 5\frac{1}{14}$ $4\frac{1}{2}$
29. $8\frac{3}{8} + 6\frac{3}{4}$ $15\frac{1}{8}$
30. $10\frac{1}{10} - 3\frac{3}{20}$ $6\frac{19}{20}$

31. Stanley rides his bicycle half way to school and then gets a flat tire. He walks his bike the next quarter mile. At that point, Mrs. Chan picks Stanley up and drives him the remaining $\frac{1}{2}$ mile to school. Find the distance between Stanley's house and the school. $1\frac{1}{2}$ mi

32. Consuela throws her hat up a 20-ft tree. The hat lands $\frac{3}{4}$ of the way up. She climbs the tree half way and reaches 4 ft for her hat. Can she get her hat back this way? Why or why not? No; she needs to reach 5 ft to get her hat.

Resources
Extra Practice
Student Study Guide
Student Study Guide, Spanish Resources, TR

8-7

Connecting to Prior Knowledge

Have students brainstorm how they can use models to show multiplication of fractions.

WORK TOGETHER

Give students these hints for making their tables:

Number Column

- Choose 20 different numbers.
- At least 4 numbers must be decimals.
- At least 4 numbers must be mixed numbers.
- At least 5 numbers must be whole numbers.

Fraction Column

- At least 5 fractions must be $\frac{1}{2}$.
- At least 5 fractions must have a numerator other than one (and still be less than one).

THINK AND DISCUSS

Before discussing the park questions, show several examples containing the word *of* used in a context where it means multiplication. You may start with sentences like these.

- *What is half of three dollars?* **($\frac{1}{2}$ • 3)**
- *I have used $\frac{3}{4}$ of the twelve boxes of chalk in the closet.* **($\frac{3}{4}$ • 12)**
- *The Smiths represent $\frac{2}{15}$ of the 4,000 S's in the phone book.* **($\frac{2}{15}$ • 4000)**

AUDITORY LEARNERS Have students discuss the differences they notice between adding and multiplying fractions.

VISUAL LEARNERS Have students draw diagrams such as the one used for Questions 2–4, to help them visualize multiplication.

> *"All you need is to tell a man that he is no good ten times a day, and very soon he begins to believe it himself."*
>
> —Lin Yutang

Organizer

1. **Focus**
   Connecting to Prior Knowledge
2. **Teach**
   Work Together
   Think and Discuss
3. **Closure**
   Try These
   Wrap Up

Skills Reviewed in Context of Lesson

- simplifying and renaming fractions

Materials and Manipulatives

- fraction bars (1 set per group)
- calculator (1 per group)

Student Resources

Extra Practice
Student Study Guide
Practice, TR Ch. 8, p. 29
Student Study Guide, Spanish Resources, TR

Teacher Resources

Teaching Transparencies 17, 19, 22–29, 75
Transparency Masters TR, pp. 21–24
Overhead Manipulatives: fraction bars
Lesson Planner, TR Ch. 8, p. 8

continues next page

What's Ahead

- Multiplying fractions and mixed numbers

8-7 Multiplying Fractions & Mixed Numbers

WHAT YOU'LL NEED

✓ Fraction bars

✓ Calculator

WORK TOGETHER

Work with a partner. Use a fraction calculator. Experiment to see what happens when you multiply by a fraction less than 1. Start with a fraction such as $\frac{1}{2}$. Multiply several different numbers by $\frac{1}{2}$. Use whole numbers, mixed numbers, decimals, and fractions. Make a table like the one at the left.

Number	Fraction	Product
10	$\frac{1}{2}$	5
5	$\frac{1}{2}$	■
3.8	$\frac{1}{2}$	■
$9\frac{1}{4}$	$\frac{1}{2}$	■
■	$\frac{1}{4}$	■

1. When you multiply a number by a fraction less than 1, is the product greater than or less than the number? Why?
   less than; The product is only a portion of the number.

THINK AND DISCUSS

Suppose your community is given a square tract of land for a park. The planning board wants to use $\frac{1}{2}$ of the land for ball fields and $\frac{1}{2}$ of the land for a picnic/play area. One third of the picnic/play area will have playground equipment. What portion of the park will have playground equipment? You can use models or multiplication to solve this problem.

2. Use the square at the left to represent the park. The shaded area represents the picnic/play area. What portion of the park is the picnic/play area? Write a fraction. $\frac{1}{2}$

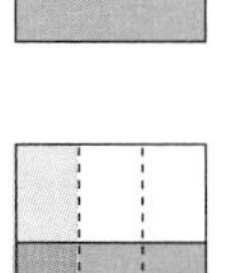

3. Now divide the square into thirds, as shown at the left. Which area on the square represents the area of the park that will have playground equipment? What portion of the square (park) is this? Write a fraction. $\frac{1}{6}$
4. The portion of the park that has playground equipment is $\frac{1}{3}$ of $\frac{1}{2}$ of the park. How does the model show this?
   One third of $\frac{1}{2}$ of the square is shaded.

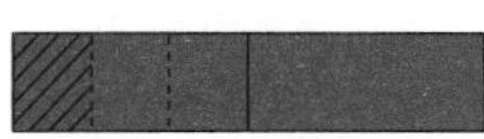

5. Does the fraction bar at the left represent $\frac{1}{3}$ of $\frac{1}{2}$? Explain.
   Yes; One third of $\frac{1}{2}$ of the fraction bar is shaded.

You can multiply to find $\frac{1}{3}$ of $\frac{1}{2}$. The word "of" means multiply.

$$\frac{1}{3} \text{ of } \frac{1}{2} = \frac{1}{3} \times \frac{1}{2} = \frac{1 \times 1}{3 \times 2} = \frac{1}{6}$$

6. Use models and multiplication to find $\frac{2}{3}$ of $\frac{3}{4}$, or $\frac{2}{3} \times \frac{3}{4}$.
   $\frac{6}{12}$ or $\frac{1}{2}$

ESL Make sure students understand what is meant by the terms *simplifying fractions* and *improper fractions.*

Example 1

Ask students: *Why can 12 be expressed as $\frac{12}{1}$?* **(because 12 divided by 1 is 12)**

Additional Example *Last Saturday night Gung-ho Middle School had a dance. Three-fifths of Mrs. Rey's class attended the dance. If Mrs. Rey has 25 students, how many of her students went to the dance Saturday night?*

Find $\frac{3}{5}$ of 25. Multiply $\frac{3}{5} \times 25$.

$\frac{3}{5} \times 25 = \frac{3}{5} \times \frac{25}{1} = \frac{3 \times 25}{5 \times 1} = \frac{75}{5} = 15$

15 students from Mrs. Rey's class attended.

Error Alert! When multiplying a whole number by a fraction, students may multiply the whole number by the denominator rather than by the numerator, because the denominator of the whole number, 1, is not evident. ***Remediation*** Be sure students show the intermediate step where the multiplication of numerators and denominators takes place. Refer students to the solutions of the Examples.

Example 2

Students may want to multiply whole numbers and then the fractions as they did when adding. Explain that the fractional parts of the mixed numbers must also be multiplied by the whole number parts.

Additional Example *Multiply $5\frac{1}{7} \times 1\frac{5}{6}$.*

Estimate: $5 \times 2 = 10$

Write $5\frac{1}{7}$ as $\frac{36}{7}$ and $1\frac{5}{6}$ as $\frac{11}{6}$

$\frac{36}{7} \times \frac{11}{6} = \frac{36 \times 11}{7 \times 6} = \frac{(36 \div 6) \times 11}{7 \times (6 \div 6)} = \frac{6 \times 11}{7 \times 1} = \frac{66}{7} = 9\frac{3}{7}$

To solve some problems, you will multiply a fraction and a whole number.

Example 1 Suppose 12 schools in your county enter a science-math competition. Two-thirds of the schools will advance to the second round of competition. How many schools will advance to the second round?

Find $\frac{2}{3}$ of 12. So multiply $\frac{2}{3} \times 12$. — "Of" means multiply.

$\frac{2}{3} \times 12 = \frac{2}{3} \times \frac{12}{1} = \frac{2 \times 12}{3 \times 1} = \frac{24}{3} = 8$ — Write 12 as $\frac{12}{1}$.

So 8 schools will advance to the second round.

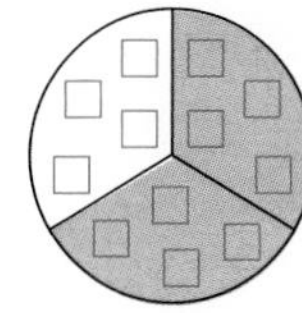

7. Does the model at the right represent $\frac{2}{3}$ of 12? Explain. Yes; Two thirds of the 12 squares are shaded.

Sometimes you can simplify before multiplying. Divide the numerator and the denominator by a common factor.

8. Look back at $\frac{2 \times 12}{3 \times 1}$ from Example 1. Notice that the 12 in the numerator and the 3 in the denominator have a common factor. What is the common factor? 3
9. Divide both the numerator and the denominator by the common factor 3 before you multiply: $\frac{2 \times (12 \div 3)}{(3 \div 3) \times 1} = \frac{■}{■}$. $\frac{8}{1}$
10. Use this method to find $\frac{4}{5} \times \frac{1}{2}$. What is the common factor? Check your answer. $\frac{4}{10}$ or $\frac{2}{5}$; 2

When you multiply with mixed numbers, first write each mixed number as an improper fraction.

Example 2 What is the area of the rectangle?

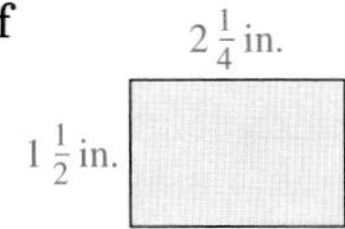

Estimate: $2 \times 2 = 4$

Write $2\frac{1}{4}$ as $\frac{9}{4}$ and $1\frac{1}{2}$ as $\frac{3}{2}$.

$2\frac{1}{4} \times 1\frac{1}{2} = \frac{9}{4} \times \frac{3}{2} = \frac{9 \times 3}{4 \times 2} = \frac{27}{8} = 3\frac{3}{8}$

The area of the rectangle is $3\frac{3}{8}$ sq. in.

11. List the steps for finding $6\frac{2}{3} \times 1\frac{1}{5}$. Then multiply. 8

FLASHBACK
To write a mixed number as an improper fraction, multiply the whole number by the denominator and add the numerator. Then write the result over the denominator.

FLASHBACK
To estimate with fractions, round to the nearest $\frac{1}{2}$. To estimate with mixed numbers, round to the nearest whole number.

Organizer, continued

Prentice Hall Technology

Multimedia Math
- Hot Page™ 8-7
- Math Tools, Fraction Strips

Computer Item Generator
- 8-7

Other Available Technology
calculator
Fast-Tract Fractions by Computer Software: Exercises 33–40 *(optional)*

Fact of the Day

The "2 by 4" description of a piece of lumber is called its nominal size, which is the board's dimension after it has been newly sawed and trimmed. This rough lumber then is seasoned and planed, which reduces its finished size to $1\frac{1}{2}$ in. by $3\frac{1}{2}$ in.

—World Book Encyclopedia

TRY THESE

Exercises 16–19: Ask students to justify their estimates.

Ongoing Assessment Have students work in pairs to adjust the recipe to feed four people rather than eight. Check that students realize they must multiply each ingredient by $\frac{1}{2}$ to change the recipe.

Recipe for Vegetable Omelette for 8

12 eggs | $4\frac{1}{2}$ slices of cheese

$1\frac{1}{4}$ green peppers | $\frac{1}{3}$ onion

$\frac{1}{4}$ lb mushrooms

6 eggs, $2\frac{1}{4}$ slices of cheese, $\frac{5}{8}$ green peppers, $\frac{1}{6}$ onion, $\frac{1}{8}$ lb mushrooms

Wrap Up

What's the Big Idea? Ask students: *Explain how multiplying fractions and multiplying mixed numbers are alike. How are they different?*

Journal Tell students you'd like them to help a student sick at home understand his mistake. Give them the following work and ask them to explain why his answer is incorrect. His paper looked like this. **(The correct answer is $30\frac{1}{4}$.)**

$$5\frac{1}{2} \times 5\frac{1}{2}$$

$$5 \times 5 + \frac{1}{2} \times \frac{1}{2}$$

$$25 + \frac{1}{4} = 25\frac{1}{4}$$

PH Multimedia Math Hot Page™ 8-7

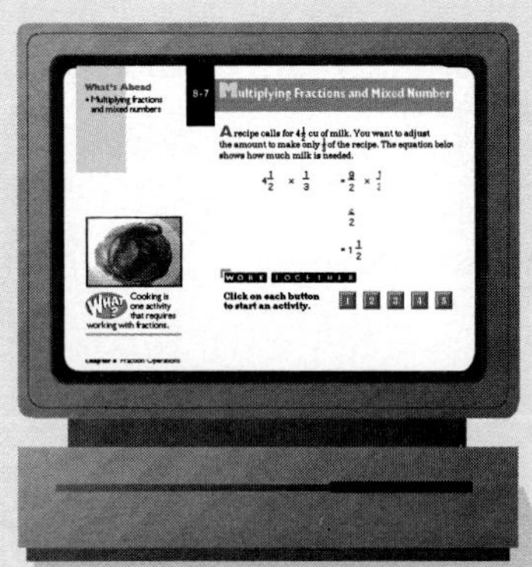

Assignment Options

Core: 27–29, 33–36, 41–44, MR all	
Reinforce: 24–26, 32, 37–40	**Enrich:** 30, 31

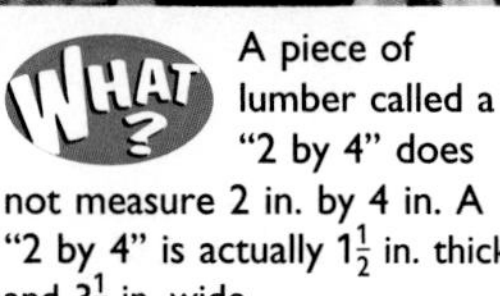

A piece of lumber called a "2 by 4" does not measure 2 in. by 4 in. A "2 by 4" is actually $1\frac{1}{2}$ in. thick and $3\frac{1}{2}$ in. wide.

Lumber Name	Thickness (in.)	Width (in.)
1 by 4	$\frac{3}{4}$	$3\frac{1}{2}$
2 by 2	$1\frac{1}{2}$	$1\frac{1}{2}$
2 by 4	$1\frac{1}{2}$	$3\frac{1}{2}$
2 by 6	$1\frac{1}{2}$	$5\frac{1}{2}$

TRY THESE

Draw a model to represent each product. See Solution Key for sample models.

12. $\frac{1}{4}$ of $\frac{1}{3}$ $\frac{1}{12}$ 13. $\frac{1}{2}$ of $\frac{3}{4}$ $\frac{3}{8}$ 14. $\frac{3}{4}$ of 16 12 15. $\frac{1}{5}$ of $\frac{5}{8}$ $\frac{1}{8}$

Estimate. Then find the product.

16. $3\frac{1}{2} \times 1\frac{1}{4}$ 4; $4\frac{3}{8}$ 17. $\frac{2}{3} \times \frac{1}{3}$ 0; $\frac{2}{9}$ 18. $\frac{3}{4} \times 9$ 9; $6\frac{3}{4}$ 19. $15 \times \frac{1}{5}$ 0; 3

Explain how to simplify. Then find the product.

20. $\frac{3}{16} \times \frac{4}{5}$ $\frac{3}{20}$ 21. $3\frac{1}{5} \times \frac{3}{4}$ $2\frac{2}{5}$ 22. $5\frac{1}{3} \times 2\frac{1}{2}$ $13\frac{1}{3}$ 23. $12 \times \frac{5}{6}$ 10

ON YOUR OWN

24. **Choose A, B, C, or D.** Which product does the model represent? C

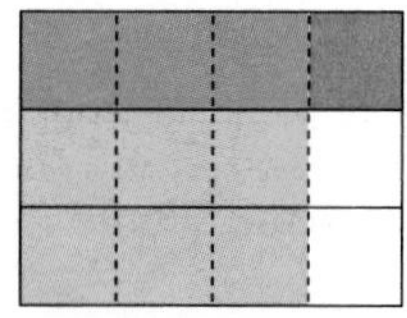

A. $\frac{3}{4} \times \frac{2}{3}$ B. $\frac{1}{3} \times \frac{1}{3}$

C. $\frac{3}{4} \times \frac{1}{3}$ D. $\frac{1}{3} \times \frac{2}{3}$

Estimate each product. Estimates may vary.

25. $2\frac{3}{4} \times 6\frac{1}{8}$ 18 26. $5\frac{1}{2} \times 1\frac{3}{10}$ 6 27. $9\frac{4}{5} \times 5\frac{7}{12}$ 60 28. $\frac{4}{7} \times 1\frac{1}{3}$ 1

Use the information at the left.

29. **Carpentry** Zahara is building the floor of a deck. She will place 32 "2 by 4" boards side by side with $\frac{1}{4}$ in. space between each board. How wide is the floor of the deck? $119\frac{3}{4}$ in.
30. **Carpentry** Simon loaded his truck with boards. He placed all the boards in a single stack. The stack had three "2 by 6" boards and six "2 by 2" boards. How high is the stack? $13\frac{1}{2}$ in.
31. **Writing** When you multiply two fractions that are each less than 1, will the product *always, sometimes,* or *never* be less than either of the fractions? Explain your answer. Always; the product is only a portion of either fraction.
32. **Sewing** A quilt pattern shows a square with $4\frac{1}{2}$ in. sides. Patty wants to reduce each side to $\frac{2}{3}$ the length shown on the pattern. Find the dimensions of the reduced square. Solve two different ways, using models and multiplication. 3 in. by 3 in.

Connections Discuss situations when knowing how to multiply mixed numbers and fractions can be useful.

- **Industrial Arts** (designing furniture and machinery, constructing buildings)
- **Consumer** (creating and adjusting recipes)

Reteaching Activity As a class, work through the procedure for finding $2\frac{2}{5} \times \frac{5}{8}$. **($1\frac{1}{2}$)** Ask students to write a list of the steps needed to find the answer. Then have students work in pairs and use their list to find $6 \times 7\frac{1}{3}$. **(44)**

ON YOUR OWN

WRITING Exercise 31 will help you assess student understanding of multiplying with fractions less than one.

TECHNOLOGY OPTION For Questions 33–40, students can use fraction software to practice multiplying fractions. Middle-school software often includes high-interest graphics and a reward system to motivate players.

CONNECTION TO SOCIAL STUDIES Exercises 41–44 use statistics concerning the literacy rate in the United States.

Find each product.

33. $\frac{5}{8} \times 16$ 10 **34.** $\frac{2}{3} \times \frac{9}{10}$ $\frac{3}{5}$ **35.** $6 \times \frac{2}{3}$ 4 **36.** $8\frac{1}{2} \times 8\frac{1}{2}$ $72\frac{1}{4}$

37. $4\frac{1}{9} \times 3\frac{3}{8}$ $13\frac{7}{8}$ **38.** $\frac{1}{5} \times 100$ 20 **39.** $\frac{2}{5} \times \frac{1}{6}$ $\frac{1}{15}$ **40.** $2\frac{1}{3} \times 10$ $23\frac{1}{3}$

Read the news article below. Use for Exercises 41–44.

Almost Half Barely Literate

Ninety million U.S. adults do not have adequate literacy skills, according to the recent National Adult Literacy Survey. From the U.S. adult population of about 191 million, a random sample of about 16,000 people 16 and older were surveyed. The study, funded by the Department of Education, placed adults in five levels of proficiency. About $\frac{1}{4}$ of the 90 million adults at low literacy levels are immigrants learning English as a second language. Of the estimated 40 million adults at the lowest of the five levels, about 37% are illiterate, not able to complete the survey.

But this is a solvable problem, according to advocates of literacy programs. In 1980, 2 million adults were enrolled in a literacy program. Today, there are 3.8 million enrolled, an increase of nearly 90%. At least $\frac{1}{3}$ of the current population of enrolled adults are learning English as a second language.

How can you help? If you would like to find out about literacy programs in your area, or if you would like to volunteer, call the Contact Literacy Center hotline at 1 (800) 228-8813 or TT1 (800) 552-9097 for the hearing impaired.

41. What numbers in the news article support the claim in the title that *almost half* are barely literate? 90 out of 191 million

42. How many of the 90 million adults at low literacy levels are immigrants learning English as a second language? What portion of the entire U.S. adult population is this? $22\frac{1}{2}$ million adults; about $\frac{3}{25}$

43. How many immigrants learning English as a second language are enrolled in a literacy program today? What portion of the immigrants at low literacy levels is this? about 1,270,000; about $\frac{1}{18}$

44. What portion of the U.S. adult population is illiterate? How many people is this? about $\frac{3}{40}$; $14\frac{4}{5}$ million

Mixed REVIEW

Simplify.

1. $8 + 3 \times 6$ 26
2. $12 \div 4 + 8 \times 2 - 1$ 18
3. How many tournament games will the champion have to play if there are 32 teams competing in a single-elimination tournament? 5
4. The lengths of three rods are 4 mm, 6 mm, and 9 mm. How can you arrange these rods to measure a length of 11 mm?
5. A clock chimes every hour. How many times will it chime in the month of July? 744 times

4. See Sol. Key.

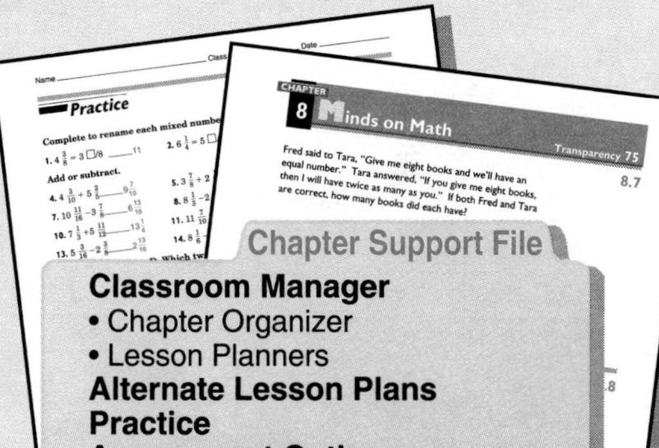

Chapter Support File

Classroom Manager
- Chapter Organizer
- Lesson Planners

Alternate Lesson Plans

Practice

Assessment Options
- Performance Based Project
- Scoring Rubric
- Student Self-Assessment Survey
- Checkpoints
- Chapter Assessments
- Cumulative Review

Minds on Math available in Teaching Transparencies

Math Minutes

Find the least common denominator (LCD) of $\frac{3}{4}$ and $\frac{5}{16}$.

16

Materials for 8-8
- fraction bars
- calculator

8-8

Connecting to Prior Knowledge

Have students discuss how they would determine how many $\frac{1}{2}$-ft pieces of wood they could cut from the same 10-ft section.

WORK TOGETHER

Give students these hints for beginning their tables.

Number Column

- Choose 20 different numbers.
- At least 4 numbers must be decimals.
- At least 4 numbers must be mixed numbers.
- At least 5 numbers must be whole numbers.

Fraction Column

- At least 5 fractions must be $\frac{1}{2}$.
- At least 5 fractions must have a numerator other than one (and still be less than one).

THINK AND DISCUSS

Use examples to show students that multiplying by $\frac{1}{2}$ is the same as dividing by 2.

Question 8: Remind students that any whole number can be written as a fraction. For example, 5 can be written as $\frac{5}{1}$.

KINESTHETIC LEARNERS Have students measure a piece of ribbon or string to confirm the answer for Example 1.

ESL **ESL** Review the meaning of the word *reciprocal* and have students work together until they are comfortable finding reciprocals. Have students work with a partner to dictate fractions and determine reciprocals.

Example 1

Students may need to be reminded to divide the numerator and denominator by the GCF of 3.

"Knowledge comes, but wisdom lingers."

—Alfred, Lord Tennyson

Organizer

1. **Focus**
   Connecting to Prior Knowledge
2. **Teach**
   Work Together
   Think and Discuss
3. **Closure**
   Try These
   Wrap Up

Vocabulary/Symbols
reciprocals

Skills Reviewed in Context of Lesson
- multiplying fractions

Materials and Manipulatives
- fraction bars (1 set per pair)
- calculator (1 per group)

Student Resources
Extra Practice
Student Study Guide
Practice, TR Ch. 8, p. 30
Student Study Guide, Spanish Resources, TR
Checkpoint, TR Ch. 8, p. 36
Alternate Lesson, TR Ch. 8, pp. 19–22

continues next page

What's Ahead

- Dividing fractions and mixed numbers

8-8 Dividing Fractions & Mixed Numbers

WHAT YOU'LL NEED

✓ Fraction bars

✓ Calculator

Number	Fraction	Quotient
10	$\frac{1}{2}$	■
5	$\frac{1}{2}$	■
3.8	$\frac{1}{2}$	■
$9\frac{1}{4}$	$\frac{1}{2}$	■
■	$\frac{1}{4}$	■

WORK TOGETHER

Work with a partner. Use a fraction calculator. Experiment to see what happens when you divide by a fraction less than 1. Start with a fraction such as $\frac{1}{2}$. Divide several different numbers by $\frac{1}{2}$. Use whole numbers, mixed numbers, decimals, and fractions. Make a table like the one at the left.

1. When you divide a number by a fraction less than 1, is the quotient greater than or less than the number? Why? greater than; Dividing a number by a fraction less than 1 is the same as multiplying by a number greater than 1.

THINK AND DISCUSS

Suppose your family and some friends order a jumbo-sized pizza. You and three friends equally share $\frac{1}{2}$ of the pizza. What portion of the pizza does each friend get to eat? You can use models, multiplication, or division to solve this problem.

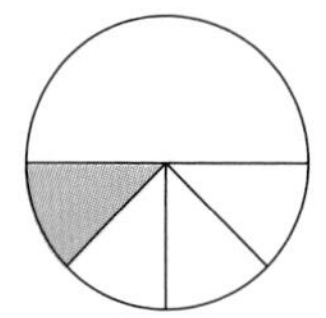

2. Use the circle at the left to represent the pizza. Since four of you will share $\frac{1}{2}$ the pizza, divide $\frac{1}{2}$ the pizza into four equal pieces. What portion of the pizza does each friend get to eat? Look at the model! $\frac{1}{8}$
3. To use multiplication to solve this problem, think about how much each friend gets. Each friend gets $\frac{1}{4}$ of $\frac{1}{2}$ of the pizza. So multiply to find $\frac{1}{4} \times \frac{1}{2}$. $\frac{1}{8}$
4. To use division to solve this problem, think about $\frac{1}{2}$ of the pizza shared by four friends. What portion will each friend get if $\frac{1}{2}$ of the pizza is divided by 4 people? So divide to find $\frac{1}{2} \div 4$. $\frac{1}{8}$
5. **Discussion** Compare the three different ways to solve this problem. Which do you prefer? Do your answers agree? Answers will vary; All answers agree.
6. Compare the multiplication and division expressions used to solve this problem. They result in the same answer, so they must be equal. Do you agree that $\frac{1}{2} \div 4 = \frac{1}{2} \times \frac{1}{4}$? Yes

Additional Example *Gary has 4 ft of string and needs $\frac{4}{5}$ ft to tie each tomato plant to a stake for support. How many tomato plants can Gary stake up?*

$4 \div \frac{4}{5}$ **Divide 4 by $\frac{4}{5}$.**

$= 4 \times \frac{5}{4}$ **Multiply 4 by the reciprocal of $\frac{4}{5}$.**

$= \frac{4 \times 5}{1 \times 4} = 5$

Gary can stake 5 tomato plants.

Example 2

Have students write 30 as $\frac{30}{1}$.

Error Alert! Some students incorrectly take the reciprocal of the first number. ***Remediation*** Have students practice saying and then verifying problems such as "6 divided by 2 is the same as one-half of 6."

Additional Example *A telephone repairman needs $2\frac{1}{3}$ ft of cord for each phone he installs. If he has 42 ft of cord in his truck, how many telephones can he install?*

Divide: $42 \div 2\frac{1}{3}$

$$42 \div \frac{7}{3} = 42 \times \frac{3}{7}$$
$$= \frac{42 \times 3}{1 \times 7}$$
$$= \frac{(42 \div 7) \times 3}{1 \times (7 \div 7)}$$
$$= \frac{6 \times 3}{1 \times 1} = 18$$

The repairman can install 18 telephones.

Journal Give students several numbers and have them call out the reciprocal. Ask them to write a short description of other things they can think of that must be turned upside down to be used. **(samples: salt shaker, hourglass)**

The numbers 4 and $\frac{1}{4}$ are *reciprocals* because their product is 1. Dividing by a number is the same as multiplying by the reciprocal of that number. You saw this in Exercise 6.

7. Find each product. What do you notice? **Each product is 1.**
   a. $\frac{1}{2} \times \frac{2}{1}$ 1 b. $\frac{2}{3} \times \frac{3}{2}$ 1 c. $\frac{1}{7} \times \frac{7}{1}$ 1 d. $8 \times \frac{1}{8}$ 1 e. $\frac{9}{2} \times \frac{2}{9}$ 1

8. Write the reciprocal of each number.
   a. $\frac{2}{3}$ $\frac{3}{2}$ b. $\frac{1}{9}$ 9 c. 5 $\frac{1}{5}$ d. 1 1 e. $\frac{7}{4}$ $\frac{4}{7}$

You will use reciprocals to divide with fractions.

Example 1 Nancy has 3 yd of ribbon. It takes $\frac{3}{8}$ yd to make one bow. How many bows can Nancy make if she uses all the ribbon?

$3 \div \frac{3}{8}$ Divide 3 by $\frac{3}{8}$.

$= 3 \times \frac{8}{3}$ Multiply 3 by the reciprocal of $\frac{3}{8}$.

$= \frac{3 \times 8}{1 \times 3} = 8$

Nancy can make 8 bows with 3 yd of ribbon.

LOOK BACK How can you check that the answer makes sense? **Sample: $8 \times \frac{3}{8}$ yd = 3 yd ribbon**

9. Draw a model for the problem and solution in Example 1. **See Solution Key.**
10. **Discussion** To divide by a number, you can multiply by its ■ instead. Why does this work? **reciprocal; multiplication undoes division**

Rhythmic gymnastics *is an Olympic event. Gymnasts dance while holding a piece of equipment such as a ribbon, hoop, rope, club, or ball.*

When you divide with mixed numbers, first write each mixed number as an improper fraction.

Example 2 Leroy made 30 c of soup. How many $1\frac{1}{4}$-c servings of soup does he have?

Divide: $30 \div 1\frac{1}{4}$

$30 \div \frac{5}{4} = 30 \times \frac{4}{5}$ Write $1\frac{1}{4}$ as $\frac{5}{4}$.

$= \frac{30 \times 4}{1 \times 5}$

$= \frac{(30 \div 5) \times 4}{1 \times (5 \div 5)}$ Simplify before you multiply.

$= 6 \times 4 = 24$

Leroy has 24 $1\frac{1}{4}$-c servings of soup.

Organizer, continued

Teacher Resources

Teaching Transparencies 17, 19, 22–29, 75
Transparency Masters, TR pp. 21–24
Overhead Manipulatives: fraction bars
Lesson Planner, TR Ch. 8, p. 9

Prentice Hall Technology

Multimedia Math
- Math Tools, Fraction Strips

Computer Item Generator
- 8-8

Other Available Technology
calculator
Division of Fractions by Computer Software: Exercises 19–26 *(optional)*

Fact of the Day

On August 2, 1990, Iraqi military forces under President Saddam Hussein invaded and occupied the Arab state of Kuwait. The Persian Gulf War of 1991, from January 16 to February 28, was fought to expel Iraq and restore Kuwaiti independence.

—ACADEMIC AMERICAN ENCYCLOPEDIA

TRY THESE

TECHNOLOGY OPTION For Exercises 19–26, students can use fraction software to practice division of fractions. Some software is specifically designed for division, explaining the process and why it is done the way it is.

Exercise 17: Have string available for students to model the problem.

Exercises 19–26: Have students write whole numbers as fractions before they begin dividing.

Ongoing Assessment

Have students work in pairs to create an expression that fits each description. Then have them find the value of the expressions. Check students' solutions.

- an expression whose quotient equals 1
- a division expression that can be simplified before dividing the fractions
- a division expression that cannot be simplified before dividing

Wrap Up

What's the Big Idea?

Ask students: *How do you divide fractions and mixed numbers?*

Reteaching Activity

Have students work in groups of four. Each group member copies a different one of the following expressions on a sheet of paper. Have them complete the activity in round-robin format. Each group member does one step, then passes the paper to the group member to the right.

a. $2\frac{1}{2} \div 4$ b. $3\frac{1}{5} \div \frac{4}{5}$ c. $1\frac{3}{4} \div 3\frac{1}{2}$ d. $5 \div 1\frac{7}{8}$

- Find the reciprocal of the divisor.
- Multiply the reciprocal by the dividend.
- Simplify if you can.
- Multiply the numerators and denominators.
- Write answer in simplest form.

(a. $\frac{5}{8}$; b. 4; c. $\frac{1}{2}$; d. $2\frac{2}{3}$)

Assignment Options

Core: 27, 29–36, 41, 42, 47, 48, 51–54, 59, MR all, CH all	
Reinforce: 37–40, 43, 44, 46, 49, 50, 55–58	**Enrich:** 28, 45

348

TRY THESE

Write the reciprocal of each number.

11. $\frac{4}{5}$ $\frac{5}{4}$ 12. 3 $\frac{1}{3}$ 13. $\frac{2}{10}$ $\frac{10}{2}$ 14. $\frac{1}{5}$ 5 15. $3\frac{1}{2}$ $\frac{2}{7}$ 16. $2\frac{5}{6}$ $\frac{6}{17}$

17. Draw a diagram to show how many $\frac{1}{3}$-ft pieces of string you can cut from a piece that is $3\frac{1}{3}$ ft long. 10 pieces; See Solution Key for diagram.

18. You have a 15-lb bag of bird seed. If the birds you feed eat $1\frac{1}{2}$ lb of seed each day, how many days will your seed last? 10 days

Divide. Write each answer in simplest form.

19. $\frac{3}{8} \div 5$ $\frac{3}{40}$ 20. $\frac{7}{8} \div \frac{3}{4}$ $1\frac{1}{6}$ 21. $4 \div \frac{3}{4}$ $5\frac{1}{3}$ 22. $\frac{1}{5} \div \frac{1}{3}$ $\frac{3}{5}$

23. $4\frac{1}{6} \div 10$ $\frac{5}{12}$ 24. $\frac{2}{3} \div 1\frac{1}{2}$ $\frac{4}{9}$ 25. $2\frac{5}{8} \div \frac{3}{4}$ $3\frac{1}{2}$ 26. $3\frac{1}{5} \div 1\frac{1}{3}$ $2\frac{2}{5}$

ON YOUR OWN

27. Samuel is cutting canvas into pieces. The canvas is $\frac{3}{4}$ yd long. How many $\frac{1}{8}$-yd pieces can he cut? 6 pieces

28. How many $\frac{1}{4}$ in. are in $\frac{1}{2}$ ft? Draw a model that shows the problem and your solution. 24

Mt. Kilimanjaro, Kenya

Land Mass	Highest Peak	Height (mi)
Africa	Kilimanjaro	$3\frac{7}{10}$
Asia	Everest	$5\frac{1}{2}$
Australia	Kosciusko	$1\frac{4}{10}$
Antarctica	Vinson Massif	$3\frac{1}{5}$
Europe	El'brus	$3\frac{1}{2}$
South America	Aconcaqua	$4\frac{3}{10}$
North America	McKinley	$3\frac{8}{10}$

The chart at the left shows the highest peaks on each of the seven major land masses on Earth.

29. How much higher is Mt. Everest than Mt. McKinley? $1\frac{7}{10}$ mi

30. Mt. Kilimanjaro is $\frac{2}{3}$ the height of which mountain peak? Everest

31. Which mountain peak is $\frac{3}{10}$ mi higher than Mt. El'brus? McKinley

32. Which peak is about 3 times as high as Mt. Kosciusko? Aconcaqua

Divide. Write each answer in simplest form.

33. $\frac{2}{3} \div \frac{1}{3}$ 2 34. $\frac{1}{8} \div \frac{1}{4}$ $\frac{1}{2}$ 35. $\frac{3}{4} \div \frac{2}{3}$ $1\frac{1}{8}$ 36. $\frac{9}{10} \div \frac{3}{5}$ $1\frac{1}{2}$

37. $\frac{5}{6} \div \frac{5}{9}$ $1\frac{1}{2}$ 38. $2 \div \frac{1}{2}$ 4 39. $\frac{4}{5} \div 6$ $\frac{2}{15}$ 40. $\frac{2}{10} \div \frac{1}{7}$ $1\frac{2}{5}$

Mental Math Find each quotient mentally.

41. $6 \div \frac{1}{2}$ 12 42. $5 \div \frac{1}{3}$ 15 43. $3 \div \frac{1}{8}$ 24 44. $7 \div \frac{1}{5}$ 35

Connections Have students discuss examples of dividing fractions.

- **Health** (adjusting prescriptions)
- **Sports and recreation** (determining rate)

ON YOUR OWN

The names of the mountain peaks are pronounced as follows:

Kilimanjaro: kil-uh-mun-JAR-oh
El'brus: el-BROOS
Kosciusko: kahs-ee-US-koh
Aconcaqua: ak-un-KAH-gwuh
Massif: ma-SEEF

MENTAL MATH In Exercises 41–44, students should see a pattern that will help them quickly solve later problems.

WRITING Exercise 45 will help you assess student understanding of division with fractions.

CHECKPOINT

The questions in this section give students more practice multiplying and dividing with fractions.

---

45. *Writing* Write a problem that can be solved by dividing 10 by $\frac{1}{3}$. Solve your problem at least two different ways. Answers will vary. Check student's work.

46. Choose A, B, C, or D. Which quotient is greater than 1? D

A. $\frac{3}{5} \div \frac{3}{5}$ **B.** $\frac{1}{4} \div \frac{3}{4}$ **C.** $\frac{1}{3} \div 4$ **D.** $2 \div \frac{1}{4}$

47. How many $\frac{1}{2}$-c servings are in an 8-c pitcher of juice? 16

48. Alejandro decides to use a $\frac{1}{4}$-gal jar to fill a 5-gal jug. How many times must Alejandro pour liquid from the jar into the jug to fill it? 20 times

49. Luella cut 3 apples into eighths. How many pieces of apple does she have? 24 pieces

50. How many $\frac{1}{2}$-in. thick cookies can you slice from a roll of cookie dough 1 ft long? 24 cookies

Divide. Write each answer in simplest form. See right.

51. $5\frac{5}{6} \div \frac{7}{8}$ **52.** $9 \div 2\frac{1}{7}$ **53.** $9\frac{1}{2} \div 3\frac{1}{2}$ **54.** $2\frac{1}{3} \div 7$

55. $1\frac{3}{4} \div 4\frac{3}{8}$ **56.** $2\frac{2}{5} \div \frac{1}{5}$ **57.** $6 \div 3\frac{1}{2}$ **58.** $6\frac{1}{3} \div 1\frac{1}{6}$

CHECKPOINT

1. Naomi cut a board in half. Then she cut each piece in half again. Then Naomi cut each of these pieces in half again. How many pieces are there? 8 pieces

2. What is the reciprocal of $\frac{7}{8}$? of 4? of $\frac{1}{3}$? of $2\frac{1}{6}$? $\frac{8}{7}$; $\frac{1}{4}$; 3; $\frac{6}{13}$

Find the product or quotient. Write each answer in simplest form. See right.

3. $2\frac{4}{5} \times 3\frac{1}{8}$ **4.** $\frac{5}{12} \times 1\frac{7}{9}$ **5.** $3 \times \frac{3}{4}$ **6.** $\frac{2}{9} \times 27$

7. $\frac{2}{3} \div 6$ **8.** $\frac{7}{36} \div \frac{1}{8}$ **9.** $6\frac{1}{4} \div \frac{3}{8}$ **10.** $5\frac{4}{7} \div 3\frac{3}{14}$

11. Choose A, B, C, or D. Which quotient is less than 1? C

A. $\frac{2}{5} \div \frac{1}{6}$ **B.** $1\frac{1}{3} \div \frac{2}{3}$ **C.** $2\frac{1}{9} \div 3\frac{4}{5}$ **D.** $\frac{2}{3} \div \frac{2}{3}$

Mixed REVIEW

Write a decimal for the given words.

1. five hundredths 0.05

2. forty-seven thousandths 0.047

Find each product. Write the answer in simplest form.

3. $4\frac{4}{5} \times 2\frac{1}{3}$ $11\frac{1}{5}$

4. $6\frac{2}{3} \times 4\frac{1}{5}$ 28

5. In a class of 40 students, 29 wore jeans, 18 wore sneakers, and 10 wore both jeans and sneakers. How many wore neither jeans nor sneakers?

3 students

51. $6\frac{2}{3}$ 52. $4\frac{1}{5}$
53. $2\frac{5}{7}$ 54. $\frac{1}{3}$
55. $\frac{2}{5}$ 56. 12
57. $1\frac{5}{7}$ 58. $5\frac{3}{7}$

3. $8\frac{3}{4}$ 4. $\frac{20}{27}$
5. $2\frac{1}{4}$ 6. 6
7. $\frac{1}{9}$ 8. $1\frac{5}{9}$
9. $16\frac{2}{3}$ 10. $1\frac{11}{15}$

Alternate Lesson

Practice

8 Minds on Math

Chapter Support File

Classroom Manager
- Chapter Organizer
- Lesson Planners

Alternate Lesson Plans

Practice

Assessment Options
- Performance Based Project
- Scoring Rubric
- Student Self-Assessment Survey
- Checkpoints
- Chapter Assessments
- Cumulative Review

Minds on Math available in Teaching Transparencies

Math Minutes

Write $\frac{3}{8}$ as a decimal.

0.375

8-9

Connecting to Prior Knowledge

Have students discuss in groups of three situations where they have measured length, weight, and capacity. Have groups share the different units of measurement they used. If possible, bring to class empty containers such as gallon or pint milk cartons.

THINK AND DISCUSS

DIVERSITY Have students who may be familiar with the metric system explain its use to the class and then discuss the differences between the two systems. Ask the students which system seems to be easier to use and then ask them why they think the customary system is still used in the United States.

ESL **TACTILE LEARNERS** Have samples of various measurement tools available for students to see and touch. You could display and label items on a table: yardstick (in., ft, yd), spring scale (lb), measuring cup (oz, c), containers (pt, qt, gal).

Question 1: This will help you assess students' prior knowledge of measurement. Most students are familiar with units of length and weight but need additional practice with units of capacity—especially pints and quarts.

Question 3: Emphasize the value of estimating before calculating.

Example 1

Some students may want to visualize 3 ft as a yard and estimate that she buys 2 yd plus $2\frac{1}{2}$ ft, which they then convert to $\frac{5}{6}$ yd.

Additional Example *A jogger ran 132 lengths of a football field on Saturday afternoon. How many miles did she run? (A football field is 100 yd long.)*

Multiply: 132 × 100 = 13,200

She ran 13,200 yd or 39,600 ft.

Divide: 39,600 ÷ 5,280 = 7.5

The jogger ran $7\frac{1}{2}$ mi.

"Knowledge is the antidote to fear."

—Ralph Waldo Emerson

Organizer

1. **Focus**
   Connecting to Prior Knowledge
2. **Teach**
   Think and Discuss
3. **Closure**
   Try These
   Wrap Up

Skills Reviewed in Context of Lesson
- operations with fractions

Student Resources
Extra Practice
Student Study Guide
Practice, TR Ch. 8, p.31
Student Study Guide, Spanish Resources, TR

Teacher Resources

Teaching Transparencies 75, 77
Lesson Planner, TR Ch. 8, p. 10

Prentice Hall Technology
Multimedia Math
- Hot Page™ 8-9

Computer Item Generator
- 8-9

MATH AND MEASUREMENT

8-9 The Customary System

What's Ahead
- Solving problems that involve changing units of length, weight, and capacity in the customary system

Customary Units of Length
12 inches (in.) = 1 foot (ft)
36 inches = 1 yard (yd)
3 feet = 1 yard
5,280 feet = 1 mile (mi)

Customary Units of Weight
16 ounces (oz) = 1 pound (lb)
2,000 pounds = 1 ton (T)

Customary Units of Capacity
8 fluid ounces (fl oz) = 1 cup
2 cups (c) = 1 pint (pt)
2 pints = 1 quart (qt)
4 quarts = 1 gallon (gal)

3. If the unit you are trying to find is larger than the unit given, you divide. If the unit you are trying to find is smaller than the unit given, you multiply.

THINK AND DISCUSS

Fractions and mixed numbers are commonly used with the customary system of measurement. For example, you may need $1\frac{1}{4}$ c of flour for a recipe. Or you may buy $\frac{1}{2}$ gal of milk for your family.

1. **Discussion** Look at the list of customary units at the left. For each unit, think of something you would measure with that unit. Give examples from your daily life. **Answers will vary. Check student's work.**

You can multiply or divide to change units of measurement.

2. a. How many inches are in 2 ft? **24 in.**
   b. How many tons are 10,000 lb? **5 T**
   c. Eighteen pints is the same amount as how many quarts? **9 qt**
   d. How many yards are in 90 ft? **30 yd**
3. **Discussion** Look back at your answers for Exercise 2. How did you know whether to multiply or divide? **See left.**

To solve many problems, you change units of measurements.

Example 1 Pat needs $8\frac{1}{2}$ ft of fabric for a sewing project. Fabric is sold in $\frac{1}{8}$-yd lengths. How many yards of fabric should Pat buy?

Think: $8\frac{1}{2}$ ft is how many yards?

Divide: $8\frac{1}{2} \div 3$

$= \frac{17}{2} \times \frac{1}{3}$

$= \frac{17}{6} = 2\frac{5}{6}$

Round $2\frac{5}{6}$ yd up to the next $\frac{1}{8}$-yd: $2\frac{7}{8}$.

Pat should buy $2\frac{7}{8}$ yd of fabric.

Example 2

After students have discussed Example 2, have them tell how the rule they developed in Question 3 is demonstrated. **(Each time they changed larger units of measurement to smaller units, they multiplied.)**

Additional Example *Teionne is serving frozen yogurt to 50 teenagers at a large party. Each serving will be $1\frac{1}{2}$ c and he has $4\frac{3}{4}$ gal on hand right now. Does Teionne have enough frozen yogurt to serve the 50 people?* **There are 76 c in $4\frac{3}{4}$ gal. Teionne needs only 75 c, so he has enough frozen yogurt.**

Question 4: This will help students solve the problem another way and give them practice changing smaller units to larger units.

Ongoing Assessment Have students match each unit of measure in Column A with its equivalent in Column B.

Column A	Column B
a. 72 oz	4 yd
b. $1\frac{1}{2}$ t	$4\frac{1}{2}$ lb
c. 144 in.	4 pt
d. $13\frac{1}{2}$ ft	3,000 lb
e. 2 ft	$4\frac{1}{2}$ yd
f. 8 c	24 in.

a. $4\frac{1}{2}$ lb; b. 3,000 lb; c. 4 yd; d. $4\frac{1}{2}$ yd; e. 24 in.; f. 4 pt

TRY THESE

Error Alert! Students may use the wrong operation to change from one unit to another. Have students recall the rules

Fact of the Day

Alaska and the Aleutian Islands were discovered in 1741 by Vitus Bering and Alexei Chirikov. The land mass of Alaska (570,374 mi^2) is equal to one-fifth of the continental United States.

—Information Please Almanac

For some problems you need to change units of measurement in order to decide if you have enough of something.

Example 2 Suppose you are planning a party. You invite 24 guests. You want to serve at least 2 c of fruit punch to each guest. You fill your punch bowl, which holds $3\frac{1}{2}$ gal. Do you have enough punch?

Think: How much punch do you need?
24 guests × 2 c per guest = 48 c

Think: How many cups are in $3\frac{1}{2}$ gal?

Change gallons to quarts. $3\frac{1}{2}$ gal = ■ qt   **1 gal = 4 qt**

$3\frac{1}{2} \times 4 = \frac{7}{2} \times 4 = 14$ qt

Change quarts to pints. 14 qt = ■ pt   **1 qt = 2 pt**
14 × 2 = 28 pt

Change pints to cups. 28 pt = ■ c   **1 pt = 2 c**
28 × 2 = 56 c

There are 56 c in $3\frac{1}{2}$ gal. You need only 48 c, so you have enough punch.

As part of the Friendship Festival, 75,000 people attended the world's largest birthday party to celebrate the 215th birthday of the United States. **How much fruit punch would you need to serve the 75,000 guests?** 9,375 gal

4. **Discussion** Solve the problem in Example 2 another way. Think: How many gallons are in 48 c? **Check student's work.**

TRY THESE

Complete.

5. 30 oz = ■ lb $1\frac{7}{8}$
6. $5\frac{1}{2}$ ft = ■ in. 66
7. 27 qt = ■ gal $6\frac{3}{4}$
8. What operation do you use to change:
   a. inches to feet? **division** b. yards to feet? **multiplication** c. gallons to cups? **multiplication**

Compare using <, >, or =.

9. 85 in. ■ 8 ft <
10. $3\frac{1}{2}$ lb ■ 56 oz =
11. $2\frac{1}{2}$ gal ■ 25 pt <
12. A regular hexagon has sides that are 9 in. long. Find the perimeter of the hexagon in feet. $4\frac{1}{2}$ ft
13. In some parts of Alaska, moose actually cause traffic jams. A moose weighs about 1,000 lb. How many tons is a moose? $\frac{1}{2}$ T

they developed: to change from smaller to larger units, divide; to change from larger to smaller units, multiply.

Exercises 9–11: Some students may need to be reminded which sign is less than and which sign is greater than.

Exercise 12: Students should recall that a hexagon has six sides.

Wrap Up

What's the Big Idea? Ask students: *How can you convert from one unit of measure to another?*

Journal Have students write a short paragraph describing how they might solve this problem. *You have to find out how many times your bicycle wheel goes around in 1 mi. The circumference of the wheel is 50 in.*

Connections Have students discuss where conversion of customary units is used.

- **Science** (gathering data about animals' weight and speed, plant growth)
- **Social Studies** (measuring distance on maps, comparing heights of structures)
- **Pharmacy** (figuring the number of doses per container)

Reteaching Activity Have students measure objects in the classroom using a yardstick. When they measure an object in inches (for example, the length of your desk), have students write: 42 in. = $3\frac{1}{2}$ ft = $1\frac{1}{6}$ yd. When they measure an object in yards (for example, the length of the classroom), have them write:

$$5\frac{3}{4} \text{ yd} = 17\frac{1}{4} \text{ ft} = 207 \text{ in.}$$

Help students see that when they change from smaller to larger units, the result is fewer units, and when they change from larger to smaller units, the result is more units.

PH Multimedia Math Hot Page™ 8-9

Assignment Options

Core: 14–16, 20–24, 30, 31, MR all	
Reinforce: 17–19, 25, 27, 28, 32	**Enrich:** 26, 29

ON YOUR OWN

Complete.

14. $6\frac{1}{4}$ ft = ■ yd $2\frac{1}{12}$
15. $1\frac{3}{4}$ mi = ■ ft 9,240
16. $2\frac{1}{2}$ qt = ■ pt 5
17. 24 oz = ■ lb $1\frac{1}{2}$
18. $3\frac{1}{2}$ T = ■ lb 7,000
19. $4\frac{1}{4}$ c = ■ fl oz 34
20. **Cooking** Cranberry "Mousse" requires 32 fl oz nonfat plain yogurt. Mary will use a measuring cup for this amount. How many cups of yogurt should she measure? 4 cups
21. **Cooking** Use the recipe at the left. Odetta bought a 6-fl oz container of nonfat plain yogurt. Did Odetta buy enough yogurt for Avocado Cream? yes

Avocado Cream
a sauce for quesadillas, salads, and tortilla chips

1 ripe avocado
juice of 1 lime
$\frac{1}{2}$ cup nonfat plain yogurt

22. **Nutrition** The American Heart Association recommends that an adult eat no more than 6 oz of cooked poultry, fish, or lean red meat each day. Scott is serving six adults a $2\frac{1}{2}$ lb roast beef for dinner. Each adult will eat about the same amount. Should they eat the whole roast? Explain. no; There should be 4 oz of roast left over.

Write >, <, or =.

23. $6\frac{1}{2}$ pt ■ 2 qt >
24. 24 fl oz ■ 3 c =
25. 6,750 lb ■ $3\frac{3}{4}$ T <

GREAT EXPECTATIONS

Veterinarian

I want to be a veterinarian because I love animals. At my house I have a fish, dog, cat, bird, and a mouse. Almost every day I walk down my lane that has 6 dogs, 5 cats, 3 donkeys, 1 mule, 1 horse, 16 geese, 4 goats and 1 pig.

A personal experience I had that made me want to become a vet was when my dog died. The veterinarian could not do anything to save him. It made me want to be a vet, so maybe that won't happen to someone else's pet. I also want to help rescue animals, like after an oil spill. I want to help save endangered species, too.

Lisa Mollmann

ON YOUR OWN

Exercise 27: Students may multiply the entire height of 555 ft $5\frac{1}{8}$ in. by 12. Remind them that the $5\frac{1}{8}$ in. part of the height is already expressed in inches.

Great Expectations

There are many valuable resources available to the students for gathering information about veterinarians. The following list includes places to write for more information and publications to read.

- College of Veterinary Medicine
  Texas A&M University
  College Station, TX 77843
- *Doc, Can You Come Out?* Leo Lemonds. (Henderson, NB: Service Press, 1987)
- *Working with Horses: A Roundup of Careers.* Karen O'Conner. (New York: Dodd, Mead, 1980).

Students can also learn from discussions with experts. Here are some possible sources.

- Invite a local veterinarian to speak to the class.
- Visit a veterinary hospital and observe the daily activities.
- Tour a school of veterinary medicine.

Encourage students to ask questions about the skills necessary for a career as a veterinarian, including these topics.

- The training and college degrees necessary to qualify
- How math is used on the job
- How computers are used to handle information

26. **Writing** Describe a situation from daily life in which you need to change from one unit of measure to another. Answers will vary. Check student's work.
27. The Washington Monument in Washington, D.C., is 555 ft $5\frac{1}{8}$ in. tall. How many inches tall is the monument? $6{,}665\frac{1}{8}$ in.
28. The Mont Blanc Tunnel goes through a mountain and connects Italy and France. Its length is 7.2 miles. What is the length of the tunnel in feet? 38,016 ft
29. La Grande Complexe is a hydroelectric power facility in Canada. One of its dams, LG2, has a spillway that allows 750,000 gal of water to pass through per second.
    a. How many gallons pass through LG2 in 1 min? See right.
    b. A gallon of water weighs about 8 lb. About how many tons of water pass through the dam's spillway in 1 s? 3,000 T

Add or subtract. Rename when necessary.

Sample	8 lb 3 oz − 4 lb 7 oz	7 lb 19 oz − 4 lb 7 oz 3 lb 12 oz	Rename 1 lb as 16 oz. 16 oz + 3 oz = 19 oz

30. 4 ft 10 in. + 1 ft 9 in. — 6 ft 7 in.
31. 5 yd 1 ft − 1 yd 2 ft — 3 yd 2 ft
32. 3 gal 3 qt + 2 gal 5 qt — 7 gal

Mixed REVIEW

Find the GCF of each set of numbers.

1. 36, 27 9
2. 24, 60, 72 12

Find each quotient. Write the answer in simplest form.

3. $\frac{7}{8} \div \frac{1}{4}$ $3\frac{1}{2}$
4. $\frac{2}{7} \div \frac{14}{15}$ $\frac{15}{49}$
5. Linda bought 4 tickets to the movies. Each ticket cost $4.25. She paid with a $20 bill. How much did it cost Linda for the tickets?

$17

29. a. 45,000,000 gallons

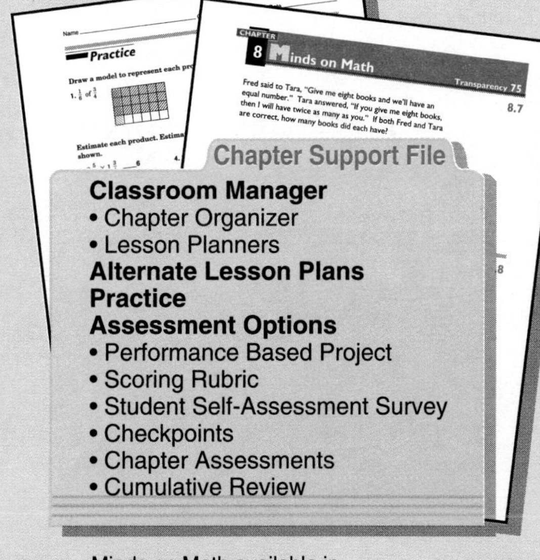

Minds on Math available in Teaching Transparencies

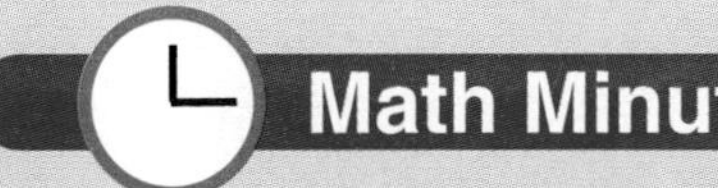

What fraction of 8 weeks is 18 days?
$\frac{9}{28}$

Dear Lisa,

I also love helping animals. I decided that I wanted to spend my time keeping them healthy and helping them when they became ill. I have two cats, a rabbit, a parrot, two parakeets, and fish—as well as a husband and two little girls.

Working hours can be long if you live and practice in a small town. You may get an emergency call in the middle of the night and not get home before office hours start the next morning. Larger cities have emergency clinics available for problems on the weekends or holidays.

It is sad that animals do not live as long as people. We see diseases that we cannot cure today. However, many veterinarians participate in research to discover new treatments for both animal and human illnesses. The more we learn, the easier it will be to save pets in the future.

Dr. Chris Stone Payne, DVM
Small Animal Veterinarian

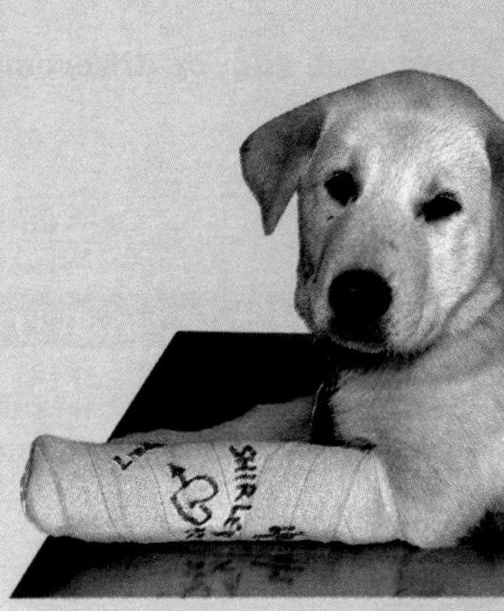

CHAPTER 8 WRAP UP

Ongoing Assessment Have students exchange papers and check each other's answers for Exercises 7–14.

Exercise 15: Ask students to show the class what patterns they found.

Exercises 25–26: Ask students to check to make sure that their answers are reasonable.

Vocabulary/Symbols
reciprocals
whole numbers

CHAPTER 8 Wrap Up

Estimating Sums and Differences 8-1

You can estimate the sum or difference of fractions by rounding each fraction to the nearest $\frac{1}{2}$. To estimate the sum or difference of mixed numbers, round each mixed number to the nearest whole number.

Estimate each sum or difference. Estimates may vary.

1. $\frac{15}{16} - \frac{7}{12}$ about $\frac{1}{2}$
2. $\frac{6}{11} + \frac{7}{8}$ about $1\frac{1}{2}$
3. $7\frac{3}{5} - 3\frac{1}{6}$ about 5
4. $4\frac{4}{9} + 1\frac{8}{15}$ about 6

Adding and Subtracting Fractions 8-2, 8-3, 8-5

You can use models to add or subtract fractions.

To add or subtract fractions first find a common denominator and then add or subtract the numerators.

5. Write an addition sentence to describe the model. $\frac{1}{5} + \frac{1}{2} = \frac{7}{10}$

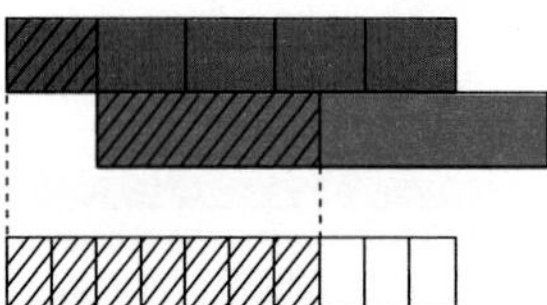

6. Write a subtraction sentence to describe the model. $\frac{5}{6} - \frac{2}{6} = \frac{3}{6} = \frac{1}{2}$

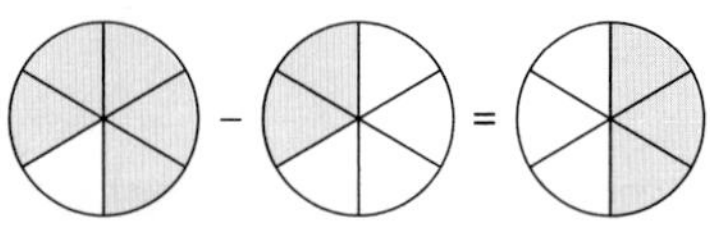

Find each sum or difference.

7. $\frac{7}{9} - \frac{2}{9}$ $\frac{5}{9}$
8. $4\frac{5}{6} - 2\frac{1}{3}$ $2\frac{1}{2}$
9. $\frac{1}{3} + \frac{3}{4}$ $1\frac{1}{12}$
10. $\frac{4}{7} + \frac{5}{7}$ $1\frac{2}{7}$
11. $\frac{7}{16} + \frac{1}{4}$ $\frac{11}{16}$
12. $6\frac{2}{5} - 2\frac{3}{4}$ $3\frac{13}{20}$
13. $3\frac{7}{8} + 1\frac{2}{12}$ $5\frac{1}{24}$
14. $\frac{9}{10} - \frac{5}{6}$ $\frac{1}{15}$

Exploring Patterns in Fraction Sums 8-4

15. Copy and complete the table. Add more rows to the table until you see a pattern in the sum. Describe the pattern. See Solution Key.

Expression	Sum	
$\frac{1}{3}$	$\frac{1}{3}$	
$\frac{1}{3} + \frac{1}{6}$	■	$\frac{3}{6}$
$\frac{1}{3} + \frac{1}{6} + \frac{1}{12}$	■	$\frac{7}{12}$

Getting Ready for Chapter 9

The skills previewed will help students understand and solve problems involving proportions.

Multiplying and Dividing Fractions 8-7, 8-8

Sometimes you can simplify before multiplying. Divide the numerator and the denominator by any common factors.

To multiply fractions, you multiply their numerators and then multiply their denominators. To divide fractions, you multiply by the reciprocal of the divisor. To find $\frac{2}{3} \div \frac{5}{6}$, multiply $\frac{2}{3} \times \frac{6}{5}$.

When you multiply or divide with mixed numbers, first write each mixed number as an improper fraction.

Find each product or quotient.

16. $\frac{3}{5} \times \frac{10}{12}$ $\frac{1}{2}$ **17.** $\frac{2}{3} \div 8$ $\frac{1}{12}$ **18.** $2\frac{1}{6} \times 3\frac{3}{4}$ $8\frac{1}{8}$ **19.** $2\frac{3}{8} \div 2\frac{1}{2}$ $\frac{19}{20}$

20. $\frac{4}{7} \div \frac{4}{7}$ 1 **21.** $4\frac{1}{7} \times 6$ $24\frac{6}{7}$ **22.** $8 \times \frac{3}{4}$ 6 **23.** $8 \div 3\frac{1}{5}$ $2\frac{1}{2}$

Strategies and Applications 8-6, 8-9

Sometimes it's helpful to draw a diagram when solving a problem.

24. Mrs. Cruz bought a rectangular piece of carpet, 12 ft wide and 18 ft long. She expects to carpet her rectangular living room, square dining room, and a hallway measuring 4 ft wide and 18 ft long.

a. Draw a diagram to show how she can make the three carpets with two cuts. See Solution Key.

b. Find the dimensions of the living room and dining room. living room: 8 ft × 10 ft, dining room: 8 ft × 8 ft.

c. Find the area of each room and the combined area of all three rooms. living room: 80 ft^2, dining room: 64 ft^2, hallway: 72 ft^2, total area: 216 ft^2.

25. In baseball, the distance from the pitcher to the batter is 60 ft. How far is this in yards?
20 yd

26. You can make 6 whole wheat pancakes with $\frac{1}{2}$ c milk. How many pancakes can you make with $\frac{1}{2}$ gal milk?
96 pancakes

GETTING READY FOR CHAPTER 9

Use equivalent fractions to fill in the ■.

1. $\frac{1}{2} = \frac{■}{14}$ 7 **2.** $\frac{6}{18} = \frac{2}{■}$ 6 **3.** $\frac{3}{5} = \frac{■}{30}$ 18 **4.** $\frac{16}{56} = \frac{■}{7}$ 2

Student Resources

Practice, p. 341
Problem Solving Practice, p. 330
Extra Practice
Student Study Guide
Student Study Guide, Spanish Resources, TR
Tools for Studying Smarter, TR
Student Self-Assessment Survey, TR Ch. 8, p. 35 *(see below)*

Name ______ Class ______ Date ______

Chapter 8 Student Self-Assessment Survey

1. Now that you have finished this chapter, think about the things you have learned about fractions. Check each topic that you feel confident you can do.
   ______ round fractions and mixed numbers (8-1)
   ______ estimate sums and differences of fractions and mixed numbers (8-1)
   ______ add and subtract fractions with like denominators (8-2)
   ______ add and subtract fractions with unlike denominators (8-3)
   ______ use spreadsheets for fraction sums (8-4)
   ______ solve problems by adding and subtracting mixed numbers (8-5)
   ______ solve a problem by drawing a diagram (8-6)
   ______ multiply fractions and mixed numbers (8-7)
   ______ divide fractions and mixed numbers (8-8)
   ______ change customary units of length, weight, and capacity (8-9)
2. Before the Chapter Assessment, I need to review ______
3. a. Check one. In general, I thought this chapter was
   ___ a snap ___ easy ___ average ___ hard ___ a monster
   b. Why do you feel this way? ______
4. In this chapter, I did my best work on ______
5. In this chapter, I had trouble with ______
6. Check each one that applies. Now that I've spent some time working with fractions, I think they are
   ___ important ___ boring ___ useful ___ fun
   ___ a waste of time ___ confusing ___ tricky ___ interesting
7. List three situations outside the classroom in which you could use fractions in your daily life.
8. Do you like using the fraction calculator? ______ Explain. ______

ASSESSMENTS

CHAPTER 8 PUTTING IT ALL TOGETHER

The projects on these pages can be used in a variety of ways:

- alternative assessment
- portfolio ideas
- additional assignments for gifted and talented students
- extra credit for all students

Follow Up

A nomograph for adding fractions with denominators of 2 through 10 needs to be marked off in 2,520ths. (2,520 is the LCD of the numbers 2 through 10.) It would operate like a simple nomograph. Mixed numbers could be added by finding the sum of their whole-number parts separately, and adding them to the sum of the fractions given on the nomograph.

EXCURSION Students may be able to find an abacus in use in a local Chinese, Indian, or Japanese business establishment. A number of books, including *Number Machines* by Forrest Mims, describe the operation of the abacus in detail.

Travel Time

As a class, brainstorm about types of travel. Students may suggest answers such as walking and riding their bicycles, but encourage them to consider all possibilities (for example: skateboarding, sledding, riding a horse, and in-line skates).

TECHNOLOGY OPTION Students can use spreadsheet software to keep records of their traveling time. Have the students designate a column to name the activity, a column designating the time spent in the activity, a column recording the time for whole activity, and a column recording the fractional part of the whole. With spreadsheet software, they can quickly calculate the total travel time.

Materials and Manipulatives

Follow Up *Excursion*
- materials for constructing abacus

How Many More
- tape measure

On a Roll
- heavy paper or index cards
- scissors
- tape

Prentice Hall Technology

Follow Up
Multimedia Math
- Math Tools, Text

Travel Time
Multimedia Math
- Math Tools, Spreadsheet

Other Available Technology

Follow Up
- *Word* by Microsoft
- *WriteNow* by Wordstar
- *II Write* by American School Publishers
- *Bank Street Writer* by Brøderbund

(all optional)

Travel Time
- *Excel; Works* by Microsoft
- *1-2-3* by Lotus
- *ClarisWorks* by Apple

(all optional)

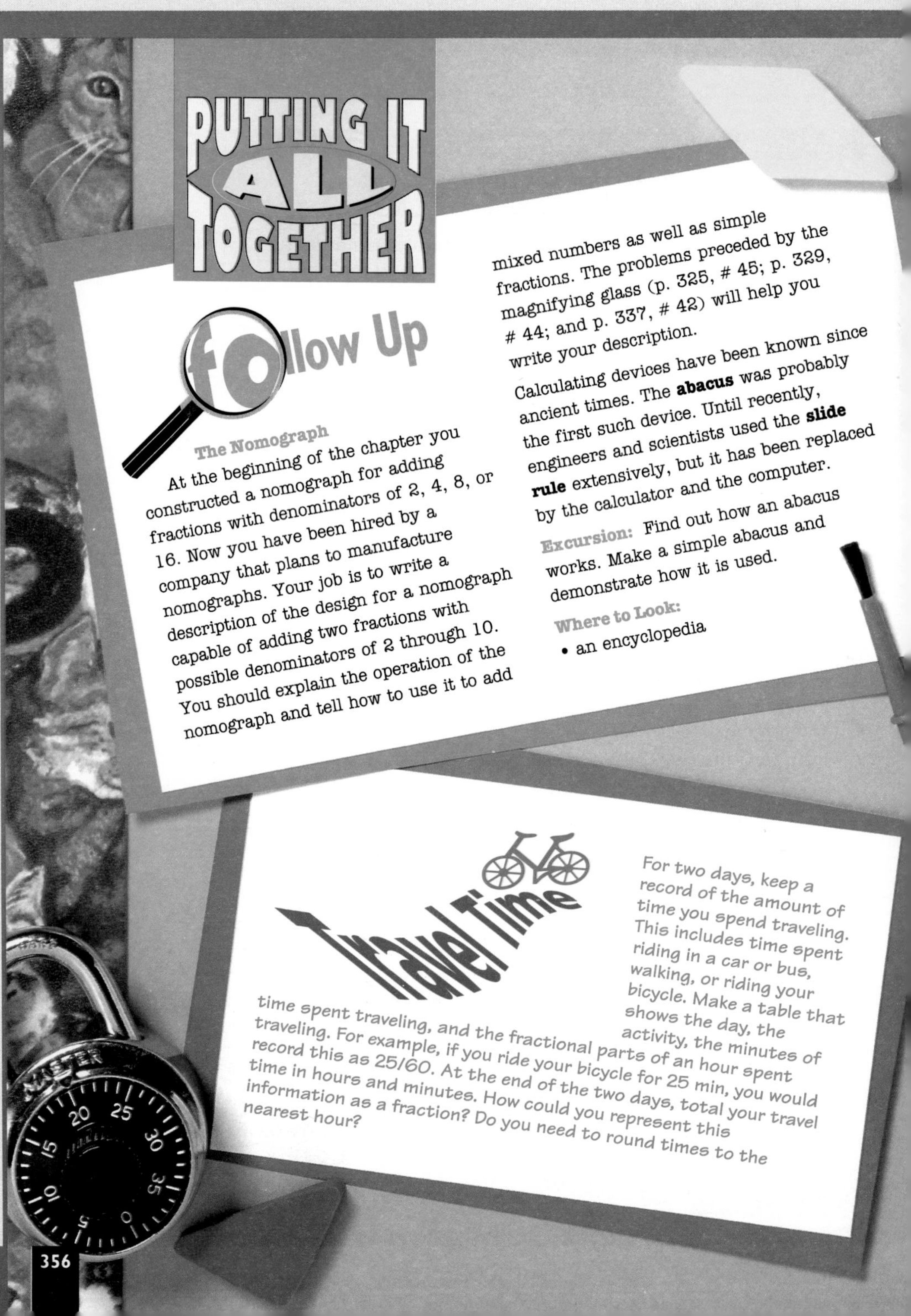

PUTTING IT ALL TOGETHER

Follow Up

The Nomograph

At the beginning of the chapter you constructed a nomograph for adding fractions with denominators of 2, 4, 8, or 16. Now you have been hired by a company that plans to manufacture nomographs. Your job is to write a description of the design for a nomograph capable of adding two fractions with possible denominators of 2 through 10. You should explain the operation of the nomograph and tell how to use it to add mixed numbers as well as simple fractions. The problems preceded by the magnifying glass (p. 325, # 45; p. 329, # 44; and p. 337, # 42) will help you write your description.

Calculating devices have been known since ancient times. The **abacus** was probably the first such device. Until recently, engineers and scientists used the **slide rule** extensively, but it has been replaced by the calculator and the computer.

Excursion: Find out how an abacus works. Make a simple abacus and demonstrate how it is used.

Where to Look:
- an encyclopedia

Travel Time

For two days, keep a record of the amount of time you spend traveling. This includes time spent riding in a car or bus, walking, or riding your bicycle. Make a table that shows the day, the activity, the minutes of time spent traveling, and the fractional parts of an hour spent traveling. For example, if you ride your bicycle for 25 min, you would record this as 25/60. At the end of the two days, total your travel time in hours and minutes. How could you represent this information as a fraction? Do you need to round times to the nearest hour?

356

How Many More?

COOPERATIVE GROUPS Have the students measure the objects with yardsticks, tape measures, and small rulers. Observe their abilities to handle the different measuring devices and how well they handle conversions to larger measurements.

On a Roll

Students will need three number cubes per group of students. Have students number the cubes, using denominators less than 12, so the game will flow with fewer computation problems.

Students can use fraction calculators to check the accumulating scores after the game is completed, or can maintain a running score using spreadsheet software.

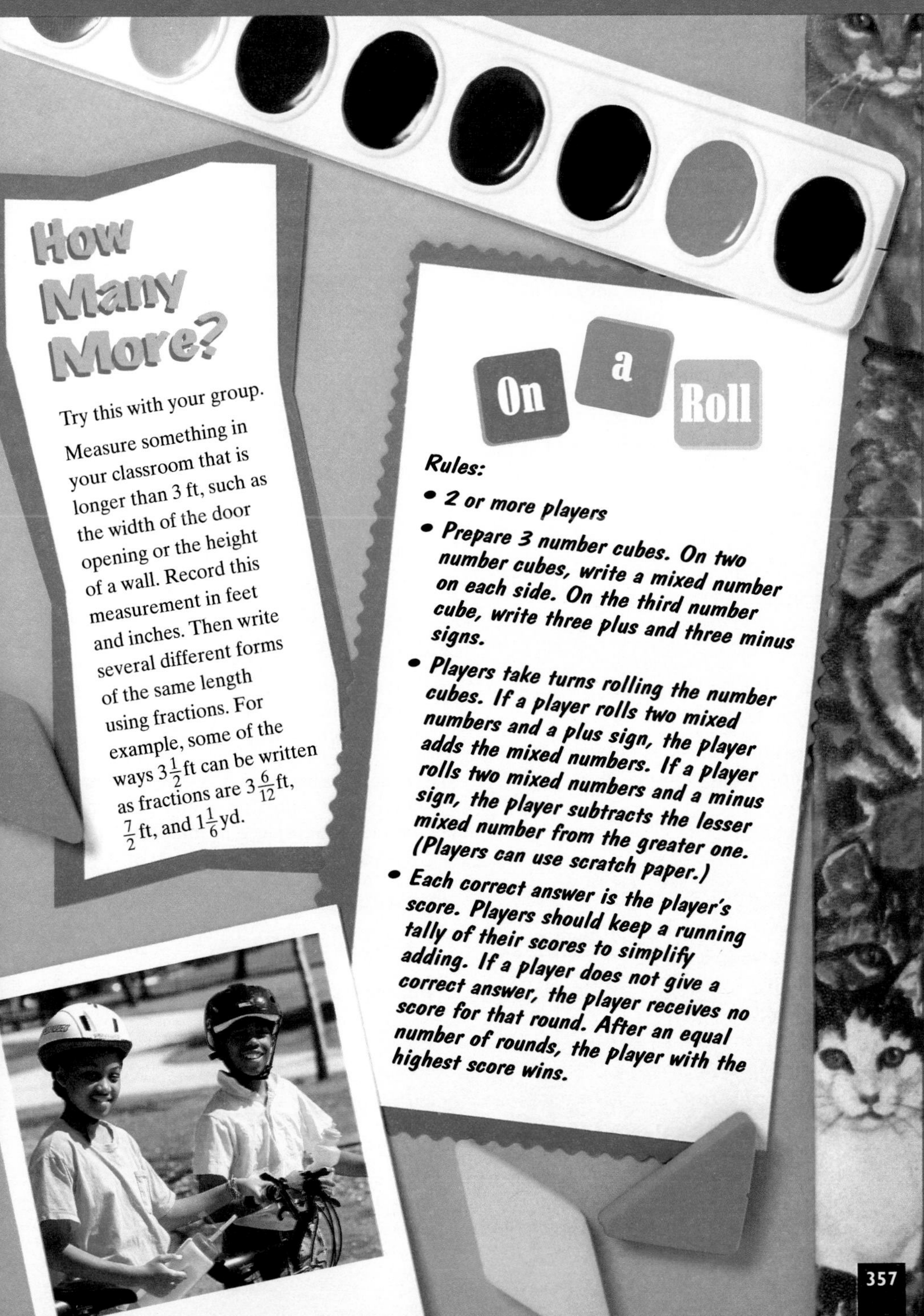

How Many More?
Try this with your group.
Measure something in your classroom that is longer than 3 ft, such as the width of the door opening or the height of a wall. Record this measurement in feet and inches. Then write several different forms of the same length using fractions. For example, some of the ways $3\frac{1}{2}$ ft can be written as fractions are $3\frac{6}{12}$ ft, $\frac{7}{2}$ ft, and $1\frac{1}{6}$ yd.
On a Roll
Rules:
• 2 or more players
• Prepare 3 number cubes. On two number cubes, write a mixed number on each side. On the third number cube, write three plus and three minus signs.
• Players take turns rolling the number cubes. If a player rolls two mixed numbers and a plus sign, the player adds the mixed numbers. If a player rolls two mixed numbers and a minus sign, the player subtracts the lesser mixed number from the greater one. (Players can use scratch paper.)
• Each correct answer is the player's score. Players should keep a running tally of their scores to simplify adding. If a player does not give a correct answer, the player receives no score for that round. After an equal number of rounds, the player with the highest score wins.
357

CHAPTER 8

ASSESSMENT

Writing Questions allow students to describe more fully their thinking and understanding of the concepts they've learned.

Exercise 5c is a writing question. If students have trouble identifying the pattern, have them add on more rows and observe what changes they see in the Sum column.

Enhanced Multiple Choice Questions are more complex than traditional multiple choice questions, which assess only one skill. Enhanced multiple choice questions assess the processes that students use as well as the end results. They are written so that students can use more than one strategy to solve the problem. Using multiple strategies is encouraged by the National Council of Teachers of Mathematics (NCTM).

Exercise 9 is an enhanced multiple choice question.

TACTILE LEARNERS Algebra tiles or slips of paper may be helpful to model Exercise 8.

Exercise 2: Provide students with graph paper to draw their models.

Exercise 7: Make sure students understand that $2\frac{1}{2}$ in. is the first year of the two-year period.

Resources

Performance Based Project, TR Ch. 8, pp. 32–34

Chapter Assessment, Forms A and B, TR Ch. 8, pp. 37–40

Spanish Chapter Assessment, Spanish Resources, TR

Computer Item Generator

CHAPTER 8

Assessment

1. Kelsey tutored for $3\frac{3}{4}$ h on Tuesday and $7\frac{1}{3}$ h on Saturday.

a. About how many more hours did Kelsey tutor on Saturday than on Tuesday? about 3 h

b. About how much time did Kelsey tutor altogether? about 11 h

2. Draw a model to find each sum or difference. See Solution Key.

a. $\frac{1}{4} + \frac{1}{4}$ $\frac{1}{2}$ **b.** $\frac{11}{12} - \frac{5}{12}$ $\frac{1}{2}$

3. Find each sum. Then write the answer in simplest form.

a. $\frac{3}{5} + \frac{11}{15}$ $1\frac{1}{3}$ **b.** $\frac{7}{12} + \frac{3}{8}$ $\frac{23}{24}$

c. $\frac{6}{15} + \frac{4}{9}$ $\frac{38}{45}$ **d.** $\frac{1}{2} + \frac{6}{7}$ $1\frac{5}{14}$

4. Find each difference. Then write the answer in simplest form.

a. $\frac{3}{4} - \frac{2}{5}$ $\frac{7}{20}$ **b.** $\frac{5}{6} - \frac{4}{15}$ $\frac{17}{30}$

c. $\frac{7}{8} - \frac{17}{32}$ $\frac{11}{32}$ **d.** $\frac{6}{7} - \frac{3}{5}$ $\frac{9}{35}$

5. Use the pattern of fraction sums given at the right.

Expression	Sum
$\frac{1}{3}$	$\frac{1}{3}$
$\frac{1}{3} + \frac{1}{9}$	■ $\frac{4}{9}$
$\frac{1}{3} + \frac{1}{9} + \frac{1}{27}$	■ $\frac{13}{27}$

a. Copy and complete the table.

b. Add another row. See Solution Key.

c. *Writing* Describe the pattern you see in the "Sum" column. See Solution Key.

6. Explain how you can mentally find the sum $3\frac{1}{4} + 2\frac{2}{3} + 5\frac{3}{4} + 1\frac{1}{3}$. Combine fourths, $3\frac{1}{4} + 5\frac{3}{4} = 8 + 1 = 9$. Combine thirds, $2\frac{2}{3} + 1\frac{1}{3} = 3 + 1 = 4$. So $9 + 4 = 13$.

7. Roscoe grew $4\frac{1}{4}$ in. over a two-year period. If he grew $2\frac{1}{2}$ in. the first year, how many inches did Roscoe grow during the second year? $1\frac{3}{4}$ in.

8. Four students are waiting in line. Bayo is behind Sarah, David is in front of Max, and Sarah is behind Max. Find the order of the four students. Front to back: David, Max, Sarah, Bayo.

9. Choose A, B, C, or D. A sales representative completed $\frac{4}{7}$ of a 1,394-mi business trip. About how many miles of the trip remain? B

A. about 100 mi **B.** about 600 mi

C. about 400 mi **D.** about 1000 mi

10. Tung has an income of $2,640 each month. He spends $\frac{1}{5}$ of his income on rent. How much does Tung spend on rent each month? $528

11. A doll maker uses $1\frac{7}{8}$ yd of material to make one doll. How many dolls can be made from a piece of material that is 45 yd long? 24 dolls

12. Write $>$, $<$, or $=$.

a. $3\frac{1}{2}$ yd ■ 7 ft $>$

b. 34 fl oz ■ $2\frac{3}{4}$ qt $<$

c. $5\frac{1}{4}$ c ■ 42 fl oz $=$

13. Complete.

a. 28 oz = ■ lb $1\frac{3}{4}$ **b.** $5\frac{3}{4}$ ft = ■ in. 69

c. $9\frac{1}{4}$ gal = ■ qt = ■ pt 37 74

CHAPTER 8 CUMULATIVE REVIEW

All the exercises in this review are enhanced multiple choice questions.

Exercises 3 and 6: Encourage students to draw diagrams.

Exercise 6: Emphasize that the question is about surface area, not volume.

Item(s)	Review Topic	Chapter
1, 4	comparing fractions and decimals	7
2, 10	multiplying fractions	8
3	area of rectangles	6
5	comparing decimals	3
6	surface area	6
7, 13	adding decimals	3
8	circles	6
9	GCF	7
11	dividing fractions	8
12	prime factorization	7

CHAPTER 8 Cumulative Review

Choose A, B, C, or D.

1. Which is *not* equivalent to five tenths? A
   A. 0.05 **B.** $\frac{5}{10}$ **C.** 0.5 **D.** fifty hundredths

2. Summer vacation is 68 days. If $\frac{3}{4}$ of vacation has gone by, how many days are left? D
   A. 12 days **B.** 51 days **C.** 23 days **D.** 17 days

3. The perimeter of a rectangle is 36 ft. One dimension is 12 ft. Find the area. A
   A. 72 ft^2 **B.** 6 ft^2 **C.** 60 ft^2 **D.** 3 ft^2

4. Which set of numbers is in order from least to greatest? C
   A. 0.67, $\frac{2}{3}$, $\frac{7}{10}$, $\frac{3}{4}$ **B.** $\frac{1}{4}$, $\frac{6}{25}$, 0.23, $\frac{2}{9}$ **C.** $1\frac{1}{4}$, $1\frac{2}{7}$, 1.3, $1\frac{1}{3}$ **D.** 0.37, $\frac{3}{8}$, $\frac{1}{3}$, 0.4

5. Which is *not* a true statement? B
   A. $0.04 > 0.01$ **B.** $0.48 < 0.4798$ **C.** $0.014 < 0.02$ **D.** $29.6 > 29.06$

6. A box is 24 cm long, 12 cm wide, and 11 cm high. Find its surface area. B
   A. 288 cm^2 **B.** 1,368 cm^2 **C.** 792 cm^2 **D.** 47 cm^2

7. Jeremiah bought a radio for $18.64. Sales tax is $1.49. How much does he need to buy the radio? D
   A. $19.03 **B.** $17.15 **C.** $33.54 **D.** $20.13

8. Find the circumference and area of a circle with a diameter of 4.6 m. Round to the nearest tenth. C
   A. $C = 16.6$ m, $A = 14.4$ m^2
   B. $C = 28.9$ m, $A = 66.4$ m^2
   C. $C = 14.4$ m, $A = 16.6$ m^2
   D. $C = 4.6$ m, $A = 5.29$ m^2

9. Which set of numbers has a GCF of 3? C
   A. 15, 30, 45 **B.** 6, 30, 24 **C.** 24, 36, 9 **D.** 36, 27, 18

10. How many hours are in $\frac{5}{6}$ of a day? A
    A. 20 **B.** 4 **C.** 9 **D.** 18

11. A relay team is competing in a $\frac{1}{2}$-mi race. Each person runs $\frac{1}{8}$ mi. How many team members are there? D
    A. 16 **B.** 2 **C.** 8 **D.** 4

12. Find the prime factorization of 300. D
    A. $2 \times 2 \times 3 \times 5$
    B. $2 \times 5 \times 5 \times 7$
    C. $2 \times 3 \times 3 \times 5 \times 5$
    D. $2 \times 2 \times 3 \times 5 \times 5$

13. The freshman car wash earned $214.35. The sophomore car wash earned $189.76. How much money did the two classes make altogether? A
    A. $404.11 **B.** $403.01 **C.** $393.01 **D.** $24.59

Resources
Cumulative Review, TR Ch. 8, pp. 41–42
Transparency Masters, TR p. 35

CHAPTER

9 Ratio, Proportion & Percent

Why Study Ratio, Proportion, and Percent?

If students ask this question, you may want to mention these areas in which ratios, proportions, and percents are used: gas consumption for a car, typing words per minute, sports, manufacturing (defects per million opportunities), cooking, architecture, toys, patterns, medicine, and money.

Graphic Display of Chapter Content

Below is one possible representation of the chapter's content and its applications to the world outside the classroom. Have students create their own graphic display and fill in applications that they have seen in their own lives.

- The center oval should state the main concept of the chapter: ratio, proportion, and percent.
- Have students draw the ovals with the next level of concepts presented in the chapter (rates, estimating, scale drawings, circle graphs, decimals, and fractions). You may want students to add any other topics that they think are appropriate.
- Ask students to draw as many application ovals as they can.
- Discuss all the applications that students identify.
- Have students make and present one display that includes all the students' ideas.

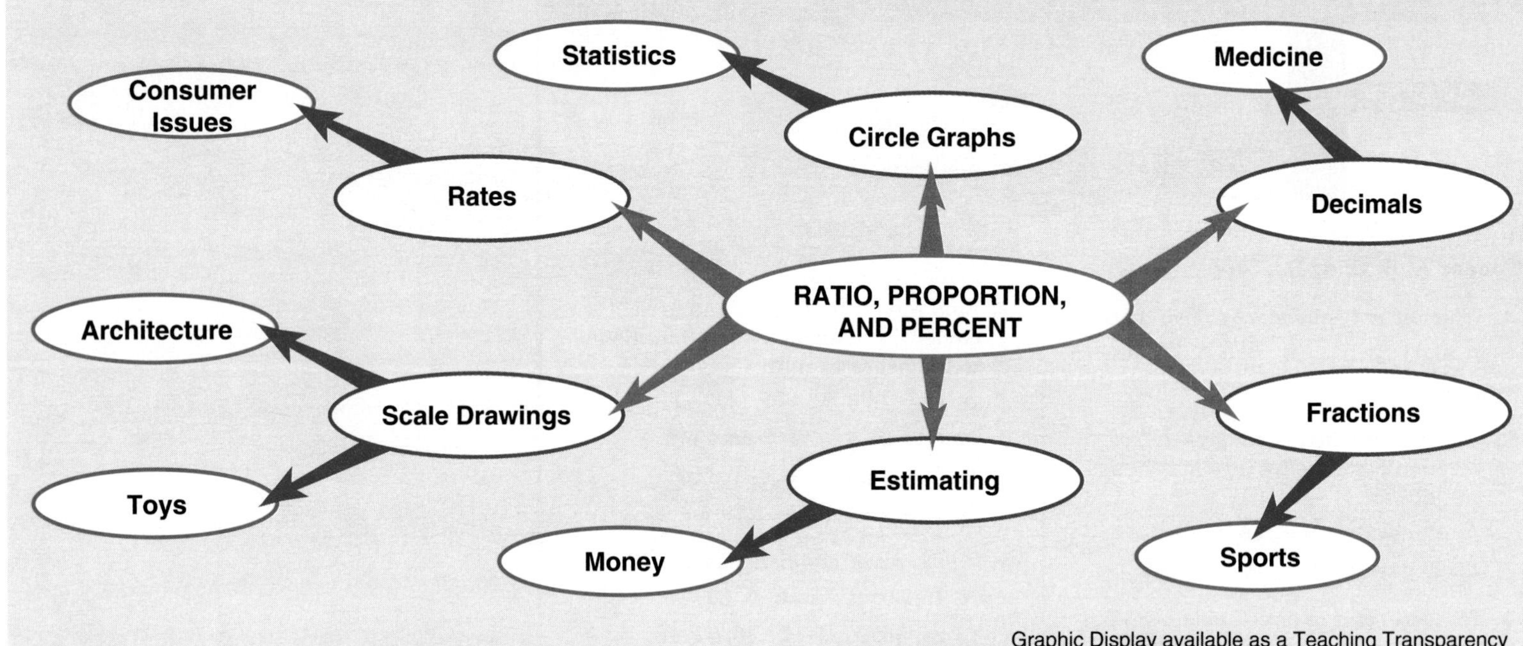

Graphic Display available as a Teaching Transparency

Vocabulary and Symbols

corresponding parts	rate
cross products	ratio
distortions	safe heart rate
equal ratios	scale
percent	unit rate
proportion	

Materials and Manipulatives

calculator	paste or tape
compass	pattern blocks
computer	protractor
geometry software	ruler
graph paper	scissors
metric ruler	stopwatch
paper	

Additional Resources

Commercially Available Technology

Calculator
fraction

Software
geometry software
Geometer's Sketchpad by Key Curriculum Press

Other Media
"Percento Bingo Game" and "Percent Video." Gamco Industries, P.O. Box 1911A7, Big Spring, TX 79721. (800) 351-1404.

"Scale Up." Films Inc Video, 5547 N. Ravenswood Ave., Chicago, IL 60640. (800) 343-4312.

"Similarity." Reston, VA: NCTM, 1989.

Materials at Little or No Cost

Center for Research in Mathematical Sciences Education, Wisconsin Center for Education Research, 1025 West Johnson St., Madison, WI 53706. Pilot programs.

Play Area Design and Use. Newton, MA: EDC. Available through ERIC.

Bibliography

For Teachers

Burton, Grace et al. *Sixth-Grade Book: Addenda Series.* Reston, VA: NCTM, 1992.

Cooney, Thomas J. *Teaching and Learning Mathematics in the 1990s.* Reston, VA: NCTM, 1990.

For Students

Boring, Mel. *Incredible Constructions.* NY: Walker, 1984.

Parker, Tom. *In One Day.* Boston: Houghton Mifflin, 1984.

Peach, S. *Technical Drawing: Design, Illustration and Model Making.* Newton, MA: EDC, 1987.

Prentice Hall Technology

Multimedia Math
- Math Tools, Fraction Strips
- Math Tools, Geometry
- Math Tools, Spreadsheet
- Hot Page™ 9-2
- Hot Page™ 9-6
- Hot Page™ 9-8
- Math Investigations, Hazard City Messengers
- Math Investigations, Crisis in Hydrotown
- Math Investigations, Mission: Mars
- Math Investigations, Measuring Elephant Populations in Africa

Computer Item Generator
- Chapter 9

Community Resources

Field Trips
- a catering business
- a manufacturing business that uses mass production
- a clearinghouse that does phone surveys or mailings

Guest Speakers
- a statistician to speak on ratios and statistics
- a carpenter
- a caterer

Backpack Take-Home Activities

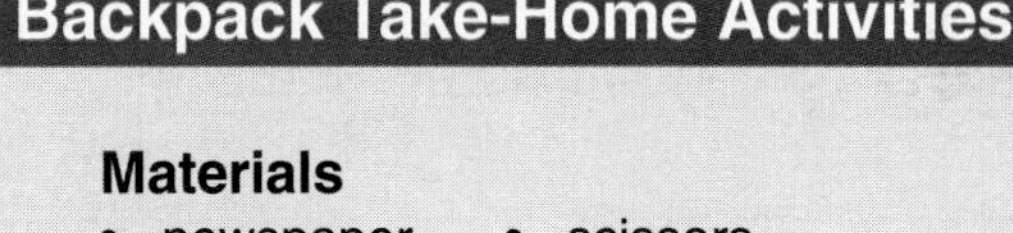

Materials
- newspaper
- tape
- pencil
- scissors
- paper

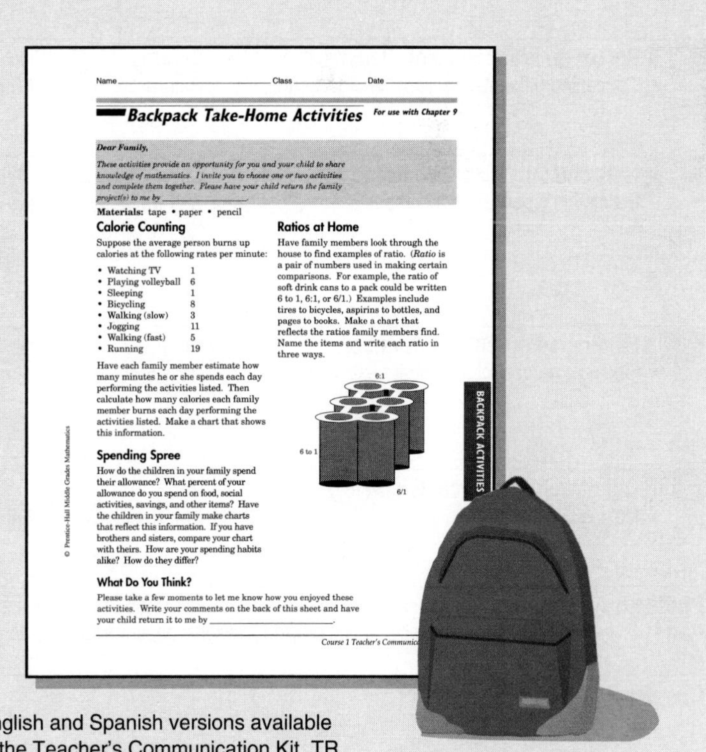

Name ____________ Class ________ Date ________

Backpack Take-Home Activities *For use with Chapter 9*

Dear Family,

These activities provide an opportunity for you and your child to share knowledge of mathematics. I invite you to choose one or two activities and complete them together. Please have your child return the family project(s) to me by ____________.

Materials: tape • paper • pencil

Calorie Counting

Suppose the average person burns up calories at the following rates per minute:

- Watching TV 1
- Playing volleyball 6
- Sleeping 1
- Bicycling 8
- Walking (slow) 3
- Jogging 11
- Walking (fast) 5
- Running 19

Have each family member estimate how many minutes he or she spends each day performing the activities listed. Then calculate how many calories each family member burns each day performing the activities listed. Make a chart that shows this information.

Spending Spree

How do the children in your family spend their allowance? What percent of your allowance do you spend on food, social activities, savings, and other items? Have the children in your family make charts that reflect this information. If you have brothers and sisters, compare your chart with theirs. How are your spending habits alike? How do they differ?

Ratios at Home

Have family members look through the house to find examples of ratio. (*Ratio* is a pair of numbers used in making certain comparisons. For example, the ratio of soft drink cans to a pack could be written 6 to 1, 6:1, or 6/1.) Examples include tires to bicycles, aspirins to bottles, and pages to books. Make a chart that reflects the ratios family members find. Name the items and write each ratio in three ways.

What Do You Think?

Please take a few moments to let me know how you enjoyed these activities. Write your comments on the back of this sheet and have your child return it to me by ____________.

BACKPACK ACTIVITIES

© Prentice-Hall Middle Grades Mathematics

Course 1 Teacher's Communica

English and Spanish versions available in the Teacher's Communication Kit, TR

Chapter 9 Planning Guide

Objectives	Assignment Options	Critical Thinking/ Problem Solving	Writing and Reading Math	Estimation Mental Math	Materials and Manipulatives
Investigation	This chapter-long project involves open-ended questioning and data collecting and provides an additional opportunity to assess students.	p. 362 p. 362	p. 362	p. 362	p. 362
9-1 Exploring Ratios • Exploring the meaning of ratio	**Core:** 8–21; MR all **Reinforce:** 22–24 **Enrich:** 25	2, 24; MR: 7 BI p. 364	24 p. 364; JL p. 364 JL Sheet		WT: 3–7; 20–23, 25 p. 364; MM p. 364 TT 79
9-2 Ratios and Rates • Finding equal ratios • Finding unit rates	**Core:** 15–21, 26–33, 37, 39; MR all **Reinforce:** 22–25, 34–36, 38, 41 **Enrich:** 40, 42	3; EX; WT: 4, 5; 25, 36, 40, 42; MR: 4 pp. 365–368; WT p. 366; BI p. 367	37–39, 42 p. 368; JL p. 367 JL Sheet	MR: 1 p. 367; MM p. 368	WT: 4a pp. 365, 367, 368; WT p. 366; RT p. 367 TT 79
9-3 Solving Proportions • Recognizing proportions • Solving proportions	**Core:** 15–22, 25, 28, 30; MR all; CH all **Reinforce:** 23, 24, 29 **Enrich:** 26, 27	EX3; 14, 24–29; CH: 1, 16; MR: 7 pp. 369, 370; BI p. 371; MM p. 372	25 p. 371; JL p. 371 JL Sheet	6–13, 15–22; CH: 12–15	EX3; 6–9, 15–18, 26 p. 372 TT 79
9-4 Problem Solving: Guess and Test • Solving problems by using guess and test	**Core:** 9, 10, 15–18; MR all **Reinforce:** 11–13, 19–23 **Enrich:** 14	All; MR: 7 pp. 373–374; BI p. 374; MM p. 375	All JL p. 374 JL Sheet	MR: 1, 2	p. 373 TT 80
9-5 Technology: Investigating Similar Figures • Exploring ratios in corresponding parts of similar figures	**Core:** 11–14, 19; MR all **Reinforce:** 15–17 **Enrich:** 18	1, 2d, 6b, 7b, 11–17, 19; MR: 5 pp. 378, 379; BI p. 379; MM p. 379	6a, 7b; WT: 10c pp. 377, 378; JL p. 378 JL Sheet	MR: 3, 4	4, 7a; WT: 10; 11–18 pp. 377, 379; WT p. 378; RT p. 379 TT 6, 80, 82; Alt. Lesson
9-6 Math and Design: Scale Drawings • Using scale drawings • Making scale drawings	**Core:** 9–11; DM all; MR all **Reinforce:** 13–16 **Enrich:** 12	2; EX; 3, 5, 6b, 7, 8; DM: 2; MR: 7 pp. 380, 381; BI p. 382; DM p. 383	8, 12–16 pp. 382, 383; JL p. 383 JL Sheet		EX; 4, 6a; DM: 1, 3, 5 p. 381; RT p. 382; DM p. 383 TT 6, 80, 82
9-7 Percent Sense • Modeling Percents	**Core:** 8–13, 15–20, 26, 29, 30; MR all **Reinforce:** 21–25, 27 **Enrich:** 14, 28	1, 6; WT: 7; 14, 26–29; MR: 7 BI p. 385	14 p. 385; JL p. 385 JL Sheet	MR: 1, 2	5; WT: a–f; 8–13, 30 pp. 384–386; WT p. 384 RT p. 385 TT 80
9-8 Percents, Fractions, and Decimals • Converting percents, fractions, and decimals	**Core:** 11–15, 18; MR all **Reinforce:** 16, 17 **Enrich:** 19	17, 18, 19c; MR: 5 p. 387; BI p. 388; MM p. 389	18 p. 389; JL p. 389 JL Sheet		WT: 1a–c; EX3; 4–9, 19 p. 388; RT p. 388 TT 1, 81
9-9 Math and Spending: Estimating with Percents • Estimating a percent of a number	**Core:** 18–24, 28–31, 38; MR all **Reinforce:** 25–27, 32, 33, 35, 36 **Enrich:** 34, 37	1, 2, 5–9; WT: 10a; 15–17, 24–27, 36, 37; MR: 7 pp. 391–393; BI p. 393; MM p. 394	8; WT: 12b pp. 391, 392; JL p. 393 JL Sheet	5; EX1, 2; WT: 11; 15–33, 35–37 pp. 391–393; WT p. 392	3, 18–23 p. 391; RT p. 393 TT 1, 81, 83
9-10 Finding a Percent of a Number • Finding a percent of a number	**Core:** 5–15, 23; MR all; CH all **Reinforce:** 16–21, 24, 25 **Enrich:** 22, 26	1–4, 14, 15, 21–26, CH: 1, 3, 12; MR: 7 pp. 395, 396; BI p. 396; MM p. 398	16 p. 397; JL p. 397 JL Sheet	17–20, 22a; MR: 3–6 p. 396	EX; 5–13; CH: 4–7 p. 395; RT p. 397; CH p. 397; MM p. 398 TT 81
9-11 Constructing a Circle Graph • Making circle graphs	**Core:** 12; MR all **Reinforce:** 13 **Enrich:** 14	WT: 2, 6b; 8, 9, 12b, 13; MR: 5 p. 399; BI p. 400;	12b p. 401; JL p. 401 JL Sheet	5, 13, 14; MR: 1, 2 RT p. 400	WT: 1, 3–7; 8d, 11–13 p. 400; WT p. 399 TT 8, 9, 81
Putting It All Together	These pages include a Follow-Up to the Investigation and other projects, which provide additional opportunities to assess the students.	pp. 404–405 pp. 404–405	p. 404 p. 404		pp. 404–405
Chapter Resources		PS Practice, CW, CA, CR PS Practice p. 384; CW pp. 410–411; CA p. 414; CR p. 415	PS Practice, CW, CA p. 360B; PS Practice p. 384; CW pp. 410–411; CA p. 414		pp. 360A, 360B Backpack Activities Manip. Kits; TT 78

Student Edition (question numbers)
Teacher's Edition (page numbers)
Other Components

BI—What's the Big Idea? CA—Chapter Assessment CH—Checkpoint CG—Computer Item Generator CR—Cumulative Review CW—Chapter Wrap Up DM—Decision Making EP—Extra Practice EX—Example FD—Fact of the Day

Cooperative Learning Activities	Technology	Data Collection & Analysis	Interdisciplinary Connections	Applications	Assessment	Review	Strand Integration	NCTM Correlation*
		p. 362	Science	design, education	p. 362 p. 362			
WT: 3–7; 25 WT p. 363; RT p. 364		FD p. 364	p. 364	p. 364; WT p. 363	p. 363	MR: All p. 363; RT p. 364 Practice p. 25	Geometry, Number, Logic/Language	1, 2, 3, 4, 5, 6, 7, 8, 12
WT: 4, 5 WT p. 366; RT p. 367	Hot Page™ 9–2	41 FD p. 366		food, sports pp. 365, 367	p. 366	MR: All p. 365; RT p. 367 Practice p. 26	Geometry, Measurement, Number, Logic/Language	1, 2, 3, 4, 5, 6, 7, 8, 12, 13
WT: 1 p. 370; WT p. 369; RT p. 371	EX3; 6–9, 15–18, 26 pp. 369, 372	29, 30 p. 372; FD p. 370	Health, Science p. 371; CH p. 372 Alt. Lesson	money, nutrition, sports, science p. 371; CH p. 372	CH: All p. 370; CH p. 372 CH TR p. 40	MR: All p. 369; RT p. 371 Practice p. 27	Algebra, Geometry, Number, Logic/Language	1, 2, 3, 4, 5, 6, 7, 8, 9, 12, 13
p. 373; RT p. 374		FD p. 374	Science pp. 374, 375	money, weather pp. 374, 375	p. 373	MR: All p. 373; RT p. 374 Practice p. 28	Discrete Math, Measurement, Number, Logic/Language	1, 2, 3, 4, 5, 7, 8, 13
WT: 8–10 WT p. 378; RT p. 379	All pp. 377, 379; WT p. 378	FD p. 378	p. 379	sports p. 379 Alt. Lesson	p. 378	MR: All p. 377; RT p. 379 Practice p. 29	Discrete Math, Measurement, Number, Logic/Language	1, 2, 3, 4, 7, 8, 12, 13
p. 381	p. 381 Hot Page™ 9–6	DM: All FD p. 381; DM p. 383	Art	design, architecture, art pp. 380, 382; RT p. 382	p. 381	MR: All p. 380; RT p. 382 Practice p. 30	Stat./Probability, Measurement, Number, Logic/Language	1, 2, 3, 4, 5, 7, 8, 9, 12, 13
WT: 7 p. 386; WT p. 384 RT p. 385	pp. 384, 385	15, 28 p. 386; FD p. 385	Science p. 386	entertainment, medicine, astronomy pp. 385, 386	pp. 384–385	MR: All p. 384; RT p. 385 Practice p. 31	Stat./Probability, Measurement, Number, Logic/Language	1, 2, 3, 4, 5, 6, 7, 8, 10, 12, 13
WT: 1, 2 pp. 387, 388; WT p. 387	EX3; 4 p. 388 Hot Page™ 9–8	16, 17, 19 p. 389; FD p. 388	p. 389	food, education p. 389	p. 388	MR: All p. 387; RT p. 388 Practice p. 32	Stat./Probability, Number, Logic/Language	1, 2, 3, 4, 5, 7, 8, 10, 12, 13
WT: 10–12 p. 394; WT p. 392 Alt. Lesson	p. 391 Alt. Lesson	WT: 10–12; 28–33, 35, 38 p. 394; WT p. 392; FD p. 392	p. 393	advertising, consumer issues, food, shopping p. 393; WT p. 392 Alt. Lesson	p. 392	MR: All p. 391; RT p. 393 Practice p. 33	Stat./Probability, Discrete Math, Number, Logic/Language	1, 2, 3, 4, 5, 7, 8, 10, 13
RT p. 397	EX; 5–13; CH: 13–15	17–20, 22, 25, 26 FD p. 396	Health p. 396	health, sports, money pp. 395, 396	CH: All p. 396; CH p. 397 CH TR p.40	MR: All p. 395; RT p. 397 Practice p. 34	Stat./Probability, Discrete Math, Number, Logic/Language	1, 2, 3, 4, 5, 7, 8, 10, 13
WT: 1–7 WT p. 399; RT p. 400	p. 399	WT: 7; 12–14 FD p. 400	pp. 399, 401	entertainment, transportation	p. 400	MR: All p. 399; RT p. 400 Practice p. 35	Geometry, Stat./Probability, Number, Logic/Language	1, 2, 3, 4, 5, 7, 8, 10, 12, 13
pp. 404–405		pp. 404–405 pp. 404–405	Science	astronomy, education, design, time	pp. 404–405 pp. 404–405			
IN, PT pp. 360–362; PT pp. 412–413 Backpack Activities	p. 360B Multimedia Math, CG	Data File 9 pp. 360–361	Health, Sports pp. 360F, 360–361 Interdisciplinary Units	sports, health, design pp. 360A, 360F, 360–361 Backpack Act., Interdisciplinary Units, Projects	IN, PT, CA pp. 360E, 362; pp. 410–414 CA, Span. CA, Self Assessment, Projects	Practice, PS Practice, CW, CR, EP, SSG CW pp. 410–411 Span. SSG, CR		

GE—Great Expectations   IN—Investigation   JL—Journal   MM—Math Minutes
MR—Mixed Review   PS—Problem Solving   PT—Putting It All Together   RT—Reteaching Activity
SSG—Student Study Guide   TT—Teaching Transparency   WT—Work Together

*For a description of the NCTM Standards, see page T15.

Assessment Options

Observation Checklist

In this chapter on ratio, proportion and percent, you have opportunities to observe your students do these tasks:

- ✓ find ratios equal to a given ratio
- ✓ solve proportions
- ✓ guess and test to solve word problems
- ✓ recognize and construct similar figures and scale drawings
- ✓ model percents using graph paper
- ✓ convert percents, fractions, and decimals
- ✓ estimate a percent of a number
- ✓ find a percent of a number exactly
- ✓ make circle graphs

In every chapter, you are given opportunities to observe your students:

- ✓ work with a partner or in a group
- ✓ write about mathematics
- ✓ participate in discussions about mathematics
- ✓ collect and analyze data
- ✓ display positive attitudes about mathematics
- ✓ use measurement tools

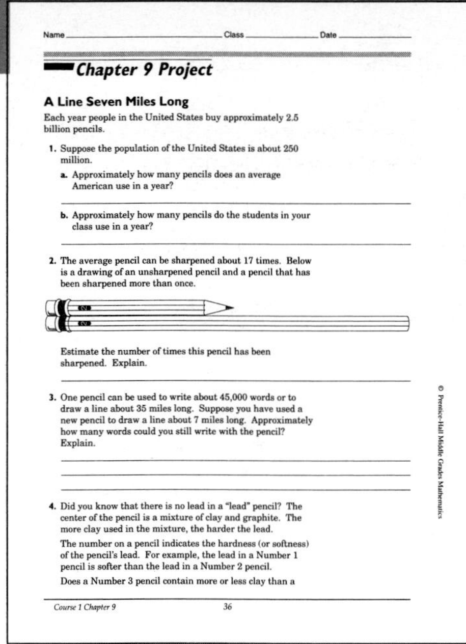

Name ______ Class ______ Date ______

Chapter 9 Project

A Line Seven Miles Long

Each year people in the United States buy approximately 2.5 billion pencils.

1. Suppose the population of the United States is about 250 million.
   a. Approximately how many pencils does an average American use in a year?
   b. Approximately how many pencils do the students in your class use in a year?
2. The average pencil can be sharpened about 17 times. Below is a drawing of an unsharpened pencil and a pencil that has been sharpened more than once.

   Estimate the number of times this pencil has been sharpened. Explain.
3. One pencil can be used to write about 45,000 words or to draw a line about 35 miles long. Suppose you have used a new pencil to draw a line about 7 miles long. Approximately how many words could you still write with the pencil? Explain.
4. Did you know that there is no lead in a "lead" pencil? The center of the pencil is a mixture of clay and graphite. The more clay used in the mixture, the harder the lead.
   The number on a pencil indicates the hardness (or softness) of the pencil's lead. For example, the lead in a Number 1 pencil is softer than the lead in a Number 2 pencil.
   Does a Number 3 pencil contain more or less clay than a

Course 1 Chapter 9 36

© Prentice-Hall Middle Grades Mathematics

Performance Based Project (with scoring rubric), Chapter Files, TR

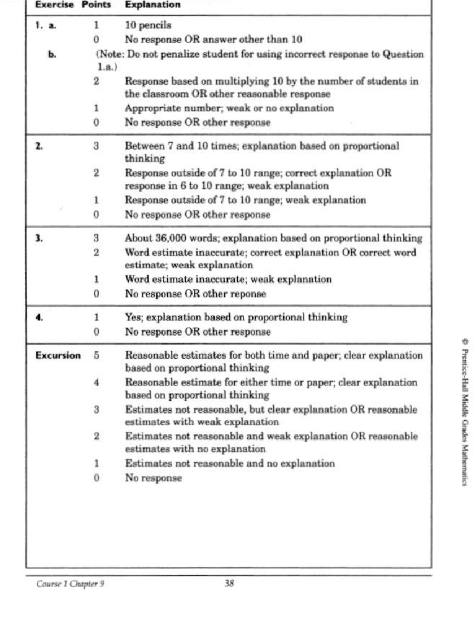

...ong Scoring Rubric

Exercise	Points	Explanation
1. a.	1	10 pencils
	0	No response OR answer other than 10
b.		(Note: Do not penalize student for using incorrect response to Question 1.a.)
	2	Response based on multiplying 10 by the number of students in the classroom OR other reasonable response
	1	Appropriate number; weak or no explanation
	0	No response OR other response
2.	3	Between 7 and 10 times; explanation based on proportional thinking
	2	Response outside of 7 to 10 range; correct explanation OR response in 6 to 10 range; weak explanation
	1	Response outside of 7 to 10 range; weak explanation
	0	No response OR other response
3.	3	About 36,000 words; explanation based on proportional thinking
	2	Word estimate inaccurate; correct explanation OR correct word estimate; weak explanation
	1	Word estimate inaccurate; weak explanation
	0	No response OR other reponse
4.	1	Yes; explanation based on proportional thinking
	0	No response OR other response
Excursion	5	Reasonable estimates for both time and paper; clear explanation based on proportional thinking
	4	Reasonable estimate for either time or paper; clear explanation based on proportional thinking
	3	Estimates not reasonable, but clear explanation OR reasonable estimates with weak explanation
	2	Estimates not reasonable and weak explanation OR reasonable estimates with no explanation
	1	Estimates not reasonable and no explanation
	0	No response

Course 1 Chapter 9 38

© Prentice-Hall Middle Grades Mathematics

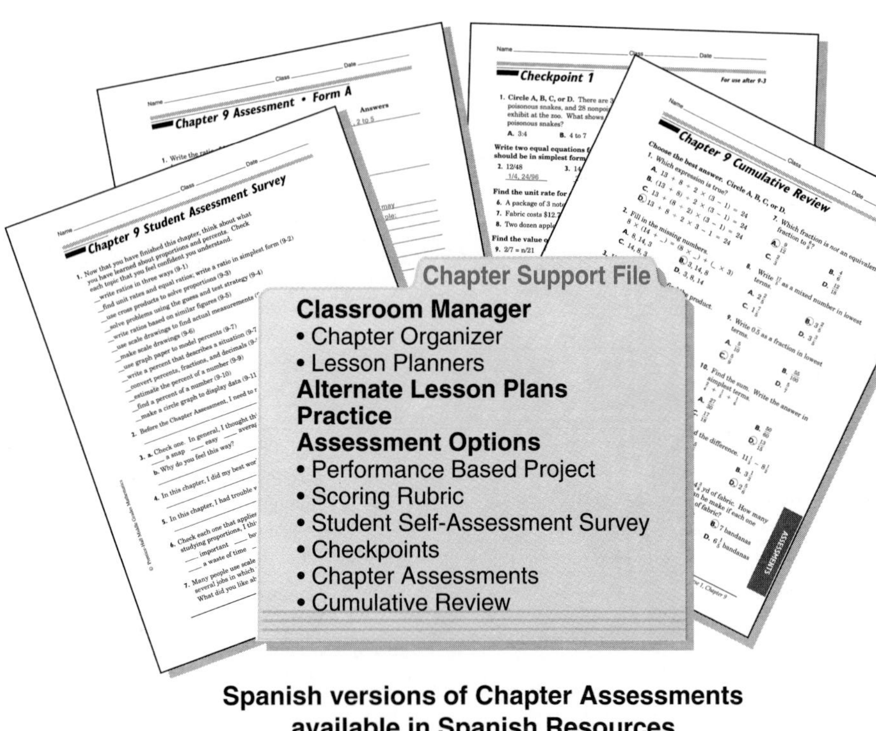

Spanish versions of Chapter Assessments available in Spanish Resources

Interdisciplinary Units
- **Travel and Geography**
- **Space Exploration**
- **Sports**
- **Consumer Awareness**
- **The Great Outdoors**

English & Spanish

These units include cross-curriculum connections and can be used at any time during the school year. See the Teacher's Guide for more information.

Working with Middle Grade Students

> *"Students should have numerous and varied experiences related to the cultural, historical, and scientific evaluation of mathematics so that they can appreciate the role of mathematics in the development of our contemporary society and explore relationships among mathematics and the disciplines it serves: the physical and life sciences, the social sciences, and the humanities."*
>
> —NCTM *Curriculum and Evaluation Standards*

Addressing a Variety of Learning Styles

The mathematical tasks in Chapter 9 involve various learning styles. Here are some examples.

- Visual learners circle cross products in a proportion (p. 370) and draw scale models (p. 381).
- Auditory learners discuss situations in which ratios are used (p. 363) and applications of the guess-and-test strategy for problem solving (p. 373).
- Kinesthetic learners find the rates at which they can print letters (p. 366), and measure circumferences to find the diameters of several game balls (p. 372).

Alternate Lesson 9-5 addresses tactile learners by having them use manipulatives.

Cultural Connections

Have each student choose a country and look up its area in an atlas. Then have students find their countries' perimeters by measuring with rulers or string, and using the legend of a map. For each country, calculate the ratio of its perimeter to its area. Using the data, compare the ratio for countries of the same approximate area but different shapes, and for countries of similar shape but different size. Draw scale models of some of the countries (or trace them from maps), and find the ratio of each scale model's perimeter to its area. Try to draw conclusions. Ask students what other ratios (area to population, for example) might be of interest for different countries.

Team Teaching Suggestion

Work with an art teacher when introducing the concepts of scale drawings. Plan a project to include scale drawings of cars, sports equipment such as volleyballs and hockey sticks, or specific objects around the school.

Mathematical Literacy

The NCTM *Standards* point out that, since our society has shifted from industry to an information base, the new goals for education must include "(1) mathematically literate workers, (2) lifelong learning, (3) opportunity for all, and (4) an informed electorate" (NCTM *Curriculum and Evaluation Standards*, p. 3). Mathematically literate workers will be able to work in groups on problems, know how to use a variety of problem solving strategies, and believe in the utility and value of mathematics.

Teaching Tip

Students in the middle grades are self-conscious about their changing bodies. Activities such as having students measure their circumference of their wrists or length of their feet can be effective teaching tools, but these activities must be carefully introduced in order to avoid embarrassment or awkwardness.

Bulletin Board

Have students make scale drawings to recreate one large picture from pieces of a smaller version of the same picture. Predetermine the ratio of the small picture to the large picture. Use this ratio to decide the size of the small squares and the large squares. Cut a small picture with uniform dimensions into small squares. Assign each student a small square to use for a scale drawing. Put a code letter or number on the back of each square. Provide each student with a large square. After each student has finished their scale drawing, have students work together to arrange the squares and recreate the picture.

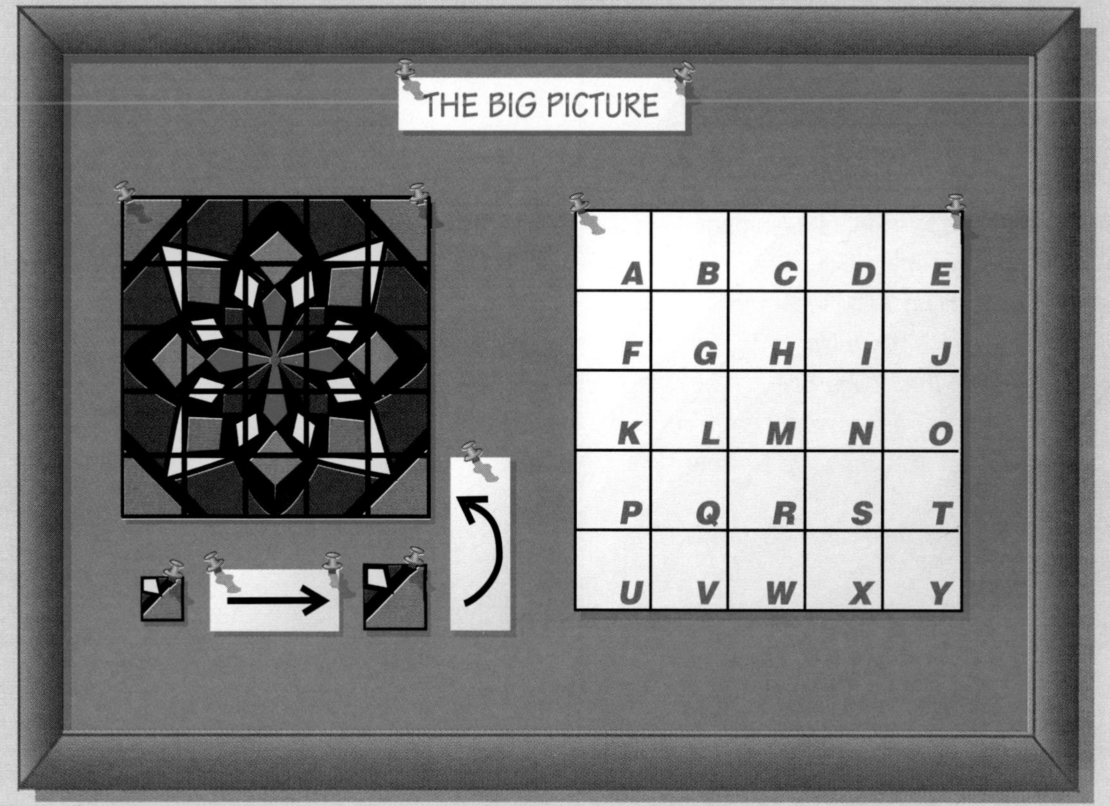

CHAPTER 9 Ratio, Proportion, and Percent

Cultural Connections Many Americans take advantage of our national park system to increase their fitness and to enjoy the challenges of hiking and exploring. Until recently, many of these recreational areas were not available to people with disabilities. Thanks to Wendy Roth and Michael Tompane, access to our national parks and historic sites has greatly increased. Wendy Roth, who lives with disabilities caused by multiple sclerosis and moves with the aid of a wheelchair, started the Easy Access Project to help others gain access to the challenges of wilderness recreation. Roth and Tompane's campaign for access led to the book *Easy Access to National Parks.* This handbook describes the accessibility of trails, campgrounds, and swimming in various national parks.

WORLD VIEW The city of Prague is the birthplace of Martina Navratilova, championship tennis player. While competing in a tournament when she was 21, Navratilova asked for asylum and permission to stay in the United States. In 1984 she won four tournaments in a row: the Australian Open, the French Open, Wimbledon, and the United States Open.

Digging for Data Ask the students to use the tables and graphs, as well as other information in the data file, to answer these questions:

- *Among teens, for what activities is female participation greater than that of males?*
  (roller skating, volleyball, and aerobics)
- *What are the dimensions of the top of the finishing post for the standard track?*
  (8 cm by 2 cm)

There may be some students in the class who might have trouble holding the pencil in the following activity. They can

Chapter 9 Contents

Data File Questions

Data File 9

CHAPTER 9 Ratio, Proportion, and Percent

In Prague, the capital of the Czech Republic, membership to a fitness club costs about $18 per month. That's about $\frac{1}{9}$ of the average salary there. In Budapest, the capital of Hungary, membership costs almost $36 a month or about $\frac{1}{6}$ of the average salary in Budapest.

Derek Turnbull made history in 1992 when he ran in a series of masters races. To compete as a master you must be at least 40 years old. Derek was a 65-year-old sheep farmer from New Zealand. He broke the world record for his age group in every race.

Derek Turnbull's Record

Event	Old Record	Turnbull in 1992
800 m	2:20.5	2:17.8
1500 m	4:41.82	4:39.8
One mile	5:05.61	4:56.4
3,000 m	10:10.2	9:47.4
5,000 m	17:43.4	16:38.8
10,000 m	36:03	34:42.8
Marathon (26 mi)	2:42:29	2:41:57

Source: *Runner's World*

Exercise Participation for Teens, Ages 12–15*

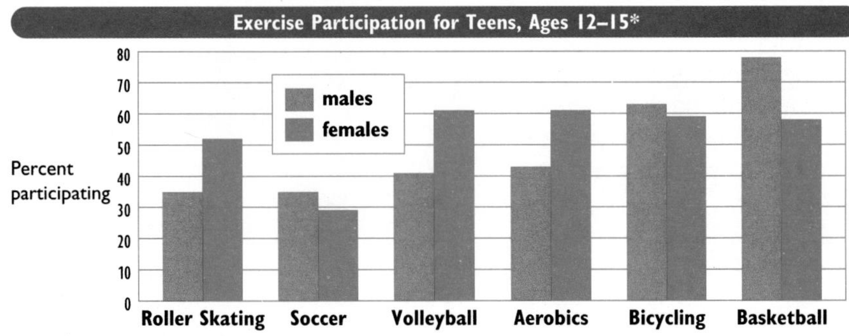

*based on 549 males and 523 females surveyed

Source: Teenage Research Unlimited

participate as timer or recorder. Have students, in groups of three, try this muscle skill and make a table of their times:

- *Straighten a wire paper clip and then bend it into a U-shape (or use a wire hairpin). On a pencil, measure and mark a spot two inches from the point of the pencil.*
- *Have one member of the group hold the pencil parallel to the desktop. Place the wire so that it is riding on the pencil at the mark. The person holding the pencil tries to keep it perfectly still and parallel to the desktop, but with the two ends of the wire just touching the desktop, without bracing the arm and without touching the desktop with the arm.*
- *The second member times how long it is before the clip "walks" off the pencil. The third member records the time.*
- *Try both right and left arms and study the data to see if there is a difference between them.*
  (A muscle contains fibers that are always in motion, some contracting, some relaxing. This causes small movements that are reflected in the movement of the wire along the pencil.)

Journal Activity Ask students to read the four objectives in What You Will Learn. Have them write which of the four sounds most interesting to them, and why. Ask them also to write which one they know the most about already.

Interdisciplinary Connection [Health] Many of the fitness programs that people use, such as yoga, Tai Chi, and other martial arts, come from other cultures. In addition to exercise, fitness is also related to other health areas such as nutrition and sleep. People differ in the amount of sleep they need, but 7 or 8 hours is the average for healthy adults. Adolescents need more because of the changes going on in their bodies. People who fall asleep without trouble and wake up feeling refreshed are probably getting enough sleep.

WHAT YOU WILL LEARN

- how to model and use ratios and proportions
- how to relate fractions, decimals, and percents
- how to use technology to investigate similar figures
- how to solve problems using guess and test

Aerobic Fitness

This chart shows the results of the 1989 one-mile walk/run test. It gives the percent of girls and boys in each age category who met the goal.

Age (years)	Goal time (min) (boys)	Goal time (min) (girls)	Percent passed (boys)	Percent passed (girls)
6	15:00	16:00	76	91
7	14:00	15:00	74	63
8	13:00	14:00	72	69
9	12:00	13:00	70	74
10–11	11:00	12:00	73	71
12	10:00	12:00	69	75
13	9:30	11:30	68	66
14–16	8:30	10:30	73	50

Source: U.S. News & World Report

Sit-ups

The goals listed below are the number of sit-ups per minute. In the 1989 study, 76% of the boys and 72% of the girls met the goals.

Children ages 5–7	20/min
Children ages 8–9	25/min
Children ages 10–11	30/min
Boys ages 12–13	35/min
Girls ages 12–13	30/min
Boys ages 14–16	40/min
Girls ages 14–16	35/min

Source: U.S. News & World Report

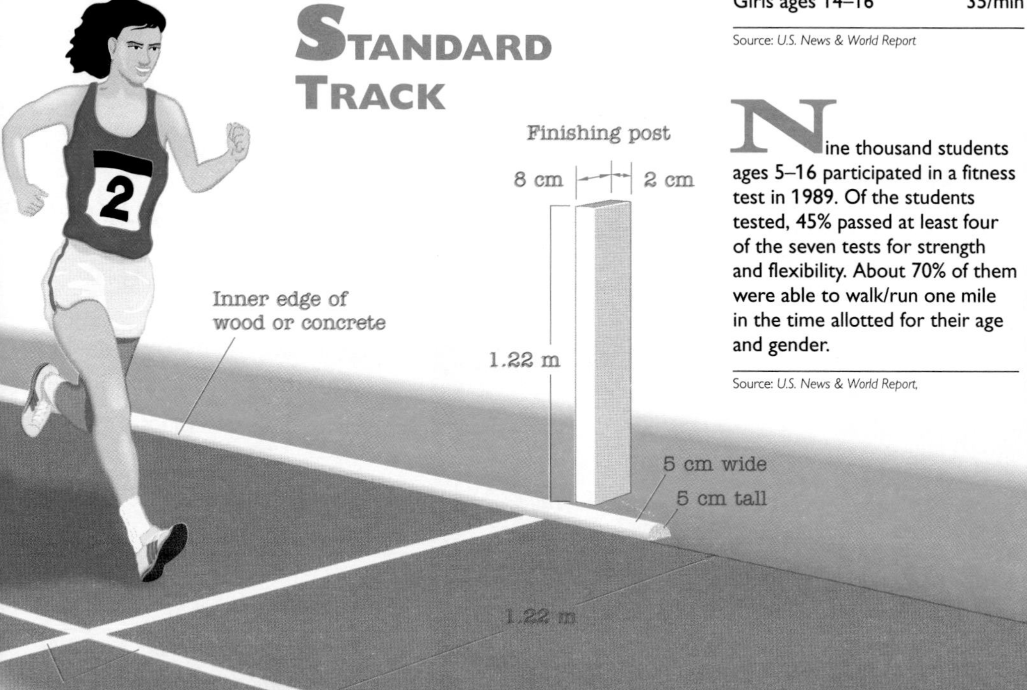

Nine thousand students ages 5–16 participated in a fitness test in 1989. Of the students tested, 45% passed at least four of the seven tests for strength and flexibility. About 70% of them were able to walk/run one mile in the time allotted for their age and gender.

Source: U.S. News & World Report.

Fact of the Day

Muscles, over 600 of them, make up nearly half the body weight of humans and are mostly protein. Muscles are made of long fibrous bundles, with the number of fibers in a bundle varying from about 5 (in the eyelid) to about 200 (in the buttocks). Each fiber in the bundle contracts for less than a second, but the fibers take turns contracting and relaxing.

—*Looking at the Body*

CHAPTER 9 INVESTIGATION

To provide an introduction to the solar system, ask students to model the parts of the sun, the planets, and the moon. Have the "sun" choose a spot in the room and have the other "planets" arrange themselves in relation to the distance to the sun. Then have the students move about the room simulating the movement of the sun and the planets.

Students should begin designing their models on paper because they soon learn that the museum project is impractical. The students will not need to proceed with the actual construction of their models.

After half the chapter has been completed, have the students show you their work on the project. If they are behind schedule, you may want to give them intermediate deadlines in order to check their work.

- *What other models have you made?*
- *What is the relationship between a model and the actual object on which it is based?*

Keeping a Project Notebook

Some suggestions for students' notebooks are:

- Include all ideas for finding sizes of the planets and the distances of planets from the sun in the model.
- List the dates and results of all discussions about the project.
- Include all calculations, together with explanations of how they were done.

Project Organizer

Related Exercises
p. 372
p. 379
p. 386
p. 394

Follow Up
p. 404

Teacher's Notes
pp. 362, 372, 379, 386, 394

Community Resources
- astronomy club
- university science department

Materials and Manipulatives
- art materials
- sports balls
- tape measure

	Diameter (mi)	Mean Distance from Sun (millions of miles)
Sun	865,120	0
Mercury	3,030	36.0
Venus	7,520	67.2
Earth	7,926	3.0
Mars	4,216	141.7
Jupiter	88,724	483.9
Saturn	74,560	885.0
Uranus	31,600	1,781.6
Neptune	30,600	2,790.2
Pluto	1,860	3,670.7

Memo

The Astro County Science Museum is raising funds to build a scale model of the solar system in the museum lobby. The lobby is 50 ft long. A brochure put out by the museum states that in the model, the sun will be the size of a basketball. According to the brochure, "Everyone committed to furthering the cause of science education in Astro County should donate to this worthy project." Would you give money for the model of the solar system?

Mission: Design your own model of the solar system with a sun the size of a basketball. Your design should include estimates of the sizes of the planets and their distances from the sun. Then decide whether you should donate money to the science museum.

- ✓ About how many times the size of Jupiter is the sun? About how many times the size of Pluto is the sun?
- ✓ How can you estimate the overall size of the model?
- ✓ What do you need to know in order to decide whether to give money to the museum?

9-1

Connecting to Prior Knowledge

Ask students to think of pairs of numbers that they often see around them. For example, ask how many students are usually in their classes. Then ask how many teachers they usually have for a class. Ask if the pairs, number of teachers and class size, are always almost the same size. Challenge them to describe the pattern in a mathematical way.

THINK AND DISCUSS

ESL **AUDITORY LEARNERS** Point to 1 to 2, 1 : 2, and $\frac{1}{2}$ as you read each ratio aloud. Tell students that the ratio can be written in different ways, and the words that are said when the ratio is read can vary also. For example, "1 to 2," "1 is to 2," "1 divided by 2," "1 per 2," "1 for each 2." Have students practice reading ratios written in different ways.

Error Alert! Students sometimes think of ratios only as fractions because they can be written in the form $\frac{a}{b}$. ***Remediation*** Discuss how the ratio of one part ginger ale to two parts fruit juice in the example does not mean that half ($\frac{1}{2}$) of the punch is ginger ale.

WORK TOGETHER

Have students work in groups of three. Encourage students to write their ratios independently and then compare and revise their answers.

Ongoing Assessment Have students meet in pairs to create fanciful recipes consisting of only two ingredients. Each student names a food, and then each pair decides at what ratio the two foods should be combined. Ask each pair to discuss its recipe and the ratio on which it is based.

What's Ahead

- Exploring the meaning of ratio

9-1 Exploring Ratios

WHAT YOU'LL NEED

✓ Pattern blocks

THINK AND DISCUSS

"There are 3 times as many peanuts as almonds in the mixture." "There are 2 counselors for every 9 campers." "Combine 1 part ginger ale to 2 parts fruit juice." Each statement involves a *ratio.* A **ratio** compares two numbers by division.

You can write the ratio of ginger ale to fruit juice in three ways.

1 to 2 1 : 2 $\frac{1}{2}$ ← $\frac{\text{ginger ale}}{\text{fruit juice}}$

1. For your class, write each ratio in three different ways. Answers may vary.
   a. boys to girls b. girls to boys
   c. boys to all students d. girls to all students

2. **Discussion** Name two situations where you might use ratios.
   Answers may vary. Samples: scale drawings, recipes.

WORK TOGETHER

3.–7. Notation may vary.

Work in groups. Use pattern blocks to explore ratios. Write a ratio to compare the areas of the following figures.

3. triangle : rhombus 1 : 2
4. triangle : triangle 1 : 1
5. triangle : trapezoid 1 : 3
6. triangle : hexagon 1 : 6
7. Copy and complete each table.

a.

Figure	triangle	trapezoid	hexagon
Area	1	■	■

3 6

b.

Figure	trapezoid	hexagon
Area	1	■

2

c. Write two ratios that compare the area of the trapezoid to the area of the hexagon. 3 : 6, 1 : 2

d. Write two ratios that compare the area of the rhombus to the area of the hexagon. 2 : 6, 1 : 3

"Knowledge comes, but wisdom lingers."
– Tennyson

Organizer

1. **Focus** Connecting to Prior Knowledge
2. **Teach** Think and Discuss, Work Together
3. **Closure** Wrap Up

Vocabulary/Symbols
ratio

Skills Reviewed in Context of Lesson
- finding area

Materials and Manipulatives
- pattern blocks (one package per group)

Student Resources
Extra Practice; Practice, TR Ch. 9, p. 25
Student Study Guide; English & Spanish

Teacher Resources

Teaching Transparency 79
Overhead Manipulatives: pattern blocks
Lesson Planner, TR Ch. 9, p. 2

Prentice Hall Technology
Computer Item Generator
- 9-1

Wrap Up

What's the Big Idea? Ask students what a ratio is. Then have students explain how to model a ratio.

Reteaching Activity Provide students with some triangles and trapezoids from a set of pattern blocks. Then have students copy and complete the table. Have them use the blocks to model the ratios in the table, and record the ratios using the smallest possible whole numbers.

Ratio of Triangles to Trapezoid	# of Triangles	# of Trapezoids	Total of Blocks
1 to 4	**(5)**	**(20)**	25
(4) to **(7)**	8	14	**(22)**
(3) to **(2)**	12	**(8)**	20
3 to 5	**(9)**	15	**(24)**

Connections Discuss ratios with these examples:

- **Art** (paint mixtures, canvas dimensions, sculpture materials)
- **Chemistry** (chemical and molecular composition, acid or base solution strengths)
- **Social Science** (comparisons of populations, religions, land area, tribes and clans, types of languages)

Journal Have students list some other relationships around them that they can express in ratios. Have students name purposes for a ratio.

ON YOUR OWN

WRITING Have students draw a diagram to help them answer Exercise 24.

ACTIVITY For Exercise 25, have students note where ratios are most commonly used in newspapers.

Assignment Options

Core: 8–21, MR all	
Reinforce: 22–24	**Enrich:** 25

Fact of the Day

The oldest known pyramid is the Step Pyramid at Saqqara, Egypt, built c. 2650 B.C.

—*Academic American Encyclopedia*

Minds on Math available in Teaching Transparencies

Math Minutes

Ask each student to use graph paper to find $\frac{1}{2} \times \frac{4}{7}$ and $\frac{3}{4} \times \frac{2}{3}$. **$\frac{4}{14}$; $\frac{6}{12}$**

Materials for 9-2

- stopwatch

Answers to Problems Unique to Spanish Edition
14. 5 : 22

Mixed REVIEW

The radius of a circle is 4 cm. Use 3.14 for π.

1. Find the circumference.
2. Find the area.

Find the perimeter of a rectangle with the following dimensions.

3. $\frac{1}{2}$ ft by 8 in. 2 ft 4 in.
4. 3 in. by $\frac{1}{4}$ ft 1 ft

Write two equivalent fractions.

5. $\frac{2}{3}$
6. $\frac{3}{5}$

7. Eight birds and squirrels are at the backyard feeder. You count 22 legs. How many birds and how many squirrels are there?

5 birds and 3 squirrels

1. About 25.12 cm
2. About 50.24 cm^2
5.–6. Answers may vary. Samples: 5. $\frac{4}{6}$, $\frac{6}{9}$
6. $\frac{6}{10}$, $\frac{9}{15}$

ON YOUR OWN

Write a ratio in three ways to compare each.

8. plates to bowls
3 to 1, 3 : 1, $\frac{3}{1}$
9. cups to bowls
2 to 1, 2 : 1, $\frac{2}{1}$
10. bowls to cups
1 to 2, 1 : 2, $\frac{1}{2}$
11. plates to cups
3 to 2, 3 : 2, $\frac{3}{2}$

Write a ratio to represent each comparison.

4 : 6 Notation may vary.
12. sunglasses to caps

13. bats to balls 5 : 7

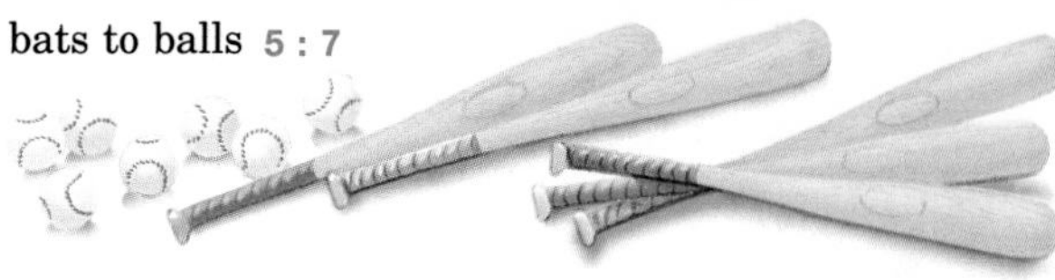

14. the number of vowels to consonants in the alphabet
5 : 21
15. the number of vowels to consonants in your name
Answers may vary.

Draw a picture to represent each ratio. See Solution Key.

16. 4 stars to 8 moons
17. $\frac{2 \text{ apples}}{6 \text{ bananas}}$
18. 3 big tiles : 7 small tiles
19. 3 shirts to 5 shorts

Name two pattern blocks with areas in the following ratio. See below.

20. 1 : 2
21. $\frac{6}{1}$
22. 2 to 3
23. $\frac{3}{1}$

24. **Writing** In Anna's class, 12 out of 16 students received a grade of B or better. Anna said that 1 out of 4 received less than a B. Is she correct? Explain your reasoning.
Yes. See Solution Key.
25. **Activity** Look in a newspaper and find two examples of ratios. You might try the sports pages or look in a supermarket ad. Answers may vary.

20. triangle to rhombus or trapezoid to hexagon 21. hexagon to triangle
22. rhombus to trapezoid 23. trapezoid to triangle or hexagon to rhombu

9-2

Connecting to Prior Knowledge

Have students list examples of ratios that they often see used around them. Ask students if the ratios always refer to the same type of unit, such as number of oranges to apples in a basket, or if the units vary. Discuss whether the speed limit on a street is a ratio of miles to hours. **(yes)**

THINK AND DISCUSS

The following steps explain the FLASHBACK.

$$\frac{3}{24} = \frac{3 \times 1}{3 \times 8} = \frac{3}{3} \times \frac{1}{8} = 1 \times \frac{1}{8} = \frac{1}{8}$$

Error Alert! Students may have trouble finding the simplest form of a ratio for problems such as Question 2. Students may give an equal ratio but not the simplest form. ***Remediation*** Encourage students not to stop trying to write a ratio in simplest form until they are sure there is no smaller equal ratio. Then have them check whether the denominator or numerator can be used to divide both terms, which is a step that is often overlooked.

TACTILE LEARNERS For Question 3, supply students with fraction bars. Direct students to find fractions with equal ratios.

Example

- *Why are both terms in the ratio divided by 12 rather than some other number?*
  (In order to have a unit rate, the comparison must be to 1. For the denominator to be 1, you have to divide by 12.)

What's Ahead
- Finding equal ratios
- Finding unit rates

WHAT YOU'LL NEED

✓ Stopwatch 

9-2 Ratios and Rates

THINK AND DISCUSS

A ratio of 1 c of unpopped corn will pop to about 8 qt of popcorn. How much popcorn can you expect from 3 c of unpopped corn?

Model the problem by showing 1 c of unpopped corn for 8 qt of popped corn.

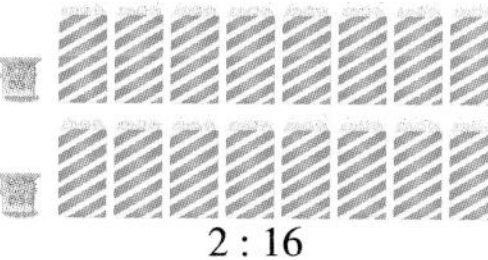

There is 1 c of unpopped corn for every 8 qt of popped corn. You can expect about 16 qt of popcorn from 2 c of unpopped corn.

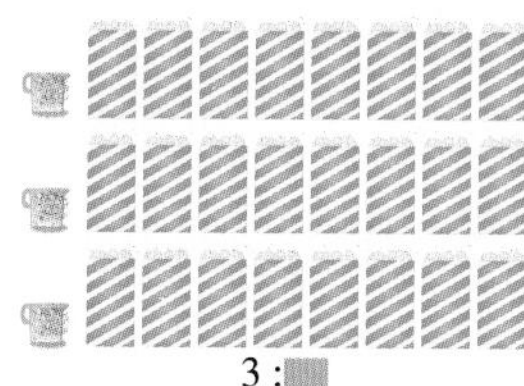

For every 3 c of unpopped corn you would expect about ■ of popcorn.
24 qt

FLASHBACK
Multiplying or dividing the numerator and the denominator of a fraction by the same number is the same as multiplying or dividing by 1.

The ratios 1 : 8, 2 : 16, and 3 : 24 are **equal ratios** since they are names for the same number. You can find equal ratios by multiplying or dividing each term in a ratio by the same nonzero number.

$$\frac{1}{8} \underset{\times 2}{\overset{\times 2}{=}} \frac{2}{16} \qquad \frac{3}{24} \underset{\div 3}{\overset{\div 3}{=}} \frac{1}{8}$$

1. Use multiplication and division to write two equal ratios.

Answers may vary. Samples given.

a. 6 : 8 — 3 : 4, 12 : 16
b. 10 to 35 — 2 to 7, 20 to 70
c. $\frac{21}{42}$ — $\frac{1}{2}$, $\frac{42}{84}$
d. 12 : 18 — 2 : 3, 24 : 36

> "First say to yourself what you would be; and then do what you have to do."
> —EPICTETUS

Organizer

1. **Focus**
   Connecting to Prior Knowledge
2. **Teach**
   Think and Discuss
   Work Together
3. **Closure**
   Try These
   Wrap Up

Vocabulary/Symbols
equal ratios
rate
unit rate

Skills Reviewed in Context of Lesson
- finding equivalent fractions

Materials and Manipulatives
- stopwatch (one per group)

Student Resources
Extra Practice
Student Study Guide
Practice, TR Ch. 9, p. 26
Student Study Guide, Spanish Resources, TR

Teacher Resources
Teaching Transparency 79
Lesson Planner, TR Ch. 9, p. 3

continues next page

- *What instrument in a car calculates a unit rate?* **(The speedometer gives the speed of the car in miles per hour.)**

Additional Example

On Saturday Leslie bicycled 45 mi in 5 h. Find the unit rate in miles per hour.

$$\frac{\text{miles}}{\text{hour}} \rightarrow \frac{45}{5}$$

$$\frac{45 \div 5}{5 \div 5} = \frac{9}{1}$$

The unit rate is 9 mi/h.

WORK TOGETHER

Separate pairs so that they do not distract each other while they are doing the timing.

- *Do you think there is a difference between your printing and your writing rates? How could you find out?* **(Time each other when printing the alphabet and then again when writing the alphabet. Calculate the unit rate for both.)**

DIVERSITY Some students experience difficulty with writing and may not wish to be timed in Question 4a. Other students may have handicaps that prevent them from writing with a pencil, and they must use a keyboard. Provide alternatives such as pointing to, touching, or saying the letters, matched appropriately to student skills.

Ongoing Assessment

Have the same pairs of students compare their writing times for one minute. Then have them compare their times in letters per second. Have students check to see that each other's rates are correct.

Organizer, continued

Prentice Hall Technology

Multimedia Math

- Hot Page™ 9-2
- Math Tools, Fraction Strips
- Math Investigations, Hazard City Messengers
- Math Investigations, Crisis in Hydrotown

Computer Item Generator

- 9-2

Fact of the Day

Forensic graphology is the science of handwriting analysis. Using this science, it is possible to determine whether a certain person wrote or signed a document.

—*Academic American Encyclopedia*

PH Multimedia Math Hot Page™ 9-2

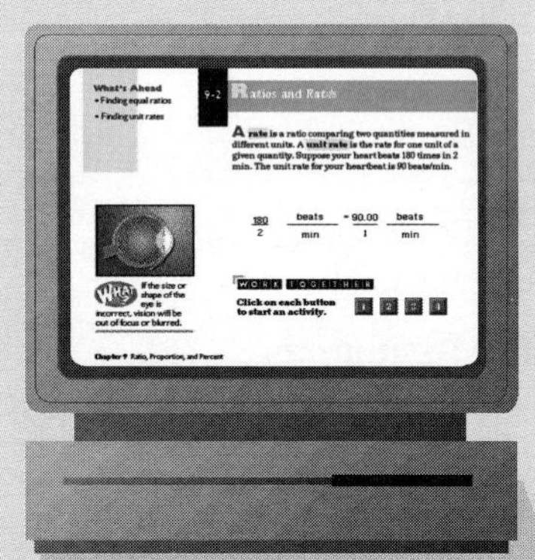

Michael Jordan, wore a new pair of sneakers for each game. After each game he signed the sneakers and donated them to charity. Even in one game the shoes got a workout. On average Michael ran 4.5 mi/game.

Source: *3-2-1 Contact*

We commonly write ratios in simplest form.

2. a. Write the fraction $\frac{25}{75}$ in simplest form. $\frac{1}{3}$
   b. How would you write the ratio $\frac{50}{150}$ in simplest form? $\frac{1}{3}$
3. **Discussion** Do equal ratios have the same simplest form? Support your answer using an example. See Solution Key.

We call a ratio that compares two items with different units a **rate.** For example, $\frac{46 \text{ mi}}{2 \text{ h}}$ compares miles traveled to hours of travel. A **unit rate** compares a quantity to a unit of one.

Example A car traveled 300 mi on 12 gal of gas. Find the unit rate in miles per gallon (mi/gal).

- $\frac{\text{miles}}{\text{gallons}} \rightarrow \frac{300}{12}$ Write the comparison as a ratio.
- $\frac{300 \div 12}{12 \div 12} = \frac{25}{1}$ Divide the numerator and the denominator by the GCF, 12.

The unit rate is $\frac{25 \text{ mi}}{1 \text{ gal}}$, or 25 mi/gal. You read this unit rate as "25 miles per gallon."

LOOK BACK How could you use a model to find the unit rate?

WORK TOGETHER

- Have a partner time you for 10 s as you print the uppercase letters of the alphabet in order from A to Z.
- Switch roles and time your partner. Count the number of letters each partner printed. 4. See Solution Key.

4. a. Find your printing rates. Compare the number of letters each printed to the time allowed.
   b. How can you use multiplication to find each unit rate for one minute? Show your work.
5. Tashia's writing rate is $\frac{24 \text{ letters}}{15 \text{ s}}$. Carol's rate is $\frac{18 \text{ letters}}{10 \text{ s}}$. Who has the faster writing rate? Carol

TRY THESE

Exercises 6–14: Have students check their answers to catch careless errors. One way to do this is to divide with the calculator. Each equal ratio will result in the same decimal answer.

Wrap Up

What's the Big Idea?

Ask students to explain how to find equal ratios and how to find unit rates.

Reteaching Activity

Group students with partners and provide each pair with two different types of blocks. Call out a ratio and have students use the blocks to model a different but equal ratio. Have each pair of students compare ratios to make sure they are equal. Continue with more difficult ratios.

Connections

Have a discussion about how rates are used. You may want to start with these examples:

- **Transportation** (gas efficiency, frequency of repair work, shipping rates)
- **Sports** (clocking a pitcher's fastball, comparing the speeds of players, determining a player's points per game)

Journal

Ask students to think of a rate they use in their daily lives. Possibilities include an estimation of walking speed, or hours spent studying daily compared to study hours in a week. Ask students to write about ratios or rates and to say which form of a ratio they prefer to read and write.

ON YOUR OWN

CRITICAL THINKING For Exercise 25, have students draw a model to represent one pizza. Then, ask students to show the fractional part of the pizza that each person ate.

TRY THESE

See Solution Key.

Write three equal ratios for each given ratio.

6. 6 : 18 2 : 6; 3 : 9; 1 : 3

7. $\frac{4}{24}$ $\frac{2}{12}, \frac{1}{6}, \frac{8}{48}$

8. 8 to 10 4 to 5; 16 to 20; 32 to 40

9. 30 : 40 3 : 4; 15 : 20; 6 : 8

10. **Sports** The team won 8 games out of 12 games played. Write the ratio of games won to games played in simplest form. $\frac{2}{3}$

Find the unit rate for each situation.

11. \$19.50 for 3 shirts $6.50/shirt

12. 300 mi in 12 h 25 mi/h

13. read 66 pages in 2 h 33 pages/h

14. type 110 words in 5 min 22 words/min

A woodpecker can pound its beak against wood at a rate of 20 pecks/s.

ON YOUR OWN

Write three equal ratios. 15.–18. Samples given.

15. $\frac{50}{100}$ 15. $\frac{1}{2}, \frac{5}{10}, \frac{100}{200}$

16. 9 to 81 16. 1 to 9, 3 to 27, 18 to 162

17. 8 : 14 17. 4 : 7, 16 : 28, 24 : 42

18. $\frac{14}{42}$ 18. $\frac{1}{3}, \frac{2}{6}, \frac{28}{84}$

Find the value that makes the ratios equal.

19. $\frac{5}{10}, \frac{■}{20}$ 10

20. 25 : 75, 1 : ■ 3

21. 6 to 9, ■ to 3 2

22. $\frac{8}{■}, \frac{2}{20}$ 80

23. 7 : ■, 14 : 42 21

24. $\frac{■}{15}, \frac{25}{75}$ 5

25. **Critical Thinking** Carlos tells you he ate $\frac{1}{3}$ of a pizza. Raylene says she ate $\frac{9}{27}$, and Maggie says she ate $\frac{2}{6}$. Which of these forms do you find easier to use? Explain your answer. See Solution Key.

Write each ratio in simplest form.

26. squares : circles $\frac{2}{5}$

27. squares : triangles $\frac{2}{3}$

28. triangles : squares $\frac{3}{2}$

29. hexagons : circles 0

Write the unit rate for each situation.

30. 16 mi in 4 h 4 mi/h

31. 175 mi in 7 da 25 mi/da

32. \$24 for 8 toys $3/toy

33. 10 pears for 5 children 2 pears/child

34. 36 balloons for 3 bunches 12 balloons/bunch

35. 144 players on 12 teams 12 players/team

Assignment Options

Core: 15–21, 26–33, 37, 39, MR all	
Reinforce: 22–25, 34–36, 38, 41	**Enrich:** 40, 42

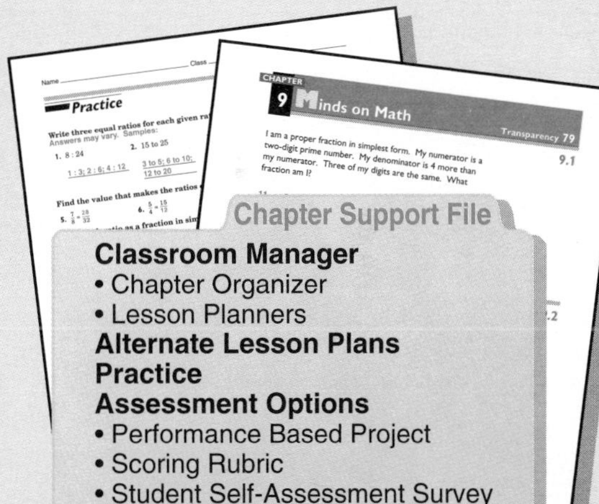

Minds on Math available in Teaching Transparencies

CONNECTION TO GEOMETRY Exercises 26–29 review geometry by having students use ratios to compare geometric figures.

CRITICAL THINKING In Exercise 40, have students show all work for their answer. Suggest that students use blocks or draw diagrams to help them.

WRITING For Exercise 42, challenge students to think of as many comparisons as they can. Then ask them to find what is alike and what is different in these areas: the written form, what is expressed, how it is useful.

Math Minutes

Ask each student to write <, >, or = to form a true statement.

$\frac{3}{4} \times 4$ ■ $\frac{3}{7} \times 7$ =

$3 - \frac{3}{4}$ ■ $3 \times \frac{3}{4}$ =

$\frac{1}{3} \times \frac{1}{3}$ ■ $\frac{1}{3}$ <

$\frac{7}{5} \times \frac{4}{3}$ ■ $\frac{5}{7} \times \frac{3}{4}$ >

Did you know you can use the digits 1 to 9 to write the ratio 4 : 5?
9876 : 12345 = 4 : 5

Source: *Curious and Interesting Numbers*

36.a. La Crystal's $4.50/lesson, Bill's $5/lesson
b. Bill, $.50 more per lesson

36. La Crystal is taking swimming lessons. She will pay $126 for 28 lessons. Bill will pay $30 for 6 lessons.

a. Write a unit rate for La Crystal's and for Bill's lesson.

b. Who is paying more per lesson? How much more?

Sign On the Dotted Line

Do you have an autograph of your favorite celebrity? Well, if you do, hold on to it. Someday it might be worth something.

Autographs of stars from the past are sometimes worth big money. Clark Gable's autograph is worth $100. Lucille Ball's is worth $75. President Harry Truman's is worth $40 and Hillary Clinton's is worth $100.

The signature of Button Gwinnett, a signer of the Declaration of Independence, recently sold for $100,000. Only 40 of his signatures are still around.

Use the article above. Write each ratio in simplest form.

37. the price of President Truman's autograph compared to Clark Gable's $\frac{2}{5}$

38. the price of Lucille Ball's autograph compared to Button Gwinnett's $\frac{3}{4000}$

39. the price of Lucille Ball's autograph compared to Hillary Clinton's $\frac{3}{4}$

40. **Critical Thinking** The ratio of water to land in Earth's southern hemisphere is 4 : 1. The ratio in the northern hemisphere is 3 : 2. Estimate Earth's ratio of water to land. 7 : 3

41. **Data File 9 (pp. 360–361)** Write each of Derek Turnbull's 1992 records as a rate. Compare distance to time.

42. **Writing** Explain how ratios and rates are similar and how they are different. Give an example of each.

41–42. See Solution Key.

Mixed REVIEW

Find each answer.

1. $\frac{2}{3} \times \frac{3}{5}$ $\frac{2}{5}$ **2.** $9\frac{1}{2} \times \frac{3}{8}$ $3\frac{9}{16}$

3. There are 24 students in Mr. Alvarez's class. Twelve students have brown eyes and four have blue eyes.

a. Find the ratio of brown-eyed students to blue-eyed students. 3 : 1

b. Write a ratio comparing the number of blue-eyed students to all students. 1 : 6

4. You have 5 coins with a total value $.75. Two of the coins are quarters. What are the other coins?

2 dimes, 1 nickel

9-3

Connecting to Prior Knowledge

Have students name ratios that are equal to the ratio $\frac{1}{2}$ and write a list of these ratios. Then ask students to discuss what math symbol could be used between any two ratios on the list. **(=)**

WORK TOGETHER

Question 1: Have students describe their results. Encourage the pairs of students to share their observations.

TECHNOLOGY OPTION After Question 1, have students write six ratios that are equal to $\frac{2}{3}$. Have students form proportions using all possible pairs of ratios. Have students compute the cross products of each proportion using a spreadsheet. Ask students to report the results.

ESL Write the word "proportion" on the board. Cover up the "pro" at the beginning of the word. Tell students that the word "portion" can mean amount. Tell students that in a proportion the two amounts are equal.

THINK AND DISCUSS

Question 4: Ask students: *Why do you think 3 × 12 and 4 × 9 are called cross products?* **(The numbers you are multiplying to find each product can be joined by crossed lines across the equal sign.)**

ESL AUDITORY LEARNERS Have auditory learners say aloud the numbers in the cross products (for example, if 2 is to 7 as 4 is to 14, then 2 times 14 should be equal to 7 times 4). Students may benefit from whispering the equations to themselves as they write them down.

What's Ahead

- Recognizing proportions
- Solving proportions

9-3 Solving Proportions

WORK TOGETHER

A **proportion** is an equation stating that two ratios are equal. For example 1 : 2 and 4 : 8 are equal. They form the proportion $\frac{1}{2} = \frac{4}{8}$.

Work with a partner to explore the proportions below. Use a calculator and any operations on the numerators and denominators. Describe as many relationships as you can.

$$\frac{180}{42} = \frac{30}{7} \qquad \frac{7}{8} = \frac{21}{24} \qquad \frac{16}{30} = \frac{8}{15}$$

1. a. Is each statement above true? How do you know?
   b. Follow these steps for each statement. Multiply the red numbers. Then multiply the blue numbers.
   c. What do you notice about the products? They are equal.

1a. Yes. See Solution Key.
b. 1260, 168, 240; 1260, 168, 240

$\frac{1}{4}$ $\frac{3}{4}$

WHO? Fra Filippo Lippi (1406–1469) was the first to draw babies using the correct proportions. Earlier artists drew babies with their heads $\frac{1}{6}$ as long as their bodies. While $\frac{1}{6}$ is correct for an adult, a baby's head is $\frac{1}{4}$ the length of its body.

Source: *The Macmillan Illustrated Almanac For Kids*

THINK AND DISCUSS

2. a. Look at the proportion $\frac{3}{4} = \frac{6}{8}$. Describe a way to tell if the proportion is true.
   b. Look at the proportion $\frac{12}{20} = \frac{21}{35}$. Describe a way to tell if the proportion is true.
   c. For which proportion above did you find it easier to show equality? Explain your reasoning.
3. a. Examine the ratios $\frac{1}{3}$ and $\frac{4}{5}$. Multiply the red numbers. Multiply the blue numbers. What do you notice?
   b. Do the ratios form a proportion? Why or why not?

True. Sample answer: $\frac{3}{4} \times \frac{2}{2} = \frac{6}{8}$
True. Sample answer: $12 \times 35 = 20 \times 21$
See Solution Key.
They are not equal.
No. Sample answer: $\frac{1}{3} = \frac{5}{15}$ and $\frac{4}{5} = \frac{12}{15}$

You can use *cross products* to tell if two ratios form a proportion. The cross products of a proportion are *always* equal.

4. The cross products of the proportion $\frac{3}{4} = \frac{9}{12}$ are 3 × ■ and 4 × ■. 12 9

> *"Fear of the future is a waste of the present."*
> —ANONYMOUS

Organizer

1. **Focus**
   Connecting to Prior Knowledge
2. **Teach**
   Work Together
   Think and Discuss
3. **Closure**
   Try These
   Wrap Up

Vocabulary/Symbols
proportion
cross products

Skills Reviewed in Context of Lesson
- simplifying fractions

Student Resources
Extra Practice
Student Study Guide
Practice, TR Ch. 9, p. 27
Student Study Guide, Spanish Resources, TR
Alternate Lesson, TR Ch. 9, pp. 13–16
Checkpoint, TR Ch. 9, p. 40

Teacher Resources
Teaching Transparency 79
Lesson Planner, TR Ch. 9, p. 4

Prentice Hall Technology
Computer Item Generator
- 9-3

Example 1
Show students that the cross products are the same if the order of the ratios is reversed.

Example 2

- *Why are both sides of the equation divided by 24 in the fourth step?* **(to isolate and solve for *n*)**

Additional Example *Find the value of n in* $\frac{14}{26} = \frac{21}{n}$.

$14n = 546$

$n = 39$

Additional Example *It takes Jake 3 hours to drive from Ashland to Lincoln, a distance of 165 miles. At this rate, how many hours will it take to drive an additional 110 miles?* **(It will take 2 hours to drive 110 miles at the current rate.)**

Error Alert! Students may have difficulty setting up the proportions correctly for a problem such as Example 3. ***Remediation*** Have students start the problem by first describing what is being compared. Then they construct a labeled proportion before beginning their solutions.

Ongoing Assessment Group students in pairs. Have each student describe to his or her partner how to find out if two ratios form a proportion and how to find a missing term in a proportion. The other partner takes notes. Have students exchange roles, and then compare and evaluate their notes.

TRY THESE

Exercises 10–13: Ask students to justify the approach they use to solve for *y*.

MENTAL MATH For Exercises 12 and 13, suggest that students first try to simplify the ratios in the proportion.

Fact of the Day

Penguins comprise about 65 percent of the total number of seabirds in the Antarctic.

—OCEAN WORLD ENCYCLOPEDIA

Example 1 Do the ratios $\frac{4}{10}$ and $\frac{20}{50}$ form a proportion?

$\frac{4}{10} \stackrel{?}{=} \frac{20}{50}$ Circle the cross products.

$4 \times 50 \stackrel{?}{=} 10 \times 20$ Write the cross products.

$200 = 200$ Simplify.

Yes, the ratios form a proportion.

You can use cross products to help you find the missing term in a proportion.

Example 2 Find the value of n in $\frac{n}{312} = \frac{5}{24}$.

$\frac{n}{312} = \frac{5}{24}$ Circle the cross products.

$n \times 24 = 312 \times 5$ Write the cross products.

$24n = 1{,}560$ Simplify.

$\frac{24n}{24} = \frac{1{,}560}{24}$ Divide both sides by 24.

$n = 65$

You can also multiply or divide by a fraction equal to 1 to find a missing term in a proportion.

5. Use division by 1 to find the value of y in $\frac{9}{39} = \frac{3}{y}$. 13

WHAT? The familiar eraser on the end of a pencil wasn't introduced until about 1860. Some teachers objected because they felt that students would make more errors if they were easy to correct.

Proportions can help you solve problems involving rates.

Example 3 Pencils at the school store are 2 for \$.15. Find the cost of buying 21 pencils.

$\frac{\text{pencils}}{\$} \rightarrow \frac{2}{0.15} = \frac{21}{c}$ Let c represent the cost.

$2 \times c = 0.15 \times 21$ Write the cross products.

.15 [×] 21 [÷] 2 [=] 1.575 Use a calculator to solve.

$c = 1.575$

Round to the next cent. The pencils cost \$1.58.

LOOK BACK How could you use a pattern to find the cost of the pencils?

Wrap Up

What's the Big Idea? Ask students to explain how to recognize and solve proportions.

Reteaching Activity Ask students to use these numbers to write as many proportions as they can: 2, 3, 4, 6, 8, 12. Then have them exchange their work with a partner to check each proportion by cross multiplication. After students correct their original proportions, ask them to write three on a page, omitting one term from each proportion. Again, have students exchange papers and find the missing term.

Connections Have a discussion about how proportions are used. You may want to start with these examples:

- **Photography** (making enlargements or reductions, cropping pictures to fit a similarly shaped but smaller frame)
- **Architecture** (making building models, using floor plans or landscaping plans)
- **Science** (mixing larger or smaller quantities of the same strength of acid or base or of the same molecular formulation)

Journal Ask students to think of ways they could use proportions to support an argument. Give students the following example: *You want to convince your parents that you are studying as much as you can, which is three hours a day. Would it be better to compare the number of study hours to waking hours in a day, or the number of weekly study hours to the number of hours in a week? Why?*

ON YOUR OWN

WRITING For Exercise 25, make sure students' definitions are consistent with their problems and solutions.

TRY THESE

Choose Use a calculator, paper and pencil, or mental math. Determine whether each pair of ratios forms a proportion.

6. $\frac{3}{9}, \frac{6}{18}$ yes 7. $\frac{9}{10}, \frac{18}{30}$ no 8. $\frac{1}{2}, \frac{50}{100}$ yes 9. $\frac{10}{20}, \frac{30}{40}$ no

Mental Math Find the value of y.

10. $\frac{48}{y} = \frac{4}{7}$ 84 11. $\frac{9}{32} = \frac{y}{48}$ 13.5 12. $\frac{4}{18} = \frac{6}{y}$ 27 13. $\frac{y}{55} = \frac{18}{22}$ 45

14. A certain flavor of frozen yogurt contains 65 calories for 2 oz. How many calories are in 10 oz of the frozen yogurt? 325 calories

ON YOUR OWN

Choose Use a calculator, paper and pencil, or mental math. Determine whether the pairs of ratios form a proportion.

15. $\frac{33}{39}, \frac{55}{65}$ yes 16. $\frac{4}{12}, \frac{6}{8}$ no 17. $\frac{42}{6}, \frac{504}{72}$ yes 18. $\frac{9}{11}, \frac{63}{77}$ yes

Find the value of the variable.

19. $\frac{2}{9} = \frac{25}{x}$ 112.5 20. $\frac{93}{60} = \frac{m}{40}$ 62 21. $\frac{18}{n} = \frac{6}{3}$ 9 22. $\frac{k}{17} = \frac{20}{34}$ 10

23. Use the digits 2, 5, 6, and 15. Write as many proportions as possible. Answers may vary. Sample answer: $\frac{2}{6} = \frac{5}{15}$

24. Marva gets paid \$7.00 for 2 h of babysitting. Saturday she babysat for the Fields. They paid her \$17.50. How long did she babysit? 5 h

25. **Writing** In your own words, define *proportion*. Write and solve a problem that uses proportions. See Solution Key.

26. **Calculator** A piano has 88 keys. The ratio of white keys to black keys is 52 to 36. A piano maker has 676 white keys. 468
    a. How many black keys does the piano maker need to have the correct ratio of white keys to black keys?
    b. How many pianos can be built? Explain how you got your answer.
    There are enough white keys for 13 pianos since $676 \div 52 = 13$.

Mixed REVIEW

Find the GCF.

1. 18, 27 9 2. 52, 78 26
3. 84, 28 28

Write two equal ratios.

4. 14 : 35 5. $\frac{6}{8}$ $\frac{3}{4}, \frac{12}{16}$
6. 8 to 20 2 to 5, 16 to 40

7. Julio, Stella, and Ted ate tuna, roast beef, or chicken for lunch. Ted didn't have roast beef or chicken. Stella didn't have roast beef. What did each person have?

Julio: roast beef, Stella: chicken, Ted: tuna

4. 28 : 70, 42 : 105

The first piano was built in 1720. The largest piano ever built weighs $1\frac{1}{3}$ T or about 2,700 lb.

Assignment Options

Core: 15–22, 25, 28, 30, MR all, CH all	
Reinforce: 23, 24, 29	**Enrich:** 26, 27

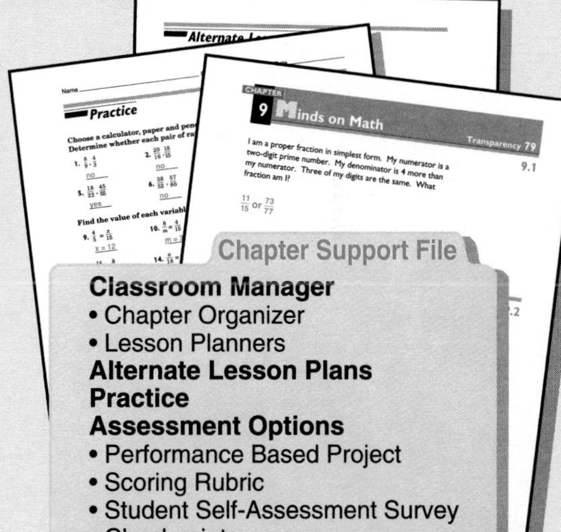

Chapter Support File

Classroom Manager
- Chapter Organizer
- Lesson Planners

Alternate Lesson Plans
Practice
Assessment Options
- Performance Based Project
- Scoring Rubric
- Student Self-Assessment Survey
- Checkpoints
- Chapter Assessments
- Cumulative Review

Minds on Math available in Teaching Transparencies

CALCULATOR Have students write a proportion for Exercise 26. Then have students use a calculator to solve the proportion.

Exercise 27: If students do not analyze their answers, they may suggest that a fraction of a coach is needed.

CHAPTER INVESTIGATION The data for Exercise 30 are available in encyclopedias and official sports rule books.

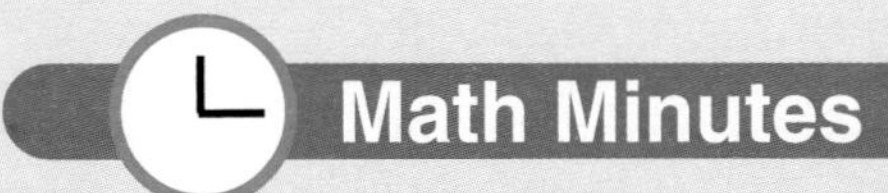

Exercise 1 is an enhanced multiple choice question.

CONNECTION TO SCIENCE Exercise 16 has students apply their knowledge of proportions to evaluate scientific data.

Math Minutes

Jeff went to the store with $25.00. If he spent $10.00, what fraction of his money does he have left? $\frac{3}{5}$

27. Sports Youth soccer teams in Hopkinton have 22 players and 3 coaches. On sign-up day, 196 students show up to play. How many coaches are needed? 27 coaches

28. At the Habra's cookout the guests ate 3 hamburgers for every 2 hot dogs. They ate 18 hamburgers. How many hot dogs did they eat? 12 hot dogs

29. Data File 5 (pp. 182–183) Suppose the alarm goes off in 220 households. About how many of these people get up? about 112 people

FLASHBACK
$C = \pi d$
$\pi \approx 3.14$

30. Investigation (p. 362) Find the diameter of a basketball. Research the size of at least three other game balls used in sports. Write ratios comparing the diameters. See Solution Key.

CHECKPOINT

1. **Choose A, B, C, or D.** Lavalle's bookstore sold 24 paperbacks, 6 hardcovers, 38 magazines, and 5 calendars. What was the ratio of magazines sold to paperbacks sold? C

   A. 24 : 38 **B.** 19 to 31 **C.** $\frac{19}{12}$ **D.** 12 : 24

Write two equal ratios for each. Sample answers given.

2. $\frac{10}{15}$ $\frac{2}{3}, \frac{20}{30}$
3. 20 to 34 10 to 17, 40 to 68
4. 18 : 40 9 : 20, 36 : 80
5. $\frac{23}{44}$ $\frac{46}{88}, \frac{69}{132}$

Write each ratio in simplest form.

6. $\frac{28}{38}$ $\frac{14}{19}$
7. 22 : 60 11 : 30
8. $\frac{18}{54}$ $\frac{1}{3}$
9. 90 : 190 9 : 19

Find each unit rate.

10. You can buy 3 tacos for $2.67. $.89/taco

11. A package of 6 batteries costs $2.10. $.35/battery

The largest iceberg ever found was 208 mi long and 60 mi wide. **How does that compare to the size of your state?**

Source: *3-2-1 Contact*

Determine whether the pairs of ratios form a proportion.

12. $\frac{8}{9}, \frac{64}{88}$ no
13. $\frac{2}{3}, \frac{28}{42}$ yes
14. $\frac{7}{12}, \frac{9}{16}$ no
15. $\frac{23}{30}, \frac{6}{8}$ no

16. Science A glacier moves about 12 in. every 8 h. About how far will a glacier move in 72 h? 108 in.

9-4

Connecting to Prior Knowledge

Ask students if they have ever made a reasonable guess that turned out to be correct. Help them describe the thinking that went into their guesses.

KINESTHETIC LEARNERS For Questions 1–5, distribute centimeter rulers and 184 cm of string to groups of students. Encourage students to guess the numbers of bracelets and rings. Then have students measure and check the accuracy of their guesses.

Error Alert! Students may use the guess and test strategy and correctly solve the problem yet still answer incorrectly. For example, for the textbook problem students may confuse the number of rings with the number of bracelets. ***Remediation*** Encourage students to be as disciplined in using this strategy as they are when using any other strategy. Point out to students that labeling their work is always helpful in avoiding careless errors. Explain to students that guessing and testing are not the same as making a lucky guess.

VISUAL LEARNERS Have students study the table for patterns in answers resulting from the different guesses.

Ongoing Assessment Challenge students to copy the original problem about the bracelets and rings on their own paper and to label the data given them in the problem. Then have students answer Questions 1–2. Students should find that the answers for the questions are already labeled correctly.

Additional Problem *The product of three consecutive whole numbers is 1,320. What are the numbers?* **(Students may want to begin by thinking of three identical numbers whose product is near 1,320; for example $10 \times 10 \times 10 = 1,000$. The three consecutive whole numbers are 10, 11, and 12.)**

What's Ahead

- Solving problems by using guess and test

PROBLEM SOLVING

9-4 Guess and Test

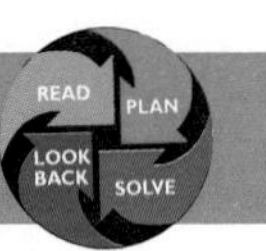

A good problem solving strategy is *Guess and Test.* First make a reasonable guess and then test it against the information you are given in the problem. If your guess is incorrect, keep trying until you find the correct answer.

> Handmade friendship bracelets use 20 cm of thread. Handmade rings use 8 cm of thread. Marny used a total of 184 cm of thread to make 14 items. **How many friendship bracelets did she make?**

READ Read and understand the given information. Summarize the problem.

Think about the information you are given and what you are asked to find.

1. a. How much thread is needed to make a friendship bracelet? a ring? **20 cm; 8 cm**
   b. How much thread did Marny use in all? **184 cm**
   c. How many items did Marny make? **14 items**
2. What does the problem ask you to find? **How many bracelets did she make?**

PLAN Decide on a strategy to solve the problem.

Guess and Test is a good strategy to use.

3. Suppose you guess that Marny made 4 bracelets.
   a. **Discussion** Why does a guess of 4 bracelets imply that Marny made 10 rings?
   b. How many centimeters of thread are used to make 4 bracelets? 10 rings? Explain how you found each answer.
   c. Does a guess of 4 bracelets result in the correct answer? Why or why not?
   d. Would your next guess for the number of bracelets be higher or lower? Explain. **Higher. Explanations may vary. Sample: Bracelets use more thread than rings. You need to increase the total thread from 160 cm to 184 cm.**

3a. The problem says she made 14 items.
b. Bracelets: 4×20 cm = 80 cm; Rings: 10×8 cm = 80 cm
c. No. 80 cm for 4 bracelets plus 80 cm for 10 rings equals 160 cm. Marny used 184 cm.

> *(Failure is) only the opportunity to begin again, more intelligently.*
> —Henry Ford

Organizer

1. **Focus**
   Connecting to Prior Knowledge
2. **Teach**
3. **Closure**
   Try These
   Wrap Up

Skills Reviewed in Context of Lesson
- multiplying whole numbers

Student Resources
Extra Practice
Student Study Guide
Practice, TR Ch. 9, p. 28
Student Study Guide, Spanish Resources, TR

Teacher Resources
Teaching Transparency 80
Lesson Planner, TR Ch. 9, p. 5

Prentice Hall Technology
Multimedia Math
- Math Investigations, Mission: Mars

Computer Item Generator
- 9-4

TRY THESE

Exercise 6: Encourage students to place their guesses in a table to help them organize the information.

ESL **ESL** In Exercise 7, remind students to find the product and not the sum. Extend this problem by suggesting that students create a similar puzzle of their own.

Wrap Up

What's the Big Idea? Ask students to explain how to solve a problem using the guess and test strategy.

Reteaching Activity Ask the class to help you create a checklist or list of procedures for using the guess and test strategy. Write students' suggestions on the chalkboard. Ask students for possible revisions to make the steps easier to follow.

Connections Have a discussion about how the guess and test strategy may be used. You may want to start with these examples:

- **Shopping** (keeping a running total while shopping, estimating tax, choosing the better value)
- **Household** (estimating bill payments, deciding on serving sizes for meals, organizing expenses)
- **Science** (making hypotheses that are then tested by experimentation)
- **Business** (ordering the number of items expected to sell in a certain amount of time, such as seasonal items or perishable goods)

Journal Have students write about ways they use the strategy of guess and test in their daily lives. Ask them to describe how a failed test helps to make the next guess a better one.

Fact of the Day

Edgar Allan Poe (1809–1849) is generally considered to be the originator of modern detective fiction.

—*Academic American Encyclopedia*

Assignment Options

Core: 9–10, 15–18, MR all	
Reinforce: 11–13, 19–23	**Enrich:** 14

SOLVE
Try out the strategy.

You can organize your guesses in a table like the one below.

Bracelets	Rings	Thread	High/Low
5 × 20 cm = 100 cm	9 × 8 cm = 72 cm	172 cm	low
8 × 20 cm = 160 cm	6 × 8 cm = 48 cm	208 cm	high
■	■	■	■

6 × 20 = 120 cm 8 × 8 cm = 64 cm 184 cm correct

4a. 6 or 7 bracelets
b. Explanations may vary. See Solution Key for sample.

4. A guess of 5 bracelets required too little thread and a guess of 8 bracelets required too much thread.
   a. What guesses would be reasonable to make next?
   b. Is one of the guesses more reasonable to make than the other? Explain.
   c. Copy and complete the table above to test your next guess. Keep guessing until you find the correct answer.
   d. How many friendship bracelets did Marny make? 6 bracelets

LOOK BACK
Think about how you solved this problem.

Make sure your answer checks against the information given in the problem.

5. Is the total number of bracelets and rings 14? Is the total amount of thread 184 cm? yes; yes

TRY THESE

Use guess and test to solve each problem.

6. One way parents in Fullerton raise money for the school is by conducting a raffle. Tickets for items are sold and then a drawing is held to determine the winner of the items. You can buy a ticket for a video game for $2 or a remote-control car for $3. On Saturday, $203 was raised by selling 80 raffle tickets. How many remote-control car tickets were sold? 43 car tickets

7. product = 96

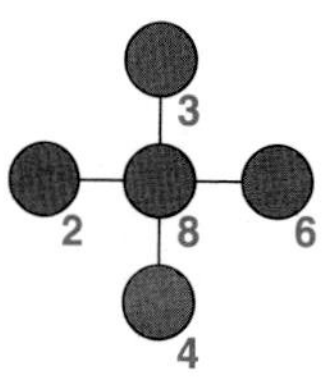

7. Place the digits 2, 3, 4, 6, and 8 in the circles at the left so that the product in both directions is the same. What is the product? Answers may vary. Sample given. See Solution Key.
8. Two numbers have a sum of 34 and a product of 285. What are the two numbers? 15 and 19

ON YOUR OWN

ESL In Exercise 11, some students may need help with the vocabulary. Read "mysteries, fantasies, and biographies" aloud and explain briefly what kind of book each word names.

CONNECTION TO SCIENCE Exercise 12 has students use a problem-solving strategy to evaluate meteorological data.

Exercise 13: Students may want to create similar puzzles for themselves.

CONNECTION TO PROPORTIONS Exercise 14 reviews proportions by having students solve for a missing term in a proportion.

CONNECTION TO PATTERNS Exercises 15–23 have students use a problem-solving strategy to solve patterns.

CONNECTION TO MEASUREMENT Exercise 14 also reviews measurement techniques by having students translate between two measurement units.

ESL In Exercises 15–23, make sure students understand the directions before they begin. For the sample 8 ↑ → = ■, draw the arrows on the pattern of numbers so the students have a physical model to follow.

ON YOUR OWN

Use any strategy to solve. Show your work.

9. Tickets for a movie cost \$4.00 for children and \$7.00 for adults. On Friday the theater collected \$720 by selling 120 tickets. How many adult tickets were sold?
80 adult tickets
10. The 182 sixth graders at the Fannie Mae Hammer Middle School are taking a trip to the museum. The entrance fee is \$1.75 per pupil and \$3.25 per adult. The bus fee is \$189 per bus. Each bus holds 44 people. What is the total cost for the students and 14 adults to visit the museum?
\$1309
11. Millie, Bob, and Fran are reading mysteries, fantasies, and biographies. The type of book each is reading does not begin with the same letter as their name. Fran is reading *The Case of the Missing Body.* Who is reading fantasies? Bob
12. Did you know that $\frac{1}{2}$ in. of rain is equal to 4 in. of snow? In April, 1921, 6 ft 4 in. of snow fell during a 24 h period, in Silver Lake, Colorado. How much rain would there have been if it hadn't been cold enough to snow? $9\frac{1}{2}$ in.
13. Place the digits 1 through 9 in the pattern at the right so that the sum is the same in both directions. What is the sum? Sums and placement of digits may vary. Sample given.

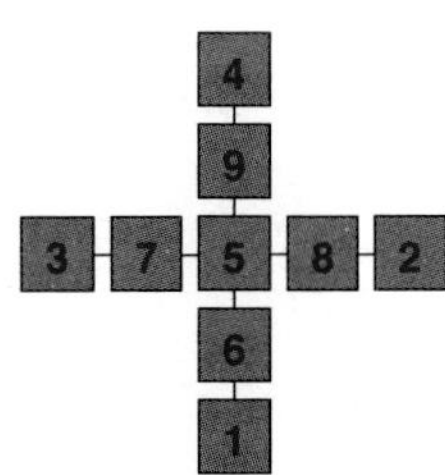

14. Making lemonade requires water and lemon juice in the ratio of 3 c water to 2 c lemon juice. You need a total of 10 gal for the fair. How many cups of lemon juice do you need? If you made 10 gal of lemonade for your class, how much would each person get? (*Hint:* 16 c = 1 gal)
64 cups lemon juice

Use the pattern at the right. Imagine the pattern continues forever.

Sample 8 ↑ → = ■ Find the number 8 in the pattern. The number above 8 is 13. The number to the right of 13 is 14. So 8 ↑ → = 14.

26	27	28	29	30	...
21	22	23	24	25	
16	17	18	19	20	
11	12	13	14	15	
6	7	8	9	10	
1	2	3	4	5	

15. 29 ↓ = ■ 24
16. 13 ← = ■ 12
17. 3 ↑ ↑ = ■ 13
18. 14 → ← = ■ 14
19. 23 ↓ ↓ → = ■ 14
20. 7 ↓ → = ■ 3
21. 18 ■ ■ = 22 ↑ ← or ← ↑
22. 2 → ↑ ← ↓ = ■ 2
23. 35 ↓ = ■ 30

Mixed REVIEW

Evaluate.

1. 5 (3 + 8) 55
2. 3 (14 − 5) 27

True or False?

3. $\frac{120}{144} = \frac{145}{75}$
4. $\frac{32}{80} = \frac{80}{200}$
5. $\frac{18}{3} = \frac{102}{17}$
6. $\frac{19}{55} = \frac{22}{71}$

7. Hank gets ready for school in 45 min. He can walk to school in 22 min. He needs to be at school by 8:05 A.M. What time should he get up?

6:58 A.M.
3. F 4. T 5. T 6. F

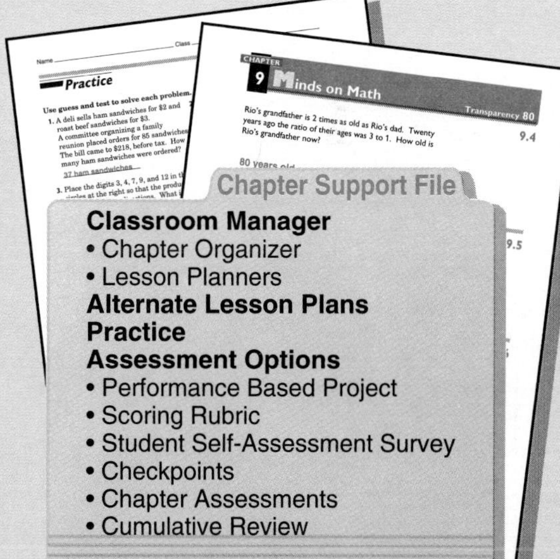

Minds on Math available in Teaching Transparencies

Math Minutes

If a certain number is squared and then multiplied by 3, the result is 48. What is the number? **4**

Materials for 9-5

- computer with geometry software *(optional)*
- protractor
- metric ruler

CHAPTER 9 PROBLEM SOLVING PRACTICE

This page provides a variety of problems that can be used to reinforce and enhance the students' problem solving skills. Encourage students to read each problem carefully. Then have them refer to the list of problem solving strategies to help them decide how to solve the problems.

Point out, however, that not all questions require a strategy for solving, nor are all the strategies in the list used on this page.

Exercise 5: Challenge students to create and exchange their own cryptarithms.

USING MANIPULATIVES Have students use a tangram to help them answer Exercise 6. Students can use different colored blocks for Exercise 8.

Answers to Problems Unique to Spanish Edition

5. Sample: 8936 + 7626 = 16562

S = 8, U = 9, M = 3, A = 6, P = 7, R = 2, G = 1, N = 5

Problem Solving Practice

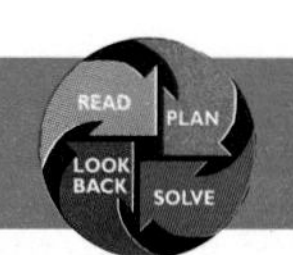

PROBLEM SOLVING STRATEGIES

Make a Table
Use Logical Reasoning
Solve a Simpler Problem
Too Much or Too Little Information
Look for a Pattern
Make a Model
Work Backward
Draw a Diagram
Guess and Test
Simulate a Problem
Use Multiple Strategies

Use any strategy to solve each problem. Show all your work.

1. The product of two consecutive pages in a book is 12,432. The sum is 223. What are the page numbers? 111, 112
2. The ratio of Peter's height to Rick's height is 5 : 3. The ratio of Rick's height to Sean's height is 1 : 3. What is the ratio of Peter's height to Sean's height? 5 : 9
3. At the sub shop Janet ate two slices of pizza and a small salad. She paid for her meal with a ten-dollar bill. Her change was \$5.11. What was the price of her meal? \$4.89
4. List the total number of triangles in the figure. 12

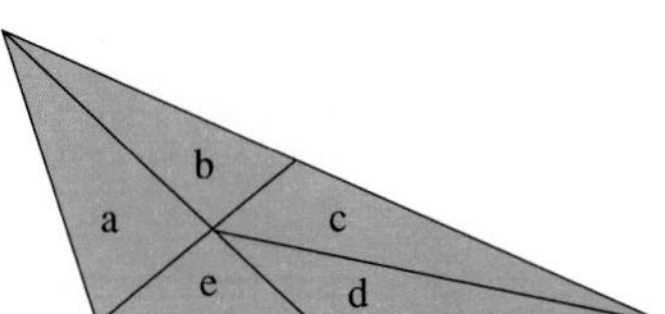

5. The following is *cryptarithm*, a puzzle where each letter represents a different digit. Find the value of each letter. (*Hint:* What is the only possible value for M?) M = 1, F = 9, A = 0

FUN + IS = MATH

Sample: 974 + 82 = 1056

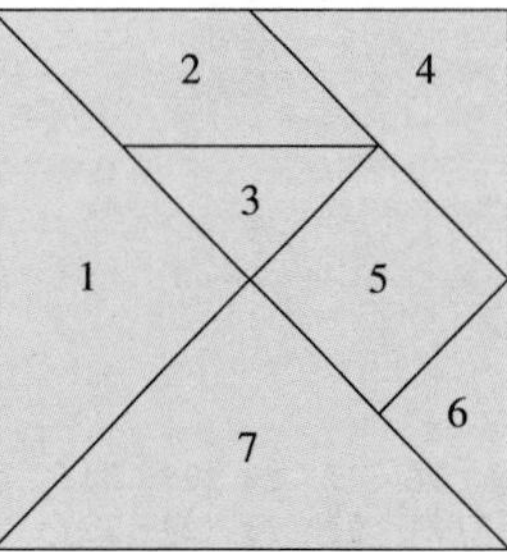

6. Examine the tangram on the left. Using any five pieces, make a rectangle. Is your answer unique? How could you tell? See Solution Key.
7. In a race, Jon was behind Marla, but ahead of Noel. Noel was behind Jon, but ahead of Dana. Order the students from fastest to slowest. Marla, Jon, Noel, Dana
8. Maxine saves quarters and dimes in a jar. Last night she counted \$6.75. The number of dimes is one more than the number of quarters. How many quarters are there? 19 quarters
9. The lengths of the sides of a rectangle are in the ratio of 1 : 3. The perimeter is 40 cm. Find the area. 75 cm^2

9-5

Connecting to Prior Knowledge

Ask students to recall the meaning of the terms *congruent* and *similar*. Have them give examples of similar figures in the classroom (for example: any two squares).

THINK AND DISCUSS

Question 1: Explain that all the figures are classified as triangles. They all have the same shape but are different sizes.

TACTILE LEARNERS Ask students to make a triangle from a sheet of typing paper in this way: *Using a corner, cut out a right triangle that has one leg half the length of the other leg. Trace the triangle samples on an overhead transparency, placing the right angles on top of one another.*

Ask students for their observations and conclusions about similar right triangles.

WRITING Question 6 helps students practice putting mathematical ideas into words. Accept statements that capture the idea of proportional sides, rather than insisting on formal mathematical definitions.

COMPUTER For Question 7, have the students do these things:

- *Create a small triangle.*
- *Use the scale or dilate feature to make a larger copy.*
- *Find the ratio of two sides on the small triangle.*
- *Find the ratio of the two corresponding sides on the large triangle.*
- *As you move a vertex to change the shape, notice that the two ratios remain equal.*

Alternate Approach For Question 7, have students who are not using a computer create similar triangles without directly using proportional sides. For example they can use a photocopier with an enlarge/reduce feature to create triangles similar to their originals. Another fast way to create similar triangles is to use one corner of a piece of typing paper. Draw lines parallel to the hypotenuse to create a series of similar triangles.

TECHNOLOGY

9-5 Investigating Similar Figures

What's Ahead

- Exploring ratios in corresponding parts of similar figures

WHAT YOU'LL NEED

✓ Computer 

✓ Geometry software 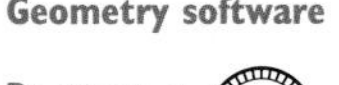

✓ Protractor 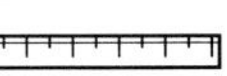

✓ Metric Ruler 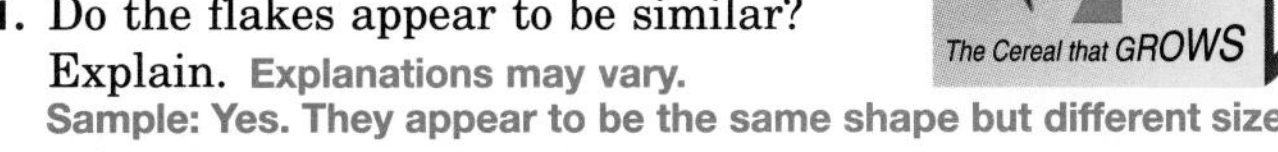

FLASHBACK

Similar figures have the same shape but they can be different sizes.

2.d. Sample answer: You might place one on top of the other, you might measure with a protractor.

4. Measurements may vary.

$AB \approx$ 1.3 cm $DE \approx$ 2.6 cm
$BC \approx$ 1.2 cm $EF \approx$ 2.4 cm
$AC \approx$ 0.7 cm $DF \approx$ 1.4 cm

THINK AND DISCUSS

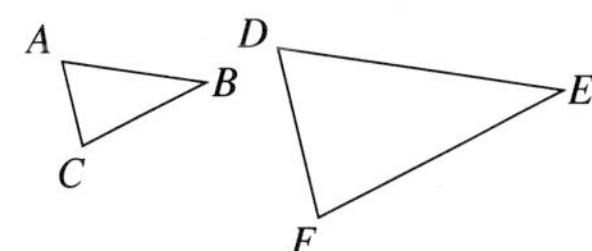

"It's soggy to eat, but fun to watch." That might be your reaction to a cereal that expands when you add milk. Look at the flakes pictured on the box of Tri-Flex.

1. Do the flakes appear to be similar? Explain. Explanations may vary. Sample: Yes. They appear to be the same shape but different sizes.

Imagine a bowl of Tri-Flex. The flakes grow as they soak up the milk. The figures show a flake before and after adding milk.

2. a. Do $\triangle ABC$ and $\triangle DEF$ appear to be similar? yes
   b. Which angle on $\triangle DEF$ used to be $\angle A$? $\angle D$
   c. What seems to be true about the sizes of the angles in $\triangle ABC$ and $\triangle DEF$? They appear to be the same.
   d. How can you compare the sizes of two angles? Describe at least two different methods.
   e. Use one of your methods to compare the measures of $\angle A$ and $\angle D$, $\angle B$ and $\angle E$, and $\angle C$ and $\angle F$. Each pair has the same measure.
3. Match the sides of $\triangle DEF$ with their original sides on $\triangle ABC$. We call matching parts of similar objects **corresponding parts.** Which side of $\triangle DEF$ corresponds to each?
   a. $\overline{AB}$ $\overline{DE}$ b. $\overline{BC}$ $\overline{EF}$ c. $\overline{AC}$ $\overline{DF}$
4. Measure the sides of $\triangle ABC$ and $\triangle DEF$.
5. The length of $\overline{AB}$, written AB, is the length from A to B. Compare the ratios.
   a. $\frac{AB}{DE}$ and $\frac{BC}{EF}$ equal b. $\frac{BC}{EF}$ and $\frac{AC}{DF}$ equal c. $\frac{AB}{DE}$ and $\frac{AC}{DF}$ equal

"Don't do what you'll have to find an excuse for."

—ANONYMOUS

Organizer

1. **Focus**
   Connecting to Prior Knowledge
2. **Teach**
   Think and Discuss
   Work Together
3. **Closure**
   Wrap Up

Vocabulary/Symbols
corresponding parts

Skills Reviewed in Context of Lesson
- using similar figures

Materials and Manipulatives
- computer *(optional)*
- geometric software *(optional)*
- protractor (one per student)
- metric ruler (one per student)

Student Resources
Extra Practice
Student Study Guide
Practice, TR Ch. 9, p. 29
Student Study Guide, Spanish Resources, TR
Alternate Lesson, TR Ch. 9, pp. 17–20

continues next page

WRITING For Question 7b, phrasing a general conjecture may be difficult for many students. Ask questions like: *What did you compare? What did you measure to get those ratios?*

Error Alert! Some students believe that two triangles that are rotated or reflected can not be congruent, or similar. The orientation of the triangles can confuse them. ***Remediation*** It may help to have the students rotate their triangles on the computer.

Ongoing Assessment Show two similar triangles, $\triangle XYZ$ and $\triangle ABC$, to students. Ask these questions to determine understanding of similarity:

- *Which angle in $\triangle XYZ$ corresponds to $\angle A$?* **($\angle X$)**
- *If $\angle C$ measures 30°, what is the measure of $\angle Z$? Explain.* **(30°; corresponding angles of similar triangles are congruent.)**
- *If AB is $\frac{1}{2}$ of AC, what is true of XY and XZ?* **(XY is $\frac{1}{2}$ of XZ.)**

Journal Ask students: *Write your own definition of similar as it applies to nonmathematical situations. How do your definition and the mathematical one compare?*

WORK TOGETHER

This activity extends the concept of proportional sides from similar triangles to similar quadrilaterals.

COMPUTER For Exercise 10, students need not find the ratio of every pair of sides. Three ratios should be enough to convince them that the sides are in proportion. ***Alternate Approach*** If a computer is not available, have the students use dot paper, squared paper, or protractors and plain paper to draw similar quadrilaterals. Then have each student or pair of students make a different shape quadrilateral. Compile results in a table on the board.

Organizer, continued

Teacher Resources

Teaching Transparencies 6, 80, 82
Transparency Masters, p. 3
Lesson Planner, TR Ch. 9, p. 6

Prentice Hall Technology

Multimedia Math
- Math Tools, Geometry

Computer Item Generator
- 9-5

Other Available Technology

Geometer's Sketchpad by Key Curriculum Press: Exercise 18 (*optional*)

Fact of the Day

In 1993, sales of ready-to-eat cereals in the United States totaled over $7,378,500,000.

—ADVERTISING AGE

6. a. Writing Summarize your results about the ratios that compare the lengths of the sides of $\triangle ABC$ and the lengths of the sides of $\triangle DEF$.

b. Discussion What does it mean to say the lengths of the sides of $\triangle ABC$ and the lengths of the sides of $\triangle DEF$ are in *proportion*?

7. a. Computer Use Geometry software to create other pairs of similar triangles and check whether the lengths of their sides are in proportion.

b. Writing Make a conjecture about the lengths of the sides of similar triangles.

6.–7. Answers may vary. See Solution Key.

WORK TOGETHER

Another cereal maker has come out with expanding flakes in the shape of quadrilaterals.

8. a. Find three pairs of flakes on the box of Fortify that appear similar. 1, 5; 2, 3; 6, 7

b. Find three pairs that do not appear to be similar. Sample answer: 1, 7; 3, 4; 5, 6

9. Look at the BEFORE and AFTER diagram of the Fortify flake shown below. Do quadrilaterals *HIJK* and *QRST* appear to be similar? Yes.

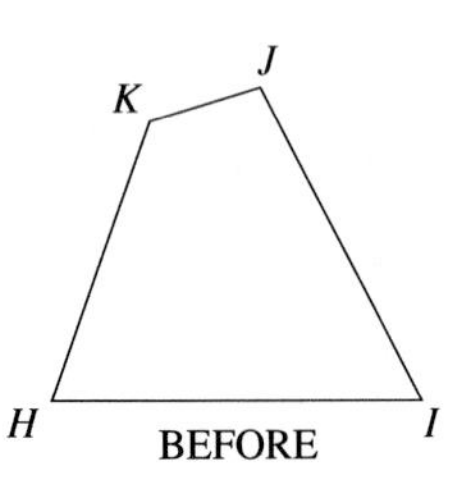

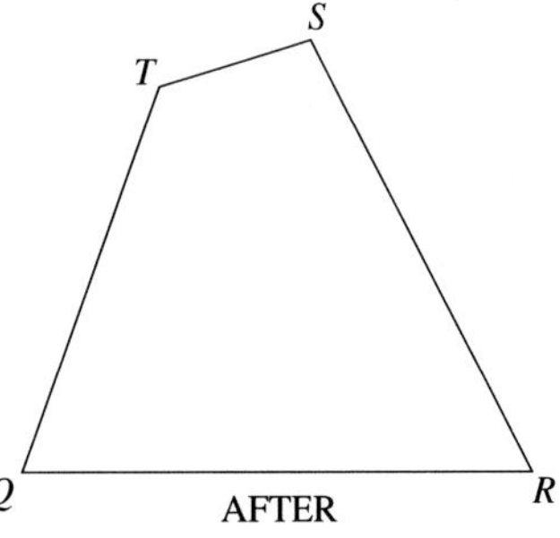

10. a. Measure to see if the sides of the two quadrilaterals are in proportion. They are in proportion.

b. Computer Use Geometry software to create other pairs of similar quadrilaterals. Check whether their sides are in proportion. Check students' work.

Wrap Up

What's the Big Idea? Ask students: *When the Tri-Flex flake ABC shown in the Think and Discuss problem grows, do all the sides increase by the same number of centimeters? Why does the flake keep its shape as it grows?*

Connections Have a discussion about using similar figures. You may wish to start with these examples:

- **City Planning** (a triangular park and the sidewalk around it)
- **Photography** (enlarging and reducing negatives)
- **Art** (scaling)

Reteaching Activity Have students work with rods or strips of paper. Use these steps to show that figures with proportional sides have the same shape.

- Make a triangle with sides of lengths 2, 3, and 4.
- Double (or triple) the length of each side and use these lengths to form another triangle.
- Compare the shapes (angles) of the two triangles.

ON YOUR OWN

CRITICAL THINKING For Exercise 17, students can also consider whether two quadrilaterals that have the same measurements for corresponding sides are similar. **(No; a square and a non-square rhombus with sides 5 in., for example, are not similar)**

COMPUTER For Exercise 18, students can use the measurement capabilities of geometry software to find the lengths of the sides of the triangles.

CHAPTER INVESTIGATION In Exercise 19, if students have difficulty understanding the concept of diameter, provide actual examples of sports balls. Demonstrate with a tape measure or ruler the circumference and the diameter of each.

c. **Writing** Make a conjecture about the lengths of the sides of similar quadrilaterals. Sample answer: The ratios of the lengths of corresponding sides are equal.

ON YOUR OWN

Try to draw a pair of figures that is not similar. If you think it is not possible, explain why. See Solution Key.

11. two rectangles
12. two squares
13. two right triangles
14. two isosceles triangles
15. two equilateral triangles
16. two parallelograms

17. **Critical Thinking** Imagine quadrilaterals *ABCD* and *EFGH*. They are not similar, but the following angles have the same measure: $\angle A$ and $\angle E$, $\angle B$ and $\angle F$, $\angle C$ and $\angle G$, and $\angle D$ and $\angle H$. Draw quadrilaterals *ABCD* and *EFGH*. See Solution Key.

18. **Computer** Use Geometry software. Make and test a conjecture about one of the following. Sample conjectures given.
    a. What can you say about the new triangle formed when you start with a triangle and you connect the midpoints of its sides? It is similar to the original triangle.

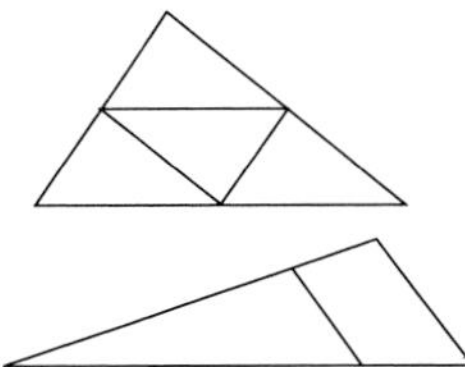

    b. Draw a segment parallel to one side of a triangle to form another smaller triangle. What can you say about the relationship between the new triangle and the original triangle? They are similar.

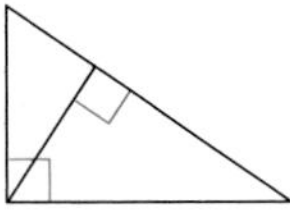

    c. Draw a right triangle. Then draw a segment from the vertex of the right angle perpendicular to the opposite side. What can you say about the relationship between the two smaller triangles? They are similar.

19. **Investigation (p. 362)** Earlier you collected data on the diameters of four sports balls. Suppose there is a photograph of the four sports balls you researched. The diameter of the basketball in the photo is 1 in. Find the diameters of the other sports balls. Round to the nearest tenth. Sample answers given.
Baseball: about 0.3 in., tennis: about 0.3 in., golf: about 0.2 in., bowling: about 0.9 in.

Mixed REVIEW

Use the figure below for 1 and 2.

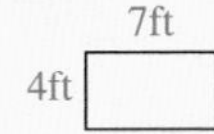

1. Find the perimeter. 22 ft
2. Find the area. 28 ft^2

Solve for *n*.

3. $\frac{1}{5} = \frac{12}{n}$ 60
4. $\frac{15}{n} = \frac{3}{25}$ 125

5. The Braxtens have two children. The sum of the children's ages is 21 and the product is 104. How old are the children? 8, 13

Assignment Options

Core: 11–14, 19, MR all	
Reinforce: 15–17	Enrich: 18

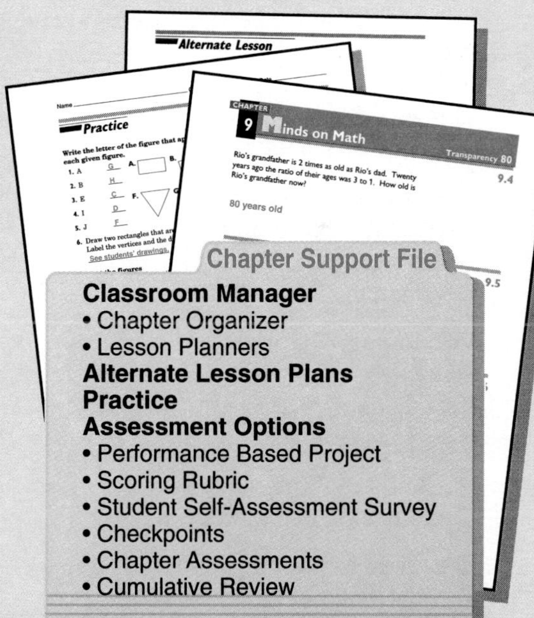

Minds on Math available in Teaching Transparencies

If Mickey earns $1,920 per month and spends $\frac{1}{4}$ of his pay on rent, how much is his rent? **$480.00**

Materials for 9-6

- ruler

9-6

Connecting to Prior Knowledge

Ask students to name toys made to scale or hobbies that use scale models, such as model airplanes or rockets, doll houses, and model cars. Challenge students to describe the size of such items in terms of a proportion.

THINK AND DISCUSS

Error Alert! Students may be confused by scales that use the same units of measurement, such as the scales for Question 1. ***Remediation*** Remind students that the scales do not represent equations. They represent ratios for displaying an object at a fraction of its actual size. Have students read each scale to themselves as, for example, "0.25 inches on the scale drawing represents 9 inches of the object at actual size."

Example

- *What is another name for the equal ratios?* **(a proportion)**
- *How are proportions used with scales to find actual measurements?* **(The scale is one ratio in the proportion, and the unknown actual measurement and the scale measurement form the other ratio. Solve for the missing term to find the actual measurement.)**

Additional Example *What is the actual height of the chair for Question 1?* **(36 in., measuring from the bottom of the back leg to the top of the back of the chair)**

DIVERSITY Some students are talented at drawing three-dimensional objects in perspective. Other students prefer to make a simple diagram for an object. Ask students to make a scale drawing of a small object of their choosing.

"Example is not the main thing in life—it is the only thing."

—ALBERT SCHWEITZER

Organizer

1. **Focus**
   Connecting to Prior Knowledge
2. **Teach**
   Think and Discuss
3. **Closure**
   Try These
   Wrap Up

Vocabulary/Symbols
scale
distortions

Skills Reviewed in Context of Lesson
- using ratio
- measuring in metric units

Materials and Manipulatives
- ruler (one per student)

Student Resources
Extra Practice
Student Study Guide
Practice, TR Ch. 9, p. 30
Student Study Guide, Spanish Resources, TR

Teacher Resources
Teaching Transparencies 6, 80, 82
Transparency Masters, p. 3
Lesson Planner, TR Ch. 9, p. 7

continues next page

MATH AND DESIGN

9-6 Scale Drawings

What's Ahead
- Using scale drawings
- Making scale drawings

WHAT YOU'LL NEED
✓ Ruler

Designers plan objects, clothes, books, and buildings that are attractive, sturdy, and functional. Designers often make drawings, blueprints, 3-D models, and fashion designs created to scale. A **scale** is a ratio that compares a length on a model to the actual length.

THINK AND DISCUSS

Examine the scale drawings below.

1. Write the scale for each drawing as a ratio in fraction form. **$\frac{0.25 \text{ in.}}{9 \text{ in.}}, \frac{1 \text{ cm}}{30 \text{ cm}}$**
2. **Discussion** Why should a scale drawing show the scale? **Answers may vary. Sample: Without the scale, you would not know the actual size.**

You can use the scale on a drawing to calculate the actual size of an object.

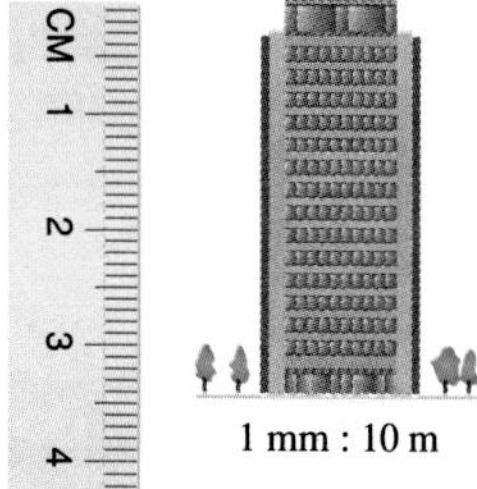

Example Use the scale drawing at the left to find the actual height of the skyscraper.

Measuring the length on the drawing shows the building is 34 mm high.

$\frac{\text{drawing (mm)}}{\text{actual (m)}} \rightarrow \frac{1}{10} = \frac{34}{h}$ — Write the scale as a ratio. Let h represent the actual height.

$1 \times h = 10 \times 34$ — Write cross products.

$h = 340$

The actual height of the skyscraper is about 340 m.

TECHNOLOGY OPTION For Questions 5–6, have students use computer assisted design (CAD) software to reduce and enlarge the given designs and answer the questions. Most drawing software can also be used to enlarge and reduce proportionally.

VISUAL LEARNERS With a copy machine, enlarge the original drawing. Have students check their enlargement with that from the copy machine. Ask students to note any distortions in their drawings.

After students have answered Question 4, ask:

- *Does the scale of 1 cm to 2 cm in the design mean that the enlargement is twice as big?*
  (The lengths and widths of the enlarged design are twice as long as the original, but the area of the enlarged design is more than twice the original area. It is 4 times as great.)

ESL Make sure that all students understand the procedure mentioned in Question 5.

Question 6: Some students will have a better understanding of scale if they actually make the enlargement and the reduction mentioned.

Ongoing Assessment Divide the class into pairs of students.

- Have one student in each pair measure the math textbook with a ruler.
- Have the student's partner use the information to construct a scale drawing using the scale 1 in. : 5 in.
- Have the first student measure the drawing.
- Ask both students to verify that the drawing is made accurately to scale.
- Challenge students to think of a better scale.

3. Discussion Are scale models and drawings and the actual figures they represent examples of similar figures? Give some examples to support your answer. See Solution Key.

You can use grid paper to reduce or enlarge designs. The designs below were created on square grids. The design on the right is an enlarged scale drawing of the original design on the left.

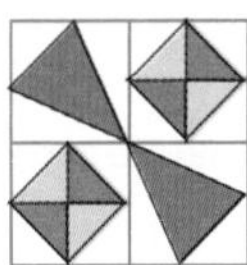

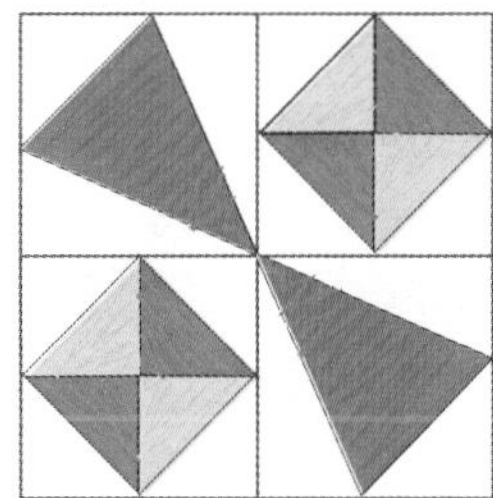

4. Find the dimensions of the grid squares in the grid on the left. Then find the dimensions of the grid squares in the grid on the right. What is the scale of the original design compared to the enlarged design?
   1 cm × 1 cm, 2 cm × 2 cm; 1 cm : 2 cm
5. Bianca used the following method to make an enlarged drawing of the design on the left. She drew a square 4 cm × 4 cm. Then, she divided the square into four smaller squares each 2 cm × 2 cm.

   "I started with the bottom right square in the original design. I measured and found that the vertex of the triangle touched the middle of each side. So I measured the square in my grid and made a mark at the halfway point of each side. I used the marks to form the triangle."

   How do you think Bianca made the top right square?
6. a. Make a scale drawing of the original design using a scale of 1 cm to 5 cm.

   b. Discussion Explain the steps you followed in making your drawing.

   c. Suppose your scale is 1 cm to 0.5 cm. How would your procedure be different?

Mixed REVIEW

Compare using >, <, or =.

1. 6.8 ■ 6.08 >
2. 10.412 ■ 10.421 <

$\triangle ABC \cong \triangle DEF$.

3. $\angle A \cong$ ■, $\angle B \cong$ ■, $\angle C \cong$ ■ $\angle D$, $\angle E$, $\angle F$
4. $\frac{AB}{BC} = \frac{DE}{■}$ EF

Write a ratio for each.

5. 27 compared to 100 $\frac{27}{100}$
6. 56 compared to 100 $\frac{56}{100}$
7. A professional baseball pitcher can pitch at 96 mi/h. Write the rate in feet per second.

140.8 ft/sec

5. Sample answer: She measured and made marks at the middle of each side, then used those marks to form the square. Next, she connected the corners of the square she drew.
6. Answers may vary. Samples given.
   b. Draw a square 10 cm × 10 cm and divide it into four smaller squares, 5 cm × 5 cm, measure 2.5 cm where needed to find the middle of the appropriate sides.
   c. Follow the same steps but draw a 1 cm × 1 cm square and divide it into four 0.5 cm × 0.5 cm squares with midpoints at 0.25 cm.

Organizer, continued

Prentice Hall Technology

Multimedia Math
- Hot Page™ 9-6

Computer Item Generator
- 9-6

Other Available Technology

Geometer's Sketchpad by Key Curriculum Press: Questions 4–6 (*optional*)

Fact of the Day

Blueprints were originally made by placing a translucent drawing over light-sensitive paper. The paper turned blue when exposed to light, leaving the lines of the drawing white.

—Academic American Encyclopedia

PH Multimedia Math Hot Page™ 9-6

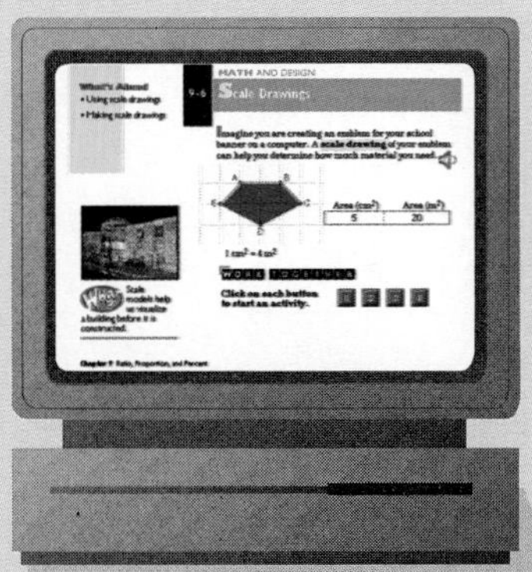

TRY THESE

WRITING For Exercise 8, have students describe the results of using each scale.

Wrap Up

What's the Big Idea? Ask students to describe how to use and make scale drawings.

Connections Have a discussion about how scale drawings are used. You may want to start with these examples:

- **Library** (storing newspapers and magazines on microfilm, microfiche, and computers)
- **Commercial Design** (using computer-generated design or art that will be enlarged or reduced for copy)
- **Special Effects** (building models of movie sets, reducing or enlarging actors to a fantastic scale)
- **Medicine** (enlarging illustrations for instructional purposes, using microscopes for surgery)

Reteaching Activity Bring a blueprint or a scale model of a building to class. Both of these are usually available from a local library. Help students find the scale of the blueprint or model. Have students measure to find the dimensions of one room and then work with them to form proportions to determine the actual size of the room.

Another alternative is to use scale models of cars or doll furniture. Many students may benefit from actually measuring and touching the figures. Determine the scale by measuring the heights of a doll's chair and a real chair and forming the ratio, $\frac{\text{height of toy chair}}{\text{height of real chair}}$. Have students use this ratio to find what the width of the chair should be. Then have students check the miniature to find if the width is appropriate.

Assignment Options

Core: 9–11, DM all, MR all	
Reinforce: 13–16	**Enrich:** 12

Sample answer: The blueprint will indicate size and location of rooms, placement of windows and doors, etc. You could make changes before construction begins.

TRY THESE

7. The height of a wall in a blueprint is 3 in. The actual wall is 96 in. high. Find the scale of the blueprint. 3 in. : 96 in. or 1 in. : 32 in.
8. **Writing** Jorge is making a scale model of an airplane. Should he use a scale of 1 in. : 1 yd or 1 yd : 1 in.? Why? 1 in. : 1 yd Sample explanation: The first measure stands for the measure on the model. If each yard on the model equals 1 in., the drawing will be larger than the actual airplane.

ON YOUR OWN

Use the scale for each drawing to find the actual size.

9. 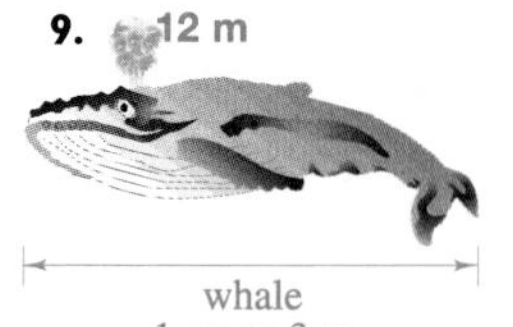

whale
1 cm to 3 m

10. 6 cm
moth
1 cm to 2 cm

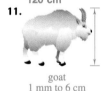

11. 120 cm
goat
1 mm to 6 cm

12. **Writing** Why would you want to see the blueprint of a house before construction starts? See left.

DECISION MAKING

Borderline

You can distort a design to produce unusual effects. Follow the directions below to learn how to create distortions.

COLLECT DATA

1. Design a border on grid paper. You might look in an art book or a book of geometric tile designs for ideas. Use at least two colors in your drawing. Refer to art books or talk to the art teacher about design considerations.

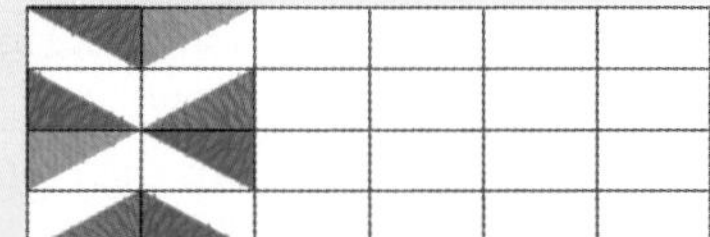

Journal Have students consider scale "models" that are not drawn or manufactured. Ask students to think of a seedling as a scale model of a tree or a puppy of a dog. Then ask students how the scale will change as the tree or dog grows.

ON YOUR OWN

WRITING For Exercise 12, have students describe what might happen if the scale is not correct.

Decision Making

Once students have decided on a pattern, have them perform the following steps.

- Decide whether to make a reduction, an enlargement, or a border that is the same size as the original.
- Decide how to distort the design. What will be the ratio of the lengths? What will be the ratio of the widths?
- Draw a square grid on a copy of the original design. Use reference points in the design for the points of the grid.
- Create a new grid to reflect your distortions.
- Copy the design on the new grid.
- Copy or trace the design onto blank paper.
- Color the design.

Encourage students to be creative in choosing their patterns. One possible creative pattern is a cartoon or a photograph. Allow students to make more than one or two distortions.

Display students' work in a border around the classroom.

Scaling Down

Have you ever noticed the detail in a toy car? Designers try to make toy cars look real.

A designer chooses a car to model and then selects a size for the toy. Next each piece on the real car is scaled down. To determine the scale the designer uses the ratio $\frac{\text{size of toy car}}{\text{size of real car}}$.

Copy the table. Use the article to complete the table.

	Part	Actual Size	Toy Size	
	Car	200 in.	3 in.	
13.	Door handle	5 in.	■	0.075 in.
14.	Headlights	8 in.	■	0.12 in.
15.	Front bumper	6 ft	■	1.08 in.
16.	Rear window	4.5 ft	■	0.81 in.

ANALYZE DATA

2. In *distortions* the scale is not the same for both dimensions of a design. The original design is on a 4 × 6 grid. What are the dimensions of the new design? Why is it not in scale with the original?

   2. The new design is also on a 4 × 6 grid. Each design has the same height, but the new design is twice as long as the original design.

3. Copy and finish the distortion of the original design. What happens to the shape of the design? It is stretched lengthwise.

4. What grid dimensions might you use if you want to distort your border design so that it is short and fat? The new design could be twice as long and half as high as the original.

MAKE DECISIONS

5. Decide on the dimensions of a grid for distorting your design. Predict what the distortion will look like. Draw the new distortion and use it as a border for stationery. Drawings may vary.

Convex and concave mirrors produce distorted images.

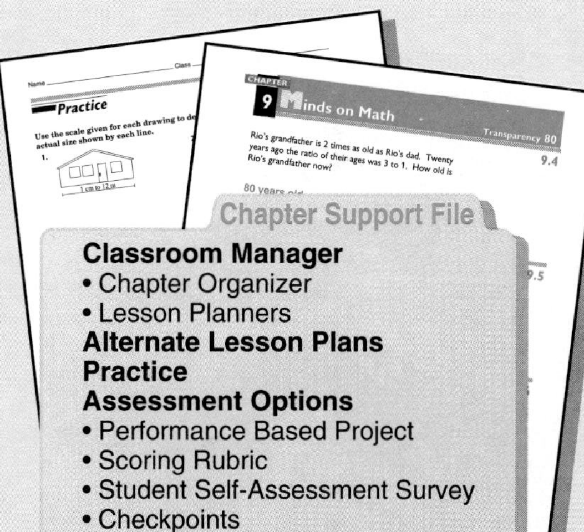

Minds on Math available in Teaching Transparencies

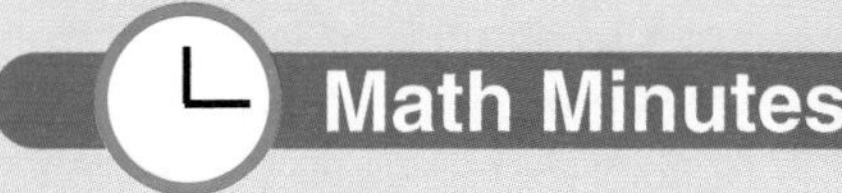

Write an expression that represents this situation. Aretha sang for a number of minutes, then she sang for 8 more minutes.
n + 8

Materials for 9-7

- metric ruler

9-7

Connecting to Prior Knowledge

Ask students to describe percents that they have seen or heard used. Then ask students the following questions:

- *How are percents written?* **(%)**
- *Is there a range percents usually fall into?* **(1–100)**
- *What is the purpose of using a percent?* **(easy to understand a comparison based on 100)**

THINK AND DISCUSS

Question 3: Help students visualize percent values by comparing percents to amounts on a scale of 100, such as 100 pennies or a 100-yard field.

TECHNOLOGY OPTION In Question 5, students can use a computer drawing program to create their own design and patterns.

Error Alert! Sometimes when a portion of a 100 grid is shaded students interpret the relationship as shaded squares to unshaded squares, rather than to the total number of squares. ***Remediation*** Remind students that a percent is by definition a comparison to 100. Have students practice reading *percent* or % as *"per one hundred."*

WORK TOGETHER

Have students work in partners or triads for this activity. Point out that the reference set for this activity is 100 cm.

Ongoing Assessment Challenge students to perform a Percent Scavenger Hunt. Provide groups of four students with a meter stick and have the groups find at least two items that fit the following descriptions.

- *an object 1% of a meter* **(width of a finger)**

"If you would be remembered, do one thing superbly well."

—Saunders Norvell

Organizer

1. **Focus**
   Connecting to Prior Knowledge
2. **Teach**
   Think and Discuss
   Work Together
3. **Closure**
   Wrap Up

Vocabulary/Symbols
percent

Skills Reviewed in Context of Lesson
- working with metric units

Materials and Manipulatives
- metric ruler (one per student)

On Your Own Exercises 21–25: graph paper, chips

Student Resources
Extra Practice
Student Study Guide
Practice, TR Ch. 9, p. 31
Student Study Guide, Spanish Resources, TR

Teacher Resources
Teaching Transparency 80
Transparency Masters, pp. 1–3, 20
Lesson Planner, TR Ch. 9, p. 8

continues next page

What's Ahead
- Modeling percents

9-7 Percent Sense

WHAT YOU'LL NEED
✓ Metric Ruler

The words *per cento,* meaning *per hundred,* have evolved since the 1400s. The words were abbreviated and eventually changed to the symbol we use today.

THINK AND DISCUSS

In a survey, 75 out of 100 people said they like to go to the movies. When you compare a number to 100 you are finding a **percent.** You can write the ratio $\frac{75}{100}$ as 75%.

1. **Discussion** Where have you seen or used percents before? **Sample answers: test scores, sale advertisements, nutrition information**

You can think of a percent as a comparison of a number to a set of 100. Study the grid at the right. The amount shaded compared to the whole is 15 out of 100. You can write this as a fraction and as a percent.

$\frac{15}{100}$ or 15%

2. What percent of each grid is shaded? not shaded?

a. 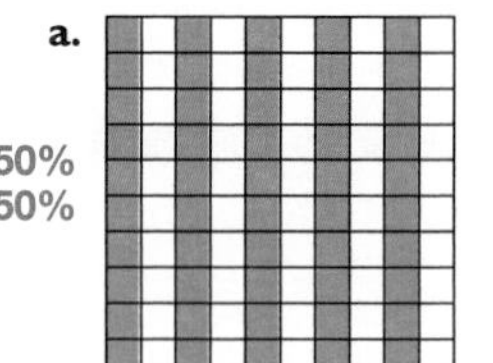
50%
50%

b. 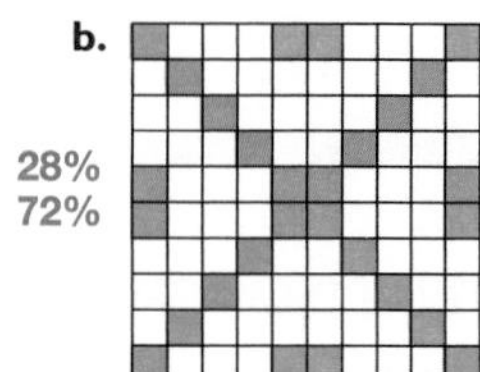
28%
72%

3. **Estimation** Estimate each percent. Choose 25%, 50%, or 75%.
   a. About what percent of the glass is full? **75%**

   b. About what percent of the pizza is eaten? **25%**
   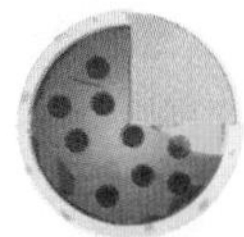
   c. About what percent of the sign is painted? **50%**

- *an object or measurement 99% of a meter* **(the height of a door knob, approximately)**

Have the groups compare their findings.

Wrap Up

What's the Big Idea? Ask students to describe how to model percents.

Reteaching Activity Group students in pairs and provide each pair with 10 × 10 grids of graph paper. Have each pair of students play a game. Students take turns shading an area between 1% and 25% of the grid. Encourage students to record their moves. The student who completes the shading of the grid loses the game. Have each pair of students describe the games and provide hints for game strategy.

Connections Have a discussion about how percents are used. You may want to start with these examples:

- **Business** (sales, sales tax, percent gains and losses, percent interest on layaway)
- **School** (grades on tests, description of school population)
- **Household** (interest on bank accounts, utility bills)

Journal Have students describe why 100 is a useful number for comparisons. Challenge students to name other numbers that would be useful. Have students evaluate the numbers and discuss what they have in common.

ON YOUR OWN

TECHNOLOGY OPTION For Exercises 8–13, use geometry software to make several copies of a 10 × 10 square grid. Have students model each percent by filling in the needed number of squares with any color.

WRITING For Exercise 14, have students compare both the scales and the amounts.

4. Use the design at the right. What percent of the design is made up of each pattern?

a. 20% **b.** 20% **c.** 38% **d.** 18% **e.** 4%

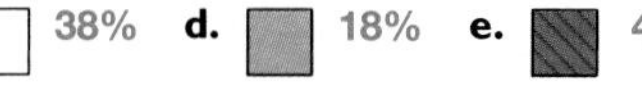

f. Find the sum of the percents in parts (a) through (e). 100%

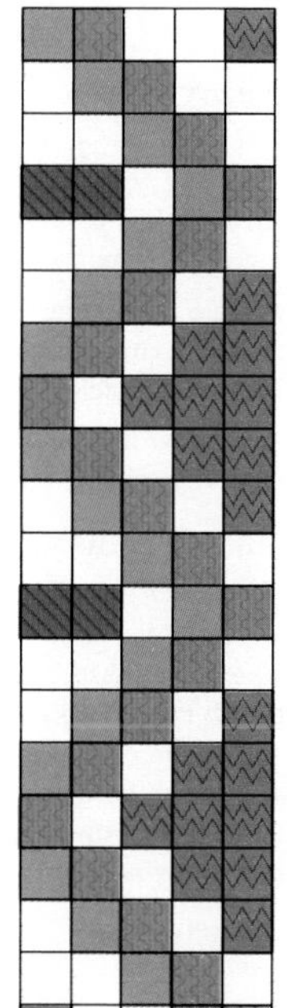

5. Draw your own percent design. Use at least three patterns. How many squares should you start with? Designs may vary; 100 squares

6. **Discussion** What's wrong with each spinner? Sample answers given.

a.

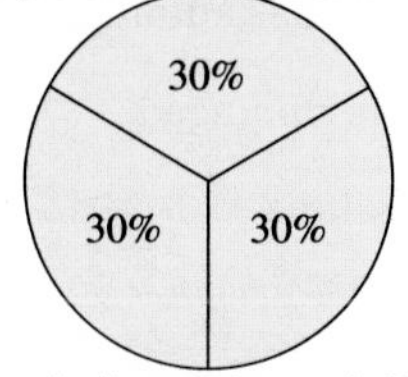

The whole must equal 100%. This totals 90%.

b.

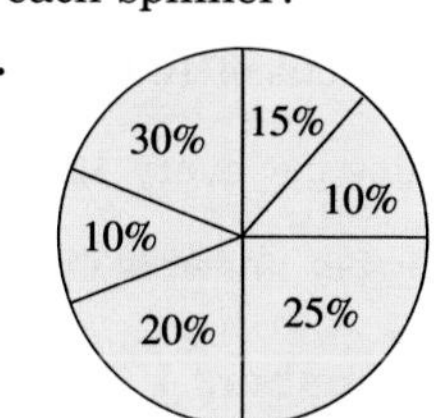

The whole cannot be greater than 100%. This totals 110%.

WORK TOGETHER

Work in small groups. Use a centimeter ruler to find each measure. What percent of a meter is each measurement?

a. length of your foot Answers may vary.

b. circumference of your head

c. a cubit (distance from tip of middle finger to elbow)

d. your hand span (Spread your fingers. Measure the distance from the tip of your thumb to the tip of your little finger.)

e. width of your smile

f. distance from your knee to the floor

FLASHBACK
100 cm = 1m

7. Why do you think a meter rather than a yard was chosen for the reference set? Answers may vary. Sample answer: Since 1m = 100 cm, meters can be more easily expressed in terms of percents.

ON YOUR OWN

Use a 10 × 10 square grid to model each percent. See Solution Key.

8. 5% **9.** 100% **10.** 75% **11.** 37% **12.** 90% **13.** 18%

Organizer, continued

Prentice Hall Technology

Computer Item Generator

- 9-7

Other Available Technology

Geometer's Sketchpad by Key Curriculum Press: Question 5, Exercises 8–13 (*optional*)

Fact of the Day

The largest prime number now known was identified in 1992. Its value is 1 less than 2 raised to the power 756,839.

—Academic American Encyclopedia

TACTILE LEARNERS For Exercises 21–25, provide students with 10 × 10 graph paper. Instruct them to write the numbers 1–100 in the squares with only one number in each square. Have students place a chip over each number that is a solution for the problem. Tell students to count the number of chips they see and that number is the percent.

CONNECTION TO PATTERNS Exercises 21–25 review patterns by having students express the numbers that fit a pattern as a percent.

CHAPTER INVESTIGATION For Exercise 30, students can find the information required of them in an encyclopedia, under the heading "Earth." Students may find there an illustration on which to base their scale drawings.

Assignment Options

Core: 8–13, 15–20, 26, 29, 30, MR all	
Reinforce: 21–25, 27	**Enrich:** 14, 28

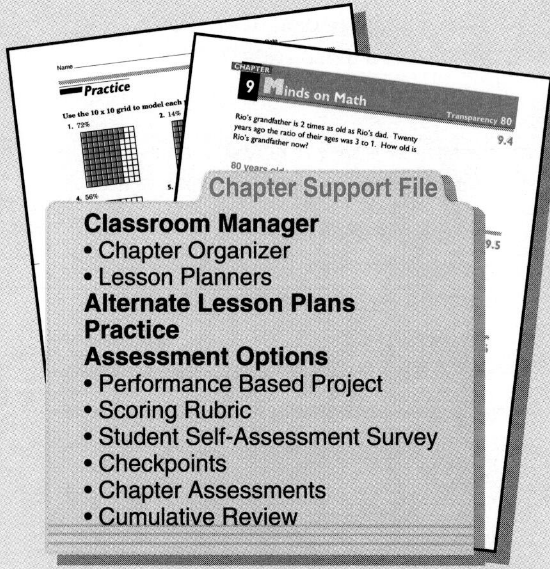

Minds on Math available in Teaching Transparencies

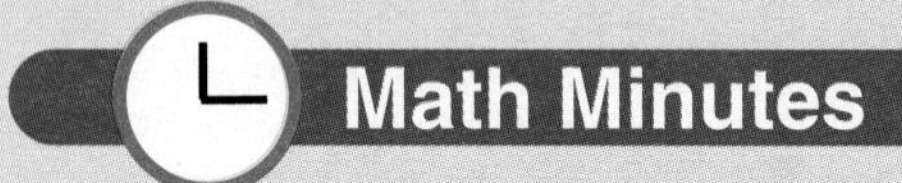

Ask students to find the prime factorization of 320. **320 = 2 × 2 × 2 × 2 × 2 × 2 × 5**

Materials for 9-8

- graph paper
- calculator

Mixed REVIEW

Find each answer.

1. $\frac{9}{16} + \frac{12}{16}$ $1\frac{5}{16}$
2. $\frac{6}{8} - \frac{3}{8}$ $\frac{3}{8}$

A drawing has a scale of 1 cm to 2 m.

3. A scale model measures 1 cm × 2.5 cm. What is the size of the table? 2 m × 5 m
4. A window is 12 mm. What is the sill length? 2.4 m

Write as a decimal.

5. $\frac{5}{20}$ 0.25
6. $\frac{9}{16}$ 0.5625

7. There are 30 students in a math class. Twelve belong to the computer club, 8 to the hiking club, and 3 to both. How many belong to neither? 13 students

FLASHBACK

A prime number has only two factors, one and itself.

Cicely Williams worked for 20 years in West Africa. Her work led to a reduced number of childhood deaths.

14. **Writing** How are 50% of a meter and 50% of $1 the same? How are they different? Sample answer: both refer to one-half of the amount; one describes length, the other money.
15. **Data File 1 (pp. 2–3)** What percent of people surveyed watch more than 21 hours of TV per week? 31%

Write each as a percent.

16. 98¢ compared to 100¢ 98%
17. 11 students out of 100 students are left handed 11%
18. 97 days out of 100 days were sunny last summer 97%
19. 4 radios per every 100 radios arrive damaged 4%
20. 85 correct answers out of 100 questions 85%

Use the numbers 1 through 100.

21. What percent are multiples of 3? 33%
22. What percent are odd? 50%
23. What percent are prime? 25%
24. What percent have at least one 7? 19%
25. What percent are neither prime nor composite? 1%
26. Thirty-five percent of a group surveyed said football was their favorite sport. What percent did not choose football? 65%
27. How much will a sales tax of 5% add to the price of a $1 item? a $10 item? $.05; $.50
28. Ask 10 people how many hours of TV they watch each week. Use a percent to tell how many watch 10 h or more. Answers may vary.
29. **Medicine** In 1790 Dr. Benjamin Rush recorded that 34% of 100 patients died before age 6. Another 41% died before age 26. What percent of his patients lived to age 26 or beyond? 25%

30. **Investigation (p. 362)** Make a scale drawing of Earth and its moon, showing size and distance. Use a diameter of 2 in. for Earth. Round distances to the nearest thousand. Drawings may vary. The diameter of the moon will be about $\frac{1}{2}$ in. (2,170 mi). The distance between Earth and the moon may vary from about $55\frac{1}{4}$ in. (221,456 mi) to about $63\frac{1}{4}$ in. (252,711 mi).

9-8

Connecting to Prior Knowledge

Ask students to think about how the same values may be expressed with percents, fractions, and decimals. Ask students the following question:

- *Express one half as a percent, a fraction, and a decimal.* **(50%, $\frac{1}{2}$ or other equivalent fraction, 0.5)**

WORK TOGETHER

Have students work in groups of four. Each student can be responsible for modeling one percent, one fraction, and one decimal. Students then match the equivalent representations.

Question 1d: Ask students to explain how they determined which fraction, decimal, and percent were equivalent. **(Each equivalent fraction, decimal, and percent covered the same area in the model.)**

THINK AND DISCUSS

Example 1

- *Why is 36% written as $\frac{36}{100}$?*

(Percent is a comparison to 100, so use the ratio $\frac{36}{100}$.)

AUDITORY LEARNERS Divide the students into groups. Have one student in each group explain how to write a percent as a fraction and as a decimal. Have the other group members follow the speaker's instructions.

Example 2

- *Why is it helpful to rewrite the fraction as having a denominator of 100?*

(A percent is a comparison to 100.)

What's Ahead

- Converting percents, fractions, and decimals

9-8 Percents, Fractions, and Decimals

WORK TOGETHER

WHAT YOU'LL NEED

✓ Graph paper

Work in groups to explore percents, fractions, and decimals. Use a 10 × 10 grid for each model.

1. a. Model the percents 30%, 75%, 20%, and 50%. **See Solution Key.**
   b. Model the fractions $\frac{3}{4}$, $\frac{1}{2}$, $\frac{3}{10}$, and $\frac{1}{5}$.
   c. Model the decimals 0.2, 0.5, 0.75, and 0.3.
   d. Match each percent with a fraction and a decimal.
2. Express each shaded area as a percent, as a fraction in simplest form, and as a decimal.

a. 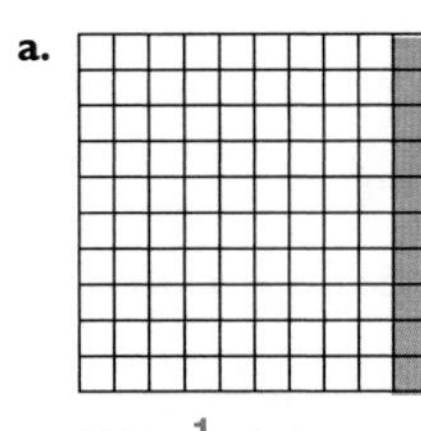

10%, $\frac{1}{10}$, 0.1

b. 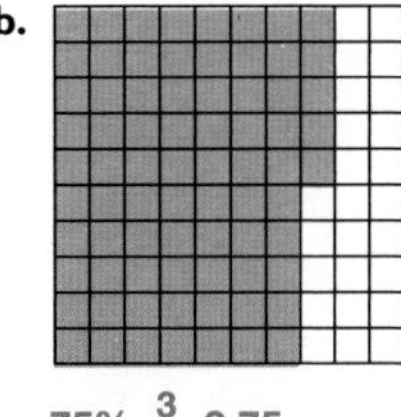

75%, $\frac{3}{4}$, 0.75

THINK AND DISCUSS

You can write a percent as a fraction and as a decimal.

Example 1 Write 36% as a fraction in simplest form and as a decimal.

$36\% = \frac{36}{100}$ — Write the percent as a fraction with a denominator of 100.

$\frac{36}{100} = \frac{9}{25}$ — Write the fraction in simplest form.

$\frac{36}{100} = 0.36$ — Write the fraction as a decimal.

$36\% = \frac{9}{25} = 0.36$

LOOK BACK How could you use a model to show 35% as a fraction and as a decimal?

WHAT? Ninety-nine percent of all types of plants and animals that have ever lived are now extinct.

Source: *The Macmillan Illustrated Almanac For Kids*

"Don't judge anyone harshly until you yourself have been through his experiences."

—GOETHE

Organizer

1. **Focus**
   Connecting to Prior Knowledge
2. **Teach**
   Work Together
   Think and Discuss
3. **Closure**
   Try These
   Wrap Up

Skills Reviewed in Context of Lesson

- simplifying fractions

Materials and Manipulatives

- graph paper (for each student)
- calculator (one per group)

Student Resources

Extra Practice
Student Study Guide
Practice, TR Ch. 9, p. 32
Student Study Guide, Spanish Resources, TR

Teacher Resources

Teaching Transparencies 1, 81
Transparency Masters, pp. 1, 2, 20
Lesson Planner, TR Ch. 9, p. 9

continues next page

Ongoing Assessment Have students draw "slow motion" conversions. Group students in pairs. Have each student write the steps for converting a percent to a fraction and a decimal, a decimal to a fraction and a percent, and a fraction to a decimal and a percent. Challenge students to make the conversions happen in "slow motion" by listing as many steps as they can for each conversion. Have partners check and compare each other's work.

Error Alert! In Question 4, some students may not use the correct keys on their calculators. ***Remediation*** Encourage students to check to see that their answers make sense in terms of the given percent.

Additional Example *Twenty-four percent of a class of sixth graders are wearing sweaters today. Use your calculator to express this as a decimal and a fraction in simplest form.* **(0.24 and $\frac{6}{25}$)**

CALCULATOR For Question 4, have students begin by making estimations so they can check their calculations.

TRY THESE

TECHNOLOGY OPTION For Exercises 5–9, use a spreadsheet to show each number as a fraction, a decimal, and a percent.

Exercise 10: Have students check their answers by finding the sum of the fractions and of the decimals. Both should be 1.

Wrap Up

What's the Big Idea? Ask students to explain how to convert among percents, fractions, and decimals.

Reteaching Activity Bring a set of dominoes to class and play a game of Domino Bingo. Randomly choose dominoes from the box and show each to students. Each student should then

Organizer, continued

Prentice Hall Technology

Multimedia Math
- Math Tools, Spreadsheet
- Hot Page™ 9-8
- Math Investigations, Crisis in Hydrotown
- Math Investigations, Measuring Elephant Populations in Africa

Computer Item Generator
- 9-8

Other Available Technology
calculator

Fact of the Day

The concept of zero was developed in India in the 9th century. It was initially used as a place holder, and is central to the Hindu-Arabic system of numbers that we use today.

—Academic American Encyclopedia

PH Multimedia Math Hot Page™ 9-8

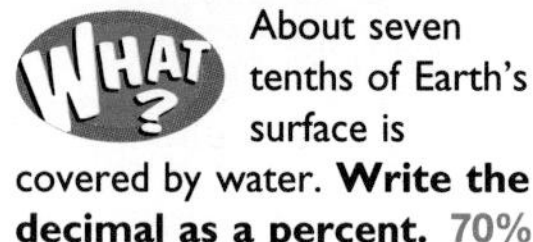

About seven tenths of Earth's surface is covered by water. **Write the decimal as a percent.** 70%

You can also write a fraction as a decimal and as a percent.

Example 2 Write $\frac{3}{10}$ as a decimal and as a percent.

$\frac{3}{10} = \frac{30}{100}$ — Rewrite the fraction as an equivalent fraction with a denominator of 100.

$\frac{30}{100} = 0.3$ — Write the fraction as a decimal.

$\frac{30}{100} = 30\%$ — Write the fraction as a percent.

$\frac{3}{10} = 0.30 = 30\%$

3. **Discussion** How would you write 0.40 as a fraction in simplest form and as a percent? $\frac{2}{5}$, 40%

You can use a fraction calculator to convert fractions, decimals, and percents.

Example 3 Use a fraction calculator to write 50% as a decimal and as a fraction in simplest form.

50 [%] 0.5 — Use the percent key.

.5 [F↔D] 5/10 — Use the fraction to decimal key.

5/10 [Simp] [=] 1/2 — Use the Simp key.

$50\% = 0.5 = \frac{5}{10} = \frac{1}{2}$

4. **Calculator** Write 58% as a decimal and as a fraction in simplest form. 0.58, $\frac{29}{50}$

TRY THESE See Solution Key.

Shade each amount on a 10 × 10 grid. Describe the shaded area as a fraction in simplest form, as a decimal, and as a percent.

5. 0.8 — $\frac{4}{5}$, 80%
6. $\frac{11}{20}$ — 0.55, 55%
7. 0.72 — $\frac{18}{25}$, 72%
8. $\frac{2}{5}$ — 0.4, 40%
9. 6% — $\frac{3}{50}$, 0.06
10. The air we breathe is about 80% nitrogen and 20% oxygen. Write each percent as a fraction in simplest form and as a decimal. $\frac{4}{5}$, 0.8; $\frac{1}{5}$, 0.2

express the domino as a fraction and convert the fraction into a percent and a decimal. Continue drawing dominoes until a student recognizes a value that has been drawn already and calls out "Bingo!" Have the student give the fraction, percent, and decimal expressions for each domino and start a new game with the remaining dominoes. Continue until all have been used.

Connections Have a discussion about how the conversions of decimals, percents, and fractions may be useful. You may want to start with the following examples:

- **Science** (diluting solutions such as acids or bases)
- **Reading graphs** (making sure a graph's visual representation matches its content)
- **Business** (making estimations of inventory changes)

Journal Ask students to compare the usefulness of the three forms and explain which forms they find easiest to use.

ON YOUR OWN

DIVERSITY For Exercise 19, have students give reasons why the graduation rate might have changed from 1940–1990. Ask them why they think students drop out of school now. Ask students to give suggestions on ways to lower the drop-out rate.

WRITING Have students use a diagram or table to support their answers for Exercise 18.

ON YOUR OWN

Copy and complete the table below. Write each fraction in simplest form.

	Fraction	Decimal	Percent
11.	■ $\frac{11}{50}$	■ 0.22	22%
12.	■ $\frac{39}{50}$	0.78	■ 78%
13.	$\frac{22}{25}$	■ 0.88	■ 88%
14.	■ $\frac{11}{20}$	0.55	■ 55%
15.	$\frac{4}{5}$	■ 0.8	■ 80%

Use the graph at the right.

16. In what percent of lunch boxes are you likely to find fruit?
23%

17. a. **Choose A, B, C, or D.** Which of the following can you *not* conclude from the graph? D
    - A. About one fourth of the lunch boxes contained fruit.
    - B. Almost 10% of the lunch boxes contained a sandwich.
    - C. Fruit was in almost twice as many lunch boxes as cookies.
    - D. Students don't take drinks in their lunch boxes.

    b. Take a lunch box survey in your class. Make a graph to show your results. Check students' work.

18. **Writing** How are fractions, decimals, and percents alike? How are they different?

19. a. The table shows the fraction of high school students who graduated from 1940 to 1990. Write each fraction as a percent.

Year	1940	1950	1960	1970	1980	1990
Graduates	$\frac{1}{4}$	$\frac{17}{50}$	$\frac{11}{25}$	$\frac{11}{20}$	$\frac{69}{100}$	$\frac{77}{100}$
Source: *Universal Almanac*	25%	34%	44%	55%	69%	77%

b. Graph the data in the table. See Solution Key.

c. Use your graph to predict the percent of high school graduates in the year 2000. Sample answer: about 87%

18. Sample answer: All three involve dividing a whole into equal parts. The number of equal parts may differ among the three forms.

Mixed REVIEW

Evaluate. 1. 2197

1. 13^3 2. 9^3 729

Write as a percent.

3. 40 out of every 100 teens choose their own clothes. 40%

4. 92 out of every 100 teens help with food shopping. 92%

5. Dwania is saving dimes. The first day she saves 1 dime and the second day 2 dimes. Each day she saves 1 more dime than the day before. How much money will she have after 2 weeks? $10.50

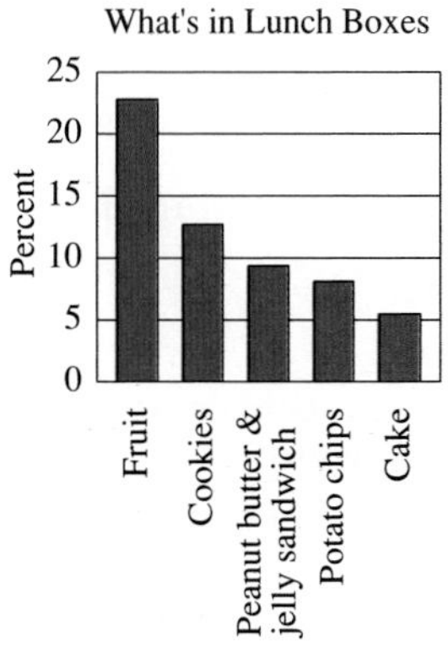

Assignment Options

Core: 11–15, 18, MR all	
Reinforce: 16, 17	Enrich: 19

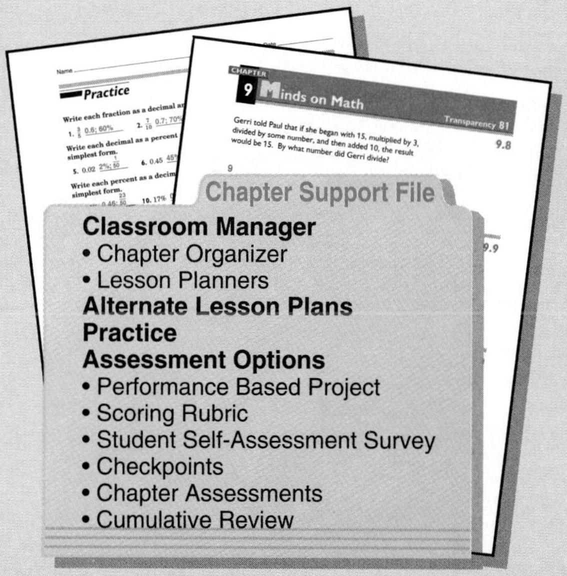

Minds on Math available in Teaching Transparencies

Math Minutes

Find the prime, common factors of 52 and 78. **2, 13**

Materials for 9-9

- graph paper

CHAPTER 9 PRACTICE

This page provides practice on the skills learned up to this point in the chapter. Daily cumulative practice can be found in the Mixed Reviews that appear in every lesson.

Exercises 1–4: Students may enjoy creating their own problems of this sort with a new word.

Exercise 25: Challenge students to change the question to *2 days* out of a week and answer it again (using a calculator). **(28.6%, $\frac{2}{7}$, 0.2857)**

Resources

Extra Practice
Student Study Guide
Student Study Guide, Spanish Resources, TR

Answers to Problems Unique to Spanish Edition

1. $\frac{3}{32}$, 3 : 32, 3 a 32
2. $\frac{2}{15}$, 2 : 15, 2 a 15
3. $\frac{6}{3}$, 6 : 3, 6 a 3
4. $\frac{17}{32}$, 17 : 32, 17 a 32
10. $\frac{5}{22}$

Practice

Write a ratio in three ways using the letters of the word SUPERCALAFRAGALISTICEXPIALIDOCIOUS.

1. the number of A's compared to the total number of letters $\frac{5}{34}$, 5 : 34, 5 to 34
2. the number of E's compared to the number of vowels $\frac{2}{16}$, 2 : 16, 2 to 16
3. the number of I's compared to the number of S's $\frac{5}{3}$, 5 : 3, 5 to 3
4. the number of consonants compared to the total number of letters
   $\frac{18}{34}$, 18 : 34, 18 to 34

Write each ratio as a fraction in simplest form.

5. 20 to 80 $\frac{1}{4}$
6. 15 : 35 $\frac{3}{7}$
7. 33 : 77 $\frac{3}{7}$
8. 14 to 56 $\frac{1}{4}$
9. 17 : 51 $\frac{1}{3}$
10. vowels to consonants in the alphabet $\frac{5}{21}$
11. vowels to consonants in your first and last name
    Answers may vary.
12. Moira is taking dance lessons. She pays \$125 for 10 lessons.
    a. Write the cost of the lessons as a unit rate. \$12.50/lesson
    b. Find the cost of 25 lessons. \$312.50

Find the value of n.

13. $\frac{n}{28} = \frac{9}{12}$ 21
14. $\frac{45}{n} = \frac{30}{48}$ 72
15. $\frac{60}{108} = \frac{n}{9}$ 5
16. $\frac{96}{144} = \frac{4}{n}$ 6
17. $\frac{3}{15} = \frac{12}{n}$ 60

Use a centimeter ruler and the scale drawing at the right.

1 cm : 1 m

18. Find the actual length of the bicycle. 3.2 m
19. Find the actual diameter of the front tire. 1.1 m

Write each as a percent, as a fraction in simplest form, and as a decimal.

20. 24 cm out of 100 cm
    24%, $\frac{6}{25}$, 0.24
21. 55 students out of 100 students
    55%, $\frac{11}{20}$, 0.55
22. 3 hats out of 25 hats
    12%, $\frac{3}{25}$, 0.12
23. 5 pens out of 20 pens
    25%, $\frac{1}{4}$, 0.25
24. 40 heads out of 100 coin tosses
    40%, $\frac{2}{5}$, 0.4
25. 2 days out of 10 days
    20%, $\frac{1}{5}$, 0.2

9-9

Connecting to Prior Knowledge

Ask students to list ways in which they can estimate sums and differences of whole numbers. Ask them how they would round 124 to the tens' place. **(120)** Have them round 125 and 126 to the nearest ten. **(130, 130)**

THINK AND DISCUSS

Error Alert! For Question 3, make sure students understand that the ten boxes in the model together total $50. Students might otherwise confuse the model for a representation of $100. ***Remediation*** Caution students to pay close attention to the value that is 100% in a problem. The value is not always 100 or a multiple of ten.

Example 1

- *When you find 10% of a number why do you divide the number by 10?*
  (Because 10% is $\frac{1}{10}$ of the total amount and you can determine $\frac{1}{10}$ of a number by dividing by 10.)
- *What quick method do you know for dividing numbers by 10?*
  (Move the decimal point one place to the left.)

ESL In Example 1, write labels such as "bill," "tip," and "percent" above the figures shown to help students follow the steps.

WRITING Challenge students to suggest different methods of estimating the tip for Question 8.

TECHNOLOGY OPTION For Example 1 and Question 8, have students estimate a 10%, 15%, and 20% tip for the cost of several meals, such as $7.50, $10.95, and $13.07. Then use a

---

What's Ahead

- Estimating a percent of a number

WHAT YOU'LL NEED

✓ Graph paper

MATH AND SPENDING

9-9 Estimating with Percents

Advertisers often use percents. "Save 25% on all cameras." "Our store has expanded. We now offer 40% more merchandise." Knowing how to estimate with percents will help you make sense of such ads.

THINK AND DISCUSS

A jacket is on sale for 60% of the regular price of $49.95. Is $25 enough to buy the jacket? You can use a model to help you visualize the situation. Round $49.95 to $50. Let 100% represent the regular price.

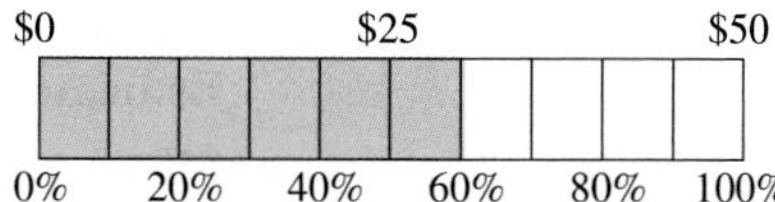

The dollar amounts are above the model and the percentages are below. **1.–3. See Solution Key for sample answers.**

1. Why do you think $50 was chosen for the rounded amount? To what might you round $43.99? $55?
2. Why do you think there are ten sections in the model? How many sections are shaded? What percent does each section represent? **6 sections; 10%**
3. Copy the model on graph paper. Write dollar amounts above 20%, 40%, 60% and 80%. What is the dollar value of each section? **$10, $20, $30, $40; $5**
4. What does the shading in the model represent? **the sale price**
5. Estimate the cost of the jacket. Explain your reasoning. **$30 Six sections are shaded. Each section represents $5.**
6. Based on your estimate, is $25 enough to buy the jacket on sale? Why or why not? **No. $25 is only 5 sections or 50%.**

WHAT? Your brain uses about 20% of the calories you eat and about 15% of your blood supply. But your brain accounts for only 2% of your body weight.

"I get quiet joy from the observation of anyone who does his job well."
—WILLIAM FEATHER

Organizer

1. **Focus**
   Connecting to Prior Knowledge
2. **Teach**
   Think and Discuss
   Work Together
3. **Closure**
   Try These
   Wrap Up

Skills Reviewed in Context of Lesson

- rounding decimals

Materials and Manipulatives

- graph paper (for each student)

Student Resources

Extra Practice
Student Study Guide
Practice, TR Ch. 9, p. 33
Student Study Guide, Spanish Resources, TR
Alternate Lesson, TR Ch. 9, pp. 21–24

Teacher Resources

Teaching Transparencies 1, 81, 83
Transparency Masters, p. 1
Lesson Planner, TR Ch. 9, p. 10

Prentice Hall Technology

Multimedia Math

- Math Tools, Spreadsheet

Computer Item Generator

- 9-9

spreadsheet to calculate the amount of the tip and the total cost of the meals. Compare the estimates with the actual cost.

Example 2

- *Why is 3% expressed as 3¢ per dollar?* **(Percent is a comparison to 100, and there are 100 pennies in a dollar. Three pennies equal 3% of a dollar.)**

Additional Example *You buy a cassette for $7.99. The sales tax is 8%. Estimate the sales tax and the final cost.* **(The sales tax is about $.64. The final cost is about $8.64.)**

VISUAL LEARNERS Students may have difficulty understanding why 42 is changed to 0.42. Rework the problem as follows.

$$\$13.99 \approx \$14.00$$

$$3\% = 0.03$$

$$\$14.00 \times 0.03 = \$0.42$$

$$\$14.00 + \$0.42 = \$14.42$$

WORK TOGETHER

Question 10: Encourage students to use models to estimate the number of students for the percent in the table.

DIVERSITY Have students generate a list of foods that reflect foods from a variety of countries and ethnic groups. Have students conduct a survey of their classmates' likes. As a follow-up activity, students could prepare one or two simple foods for their classmates to sample.

Ongoing Assessment Have students describe the steps involved in estimating 18% of 130. **(about 26)**

WRITING For Question 12b, have students suggest reasons why the two surveys may differ.

Fact of the Day

Louis Jacques Mandé Daguerre (1787–1851) is considered the inventor of photography. In 1839 he introduced the daguerrotype, the first commonly produced photograph.

—*Encyclopedia of Photography*

You can use mental math to estimate percents.

Example 1 You have breakfast at the Blue Diner. Estimate a 10% tip for a bill of $6.42.

$6.42 ≈ $6.50 — Round to a convenient place.

10% = 0.10 — Think of the percent as a decimal.

0.10 × 6.50 = 0.65 — Multiply mentally.

The tip is about $.65.

7.–8. See Solution Key.

7. Look at Example 1. Why do you think $6.42 was rounded to $6.50 rather than to $6 or $7?

8. **Writing** Describe a method for estimating a 15% tip. Include guidelines for rounding the amount of the bill.

Some states charge a sales tax on a variety of things. You can use mental math to estimate the added cost of sales tax.

Example 2 You buy a CD for $13.99. The sales tax is 3%. Estimate the sales tax and the final cost.

$13.99 ≈ $14.00 — Round to a convenient place.

3% → 3¢ per dollar — Think of the percent as cents per dollar.

14 × 3 = 42 — Multiply mentally.

14 + 0.42 = 14.42 — Add the estimates.

The sales tax is about $.42. The final cost is about $14.42.

9. Look at Example 2. Would you ever want to round the price of an item down before estimating the sales tax? Why or why not? Sample answer: No. Rounding down would underestimate the amount of the tax.

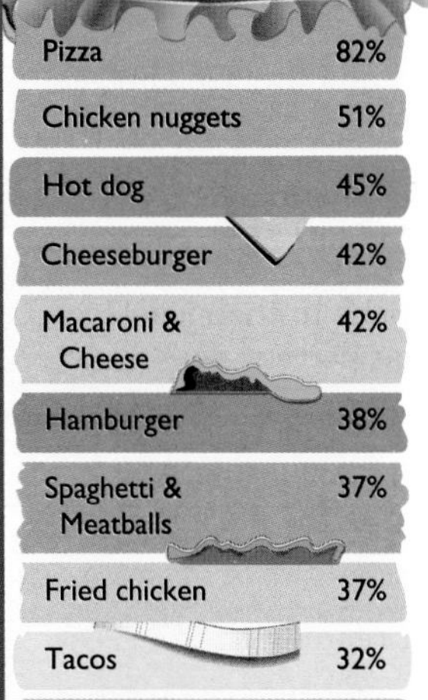

Kids' Top Ten Foods
Pizza 82%
Chicken nuggets 51%
Hot dog 45%
Cheeseburger 42%
Macaroni & Cheese 42%
Hamburger 38%
Spaghetti & Meatballs 37%
Fried chicken 37%
Tacos 32%
Grilled cheese 22%

Source: Gallup Organization

WORK TOGETHER

When asked to list their favorite foods, a group of students gave the responses shown at the left. Pizza was the favorite food of 82% of the students.

10. a. **Discussion** Suppose 103 students were surveyed. Would the statement "About 30 students chose tacos." make sense? Why or why not? Sample answer: Yes. You could estimate that 30% × 100 = 30 students.

TRY THESE

ESL In Exercise 15, point out that the boots are not 80% *off,* but 80% *of* the regular price. Make sure students understand the difference by asking them to compare 80% of and 80% off of the original price.

Wrap Up

What's the Big Idea? Ask students to describe how to estimate a percent of a number.

Connections Have a discussion about how estimating a percent of a number is useful. You may want to start with these examples:

- **Biology** (estimating an animal's age by its size, quickly determining the losses or increases in a herd)
- **Business** (budgeting time and labor for a temporary project, estimating raises or production increases)
- **Science** (estimating the composition of a mixture)

Reteaching Activity The visual model in Think and Discuss may be clearer for some students if it is presented vertically rather than horizontally. In a vertical presentation, the division between the numbers and the percents may be more obvious. Have students make a vertical model for the Think and Discuss problem. Ask students to compare their models to the one in the textbook.

Journal Have students write a realistic scene in which they solve a problem by estimating a percent.

ON YOUR OWN

CRITICAL THINKING In Exercise 25, students must read carefully to see that *off* is not *of.*

b. Suppose 207 students were surveyed. How could you estimate the number of students that chose each food? See Solution Key for sample answer.

11. Use the *Kids Top Ten Foods* chart. Estimate the number of students in your class who will choose pizza as number 1, chicken nuggets as number 2, and so on for all ten foods. You may want to use a model. Answers may vary.

12. a. Conduct a survey among your classmates. Have each student rank the foods in the chart from 1 to 10. Write the results as percents. Survey results may vary.

b. Writing How do your survey results compare with your estimates in Exercise 11? Answers may vary.

TRY THESE

What dollar amount does the shaded part represent?

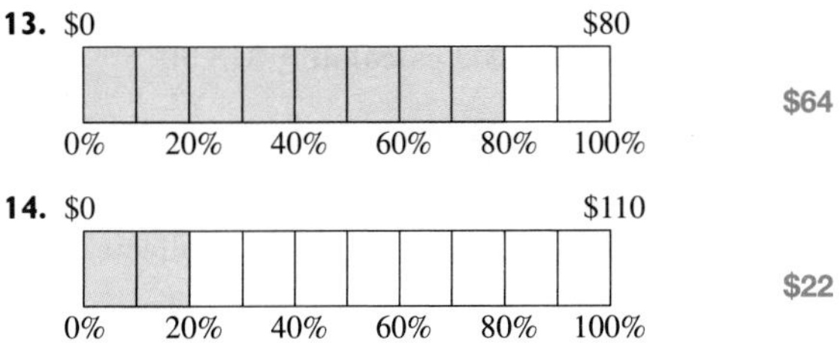

13. $64

14. $22

15. The regular price for a pair of boots is $23.99. They are on sale for 80% of the regular price. Estimate the sale price. Sample answer: $19.20

16. Estimate a 10% tip, a 15% tip, and a 20% tip for a meal that costs $5.83. Sample answer: $.59, $.89, $1.18

17. Estimate the sales tax and final cost for a hat that costs $18.59 with a sales tax of 5%. Sample answer: $.93, $19.53

ON YOUR OWN

Draw a model to help you estimate each amount.

18. 90% of 41 **19.** 20% of 486 **20.** 10% of 129

21. 25% of 53 **22.** 75% of 98 **23.** 15% of 21

18.–23. See Solution Key for sample answers.

Mixed REVIEW

Evaluate.

1. $\frac{2}{5} + \frac{1}{3}$ $\frac{11}{15}$ 2. $\frac{7}{12} - \frac{3}{8}$ $\frac{5}{24}$

Write as a percent.

3. $\frac{9}{36}$ 25% 4. $\frac{21}{28}$ 75%

Write as a fraction.

5. 40% $\frac{2}{5}$ 6. 85% $\frac{17}{20}$

7. How many 3-digit numbers are divisible by 13? Explain your method.

69

7. Sample method: truncate 1,000 ÷ 13 ~ 76, and subtract the 2-digit numbers. 76 − 7 = 69

Assignment Options

Core: 18–24, 28–31, 38, MR all	
Reinforce: 25–27, 32, 33, 35, 36	**Enrich:** 34, 37

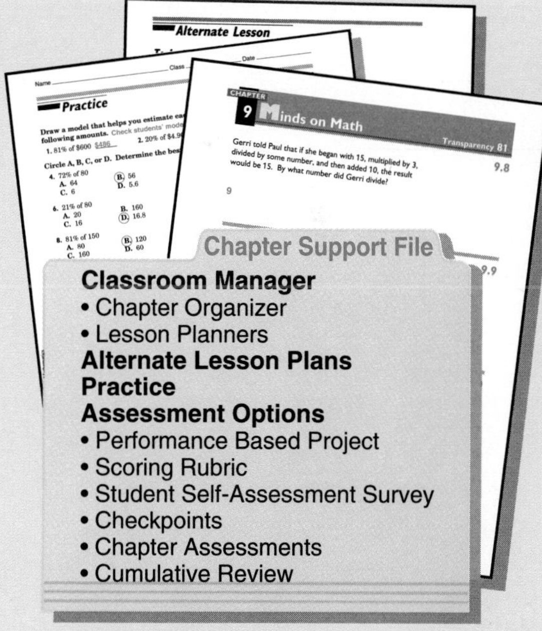

Minds on Math available in Teaching Transparencies

ACTIVITY In Exercise 34, note that there may also be a city sales tax in some areas.

CHAPTER INVESTIGATION The information called for in Exercise 38 can be found in books on space or the solar system or in an encyclopedia under those headings.

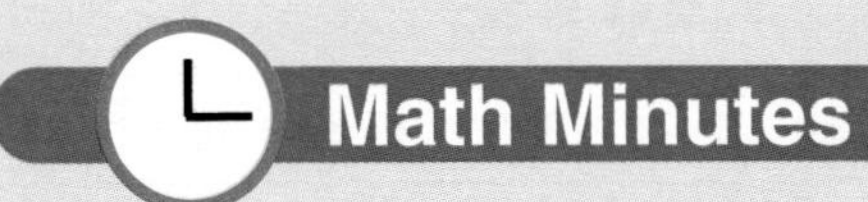

The school store had the following sale: *Buy one pen for $.69 and pay $.50 for each additional pen.* Pedro spent $4.19 on pens. How many did he buy? **8**

24. A baseball mitt is on sale for 75% of the original price of $39.99. Estimate the sale price of the mitt. Sample: $32

25. Critical Thinking The regular price of a chair is $349. Estimate the amount saved for each sale price. Sample answers
   a. 20% off $70 b. 30% off $105 c. 75% off $262.50

26. By the age of two a child's height is usually about 50% of its full adult height. Estimate the adult height of a 2-year old whose height is 2 ft 9 in. About 5 ft 6 in.

27. Miguel received the following tips. Estimate the value of each. Which tip was for the greatest amount? c
   a. 15% of $4.20 $.63 b. 10% of $4.75 $.48 c. 12% of $6.00 $.72

Use the sales tax chart at the left. Estimate the sales tax and final cost of the item in each state. See Solution Key for sample answers.

State Sales Tax	
State	Tax
Colorado	3%
Florida	6%
Georgia	4%
Massachusetts	5%
New Jersey	7%

Source: *The World Almanac and Book of Facts.*

28. roller blades; $75
29. dictionary; $14.59
30. poster; $9.99
31. calculator; $18.50
32. game; $21.03
33. erasers; $.79

34. Activity Find out if there is a sales tax in your state. Then, find out how the state uses the money collected from the sales tax. Answers may vary.

35. Data File 9 (pp. 360–361) Estimate the number of girls in each age group that passed the aerobic fitness test. Assume 250 girls per age group took the test. See Solution Key.

36. Shopping A store is having a sale. All items are marked down 30%. Estimate the savings for each item. Answers may va
   a. a tee-shirt regularly priced at $16.99 about $5.10
   b. a jacket regularly priced at $129 about $39

37. Sample answer: rounding to $16, $9.20 each

37. Juanita and Tanisha ate lunch at T.J.'s Cantina. The bill was $15.75. They want to add a 15% tip and then share the bill equally. Estimate the amount each should pay.

38. Investigation (p. 362) Make a list of objects that might appear in a model of the solar system other than the sun, the Earth, the moon, and the planets.
Sample answers: asteroids, comets, other planets' moons

9-10

Connecting to Prior Knowledge

Ask students: *If a savings account pays between 10% and 7% per year, and you have $100 invested, what is the range for the money you might earn?* **($10 to $7)** Discuss strategies for finding the range.

THINK AND DISCUSS

VISUAL LEARNERS Have students write on an index card the steps for changing a percent to a fraction and a decimal. Have them place the card on their desk for reference.

Example

- *Which method is usually easiest to use when a calculator is available?*
  (Method 3)
- *When might you want to use the Method 2, expressing the percents as fractions?*
  (when the percent is equivalent to a simple fraction)

Additional Example *A karat is a measure of purity in gold. Pure gold is 24 karats. However, gold for jewelry is often mixed with another metal to give it strength.*

- *How many karats is jewelry that is 75% pure gold?*
  (18 karats)
- *In some parts of the world you can find gold jewelry that is 92% pure gold. How many karats is this?*
  (about 22 karats)
- *Which method would you use to solve each gold problem?*
  (The first can be solved by using fractions since 75% is equivalent to $\frac{3}{4}$. The second is easier to solve by using decimals. A visual model can be used for both.)

What's Ahead

- Finding a percent of a number

9-10 Finding a Percent of a Number

THINK AND DISCUSS

Your heart rate or pulse increases when you exercise. A safe exercise range is between 60% and 80% of your maximum *safe heart rate*. You can find your maximum safe heart rate by subtracting your age from 220.

There are at least three different methods you can use to find a person's safe exercise range.

Example Find the safe exercise range for a 12-year-old.

$220 - 12 = 208$ Find the maximum safe heart rate.

Method 1 Use a model.

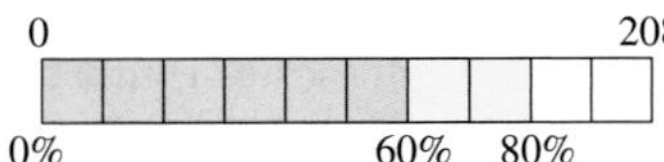

Each section represents 20.8 heart beats.

Method 2 Write the percents as fractions.

$$60\% = \frac{60}{100} \times 208 = \frac{12,480}{100} = 124.8 \approx 125$$

$$80\% = \frac{80}{100} \times 208 = \frac{16,640}{100} = 166.4 \approx 166$$

Method 3 Write the percent as decimals. Use a calculator.

60 [%] [×] 208 [=] 124.8 ≈ 125

80 [%] [×] 208 [=] 166.4 ≈ 166

Each method gives the same result. The safe exercising range for a 12-year-old is about 125 to 166 heart beats per minute.

1. Find the safe exercise range for a 20-year-old and for a 50-year-old. How does the safe exercise range change as a person grows older? 120 to 160 heart beats per minute, 102 to 136 heart beats per minute; the range decreases.

You can check your heart rate or use the *talk test* to tell whether you are exercising in the right range. If you're so out of breath that you can't talk, slow down. If you can sing, you can pick up the pace. When you can talk comfortably while exercising you are on target.

Source: *Prentice Hall Health*

"He that wrestles with us strengthens our nerves and sharpens our skill. Our antagonist is our helper."

—Edmund Burke

Organizer

1. **Focus**
   Connecting to Prior Knowledge
2. **Teach**
   Think and Discuss
3. **Closure**
   Try These
   Wrap Up

Vocabulary/Symbols
safe heart rate

Skills Reviewed in Context of Lesson
- multiplying fractions

Materials and Manipulatives
On Your Own Exercises 4–7: graph paper

Student Resources
Extra Practice
Student Study Guide
Practice, TR Ch. 9, p. 34
Student Study Guide, Spanish Resources, TR
Checkpoint, TR Ch. 9, p. 40

Teacher Resources
Teaching Transparency 81
Lesson Planner, TR p. 11

continues next page

Ongoing Assessment Ask students to find the exercising range for a 45-year-old. Have them write out their steps and use two of the three methods discussed. Ask students the following questions:

- *Will the safe pulse range for a 45-year-old be smaller or larger than your safe pulse range?* **(The safe range for a 45-year-old is smaller than a sixth grader's range.)**
- *Will 90% of the maximum heart rate for a 45-year-old be higher or lower than 90% of your maximum heart rate? Why?* **(90% of the maximum heart rate for a 45-year-old is lower than a sixth-grader's.)**
- *How does one's safe heart rate change as one grows older?* **(decreases)**

Error Alert! Students may make careless errors in problems such as Question 2. ***Remediation*** Encourage students to check their answers by estimating.

TRY THESE

Exercise 4: Have students compare their answers and estimates.

DIVERSITY For Exercise 4c, remember that some students who wear contact lenses or glasses may be self-conscious about that fact.

Wrap Up

What's the Big Idea? Ask students to describe different ways to find a percent of a number.

Connections Have a discussion about how finding a percent of a number is used. You may want to start with these examples:

- **Social Studies** (finding language distribution, voting patterns)

Organizer, continued

Prentice Hall Technology
Computer Item Generator
- 9-10

Fact of the Day

An expenditure of 3500 calories, either in the form of decreased consumption or increased activity, is required to consume one pound of fat.

—ACADEMIC AMERICAN ENCYCLOPEDIA

Sometimes one method is more appropriate or convenient to use than another.

2. Which method would you use to answer each question? Explain your reasons. Use a 24 h day.
   a. Catherine spends 25% of her day in school. How many hours does Catherine spend in school each day?
   b. Ian practices the piano for 5% of the day. For how many hours does Ian practice the piano each day?
   c. **Discussion** Describe a way to calculate each percent using mental math.

2. Sample answers:
   a. fraction method, 6 h
   b. decimal method, 1.2 h
   c. Since 25% is $\frac{1}{4}$, divide 24 by 4. Find 10% of 24 and then divide by 2.

TRY THESE

3. Approximately 67% of body weight is water. Suppose a person weighs 114 lb. About how many pounds is water? about 76 lb
4. In the United States, about 46% of the population wears glasses or contact lenses.
   a. How many people would you expect to wear glasses or contact lenses in a group of 85 people? about 39 people
   b. Explain how you found your answer and why you chose that method.
   c. How many people in your classroom would you expect to wear glasses or contact lenses? Answers may vary. About 14 in a class of 30

4.b. Decimal method. 46% is not easy to find with a model. $\frac{23}{50} \times 85$ is not easy to find.

ON YOUR OWN

Find each percent. Use any method.

5. 50% of 786 — 393
6. 43% of 61 — 26.23
7. 10% of 56 — 5.6
8. 75% of 84 — 63
9. 37% of 140 — 51.8
10. 80% of 255 — 204
11. 12% of 72 — 8.64
12. 25% of 112 — 28
13. 66% of 99 — 65.34
14. **Sports** The Lions won 75% of their 28 games this year. How many games did they win? 21 games
15. During the summer Rosa earned $950. She saved 40%. How much money did she save? $380

Mixed REVIEW

Compare. Use >, <, or =.

1. $\frac{3}{8}$ ■ $\frac{2}{4}$ < 2. $\frac{6}{15}$ ■ $\frac{2}{3}$ <

Estimate a 15% tip for each amount.

3. $4.00 4. $15.50

Solve for *n*.

5. $\frac{1}{3} = \frac{n}{360}$ 120
6. $\frac{3}{8} = \frac{n}{360}$ 135

7. The chorus director can arrange singers in rows of 10, 12, or 15 with no one left over. What is the least number of singers in the chorus? 60 singers

3. sample answer: $.60
4. sample answer: $2.33

- **Geography** (analyzing land masses by type of terrain, comparing heights of mountains)
- **Science** (comparing experimental groups, analyzing mineral content of rock samples)

Reteaching Activity Have students model percents of a number by using two colors of blocks. Provide pairs of students with blocks. Have each student take turns modeling and finding the percent of the blocks that are a certain color. Partners should check each other's answers.

Journal Ask students to compare the different methods of finding a percent. Have students name the method they prefer and explain their preferences.

ON YOUR OWN

WRITING For Exercise 16, have students support their answers with examples.

ESL For Exercise 22, encourage students to conjecture whether the frequency table remains the same for other languages. Challenge students to work in pairs on a project to test their conjecture, using a written passage in another language.

CONNECTION TO LANGUAGE ARTS Exercises 17–22 have students apply their knowledge of percents to analyze the frequency of vowels in written passages.

CHECKPOINT

Exercise 12 is an enhanced multiple choice question.

Students will need 10 × 10 grids for Exercises 4–7.

16. **Writing** Explain how you would decide when to use each of the three methods in this lesson when finding the percent of a number. Answers may vary. You can look for numbers that work easily together.

Frequency of Vowels in Written Passages

Letter	A	E	I	O	U	Y
Frequency	8%	13%	6%	8%	3%	2%

Use the table above to estimate the number of letters you would expect in each passage.

17. the number of E's in a passage of 300 letters about 39
18. the number of A's in a passage of 1400 letters about 112
19. the number of U's in a passage of 235 letters about 7
20. the number of I's in a passage of 695 letters about 42
21. Why don't the percents in the table add to 100%? Answers may vary. Consonants also occur.
22. a. Examine a short passage in a book. Count the number of letters in the passage. Use the percents from the table to estimate the number of each vowel to expect.
    b. Count the number of A's. Is your count the same as your expected number in (a.)? Why or why not?
    c. Count the number of B's. Write the number as a percent of the total letters in the passage. 2; about 1%
    d. Do you think you have enough data to draw any conclusions about the general frequency of the letter B in written passages? Why or why not?
23. Nail biting is a hard habit to kick. About 40% of children and teenagers bite their nails. A town has 1,618 children and teenagers. How many would you expect to be nail biters? 647 children and teenagers
24. The dance club is holding its annual show. The club printed 400 tickets and sold 85% of the tickets. How many tickets did the club sell? 340 tickets

Only two words in the English language use all the vowels a, e, i, o, u, in order. They are *facetious* and *abstemious*. **Find out what each word means.**

Source: *The Macmillan Illustrated Almanac For Kids*

22.a. Sample: No. of letters = 230.

Vowel	A	E	I	O	U	Y
Expected Number	18	30	14	18	7	5

22.b. 16; yes; the numbers were close. Frequency reflects an average. Passages will vary.

22.d. Answers may vary. You might conclude that B occurs less frequently than some vowels. To determine a frequency, you would need to consider more samples.

Assignment Options

Core: 5–15, 23, MR all, CH all	
Reinforce: 16–21, 24, 25	**Enrich:** 22, 26

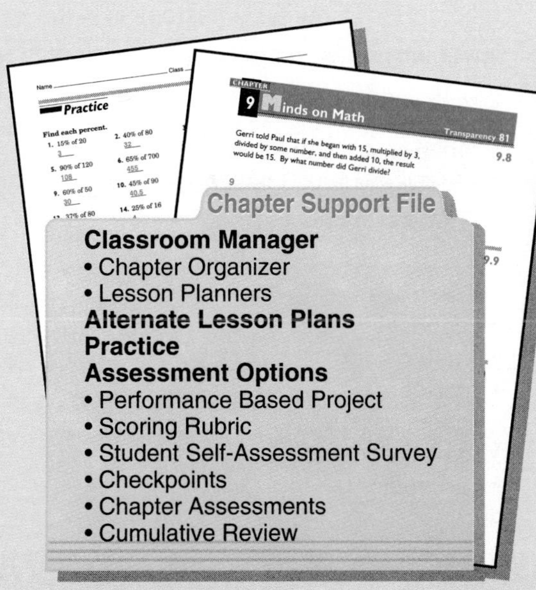

Minds on Math available in Teaching Transparencies

Math Minutes

Put students in groups of four, and ask them to draw a map and find a distance based on the following information. On the map of Rock County, Limestone is in the lower left corner, Slate is $1\frac{3}{8}$ in. north of it, Basalt is $2\frac{3}{4}$ in. east of Limestone, and Granite is $\frac{5}{16}$ in. south of Slate. About how far is Granite from Limestone?
$1\frac{1}{16}$ in. north of Limestone

Materials for 9-11

- paper
- metric ruler
- scissors
- paste or tape
- safety compass
- protractor

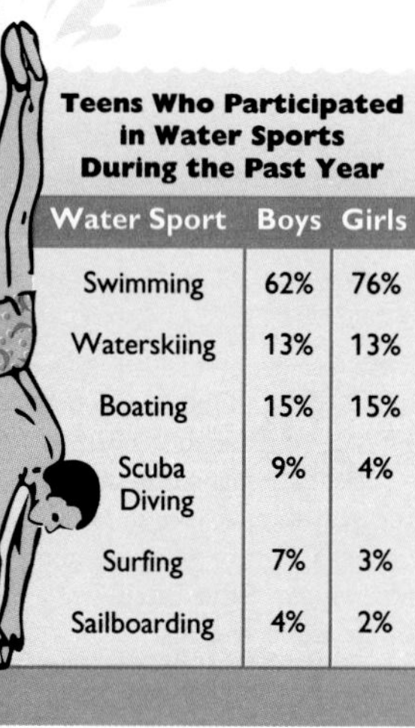

Teens Who Participated in Water Sports During the Past Year

Water Sport	Boys	Girls
Swimming	62%	76%
Waterskiing	13%	13%
Boating	15%	15%
Scuba Diving	9%	4%
Surfing	7%	3%
Sailboarding	4%	2%

ource: *Teenage Research Unlimited*

25. Data File 9 (pp. 360–361) Use the number of teens surveyed. How many females participate in volleyball? how many males? males—about 225; females—about 319

Use the table at the left.

26. An interviewer talked to 250 males and 250 females between the ages of 12 and 15. How many would you expect to have been swimming in the past year?
345 people

CHECKPOINT

1. The average of three consecutive numbers is 9. Their sum is 27. What are the numbers? 8, 9, 10

2. Find the value of x. The figures are similar. $x = 10$

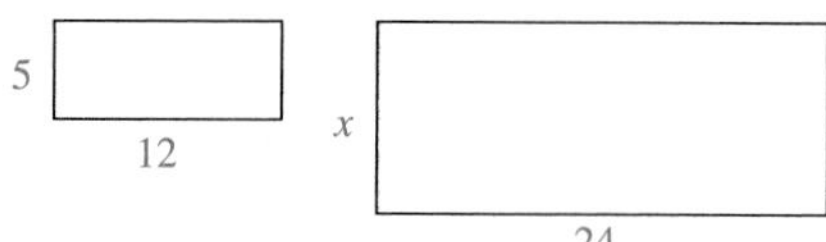

3. A map has a scale of 1 cm : 75 km. The distance on the map from Hondo to Cheyenne is 3.5 cm. What is the actual distance? 262.5 km

Use a 10 × 10 grid to model each percent.

4. 17% **5.** 46% **6.** 89% **7.** 71%
Check students' drawings. See Solution Key.

Write as a percent.

8. $\frac{6}{8}$ 75% **9.** 0.45 45% **10.** 0.67 67% **11.** $\frac{15}{25}$ 60%

12. Choose A, B, C, or D. Which of the following is *not* a way to find 88% of 40? C

A. 0.88×40 **B.** $\frac{88}{100} \times 40$

C. $\frac{40}{n} = \frac{88}{100}$ **D.** 0.40×88

Find each percent.

13. 58% of 72
41.76

14. 86% of 41
35.26

15. 8% of 40
3.2

9-11

Connecting to Prior Knowledge

Ask students the following questions:

- *Where have you seen circle graphs used?* **(A possible answer is in social studies.)**
- *How are circle graphs different from other graphs such as line graphs?* **(Circle graphs are used to compare data within a whole, while line graphs often show changes over time.)**

WORK TOGETHER

KINESTHETIC LEARNERS For Question 5, have students use their compass to draw another circle that is the same size as the circle they drew for Question 4. Direct students to cut the new circle in half and then to cut one of the halves in half. Tell students to label these pieces 50% or 25%. Instruct students to use these pieces to determine if the sections of their graph are the correct size.

DIVERSITY Some students may not be physically able to construct the circle graph. Assign these students to a partner who can make the construction while the physically challenged student takes notes or records the results.

Question 6a: This question reviews measuring with a protractor.

Question 7: Form heterogeneous groups of four for this question. If possible, allow the groups of students to survey other classrooms.

TECHNOLOGY OPTION After students have completed Questions 1–7, have them use a spreadsheet to construct the circle graphs. Then compare the resulting circle graphs with ones they constructed by hand.

What's Ahead

- Making circle graphs.

9-11 Constructing a Circle Graph

WHAT YOU'LL NEED

- ✓ Dot paper
- ✓ Metric Ruler
- ✓ Scissors
- ✓ Glue
- ✓ Compass
- ✓ Protractor

WORK TOGETHER

Circle graphs provide a good visual representation of percent data. The table shows the results of a survey of 1,000 adults who were asked to think about the amount of time they spend watching TV. Work with a partner to construct a circle graph for the data. See Solution Key.

Too much	Too little	About right	Don't know
49%	18%	31%	2%

Source: *Gallup Organization*

1. Use the data to make a circle graph.
   - draw a strip 10 cm long, leaving a tab at the end. Since 10 cm = 100 mm, each millimeter represents 1%.
   - Mark the strip with the percentages given in the table.

49%	18%	31%	2%	Tab

(100% spans the first four sections)

2. Should the percents that make up a circle graph always add to 100%? Why or why not? Yes. Explanations will vary. The information represented consists of parts of one whole.

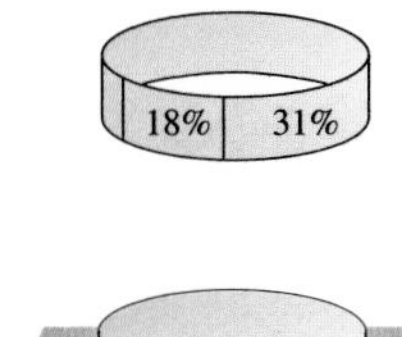

3. Use the strip to form a percent circle. Cut the strip out carefully. Shape the strip into a circle and paste or tape the ends. Make sure to align the beginning and end of the strip.

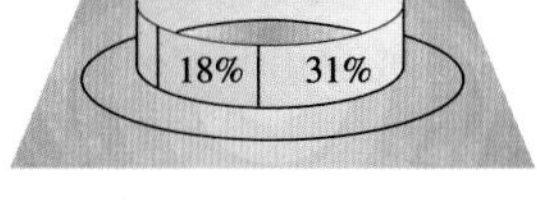

4. Use a compass to draw a circle slightly larger than your percent circle. Place a dot at the center of your circle. Use your percent circle to mark off the percentages around the circumference of the circle. Use a ruler to connect the marks to the center of the circle.

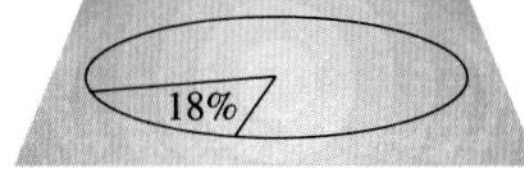

5. Label your graph and give it a title. Does your graph make sense? Use estimation to decide if each section appears to be the correct size. Check students' graphs.

"In the ideal sense nothing is uninteresting; there are only uninterested people."

—Brooks Atkinson

Organizer

1. **Focus**
   Connecting to Prior Knowledge
2. **Teach**
   Work Together
   Think and Discuss
3. **Closure**
   Try These
   Wrap Up

Skills Reviewed in Context of Lesson

- finding percent of a number
- measuring angles

Materials and Manipulatives

- paper (for each group)
- metric ruler (one for each group)
- scissors (one for each group)
- paste or tape (for each group)
- compass (one for each group)
- protractor (one for each group)

Student Resources

Extra Practice
Student Study Guide
Practice, TR Ch. 9, p. 35
Student Study Guide, Spanish Resources, TR

continues next page

THINK AND DISCUSS

Error Alert! Students may try to use the number 1,000 to find the number of degrees for Question 8a. ***Remediation*** Point out to students that it is easier to use the ratio from the percent data than to form a ratio from the actual number of respondents. Remind students to look for the least complicated method of solving a problem.

Ongoing Assessment Have students compare the different methods and describe situations for which they are best suited. Encourage students to provide examples.

TRY THESE

Exercise 11: Have students compare their graphs.

Wrap Up

What's the Big Idea? Ask students to explain how to make circle graphs.

Reteaching Activity Group students in pairs. Have each student in a pair take turns providing his or her partner with a time, such as 3:30. Ask the other student to reply by estimating the angle the hands make on a clock face at that time as a percent of a circle. At 3:30, the percent of a circle is about 25% of a circle, or 90°.

Connections Have a discussion about where circle graphs are used. You may want to start with these examples:

- **Newspapers** (showing the national budget deficit or the unemployment rate)
- **Geography** (comparing the land masses of the continents or the areas of the oceans)
- **Household** (displaying monthly expenses)

Organizer, continued

Teacher Resources

Teaching Transparencies 8, 9, 81
Transparency Masters, p. 3
Overhead Manipulatives: protractor
Lesson Planner, TR Ch. 9, p. 12

Prentice Hall Technology

Multimedia Math
- Math Tools, Spreadsheet

Computer Item Generator
- 9-11

Fact of the Day

In 1731, Benjamin Franklin founded the Library Company of Philadelphia, the first subscription library in America. It served as a model for the modern public library.

—ACADEMIC AMERICAN ENCYCLOPEDIA

Measures may vary slightly. Accept reasonable measures. 176°, 65°, 112°, 7°

6. a. Use a protractor to find the measure of each angle on your completed circle graph.
   b. Can you think of another way to find the measure of each angle? Yes; find percentages of 360°.
7. Conduct a survey in your classroom to see how your classmates feel about their TV viewing habits. Give the same choice of responses. Make a circle graph of your data. Answers may vary.

THINK AND DISCUSS

You can also make a circle graph by combining some math skills you already know.

- finding the percent of a number
- the number of degrees in a circle
- using a protractor to draw an angle with a given measure

The most overdue library book in the U.S. was borrowed in 1823. The great-grandson of the borrower returned the book on December 7, 1968. The fine for the overdue book would have been $2,264.

Source: *Guinness Book of Records*

The table below shows the responses of 1,000 adults who were asked whether they spent too much or too little time reading for pleasure.

Too much	Too little	About right	Don't know
7%	73%	16%	4%

Source: *Gallup Organization*

8. **Discussion** Suppose you want to make a circle graph. How could you find the measure of each section using proportions? using percents?
   a. Use a proportion to find the number of degrees for the response "Don't know." $\frac{4}{100} = \frac{n}{360}$; $n = 14.4$; about 14°
   b. Use a percent to find the number of degrees for the response "Too little." $0.73 \times 360 \approx 262.8$; about 263°
   c. Use any method to find the number of degrees for the response "About right." Which method do you think is easiest? Why?
   d. Use a compass to draw a circle and a radius. Use your protractor to draw each angle. Label your graph and give it a title. Check students' drawings. See Solution Key.

8. Place the number of the percent over 100 and set equal to $\frac{n}{360}$. Write the percent as a decimal and multiply by 360.
8.c. About 58° Answers may vary. Sample: using percents requires only one operation.

Journal Ask students to compare the different ways to create a circle graph. Have students name their preferences and support their answers.

ON YOUR OWN

ESL For Exercise 12a, suggest that students use pictures or icons such as a bus or a car on tables. "Very willing" could be represented by a smiling face. "Somewhat willing" could use a face with a smaller smile. "Not very willing" could be a face with a frown, and "Don't know" could be a question mark. Encourage students to make their own tables and use pictures as labels.

WRITING For Exercise 12b, have students support their answers with a percent.

9. **Discussion** When are circle graphs a better way to display data than tables? Use examples to support your answer.

9. Answers will vary. When the data can be thought of as parts of one whole and you want to compare the parts; for example, the parts of a budget

TRY THESE

10. The graph at the right has the labels in the wrong sections. Tell which section should have each percent label. A: 53%; B: 25%; C: 22%

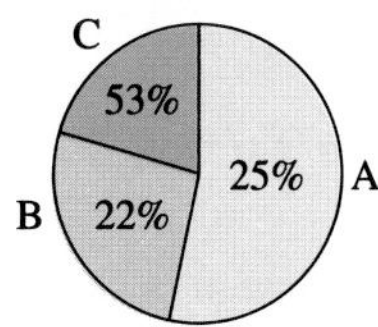

11. La Monte Middle School held several fundraising events. The percent raised from each activity is shown in the table below. Display the data in a circle graph. See Solution Key.

Car wash	Paper drive	Book sale	Food stand
42%	28%	18%	12%

ON YOUR OWN

12. a. Construct two circle graphs. One that shows the bus data and another that displays the car pool data. Remember to label your graphs and give them a title. See Solution Key.

What Teen Drivers Will Do for Air Quality				
	Very willing	Somewhat willing	Not very willing	Don't know
Use the bus more often	22%	25%	50%	3%
Car pool more often	49%	26%	23%	2%

Source: *Gallup Organization*

b. **Writing** Which option for preserving air quality seems more likely to succeed? Why? Car pooling; percent very willing is greater than percent very willing to use bus.

c. Think of another option for preserving air quality. Use the same response choices as in the table and survey 25 students. Make a circle graph to show your results. Answers may vary. Samples: walk, bicycle

13. List the things you do on a Saturday. Estimate the hours you spend on each activity. Write the time as a percent of a 24-hour day. Construct a circle graph. Check students' graphs.

14. **Data File 1 (pp. 2–3)** Estimate the percent of hours spent on each type of commercial during 604 h of kid's TV.

Mixed REVIEW

Evaluate.

1. $\frac{3}{4} \div \frac{4}{5}$ $\frac{15}{16}$
2. $\frac{8}{15} \div \frac{2}{3}$ $\frac{4}{5}$

Find each percent.

3. 55% of 386 212.3
4. 33% of 58 19.14
5. Which number doesn't belong? Give a reason for your choice.

2992 1919

4949 2929

Answers may vary. 2992 does not have alternating digits.

14. Answers may vary. Accept any reasonable estimates. Toys: about 30%, breakfast foods: about 20%; snacks and drinks: about 20%; fast foods: about 6%; health foods: about 3%; others: about 20%

Assignment Options

Core: 12, MR all	
Reinforce: 13	**Enrich:** 14

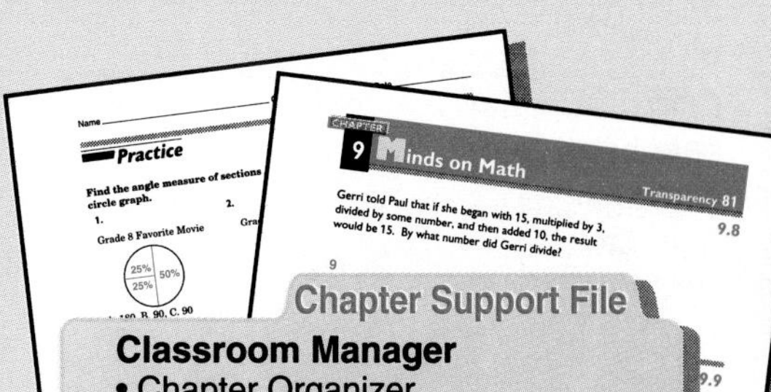

Classroom Manager
- Chapter Organizer
- Lesson Planners

Alternate Lesson Plans

Practice

Assessment Options
- Performance Based Project
- Scoring Rubric
- Student Self-Assessment Survey
- Checkpoints
- Chapter Assessments
- Cumulative Review

Minds on Math available in Teaching Transparencies

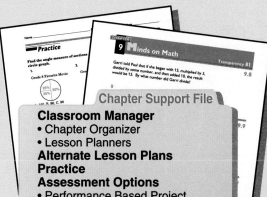

Math Minutes

Choose any two fractions that are not equivalent. How many fractions are between the two? Justify your answer. **infinitely many; you can always divide the difference of two fractions in half to find an intermediate fraction.**

CHAPTER 9 WRAP UP

For Exercises 3–8, have students circle the cross products before solving each proportion.

Ongoing Assessment Have students work with partners. One partner can do the odd numbered exercises, the other partner the even numbered exercises. Have the partners exchange papers and check each of their answers. For Exercise 20, you may want both partners to work on constructing the circle graph.

Exercise 13: You may want to tell students that 80% of the regular price is the sale price.

Exercise 14 is an enhanced multiple choice question.

Vocabulary/Symbols

corresponding parts
cross products
distortions
equal ratios
percent
proportion
rate
ratio
safe heart rate
scale
unit rate

Ratios, Rates, and Proportions 9-1, 9-2, 9-3

A ***ratio*** is a comparison of two numbers.

A ***rate*** is a ratio that compares two measures with different units.

A ***proportion*** is an equation stating that two ratios are equal. You can use cross products to find the missing term in a proportion.

1. A moonrat is a member of the hedgehog family. An adult male's body is about 45 cm long. Write the ratio to compare a moonrat's body length to 1 m in three ways. (1 m = 100 cm) 45 to 100, $\frac{45}{100}$, 45 : 100

2. A package of three videotapes is on sale for \$5.97. A package of 2 videotapes is on sale for \$3.76. Find the unit rate for each. Which tape has the higher unit cost? three tapes: \$1.99 two tapes: \$1.88 The tape in the package of three.

Find the value of *n*.

3. $\frac{3}{5} = \frac{n}{35}$ $n = 21$
4. $\frac{6}{9} = \frac{18}{n}$ $n = 27$
5. $\frac{n}{6} = \frac{12}{24}$ $n = 3$
6. $\frac{32}{n} = \frac{8}{4}$ $n = 16$
7. $\frac{n}{15} = \frac{5}{25}$ $n = 3$
8. $\frac{17}{51} = \frac{3}{n}$ $n = 9$

Similar Figures and Scale Drawings 9-5, 9-6

If two figures are ***similar,*** their corresponding angles are congruent and the ratios of the lengths of their corresponding sides are equal.

A ***scale*** is a ratio that compares length on a drawing or model to the actual length of an object.

9. **Writing** The triangles have equal angle measures. Tell how you would show that the triangles are similar. Measure each side of the triangles. Compare the ratios of the lengths of the corresponding sides.

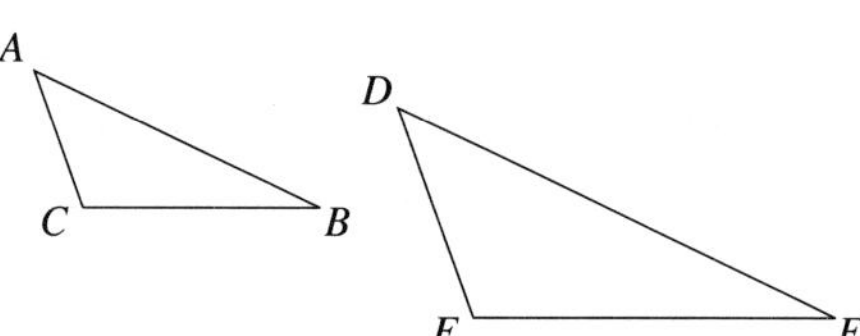

10. A scale on a landscape blueprint is 1 in. : 6 ft. A stone wall is 4 in. long on the blueprint. How long is the wall? 24 ft

11. A drawing of a leatherback turtle has a scale of 2 cm : 1 m. The drawing of the turtle is 3 cm long. How long is the turtle? 1.5 m

Getting Ready for Chapter 10

The skills previewed will help students understand and solve problems based upon permutations and combinations.

Percents, Fractions, and Decimals — 9-7, 9-8, 9-9

A ***percent*** is a ratio that compares a number to 100. You can write a percent as a decimal or as a fraction. You can estimate with a percent.

12. Write 65% as a decimal and as a fraction in simplest form. 0.65, $\frac{13}{20}$

13. An office chair is on sale for 80% of the regular price of \$87.95. Estimate the sale price. Accept any reasonable estimate. about \$70

14. Choose A, B, C, or D. Find the best estimate for 72% of 90. C

A. 72 **B.** 45 **C.** 68 **D.** 90

Percent of a Number and Circle Graphs — 9-10, 9-11

You can use a model, a fraction, or a decimal to find a percent of a number.

You can make a circle graph to show percent data.

Find each percent.

15. 75% of 40 30
16. 23% of 19 4.37
17. 60% of 80 48
18. 10% of 235 23.5
19. 5% of \$15.98 \$.80

20. Use the data at the right to construct a circle graph. See Solution Key.

Ways to Get to School

Car	Bus	Bike	Walk
24%	57%	4%	15%

Strategies and Applications — 9-4

Sometimes *Guess and Test* is a good strategy to solve problems. Make a reasonable guess, test it against the problem, and keep trying until you find the correct answer.

21. Todd's class is making plastic birdfeeders in two sizes. Small birdfeeders use 2 dowels, large birdfeeders use 3 dowels. The class used 103 dowels to make 38 feeders. How many small birdfeeders did that class make? 11 small feeders

GETTING READY FOR CHAPTER 10

22. Lian planned to call her new friend Onida, but the last two digits of her phone number are smudged. 375-04■■
How many possibilities are there for Onida's number? 100 possibilities

Student Resources

Practice, p. 390
Problem Solving Practice, p. 376
Extra Practice
Student Study Guide
Student Study Guide, Spanish Resources, TR
Tools for Studying Smarter, TR
Student Self-Assessment Survey, TR Ch. 9, p. 39

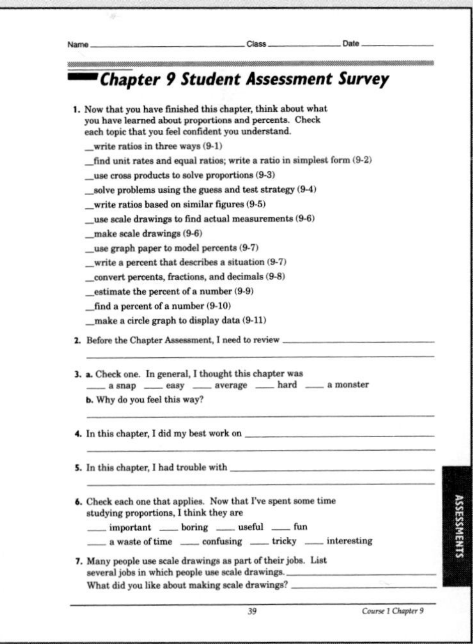

Name ______ Class ______ Date ______

Chapter 9 Student Assessment Survey

1. Now that you have finished this chapter, think about what you have learned about proportions and percents. Check each topic that you feel confident you understand.
__write ratios in three ways (9-1)
__find unit rates and equal ratios; write a ratio in simplest form (9-2)
__use cross products to solve proportions (9-3)
__solve problems using the guess and test strategy (9-4)
__write ratios based on similar figures (9-5)
__use scale drawings to find actual measurements (9-6)
__make scale drawings (9-6)
__use graph paper to model percents (9-7)
__write a percent that describes a situation (9-7)
__convert percents, fractions, and decimals (9-8)
__estimate the percent of a number (9-9)
__find a percent of a number (9-10)
__make a circle graph to display data (9-11)

2. Before the Chapter Assessment, I need to review ______

3. a. Check one. In general, I thought this chapter was
__ a snap __ easy __ average __ hard __ a monster
b. Why do you feel this way?

4. In this chapter, I did my best work on ______

5. In this chapter, I had trouble with ______

6. Check each one that applies. Now that I've spent some time studying proportions, I think they are
__ important __ boring __ useful __ fun
__ a waste of time __ confusing __ tricky __ interesting

7. Many people use scale drawings as part of their jobs. List several jobs in which people use scale drawings. ______
What did you like about making scale drawings? ______

ASSESSMENTS

39 Course 1 Chapter 9

CHAPTER 9

PUTTING IT ALL TOGETHER

The projects on these pages can be used in a variety of ways.

- alternative assessment
- portfolio ideas
- additional assignments for gifted and talented students
- extra credit for all students

Follow Up

- Recall the human model of the solar system students formed on the first day of the project. Ask students to list ways they would change the model to reflect facts they have learned since the beginning of the project.
- Have students list the main points concerning their investigation that they feel need to be addressed in their letter to the editor.
- Ask them to outline their letters for your review before they are written.

EXCURSION The nearest star, Alpha Centauri, is about 4.3 light-years from the Sun. In a model with a 10-inch diameter Sun, Alpha Centauri would appear about 3,500 miles from the Sun.

Round and Round

COOPERATIVE GROUPS Students can work together to find circle graphs, because these graphs are not as prevalent as line graphs and bar graphs.

EXCURSION If a computer is not available, have students display the two graphs (circle graph and second choice) on poster board and present it to the class.

TECHNOLOGY OPTION If statistical software is available, students can input the data from a circle graph and then test other formats of graphs.

Materials and Manipulatives

Follow Up
- basketball
- tape measure

Round and Round
- newspapers
- magazines
- art supplies

Scaled Down
- graph paper

Other Available Technology

Round and Round
- *Data Insights* by Sunburst

PUTTING IT ALL TOGETHER

Follow Up

Modeling the Solar System

The Astro County Science Museum has begun its final push for donations to help build its model of the solar system. It's time for you to do your part. Write a letter to the editor of the Astro County Gazette. In your letter, explain why you believe local citizens should donate to the project or why they should oppose the project. Explain your reasons for your position. The following are suggestions to help you compose your letter.

- ✓ Use ratios.
- ✓ Use proportions.
- ✓ Use a scale drawing.

The problems preceded by the magnifying glass (p. 372, # 30; p. 379, # 19; p. 386, # 30, and p. 394 # 38) will help you support your argument.

The museum was right to emphasize the importance of science education in its brochure. Surveys regularly reveal that the American public is greatly misinformed about even the most basic science facts. One recent survey showed that 20% of Americans believe that the Sun revolves around the Earth.

Excursion: In a scale model of our galaxy with the Sun the size of a basketball, how far away would the nearest star (after the Sun) appear?

Where to Look:
- an encyclopedia or an astronomy text

Round and Round

Do this with your group.

Look through newspapers and magazines for examples of at least 3 circle graphs. For each circle graph, write two word problems that can be solved by using the information displayed in the graph.

Excursion: Look closely at each circle graph. Could the information displayed in any of the circle graphs be displayed by using another kind of graph? Choose one circle graph and make another kind of graph that displays the same information.

404

Scaled Down

Students need to be careful to scale furniture as well as the dimensions of the bedroom. Make sure the scale is clearly marked on the drawing.

RESEARCH Students may wish to visit an architect's office to see the process of designing houses and offices. Many architects have sophisticated computer programs to help them perform the designing tasks.

Dream Day

For the 10-hour period, students may wish to convert the time to minutes, hours and minutes, hours, by blocks of time, or any combination of time. Using their creative talents to dream, students may decide to fly in an airplane westward to gain extra hours.

Ask students to display the time spent on each activity so that the total can be easily calculated for accuracy.

SCALED DOWN
Use graph paper to make a scale drawing of your bedroom or another room in your home. Find the length and width of your room. You will also need to decide on an appropriate scale for your drawing.
After you have completed your scale drawing, cut out different figures that can be used to represent furniture such as a bed, bureau, and bookcase. Try to show at least two different ways the furniture in the room can be arranged. How would you arrange the furniture in the room to achieve the largest open area possible?
Dream Day
• Imagine that you could spend a day doing anything you wanted, such as spending time with friends, going to a concert, or shopping at your favorite stores.
• Create a schedule of your day that consists of activities from 9:00 A.M. to 7:00 P.M. After you complete your schedule, make a table that displays in hours and minutes the amount of time spent on each activity.
• Below the table, make a list of statements that describe the time spent on each activity in fractional terms, such as "One-tenth of my time was spent at a soccer game."
405

CHAPTER 9 ASSESSMENT

ESTIMATION For Exercise 10, suggest to students that they first estimate the decimal equivalent for $\frac{5}{12}$.

Enhanced Multiple Choice Questions are more complex than traditional multiple choice questions, which assess only one skill. Enhanced multiple choice questions assess the processes that students use as well as the end results. They are written so that students can use more than one strategy to solve the problem. Using multiple strategies is encouraged by the National Council of Teachers of Mathematics (NCTM).

Exercise 4 is an example of an enhanced multiple choice question.

Writing Questions allow students to describe more fully their thinking and understanding of the concepts they've learned.

Exercise 2 is a writing question.

Resources

Performance Based Project, TR Ch. 9, pp. 36–38
Chapter Assessment, Forms A and B, TR Ch. 9, pp. 41–44
Spanish Chapter Assessment, Spanish Resources, TR
Computer Item Generator

CHAPTER 9

Assessment

1. Which is another way to write the ratio 6 : 3? D

A. 3 : 6 **B.** 6 , 3 **C.** $\frac{3}{6}$ **D.** 6 to 3

2. Writing Are the ratios 9 apples to 12 apples and 6 apples to 10 apples equal? Explain your answer. No. Sample explanation: write a proportion, check cross products.

3. Write a ratio comparing the shaded region to the unshaded region as a fraction in lowest terms. $\frac{2}{3}$

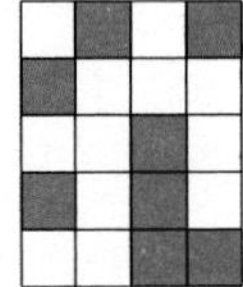

4. Find a ratio equal to $\frac{3}{12}$. C

A. $\frac{9}{24}$ **B.** $\frac{4}{1}$ **C.** $\frac{8}{32}$ **D.** $\frac{5}{15}$

5. Solve for n.

a. $\frac{21}{35} = \frac{9}{n}$ $n = 15$ **b.** $\frac{n}{63} = \frac{4}{14}$ $n = 18$

6. A scale drawing has a scale of 1 cm to 1.5 m. A tree in the drawing measures 4.5 cm. Find the height of the tree. 6.75 m

7. Write each as a percent.

a. $\frac{11}{20}$ 55% **b.** 0.7 70%

8. Write each as a fraction in lowest terms.

a. 38% $\frac{19}{50}$ **b.** 0.62 $\frac{31}{50}$

9. Express each as a decimal.

a. $\frac{6}{20}$ 0.3 **b.** 55% 0.55 **c.** 6% 0.06 **d.** $\frac{78}{100}$ 0.78

10. Estimation Choose the best estimate for $\frac{5}{12}$. Explain how you arrived at your estimate. B; $\frac{6}{12}$ = 50% and $\frac{4}{12}$ = $33\frac{1}{3}$%

A. 50% **B.** 40% **C.** 30%

11. Draw a model to show each percent.

a. 75% of 200 **b.** 30% of 210
See Solution Key.

12. Find each percent.

a. 52% of 96 49.92
b. 20% of 400 80
c. 38% of 150 57

13. Use the data in the table to make a circle graph. See Solution Key.

Types of Books Preferred

Mysteries	Biographies	Fiction	Humor
22%	13%	55%	10%

14. Marisa spent \$4.25 on stamps. She bought some for \$.29 each and some for \$.35 each. How many of each type did she buy? five \$.29 stamps and eight \$.35 stamps

15. Gerald bought art supplies that totalled \$15.78. The tax is 3%. Estimate the amount of the tax and the total cost of the art supplies. about \$.48 tax; about \$16.25

16. Estimate a 15% tip on each bill.

a. \$25.35 \$3.80 **b.** \$9.35 \$1.40

For Exercises 15–16, accept any reasonable estimates.

CHAPTER 9

CUMULATIVE REVIEW

Exercise 3 is an enhanced multiple choice question.

Item(s)	Review Topic	Chapter
1	ratios	9
2	numerical expressions	5
3	prime factorization	7
4	estimating area	6
5	exponents	5
6	points, lines, and planes	2
7	subtracting mixed numbers	8
8	finding elapsed time	3
9	distributive property	4
10	averages	1

Resources

Cumulative Review, TR Ch. 9, pp. 45–46
Transparency Masters, TR p. 35

CHAPTER 9

Cumulative Review

Choose A, B, C, or D.

1. What is the ratio of the number of squares to the number of triangles? B

A. 1:1 **B.** 1:2
C. 2:1 **D.** 1:4

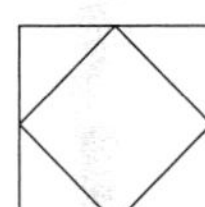

2. A garage charges $2.00 for the first 90 min and $1.00 for each additional half hour. Which expression can you use to find the cost of parking for 4 h? C

A. 2.00 + 4(1.00)
B. 2.00 + 2.5(1.00)
C. 2.00 + 5(1.00)
D. 4(2.00 + 1.00)

3. Which number is *not* a prime factor of 2,420? B

A. 2 **B.** 3 **C.** 5 **D.** 11

4. What is the best estimate for the area of the shaded region? C

A. 18 square units
B. 20 square units
C. 25 square units
D. 40 square units

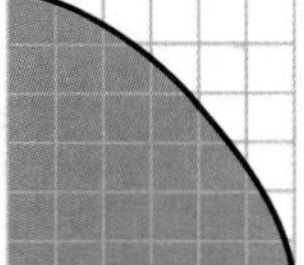

5. Find the value of the expression $3 + b^2$ when $b = 5$. D

A. 64 **B.** 13
C. 16 **D.** 28

6. Which statement is *not* true about points, A, B, and C shown? A

A. A, B, and C are collinear
B. A, B, and C are coplanar
C. $\angle ABC$ is acute
D. A does not lie on $\overleftrightarrow{BC}$

A
B C

7. What should you do first to find the difference $5\frac{1}{4} - 3\frac{2}{3}$? B

A. Find the difference 5 − 3
B. Write $5\frac{1}{4}$ as $4\frac{5}{4}$.
C. Find the difference $5 - 3\frac{2}{3}$.
D. Write $3\frac{2}{3}$ as $2\frac{5}{3}$.

8. Sukie boarded the school bus at 7:48 A.M. and arrived at school at 8:13 A.M. How many minutes did she spend on the bus? C

A. 13 min **B.** 65 min
C. 25 min **D.** 15 min

9. Which expression is equivalent to 35 • 10? A

A. 35 (100 ÷ 10)
B. 35 (100 • 10)
C. 35 + (100 • 10)
D. 35 + (100 + 10)

10. Find the mean of the allowances: $4, $2, $2.50, $4, $3. D

A. $4.00 **B.** $2.50
C. $2.75 **D.** $3.10

CHAPTER

10 Probability

Why Study Probability?

This branch of mathematics helps students find out how likely it is that a particular outcome, related to some event, will occur. Some possible reasons for studying this topic include its use in the social sciences, genetic studies, quantum mechanics, industry, commerce, and the insurance business.

Graphic Display of Chapter Content

Below is one possible representation of the chapter's content and its applications to the world outside the classroom. Have students create their own graphic display and fill in applications that they have seen in their own lives.

- The center oval should state the main concept of the chapter: probability.
- Have students draw the ovals with the next level of concepts presented in the chapter (probability events, experimental probability, tree diagrams, independent events, and arrangements). You may want students to add other topics that they think are appropriate.
- Ask students to draw as many application ovals as they can.
- Discuss all the applications that students identify.
- Have students make and present one display that includes all the students' ideas.

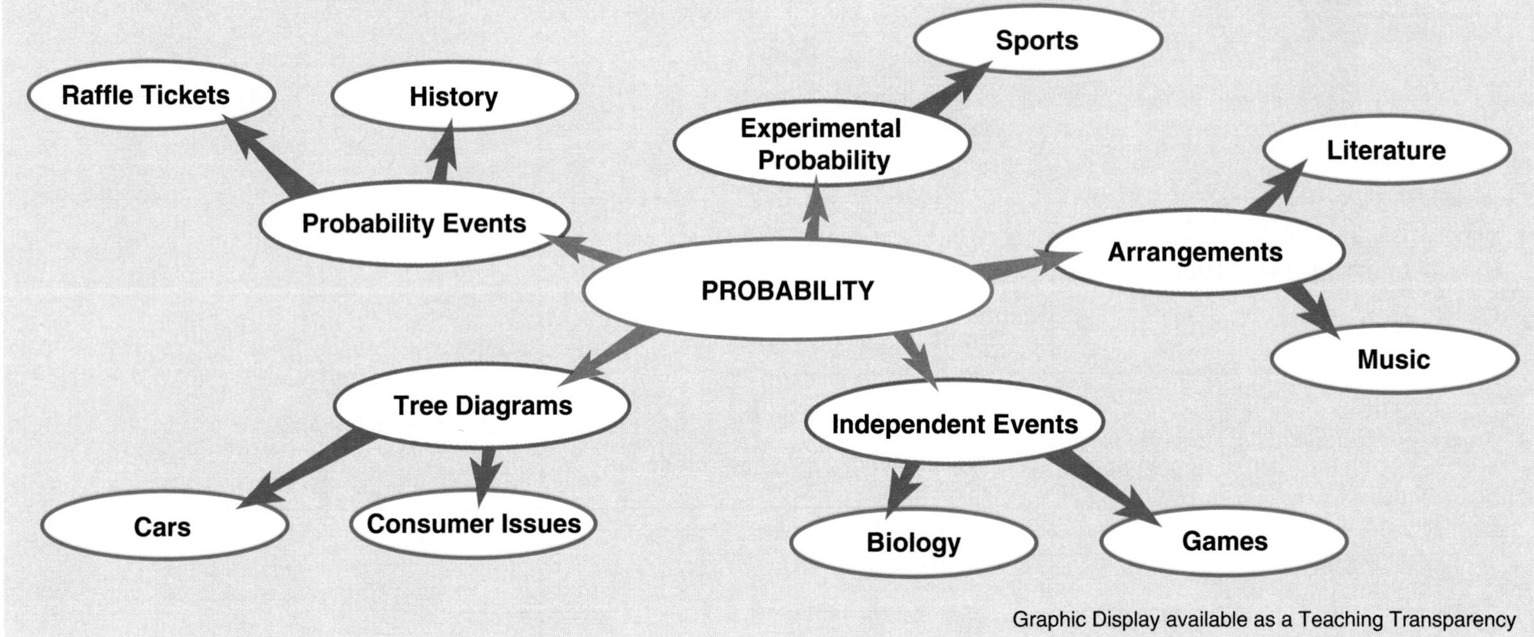

Graphic Display available as a Teaching Transparency

Vocabulary and Symbols

certain
counting principle
equally likely
experimental probability
fair
favorable
impossible
independent
model
population sample
random
representative
simulate
tree diagram
trial

Materials and Manipulatives

a number of beans, chips, cubes, or other objects that differ only in color	software with random number and graphing capabilities
bag or container	red and blue cubes
computer	spinners
square tiles	stack of pennies

Additional Resources

Commercially Available Technology

Calculator
fraction

Software
probability software
- *A Chance Look* by Sunburst
- *ClarisWorks* by Apple
- *Excel; Works* by Microsoft
- *Taking Chances* by Sunburst

Other Media
"Math...Who Needs It?!" PBS Video, 1320 Braddock Place, Alexandria, VA 22314-1698. (800) 344-3337.
"Probability." Films Inc Video, 5547 N. Ravenswood Ave., Chicago, IL 60640. (800) 343-4312.
"Probability." Aims Media, 9710 DeSoto Avenue, Chatsworth, CA 91311-4409.

Materials at Little or No Cost

Advertising. Newton, MA: EDC. Available through ERIC. Activity.
Manufacturing. Newton, MA: EDC. Available through ERIC. Activity.

Bibliography

For Teachers
Artz, Alice F. and Claire M. Newman. *How to Use Cooperative Learning in the Mathematics Class*. Reston, VA: NCTM, 1990.
Schulte, Albert P., ed. *Teaching Statistics and Probability*. Reston, VA: NCTM, 1981.

For Students
Churchill, E. Richard. *I Bet I Can, I Bet You Can't*. NY: Sterling, 1982.
Cushman, Jean. *Do You Wanna Bet?* Boston: Houghton Mifflin, 1991.
Sharp, Richard M. and Seymour Metzner. *The Sneaky Square and 113 Other Math Activities for Kids*. Blue Ridge Summit, PA: TAB Books, 1990.

Prentice Hall Technology 

Multimedia Math
- Hot Page™ 10-1
- Hot Page™ 10-2
- Hot Page™ 10-5
- Hot Page™ 10-8
- Math Investigations, Hazard City Messengers
- Math Investigations, Measuring Elephant Populations in Africa

Computer Item Generator
- Chapter 10

Community Resources

Field Trips
- a car dealership to explore combinations of options on cars
- a pizza place to explore combinations of toppings

Guest Speakers
- a biologist
- a market researcher
- an actuary

Backpack Take-Home Activities

Materials
- 2 number cubes or dice
- 2 pennies, nickels, dimes, or quarters
- 5 pairs of socks (each pair a different color or pattern)
- paper bag
- paper
- pencil

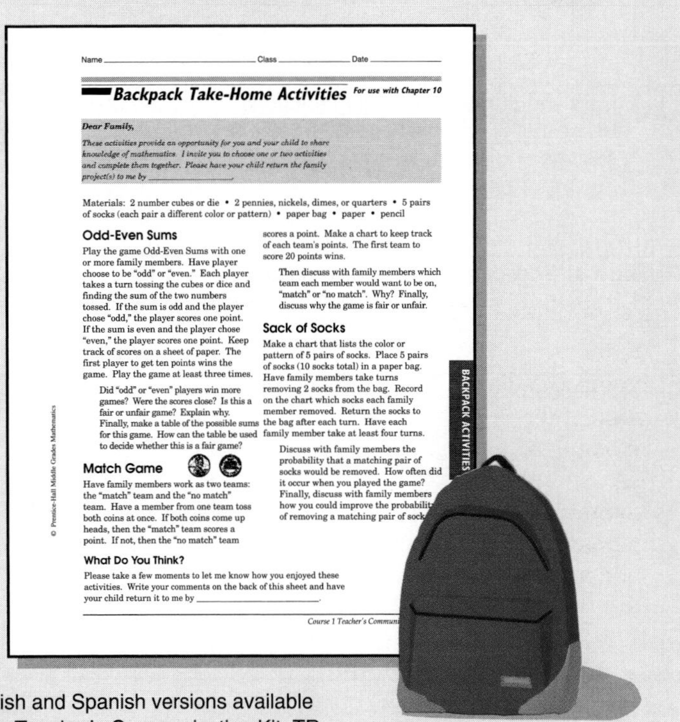

Name ____________ Class ____________ Date ____________

Backpack Take-Home Activities *For use with Chapter 10*

Dear Family,

These activities provide an opportunity for you and your child to share knowledge of mathematics. I invite you to choose one or two activities and complete them together. Please have your child return the family project(s) to me by ____________.

Materials: 2 number cubes or die • 2 pennies, nickels, dimes, or quarters • 5 pairs of socks (each pair a different color or pattern) • paper bag • paper • pencil

Odd-Even Sums
Play the game Odd-Even Sums with one or more family members. Have player choose to be "odd" or "even." Each player takes a turn tossing the cubes or dice and finding the sum of the two numbers tossed. If the sum is odd and the player chose "odd," the player scores one point. If the sum is even and the player chose "even," the player scores one point. Keep track of scores on a sheet of paper. The first player to get ten points wins the game. Play the game at least three times.

Did "odd" or "even" players win more games? Were the scores close? Is this a fair or unfair game? Explain why. Finally, make a table of the possible sums for this game. How can the table be used to decide whether this is a fair game?

Match Game
Have family members work as two teams: the "match" team and the "no match" team. Have a member from one team toss both coins at once. If both coins come up heads, then the "match" team scores a point. If not, then the "no match" team scores a point. Make a chart to keep track of each team's points. The first team to score 20 points wins.

Then discuss with family members which team each member would want to be on, "match" or "no match". Why? Finally, discuss why the game is fair or unfair.

Sack of Socks
Make a chart that lists the color or pattern of 5 pairs of socks. Place 5 pairs of socks (10 socks total) in a paper bag. Have family members take turns removing 2 socks from the bag. Record on the chart which socks each family member removed. Return the socks to the bag after each turn. Have each family member take at least four turns.

Discuss with family members the probability that a matching pair of socks would be removed. How often did it occur when you played the game? Finally, discuss with family members how you could improve the probabilit[y] of removing a matching pair of sock[s].

What Do You Think?
Please take a few moments to let me know how you enjoyed these activities. Write your comments on the back of this sheet and have your child return it to me by ____________.

Course 1 Teacher's Communi[cation Kit]

BACKPACK ACTIVITIES

English and Spanish versions available in the Teacher's Communication Kit, TR

Chapter 10 Planning Guide

Objectives	Assignment Options			Critical Thinking/ Problem Solving	Writing and Reading Math	Estimation Mental Math	Materials and Manipulatives
Investigation	This chapter-long project involves open-ended questioning and data collecting and provides an additional opportunity to assess students.			p. 410 p. 410	p. 410	p. 410	p. 410
10-1 Exploring Fair and Unfair Games • Determining if a game is fair or unfair • Finding experimental probability	**Core:** 14, 15, 17, 19, 20; MR all	**Reinforce:** 16, 18	**Enrich:** 21	WT: 3; 6–13, 17–21 p. 413; WT p. 411; BI p. 412; MM p. 413	20 p. 413; JL p. 412 JL Sheet	MR: 4, 5	WT: 2–5; 18, 21 pp. 412, 413; WT p. 411; RT p. 412 TT 85
10-2 Problem Solving: Simulate a Problem • Solving problems by simulation	**Core:** 15, 17–19, 22; MR all	**Reinforce:** 14, 21	**Enrich:** 16, 20	All; MR: 3–5 p. 414; BI p. 415; MM p. 416	All p. 416; JL p. 415 JL Sheet	14	6, 8, 12, 13, 17 pp. 414, 415 TT 85
10-3 Technology: Experimental Probability & Simulations • Using computers to explore experimental probability • Using random digits to simulate probability problems	**Core:** 11–13; MR all	**Reinforce:** 14, 15	**Enrich:** 16	1, 3, 5c, 6d–e; WT: 10; 11–16; MR: 3–5 p. 417; BI p. 418; MM p. 419	WT: 9; 14 JL p. 418 JL Sheet		2, 6; WT: 8 p. 417; WT p. 418 TT 85, 88, 89
10-4 Probability • Determining the probability of an event	**Core:** 20–23, 26, 27; MR all; CH all	**Reinforce:** 24, 29, 30	**Enrich:** 25, 28	1, 7, 9d; WT: 10; 13, 25, 26, 28, 30; CH: 2, 3; MR: 3 pp. 421–423; BI p. 422; RT p. 423	27b, 28 p. 424; JL p. 423 JL Sheet	MM p. 424	5, 19, 30b p. 422 TT 86
10-5 Tree Diagrams & the Counting Principle • Displaying and counting all possible outcomes • Finding probabilities using tree diagrams and the counting principle	**Core:** 12, 13, 15, 16; MR all	**Reinforce:** 11, 17	**Enrich:** 14	3, 4; EX3; 5, 6; EX4; 8, 9, 12–17 pp. 425–427; BI p. 427; MM p. 428	13 p. 428; JL p. 428 JL Sheet		p. 428; RT pp. 427–428 TT 86
10-6 Independent Events • Determining the probability of two independent events • Deciding whether or not events are independent	**Core:** 16–20; MR all	**Reinforce:** 13–15, 21	**Enrich:** 22, 23	WT: 2; 4, 6, 8, 9, 12, 13, 20–23 pp. 429, 430; BI p. 430; MM p. 431	20 p. 431; JL p. 431 JL Sheet		WT: 2; 13–18 MR: 1, 2 RT p. 430 TT 86; Alt. Lesson
10-7 Exploring Arrangements • Determining the number of arrangements of a group of items	**Core:** 14, 16, 18, 19; MR all; CH all	**Reinforce:** 13, 15, 17	**Enrich:** 20	5, 6, 9–12, 14, 15, 17–20; CH: 2–4; MR: 5 p. 433; WT p. 432; BI p. 433; MM p. 434	20 p. 434; JL p. 433 JL Sheet	MR: 1, 2	WT: 3; CH: 1, 3 p. 432; RT p. 433; CH p. 434 TT 87
10-8 Math and Surveys: Making Predictions • Making predictions about a population based on a sample	**Core:** 12–16, 20; MR all	**Reinforce:** 10, 11, 17	**Enrich:** 18, 19	3, 4; WT: 6, 9; 11–16, 18, 20; MR: 3, 4 pp. 437, 438; BI p. 437; MM p. 439	10, 11, 19 p. 438; JL pp. 437–438 JL Sheet	MR: 1, 2	WT: 5–8; 19, 20 pp. 437, 438; WT p. 436; RT p. 437 TT 87
Putting It All Together	These pages include a Follow-Up to the Investigation and other projects, which provide additional opportunities to assess the students.			pp. 442–443 pp. 442–443	pp. 442–443		pp. 442–443 p. 442
Chapter Resources				PS Practice, CW, CA, CR PS Practice p. 420; CW pp. 440–441; CA p. 444; CR p. 445	PS Practice, CW, CA p. 408B; PS Practice p. 420; CW pp. 440–441; CA p. 444		pp. 408A, 408B Backpack Activities, Manip. Kits TT 84

Student Edition (question numbers)
Teacher's Edition (page numbers)
Other Components

BI—What's the Big Idea? CA—Chapter Assessment CH—Checkpoint CG—Computer Item Generator CR—Cumulative Review CW—Chapter Wrap Up DM—Decision Making EP—Extra Practice EX—Example FD—Fact of the Day

Cooperative Learning Activities	Technology	Data Collection & Analysis	Interdisciplinary Connections	Applications	Assessment	Review	Strand Integration	NCTM Correlation*
		p. 410 p. 410	Science	weather	p. 410 p. 410			
WT: 1–5; 18 p. 412; WT p. 411; RT p. 412	p. 413 Hot Page™ 10-1	WT: 2, 3; 9, 12, 13, 17, 18 p. 413; RT p. 412; FD p. 412	p. 413	games pp. 411–413	p. 412	MR: All p. 411; RT p. 412 Practice p. 22	Stat./Probability, Discrete Math, Logic/Language	1, 2, 3, 4, 5, 7, 8, 9, 10, 11
RT p. 415	p. 414 Hot Page™ 10-2	7–9, 12, 13, 15, 17, 18, 21 pp. 414, 416; FD p. 415	Science p. 416	jobs, sports, money, weather biology pp. 414–416	p. 414	MR: All p. 414; RT p. 415 Practice p. 23	Stat./Probability, Discrete Math, Logic/Language	1, 2, 3, 4, 5, 7, 8, 10, 11
WT: 7–10 WT p. 418; RT p. 419 Alt. Lesson	All p. 417; WT p. 418	6; WT: 7, 9, 10; 12 FD p. 418	Sports	sports, entertainment, weather p. 419	p. 418	MR: All p. 417; RT p. 419 Practice p. 24	Stat./Probability, Discrete Math, Logic/Language	1, 2, 3, 4, 5, 7, 8, 9, 10, 11
WT: 10–12; 19 p. 422; WT p. 422 Alt. Lesson	Alt. Lesson	27 p. 424; FD p. 422		games, weather pp. 421, 423	CH: All p. 422; CH p. 424 CH TR p. 34	MR: All p. 421; RT p. 423 Practice p. 25	Stat./Probability, Discrete Math, Logic/Language	1, 2, 3, 4, 5, 7, 8, 9, 10, 11
p. 427; RT pp. 427–428	p. 428 Hot Page™ 10-5	FD p. 426	Physical Education	sports, cars, travel, consumer issues p. 428	p. 427	MR: All p. 425; RT pp. 427–428 Practice p. 26	Stat./Probability, Discrete Math, Logic/Language	1, 2, 3, 4, 5, 7, 8, 9, 10, 11
WT: 1, 2 WT p. 429; RT p. 430		WT: 2 WT p. 429; RT p. 430; FD p. 430	Science pp. 430, 431	games, biology, clothing pp. 430, 431 Alt. Lesson	p. 430	MR: All p. 429; RT p. 430 Practice p. 27	Stat./Probability, Discrete Math, Logic/Language	1, 2, 3, 4, 5, 7, 8, 9, 10, 11
WT: 1–4 WT p. 432; RT p. 433; CH p. 434		WT: 1–4 FD p. 433	Language Arts	sports, literature, music p. 433	CH: All p. 432; CH p. 434 CH TR p. 34	MR: All p. 432; RT p. 433 Practice p. 28	Stat./Probability, Discrete Math, Logic/Language	1, 2, 3, 4, 5, 7, 8, 9, 10, 11
WT: 5–9 WT pp. 436–437; RT p. 437	p. 437 Hot Page™ 10-8	WT: 5–8; 17, 18, 20 pp. 437, 438; WT p. 436; RT p. 437; FD p. 437	History, Science p. 438	surveys, politics, entertainment, farming, weather pp. 436, 438; RT p. 437; GE pp. 438–439	p. 437	MR: All p. 436; RT p. 437 Practice p. 29	Stat./Probability, Discrete Math, Logic/Language	1, 2, 3, 4, 5, 7, 8, 10, 11
pp. 442–443		pp. 442–443 pp. 442–443	Science	weather, insurance, recreation	pp. 442–443 pp. 442–443			
IN, PT pp. 408–410; PT pp. 442–443 Backpack Activities	p. 408B Multimedia Math, CG	Data File 10 pp. 408–409	Science, Geography pp. 408F, 408–409 Interdisciplinary Units	earthquakes, geography pp. 408A, 408F, 408–409 Backpack Activities, Projects Interdisciplinary Units	IN, PT, CA pp. 408E, 410; CW pp. 440–441; PT pp. 442–443; CA p. 444 CA, Span. CA, Self Assessment, Projects	Practice, PS Practice, CW, CR, EP, SSG CW pp. 440–441 Span. SSG, CR		

GE—Great Expectations IN—Investigation JL—Journal MM—Math Minutes
MR—Mixed Review PS—Problem Solving PT—Putting It All Together RT—Reteaching Activity
SSG—Student Study Guide TT—Teaching Transparency WT—Work Together

*For a description of the NCTM Standards, see page T15.

Assessment Options

Observation Checklist

In this chapter on probability, you have opportunities to observe your students do these tasks:

- ✓ find experimental probabilities to decide whether games are fair or unfair
- ✓ solve problems by simulation using technology and other methods
- ✓ determine probability of some events
- ✓ use tree diagrams to find sample spaces
- ✓ use the counting principle to determine the number of possible outcomes
- ✓ find the number of possible arrangements of a group of items
- ✓ use random sampling to make predictions about populations

In every chapter, you are given opportunities to observe your students:

- ✓ work with a partner or in a group
- ✓ write about mathematics
- ✓ participate in discussions about mathematics
- ✓ collect and analyze data
- ✓ display positive attitudes about mathematics
- ✓ use measurement tools

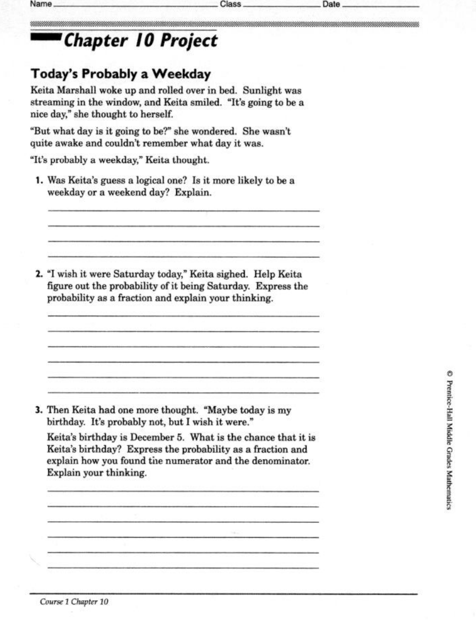

Name ________ Class ________ Date ________

Chapter 10 Project

Today's Probably a Weekday

Keita Marshall woke up and rolled over in bed. Sunlight was streaming in the window, and Keita smiled. "It's going to be a nice day," she thought to herself.

"But what day is it going to be?" she wondered. She wasn't quite awake and couldn't remember what day it was.

"It's probably a weekday," Keita thought.

1. Was Keita's guess a logical one? Is it more likely to be a weekday or a weekend day? Explain.

2. "I wish it were Saturday today," Keita sighed. Help Keita figure out the probability of it being Saturday. Express the probability as a fraction and explain your thinking.

3. Then Keita had one more thought. "Maybe today is my birthday. It's probably not, but I wish it were."
Keita's birthday is December 5. What is the chance that it is Keita's birthday? Express the probability as a fraction and explain how you found the numerator and the denominator. Explain your thinking.

Course 1 Chapter 10

Performance Based Project (with scoring rubric), Chapter Files, TR

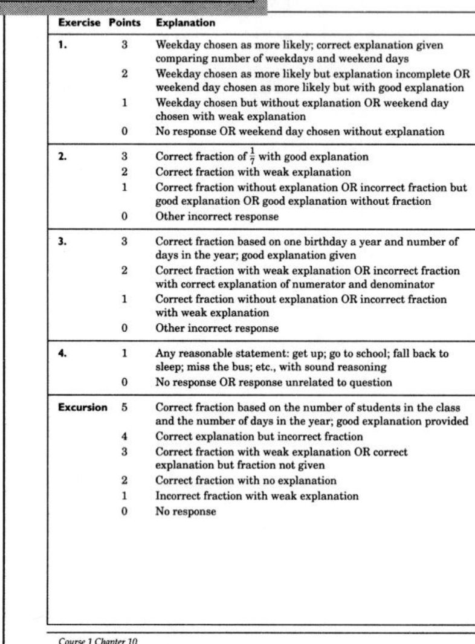

Weekday Scoring Rubric

Exercise	Points	Explanation
1.	3	Weekday chosen as more likely; correct explanation given comparing number of weekdays and weekend days
	2	Weekday chosen as more likely but explanation incomplete OR weekend day chosen as more likely but with good explanation
	1	Weekday chosen but without explanation OR weekend day chosen with weak explanation
	0	No response OR weekend day chosen without explanation
2.	3	Correct fraction of $\frac{1}{7}$ with good explanation
	2	Correct fraction with weak explanation
	1	Correct fraction without explanation OR incorrect fraction but good explanation OR good explanation without fraction
	0	Other incorrect response
3.	3	Correct fraction based on one birthday a year and number of days in the year; good explanation given
	2	Correct fraction with weak explanation OR incorrect fraction with correct explanation of numerator and denominator
	1	Correct fraction without explanation OR incorrect fraction with weak explanation
	0	Other incorrect response
4.	1	Any reasonable statement: get up; go to school; fall back to sleep; miss the bus; etc., with sound reasoning
	0	No response OR response unrelated to question
Excursion	5	Correct fraction based on the number of students in the class and the number of days in the year; good explanation provided
	4	Correct explanation but incorrect fraction
	3	Correct fraction with weak explanation OR correct explanation but fraction not given
	2	Correct fraction with no explanation
	1	Incorrect fraction with weak explanation
	0	No response

Course 1 Chapter 10

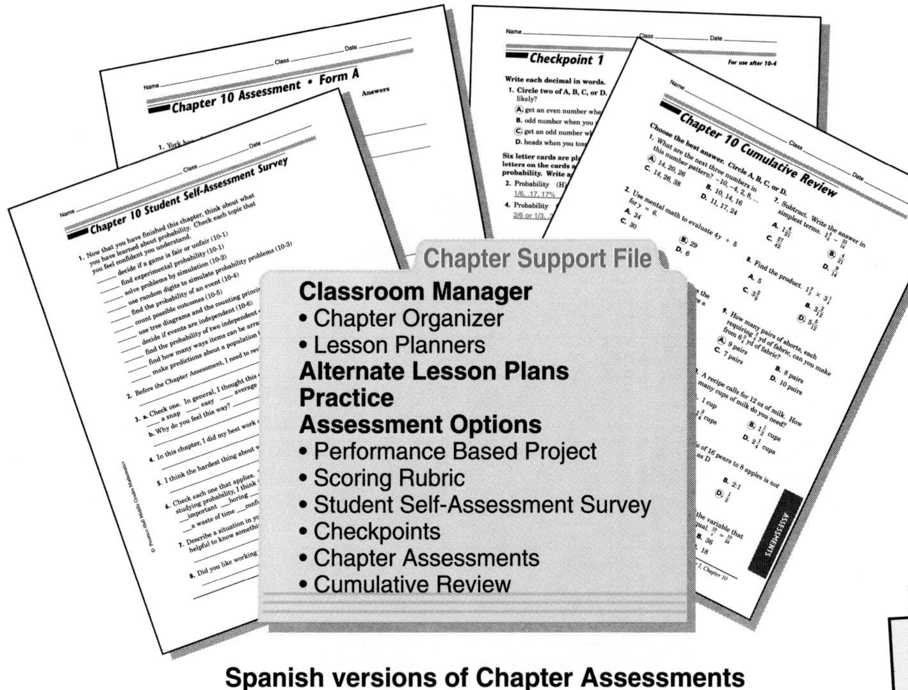

Spanish versions of Chapter Assessments available in Spanish Resources

Interdisciplinary Units

- **Travel and Geography**
- **Space Exploration**
- **Sports**
- **Consumer Awareness**
- **The Great Outdoors**

English & Spanish

These units include cross-curriculum connections and can be used at any time during the school year. See the Teacher's Guide for more information.

Working with Middle Grade Students

> *“ We didn't all come over on the same ship, but we're all in the same boat. ”*
>
> —Bernard Baruch

Addressing a Variety of Learning Styles

Chapter 10 utilizes various learning styles.

- Visual learners read line plots (p. 413) and analyze spinners (p. 423).
- Tactile learners draw diagrams (p. 412), use computers (p. 417), and draw tree diagrams (p. 425).
- Auditory learners discuss ways to simulate a problem (p. 415) and compare the likeliness of generating random numbers (p. 417).
- Kinesthetic learners play games to determine if they are fair or unfair (p. 411) and investigate weather information (p. 416).

Alternate lesson 10–6 addresses tactile learners by having them use manipulatives.

Cultural Connections

Mathematicians first became interested in probability in 1654, when the Chevalier de Méré asked the mathematician Blaise Pascal to solve a gambling problem for him. Here is a riddle from the time when probability theory was just beginning.

Suppose that there are two identical chests, each with two drawers. Chest A has a gold coin in each drawer. Chest B has one drawer with a gold coin and one empty drawer. You pick a chest and a drawer at random. There is a gold coin in it. What is the probability that the other drawer of the same chest also contains a gold coin? Have the class do a simulation to find out. The theory of probability gives $\frac{2}{3}$ as the correct answer.

Team Teaching Suggestion

Have a physical education teacher come and work with the class to introduce the concept of probability used in athletic events. The expectations for success in the standing long jump can be listed for each student based on his or her height and body mass. After the students have each performed three long jumps, compare the results with the expectations.

Math and the Melting Pot

According to *Everybody Counts*, “mathematics is a key to opportunity and careers,” yet minorities and women are underrepresented in scientific careers. An effective teacher provides high expectations for each child, but ones that are individually appropriate. All students thrive when they receive attention and experience success.

Teaching Tip

Students in middle school often have negative feelings about how their abilities and appearance compare with those of other students. To help turn these concerns into motivation, discuss ways people differ in their talents and abilities. Encourage students to try different approaches to mathematics problems. Help them understand that there may be more than one good way to solve a problem and there may even be more than one good answer.

Bulletin Board

Post possible choices for T-shirt colors and designs. Periodically add new designs based on students' suggestions. For example, you may want to start with two T-shirt colors and as the number of designs increases, add a third T-shirt color. Each student chooses a combination, sketches and colors it, and puts it on the board. Encourage students to make as many different combinations of T-shirt designs as possible. As the number of combinations changes, have students predict the total number of combinations possible. Review these predictions with the class on a regular basis.

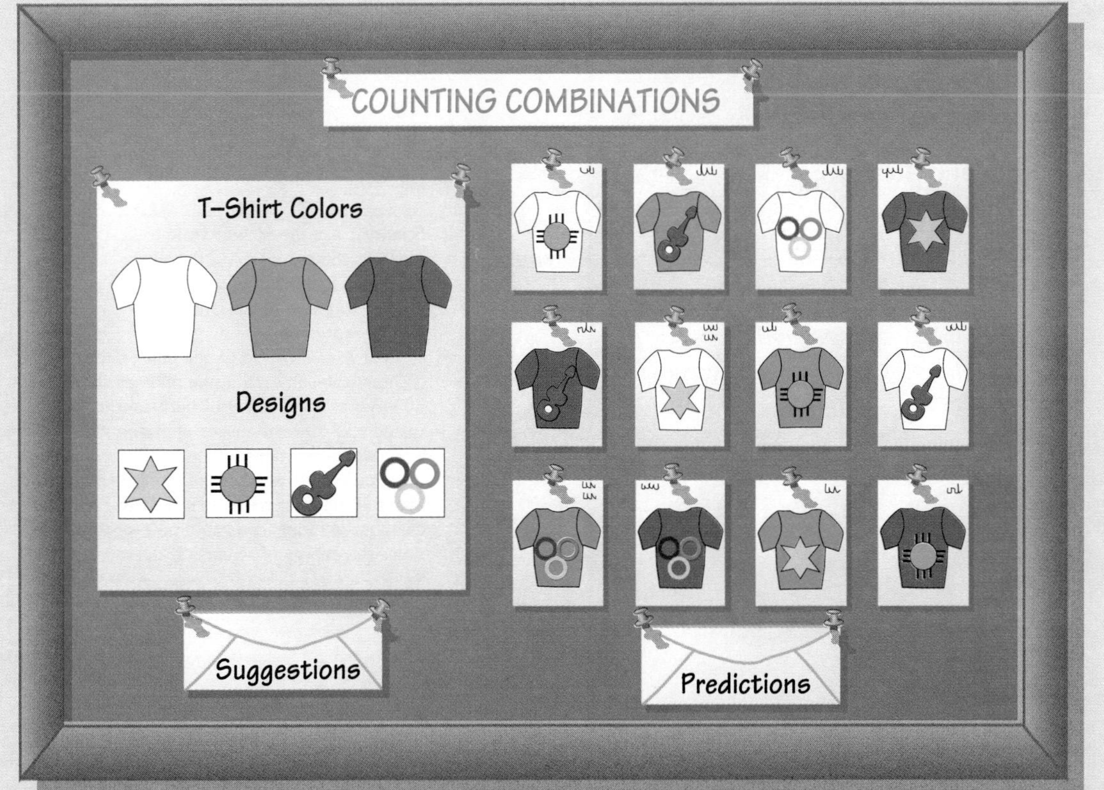

CHAPTER 10 Probability

Cultural Connections Since China has experienced many devastating earthquakes, it is understandable that the Chinese have kept detailed historical records and were also the first to invent a seismograph. Chang Heug (78–139 A.D.), a mathematician, astronomer, and geographer, set up an instrument consisting of eight carefully balanced balls arranged in a circle around a compass. Earthquake tremors caused one of the balls to roll off, indicating the direction from which the vibrations were coming.

The first seismograph to use electrical currents (produced by electromagnets) was invented by Prince Boris Golitsyn, a Russian physicist, in 1905.

WORLD VIEW China has experienced more catastrophic earthquakes than any other country. Not very many earthquakes kill more than 100,000 people, but all five such earthquakes recorded in history have occurred in China. At least 100,000 were killed in each of two earthquakes in 1290 and in 1920. About 200,000 deaths occurred in a 1927 earthquake. A deadly earthquake near Peking killed about 700,000 people in 1976. The worst earthquake ever recorded happened in the Shensi region of China on January 24, 1556, killing about 825,000 people.

Digging for Data
Ask if students have seen earthquake reports on news shows.

- *What did you notice from the pictures?* (**demolished buildings, twisted bridges, and so forth**)
- *Where would an earthquake generally fit on the Richter scale chart measurement to produce such damage?*

Chapter 10 Contents

Data File Questions

p. 416

Data File 10

CHAPTER 10 Probability

SHAKE, RATTLE, & ROLL

The map shows the San Andreas fault in California. The numbers at each location show the likelihood of an earthquake and the expected measure on the Richter scale.

Southern Santa Cruz Mountains 30%
San Francisco 20%
Parkfield 90%
North Coast Less than 10%
8
7
6.5
6
San Francisco
San Andreas Fault

The Richter Scale

Scientists use the Richter scale to measure the size of an earthquake. Charles F. Richter developed the scale in 1935 to measure the amount of ground motion.

For each increase of one unit on the Richter scale, an earthquake releases about 30 times as much energy. This means it would take 30 earthquakes of magnitude 6 to release the same energy as just one of magnitude 7. An earthquake rating 6 releases about 30 times as much energy as an earthquake rating 5 and about 30^2 or 900 times the energy of an earthquake rating 4.

Source: *Earthquakes,* Bruce A. Bolt

Earthquake Damage

Richter Scale	Typical Damage
8	Total damage.
7	Buildings collapse.
6	Buildings crack and things fall off shelves.
5	Furniture and pictures move.
3–4	People feel a rumble and hear noise.
1–2	Most people don't notice anything.

Source: *Junior Scholastic*

- Have students ask friends and neighbors if they know anyone living in a major earthquake zone. Then have students locate those areas on the map.
- Discuss the lengths of time for a seismograph to register the P-waves and S-waves at different distances, using the chart.

Journal Activity

- Ask students to read the four objectives for the chapter and write down what they think they know about probabilities and predictions.
- Using the chart on earthquake damage, have students write stories describing the effects of an earthquake at various levels on the Richter scale.
- Looking at the map of California, where would the students most likely want to live, considering the likelihood of earthquakes? Have them explain the reasons for their choices.

Interdisciplinary Connection [Science and Geography]

Seismographs measure the strength of an earthquake, reporting the numbers as Richter readings (named after earthquake specialist Charles Richter). Some scientists believe that the earthquake that destroyed Lisbon, Portugal, in 1755 may have been the strongest in history since it even shook lakes in Norway (1,700 mi away). Locate these areas on maps.

WHAT YOU WILL LEARN

- how to determine fair and unfair games
- how to use tree diagrams and formulas to determine probability
- how to use technology to simulate probability experiments
- how to use probability to make predictions

Earthquake Zones in the United States

Damage

None | Moderate | Minor | Major

Source: *Earthquakes*, Seymour Simon

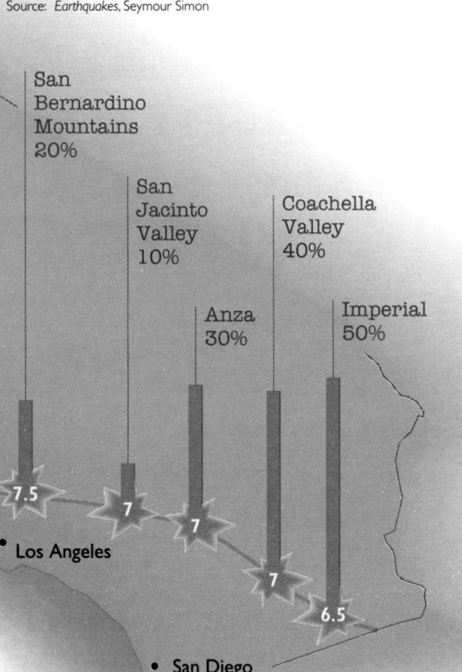

In 1976, more than 240,000 people were reported killed in an earthquake in Tangshan, China. The earthquake measured 8.2 on the Richter scale and was felt up to 800 km away.

Earthquake Waves

Time (min): 0, 4, 8, 12, 16, 20, 24, 28

S-wave

P-wave

Distance from Seismograph (km): 0, 2,000, 4,000, 6,000, 8,000, 10,000, 12,000

Waves of an Earthquake

Primary (P) waves travel with a push-pull motion through the earth at a speed of about 7.7 km/s. Secondary (S) waves travel with a side-to-side motion at a slower speed of about 4.4 km/s.

The graphs show the time for P-waves and S-waves to travel a given distance from an earthquake. A seismograph records the wave vibrations and their arrival time. You can use the graph to estimate the distance between the seismograph and the earthquake. Suppose a seismograph is 1,000 km from an earthquake. It would record P-waves after 2 min and S-waves after 4 min.

Source: *Brief Review in Earth Science*, Prentice Hall; *Movers & Shakers*, State Farm Insurance

Fact of the Day

Tsunamis are ocean waves caused by earthquakes. A single earthquake in 1960 sent tsunamis to places as far apart as Chile and Japan. One tsunami that hit Alaska after a 1964 earthquake was nearly 220 feet high.

—*Amazing Facts*

CHAPTER

10 INVESTIGATION

Memo

Some people claim that they can feel when the weather is going to change. People with rheumatism, for example, sometimes claim to feel a peculiar ache in their bones before a rainstorm. Ask students to relate scientific ways to forecast the weather.

Mission

Throughout the chapter students will be gathering information that will deepen their understanding of meteorology. Make "predict tomorrow's weather" a part of their math assignment once a week. Have groups keep lists of methods they can use to predict the local weather. Check these lists periodically to be sure groups are continuing to add to them.

Additional Leads to Follow

- *How can you find out whether a possible weather predictor is reliable?*
- *How can you express in mathematical terms the likelihood that your prediction will come true?*

Keeping a Project Notebook

Some suggestions for students' notebooks are these.

- Collect methods you can use to predict the weather. Try them out, recording how you used each method, what was supposed to happen, and what happened.
- Keep a daily weather log. Suggested categories: general description of the day's weather, high and low temperatures, wind direction, amount of precipitation.
- List the dates and results of all discussions about the project.
- Include all calculations, together with explanations for how they were done.

Project Organizer

Related Exercises
p. 416
p. 423
p. 439

Follow Up
p. 442

Teacher's Notes
pp. 410, 416, 424, 438, 442

Community Resources
- local U.S. Weather Service station
- TV meteorologist

Materials and Manipulatives
- meteorological instruments, possibly including thermometer, barometer, rain gauge, wind sock

Memo

Forecasting the weather accurately is an extremely difficult challenge. Some weather forecasters use the "butterfly effect" to explain the difficulty of their job. Imagine a butterfly in Brazil fluttering its wings on Monday morning. The fluttering disturbs the air near the butterfly. The disturbance moves on and on, affecting air currents farther and farther away. By Friday afternoon, the disturbance is affecting storm patterns in Chicago.

Now think of all the tiny air movements at any given moment in the world. How is it possible to predict the combined effects they will have on the weather?

Mission: Predict tomorrow's weather. Your prediction should include an estimate of the high and low temperatures, the amount of precipitation, and any other information you consider important. Explain how you arrived at your prediction and estimate how likely it is to come true.

- ✓ What information can you gather that might be useful in making your prediction?
- ✓ What are the main forces that affect the weather in your area?

10-1

Connecting to Prior Knowledge

Ask students to name games and sports they like to play. Then have students explain why each game or sport has rules. Challenge students to determine the purposes of a set of rules. Then ask students to explain how the rules for a game like checkers make it a fair game.

WORK TOGETHER

Provide each pair of students with two colors of chips or blocks and a bag. Before students begin playing the games, have them prepare and label a table for each of the three games. Also, if necessary, have a discussion of the mathematical meaning of a fair game.

Make sure that students write down their answers for each of the Questions 1–4 so that the discussion in Question 5 can be organized and meaningful.

Question 5: Challenge students to support their answers with their data and to make general theories about the fairness or unfairness of each game.

KINESTHETIC LEARNERS Game playing actively involves the learner in the process of analysis. Ask questions as you observe players, such as: *Is this outcome what you expected?*

DIVERSITY Some people may be concerned because they equate probability and playing games with dice or cards with gambling. Explain that the mathematics of probability is used in fields as varied as theoretical physics, weather prediction, and farming. Point out that playing games is as old as human civilization (see the WHO?) and does not have to be associated inevitably with gambling for money.

What's Ahead

- Determining if a game is fair or unfair
- Finding experimental probability

WHAT YOU'LL NEED

✓ Bag or container

✓ Red or blue cubes (or other objects of two colors)

10-1 Exploring Fair and Unfair Games

WORK TOGETHER

Play these three games with a partner.

A game is **fair** if each player has the same chance of winning. Players are *equally likely* to win.

1. Before you play Game 1, answer this question: Do you think the game is fair or unfair? If it is unfair, which player is more likely to win? Fair

Game 1 Place 1 red cube and 1 blue cube in a bag. Draw 1 cube from the bag without looking. If the cube is red, player A wins. If the cube is blue, player B wins.

2. Decide who will draw the cubes and who will record data. Play the game 20 times. Record your results in a table.
Answers may vary.

Number of times player A won	■
Number of times player B won	■
Number of times we played the game	20

3. Does it seem as if the game is fair or unfair? Explain.
See below.
4. Complete Questions 1–3 for Games 2 and 3.
See Sol. Key.

Game 2 Place 2 red cubes and 2 blue cubes in a bag. Draw 2 cubes from the bag without looking. If they are the same color, player A wins. If they are not the same color, player B wins.

Game 3 Place 3 red cubes and 1 blue cube in a bag. Draw 2 cubes from the bag without looking. If they are the same color, player A wins. If they are not the same color, player B wins.

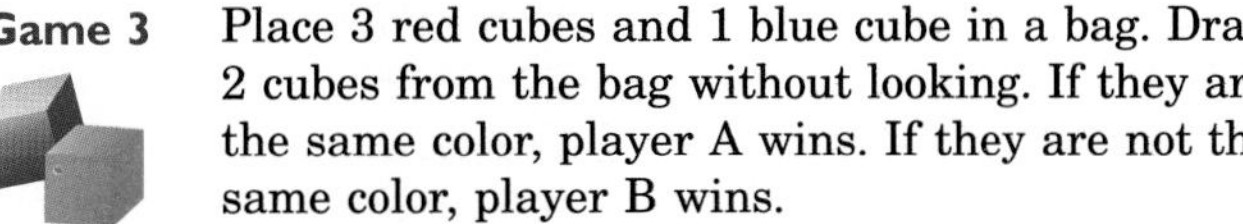

5. As a class, decide which of the three games are fair and which are unfair. Games 1 and 3 are fair. Game 2 is unfair.

3. Answers may vary. Sample answer: If both players win nearly the same number of times, the game will seem fair.

The Mandan people along the Missouri River played a game of chance involving tossing decorated bone dice in a basket. The score depended on which sides of the dice landed facing up.

“*A bird is known by its note, and a man by his talk.*”

—Proverb

Organizer

1. **Focus**
   Connecting to Prior Knowledge
2. **Teach**
   Work Together
   Think and Discuss
3. **Closure**
   Wrap Up

Vocabulary/Symbols
fair
equally likely
experimental probability

Skills Reviewed in Context of Lesson
- working with ratios

Materials and Manipulatives
- bag or container (1 for each group)
- 3 red and 2 blue cubes (for each group)

On Your Own Exercise 18: 2 coins
Exercise 21: coins, dice, spinners or color cubes *(optional)*

Student Resources
Extra Practice; Practice, TR Ch. 10, p. 22
Student Study Guide: English & Spanish

Teacher Resources
Teaching Transparency 85
Lesson Planner, TR Ch. 10, p. 2

continues next page

THINK AND DISCUSS

Question 6: Have students compare examples.

Error Alert! Students may be under the illusion that the past trials affect present ones and may therefore answer Question 8 with "red." ***Remediation*** Point out to students that the cubes do not have memories. The red and blue cubes each have an equal chance of being drawn in Game 1 regardless of past drawings. Emphasize to students that a larger number of tests will usually give a more accurate reflection of the probability.

Ongoing Assessment Have students list the player they would choose to be for each game. Ask students to explain their reasons in terms of probability. Then have students compare observations with a partner.

Wrap Up

What's the Big Idea? Ask students to explain how to determine if a game is fair or unfair. Then have students describe how to find experimental probability.

Reteaching Activity Use the example of a coin toss to review determining fair and unfair games. Ask students the following questions:

- *Compare the probabilities of tossing a head or a tail.* **(equal)**
- *Is tossing a coin a fair or unfair game? Why?* **(Fair; each side has an equal chance.)**

Then group students in pairs and provide each pair with a coin. Ask each pair to record 20 flips of the coin and compile the results as a class.

Journal Ask students to name some real-life situations that might be interpreted as fair or unfair games. Have them explain their reasoning.

Organizer, continued

Prentice Hall Technology

Multimedia Math
- Hot Page™ 10-1

Computer Item Generator
- 10-1

Other Available Technology

A Chance Look by Sunburst: Question 9, Exercise 18 *(optional)*

Fact of the Day

Every day, the United States Mint stamps out 3.5 million quarters, 3.7 million dimes, 3 million nickels, and 39 million pennies.

—*In One Day*

PH Multimedia Math Hot Page™ 10-1

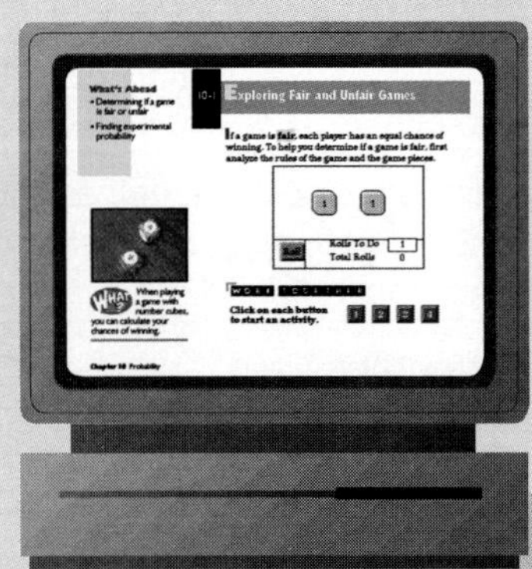

412

Mixed REVIEW

Calculate.

1. $\frac{9}{10} + \frac{4}{17}$ $1\frac{23}{170}$
2. $2\frac{3}{4} - 1\frac{2}{5}$ $1\frac{7}{20}$
3. Construct a circle graph. 3. See Solution Key.

Favorite Fruit	
Apples	65%
Oranges	15%
Other	20%

Complete each pattern.

4. 2, 4, 7, 11, ■, ■, ■ 4. 16, 22, 29
5. 0.75, 1.05, 1.35, 1.65, ■, ■, ■ 1.95, 2.25, 2.55

9. Answers may vary. Sample answer: If the game is fair, for a large number of trials, we would expect the outcomes of each player to be nearly the same.

R1 — R2, B1 — B2 (diagram)

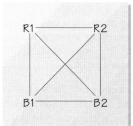

12. a. R1, B1; R1, B2; R1, R2; B1, B2; B1, R2; R2, B2
b. 2; 4; No
c. Unfair; Answers may vary. See Exercise 9.

THINK AND DISCUSS

6. Does a fair game always seem fair? Give examples. No; Sample: Players' outcomes needn't be equal for a game to be fair.
7. Si and Karen played Game 1. Karen won 7 times and Si won 13 times. How can this happen if the game is fair? Sample answer: The outcomes are due to chance.
8. Ki-Jana and Susana played Game 1. The first 3 cubes drawn were blue. Is the fourth cube more likely to be red or blue? Neither, since Game 1 is fair.

You can use a ratio to show the fraction of the time that a player wins. This ratio is the *experimental probability* of winning the game. You write this ratio as shown below.

$$\text{Probability(A wins)} = \frac{\text{number of times A won}}{\text{total number of times played}}$$

$$\text{Probability(B wins)} = \frac{\text{number of times B won}}{\text{total number of times played}}$$

9. Combine the class data for each game on the previous page. Find Probability(A wins) and Probability(B wins) for each game. What does this tell you about the games? See left.
10. If you play the games tomorrow, will the experimental probabilities be the same as they were today? Explain. Not necessarily; Sample answer: Each actual outcome is due to chanc

You can decide if a game is fair or unfair by considering all the possible outcomes.

11. In Game 1, the 2 possible outcomes are red and blue. Are they equally likely? How do you know? Yes; Sample answer: There are only 2 cubes in the bag with one of each color.
12. For Game 2, Eduardo drew the diagram at the left. Eduardo named the cubes R1, R2, B1, and B2. Each line represents a draw of two cubes. See left.
    a. List all possible outcomes. For example, R1 B1 is one outcome. How many possible outcomes are there? 6
    b. How many outcomes give player A a win? How many give player B a win? Are A and B equally likely to win?
    c. Is the game fair or unfair? How is this result related to the experimental probabilities you found in Question 9?
13. Draw a diagram for Game 3. List all possible outcomes. Are players A and B equally likely to win? Is the game fair or unfair? See Solution Key for diagram; outcomes: R1, R2; R1, R3; R2, R3; B, R1; B, R2; B, R3; Yes; fair

Connections Have a discussion about how the concept of fairness from equal probability is used. You may want to start with the following examples:

- **Government** (anti-discrimination legislation, equal voting rights, traffic laws)
- **Sports** (coin toss to determine kicking team in football, game rules that standardize equipment, schedules that balance home and away games)
- **Science** (experiments that are objective and controlled)

ON YOUR OWN

Students will need two coins for Exercise 18.

ESL For Exercise 16, make sure students know what dice look like. For Exercise 18, show them that the side of a coin that has a person's head on it is called "heads." The other side is called "tails."

CONNECTION TO STATISTICS Exercise 16 has students use a line plot and a grid to find probabilities.

ACTIVITY For Exercise 18, have students describe the limitations of using experimental data for part c.

TECHNOLOGY OPTION For Exercise 18, students can use computer software to simulate flipping two coins 1,000 times and compare the results with the theoretical probabilities. Discuss the fact that as the number of trials increases, the experimental probabilities will approximate the theoretical probabilities.

WRITING Have students describe their preferred methods for Exercise 20.

CRITICAL THINKING Encourage students to test their games for Exercise 21 and to alter the rules as necessary.

ON YOUR OWN

14. Mia and Jo played a game and completed the table at the right. Find Probability(A wins) and Probability(B wins). $\frac{9}{20}$; $\frac{11}{20}$

Game Results	
A wins	卌 ||||
B wins	卌 卌 |
Times played	卌 卌 卌 卌

15. If Probability(A wins) = Probability(B wins), what do you know about a game? The game seems fair.

16. Leroy rolled 2 dice and found the sum. He played the game many times and recorded the sums in the line plot.

Sum	2	3	4	5	6	7	8	9	10	11	12
	×	×××	×	××	×××××	×××	×××××××	×××××	××	×	

a. Which sum did Leroy get most often? 8

b. Complete a grid like the one at the right to show all possible outcomes. Which sum is most likely? Compare to your answer in part (a). See Solution Key; 7; the answers are different.

c. Use Leroy's data to find Probability(10) and Probability(1). $\frac{2}{30}$; 0

Sums of Two Dice

	1	2	3	4	5	6
1	2	3	4	■	■	■
2	3	4	■	■	■	■
3	4	■	■	■	■	■
4	5	■	■	■	■	■
5	■	■	■	■	■	■
6	■	■	■	■	■	■

17. Leroy said to Tim, "If the sum of the 2 dice is prime, you win. If the sum is not prime, I win." Use your grid from Exercise 16(b). Is this game fair or unfair? Explain.
Unfair; There are 15 possible prime sums and 21 possible composite sums.

FLASHBACK
A prime number has exactly two factors, the number itself and 1. A composite number has more than two factors.

18. a. **Activity** Toss 2 coins at least 25 times. If you toss 2 heads or 2 tails, player A wins. If you toss 1 head and 1 tail, player B wins. Record your results in a table. See right.

b. Does the game seem fair or unfair? Explain.

c. Consider all possible outcomes for the game. Is it fair or unfair? Support your answer without using your recorded data. Fair; the outcomes are T, H; H, H; H, T; T, T; each player has an equal chance of winning.

18.a. Check students' tables.
b. Answers may vary.

19. Bodaway and Litisha played a game 10 times and decided it was unfair. Jaime and Marta played 50 times and decided it was fair. Who do you think is correct? Why?
Jaime and Marta; Sample answer: They played the game 40 more times.

20. **Writing** You have learned ways to decide if a game seems to be fair or unfair. Which way do you prefer? Why?
Answers may vary.

21. **Critical Thinking** Design one game that is fair and one that is unfair. Use coins, dice, spinners, or colored cubes.
See Solution Key.

Assignment Options

Core: 14, 15, 17, 19, 20, MR all	
Reinforce: 16, 18	Enrich: 21

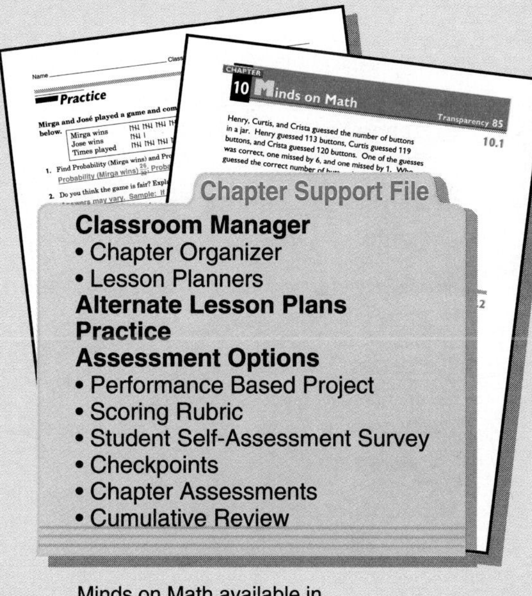

Minds on Math available in Teaching Transparencies

Math Minutes

If Stacy paid $12.00 for 15 juice bars at a fair, what did each cost?
$.80

Materials for 10-2

- spinners

10-2

Connecting to Prior Knowledge

Ask students to explain why a play's production might stage a rehearsal before its opening date, or why the members of a football team might scrimmage among themselves. Then tell students that modeling a situation is also called a simulation. Ask students to brainstorm for reasons why a scientist might want to make a simulation of the atmosphere on Venus, for example. **(to study its effects on different substances or its capacity for plant life, and so on)**

ESL **TACTILE LEARNERS** By simulating the problem, students get involved and increase their understanding.

Additional Problem *Yan's restaurant has run out of its supply of fortune cookies and will not receive a new shipment for two weeks. Yan has found a temporary supply to use for the two weeks, but is worried because the new supply has only six different fortunes. Each of the six fortunes is equally represented.*

What is the probability that a regular customer who comes in once a week will receive the same fortune as was received the previous week? **(Have students roll two dice to simulate the problem. Ask students to combine their data. Students' data should reflect about a $\frac{1}{6}$ chance.)**

Ongoing Assessment After students have answered Question 11, have them write a paragraph on what they have learned about simulating problems. Ask students particularly to describe how to use various models for simulations. Then arrange students in groups of four or five and have the members of each group compare observations and ideas.

TRY THESE

TECHNOLOGY OPTION For Exercise 12, students can simulate the problem using probability software.

“Learn, but learn from the learned.”
—CATO

Organizer

1. **Focus**
   Connecting to Prior Knowledge
2. **Teach**
3. **Closure**
   Wrap Up

Vocabulary/Symbols
simulate model trial

Skills Reviewed in Context of Lesson
- working with time

Materials and Manipulatives
- spinners (1 for each group)

On Your Own Exercise 17: almanac or newspaper

Student Resources
Extra Practice; Practice, TR Ch. 10, p. 23
Student Study Guide
Student Study Guide: English & Spanish

Teacher Resources
Teaching Transparency 85
Overhead Manipulatives: clear spinner
Lesson Planner, TR Ch. 10, p. 3

Prentice Hall Technology
Multimedia Math
- Hot Page™ 10-2

Computer Item Generator
- 10-2

continues next page

PROBLEM SOLVING

10-2 Simulate a Problem

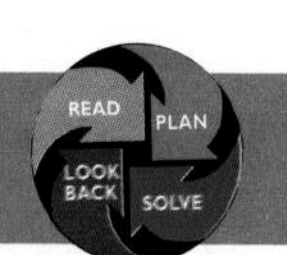

What's Ahead
- Solving problems by simulation

WHAT YOU'LL NEED
✓ Spinner

You can often solve a probability problem by simulating it. You can use a model, collect data based on the model, and then use the data to solve the problem.

> Sam delivers newspapers to many of his neighbors, including Mrs. Smith. Sam delivers Mrs. Smith's newspaper between 6:30 A.M. and 7:30 A.M. Mrs. Smith leaves for work between 7:00 A.M. and 8:00 A.M. What is the probability that Mrs. Smith gets her newspaper before she leaves for work?

READ Read and understand the given information. Summarize the problem.

1. Will Mrs. Smith get the newspaper before she leaves for work if Sam delivers it at each time?
   a. before 7:00 A.M. **yes** b. after 7:00 A.M. **possibly**
2. How much of the time does Sam deliver Mrs. Smith's newspaper before 7:00 A.M.? after 7:00 A.M.? **about half; about**
3. If Sam always wants Mrs. Smith to receive her newspaper before she leaves for work, during what time interval should he deliver her newspaper? **6:30 A.M.–7:00 A.M.**
4. If Mrs. Smith always wants to get her newspaper before she leaves for work, during what time interval should she leave? **7:30 A.M.–8:00 A.M.**
5. Two times are important in this problem: the time at which Sam delivers Mrs. Smith's newspaper, and the time at which Mrs. Smith leaves for work. Do the two times depend on each other or are they independent? **They are independent.**

PLAN Decide on a strategy to solve the problem.

Instead of collecting data on Sam and Mrs. Smith themselves, you can represent their situation with a model. Ways of using a model to simulate the problem include drawing cubes, tossing coins, spinning spinners, rolling dice, and using random numbers.

Error Alert! Students may have difficulty simulating the problem for Exercise 13, because it differs from the example problem and Exercise 12. ***Remediation*** Point out to students that they can still use spinners to simulate the problem. Instead of designing the spinners with time periods, students can designate 75% of each circle as a free throw and the other 25% as a miss.

Wrap Up

What's the Big Idea? Ask students to describe how to solve problems by simulation.

Reteaching Activity Review with students the steps involved in simulating the example problem. Encourage students to describe the purpose of each step. For example, the step in Question 6 could be described as "Choose a model for the simulation." Then ask for students' descriptions one step at a time to compile a class strategy sheet for simulating problems.

Connections Have a discussion about how simulations are used. You may want to start with the following examples:

- **Space Travel** (training astronauts for weightlessness, testing rockets and other equipment)
- **Environmentalism** (testing ways to preserve an endangered species, determining the effects of environmental changes on an ecosystem)
- **Commercial Design** (testing a car's aerodynamics, determining the appeal of packaging)

Journal Ask students: *Is simulation relatively easy or difficult? useful or not so useful? Explain.*

ON YOUR OWN

CONNECTION TO STATISTICS Exercise 15 has students evaluate the data presented in a table.

6. The spinner at the right represents the times at which Sam delivers newspapers. Draw a spinner to represent the times that Mrs. Smith leaves for work. See Solution Key.

7. Spinning each spinner once simulates what happens on one morning. Each time you simulate the problem, you complete one **trial.** How many trials will you complete? Answers will vary. Sample answer: at least 20 trials

SOLVE — Try out the strategy.

8. Simulate the problem many times. Record your results in a table. You may want to combine all class data. Check students tables.
9. Use the data to find the experimental probability that Mrs. Smith will get her newspaper before she leaves for work in the morning. What does this tell you? See below.
10. Discussion Does your answer seem reasonable? Is this the only possible answer? Answers may vary; No

LOOK BACK — Think about how you solved this problem.

11. Discussion Can you think of another way to simulate or solve this problem? See Solution Key for sample answer.

9. Answers may vary. Sample answer: For a large number of trials, Mrs. Smith should receive the newspaper before leaving $\frac{3}{4}$ of the time

TRY THESE

Simulate and solve each problem. Show all your work.

1–4. See Sol. Key.

12. You practice the piano 15 min every weekday between 4:00 P.M. and 5:00 P.M. Your father gets home from work every weekday between 4:30 P.M. and 5:30 P.M. What is the experimental probability that your father gets home from work while you are practicing the piano? See below.
13. Sports A professional basketball player makes 75% of his free throws. What is the experimental probability that he will make two free throws in a row?

12–13. Answers may vary. See Solution Key for sample answers.

ON YOUR OWN

Use any strategy to solve each problem. Show all your work.

14. Suppose your class plans an end-of-the-year picnic. Each student gets one sandwich and one juice box. Three juice boxes cost $1.29. Sandwiches cost $1.85 each. Estimate the cost for the picnic for *your* mathematics class. Answers may vary. Sample answer: $47.88 for a class of 21 students.

Mixed REVIEW

Draw a model to find each quotient.

1. 0.2 ÷ 0.04
2. 0.9 ÷ 0.03
3. Sharon and Ashur played a game 30 times. Sharon won 18 times and Ashur won 12 times. Is this a fair game? Explain.
4. Suppose you roll a die 10 times and get a 3 every time. Is this a fair die? Explain.
5. I'm thinking of a number. If I multiply by 3 and then subtract 11, the result is 43. What is the number? 18

Organizer, continued

Other Available Technology
A Chance Look by Sunburst: Questions 6–8, Exercise 12 *(optional)*

Fact of the Day

Every day, Americans use 187,000 tons of paper. If it were all newsprint, it could completely cover Long Island, NY.

—*In One Day*

PH Multimedia Math Hot Page™ 10-2

Assignment Options

Core: 15, 17–19, 22, MR all	
Reinforce: 14, 21	**Enrich:** 16, 20

CHAPTER INVESTIGATION Encourage students to use the school library or a public library to find the required information for Exercise 17.

WRITING For Exercise 20, encourage students to imagine what will happen at the carpet store to help them with their answers.

CONNECTION TO SCIENCE Exercise 22 has students solve a problem that involves scientific data.

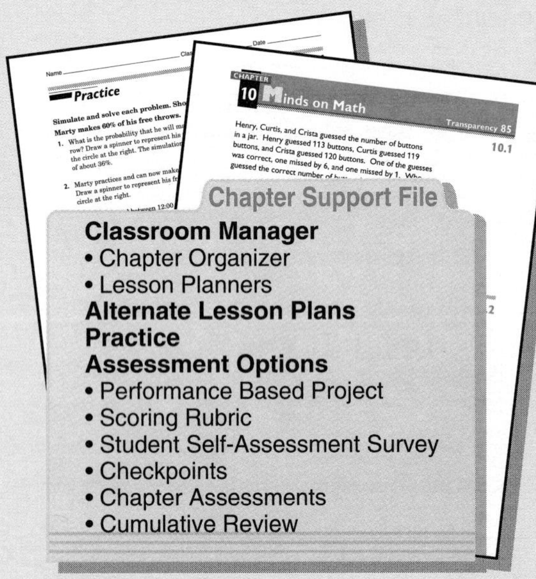

Minds on Math available in Teaching Transparencies

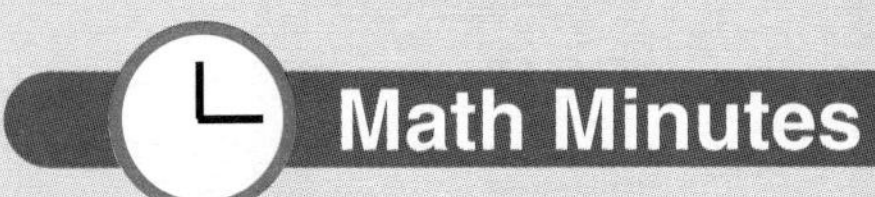

At the Grand Towers Youth Camp, 6 children sleep in a cabin. If 140 children came to the camp, how many cabins would they occupy?
24

Materials for 10-3

- computer *(optional)*
- software with random number and graphing capabilities *(optional)*

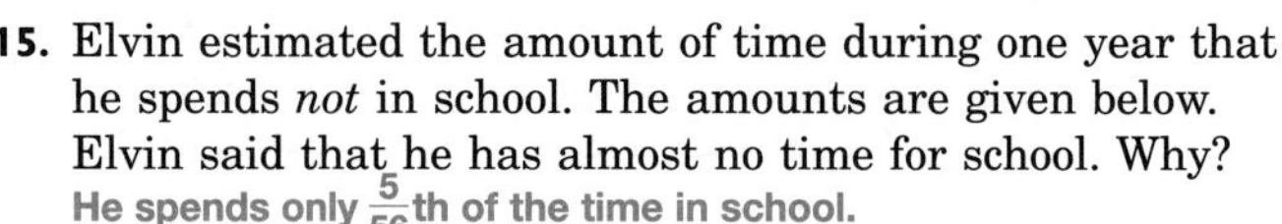

15. Elvin estimated the amount of time during one year that he spends *not* in school. The amounts are given below. Elvin said that he has almost no time for school. Why? He spends only $\frac{5}{56}$th of the time in school.

Time Spent Not in School			
Sleeping	Eating	School vacations	Weekends
$\frac{1}{4}$	$\frac{1}{8}$	$\frac{1}{4}$	$\frac{2}{7}$

16. What is the least number of people you could have in a group and still be sure that at least two of them have birthdays in the same month? What is the least number so that three of them have birthdays in the same month? 13; 25
17. **Investigation (p. 410)** Find the average temperature and precipitation for the current month in your city or region. Use an almanac or newspapers to find this information. Compare with today's temperature and precipitation. Answers may vary.
18. **Data File 10 (pp. 408–409)** Is San Francisco or Anza more likely to have an earthquake? Explain. Anza; 30% > 20%
19. An 8-by-8 checkerboard has one pair of opposite corners missing. One domino covers two squares of the checkerboard. Can you cover the entire checkerboard with dominoes? If so, draw a diagram that shows your solution. If not, explain why it is impossible. No; two nonadjacent squares would always be left uncovered.
20. **Writing** Velmanette is getting new bedroom carpet. Write down all the information she needs to take to the carpet store so that she can order new carpet. Answers may vary. Sample answers: size of floor space, color of room
21. A gumball machine holds many giant gumballs in four flavors: grape, lime, raspberry, and banana. Madeleine wants one of each flavor. Each gumball costs 25¢. About how much money will Madeleine spend in order to get the four different flavors of gumballs? Use a simulation representing a given gumball machine; at least $1.
22. **Biology** Some jumping spiders can jump 40 times their own length. About how far in centimeters could a 15 mm jumping spider jump? 60 cm

Jumping spiders hunt by stalking. They follow an insect, then jump to grab it. Before jumping, they secure a silk thread on which they can climb if they miss their prey!

Source: *Wild, Wild World of Animals, Insects and Spiders*

10-3

Connecting to Prior Knowledge

Have students recall how they used cubes or spinners to simulate random events in order to solve problems. Tell the students that here they will be conducting simulations using random numbers (generated by computer or from a random number table).

THINK AND DISCUSS

Question 3: Ask the students: *How could you use a number cube to model the tossing of a coin?* **(Tossing the numbers 1, 2, or 3 represents "heads" and 4, 5, or 6 represents "tails"; odd number for heads, even for tails; or any other grouping of 3 digits for heads and the other 3 for tails.)**

COMPUTER If you are using a computer spreadsheet with a random number function, demonstrate how to use the random number function. To save time in tallying results:

- Generate sets of digits in several columns (4 digits per cell).
- Cut the printout into sections.
- Give a section to each pair of students.
- Have each pair circle the sets that begin with 111 or 222.
- Compile the results from all the groups.

If you are using a computer with probability software or your own program, demonstrate the Random Number command and then tally an example or two by hand so students understand how the simulation works. Let the computer tally the rest of the data. ***Alternate Approach*** If a computer is not available, use a random number table and decide with students on how to interpret digits. (Even digits can be heads and odd digits can be tails; 0–4 can be heads and 5–9 can be tails.)

VISUAL LEARNERS Have these students mark the tallies for the exercises or circle the digits required in the simulation.

Error Alert! Students' tally marks can become crossed, lost, or marked on top of another tally. The more times that tally marks are required for the simulation, more instances of missed

What's Ahead

- Using computers to explore experimental probability
- Using random digits to simulate probability problems

WHAT YOU'LL NEED

✓ Stack of pennies

✓ Computer

✓ Software with random number and graphing capabilities

TECHNOLOGY

10-3 Experimental Probability & Simulations

THINK AND DISCUSS

The coin spins upward from the referee's hand. Your coach has chosen you as the captain of the soccer team. You must call heads or tails to see which team gets the ball. In the first three games, the coin has landed heads.

1. Will you call heads or tails? Why? **Answers will vary.**
2. You can act out the problem by tossing a coin.
   a. You must first toss three heads in a row. What do these tosses represent? **the referee's first three coin tosses**
   b. You can then toss the coin a fourth time. What does this toss represent? **the referee's coin toss for the fourth game**
   c. Why does acting out the problem take so long? **Answers may vary. Sample answer: It's difficult to get 3 heads in a row.**
3. Can you use a spinner like the one at the left to simulate the problem? Would this method be faster than tossing a coin? Explain. **Yes; No, you still have to get 3 of one color in a row.**

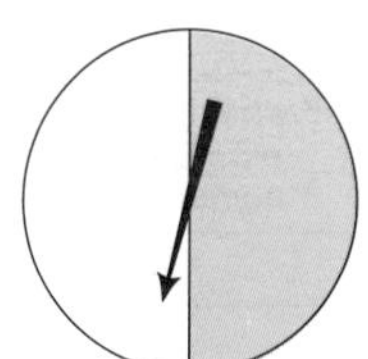

You can also use a computer to simulate the problem. A computer can quickly generate a list of *random digits.* Because they are random, all digits are equally likely to occur.

4. a. Suppose the digit 1 represents a coin toss landing heads. What series of digits would represent the coin tosses made by the referee in the first three games? **111**
   b. What is represented by the digits 1112? 1111? **a tails after 3 heads; a heads after 3 heads.**
5. Use the list of random digits at the left.
   a. How many times does 1112 appear in the list? **3**
   b. How many times does 1111 appear in the list? **3**
   c. **Discussion** Do you think it is more likely that the referee will toss a heads or a tails at the start of the fourth game? Explain. **Heads and tails are equally likely to be tossed.**

List of Random 1's and 2's
1121212221122121 2
1111212121212222 12
2212111121212222 1
1212112211112222 12

> *"A fool must now and then be right by chance."*
>
> —William Cowper

Organizer

1. **Focus**
   Connecting to Prior Knowledge
2. **Teach**
   Think and Discuss
   Work Together
3. **Closure**
   Wrap Up

Skills Reviewed in Context of Lesson

- working with experimental probability
- reading/interpreting tables
- working with percents

Materials and Manipulatives

- computer (1 for each group; *optional*)
- software with random number and graphing capabilities (for each computer; *optional*)
- random number table *(optional)*
- graph paper *(optional)*

Student Resources

Extra Practice
Student Study Guide
Practice, TR Ch. 10, p. 24
Student Study Guide, Spanish Resources, TR
Alternate Lesson, TR Ch. 10, pp. 10–13

continues next page

marks can occur. ***Remediation*** It may help to remind students to separate their tallies by groups of five, keep space between tally marks, or have another student help them record the tally marks.

ESL **ESL** Most students will enjoy these problems because they are similar to games. Encourage students to ask questions when the problems are not clear. One way to do this is to reward any question with positive attention, careful listening, and feedback such as "good question," or "I'm glad you asked."

Journal Ask students to describe a situation in which running a random number simulation would save a lot of time.

WORK TOGETHER

The intuitive but erroneous misconception that the odds change when one event has happened several times in a row is sometimes called the "gambler's fallacy." You may wish to ask students: *Has the coin changed after several heads in a row? Does the coin have a memory?*

Question 7: Have students compute the ratios in column 4 with calculators.

COMPUTER For Question 8, students can use software with graphing capabilities. In some spreadsheet programs, the data to be graphed should be in adjacent columns, so you would need to move "tosses" to the third column, next to the ratio of heads/tosses. ***Alternate Approach*** If a computer is not available, have the students make the graph by hand.

Ongoing Assessment Suppose 5 heads in a row have been tossed. Ask the students to describe how they could use a simulation to determine whether it is more likely that a head or a tail will be tossed the sixth time.

Wrap Up

What's the Big Idea? Ask students: *In a simulation, what would happen if you made a decision based on too few trials?*

Organizer, continued

Teacher Resources

Teaching Transparencies 85, 88, 89
Lesson Planner, TR Ch. 10, p. 4

Prentice Hall Technology

Computer Item Generator
- 10-3

Other Available Technology
ClarisWorks by Apple *(optional)*

Fact of the Day

In the 18th Century, Abraham de Moivre studied games of chance and developed the distribution of possible outcomes known as the bell-shaped curve or normal distribution. This curve was also independently developed in the 18th century by the French mathematician Pierre Simon de Laplace, who applied it to astronomical observations.

—Academic American Encyclopedia

Number of times three heads were tossed, then another heads (1111)	■
Number of times three heads were tossed, then a tails (1112)	■

6. a. **Computer** Generate and print at least 500 random 1's and 2's digits. Check students' work.
   b. Complete the table at the left. Answers will vary.
   c. Find Probability(fourth toss heads) and Probability(fourth toss tails). Answers will vary.
   d. Now what do you think about your answer to Question 1? Explain. Answers will vary. Students should realize that heads and tails are equally likely to be tossed.
   e. **Discussion** If you printed a list of 1,000 random digits, will you be more sure of your solution? Explain. Yes, as the number of tries increases, the better able you are to predict the answer.

WORK TOGETHER

Work in pairs. Use the data you generated in Question 6 to simulate what happens with more and more tosses of a coin. Each pair of students should use a different section of the data and count the number of 1's and 2's.

7. Combine class data to complete the table below. Check students' tables.

Number of tosses	Number of heads	Number of tails	Probability(heads) $= \frac{\text{number of heads}}{\text{number of tosses}}$
10	■	■	■
20	■	■	■
30	■	■	■
40	■	■	■
50	■	■	■
100	■	■	■
200	■	■	■
500	■	■	■
1,000	■	■	■

8. **Computer** Make a line graph to show what happens to Probability(heads) as the number of tosses increases. Check students' graphs.
9. **Writing** Do you see trends or patterns in the graph? Use the data or the graph to make at least one true statement. Answers will vary. Sample answer: Probability(heads) approaches $\frac{1}{2}$.
10. **Critical Thinking** What do you think will happen to Probability(heads) if you simulate another 10,000 tosses? Probability(heads) should be very close to $\frac{1}{2}$.

1. $\frac{2}{3}, \frac{4}{6}$ 2. $\frac{1}{3}, \frac{3}{9}$

Mixed REVIEW

Write two equal ratios.

1. 12 to 18 2. $\frac{15}{45}$ See above.
3. The Leopards played their first field hockey game Monday, September 20, and played a game every Monday thereafter. What was the date of their seventh game? Nov. 1
4. Brett makes 40% of his free throws. What is the probability that he will make three free throws in a row? $\frac{8}{125}$
5. How many different ways can you make change for 31¢? 18

Connections Have a discussion about simulations. You may want to start with these examples:

- **State Lottery** (depending on the type of game offered, discuss the method of simulation)
- **Television Game Shows** (discuss the variables that affect the games' results after each game played)

Reteaching Activity Have the students discuss the steps in setting up a simulation (for example: choosing an appropriate model, performing a trial of the situation, recording the results of the trial, repeating the trials as many times as possible).

ON YOUR OWN

Exercise 11: Although students should recognize that the probability of tossing another head is 0.5, it is still compelling to the students to think that tails "is bound to come up." How students answer this problem will help you determine their understanding of probability.

Exercise 12: Ask students to write about their solution and their analysis of the problem.

ON YOUR OWN

11. Sports Suppose your opponent tosses a dime to see who serves first in a tennis game. You must call heads or tails.
    a. The last nine tosses were tails. What will you call? Why?
    b. The last toss was heads. What will you call? Why?

11a–b. Answers may vary. Sample answer: It doesn't matter. Heads and tails are equally likely to be tossed.

12. a. How likely are "doubles" when you roll two dice? Simulate this by using the list. Use 2 digits at a time. Complete the table.

Number of doubles	■	6
Number of times dice were rolled	■	36
Probability(doubles)	■	$\frac{1}{6}$

    b. Now analyze the problem by listing all possible outcomes. How likely are doubles? Show your solution. See right.

12b. See Solution Key for outcomes; $\frac{1}{6}$

List of Random Digits 1–6

2341632411253452 4
3514263523243464 4
2412336231326455 4
3631141342453141 5
2622

13. A movie theater prints one digit 0–9 on each ticket. You collect tickets from movies you've seen. When you have each digit, you get a free ticket. How many movies will you have to see before you get a free ticket? Use the random digits at the right to simulate and solve this problem. about 22

List of Random Digits 0–9

5820321984560321 6
6198723047282270 1
3639390265831088 6
8429750182395470 6

14. Writing A basketball player usually makes 50% of her free throws. Explain how to use a computer simulation to find the experimental probability that she makes 7 out of 10 free throws. See Solution Key.

15. Here is a new game. Toss three coins. If you get exactly two heads or two tails, you win. Otherwise, your opponent wins. Is the game fair or unfair? Show your solution. See Solution Key.

16. **Choose A, B, or C.** Suppose there is a 50% chance of rain for the next three days. Which method will *not* work to find out how likely it is to have three days of rain? C
    A. Toss a coin. Let heads be "rain" and tails be "no rain."
    B. Use a computer to list random digits 0–9. Let even numbers be "rain" and let odd numbers be "no rain."
    C. Spin a spinner with three equal sections: one day of rain, two days of rain, and three days of rain.

***While in prison** during World War II, John Kerrich tossed a coin 10,000 times. He tossed 5,067 heads. The experimental probability of tossing a head was 50.67%.*

Assignment Options

Core: 11, 12, 13, MR all	
Reinforce: 14, 15	Enrich: 16

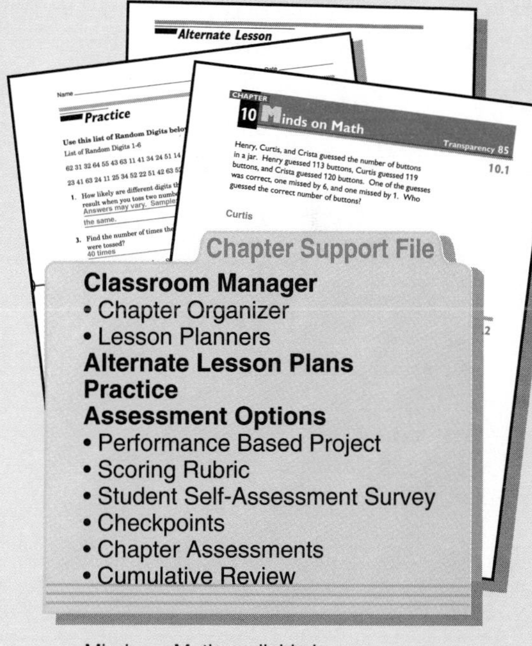

Alternate Lesson
Practice
10 Minds on Math
Chapter Support File
Classroom Manager
• Chapter Organizer
• Lesson Planners
Alternate Lesson Plans
Practice
Assessment Options
• Performance Based Project
• Scoring Rubric
• Student Self-Assessment Survey
• Checkpoints
• Chapter Assessments
• Cumulative Review

Minds on Math available in Teaching Transparencies

How many weeks are in 231 days?
33 weeks

CHAPTER

10 PROBLEM SOLVING PRACTICE

This page provides a variety of problems that can be used to reinforce and enhance the students' problem solving skills. Encourage students to read each problem carefully. Then have them refer to the list of problem solving strategies to help them decide how to solve the problems.

Point out, however, that not all questions require a strategy for solving, nor are all the strategies in the list used on this page.

WRITING For Exercise 4, encourage students to make a table that shows the number of border dots, the number of inside dots, and the area. For enrichment, have students try to discover Pick's rule for determining the area of a lattice polygon. Pick's rule is $A = I + \frac{B}{2} - 1$, where I is the number of dots *inside* the polygon and B is the number of dots *on* the polygon.

Materials and Manipulatives

- dot paper

Problem Solving Practice

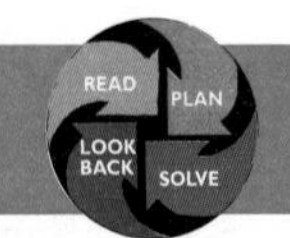

PROBLEM SOLVING STRATEGIES

Make a Table
Use Logical Reasoning
Solve a Simpler Problem
Too Much or Too Little Information
Look for a Pattern
Make a Model
Work Backward
Draw a Diagram
Guess and Test
Simulate a Problem
Use Multiple Strategies

Solve. The list at the left shows some possible strategies you can use.

1. Philip Astley, an Englishman, started the circus as we know it today. He presented trick riding shows to the public. Use the clues to find the year the circus began.
   - The sum of the digits equals 22.
   - The year is divisible by 4.
   - The American Revolution occurred in this century.

   1768
2. Did you know that a circus ring is a specific size? Philip Astley discovered that the ideal circle for bareback riding has a diameter of 42 ft. Find the area of this circle. about 1,384.74 sq. ft.
3. A survey reports that 73% of moviegoers buy popcorn at the movie theater. You own a theater with 360 seats. You sell containers of popcorn.
   a. If both movies sell out, how many containers of popcorn do you expect to sell each day? about 525
   b. Each container of popcorn costs you 45¢ and sells for $1.50. What profit do you expect from popcorn each day? $551.25

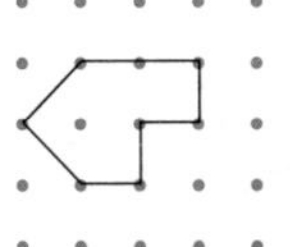

4. **Writing** Copy the polygon at the left onto dot paper. Find the area of the polygon. Notice that there is one dot inside the polygon. Also, there are 8 dots on the border of the polygon. Make five other polygons of this type. Find the area of each polygon. What do you observe? Each polygon has an area of 4 sq. units.
5. A restaurant has 25 of each type of sticker: soup, sandwich, salad, and drink. One sticker is put on each menu. Each time you visit the restaurant, you receive a menu. The item listed on the sticker is free. How many times will you need to visit the restaurant to get each type of item free? Use a simulation. Answers may vary; sample: at least 4.
6. Suppose a planet has two hemispheres. In each hemisphere there are three continents. On each continent there are four countries. In each country there are five states. How many states are on the planet? 120

10-4

Connecting to Prior Knowledge

Have students discuss probability and its applications in their own lives. Start the discussion by asking students to describe the context in which they last used the word *probably.* Ask students what they mean when they use the word. Then challenge students to name times when they have had to be more specific about the chances of an event.

THINK AND DISCUSS

ESL **AUDITORY LEARNERS** There is a great deal of vocabulary associated with probability. Students may not be familiar with the words or phrases and their implied meanings. Discuss the meaning of words such as *outcome, event, improbable, likely, favorable, certain,* and *impossible* as they occur.

Example

- *Where did the 4 in the denominator come from ?* **(There are 4 cubes in the bag.)**
- *Would you expect the probability for blue to be higher or lower? Why?* **(lower; fewer blue cubes)**

Additional Example *A bag contains 2 red cubes, 3 blue cubes, and 5 white cubes. What is the probability of each color cube being drawn?*

Probability(red) = $\frac{2}{10}$ = $\frac{1}{5}$ or 0.20 or 20%

Probability(white) = $\frac{5}{10}$ = $\frac{1}{2}$ or 0.50 or 50%

Probability(blue) = $\frac{3}{10}$ or 0.30 or 30%

Error Alert! Students may not understand the ratio for probability and so make mistakes in problems such as

---

What's Ahead

- Determining the probability of an event

10-4 Probability

> *"In this world, nothing is certain but death and taxes."*
>
> —Benjamin Franklin

THINK AND DISCUSS

Think back to Game 3 on page 411. There were 3 red cubes and 1 blue cube in a bag.

In the hand game one player holds an unmarked object in one hand and a marked object in the other. An opponent wins by guessing which hand holds the unmarked object. ***What is the probability of choosing the correct hand?*** $\frac{1}{2}$

1. Suppose you draw 1 cube from the bag. Which is more likely, red or blue? How do you know? red; There are more red cubes than blue.
2. Suppose you draw 1 cube from the bag and replace it 4 different times. How many times do you expect to get red? How many times do you expect to get blue? 3; 1
3. Are all 4 cubes in the bag equally likely to be drawn? Yes.

Probability tells how likely it is that an event will happen. When all outcomes are equally likely, the probability that an event will occur is the ratio below. You can write this ratio as a fraction, a decimal, or a percent.

$$\text{Probability(event)} = \frac{\text{number of favorable outcomes}}{\text{number of possible outcomes}}$$

Example A bag contains 3 red cubes and 1 blue cube. What is the probability that a red cube is drawn?

- Find the probability that a cube drawn is red.

$$\frac{\text{number of favorable outcomes}}{\text{number of possible outcomes}} = \frac{\text{red cubes}}{\text{all cubes}} = \frac{3}{4}$$

$$\text{Probability(red)} = \frac{3}{4} = 0.75 = 75\%$$

4. Find the probability that a cube drawn is blue. $\frac{1}{4}$
5. Design a spinner you could use to simulate this problem. See Solution Key.
6. How many blue cubes could you add to the bag so that Probability(blue) = Probability(red)? 2
7. **Discussion** What does the word *favorable* mean in the formula for probability? Favorable is the outcome you want to occur.

Organizer

1. **Focus**
   Connecting to Prior Knowledge
2. **Teach**
   Think and Discuss
   Work Together
3. **Closure**
   Try These
   Wrap Up

Vocabulary/Symbols
favorable
certain
impossible

Skills Reviewed in Context of Lesson
- working with ratios

Student Resources
Extra Practice
Student Study Guide
Practice, TR Ch. 10, p. 25
Student Study Guide, Spanish Resources, TR
Checkpoint, TR Ch. 10, p. 34
Alternate Lesson, TR Ch. 10, pp. 14–17

Teacher Resources
Teaching Transparency 86
Lesson Planner, TR Ch. 10, p. 5

continues next page

Questions 8 and 9. ***Remediation*** Point out to students that the first step in determining probability is to consider all the possibilities. In a problem such as the Example, each cube has an equal chance of being drawn. Each cube must then be accounted for as a possibility, and so the number of possible outcomes is the number of cubes.

DIVERSITY Some students may have experience in thinking about probability. Others may be totally unfamiliar with these issues. Make sure that all students have a chance to participate in each probability experiment. Have students with better understanding explain their reasoning to others.

Ongoing Assessment Have each student design a simple game that involves rolling two dice. Encourage students to evaluate the probability of a favorable outcome and the probability of an unfavorable outcome for their games. Then arrange students in groups of four so that students can assess each other's games.

WORK TOGETHER

Question 12: Encourage students to think of other words to include on the number line.

TRY THESE

Exercise 18: Encourage students to compare and discuss their answers.

ACTIVITY Arrange students in groups of four for Exercise 19. Each student in a group can be responsible for designing one portion of the spinner. Group members can check each other's work.

Wrap Up

What's the Big Idea? Ask students to explain how to determine the probability of an event.

Organizer, continued

Prentice Hall Technology

Multimedia Math

- Math Investigations, Hazard City Messengers

Computer Item Generator

- 10-4

Fact of the Day

The language with the greatest number of distinct consonantal sounds is Ubykhs in the Caucasus, with 80–85. The language with the least is Rotokas, with six.

—GUINNESS BOOK OF RECORDS

8.a. 5; Yes, if the marbles are exactly the same except for color.

8. One marble is drawn from the bag at the left.

a. How many possible outcomes are there? Are all marbles in the bag equally likely to be drawn?

b. Find Probability(red). Write as a fraction, as a decimal, and as a percent. How many outcomes are favorable? $\frac{2}{5}$, 0.4, 40%; 2

9. Suppose you roll a die once.

a. List all the possible outcomes. 1, 2, 3, 4, 5, 6

b. What is the probability of rolling an even number? $\frac{3}{6}$

c. What is the probability of *not* rolling an even number? Describe this another way. $\frac{3}{6}$; rolling an odd number

d. Find the sum Probability(even) + Probability(not even). Are you surprised? Why or why not? 1; No; The total probability should always equal 1.

WORK TOGETHER

When the probability of an event is 1, the event is *certain* to happen. When the probability of an event is 0, the event is *impossible*.

10. Work with a partner to think of at least 3 examples of each type of event. Write down all your ideas.

a. certain **b.** impossible **c.** possible but uncertain
Answers will vary. See left for sample answers.

11. Find the probability of each example you gave. Write each probability as a fraction, a decimal, and a percent. Answers will vary. See left.

12. Draw a number line to display the range of numbers used to describe probability. Label it with commonly used fractions, decimals, and percents. On the number line, write these words at appropriate places: See Solution Key for sample answer.
certain, impossible, very likely, little chance, happens about half of the time

10.a. getting a heads or tails with one flip of a coin, getting an odd or even no. with 1 roll of a die, getting a sum greater than 1 with 2 rolls of a die
b. getting an 8 with 1 roll of a die, getting a sum of 13 with 1 roll of 2 dice, getting a 0 with 1 roll of a die
c. getting an even no. with 1 roll of a die, getting a sum of 8 with 1 roll of 2 dice, getting a heads with 1 flip of a coin

Low High

11.(10.a.) $\frac{1}{1}$, 1.0, 100%
(10.b.) 0, 0.0, 0%
(10.c.) $\frac{3}{6}, \frac{5}{36}, \frac{1}{2}$

TRY THESE

13. Suppose your teacher writes the name of each student in your class on a card. To select a winner, your teacher draws one card from a box. Use your class data to find Probability(you win). Find Probability(you do not win). $\frac{1}{\text{total no. students in class}}$; $\frac{\text{no. students in class} - 1}{\text{total no. students in class}}$

Reteaching Activity Tell students to imagine that at some point during the class a tile from the ceiling is certain to fall and land on someone's desk. Ask students the following questions:

- *What is the first step in determining the probability of the tile landing on your desk?* **(finding number of possible outcomes—in this case, number of students)**
- *What is the number of possible outcomes?* **(Answers will vary.)**
- *What is the probability of the tile falling on your desk?* **(Answers will vary.)**
- *Given that only one tile will fall, what is the probability that no tiles will fall? that one tile will fall? two?* **(0; 1; 0)**

  Have students discuss their answers after each question.

Connections Have a discussion about how probability is used. You may want to start with the following examples:

- **Meteorology** (forecasting weather, predicting the path of a hurricane or snowstorm)
- **Sports** (evaluating the fairness in a game or the balance between offense and defense on different teams)
- **Medicine** (evaluating injuries or diseases in terms of recovery or relapse)
- **Public Safety** (evaluating the probabilities of various accidents in order to help people be safe)

Journal Ask students to think of the probabilities of events in their daily life. Have students evaluate the probabilities and determine whether most are certain, impossible, or somewhere in between. Ask students how their conclusions reflect the usefulness of probability.

ON YOUR OWN

CRITICAL THINKING For Exercise 25, encourage students to draw a diagram or use tally marks to represent possible outcomes.

A computer generates random digits 0–9. Find each probability. Write as a fraction, decimal, and percent.

14. Probability(6) $\frac{1}{10}$, 0.1, 10%
15. Probability(even number) $\frac{5}{10}$, 0.5, 50%
16. Probability(not 6) $\frac{9}{10}$, 0.9, 90%
17. Probability(1 or 2 or 3) $\frac{3}{10}$, 0.3, 30%
18. Do you agree or disagree with the following statement? An event with probability of 0 will never happen, and an event with probability of 1 will always happen. Agree
19. Activity Work with a group to design a spinner with Probability(A) = 50%, Probability(B) = 10%, Probability(C) = 0%, and Probability(D) = 40%. See Solution Key.

ON YOUR OWN

A die is rolled once. Find each probability. Write as a fraction, decimal, and percent.

20. Probability(4) $\frac{1}{6}$, $0.1\overline{6}$, $16\frac{2}{3}$%
21. Probability(9) 0, 0.0, 0%
22. Probability(not 5) $\frac{5}{6}$, $0.8\overline{3}$, $83\frac{1}{3}$%
23. Probability(1 or 3 or 6) $\frac{1}{2}$, 0.5, 50%
24. Find Probability(red) and Probability(blue) for the spinner at the right. $\frac{1}{3}$, $\frac{2}{3}$
25. Critical Thinking An icosahedron is a die with 20 faces. All outcomes are equally likely. Each face is colored red, blue, yellow, or green. You know Probability(yellow) = Probability(blue) = Probability(green) = Probability(red). How many faces are colored red? 5
26. One thousand raffle tickets are sold. You buy two of them. One winning ticket is drawn.
    a. What is the probability that you win? $\frac{1}{500}$
    b. What is the probability that you do not win? $\frac{499}{500}$
27. Investigation (p. 410) Find the chance of precipitation for your region tonight and tomorrow. Answers may vary. Check students' papers.
    a. Does the media report the probability as a fraction, a decimal, a percent, or with words?
    b. Writing Write a sentence about your investigation.

Mixed REVIEW

1. The radius of a circle is 15 m. What is the diameter? 30 m
2. The diameter of a circle is 22 ft. What is the radius? 11 ft.
3. You program a computer to list random 6's, 7's, and 8's. It lists four 6's in a row. Is it more likely to list a 6, a 7, or an 8 next? Explain. See below.
4. Could the pattern be folded along the dashed lines to make a cube? No

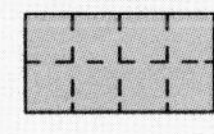

3. none of them; they all have an equal chance of occurring.

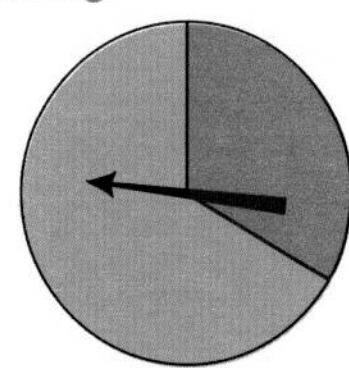

Assignment Options

Core: 20–23, 26, 27, MR all, CH all	
Reinforce: 24, 29, 30	**Enrich:** 25, 28

CHAPTER INVESTIGATION Challenge students to consult different sources for the information required in Exercise 27. Ask students if different sources have different ways of reporting probability.

WRITING Check students' answers to Exercise 28 to make sure they understand that each way of expressing probability is sufficient. Students' answers should reflect personal opinions.

Exercise 29: Students could use a number line for ordering the events.

CHECKPOINT

Enhanced multiple choice questions are more complex than traditional multiple choice questions, which assess only one skill. Enhanced multiple choice questions assess the processes that students use as well as the end results. They are written so that students can use more than one strategy to solve the problem.

Using multiple strategies is encouraged by the National Council of Teachers of Mathematics (NCTM).

Exercise 3 is an example of an enhanced multiple choice question.

Exercise 2: Ask students if the results from a bigger sample might differ from those in the problem.

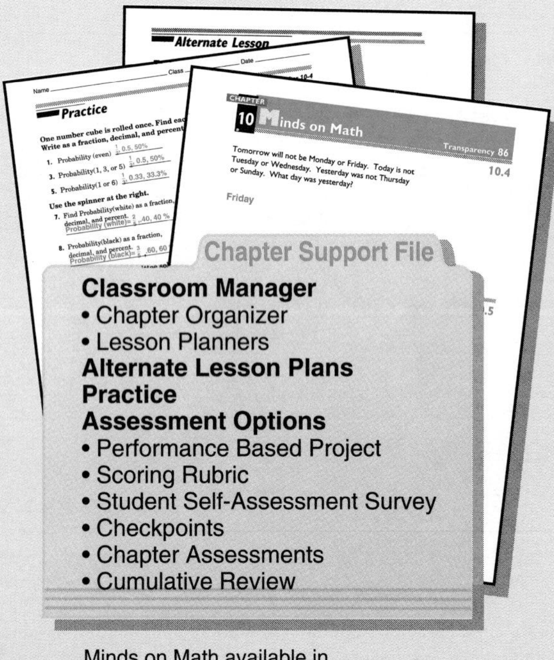

Minds on Math available in Teaching Transparencies

Math Minutes

Evaluate each expression when $a = 4$ and $b = 9$:

1. $(4 + b) - a$ **9**
2. $(b + a) \cdot 6$ **78**
3. $(a \cdot b) + (a + b)$ **49**

The probability of seeing a whale during a whale watch boat ride increases with the area of ocean, the season, the time of day, and the knowledge of the guide.

28. **Writing** Does it make more sense to you to think of probability as a fraction, a decimal, or a percent? Why? Answers will vary.
29. Order the following events from most likely to least likely. Answers may vary; sample answer: A, B, E, G, C, D, F.
    - **A.** The sun rises tomorrow.
    - **B.** You have a homework assignment tonight.
    - **C.** The next coin you toss comes up heads.
    - **D.** It snows somewhere in your state this week.
    - **E.** You complete a homework assignment tonight.
    - **F.** You live to be 195 years old.
    - **G.** You make a basket next time you play basketball.
30. A bag contains only red and green cubes. Probability(red) $= \frac{3}{8}$. You select one cube without looking.
    - **a.** Find Probability(green). $\frac{5}{8}$
    - **b.** Draw a spinner you could use to simulate this problem. See Solution Key.
    - **c.** How many of each color cube might the bag contain? for red: multiples of 3; for green: corresponding multiples of 5

CHECKPOINT

1. A computer generates random digits 1–5. Find each probability. Write as a fraction, decimal, and percent.
   - **a.** Probability(3)
   - **b.** Probability(odd number)
   - **c.** Probability(2 or 3) $\frac{2}{5}$, 0.4, 40%
   - **d.** Probability(not 5) $\frac{4}{5}$, 0.8, 80%

   1.a. $\frac{1}{5}$, 0.2, 20%
   b. $\frac{3}{5}$, 0.6, 60%

2. Lei-Li and Earline played a game and completed the table at the left.

Game Results	
Earline wins	14
Lei-Li wins	16
Times played	30

   - **a.** Find the experimental probability that Earline wins. $\frac{7}{15}$
   - **b.** Find the experimental probability that Lei-Li wins. $\frac{8}{15}$
   - **c.** Is the game fair? Explain. The game seems fair because the probabilities are close to $\frac{1}{2}$.
3. **Choose A, B, C, or D.** Which event is most likely? D
   - **A.** "tails" when you toss a coin
   - **B.** "consonant" when you randomly choose a letter A–Z
   - **C.** "9" when a computer lists random digits 0–9
   - **D.** "not 3" when you roll a number cube

10-5

Connecting to Prior Knowledge

Ask students how they determine the number of possible outcomes of the roll of two dice. Have students compare methods and then show them a tree diagram of the possibilities on the chalkboard. **(For each possible number for the first die, draw branches to the numbers 1–6 for the second die.)** Ask students to describe this method.

THINK AND DISCUSS

VISUAL LEARNERS Students may wish to draw tree diagrams for most of the problems in this lesson. When the numbers become large they can sketch an abbreviated version of a tree in order to visualize the appropriate action.

ESL Some students may not understand why these diagrams are called "tree" diagrams. Use a sketch to relate the diagram for Example 1 to a branching tree lying on its side with a single trunk at V and three main limbs connecting to V, S, and B. Other branches can spread out from there if there are more choices.

Example 1

Point out to students that no combination is listed twice, and that the order is important. VS is not the same as SV.

Additional Example *How many different choices are there for 4 sports instead of 3? Assume the added sport is football.*

V	V—VV		S	V—SV		B	V—BV		F	V—FV
	S—VS			S—SS			S—BS			S—FS
	B—VB			B—SB			B—BB			B—FB
	F—VF			F—SF			F—BF			F—FF

(There are now 16 different ways to choose activities.)

What's Ahead

- Displaying and counting all possible outcomes
- Finding probabilities using tree diagrams and the counting principle

10-5 Tree Diagrams & the Counting Principle

THINK AND DISCUSS

Students in a physical education class can choose what activity to do for a ten-week period. The choices are volleyball, soccer, and baseball. After the ten weeks are over, students choose again for the next ten-week period. They can choose the same activity.

1. How many choices do students have for the first activity? 3

A **tree diagram** displays all possible choices. Each branch of the tree diagram shows one choice. You use a tree diagram when all outcomes are equally likely to occur and when an event has two or more stages.

Example 1 Draw a tree diagram for the physical education activities. How many different ways can students choose?

Use the letter V for volleyball, S for soccer, and B for baseball.

First Activity	Second Activity	Possible Choices
V	V	VV
	S	VS
	B	VB
S	V	SV
	S	SS
	B	SB
B	V	BV
	S	BS
	B	BB

There are 9 different ways to choose activities.

2. Draw a tree diagram that shows all possible outcomes when you toss 3 coins. **See left.**

2. 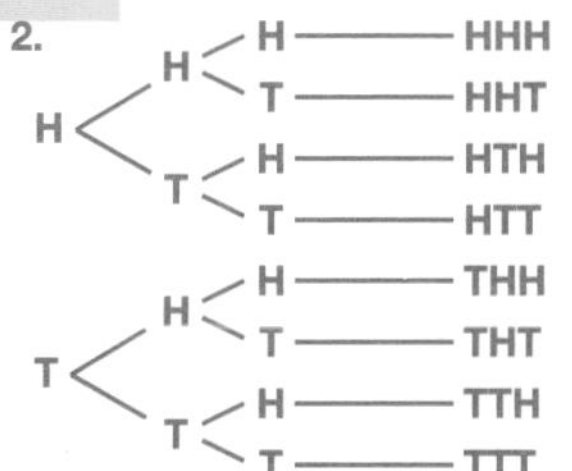

On September 4, 1993, *Jim Abbott of the New York Yankees pitched a no-hitter against the Cleveland Indians.*

" Learning makes the wise wiser, but the fool more foolish. "

—PROVERB

Organizer

1. **Focus**
   Connecting to Prior Knowledge
2. **Teach**
   Think and Discuss
3. **Closure**
   Try These
   Wrap Up

Vocabulary/Symbols
tree diagram
counting principle

Skills Reviewed in Context of Lesson
- working with probability

Student Resources
Extra Practice
Student Study Guide
Practice, TR Ch. 10, p. 26
Student Study Guide, Spanish Resources, TR

Teacher Resources
Teaching Transparency 86
Lesson Planner, TR Ch. 10, p. 6

Prentice Hall Technology
Multimedia Math
- Hot Page 10-5

Computer Item Generator
- 10-5

continues next page

Question 2: Point out to students that they can use four columns for this problem: First toss, second toss, third toss, and possible outcome for all 3 tosses.

Error Alert! Students may be confused about how many tree diagram columns to use for problems such as those in Question 2. ***Remediation*** Point out to students that in a tree diagram each decision requires a column. The rows for each column indicate the number of choices for each decision. The last column lists all possible choices.

Example 2

Point out to students that choices in which the student plays soccer during the second period end in S.

Additional Example *Find the probability of playing soccer during the second period when there are 4 choices of sports .*
possible outcomes: 16; favorable outcomes: 4;
probability $= \frac{4}{16} = \frac{1}{4}$

CRITICAL THINKING Have students compare their answers for Question 4. Challenge students to create a rule describing the relationship.

Examples 3 and 4

Encourage students to check the application of the counting principle by drawing a tree diagram.

Additional Example *A supply of sandwiches is prepared for the math club field trip. Each sandwich has one of the following: avocado, cheese, turkey, ham, or chicken salad. Each sandwich is also prepared with either mustard or mayonnaise and is on either white or wheat bread. How many different sandwiches can there be?*

Type of Sandwich		Condiment		Type of Bread		
5 choices		2 choices		2 choices		
5	×	2	×	2	=	20

(There can be 20 different sandwiches.)

Organizer, continued

Other Available Technology
Excel; Works by Microsoft: Exercise 15 *(optional)*

Fact of the Day

Americans eat 6.5 million gallons of popcorn every day.

—In One Day

You can use a tree diagram to find the probability of an event.

Example 2 Use the tree diagram in Example 1. Suppose a student chooses randomly. What is the probability she plays soccer during the second period?

- Count all possible outcomes: 9.
- Find the number of favorable outcomes: 3.

  Favorable outcomes are volleyball/soccer, soccer/soccer, and baseball/soccer.

Probability(soccer in second period) $= \frac{3}{9} = \frac{1}{3}$

3. **Critical Thinking** Is there a relationship among the number of first-period activities, the number of second-period activities, and the number of possible choices? If so, what is it? Yes. The number of possible choices is the product of the number of first activities and the number of second activities.
4. Do you see a way to count all possible outcomes without using a tree diagram or a grid? Explain. Yes. Multiply together the number of outcomes for each stage.

Another way to find the number of possible outcomes is to use *the counting principle.*

The Counting Principle

The number of outcomes for an event with two or more distinct stages is the product of the number of outcomes at each stage.

Example 3 You and your friends want to buy a pizza. You have only enough money for a medium size with one topping. How many different types of pizza can you buy?

Use the counting principle.

Topping (6 choices)		Crust (2 choices)		Types of pizza
6	×	2	=	12

You can buy 12 different types of pizza.

Pizza PALACE
Toppings
mushrooms
onions
pepperoni
sausage
peppers
extra cheese
Crusts
thick
thin

- *If one of each type of sandwich is made, what is the probability of randomly getting a sandwich with mustard?*
possible outcomes: 20; number of favorable outcomes: 10; probability (sandwich with mustard) = $\frac{10}{20} = \frac{1}{2}$

Ongoing Assessment Ask students to write their own definitions of the counting principle. Then have students compare definitions within their groups. Ask students to make sure that each definition shows the relationship between the numbers of choices in each stage of an event. After students have completed and compared definitions, have a class-wide discussion to summarize.

DIVERSITY Only in the United States, according to *Everybody Counts* (National Research Council), is it a common belief that only those with special ability can do well in math. In other countries, the expectation is that most students can master math if they work hard enough.

TRY THESE

Exercise 8: Remind students that (5, 6) is a different outcome from (6, 5) if order matters. If students use a table (similar to a multiplication table for 1 to 6), they can see that all the cells on one side of the diagonal can be eliminated as duplicates if order doesn't matter.

Wrap Up

What's the Big Idea? Ask students: *How do you use tree diagrams and the counting principle to determine the number of outcomes and to find the probabilities?*

ESL Reteaching Activity Have groups of students work together with packs of 6 index cards per group. Label three cards in each pack "green shirt," "red shirt," and "yellow shirt." Label the other three cards "green pants," "red pants," and "yellow pants." Ask students to use their pack of cards to determine all possible outcomes for an outfit of shirt and pants. Review with

5. Pizza Palace decides to offer one more topping. How many more types of pizza can you and your friends buy? 2

6. **Discussion** What information do you get with a tree diagram that you do not get with the counting principle? **Sample answer: You can see the actual outcomes.**

You can also use the counting principle to find the probability of an event.

Example 4 Use the information from Example 3. Suppose you and your friends choose a pizza at random. What is the probability that you choose a mushroom pizza with a thin crust?

- Count all possible outcomes: 12.
- Find the number of favorable outcomes: 1.

Probability(mushroom, thin crust) = $\frac{1}{12}$

7. Find the probability of choosing each type of pizza.
   a. a thick crust $\frac{1}{2}$ b. a pepperoni pizza $\frac{1}{6}$

8.b. The question asks for the total number of outcomes, not a list of the actual outcomes.

TRY THESE

8. a. Suppose you roll two dice. Use the counting principle to find the number of possible outcomes. **36**
   b. Why would using the counting principle be easier than drawing a tree diagram? **See above**
   c. What is the probability of rolling two 5's? $\frac{1}{36}$

9. **Cars** When you order a car, you choose the exterior and interior colors. A dealership offers a new car in 10 exterior colors: black, silver, teal, white, navy, royal blue, red, burgundy, forest green, and brown. Each exterior color has 3 different interior colors. How many different color combinations are there? **30**

10. **Cars** A navy car is available with a gray, blue, or black interior. A silver car is available with a gray, blue, black, or red interior. Draw a tree diagram to show all possible color combinations. **See Solution Key.**

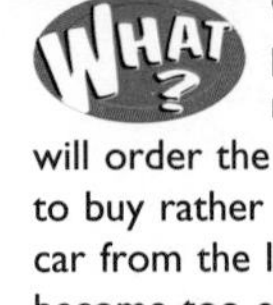

Car dealerships predict that more people will order the car they want to buy rather than choose a car from the lot. It has become too expensive for car dealerships to stock all the different cars that are available. Consumers are happier because they get the cars they want!

PH Multimedia Math Hot Page 10-5

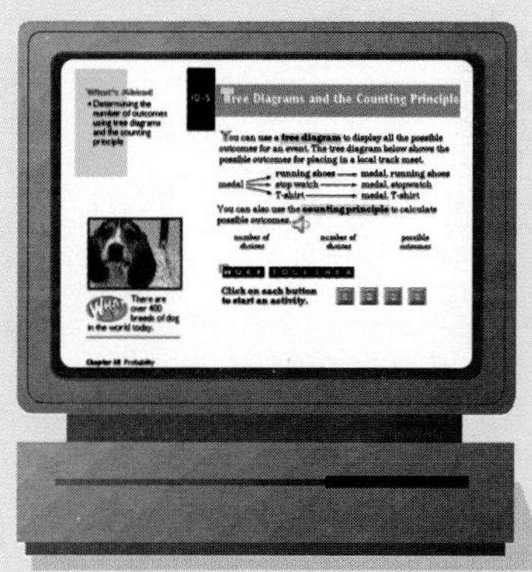

Assignment Options

Core: 12, 13, 15, 16, MR all	
Reinforce: 11, 17	**Enrich:** 14

students how these same outcomes can be determined using a tree diagram. Have students draw the tree diagram. Then discuss how the counting principle can also be used to find the total number of outcomes.

Connections Have a discussion about how tree diagrams and the counting principle can be used. You may want to start with the following examples:

- **Restaurants** (preparing for daily specials that involve two or more choices)
- **Household** (determining the number of recipes that use a set of ingredients, making different outfits from the same clothing items)
- **Publishing** (issuing books under more than one cover, issuing CDs with optional songs and different covers)

Journal Ask students to write about the benefits of organizing a set of choices. Then ask students to determine which method they like better, tree diagrams or the counting principle. Have students support their answers.

ON YOUR OWN

WRITING Make sure students' problems for Exercise 13 account for all possibilities.

CONNECTION TO STATISTICS Exercise 14 has students use a table to compare prices.

TECHNOLOGY OPTION In Exercise 14, you may wish to have students use spreadsheet software to explore prices for different combinations of equipment.

CONNECTION TO ECONOMICS Exercise 14c has students evaluate a range of costs for different computer setups.

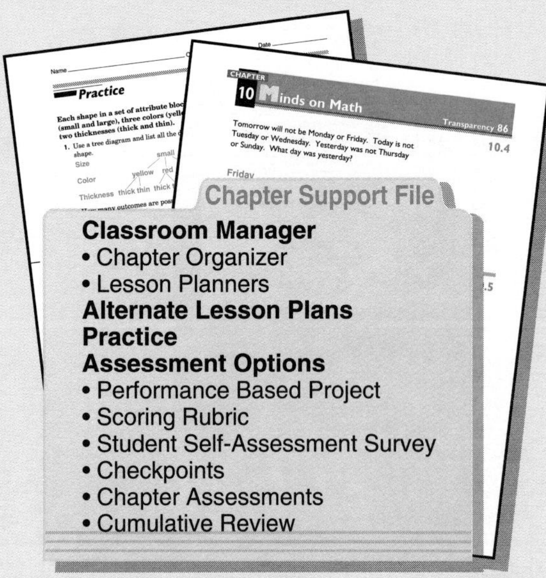

Minds on Math available in Teaching Transparencies

Math Minutes

Grace is tying carnations into bunches of one dozen. If she has 336 carnations, how many bunches can she make? Will she have any carnations left over? Explain.
28 bunches, none left over; 336 is divisible by 12

Materials for 10-6

- blue and red cubes
- bags or containers

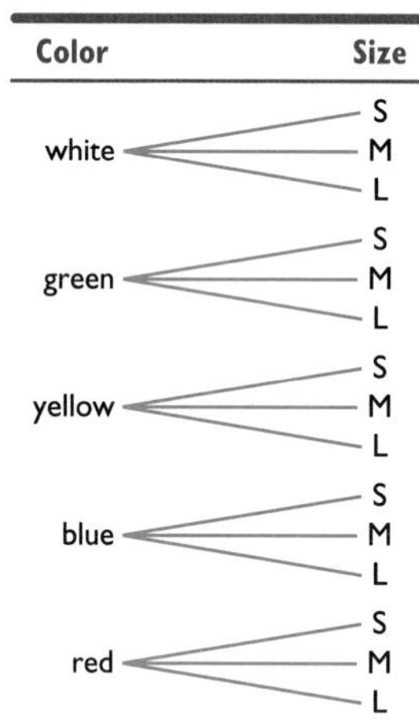

14.c. standard, monochrome, stylewriter; adjustable, color 16-in., laser; $1,700

Mixed REVIEW

Use Napier's rods to find each product.

1. 297 × 5 1,485
2. 3,429 × 7 24,003

Find the probability of each event.

3. a month chosen at random has exactly 30 days $\frac{1}{3}$
4. a letter chosen at random from the word SCIENCE is a vowel $\frac{3}{7}$
5. Find the sum of the even whole numbers from 10 through 48. 580

ON YOUR OWN

11. Small and large blocks in a special set come in five shapes: cube, pyramid, cone, cylinder, and triangular prism. List all the different types of blocks in the set. See Solution Key.
12. **Travel** Four airlines fly nonstop from Washington to Columbus. Five airlines fly nonstop from Columbus to Seattle. How many different pairs of airlines can you use to fly from Washington to Seattle through Columbus? 20
13. **Writing** Write a problem that can be solved using the tree diagram at the left. Solve your problem. See Solution Key.
14. **Consumer Issues** The table below gives some of the choices available when you buy a computer. Suppose you choose one keyboard, one monitor, and one printer.

Keyboards	Monitors	Printers
Standard $105	Monochrome $329	Laser $819
Extended $185	Color 14-in. $539	Stylewriter $339
Adjustable $195	Color 16-in. $1,459	Dot-matrix $439

a. How many outcomes are possible? 27
b. You want a color monitor but you do not want an adjustable keyboard. How many outcomes are left? 12
c. Which computer costs the least? Which computer costs the most? Write the range of costs for these computers. See left.

15. A cafeteria serves the same three main courses and three desserts at lunch each day. You choose a different meal each day, but you always take one main course and one dessert. After how many days will you run out of choices? 9
16. To play a board game, you spin a spinner and take a card. The spinner has sections that tell you to move 1, 2, 3, or 4 spaces. The cards state Free Turn, Lose a Turn, or No Change. What is the probability you move 3 spaces and lose a turn? $\frac{1}{12}$
17. **Cars** When you order a car, you must choose from 8 exterior colors and either cloth or leather interior. Cloth is available in 3 different colors. Leather is available in dark or light. How many different types of car are possible? 40

10-6

Connecting to Prior Knowledge

Remind students of the fact that the probabilities of heads and tails in a coin toss remain equal even after tosses of three tails in a row. Ask students to describe the relationship, or lack of a relationship, between the coin tosses in terms of cause and effect.

WORK TOGETHER

Question 2: Students may need to compare results with another group to detect a pattern in the experimental data.

DIVERSITY This chapter helps students move from the concrete operations stage of thinking to the formal operation stage. Formal operations ask a student to think about thinking and to see a concept as part of a larger system. The educator Piaget thought that the majority of children enter the formal thinking stage between 12 and 14. Later research suggests, however, that some children can think formally on some tasks before they can do so on others, and that some never enter the stage of formal thinking on some tasks. Help your students cross the bridge between concrete and formal thinking by encouraging them to use manipulatives as long as they help, but to also write the more formal mathematical expressions.

THINK AND DISCUSS

CRITICAL THINKING For Question 9, encourage students to name events that do not involve games.

AUDITORY LEARNERS Students often need several discussions about independent events. Most people hold fallacious beliefs about probability, and the facts often seem counter-intuitive.

Error Alert! Students may not understand the connection between multiplying to find probability and using the counting principle for problems such as Question 12. ***Remediation*** Remind students that multiplication can be expressed as

---

What's Ahead

- Determining the probability of two independent events
- Deciding whether or not events are independent

WHAT YOU'LL NEED

✓ Red or blue cubes (or other objects of two colors)

✓ Bag or container

2. Unfair; the game favors player A.

10-6 Independent Events

WORK TOGETHER

Work with a partner. Let's look at Game 3 from page 411 again!

1. Recall your results for Game 3. Is Game 3 fair or unfair? If necessary, play the game or draw a diagram to consider all possible outcomes again. Fair
2. Now change Game 3 to Game 3A. Instead of drawing 2 cubes at a time, draw 1 cube at a time. Play Game 3A at least 20 times. Is Game 3A fair or unfair? Explain.

Game 3A Place 3 red cubes and 1 blue cube in a bag. Draw a cube from the bag without looking. Record the color, put the cube back into the bag, and again draw a cube. If the 2 cubes are the same color, player A wins. If not, player B wins.

THINK AND DISCUSS

The tree diagram at the left shows 16 equally likely outcomes.

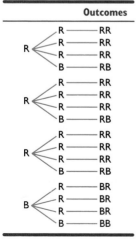

First	Second	Outcomes
R	R	RR
	R	RR
	R	RR
	B	RB
R	R	RR
	R	RR
	R	RR
	B	RB
R	R	RR
	R	RR
	R	RR
	B	RB
B	R	BR
	R	BR
	R	BR
	B	BB

3. Is the tree diagram for Game 3, Game 3A, or both games? 3A
4. **Discussion** Use the tree diagram to decide whether this game is fair or unfair. Make sure you all agree. Unfair
5. In Game 3A, are all 4 cubes equally likely to be drawn on the first draw? on the second draw? Does the second cube drawn depend on the first cube drawn? Yes; Yes; No
6. In Game 3, does the second cube drawn depend on the first cube drawn? Why or why not? Yes, since the cubes are not replaced.

If the outcome of one event does not depend on the outcome of another event, the events are **independent.**

7. Does Game 3 or Game 3A have independent events? 3A

"Shallow men believe in luck, believe in circumstances. Strong men believe in cause and effect."

—Ralph Waldo Emerson

Organizer

1. **Focus**
   Connecting to Prior Knowledge
2. **Teach**
   Work Together
   Think and Discuss
3. **Closure**
   Wrap Up

Vocabulary/Symbols
independent

Skills Reviewed in Context of Lesson
- working with tree diagrams
- multiplying fractions

Materials and Manipulatives
- 1 blue and 3 red cubes (or other objects of two colors; for each group)
- bag or container (1 for each group)

Student Resources
Extra Practice
Student Study Guide
Practice, TR Ch. 10, p. 27
Student Study Guide, Spanish Resources, TR
Alternate Lesson, TR Ch. 10, pp. 18–21

continues next page

repeated addition. A tree diagram works by adding the choices together. The counting principle requires finding the product of the number of outcomes.

Ongoing Assessment Ask students to solve this problem. Look to see if students understand that the events are independent and if they understand how to determine all possible outcomes.

- *A spinner has equal sections that are green, red, yellow, and blue. The spinner is spun once and a coin is tossed. What is the probability that the outcome will be green and tails?* $\frac{1}{4} \times \frac{1}{2} = \frac{1}{8}$

Wrap Up

What's the Big Idea? Ask students: *What are independent events? How do you determine the probability of two independent events both happening?*

Reteaching Activity Have students flip two coins, one after the other, and record the results for the first toss and second toss. Have students meet to combine the results of at least 100 trials to determine the experimental probabilities for (heads, heads), (heads, tails), (tails, heads), and (tails, tails). Then have students use tree diagrams to determine the theoretical probability for each outcome. Have them compare both sets of results with the probabilities found by multiplying the independent probabilities.

Connections Have a discussion about how probability and independent events are used. You may want to start with these examples:

- **Medicine** (diagnosing patients, evaluating treatment options)
- **Science** (isolating the factors that affect an experiment, recognizing causes and their effects)
- **Sports** (discovering successful strategies, analyzing risks)

Organizer, continued

Teacher Resources

Teaching Transparency 86
Lesson Planner, TR Ch. 10, p. 7

Prentice Hall Technology

Computer Item Generator

- 10-6

Fact of the Day

Aristotle was the first to set forth the theory of *syllogisms,* which are arguments in logic. Venn diagrams can be used to demonstrate the validity or invalidity of syllogisms.

—Academic American Encyclopedia

Assignment Options

Core: 16–20, MR all	
Reinforce: 13–15, 21	Enrich: 22, 23

8.a. No.
b. No.
c. Yes.
d. Yes.
e. No.
9. independent events: winning 2 different lotteries; dependent events: two people each receiving their selection from a vending machine.

1–3. See Solution Key.

Mixed REVIEW

Use a protractor to draw an angle with each measure.

1. 45° 2. 130°
3. Draw a tree diagram to show all possible outcomes when you toss a coin and roll a die.
4. What is the probability of getting a heads and an even number in Exercise 3? $\frac{1}{4}$

Use the Venn diagram.

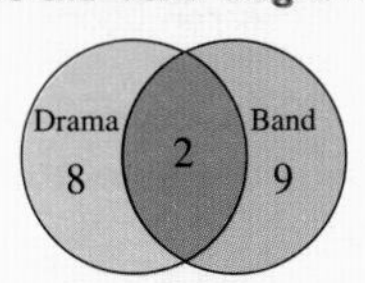

5. How many students are members of the drama club? 10
6. How many students are in the band and members of the drama club? 2

See left.

8. Are the two events independent? Why or why not?
   a. A card is drawn from a deck and is not replaced. Another card is drawn from the deck.
   b. Cleotha studies mathematics 30 min every evening. Cleotha gets an A on her next mathematics quiz.
   c. It snows in Washington, D.C. A new President of the United States is elected.
   d. At a soccer game, a coin is tossed and comes up heads. At the next game, the coin comes up tails.
   e. Faraj runs 6 mi every day. Faraj placed first in a cross country race.
9. **Critical Thinking** List some events that are independent and some that are not. Think of events that are not already described in this chapter. Answers will vary. See sample at left.
10. When you toss a coin, what is the probability of tossing three tails in a row? Draw a tree diagram to show all possible outcomes. Are these independent events? $\frac{1}{8}$; see Solution Key for diagram; Yes.

Another way to find the probability of independent events is to multiply the probabilities.

Probability(A and B) = Probability(A) × Probability(B)

11. Use multiplication to find the probability of tossing 3 tails in a row. Complete: Probability(tails, tails, tails) = Probability(tails) × Probability(tails) × Probability(tails) = ■ × ■ × ■ = ■. Compare with Question 10. $\frac{1}{2}$; $\frac{1}{2}$; $\frac{1}{2}$; $\frac{1}{8}$; The answer is the same.
12. Mei-Ling has 3 sweaters: pink, white, blue. She has 2 pairs of jeans: white, blue. She has 5 pairs of socks: 3 white, 1 blue, 1 pink. She randomly selects 1 sweater, 1 pair of jeans, and 1 pair of socks. What is the probability that she selects all blue?
    a. Use the counting principle to find the number of possible outcomes. Then find the probability. 30; $\frac{1}{30}$
    b. Use multiplication to find the probability. $\frac{1}{3} \times \frac{1}{2} \times \frac{1}{5} = \frac{1}{30}$
    c. Compare your answers for parts (a) and (b). Which method do you prefer for finding the probability? Why? See below.
    d. Explain why you might not want to use a tree diagram to find this probability. Sample answer. The question doesn't ask for a list.

12.c. They are equal; Answers may vary.

Journal Ask students to list the benefits and disadvantages of each way of finding the probability of independent events. Have students write an explanation of their answers.

ON YOUR OWN

WRITING For Exercise 20, have students give reasons why each example is a case of independent events.

CONNECTION TO SCIENCE Exercises 22 and 23 have students use probability to evaluate biological events.

ON YOUR OWN

Use the spinner for Exercises 13–15. It is spun twice.

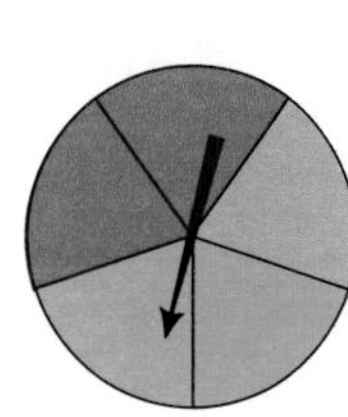

13. Are the two spins independent events? Explain. Yes; the second spin doesn't depend on the first.
14. Use multiplication to find the probability that the first spin is blue and the second spin is red. $\frac{4}{25}$
15. Draw a tree diagram to show all possible outcomes. Find the probability that the two spins are the same color. See Solution Key; $\frac{9}{25}$

Use the two boxes at the right for Exercises 16–18. Box 1 contains 4 cards, and Box 2 contains 5 cards.

Box 1

Box 2

16. A card is drawn from Box 1. Find Probability(M). $\frac{1}{4}$
17. A card is drawn from Box 1. Then a card is drawn from Box 2. Find Probability(ME). $\frac{1}{10}$
18. A card is drawn from Box 1 and put back. Then another card is drawn. Find Probability(HA). $\frac{1}{16}$
19. In a game you toss a coin and roll two dice. How many possible outcomes are there for each of the following?
    a. one coin 2
    b. one die 6
    c. one coin and one die 12
    d. the game 72
20. **Writing** Use your own words to explain to a friend what independent events are. Give some examples. See Solution Key.
21. **Choose A, B, or C.** Which events are not independent? B
    A. Your computer randomly lists a 1 and then a 2.
    B. You draw two colored cards at one time from a deck and get one red and one blue.
    C. You roll a die twice and get 6 both times.
22. **Biology** Assume that "boy" and "girl" are equally likely outcomes for a baby. What is the probability that someone has five baby girls in a row? Show your solution in at least two different ways. $\frac{1}{32}$; Sample ways: tree diagram, counting principle
23. **Biology** Diana thinks that having two babies of the same gender is as likely as having two babies of different genders. Do you agree or disagree? Show your solution. Answers may vary. Sample answer: Yes; the probability of same gender (GG or BB) is the same as the probability of different genders (GB or BG).

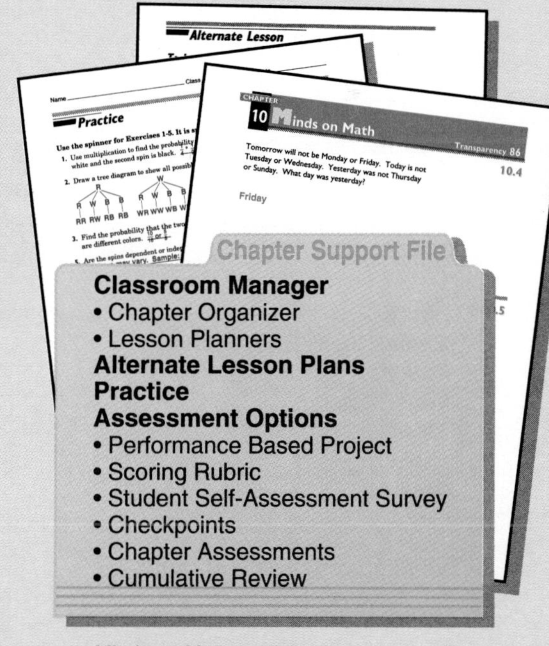

Alternate Lesson
Practice
CHAPTER 10 Minds on Math
Transparency 86
10.4
Tomorrow will not be Monday or Friday. Today is not Tuesday or Wednesday. Yesterday was not Thursday or Sunday. What day was yesterday?
Friday
Chapter Support File
Classroom Manager
• Chapter Organizer
• Lesson Planners
Alternate Lesson Plans
Practice
Assessment Options
• Performance Based Project
• Scoring Rubric
• Student Self-Assessment Survey
• Checkpoints
• Chapter Assessments
• Cumulative Review

Minds on Math available in Teaching Transparencies

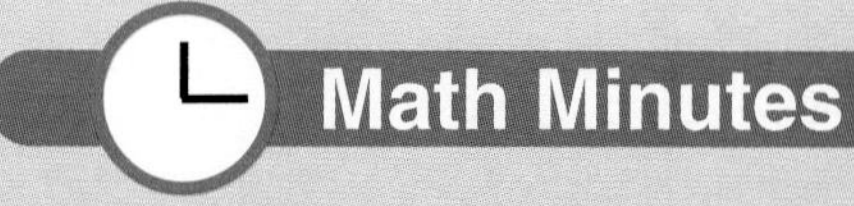

Sixteen teams play in a tournament. Each team plays until it loses. How many games must be played to determine the winner?
15 games

Answers to Problems Unique to Spanish Edition

16. $\frac{1}{4}$
17. $\frac{1}{4} \times \frac{2}{5} = \frac{2}{20} = \frac{1}{10}$
18. $\frac{1}{4} \times \frac{1}{4} = \frac{1}{16}$

10-7

Connecting to Prior Knowledge

Ask students to recall the method of using a tree diagram to find possible outcomes for an event. Have students brainstorm for situations in which making an organized list of combinations or arrangements of items would be helpful.

WORK TOGETHER

ESL Make sure students can explain the meaning or give examples of these words: *prediction, different, arrangements, tree diagram,* and *counting principle.* Flashcards with definitions and examples will help students with these terms.

KINESTHETIC LEARNERS It is important for students to act out this activity. Have students record the arrangements.

Ongoing Assessment Look over students' answers for Question 4 to determine if students understand what makes a good strategy for determining the number of arrangements of a group of items. Ask students the following questions:

- *Are all arrangements accounted for in your list?*
- *Have you repeated any arrangements?*
- *Can you think of a better strategy for making an organized list of possible arrangements?*

Lead students to consider the use of a tree diagram or the counting principle.

THINK AND DISCUSS

Error Alert! Students may not understand the application of the counting principle for Questions 10–12. ***Remediation*** Encourage students to think about the choices for each stage. If one student out of four takes the first place in line, there is one

> *"Chance is the providence of adventurers."*
> —NAPOLEON BONAPARTE

Organizer

1. **Focus**
   Connecting to Prior Knowledge
2. **Teach**
   Work Together
   Think and Discuss
3. **Closure**
   Wrap Up

Skills Reviewed in Context of Lesson
- working with tree diagrams

Materials and Manipulatives
Checkpoint Exercises 1, 3: colored chips or cubes *(optional)*

Student Resources
Extra Practice
Student Study Guide
Practice, TR Ch. 10, p. 28
Student Study Guide, Spanish Resources, TR
Checkpoint, TR Ch. 10, p. 34

Teacher Resources

Teaching Transparency 87
Lesson Planner, TR Ch. 10, p. 8

Prentice Hall Technology
Computer Item Generator
- 10-7

What's Ahead
- Determining the number of arrangements of a group of items

10-7 Exploring Arrangements

WORK TOGETHER

Work in groups of four students.

1. Make a prediction and write it down for this question: How many different ways can you arrange your group members in a line? 24 different ways for a group of 4

2. Stand up and form one line of all your group members. Then form as many different lines as you can. How many different lines can you form? See Question 1.

3. Simulate this problem. Represent each member with an object, such as a pencil or a book. Arrange the objects in as many different lines as you can. Did you get the same number of possible arrangements? Yes; see Question 1.

Suppose only** 3 people are in line. **How many different ways can the 3 people form a line? 6

4. Use a letter or a number to represent each group member. Make an organized list of all possible arrangements.
   a. How many arrangements are in your list? See Question 1.
   b. Compare this number with your prediction and your answers to Questions 2 and 3. Answers should be the same.

THINK AND DISCUSS

You can use several different methods to find the number of arrangements of a set of objects.

5. **Discussion** In the activity above, you used several methods to find the number of different arrangements of your group members. Name each method. What did you like or dislike about each method? acting it out, using simulation with books, using a list; Answers will vary.
6. **Discussion** As a class, agree on the number of possible arrangements for groups with 3 members, 4 members, and 5 members. 6, 24, 120

less student to decide between for the second place, and so on. Have students model the line with blocks or markers or act it out.

Wrap Up

What's the Big Idea? Ask students: *How can you use the counting principle and tree diagrams to determine the number of arrangements of any number of items?*

Reteaching Activity Have students work in groups of three to examine the number of ways three people can be cast in a play based on *The Wizard of Oz* (the Scarecrow, Tin Man, and Lion). Make signs with the three parts that students can hold. Have them line up and trade signs to show all of the arrangements and then have students record the information on paper. Ask students the following questions:

- *How many choices are there for the role of the Scarecrow?* **(3)**
- *If someone is chosen as the Scarecrow, how many choices are left for the role of the Tin Man?* **(2)**

Connections Have students discuss situations in which the arrangement of items in order is useful. You may want to start with these examples:

- **Communications** (assigning telephone numbers)
- **Sports** (determining order of contestants, order of events in competitions, or the lineups of teams)
- **Florist** (making flower arrangements, determining order of stops for deliveries)

Journal Ask students to write about how their ideas on probability have changed and why.

ON YOUR OWN

CRITICAL THINKING Remind students that Exercise 19 requires finding all possible arrangements for seven items. Students may want to use the fastest method they know.

You can draw a tree diagram or make an organized list. Then count all the possible arrangements.

7. The tree diagram at the right shows all possible arrangements of the numbers 1, 2, and 3. Draw a tree diagram that shows all possible arrangements of the numbers 1, 2, 3, and 4. See Solution Key.

			Outcomes
1	2	3	123
	3	2	132
2	1	3	213
	3	1	231
3	1	2	312
	2	1	321

8. To count the number of arrangements of A, B, C, and D, Veronica started to make the list at the right. Complete the list. Would you organize the list this way? See Solution Key.

Veronica's List
ABCD BCDA CDAB ···
ABDC
ACBD
⋮

9. **Discussion** Which method do you prefer, drawing a tree diagram or making a list? Do they give the same results? Answers may vary; Yes.

You can also use the counting principle. For example, to find the number of arrangements of four students, think about each place in a line.

First place in line		Second place in line		Third place in line		Fourth place in line	
4	×	3	×	2	×	1	= 24

10. **Discussion** Why are there 4 choices for the first place in line, but only 3 choices for the second place in line? Sample answer: When someone is in first place, he or she can no longer be in second place.
11. **Discussion** Does this method make sense to you? When might this method be the most practical one to use? Yes; when the numbers are large.
12. **Sports** A coach must decide on a batting order for nine baseball players. Use the counting principle to find the number of choices the coach has for a batting order. 362,880

Problem Solving Hint
Write the product you need to find. Then use a calculator to find the product.

ON YOUR OWN

13. Make an organized list of all possible arrangements of the letters in the word SING. How many are English words? See Solution Key.
14. Many daily newspapers have a feature called "Scramble." Imagine that you write this feature. How many different ways can you scramble the letters in the word RANDOM? 720
15. The school choir will sing five songs for an assembly. How many different ways can the director order the songs? 120

Fact of the Day

The oldest known bobsled dates from 6500 B.C., and came from Heinola, Finland. The first known bobsled race took place at Davos, Switzerland, in 1889.

—GUINNESS BOOK OF RECORDS

Assignment Options

Core: 14, 16, 18, 19, MR all, CH al	
Reinforce: 13, 15, 17	**Enrich:** 20

Answers to Problems Unique to Spanish Edition

13. SOPA OSPA POAS APOS
SOAP OSAP POSA APSO
SPOA OASP PASO ASPO
SPAO OAPS PAOS ASOP
SAPO OPAS PSAO AOPS
SAOP OPSA PSOA AOSP
Four combinations form words in Spanish: SOPA, SAPO, POSA, PASO.
14. 720; 6 × 5 × 4 × 3 × 2 × 1

WRITING Make sure students work through their problems for Exercise 20 to make sure they are applicable and solvable.

CHECKPOINT

Exercises 1–4: Encourage students to use blocks or tiles to model any of these problems. For Exercises 1 and 3, have students simulate the situations described.

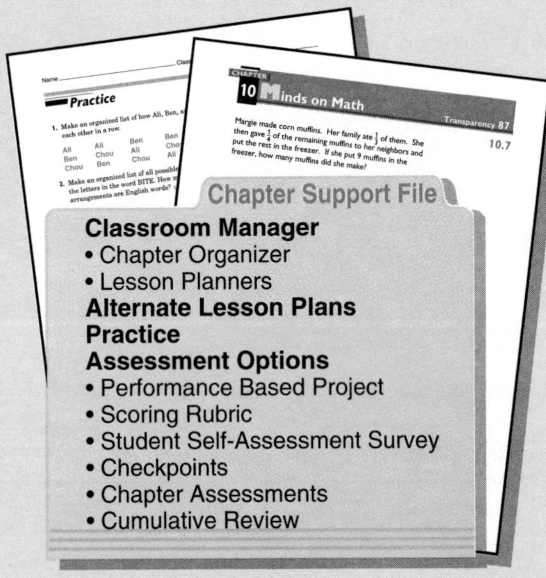

Minds on Math available in Teaching Transparencies

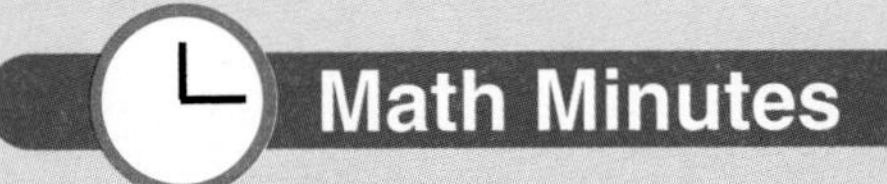

In a group of six boys and girls, each person shakes hands once with each of the other people in the group. How many handshakes are exchanged?
15

Materials for 10-8

- beans, chips, cubes, or other objects that differ only in color

The Jamaican bobsled team was the subject of a 1993 movie called "Cool Runnings."

Answers will vary. Sample: A red, a white, and a blue marble are in a box. You select a marble without replacement, and then select another marble. Make a list of possible outcomes.

Mixed REVIEW

Simplify.

1. $15 + 6 \div 3$ 17
2. $8 \times 2^2 - 4 \div 2$ 30

A die is rolled twice. Find the probability of each event.

3. 3, then odd $\frac{1}{12}$
4. 5, then 5 $\frac{1}{36}$
5. Two numbers have a product of 364 and a difference of 15. What are the two numbers? 28, 13

16. **Sports** Bobsled teams like to be one of the first down the track because the track becomes slower with use. Draw a tree diagram to show all the different arrangements of bobsled teams from Switzerland, Germany, and Italy. See Solution Key.
17. **Literature** A library received a seven-volume set of books by C.S. Lewis called *The Chronicles of Narnia.*
    a. How many ways can the books be arranged in a row on a shelf? 5,040
    b. The seven books are placed in a random order on a shelf in the library. What is the probability that the books are in the correct order from left to right? $\frac{1}{5,040}$
18. **Music** A radio disc jockey has ten songs to play in the next hour. How many different ways can he arrange the songs? 3,628,800
19. **Critical Thinking** Tanya said that her phone number has every digit from 3 to 9. Kenna decides to try every possible phone number until she reaches Tanya. Suppose Kenna is as unlucky as possible. How many different phone numbers will Kenna try before she reaches Tanya? 5,040
20. **Writing** Write a problem that can be solved by using the tree diagram. Solve the problem another way.

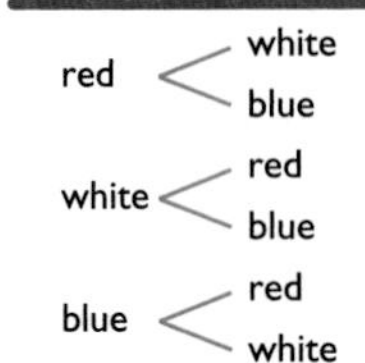

CHECKPOINT

1. A blue, red, or yellow chip is selected, and a coin is tossed.
    a. Draw a tree diagram to show all possible outcomes.
    b. Find Probability(yellow, then tails). $\frac{1}{6}$ See Solution Key.
2. When ordering the luncheon special, you can choose from 3 entrees, 2 soups, and 2 desserts. Use the counting principle to find the number of possible combinations. 12
3. A bag contains 3 green cubes and 4 red cubes. A cube is drawn and replaced. Another cube is drawn. What is the probability that 2 red cubes are drawn? $\frac{16}{49}$
4. How many different ways can 6 students be lined up shoulder-to-shoulder for a photograph? 720

CHAPTER 10 PRACTICE

This page provides practice on the skills learned up to this point in the chapter. Daily cumulative practice can be found in the Mixed Reviews that appear in every lesson.

CALCULATOR For Exercise 19, have students write an expression for the solution before they do the calculation.

Practice

1. Is Game 4 fair or unfair?
Game 4: Place 3 red cubes and 3 blue cubes in a bag. Draw 2 cubes from the bag without looking. If they are the same color, player A wins. If they are not the same color, player B wins. unfair

2. **Sports** Solve by simulation.
A batting average is the ratio of the number of hits to the number of times at bat. Andre's batting average is 0.250. Find the probability that he gets 2 hits the next 2 times at bat. Answers may vary; For a large number of trials, $\frac{1}{16}$.

3. Kaylee tossed a coin 20 times with these results: 12 heads, 8 tails. Use her data to find the experimental probability of getting heads. $\frac{3}{5}$

4. Explain how you can use random digits to simulate the probability of heads when you toss a coin. Discuss the number of trials you would do. Answers will vary. Sample: Use 2 random digits. Do 50 trials. The probability should be about $\frac{1}{2}$.

A die with 12 faces numbered 1–12 is rolled. All outcomes are equally likely. Find each probability.

5. Probability(even) $\frac{1}{2}$
6. Probability(13) 0
7. Probability(not 1) $\frac{11}{12}$
8. Probability(7 or 8) $\frac{1}{6}$
9. Probability(number less than 10) $\frac{3}{4}$

10. Suppose you read in the newspaper that the probability of precipitation is 10%. Write this probability two other ways and describe it using words. $\frac{1}{10}$; 0.1; sample: a small chance of precipitation

11. Describe one event that is certain, one event that is impossible, and one event that may or may not happen. What is the probability of each event? See below.

12. Sweatshirts are available in green, gray, black, blue, and orange. The sizes are small, medium, and large. Draw a tree diagram to show all possible outcomes for a sweatshirt. See Solution Key.

13. Sweatshirts at another store are available in 10 different colors, 3 different styles, and 4 different sizes. Use the counting principle to find the number of possible outcomes. 120

Are the two events independent? Why or why not?

14. It snows overnight. You decide to go sledding the next day. No.

15. You reach into a bag with red and blue cubes and draw 2 red cubes. No.

16. You toss a coin twice. Yes.

17. A computer randomly lists 1, then 2. Yes.

18. What is the probability of getting two 6's when you roll two dice? $\frac{1}{36}$

19. **Calculator** How many different ways can you arrange 11 books on a shelf? 39,916,800

11. Answers will vary. Sample answer: rolling a number less than 10 with one die; rolling a sum of one with 2 dice, flipping a coin and getting a heads; 1, 0, $\frac{1}{2}$.

Resources
Extra Practice
Student Study Guide
Student Study Guide, Spanish Resources, TR

10-8

Connecting to Prior Knowledge

Ask students to think of situations in which sampling and predicting take place, such as Gallup polls, telephone sampling, or Nielsen ratings. Ask students to name the purposes of these methods.

THINK AND DISCUSS

ESL Error Alert! Students may be confused by the specialized use of the words *population* and *sample* for Questions 2 and 3. ***Remediation*** Have students give everyday definitions for the terms and write the definitions on the chalkboard. Then lead students to view the relationship between the terms *population* and *sample* as "whole to part." Tell students that one way of testing the whole is to sample a part. Ask students to provide examples, such as tasting a dish to determine if it is ready to eat.

Question 2: Ask students to differentiate between voters and general population for the survey's population and the telephone book listings and the respondents for the survey's sample.

Question 4: Encourage students to think of other possible reasons for a poll being so inaccurate.

WORK TOGETHER

Divide the class into four groups and have groups change partners after each survey. Limit groups' populations to fewer than 400 items. If there are not enough cubes or blocks, encourage groups to make their populations from colored squares on a sheet of graph paper. Different kinds of beans also work well for this activity.

Challenge each group to draw up a sample and evaluation plan while the other group is assembling its population. Then have the population group check the surveying group's method and calculations.

"Knowledge is power."
—Francis Bacon

Organizer

1. **Focus**
   Connecting to Prior Knowledge
2. **Teach**
   Think and Discuss
   Work Together
3. **Closure**
   Wrap Up

Vocabulary/Symbols
population, representative, sample, random

Skills Reviewed in Context of Lesson
- working with percents

Materials and Manipulatives
- a number of beans, chips, cubes, or other objects that differ only in color

On Your Own Exercises 19, 20: newspaper or magazine

Student Resources
Extra Practice
Student Study Guide
Practice, TR Ch. 10, p. 29
Student Study Guide, Spanish Resources, TR

Teacher Resources
Teaching Transparency 87
Lesson Planner, TR Ch. 10, p. 9

continues next page

MATH AND SURVEYS

10-8 Making Predictions

What's Ahead
- Making predictions about a population based on a sample

WHAT YOU'LL NEED
✓ A number of beans, chips, cubes, or other objects that differ only in color

THINK AND DISCUSS

For the 1936 presidential election, *Literary Digest* did a survey to predict the results of the election. They mailed questionnaires to 10 million people. They used names and addresses from telephone books to select who would receive questionnaires. Only 2.4 million people sent questionnaires back. Here are the survey and election results.

	Survey Results	Actual Election Results
Franklin Roosevelt	43%	62%
Alfred Landon	57%	38%

1. Which candidate won the *Literary Digest* survey? Which candidate won the election? Were the survey results accurate? Landon; Roosevelt; No

"Polling is merely an instrument for gauging public opinion. When a president or any other leader pays attention to poll results, he is in effect, paying attention to the views of the people."
—George H. Gallup (1901–1984)

A **population** is a group of people or other objects about whom you want information. A **sample** is the part of the population you use to make predictions about the population. In order to make accurate predictions, the sample must be *representative* of the whole population. With a *random* sample, each member of the population has the same chance of being in the sample. A random sample usually results in a representative sample.

2. For the *Literary Digest* survey, what is the population? What is the sample? registered voters; 10 million people listed in telephone books
3. Two major problems with the *Literary Digest* survey led to poor predictions.
   a. **Discussion** Not everyone is listed in the telephone book! In fact, many Democrats who voted for Roosevelt did not have telephones. Was the sample representative? Was the sample random? Explain your answers.
   b. **Discussion** Only 2.4 million people sent their questionnaires back. Why is this a problem?

3.a. No; No; The sample was not chosen from the entire population.
b. A 24% return rate may not be representative of the sample.

Emphasize to students that there are no correct answers to the activity, only thorough and well-planned methods that students should use.

TACTILE LEARNERS Make sure all students have a chance to manipulate, arrange, and count the objects for Questions 5–9.

TECHNOLOGY OPTION For Questions 5–9, students can use software that explores sampling.

Question 8: Have the different groups compare both their results and their methods.

Ongoing Assessment Ask students to answer the following questions and to explain their reasoning.

- *You have taken a sample of 100 beans from a population of 400 and obtained these results: 35 kidney, 17 pinto, and 48 lima. Based on this sample, what is your prediction for the population?* **(About 140 kidney, 68 pinto, 192 lima; students' methods will vary.)**
- *Is the sample size adequate?* **(Answers will vary.)**

Wrap Up

What's the Big Idea? Ask students: *What is a random sample and how can it be used to make predictions about a population?*

Reteaching Activity Bring to class several polls and surveys from newspapers and magazines. Have students examine the polling methods and evaluate the polls. Challenge students to describe as precisely as possible the population and the sample in the poll.

Journal Point out to students that it is always difficult and sometimes dangerous to generalize about groups of people. Ask students to think of ways polls and surveys can take people's differences and individuality into account.

For the 1948 presidential election, three different surveys predicted that the Republican candidate Dewey would win. Instead, Truman won! All the surveys did personal interviews to collect data. Each interviewer asked a certain number of people from specific categories for whom they would vote. Here are the results.

	Crossley Predictions	Gallup Predictions	Roper Predictions	Election Results
Harry Truman	45%	44%	38%	50%
Thomas Dewey	50%	50%	53%	45%

Harry Truman was elected President, even though 3 surveys predicted that he would lose!

4. **Discussion** The problem was that interviewers chose whom to interview within each category. So they visited affluent neighborhoods where mainly Republicans lived. How and why did this lead to poor predictions?
The sample would be biased towards the Republican candidate, Dewey.

WORK TOGETHER

Work in teams to experiment with random samples. Take turns being Team 1 and Team 2. Then answer the questions.

Team 1: Create a population of objects that are the same except for color. For example, use red, white, and blue cubes. Use 2–4 different colors. Write down the number of each color in the population. Tell Team 2 only the number of objects in your population and the number of different colors you used.

Team 2: Take a random sample of the population. Then predict the distribution of colors within the population. For example, if the population contains 400 white and red cubes, you might predict that there are 100 white cubes and 300 red cubes.

5.–6. Sample answers are given.

5. How did you make sure that the samples were random?
The sample was chosen without looking into the bag.
6. How many objects did you use for a sample? Why? The larger a random sample is, the better it should represent the population.
7. How well did your sample represent the population?
Answers may vary.
8. How accurate were your predictions? Are you surprised?
Answers may vary.
9. **Discussion** Why take a random sample instead of counting or surveying the whole population? Sample answer: when the population is very large, using a random sample takes less time and effort.

Mixed REVIEW

Evaluate.

1. $2x + 5$ for $x = 9$ 23
2. $b^2 + 4b$ for $b = 3$ 21
3. A recruiter needs to schedule 7 people for interviews. How many different ways can the recruiter arrange the interviews? 5,040
4. In how many different ways can 4 people be seated in a row of 4 seats? 24
5. How many squares are there in the figure below? 30

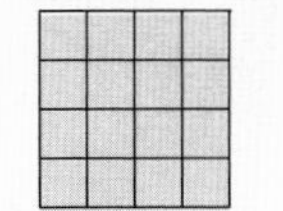

Organizer, continued

Prentice Hall Technology

Multimedia Math
- Hot Page 10-8
- Math Investigations, Measuring Elephant Populations in Africa

Computer Item Generator
- 10-8

Other Available Technology

Taking Chances by Sunburst: Questions 5–9 *(optional)*

Fact of the Day

Since the introduction of the popular vote in presidential elections in 1872, the greatest majority won was 17,994,460 votes in 1972, when President Richard M. Nixon defeated George S. McGovern.

—Guinness Book of Records

Connections Have a discussion about how surveys are used. You may want to begin with the following examples:

- **Entertainment** (surveying stores to determine top albums, theaters to follow a film's gross, and TV viewers for their opinions for a talk show)
- **Sports** (surveying coaches and reporters to determine top high school and college rankings, surveying cities to decide to whom to award expansion teams)
- **Media** (surveying viewers or readers to describe population to potential advertisers)
- **Consumer** (grading products by survey results)

ON YOUR OWN

CRITICAL THINKING For Exercise 16, have students explain how their examples fit both descriptions.

WRITING For Exercise 19, encourage students to write a local newspaper if they can for the fastest results.

CHAPTER INVESTIGATION Students can find the data required for Exercise 20 in back issues of a local newspaper or with the Weather Service. Have students make tables of the data they find.

CONNECTION TO SCIENCE Exercise 20 has students make predictions about the weather based on past data.

PH Multimedia Math Hot Page™ 10-8

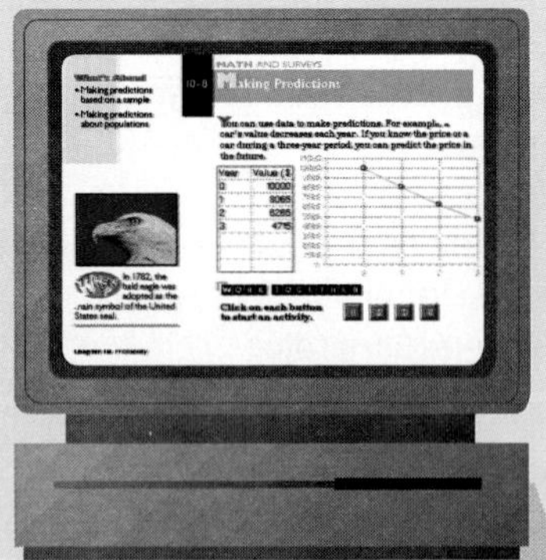

Assignment Options

Core: 12–16, 20, MR all	
Reinforce: 10, 11, 17	**Enrich:** 18, 19

What Do You Think?

Call the number below to give your opinion on the following questions. Each call costs 75¢. Use only a touch-tone phone. Press 1 for YES. Press 3 for NO. After you answer the questions, enter your age. This opinion poll lasts only until midnight EST on Tuesday, May 15. This magazine will publish the results in a future issue.

ON YOUR OWN

The partial news article was distributed nationally.

10. Identify the population and sample for this survey. See Solution Key.
11. Give at least three reasons why the data collected from the survey will not be representative of the population. See Solution Key.

Is each sample random? representative? Explain.

12. A company wants to know the opinions of sixth graders in a certain town. The name of every sixth grader in town is placed in a revolving bin, and 30 names are drawn. yes; possibly.
13. To find the cost to rent a two-bedroom apartment in the United States, 100 two-bedroom apartment dwellers in New York City are questioned. No; No.
14. To determine the most popular car in your city, data is collected on all the cars in the high school parking lot. No; No.
15. To taste a bowl of soup, you take a spoonful. Yes; possibly.
16. Critical Thinking Is it possible to have a sample that is representative but not random? random but not representative? Use examples to explain your answer. Yes; Yes.

GREAT EXPECTATIONS

Farmer

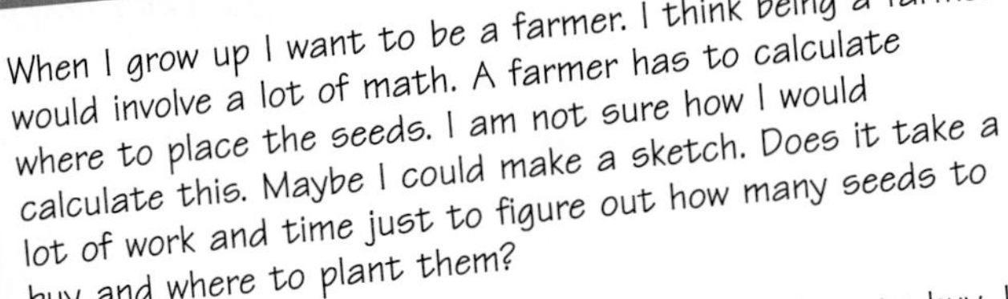

When I grow up I want to be a farmer. I think being a farmer would involve a lot of math. A farmer has to calculate where to place the seeds. I am not sure how I would calculate this. Maybe I could make a sketch. Does it take a lot of work and time just to figure out how many seeds to buy and where to plant them?

A farmer also has to calculate how much fertilizer to buy. I will have to know about crop rotation so I always have rich soil. I think this is how I will use math if I am a farmer.

Carri Chan

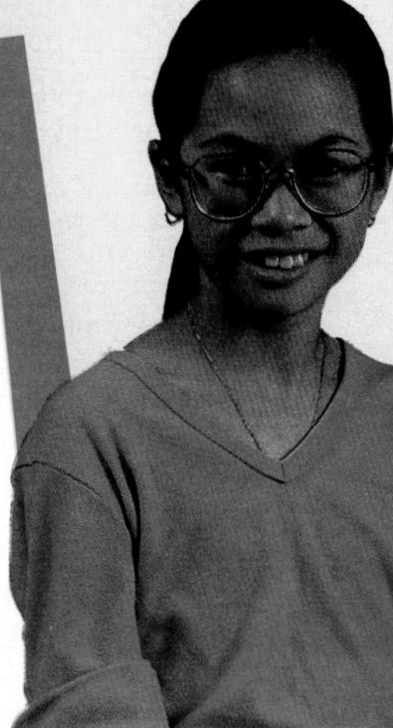

Great Expectations

There are many valuable resources available to the students for gathering information about being a farmer. The following list includes places to write for more information and publications to read.

- Texas Agricultural Extension Service
  Texas A&M University
  College Station, TX 77843
- *The Minority Farmer: A Disappearing American Resource,* United States Congress House Committee on Government Operations, Washington, D.C.: U.S.G.P.O., 1990.
- *Farm: A Year in the Life of an American Farmer.* Richard Rhodes. (NY: Simon & Schuster, 1989).
- *Math on the Job: Grain Farmer.* (Columbus, Ohio: National Center for Research in Vocational Education, Ohio State University, 1985).

Students can also learn from discussions with experts. Here are some possible sources.

- Invite a local farmer to speak to the class.
- Ask the manager of a local grain elevator to give a guided tour and explain the process of the harvest.
- Visit the laboratory farm of a university.

Encourage students to ask questions about the skills necessary for a career as a farmer, including these topics.

- The training and college degrees necessary to become a farmer
- How math is used on the job (discuss fractions, algorithms, patterns, estimation, geometry, area, probability)
- How computers are used to maintain records

Answers may vary. Samples are given.

17. A UFO is an "unidentified flying object." Two surveys asked a random sample of Americans if UFOs were real or just in people's imaginations.

a. Estimate the probability that a person you meet tomorrow will believe that UFOs are real. 47%

b. If you tell 300 people that UFOs are in people's imaginations, how many do you think will agree? about 93

c. Why do you think the data changed from 1978 to 1990? People may have been influenced by TV programs about UFOs.

UFO Survey Results

	1978	1990
Real	57%	47%
Imagination	27%	31%
Not sure	16%	22%

18. Data File I (pp. 2–3) Data is given for the number of hours that people watch TV in a week. Can you tell if the sample is random or representative? Do you think the predictions are accurate? See Solution Key.

19. Writing Find an article in a newspaper or magazine that includes data collected from a survey. Write a letter to the editor. Ask the editor about the sample, the population, and the methods they used. Send your letter! Check students' letters.

20. Investigation (p. 410) Collect data on the daily weather for your region from the last two weeks. Look for patterns or trends. Predict the weather in your region for tomorrow. Explain how you made the prediction. Why might your prediction not be accurate? See Solution Key.

Dear Carri,

Congratulations on having a career goal of being a farmer. Farmers are very important people. They produce a high-quality food supply for our country and other countries.

Math is very important in running a farm business. The farmer must calculate the number of dollars needed to plant crops and feed the animals. Farmers develop budgets, calculate interest, account for expense and income, understand profit and loss, and balance their record books.

Farmers must work with nature to produce the highest quality food. They keep charts and records of the rainfall and temperature to make decisions for growing plants and animals.

Farmers use percent to balance the feed rations for animals and fertilizer mixes for plants.

Best wishes for a successful farming career.

Larry D. Case

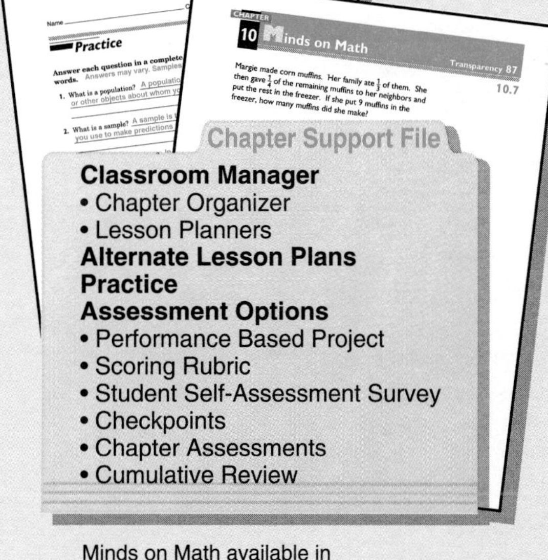

Practice
10 Minds on Math
Chapter Support File
Classroom Manager
• Chapter Organizer
• Lesson Planners
Alternate Lesson Plans
Practice
Assessment Options
• Performance Based Project
• Scoring Rubric
• Student Self-Assessment Survey
• Checkpoints
• Chapter Assessments
• Cumulative Review

Minds on Math available in Teaching Transparencies

Math Minutes

At an amusement park, deluxe hamburgers cost $2.75 each. How many can Antria buy with a $20 bill? How much change will she receive?

7 hamburgers; $.75 change

CHAPTER 10 WRAP UP

Ongoing Assessment Have students work in pairs on the exercises. Then have each pair compare and discuss results with another pair. Tell students that they should be able to give reasons for their answers.

If students have difficulty with a particular problem, encourage them to go back through the lessons to find similar problems they have already solved.

Vocabulary/Symbols

certain
counting principle
equally likely
experimental probability
fair
favorable
impossible
independent
model
population sample
random
representative
simulate
tree diagram
trial

Materials and Manipulatives

- number cubes

Fair and Unfair Games 10-1

A game is ***fair*** if each player has the same chance of winning.

One way to decide if a game is fair or unfair is to consider all the possible outcomes of the game.

1. Players take turns tossing two number cubes. If the sum of the numbers on the two cubes is even, Player A scores a point. If the sum is odd, Player B scores a point. The player with the most points at the end of 10 rounds wins.

a. List all possible outcomes. See right.

b. Writing Is the game fair or unfair? Explain. Fair; the number of even sums is equal to the number of odd sums.

1.a.	1	2	3	4	5	6
1	2	3	4	5	6	7
2	3	4	5	6	7	8
3	4	5	6	7	8	9
4	5	6	7	8	9	10
5	6	7	8	9	10	11
6	7	8	9	10	11	12

Experimental Probability and Simulations 10-1, 10-2, 10-3

You can also use experimental probability to determine if a game is fair or unfair. ***Experimental probability*** is a ratio that shows the fraction of the time a player wins a game.

A situation can be represented with a ***model.*** You can ***simulate*** a problem using a model or random digits.

2. Results of a game are shown below.

<table>
<tr><td>A wins</td><td>|||</td></tr>
<tr><td>B wins</td><td>卌 ||</td></tr>
<tr><td>Times played</td><td>卌 卌</td></tr>
</table>

a. Find Probability(A wins) and Probability(B wins). $\frac{3}{10}$; $\frac{7}{10}$

b. Is the game fair or unfair? Explain. Unfair; the experimental probability of B winning is much greater than A.

3. You take your dog for a 20 min walk every weekday any time between 5:00 P.M. and 6:00 P.M. Your mother gets home from work every weekday any time between 5:30 P.M. and 6:30 P.M. What is the experimental probability that your mother gets home from work while you are walking your dog? Check student's work.

4. How likely are "consecutive numbers" when you toss two dice? Use the list of random digits at the right to simulate this problem. $\frac{2}{9}$

List of Random Digits 1–6

23	41	63	24	11	25	34	52	22	51	42	63
52	32	43	41	11	24	12	33	62	31	32	64
55	43	63	11	41	34	24	51	14	15	26	32

Getting Ready for Chapter 11

These exercises preview the concept of integers.

Probability 10-4

You can describe the ***probability*** of an event occurring as the ratio of the number of favorable outcomes to the number of possible outcomes.

5. A bag contains the letters of the word MATHEMATICS. Find each probability.

a. selecting the letter M $\frac{2}{11}$ **b.** selecting the letter R 0 **c.** selecting a vowel $\frac{4}{11}$

Tree Diagrams, the Counting Principle, and Independent Events 10-5, 10-6

You can use a ***tree diagram*** or the ***counting principle*** to find the number of possible outcomes.

If the outcome of one event does not depend on the outcome of another event, the events are ***independent.***

6. A company makes 5 car styles. Each car comes in 6 colors. Each car can have 4 interior styles and automatic or standard transmission. Harold wants one of each kind of car for his lot. How many cars must he order? 240 cars

7. Suppose you play a game using the spinner at the right. Find the probability that the first spin is yellow and the second spin is green. $\frac{15}{64}$

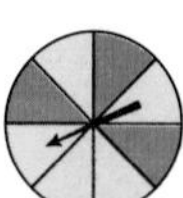

Arrangements and Making Predictions 10-7, 10-8

You can find the number of arrangements of a set of objects by making a list, drawing a tree diagram, using the counting principle, or simulating the problem.

A sample is *random* if each member of a population has an equal chance of being in the sample.

8. Zalika will play 5 songs for her piano recital. In how many ways can Zalika order the songs? 120 ways

9. To find the favorite sport of boys in your school, you survey all boys who play on the soccer team. Is the sample random? Explain. no; not all boys in school have an equal chance of being surveyed.

GETTING READY FOR CHAPTER 11

Would you represent each situation by a positive or a negative number?

1. a debt of $12 negative **2.** a gain of 10 yd positive **3.** 100 ft below sea level negative **4.** 3 steps forward positive

Student Resources

Practice, p. 435
Problem Solving Practice, p. 420
Extra Practice
Student Study Guide
Student Study Guide, Spanish Resources
Tools for Studying Smarter, TR
Student Self-Assessment Survey, TR Ch. 10, p. 33 *(see below)*

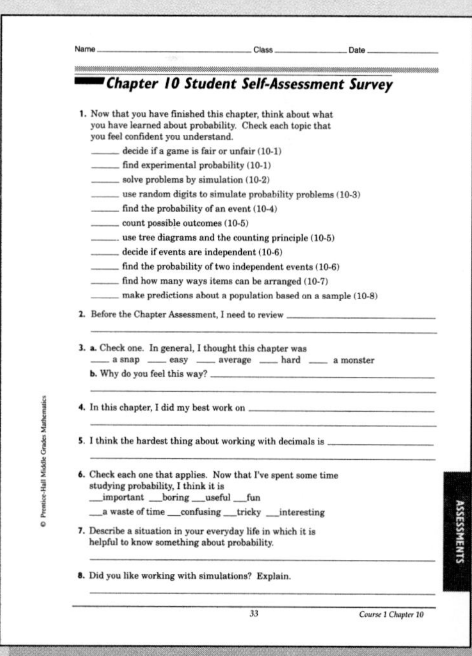

Name ____________ Class ________ Date ________

Chapter 10 Student Self-Assessment Survey

1. Now that you have finished this chapter, think about what you have learned about probability. Check each topic that you feel confident you understand.
   ______ decide if a game is fair or unfair (10-1)
   ______ find experimental probability (10-1)
   ______ solve problems by simulation (10-2)
   ______ use random digits to simulate probability problems (10-3)
   ______ find the probability of an event (10-4)
   ______ count possible outcomes (10-5)
   ______ use tree diagrams and the counting principle (10-5)
   ______ decide if events are independent (10-6)
   ______ find the probability of two independent events (10-6)
   ______ find how many ways items can be arranged (10-7)
   ______ make predictions about a population based on a sample (10-8)
2. Before the Chapter Assessment, I need to review ____________
3. a. Check one. In general, I thought this chapter was
   ____ a snap ____ easy ____ average ____ hard ____ a monster
   b. Why do you feel this way? ____________
4. In this chapter, I did my best work on ____________
5. I think the hardest thing about working with decimals is ____________
6. Check each one that applies. Now that I've spent some time studying probability, I think it is
   ___important ___boring ___useful ___fun
   ___a waste of time ___confusing ___tricky ___interesting
7. Describe a situation in your everyday life in which it is helpful to know something about probability.
8. Did you like working with simulations? Explain.

ASSESSMENTS

33 *Course 1 Chapter 10*

Answers to Problems Unique to Spanish Edition

5. a. $\frac{2}{11}$ b. 0 c. $\frac{5}{11}$

CHAPTER 10

PUTTING IT ALL TOGETHER

The projects on these pages can be used in a variety of ways.

- alternative assessment
- portfolio ideas
- additional assignments for gifted and talented students
- extra credit for all students

Follow Up

Students should not be expected to draw up day-to-day forecasts but rather general predictions for the period. Some may simply compare the upcoming period with annual averages, for example, "heavier than usual precipitation."

Have students record their predictions. Check the predictions at the end of 30 days.

RESEARCH The "morgue" at the offices of the local newspaper will have copies of back issues of the paper for student research on local weather. Often the library will have recent back issues also.

EXCURSION Among natural phenomena that could affect insurance rates are floods, hurricanes, earthquakes, and tornadoes.

That's the Way the Spinner Spins

COOPERATIVE GROUPS Have students color the spinner the four colors mentioned in the table plus an extra purple and blue section. As part of the experiment, students can alternate spinning the spinner and recording the tally marks. Ask students whether replacing the spinner with other chance devices (for example, cards or dice) would make a difference to the outcome. Again, have the students conduct an experiment and compare the results.

Materials and Manipulatives

Follow Up
- back issues of newspapers

That's the Way the Spinner Spins
- paper clips
- spinners

Hexamania
- copies of game board

Words Words Words
- newspaper or magazine
- Scrabble game

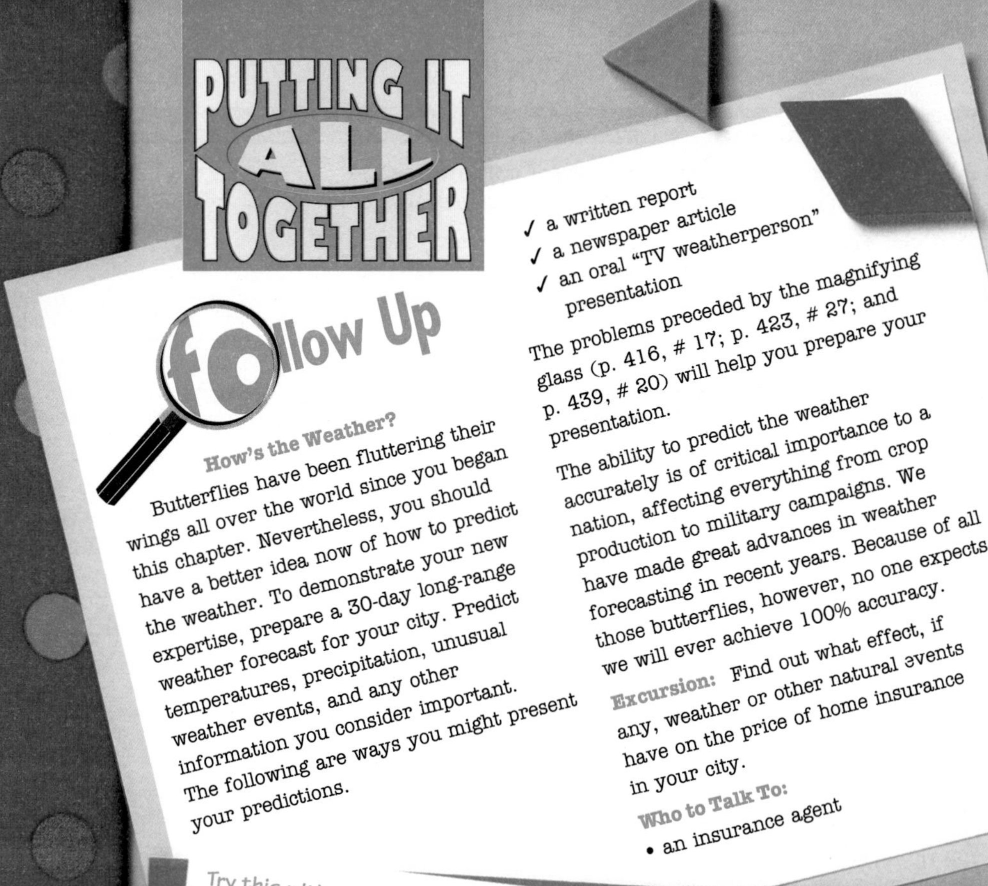

PUTTING IT ALL TOGETHER

Follow Up

How's the Weather?

Butterflies have been fluttering their wings all over the world since you began this chapter. Nevertheless, you should have a better idea now of how to predict the weather. To demonstrate your new expertise, prepare a 30-day long-range weather forecast for your city. Predict temperatures, precipitation, unusual weather events, and any other information you consider important. The following are ways you might present your predictions.

✓ a written report
✓ a newspaper article
✓ an oral "TV weatherperson" presentation

The problems preceded by the magnifying glass (p. 416, # 17; p. 423, # 27; and p. 439, # 20) will help you prepare your presentation.

The ability to predict the weather accurately is of critical importance to a nation, affecting everything from crop production to military campaigns. We have made great advances in weather forecasting in recent years. Because of all those butterflies, however, no one expects we will ever achieve 100% accuracy.

Excursion: Find out what effect, if any, weather or other natural events have on the price of home insurance in your city.

Who to Talk To:
- an insurance agent

That's the Way the Spinner Spins

Try this with your group.

This table shows the results of 60 spins on a spinner divided into 6 sections.

Use the data in the table to determine how many sections of each color were on the spinner. Then make a copy of the spinner.

Purple	𝍸𝍸𝍸 IIII	19/60
Green	𝍸𝍸	10/60
Blue	𝍸𝍸𝍸𝍸	20/60
Orange	𝍸𝍸 I	11/60

You can make a spinner with a pencil and paper clip. Hold the pencil upright with the point inside one of the ends of the paper clip. Use your thumb and forefinger to tap the paper clip to make it spin. Spin the spinner 60 times. Keep a tally and compare your results with the results shown in the table.

Hexamania

Have students play this game once with a partner. Remind students that the game is an experiment. No matter who wins the first game, both partners should make notes. Partners may also discuss the game when it is finished, and try to figure out together why the winner won.

Before the next game, have students change partners. Repeat the procedure of the first game. Change partners again before each game, so that each student plays with at least five different partners.

After five or ten games, have students share their ideas about winning strategies. If the class can agree on a winning strategy, have students test it in pairs to see whether it works.

Words Words Words

COOPERATIVE GROUPS Have students construct a chart for tallying letters of the alphabet that are used in the selected passage. The letter e should occur more often than any of the other letters.

EXCURSION Of the 100 tiles in the game of Scrabble, the letter e is displayed the most (12 tiles). The more common letters (for example, n, t, and r) have more tiles for each letter, but less common letters (for example, x, q, z, and j) have higher point values.

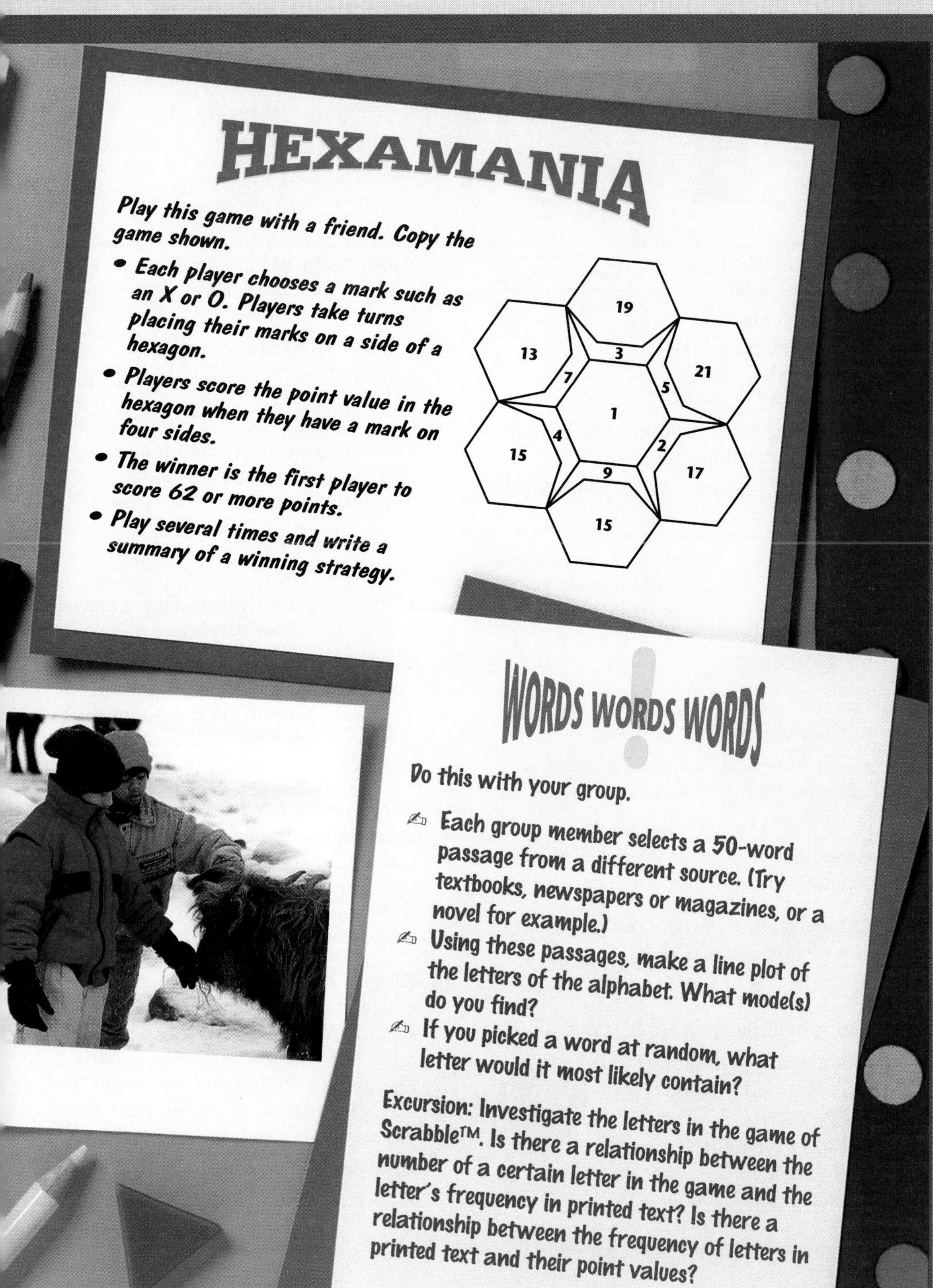

HEXAMANIA
Play this game with a friend. Copy the game shown.
• Each player chooses a mark such as an X or O. Players take turns placing their marks on a side of a hexagon.
• Players score the point value in the hexagon when they have a mark on four sides.
• The winner is the first player to score 62 or more points.
• Play several times and write a summary of a winning strategy.
19
13
3
7
21
5
1
4
2
15
9
17
15
WORDS WORDS WORDS
Do this with your group.
Each group member selects a 50-word passage from a different source. (Try textbooks, newspapers or magazines, or a novel for example.)
Using these passages, make a line plot of the letters of the alphabet. What mode(s) do you find?
If you picked a word at random, what letter would it most likely contain?
Excursion: Investigate the letters in the game of Scrabble™. Is there a relationship between the number of a certain letter in the game and the letter's frequency in printed text? Is there a relationship between the frequency of letters in printed text and their point values?
443

CHAPTER

10 ASSESSMENT

Enhanced Multiple Choice Questions are more complex than traditional multiple choice questions, which assess only one skill. Enhanced multiple choice questions assess the processes that students use as well as the end results. They are written so that students can use more than one strategy to solve the problem. Using multiple strategies is encouraged by the National Council of Teachers of Mathematics (NCTM).

Exercise 10 is an example of an enhanced multiple choice question.

Writing Questions allow students to describe more fully their thinking and understanding of the concepts they've learned.

Exercise 1c is a writing question.

Resources

Performance Based Project, TR Ch. 10, pp. 30–32
Chapter Assessment, Forms A and B, TR Ch. 10, pp. 35–38
Spanish Chapter Assessment, Spanish Resources, TR
Computer Item Generator

Answers to Problems Unique to Spanish Edition

3.c. 19,683

CHAPTER 10

Assessment

1. Sal and Matt played a game of chance.

Game Results	
Sal wins	7
Matt wins	13
Times played	20

 a. What is the experimental probability that Sal wins? $\frac{7}{20}$
 b. Find the experimental probability that Matt wins. $\frac{13}{20}$
 c. **Writing** Does the game seem fair? Explain. No; the experimental probabilities are not equal.

2. A number cube has six sides numbered 1 through 6. The number cube is rolled twice. What is the probability of getting a 2 on the first roll and a 5 on the second roll? $\frac{1}{36}$

3. Use the counting principle to find the number of possible outcomes.
 a. selecting a meal from 5 entrees, 4 soups, and 3 desserts 60
 b. tossing a coin four times 16
 c. number of possible groups of three letters for a monogram 17,576

4. **Choose A, B, C, or D.** The probability of a certain event is ■. B

 A. 0 **B.** 1 **C.** $\frac{1}{2}$ **D.** $\frac{1}{4}$

5. The spinner is spun three times.

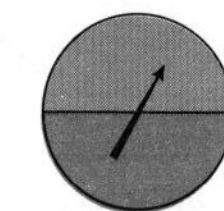

 a. Make a tree diagram to show all possible outcomes.
 b. Find Probability(green, red, green). $\frac{1}{8}$
 c. Find Probability(all red). $\frac{1}{8}$

5.a. See Solution Key.

6. A bag contains blue and green chips. The probability of drawing a blue chip is $\frac{5}{12}$.
 a. Find Probability(green). $\frac{7}{12}$
 b. Draw a spinner you could use to simulate this problem. See Solution Key.

7. Find the probability that a digit selected at random from the number 216,394 is a multiple of 3. $\frac{1}{2}$

8. Determine if the events are independent.
 a. Two dice are thrown. One die shows a 3. The other displays a 1. independent
 b. You choose a red marble from a bag containing red and yellow marbles. You do not put the marble back. You choose again and get another red marble. not independent

9. Every year a business gives 3 equal scholarships to eligible high school seniors. There are 7 seniors eligible this year to receive these scholarships. In how many ways can 3 seniors out of 7 be selected for the scholarships? 210

10. **Choose A, B, C, or D.** A marine biologist catches 75 fish from a lake, tags them, and then releases them back into the lake. The next month she catches 75 fish and finds that 5 of them are tagged. Estimate the fish population of the lake. C

 A. about 80 **B.** about 325
 C. about 1,125 **D.** about 28,125

CHAPTER 10 CUMULATIVE REVIEW

Exercises 6 and 8 are enhanced multiple choice questions.

Item(s)	Review Topic	Chapter
1	finding reciprocals	8
2	patterns	5
3, 6	probability	10
4, 9	solving proportions	9
5	solving equations	5
7	adding fractions	8
8	exploring arrangements	10
10	scale drawings	9

CHAPTER 10 Cumulative Review

Resources
Cumulative Review, TR Ch. 10, pp. 39–40
Transparency Masters, TR p. 35

Choose A, B, C, or D.

1. What is the reciprocal of $4\frac{2}{5}$? C

   A. $6\frac{1}{5}$ B. $\frac{5}{2}$ C. $\frac{5}{22}$ D. $\frac{1}{4}$

2. Find the next two terms in the number pattern 2, 6, 12, 20, . . . B

   A. 28, 36 B. 30, 42
   C. 24, 32 D. 32, 44

3. You and a friend play the game "Rock, paper, scissors" by putting one hand behind your backs and, on the count of three, showing your hands in one of the positions. What is the probability that you each show "paper"? D

   A. $\frac{1}{3}$ B. $\frac{1}{2}$ C. $\frac{1}{6}$ D. $\frac{1}{9}$

4. What is the value of m if $\frac{2m}{21} = \frac{8}{35}$? D

   A. 7 B. $\frac{5}{12}$ C. 12 D. 2.4

5. Estimate the solution to the equation $x - 17.16 = 33.4$. B

   A. About 16 B. About 50
   C. About 2 D. About 0.5

6. Which event is least likely to occur? C

   A. You roll a die once and get a 6.
   B. You toss a coin twice and get two heads.
   C. You draw a card from a standard 52-card deck and get an ace.
   D. One of the next 7 days is Saturday.

7. Which value of d will make the sum $\frac{8}{1} + \frac{3}{d}$ greatest? A

   A. 4 B. 5
   C. 6 D. 7

8. How many different three-digit numbers can you make using the digits 1, 3, 5, and 7? (Use each digit at most once.) A

   A. $4 \times 3 \times 2$
   B. $7 \times 5 \times 3$
   C. $3 \times 2 \times 1$
   D. $4 \times 4 \times 4$

9. Which is the best buy? B

   A. a half-dozen muffins, if a dozen costs \$6.59
   B. a half-dozen muffins for \$3.19
   C. a half-dozen muffins if each costs \$.59
   D. a half-dozen muffins if muffins cost \$1.19 for 2

10. You want to draw a map of your neighborhood on a piece of paper that is $8\frac{1}{2}$ in. by 11 in. What scale should you use to map an area 1,000 yd by 750 yd? D

    A. 1 in. = 75 yd
    B. 1 in. = 80 yd
    C. 1 in. = 85 yd
    D. 1 in. = 95 yd

CHAPTER

11 Integers and Coordinate Graphing

Why Study Integers and Coordinate Graphing?

If students ask this question, you may want to mention the following people who use integers: mapmakers, weather forecasters, health analysts, accountants, physicists, pilots, navigators, computer programmers, and game designers.

Graphic Display of Chapter Content

Below is one possible representation of the chapter's content and its applications to the world outside the classroom. Have students create their own graphic display and fill in applications that they have seen in their own lives.

- The center oval should state the main concept of the chapter: integers and coordinate graphing.
- Have students draw the ovals with the next level of concepts presented in the chapter (number lines, modeling integers, graphing, translations and reflections). You may want students to add other topics that they think are appropriate.
- Ask students to draw as many application ovals as they can.
- Discuss all the applications that students identify.
- Have students make and present one display that includes all the students' ideas.

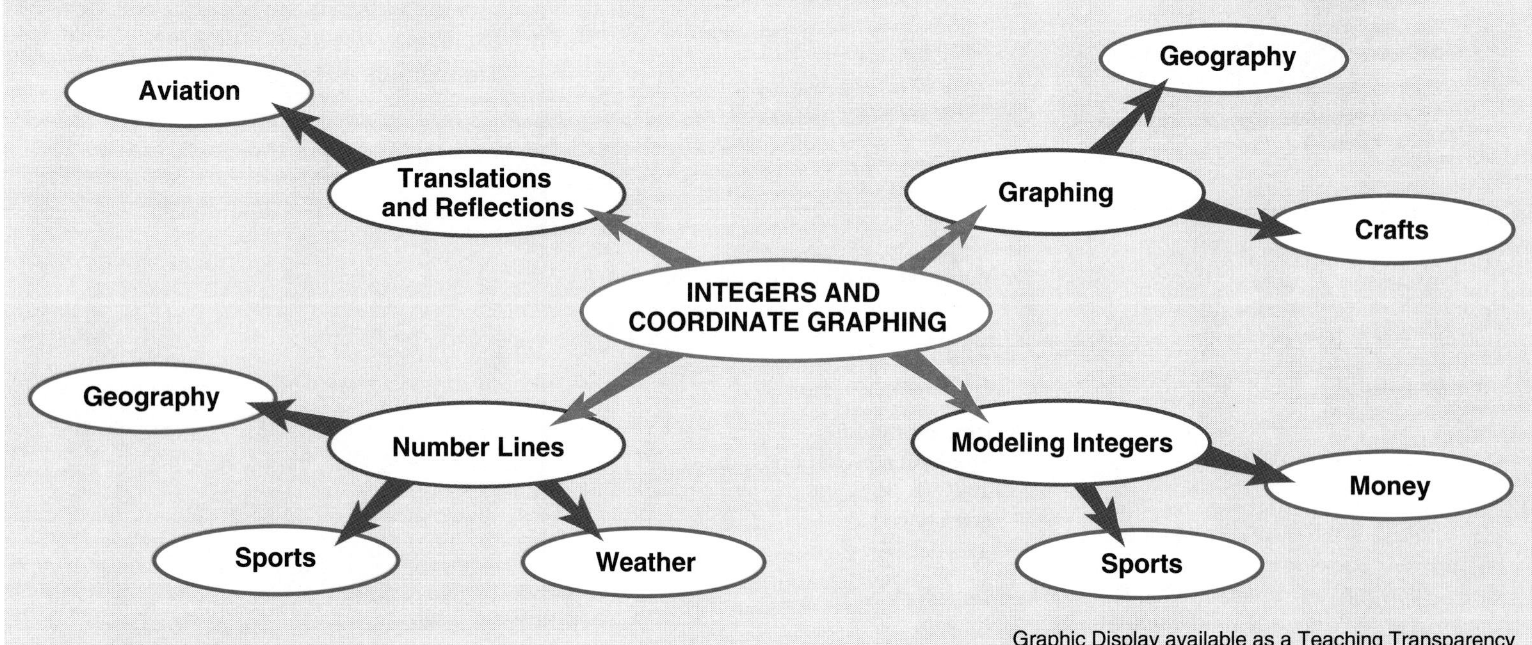

Graphic Display available as a Teaching Transparency

Vocabulary and Symbols

balance
balance sheet
coordinate plane
coordinates
first coordinate
image
integers
negative integers
opposites
ordered pair
origin
positive integers
quadrants
reflection
second coordinate
slide
translation
x-axis
y-axis

Materials and Manipulatives

algebra tiles	calculator
computer	coordinate geometry software
geoboard	paper bag
rubber bands	two dice of different colors

Additional Resources

Commercially Available Technology

Calculator
fraction

Software
algebra software
- *Math Connections: Algebra I* by Sunburst
- *Label Land* by Sunburst

geometry software
- *Geometric Connections* by Sunburst
- *Geometric Connections: Transformations* by Sunburst

spreadsheet software
- *1-2-3* by Lotus
- *ClarisWorks* by Apple
- *Excel; Works* by Microsoft

Other Media

"Graphing Inequalities." Aims Media, 9710 DeSoto Avenue, Chatsworth, CA 91311.

"Graphs Rule, OK?" Films Inc Video, 5547 N. Ravenswood Ave., Chicago, IL 60640. (800) 343-4312.

"Word Problem Game Show: Level C." Gamco Industries, P.O. Box 1911A7, Big Spring, TX 79721. (800) 351-1404.

Materials at Little or No Cost

American Mathematical Society, P.O. Box 6248, Providence, RI 02940. (401) 455-4000. Publications and newsletters.

Editorial Projects in Education, Inc., 4301 Connecticut Ave, NW, Washington, DC 20008. Publisher of *Teacher* magazine.

Bibliography

For Teachers

Charles, Randall, et al. *How to Evaluate Progress in Problem Solving*. Reston, VA: NCTM, 1987.

Rowan, Thomas E. and Lorna J. Morrow. *Implementing the K–8 Curriculum and Evaluation Standards*. Reston, VA: NCTM, 1988.

For Students

Aaseng, Nathan. *Twentieth Century Inventors*. NY: Facts on File, 1991.

Bell, Neill. *The Book of Where or How to Be Naturally Geographic*. Boston: Little, Brown, 1982.

Cooper, Chris and Tony Osmon. *How Everyday Things Work*. NY: Facts on File, 1984.

Prentice Hall Technology 

Multimedia Math
- Math Tools, Frames
- Math Tools, Manipulatives
- Hot Page™ 11-1
- Hot Page™ 11-6
- Hot Page™ 11-8
- Math Investigations, Mission: Mars

Computer Item Generator
- Chapter 11

Community Resources

Field Trips
- a football game or golf tournament
- an airport
- an archeological dig site

Guest Speakers
- a weather forecaster
- a pilot
- an archeologist

Backpack Take-Home Activities

Materials
- paper
- pencil
- tape
- science or history textbook
- newspaper
- several food cans and boxes
- scissors

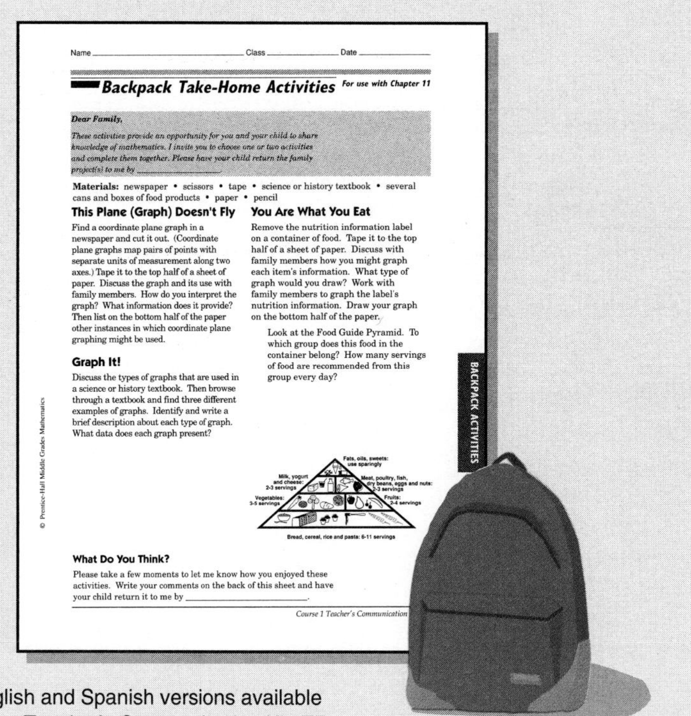

Name ______ Class ______ Date ______

Backpack Take-Home Activities *For use with Chapter 11*

Dear Family,

These activities provide an opportunity for you and your child to share knowledge of mathematics. I invite you to choose one or two activities and complete them together. Please have your child return the family project(s) to me by ______

Materials: newspaper • scissors • tape • science or history textbook • several cans and boxes of food products • paper • pencil

This Plane (Graph) Doesn't Fly

Find a coordinate plane graph in a newspaper and cut it out. (Coordinate plane graphs map pairs of points with separate units of measurement along two axes.) Tape it to the top half of a sheet of paper. Discuss the graph and its use with family members. How do you interpret the graph? What information does it provide? Then list on the bottom half of the paper other instances in which coordinate plane graphing might be used.

Graph It!

Discuss the types of graphs that are used in a science or history textbook. Then browse through a textbook and find three different examples of graphs. Identify and write a brief description about each type of graph. What data does each graph present?

You Are What You Eat

Remove the nutrition information label on a container of food. Tape it to the top half of a sheet of paper. Discuss with family members how you might graph each item's information. What type of graph would you draw? Work with family members to graph the label's nutrition information. Draw your graph on the bottom half of the paper.

Look at the Food Guide Pyramid. To which group does this food in the container belong? How many servings of food are recommended from this group every day?

What Do You Think?

Please take a few moments to let me know how you enjoyed these activities. Write your comments on the back of this sheet and have your child return it to me by ______.

BACKPACK ACTIVITIES

© Prentice-Hall Middle Grades Mathematics

Course 1 Teacher's Communication

English and Spanish versions available in the Teacher's Communication Kit, TR

Chapter 11 Planning Guide

Objectives	Assignment Options	Critical Thinking/ Problem Solving	Writing and Reading Math	Estimation Mental Math	Materials and Manipulatives
Investigation	This chapter-long project involves open-ended questioning and data collecting and provides an additional opportunity to assess students.	p. 448 p. 448	p. 448		p. 448
11-1 Using a Number Line • Graphing integers on a number line • Comparing and ordering integers	**Core:** 24–27, 32–35, 37, 38, 40, 43, 44, 46; MR all **Reinforce:** 28–31, 36, 39, 41, 45 **Enrich:** 42	9, 26, 42; MR: 3, 4 pp. 449, 450; BI p. 451; MM p. 452	42 p. 452; JL p. 451 JL Sheet	8, 24, 25, 28 p. 451; MM p. 452	1, 2, 6, 7, 12, 27b, 43–45 p. 452; RT p. 451 TT 91
11-2 Modeling Integers • Representing positive integers, negative integers, and zero using models	**Core:** 10–16; MR all **Reinforce:** 9, 17 **Enrich:** 18, 19	3, 8d, 9, 19 pp. 453, 454; BI p. 454; MM p. 454	9 p. 454; JL p. 453 JL Sheet	5, 6, 17	4, 10–13, 18 pp. 453, 454; WT p. 454; RT p. 454 TT 91
11-3 Modeling Addition of Integers • Adding integers using models	**Core:** 20–22, 26–30, 33–35; MR all; CH all **Reinforce:** 23–25, 31, 32, 36–39 **Enrich:** 40, 41	8, 30–35, 40, 41; MR: 3, 5 pp. 455, 456; BI p. 456	41 p. 458; JL p. 457 JL Sheet	14–19, 26–29, 36–39; MR: 4 pp. 456, 458	2; EX1; 4; EX2; 6, 11–13, 20–25; CH: 4, 6–12 pp. 455–457; CH p. 458; MM p. 458 TT 91
11-4 Modeling Subtraction of Integers • Subtracting integers using models	**Core:** 15–17, 21, 22, 28, 29, 31, 36–40; MR all **Reinforce:** 18–20, 23–27, 41–44 **Enrich:** 30, 32–35	3, 4, 28–30, 36–40, 42–44; MR: 5 pp. 459–462; BI p. 461; MM p. 462	30 p. 462; JL p. 461 JL Sheet	21–24, 32–35; MR: 1, 2, 4	1; EX1; 2; EX2, 3; 5, 8–20 pp. 459–462; WT p. 460; RT p. 461 TT 92 Alt. Lesson
11-5 Problem Solving: Use Multiple Strategies • Solving problems using multiple strategies	**Core:** 13, 15, 16, 18; MR all **Reinforce:** 14, 19, 20 **Enrich:** 17, 21	All; MR: 5 pp. 464–466; BI p. 465; RT p. 465; MM p. 466	All JL p. 465 JL Sheet		MR: 1, 2 p. 465 TT 92
11-6 Graphing on the Coordinate Plane • Using a coordinate plane to graph points • Naming the coordinates of points on a coordinate plane	**Core:** 21–24, 26, 27, 32–35; MR all **Reinforce:** 25, 29 **Enrich:** 28, 30, 31, 36	2, 3, 20, 26c, 35; MR: 1, 2, 5 pp. 467, 469; BI p. 468	27–29, 35 p. 469; JL p. 469 JL Sheet	27; MR: 3 MM p. 470	EX1; 25, 26, 28, 29a, 31, 36; MR: 4 pp. 467–469; WT p. 467; RT p. 469 TT 3, 92
11-7 Technology: Translations and Reflections • Exploring translations and reflections on a coordinate plane using computers	**Core:** 11–17, 19, 20; MR all; CH all **Reinforce:** 18, 21 **Enrich:** 22	5, 8; WT: 10d; 19, 21e; CH: 1, 10; MR: 5 p. 474; WT p. 473; BI p. 474; MM p. 475	WT: 10c; 19 p. 475; WT p. 473; JL p. 474 JL Sheet	MR: 3, 4	7b, 8c, 9; WT: 10a; 18b, 21a–c, 22; CH: 11–13 pp. 472, 473, 475; WT p. 473; RT p. 474; CH p. 475 TT 3, 93 Alt. Lesson
11-8 Math and Budgets: Applying Integers and Graphs • Using a balance sheet to determine profit or loss • Drawing and interpreting graphs involving integers	**Core:** 17–19, 25–29; MR all **Reinforce:** 20–23 **Enrich:** 24	1–3; EX1; 28; MR: 5 pp. 476, 477; BI p. 478; MM p. 479	24; MR: 5 p. 478; JL p. 477 JL Sheet	17–22; MR: 1, 2 p. 476	EX1; 4; EX2; 10–12, 17–22, 23b, 25–29 pp. 476–479; RT p. 478 TT 19, 93
Putting It All Together	These pages include a Follow-Up to the Investigation and other projects, which provide additional opportunities to assess the students.	pp. 482–483 pp. 482–483			pp. 482–483 pp. 482–483
Chapter Resources		PS Practice, CW, CA, CR PS Practice p. 471; CW pp. 480–481; CA p. 484; CR p. 485	PS Practice, CW, CA p. 446B; PS Practice p. 471; CW pp. 480–481; CA p. 484		pp. 446A, 446B Backpack Activities, Manip. Kits TT 90, 94, 95

Student Edition (question numbers)
Teacher's Edition (page numbers)
Other Components

BI—What's the Big Idea? CA—Chapter Assessment CH—Checkpoint
CG—Computer Item Generator CR—Cumulative Review CW—Chapter Wrap Up
DM—Decision Making EP—Extra Practice EX—Example FD—Fact of the Day

Cooperative Learning Activities	Technology	Data Collection & Analysis	Interdisciplinary Connections	Applications	Assessment	Review	Strand Integration	NCTM Correlation*
		p. 448	Social Studies, Science	time, history, geology	p. 448			
					p. 448			
	6, 7, 43–45	24–28, 41	Geography, Science	sports, jobs, weather		MR: All	Geometry, Number, Logic/Language	1, 2, 3, 4, 6, 8, 9, 10, 12, 13
p. 450; RT p. 451	p. 452 Hot Page™ 11-1	FD p. 450	pp. 451, 452	pp. 449–452	p. 450	p. 449; RT p. 451 Practice p. 22		
WT				money		MR: All	Algebra, Number, Logic/Language	2, 3, 4, 6, 8, 9
p. 453; WT p. 454	MM p. 454	FD p. 454		p. 454	p. 453	p. 453; RT p. 454 Practice p. 23		
WT; 17–19		35	Science	hobbies, weather, money, sports	CH: All	MR: All	Algebra, Number, Logic/Language	1, 2, 3, 4, 5, 7, 8, 9, 13
p. 456; WT p. 456; RT p. 457 Alt. Lesson	p. 456 Alt. Lesson	p. 457; FD p. 456	p. 457	pp. 455, 457	p. 456; CH p. 458 CH TR p. 34	p. 455; RT p. 457 Practice p. 24		
WT		25–27, 31, 41a	Science, Geography	money, sports, weather, time		MR: All	Algebra, Number, Logic/Language	1, 2, 3, 4, 5, 7, 8, 9, 13
WT p. 460; RT p. 461	p. 460	p. 462; FD p. 460	pp. 461, 462 Alt. Lesson	pp. 459, 461, 462	p. 461	p. 459; RT p. 461 Practice p. 25		
		7–10		games, consumer issues		MR: All	Discrete Math, Number, Logic/Language	1, 2, 3, 4, 5, 7, 8, 9, 10, 13
pp. 464, 465; RT p. 465	p. 465	FD p. 465		p. 465	p. 465	p. 464; RT p. 465 Practice p. 26		
WT	36a; MR: 4	27, 28, 29	Art, Geography	crafts, map making		MR: All	Geometry, Discrete Math, Logic/Language	2, 3, 4, 5, 8, 9, 10, 12
p. 468; WT p. 467; RT p. 469	pp. 468, 469 Hot Page™ 11-6	p. 469; FD p. 468	p. 469	pp. 467, 469	p. 468	p. 467; RT p. 469 Practice p. 27		
WT: 10	All; CH: 11–13	6; WT: 10b, c; 20	Science	navigation	CH: All	MR: All	Geometry, Discrete Math, Logic/Language	1, 2, 3, 4, 5, 8, 9, 12
WT p. 473; RT p. 474 Alt. Lesson	p. 475; WT p. 473; CH p. 475	p. 475; FD p. 473		p. 474	p. 474; CH p. 475 CH TR p. 34	p. 472; RT p. 474 Practice p. 28		
	EX1; 4, 10–12, 17–22, 25–29	5–9, 23a, 28, 29		budgets, business, jobs		MR: All	Geometry, Stat./Probability, Logic/Language	1, 2, 3, 4, 5, 7, 8, 9, 10, 12
pp. 476, 478; RT p. 478	pp. 477, 479 Hot Page™ 11-8	FD p. 477		pp. 476, 478; GE p. 479	p. 478	p. 476; RT p. 478 Practice p. 29		
pp. 482–483		pp. 482–483	Social Studies, Science	history, geology, time, art	pp. 482–483			
pp. 482–483		pp. 482–483			pp. 482–483			
IN, PT		Data File 11	Science, Social Studies	geography, weather, earth science	IN, PT, CA	Practice, PS Practice, CW, CR, EP, SSG		
pp. 446–448; PT pp. 482–483 Backpack Activities	p. 446B Multimedia Math, CG	pp. 446–447	pp. 446F, 446–447 Interdisciplinary Units	pp. 446A, 446F, 446–447 Backpack Activities, Projects, Interdisciplinary Units	pp. 446E, 448; pp. 480–484	CW pp. 480–481 Span. SSG, CR		

GE—Great Expectations IN—Investigation JL—Journal MM—Math Minutes
MR—Mixed Review PS—Problem Solving PT—Putting It All Together RT—Reteaching Activity
SSG—Student Study Guide TT—Teaching Transparency WT—Work Together

*For a description of the NCTM Standards, see page T15.

Assessment Options

Observation Checklist

In this chapter on integers and coordinate graphing, you have opportunities to observe your students do these tasks:

- ✓ compare positive and negative integers and arrange them on a number line
- ✓ use algebra tiles to model addition and subtraction of integers
- ✓ use multiple strategies to solve word problems
- ✓ graph points on the coordinate plane
- ✓ use computers to graph translations and reflections on a coordinate plane
- ✓ use graphs and integers to show profit and loss

In every chapter, you are given opportunities to observe your students:

- ✓ work with a partner or in a group
- ✓ write about mathematics
- ✓ participate in discussions about mathematics
- ✓ collect and analyze data
- ✓ display positive attitudes about mathematics
- ✓ use measurement tools

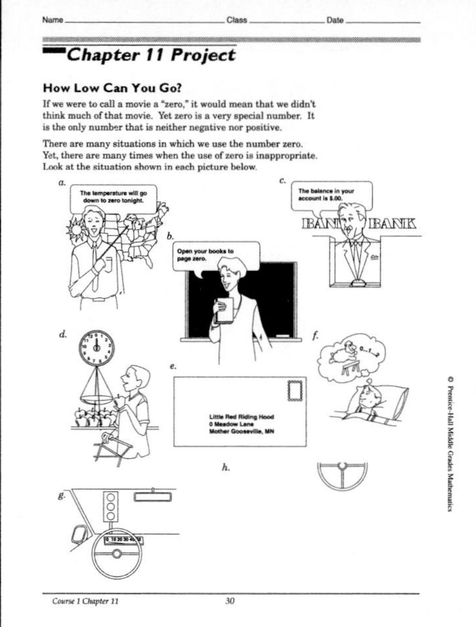

Name ______________ Class ______________ Date ______________

Chapter 11 Project

How Low Can You Go?

If we were to call a movie a "zero," it would mean that we didn't think much of that movie. Yet zero is a very special number. It is the only number that is neither negative nor positive.

There are many situations in which we use the number zero. Yet, there are many times when the use of zero is inappropriate. Look at the situation shown in each picture below.

Course 1 Chapter 11 30

© Prentice-Hall Middle Grades Mathematics

Performance Based Project (with scoring rubric), Chapter Files, TR

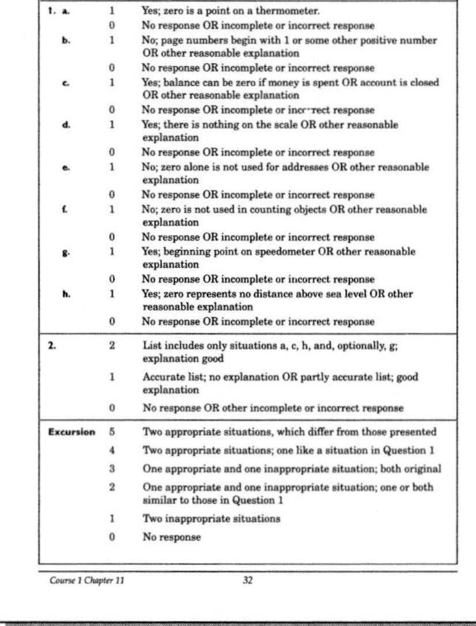

…ou Go? Scoring Rubric

Exercise	Points	Explanation
1. a.	1	Yes; zero is a point on a thermometer.
	0	No response OR incomplete or incorrect response
b.	1	No; page numbers begin with 1 or some other positive number OR other reasonable explanation
	0	No response OR incomplete or incorrect response
c.	1	Yes; balance can be zero if money is spent OR account is closed OR other reasonable explanation
	0	No response OR incomplete or incorrect response
d.	1	Yes; there is nothing on the scale OR other reasonable explanation
	0	No response OR incomplete or incorrect response
e.	1	No; zero alone is not used for addresses OR other reasonable explanation
	0	No response OR incomplete or incorrect response
f.	1	No; zero is not used in counting objects OR other reasonable explanation
	0	No response OR incomplete or incorrect response
g.	1	Yes; beginning point on speedometer OR other reasonable explanation
	0	No response OR incomplete or incorrect response
h.	1	Yes; zero represents no distance above sea level OR other reasonable explanation
	0	No response OR incomplete or incorrect response
2.	2	List includes only situations a, c, h, and, optionally, g; explanation good
	1	Accurate list; no explanation OR partly accurate list; good explanation
	0	No response OR other incomplete or incorrect response
Excursion	5	Two appropriate situations, which differ from those presented
	4	Two appropriate situations; one like a situation in Question 1
	3	One appropriate and one inappropriate situation; both original
	2	One appropriate and one inappropriate situation; one or both similar to those in Question 1
	1	Two inappropriate situations
	0	No response

Course 1 Chapter 11 32

© Prentice-Hall Middle Grades Mathematics

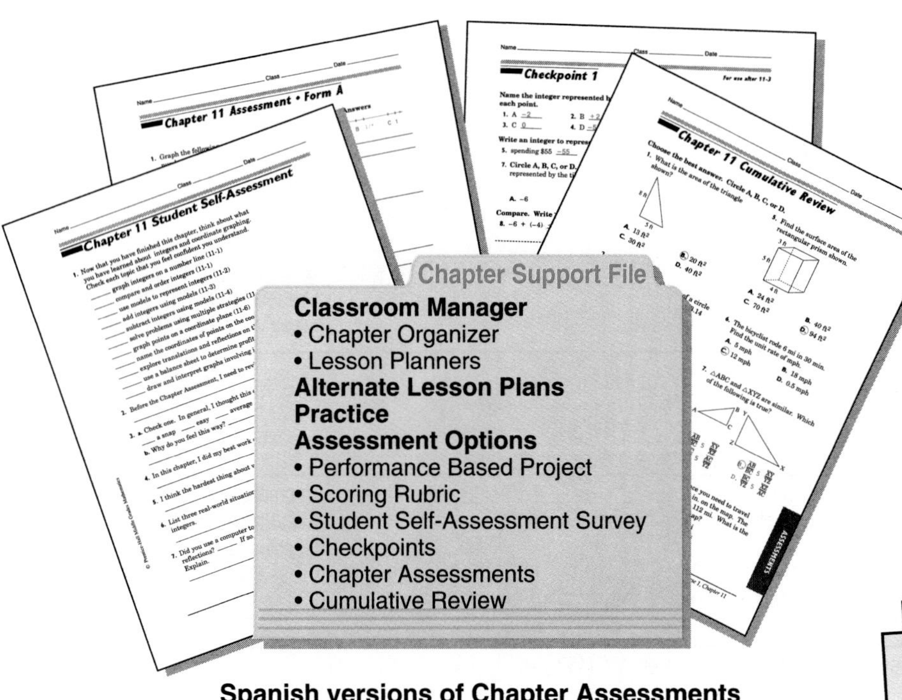

Chapter Support File

Classroom Manager
- Chapter Organizer
- Lesson Planners

Alternate Lesson Plans

Practice

Assessment Options
- Performance Based Project
- Scoring Rubric
- Student Self-Assessment Survey
- Checkpoints
- Chapter Assessments
- Cumulative Review

Spanish versions of Chapter Assessments available in Spanish Resources

Interdisciplinary Units
- **Travel and Geography**
- **Space Exploration**
- **Sports**
- **Consumer Awareness**
- **The Great Outdoors**

English & Spanish

These units include cross-curriculum connections and can be used at any time during the school year. See the Teacher's Guide for more information.

Working with Middle Grade Students

> *"When students make graphs, data tables, expressions, equations, or verbal descriptions to represent a single relationship, they discover that different representations yield different interpretations of a situation. In informal ways, students develop an understanding that functions are composed of variables that have a dynamic relationship: Changes in one variable result in change in another. . . ."*
>
> —NCTM CURRICULUM AND EVALUATION STANDARDS

Addressing a Variety of Learning Styles

The mathematical tasks in Chapter 11 involve various learning styles. Here are some examples:

- Visual learners graph numbers on a number line (p. 449) and use a map of time zones to add and subtract hours (p. 462).
- Tactile learners use colored tiles to model integers (p. 453) and roll dice to subtract integers (p. 460).
- Auditory learners work with partners to describe real world situations using integers (p. 454) and describe shapes created on a geoboard (p. 467).
- Kinesthetic learners pull tiles from a bag to represent positive and negative integers (p. 456) and research events that happened in their school before they entered (p. 458).

Alternate Lessons 11-4 and 11-7 address tactile learners by having them use manipulatives.

Cultural Connections

Heron, a Greek mathematician who lived in Alexandria, Egypt, in the first century A.D., asked the following question. Suppose you have a line l and points A and B in the plane on the same side of l. Where on line l should you put point C to make the combined distances $AC + CB$ the shortest?

Heron solved this problem by drawing B', the image of B reflected in l. Then he noticed that no matter where he put C on l, $AC + CB$ was the same as $AC + CB'$. He put C where the line connecting A and B' hit line l. This made $AC + CB'$ as short as possible. Since $AC + CB'$ was as short as possible, $AC + CB$ was also as short as possible.

Team Teaching Suggestion

Work with a science teacher to help students see actual use of recording science measurements and graphing the results. A good example might be temperature and volume changes or electric conductivity vs. concentrations of solutions.

A Ladder or a Stepping Stone?

Mathematics has often been taught as if it were a ladder; a student could not step to a given rung without first having climbed all rungs below it. Instead of insisting that students do problems in one "correct" way, encourage them to work problems by any method they know. If students are free to approach mathematics by any path they can find, mathematics will become available to them.

Teaching Tip

Remind students that increments along the axes should be evenly spread and that it is not always necessary to extend the axes far above or below the number used.

Bulletin Board

Post a large grid on the bulletin board with a small plane at the origin. Ask students what kinds of things pilots have to veer around when in flight, and have students work in groups to produce a picture of each idea. Place these pictures on the grid. (Do not cover the x- or the y-axis.) Ask students to identify flight paths using as few coordinates as possible. Tell students that every point they use represents a turn in the flight path. A flight path from O to B is shown. There are many flight paths for each destination. Have students form translations and reflections of these flight paths about the x- and y-axis.

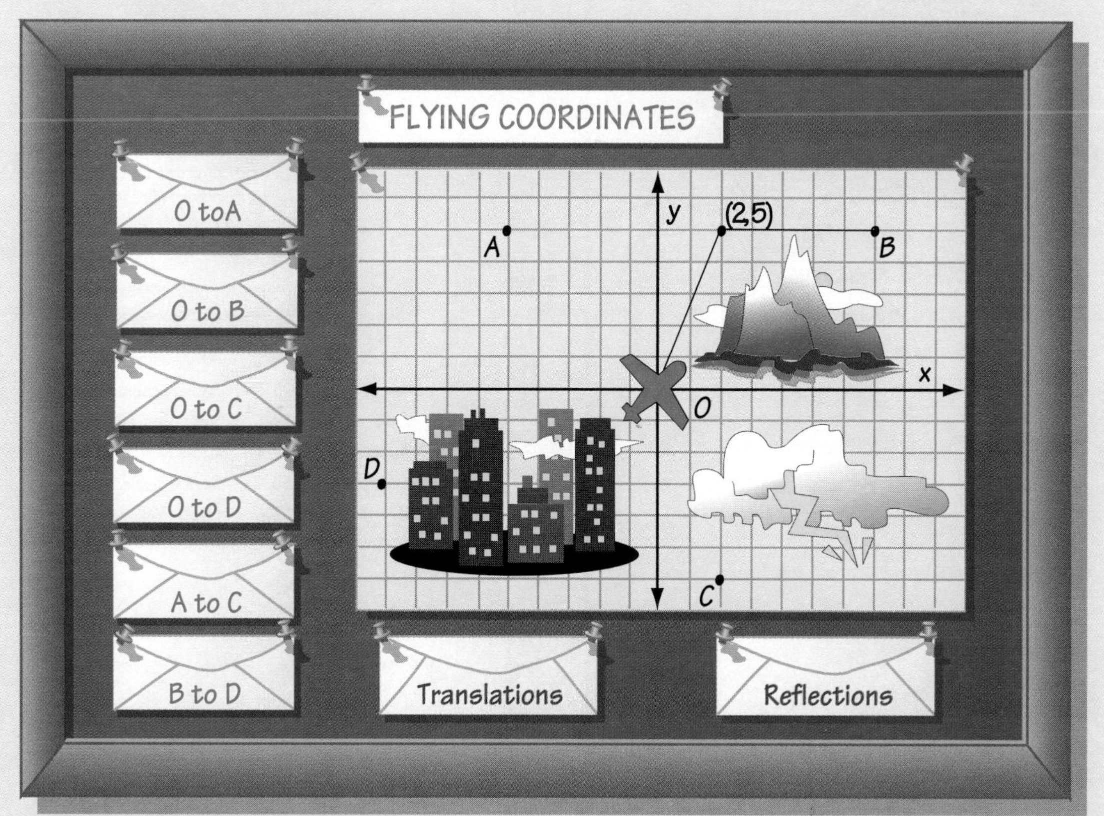

CHAPTER 11 Integers and Coordinate Graphing

Cultural Connections Temperatures and climates can change when the atmosphere around the planet changes. Much concern has been focused on our ozone layer and the amount of carbon dioxide dispersed into our atmosphere. Even though most of the discussions and studies about climate changes due to pollution have occurred during recent years, the debate has been around for about a century. In 1896 Svante Arrhenius, a Swedish chemist, made calculations about the use of coal furnaces in industry and warned about carbon dioxide being released into the atmosphere. Arrhenius described how the planet could become warmer because of gases in our atmosphere; this has come to be called the "greenhouse effect." Scientists now know that other gases such as chlorofluorocarbons—CFCs from refrigeration and air conditioning—also contribute to this situation. Like carbon dioxide, these gases in the atmosphere trap heat radiated from the earth's surface and reflect it downward again.

WORLD VIEW The earth's crust is made up of at least seven large rigid plates and eight smaller ones. These plates, about 60 mi thick, move slowly from one-half to four inches per year, but not all in the same direction. Theorists propose that if the movements continue in their current pattern, North America will collide with Asia in about 200 million years, and Australia may reach China.

Digging for Data Discuss the information in the tables and have students find the approximate locations of the listed places on a map.

- Have students ask family members and neighbors to tell them the highest and lowest temperatures they have experienced, and any special stories related to these temperature extremes.

Chapter 11 Contents

Data File Questions

pp. 296, 452, 469

Data File 11

CHAPTER 11 Integers and Coordinate Graphing

Here is the formula to change from degrees *Celsius* (°C) to degrees *Fahrenheit* (°F):

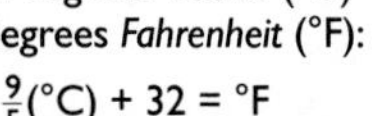

$$\frac{9}{5}(°C) + 32 = °F$$

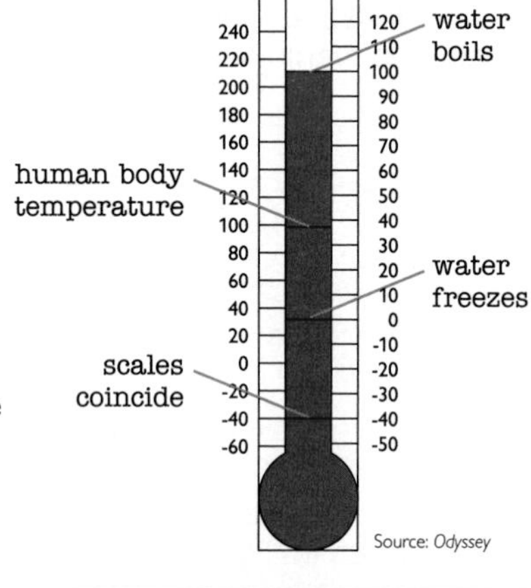

Source: *Odyssey*

Highest Recorded Temperatures in Each of the Seven Continents		
Africa	58°C	Al' Aziziyah, Libya
Antarctica	15°C	Bahia, Esperanza
Asia	54°C	Tirat Tsvi, Israel
Australia	53°C	Cloncurry, Queensland
Europe	50°C	Seville, Spain
N. America	57°C	Death Valley, California
S. America	49°C	Rivadavia, Argentina

Lowest Recorded Temperatures in Each of the Seven Continents		
Africa	-24°C	Ifrane, Morocco
Antarctica	-89°C	Vostok
Asia	-68°C	Oimekon, Russian Federation
Australia	-22°C	Charlotte Pass, NSW
Europe	-59°C	Ust'Schugor, Russian Federation
N. America	-63°C	Snag, Yukon
S. America	-33°C	Colonia, Sarmiento, Argentina

Source: *Encyclopedia Britannica*

Ocean Floor Profile Along the Equator

Elevation and depth (m)

6,000
4,000
2,000
Sea Level
2,000
4,000
6,000

Andes Mountains
Galapogos Islands
Pacific Ocean
South America

- Have students ask people who have lived in different places what the weather was like and to describe the type of terrain. Guide students to generalize about latitude, altitude, and distance from the ocean in terms of weather patterns.

Journal Activity

- Have students read the four objectives for the chapter and explain what they would like to learn in this chapter.
- Have students write about a climate in which they would like to live and explain why.

Interdisciplinary Connection [Science and Economics]

Much information has been presented about the long-range problems of atmospheric and ground pollution. The world has changed from farming and fishing to industries and factories. The modern world is aimed at technology and high finance, and the methods of achieving these goals involve big business. Some areas have continued to cut down forests, not only to use wood, but also to clear land for plantations and ranches. There is evidence that deforestation accelerates the release of carbon dioxide into the atmosphere, since trees are absorbers of this gas.

Discuss the pros and cons of cutting down forests to build industries and make plantations and ranches. Consider why lawmakers are often not concerned about distant issues. Have students consider the alternatives to fossil fuels (geothermal, hydroelectric, wind, burning garbage, and solar energy, for example).

WHAT YOU WILL LEARN

- how to model addition and subtraction with integers
- how to create and use a coordinate system
- how to use technology to explore translations and reflections
- how to use multiple strategies to solve problems

The World's Climate Regions

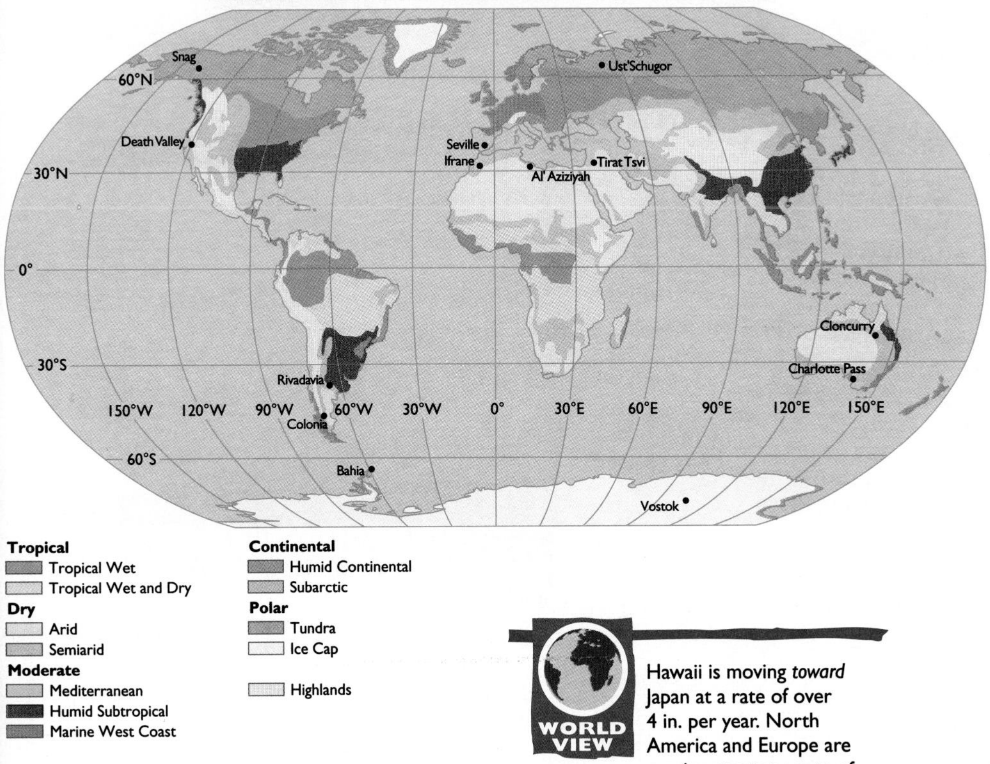

WORLD VIEW

Hawaii is moving *toward* Japan at a rate of over 4 in. per year. North America and Europe are moving *apart* at a rate of about 1 in. per year.

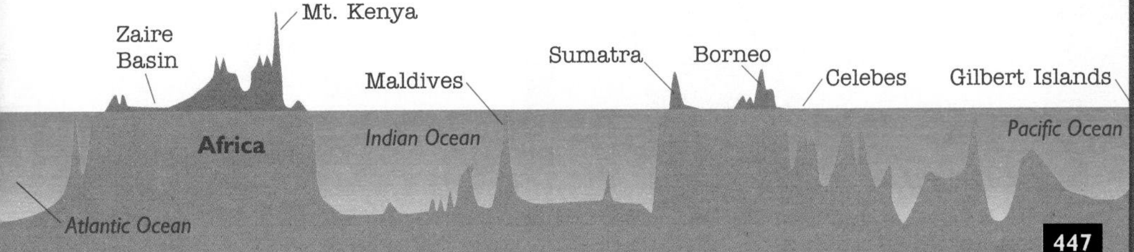

Fact of the Day

The places with the greatest temperature range are parts of northeast Siberia in the former Soviet Union. The temperatures at Verkhoyansh have varied from –94°F to 98°F, a range of 192 degrees.

—*The Superbook of Our Planet*

447

CHAPTER 11

INVESTIGATION

Memo

You may wish to have students bring diaries, yearbooks, and calendars to class to help them remember events of the past. Have students list the events that have happened since the selected date:

- *What events are repeated by each group member?*
- *List the events in order of importance to the school, that is, ones that have caused changes to take place.*
- *Before students begin work, be sure they understand the various events that are important.*

Mission

Students can draw a scaled timeline that can be divided into years and months and weeks. They can modify the length of the line before deciding on the placement of their selected events.

After about half the chapter has been completed, have students show you their work on the project. If they are behind schedule, give them intermediate deadlines.

Additional Leads to Follow

- *Look at event placement. Is one area more dense than others? Which events can you combine into one event? Which events can be elaborated?*
- *Which events would you like to repeat?*

Keeping a Project Notebook

Here are some suggestions for students' notebooks:

- Keep a list of all events (with dates, descriptions, and reasons for importance) mentioned in discussions with group members that might be used in the timeline.
- Keep copies of all preliminary designs.
- List the dates and results of all discussions about the project.

Project Organizer

Related Exercises
p. 452
p. 458
p. 462
p. 474

Follow Up
p. 482

Teacher's Notes
pp. 448, 452, 457, 462, 475, 482

Community Resources
- librarian
- historian

Materials and Manipulatives
- diaries, yearbooks, or calendars
- manila folders or construction paper
- colored pens

investigation

Project File

Memo

A **timeline** is a visual representation of the dates of a series of events. You can use timelines to represent past events, such as important events in history. You can also use timelines as planning devices to show how future events may unfold. For example, you could draw a timeline to show expected progress in a fund-raising drive.

Fund Raising for Class Trip

Mission: Create a timeline of important events that have occurred at your school. Begin your timeline at "Year 0," your first year in the school (or your first year as a member of your group). Your timeline should include descriptions of events and dates of events, numbered from zero, along with any other information you consider important.

LEADS TO FOLLOW

✓ How can you decide whether an event is important enough to include on your timeline?

✓ Should you number your timeline by years, months, weeks, or by some other interval?

448

11-1

Connecting to Prior Knowledge

Ask students to name situations in which they have seen examples of numbers less than zero. Give students examples such as golf scores (strokes under par), stock reports, temperatures in the newspaper, and so on. Ask students how they might describe negative numbers.

THINK AND DISCUSS

ESL Help students distinguish the operation of subtraction (7 minus 4) from the type of number (negative 5) by reminding them to use the word *minus* only when the symbol – occurs between two numbers and is an operation (or verb, meaning subtract). Thus –4 is said "negative 4" and *not* "minus 4" or "subtract 4."

Question 2: Have students compare their graphs. Ask students to label the numbers on their number lines *positive* or *negative.*

KINESTHETIC LEARNERS Have students go to a number line on the board and find points on the line.

ESL Make sure students do not get negative integers confused with subtraction of integers. Using a number line, demonstrate that the negative integers are less than zero.

DIVERSITY Ask a student who understands football to draw a diagram on the board and explain the yard line markings.

Example 1

- *Is the lower number always to the left or to the right on the number line?* **(left)**
- *Both numbers are what type of integer?* **(negative)**

Additional Example *Tricia's golf score was –6. Ann's was 0. Who had the lower score?* **(Tricia: –6 < 0)**

CRITICAL THINKING For Question 9, encourage students to refer to a number line.

What's Ahead

- Graphing integers on a number line
- Comparing and ordering integers

11-1 Using a Number Line

THINK AND DISCUSS

In a football game, a receiver caught the football and gained 4 yd. Later a running back gained −3 yd, which means he lost 3 yd. In the second half the quarterback was sacked and gained −6 yd. Here's how you read the numbers of yards gained.

+4: *positive 4* −3: *negative 3* −6: *negative 6*

FLASHBACK
To graph a number on a number line, draw a point at that number.

To keep track of the yardage, you can graph the gains on a number line. Extend the number line to the left of 0 to show negative numbers.

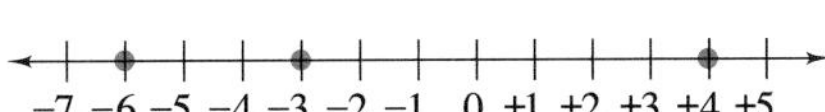

1. Another football player lost four yards on a carry. Write this amount as a number and graph it on a number line. −4
2. Graph the numbers −1, 5, and 0 on a number line. See Solution Key.

The numbers . . . −3, −2, −1, 0, +1, + 2, +3, . . . are **integers.** The numbers +1, +2, +3, . . . are **positive integers.** The numbers −1, −2, −3, . . . are **negative integers.** The number 0 is neither positive nor negative. You can write positive numbers with or without a "+" sign. For example, +2 = 2.

Two numbers that are the same distance from 0 on a number line, but in different directions, are **opposites.**

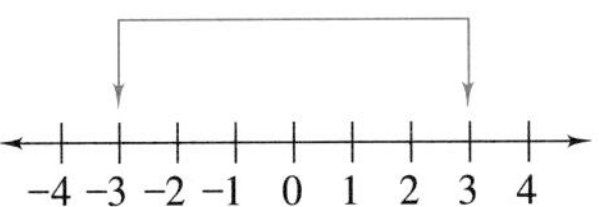

3 and −3 are three units from 0.
3 and −3 are opposites.

3. Name the opposite of each integer.
   a. 4 −4 b. −6 6 c. 15 −15 d. 0 0
4. Name two integers that are opposites. How far from 0 is each integer? Answers will vary. Sample: −7 and 7; 7 units.

WHAT? The longest field goal recorded is 63 yd. Tom Dempsey kicked the record-breaking field goal for the New Orleans Saints in 1970.

Source: *The Guinness Book of Records*

> *"Mankind owes to the child the best it has to give."*
> —United Nations Declaration

Organizer

1. **Focus**
   Connecting to Prior Knowledge
2. **Teach**
   Think and Discuss
3. **Closure**
   Try These
   Wrap Up

Vocabulary/Symbols
integers
positive integers
negative integers
opposites

Skills Reviewed in Context of Lesson
- using a number line

Student Resources
Extra Practice
Student Study Guide
Practice, TR Ch. 11, p. 22
Student Study Guide, Spanish Resources, TR

Teacher Resources
Teaching Transparency 91
Transparency Masters, TR p. 26
Lesson Planner, TR Ch. 11, p. 2

continues next page

Example 2
Have students copy the number line and label each point with a name to make sure students make the connection between the data in the table and on the line.

Additional Example *Another group of friends had the golf scores –1, 3, 0, 1, and –4. List the scores in order from least to greatest.* **(–4, –1, 0, 1, 3)**

Error Alert! For problems such as Examples 1 and 2, students may be confused why a number with a greater absolute value, such as –6, should be less than –1. ***Remediation*** Encourage students to plot any integers they are unsure about on a number line. Also, ask students: *Which would you rather have, a debt of $6 or a debt of $1?*

Ongoing Assessment Have students return to the example of the running back in Question 1. Give students the following situation to evaluate: *Your football team is on the opposing team's five-yard line. Someone asks you how many yards you hope the team makes on the next play: –9, 0, 5, or –1. Which do you choose and why?* **(An answer of 5 yd would be best because it is the greatest possible positive yardage and a touchdown. Have students compare the integers on a number line.)**

ESL VISUAL LEARNERS The best way to help students understand the concept of size with relation to negative numbers is to give them ample opportunity to use number lines. Have students verbalize how they are locating numbers on the number line.

TRY THESE

AUDITORY LEARNERS For Exercises 12–23, have students work in pairs. One student reads the question and the other gives the answer. Students can take turns reading the questions and giving the answers.

Organizer, continued

Prentice Hall Technology
Multimedia Math
• Hot Page 11-1
Computer Item Generator
• 11-1

Fact of the Day

The Indian Ocean has an area of 25,300,000 mi^2. Although it has an average depth of 3,963 m (13,002 ft), the Indian Ocean's deepest point is the Sunda Trench, which reaches 7,455 m (24,460 ft) below sea level.

—INFORMATION PLEASE ALMANAC

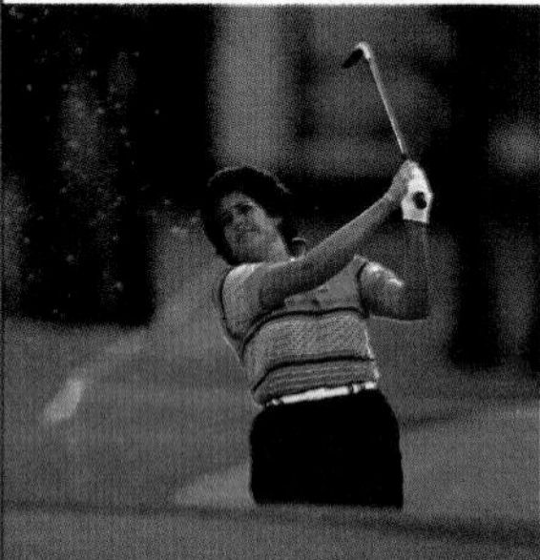

Nancy Lopez won the Rail Charity Golf Classic tournament in 1992 with a score of −17.

Source: *Sports Illustrated Sports Almanac.*

5. a. What is the opposite of gaining nine yards in football? Losing 9 yd
   b. Write the gain and its opposite as integers. 9, −9

You can use the [+/−] key to write the opposite of a number.

5 [+/−] → −5   5 [+/−] [+/−] → 5

6. A calculator displays −12. If you press the [+/−] key, what does the calculator display? 12

7. Why is the [+/−] key called the "change-sign" key? The key changes positive numbers to negative numbers and vice versa.

Golfers keep score by counting how many times they hit the golf ball. Then they compare that number to an accepted standard for the hole or course. A score of −2 means that you hit the ball two less times than the standard. In golf, the lowest score is the best.

Stoneham Golf Course	
Eugenio	−1
Mwita	−5

Example 1 Who had a lower score, Eugenio or Mwita?

• Graph each score on a number line.

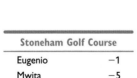

−5 is to the left of −1.
−5 < −1 or −1 > −5

Mwita had a lower score than Eugenio.

8. Compare using <, >, or =.

a. 10 ■ 6 > b. −7 ■ 0 < c. 3 ■ −4 > d. −13 ■ −11 <

FLASHBACK
Numbers on a number line increase in value from left to right.

9. **Critical Thinking** Complete with *always, sometimes,* or *never.*
   a. 0 is ■ greater than a negative integer. always
   b. 0 is ■ greater than a positive integer. never
   c. A negative integer is ■ less than another negative integer. sometimes

Golf Scores	
2	Ilana
0	Dwayne
−4	Luisa
3	Shani
−2	William

Example 2 List the scores in order from least to greatest.

• Graph each score on a number line.

• Write the scores from left to right.

In order, the scores are −4, −2, 0, 2, and 3.

CONNECTION TO SCIENCE Exercise 19 has students use integers to describe the depth of a cave, and Exercise 20 has students use integers to describe the height of a mountain.

CONNECTION TO GEOGRAPHY For Exercises 19 and 20, have students locate Carlsbad Caverns and Mt. Whitney on a map.

Wrap Up

What's the Big Idea? Ask students: *How can you graph integers on a number line? How can you compare and order integers?*

Connections Have the students discuss how positive and negative integers are used. You may want to start with these examples:

- **Banking** (deposits and withdrawals)
- **Consumer Issues** (coupons and refunds)
- **Accounting** (credits and debits)

Reteaching Activity Bring to class a listing of golf tournament scores from the sports page in a newspaper. Arrange students in groups of four. Have each group make a number line comparing a set of scores. Make sure students label and title their number lines. Then have groups compare their number lines to the list of placings and make a conjecture that relates the two. **(The lower the score, the higher the standing.)**

Journal Ask students to explain why negative integers are so useful and important.

ON YOUR OWN

CONNECTION TO STATISTICS In Exercises 24–27, students express data displayed in a bar graph as integers.

ESTIMATION For Exercises 24 and 25, have students explain the reasoning behind their estimates.

10. Which two players had opposite scores? William and Ilana

11. List in order from least to greatest: 7, −4, 11, 0, −8.
−8, −4, 0, 7, 11

TRY THESE

12. Graph these integers on a number line: 6, −9, 7, −1, 0, 3.
See Solution Key.

Name the integer that is represented by each point.

13. M 1 14. N −4

15. P 5 16. Q −6

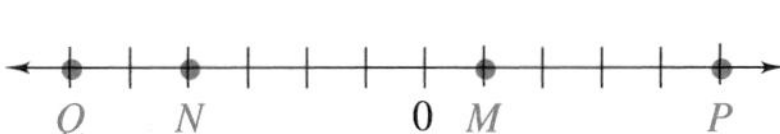

Write an integer to represent each situation.

17. earnings of $25 25

18. 14 degrees below zero −14

19. **Geography** Carlsbad Caverns in New Mexico are the deepest caves in the United States at 1,565 ft deep. −1,565

20. **Geography** Mt. Whitney in California has an elevation of 4,418 m. 4,418

Compare using <, >, or =.

21. −7 ■ 2 <

22. −12 ■ −9 <

23. −17 ■ −23 >

ON YOUR OWN

Use the bar graph at the right.

24. **Estimation** Estimate the change in the number of farmers by the year 2005. Estimates may vary. Sample: −225,000

25. **Estimation** Estimate the change in the number of lawyers by the year 2005. Estimates may vary. Sample: +210,000

26. Will bank tellers or typists lose more jobs? Explain. See right.

27. a. List the jobs in order from the most gained to the most lost. teacher aide, cook, lawyer, bank teller, typist, farmer

b. Redraw the graph with the jobs in that order.
See Solution Key.

26. typists; Typists will lose about 100,000 jobs while bank tellers will only lose about 25,000 jobs.

Employment Change from 1990 to 2005 (thousands of jobs)

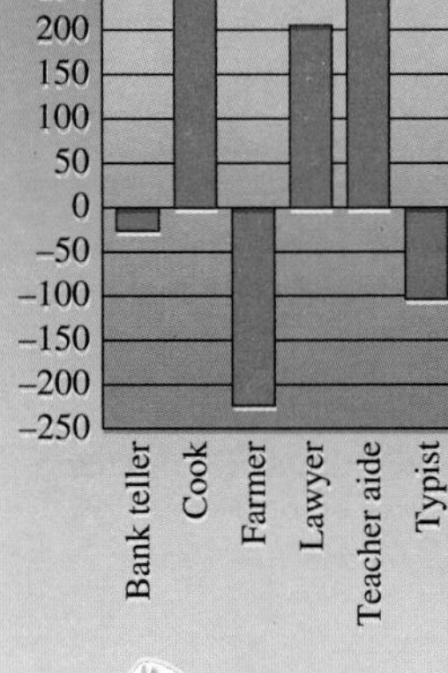

PH Multimedia Math Hot Page™ 11-1

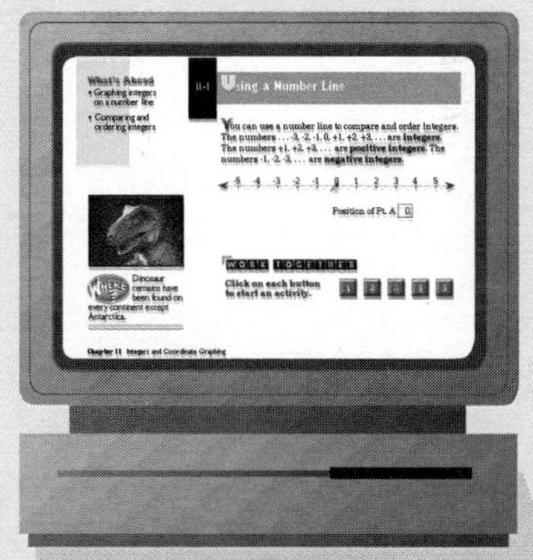

Assignment Options

Core: 24–27, 32–35, 37, 38, 40, 43, 44, 46, MR all	
Reinforce: 28–31, 36, 39, 41, 45	**Enrich:** 42

CONNECTION TO SCIENCE Exercise 40 has students compare and order temperatures.

WRITING For Exercise 42, have students provide at least three examples of positive integers and three examples of negative integers.

CALCULATOR Have students write and exchange their own problems similar to Exercises 43–45.

CHAPTER INVESTIGATION For Exercise 46, encourage students to compare their time lines to a number line.

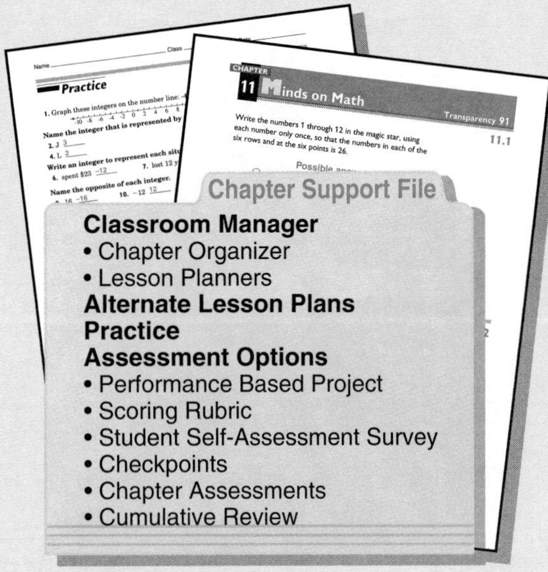

Minds on Math available in Teaching Transparencies

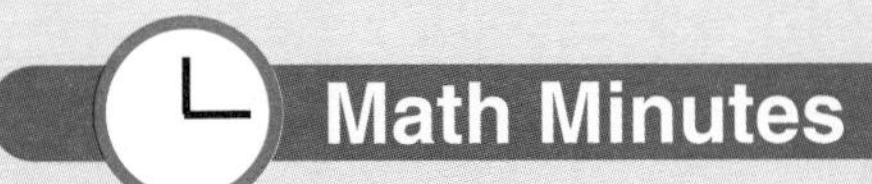

If you tossed a coin 200 times, what is the mathematical probability of getting a head on the 143rd toss?

$P(\text{head}) = \frac{1}{2}$

Materials for 11-2

- algebra tiles

452

Mixed REVIEW

Find each sum or difference.

1. $5\frac{2}{3} + 3\frac{1}{6}$ $8\frac{5}{6}$
2. $2\frac{7}{8} - 1\frac{2}{3}$ $1\frac{5}{24}$

See below.

3. Explain why a sample should be chosen randomly.
4. A poll of voters found that 43% favored an increase in taxes. What is the probability that another voter, when asked, would favor an increase in taxes?
5. What is the sum of the first 10 even integers? 110

3. to be sure that the sample is representative
4. 43%

At age 14 Sarah Billmeier from Vermont won three skiing events at the 1992 Paralympics in France.

28. Data File 11 (pp. 446–447) Estimate the depth of the Indian Ocean. Write the amount as an integer compared to sea level. −4,000 m

Write an integer between the given integers.
Answers may vary. Sample given.

29. −7, 3 −3 **30.** 0, −6 −3 **31.** −5, −13 −8

Name the opposite of each integer.

32. 13 −13 **33.** −8 8 **34.** 150 −150 **35.** −212 212

36. Name three pairs of situations that are opposites. For example, walk up two stairs; walk down two stairs. See Solution Key.

Write an integer that makes each statement true.
Answers may vary. Sample given.

37. $-5 <$ ■ −2 **38.** ■ < 6 2 **39.** opposite of ■ > 0 −7

40. Weather List the temperatures from least to greatest.
- Normal body temperature is about 37°C.
- An average winter day on the polar ice cap is −25°C.
- The warmest day in Canada was 45°C.
- Water freezes at 0°C. Ski resorts can make artificial snow at this temperature.
- The coldest day in Alaska was −62°C.

−62°C, −25°C, 0°C, 37°C, 45°C

41. Data File 11 (pp. 446–447) List the lowest recorded temperatures from least to greatest.
−89°C, −68°C, −63°C, −59°C, −33°C, −24°C, −22°C

42. Writing Explain what integers are and describe opposites. Include number lines in your descriptions. See Solution Key.

Calculator **Name the integer that results from each calculator key sequence.**

43. 8 [+/−] −8 **44.** 9 [+/−] [+/−] 9 **45.** 6    −6

46. Investigation (p. 448) See Solution Key.

a. How is a time line similar to a number line? How is it different?

b. What type of points on your time line represents events that happened before you entered school? after you entered school?

11-2

Connecting to Prior Knowledge

Have students recall examples of using negative numbers and zero. Ask students how the values were represented.

THINK AND DISCUSS

CRITICAL THINKING For Question 3, have students share their observations.

Error Alert! For Question 7, students may remove pairs of one color of tile. ***Remediation*** Remind students that zero pairs are made up of two opposites or two different-colored tiles.

Ongoing Assessment Have students plot opposites on a number line. Then have students draw a model for the integers. Ask students to name the sum of each pair of opposites. **(zero)**

TACTILE LEARNERS This entire lesson is excellent for tactile learners because the activities focus on using different-colored tiles to represent positive and negative integers. Have students use the tiles as directed in the activities. If there are not enough tiles available for all students, have each pair make one model.

Journal Challenge students to think of other ways to model integers. Ask students to compare these to the tiles model.

ESL Discuss with students in informal language the meaning of the word "integer." Elicit the fact that "integer" does not include decimals or fractions and that an integer can be positive, negative, or zero. Make sure students also know what is meant by a "zero pair" **(a positive and a negative integer whose sum is zero; integers are opposites)** and why removing these two different-colored tiles does not change the value of the integer represented by the model.

> *"A child is the root of the heart."*
>
> —Caroline Maria De Jesus

11-2 Modeling Integers

What's Ahead

- Representing positive integers, negative integers, and zero using models.

WHAT YOU'LL NEED

✓ Algebra tiles

→ 1 → −1

→ 3

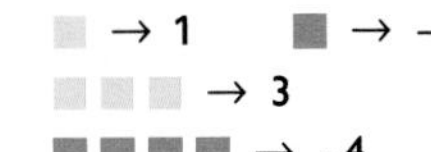
→ −4

THINK AND DISCUSS

You can use colored tiles to model integers. Yellow tiles represent positive integers. Red tiles represent negative integers.

1. What integer is represented by the tiles?
   a. −2 b. 7
   c. 5 d. −5
2. Which integers in Question 1 are opposites? 5 and −5
3. **Critical Thinking** What do you notice about the sets of tiles that represent a number and its opposite? the same number of tiles is in each set but the sets are different colors
4. Use tiles to represent each integer and its opposite.
   a. 4 b. −3 c. 2 d. −8
   See Solution Key.

Suppose you earned $1 and then spent $1. Then ■ represents the $1 that you earned and ■ represents the $1 that you spent. You have *no more* or *no less* money than before.

■■ represent 0, or ■ + ■ = 0

5. Suppose you have seven positive tiles. How many negative tiles do you need to represent zero? 7
6. Suppose you have ten negative tiles. How many positive tiles do you need to represent zero? 10

0 0 −3

= −3

You can use zero pairs of tiles to write integers when you have tiles of both colors together.

- Group the pairs of tiles that represent zero.
- Remove the pairs from the other tiles.
- Write the integer that the remaining tiles represent.

7. Write the integer that is represented by the tiles.
   a. −1 b. −4 c. 6

Organizer

1. **Focus**
   Connecting to Prior Knowledge
2. **Teach**
   Think and Discuss
   Work Together
3. **Closure**
   Wrap Up

Skills Reviewed in Context of Lesson
- identifying integers

Materials and Manipulatives
- algebra tiles (1 set per student)

On Your Own Exercises 10–13: algebra tiles

Student Resources
Extra Practice
Student Study Guide
Practice, TR Ch. 11, p. 23
Student Study Guide, Spanish Resources, TR

Teacher Resources
Teaching Transparency 91
Transparency Masters, TR p. 27
Overhead Manipulatives: algebra tiles
Lesson Planner, TR Ch. 11, p. 3

Prentice Hall Technology

Multimedia Math
- Math Tools, Manipulatives

Computer Item Generator
- 11-2

WORK TOGETHER

Provide each pair of students with tiles of two different colors.

DIVERSITY Some students may not be able to arrange tiles to represent integers because of physical disabilities or color blindness. Have these students work with other students who can manipulate the tiles.

Wrap Up

What's the Big Idea? Ask students to explain how to use models to represent positive and negative integers and zero.

Reteaching Activity Place two different colors of tiles in a bag. Randomly draw 6 to 12 tiles from the bag and have students find the integer the tiles model.

Connections Have a discussion about how zero pairs are used. You may want to start with these examples:

- **Measurement** (using a balance scale)
- **Household** (repaying debts)

ON YOUR OWN

Students will need colored tiles for Exercises 10–19.

WRITING For Exercise 9, have students draw models for at least one positive integer, one negative integer, and zero.

CRITICAL THINKING Have students organize their answers to Exercise 19 according to the different possible arrangements.

Fact of the Day

The dollar is the main currency unit of the United States, Canada, New Zealand, Australia, Ethiopia, Liberia, and several former British colonies. It was adopted in the United States in 1792 and was based on a Spanish coin that circulated in the colonies before the American Revolution.

—*Academic American Encyclopedia*

Assignment Options

Core: 10–16, MR all	
Reinforce: 9, 17	**Enrich:** 18, 19

Minds on Math available in Teaching Transparencies

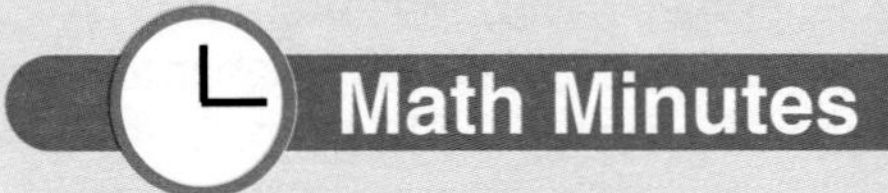

Math Minutes

Calculate the interest if you borrow $200 at a simple interest rate of 12% for two years. **$48.00**

Materials for 11-3

- algebra tiles
- paper bag

454

8. a. What integer is represented by ■■□□□□? 2
   b. What integer is represented by □□□□□■■■? 2
   c. How do the answers to parts (a) and (b) compare? =
   d. Critical Thinking How many ways are there to represent an integer with tiles? Explain. Answers may vary. Sample: There are infinitely many since for every positive integer there is a negative integer.

WORK TOGETHER

Check student's work.

Work with a partner. Repeat this activity four times.

- State a real world situation that can be represented by an integer. Have your partner name the integer and represent it with tiles.
- Have your partner describe the opposite real world situation. You name this opposite and represent it with tiles.

ON YOUR OWN

9. Writing Explain how you can use tiles to represent integers. Include examples and diagrams. See left.

9. You could use yellow tiles to represent positive integers and red tiles to represent negative integers. Zero could be represented by an equal number of white and red tiles.

Use tiles to represent each integer in two ways.
See Solution Key.

10. 1   11. −7   12. 0   13. 5

Write the integer that is represented by the tiles.

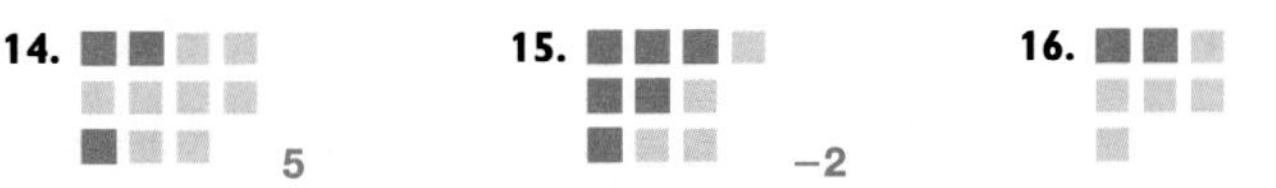

14. 5   15. −2   16. 3

17. What integer is represented by 13 negative tiles and 7 positive tiles? −6

18. a. Think of two integers. Model them with tiles.
    b. Use a different number of tiles to represent the opposite of each integer. See Solution Key.

19. Critical Thinking Suppose you had 6 tiles and didn't know the colors of the tiles.
    a. How many different ways can you color the tiles? 64 ways
    b. List all the integers that the tiles can represent. −6, −5, −4, −3, −2, −1, 0, 1, 2, 3, 4, 5, 6

Mixed REVIEW

Find the value of x. 56

1. $\frac{20}{21} = \frac{x}{63}$ 60   2. $\frac{4}{28} = \frac{8}{x}$

Write the opposite of each integer.

3. −4 4   4. 21 −21

5. Draw a pair of triangles that are similar but not congruent.

See Solution Key.

11-3

Connecting to Prior Knowledge

Ask students to think of ways to model the addition of integers based on the methods they have used so far to model integers. Discuss with students the advantages and disadvantages for each method.

THINK AND DISCUSS

KINESTHETIC LEARNERS Have the students make paper frogs and have them model the frog jumps on a number line marked off on the floor. They can use the chart of Toadstool's jumps to find the distance he jumped each time. For each attempt, have them record the sum of the first and second jumps.

ESL DIVERSITY Some students may never have heard of a frog jumping contest. Explain how the contest works. Encourage students to look in the library for articles and stories about jumping frogs.

Example 1

Encourage students to be consistent in the color they use for a positive integer and for a negative integer.

Additional Example *Find the sum −3 + (−5).*

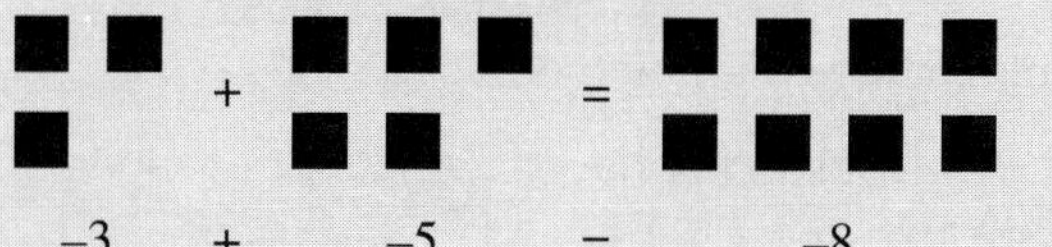

−3 + −5 = −8

Example 2

Remind students that zero pairs are pairs of opposites, which together equal zero.

Additional Example *Find the sum −7 + 5.*

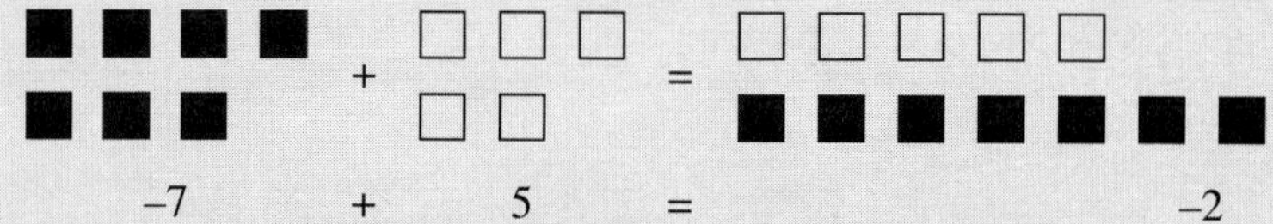

−7 + 5 = −2

> *There is nothing either good or bad, but thinking makes it so.*
> —WILLIAM SHAKESPEARE

11-3 Modeling Addition of Integers

What's Ahead

- Adding integers using models

WHAT YOU'LL NEED

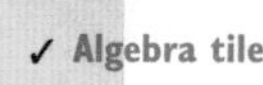

✓ Algebra tiles

✓ Paper bag

Toadstool's Practice Jumps

Attempt	First Jump	Second Jump
1	3 ft	7 ft
2	−5 ft	−2 ft
3	6 ft	−4 ft
4	−7 ft	3 ft
5	4 ft	−4 ft

THINK AND DISCUSS

People in Frogville train frogs for the Annual Frog Jumping Festival. The main event is the Double Jump, in which the distances for two leaps are combined. Last year's champion Toadstool is giving his owner Pamela a little trouble. Sometimes he jumps backward! Pamela kept track of Toadstool's practice jumps for the Double Jump.

You can model the lengths of Toadstool's jumps with tiles to find the sum of his jumps. To find the sum of his first attempt, write this number sentence.

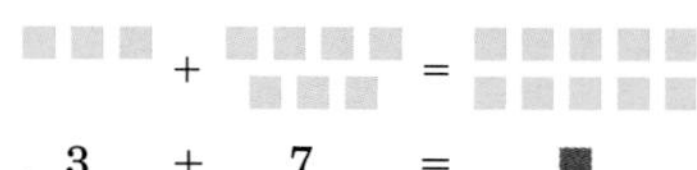

3 + 7 = ■

1. Complete the number sentence above. How many total feet did Toadstool jump in his first attempt? 10 ft
2. Show how tiles can be used to find the sum 9 + 4. See Solution Key.
3. Complete: Adding two positive integers always results in a ■ integer. positive

Example 1 What was the sum of Toadstool's jumps in his second attempt?

- Model each integer with tiles. Then count the tiles.

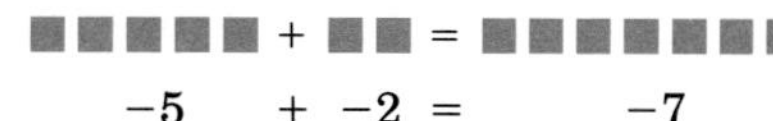

−5 + −2 = −7

He jumped a total of −7 ft.

4. Use tiles to find each sum.
   a. $-8 + (-1)$ −9
   b. $-3 + (-6)$ −9
   c. $-12 + (-9)$ −21
   d. $-7 + (-8)$ −15

WHAT? The United States record for a jumping frog is 21 ft $5\frac{1}{2}$ in. total for 3 jumps and occurred at the Calaveras County, CA, Jumping Frog Jubilee.

Source: *The Guinness Book of Records*

Organizer

1. **Focus**
   Connecting to Prior Knowledge
2. **Teach**
   Think and Discuss
   Work Together
3. **Closure**
   Try These
   Wrap Up

Skills Reviewed in Context of Lesson
- modeling integers

Materials and Manipulatives
- algebra tiles (1 set per students, 20 yellow and 20 red)
- paper bag (1 per group)

On Your Own Exercises 20–25: algebra tiles

Student Resources
Extra Practice
Student Study Guide
Practice, TR Ch. 11, p. 24
Student Study Guide, Spanish Resources, TR
Checkpoint, TR Ch. 11, p. 34
Alternate Lesson, TR Ch. 11, pp. 10–13

continues next page

Error Alert! In Question 6, students may model correctly but use the wrong sign for the answer. ***Remediation*** Remind students that the tiles that are left over after making zero pairs represent the integer that is the sum. Encourage students to make a note of the color of the tiles for each sum. Students can refer to a key such as "yellow = positive; red = negative." Encourage them to verbalize their findings as they model the sums.

CRITICAL THINKING For Question 8, have students draw models that support their answers.

WORK TOGETHER

Provide each pair of students with a paper bag, 20 yellow tiles, and 20 red tiles. Encourage each student in a pair to keep an individual scorecard so that students can later compare their findings to those of their partner.

TRY THESE

TECHNOLOGY OPTION For Exercises 11–13, students can use algebra software to practice adding integers.

MENTAL MATH Encourage students to visualize zero pairs as appropriate for Exercises 14–16.

Ongoing Assessment Use the student answers from Exercises 17–19. Have each pair of students meet with at least two other pairs to compare exercises. Encourage students to check each other's addition and to model each sum with tiles.

Wrap Up

What's the Big Idea? Ask students how to add integers using models.

Organizer, continued

Teacher Resources

Teaching Transparency 91
Transparency Masters, TR p. 27
Overhead Manipulatives: algebra tiles
Lesson Planner, TR Ch. 11, p. 4

Prentice Hall Technology

Multimedia Math
- Math Tools, Frames
- Math Tools, Manipulatives

Computer Item Generator
- 11-3

Other Available Technology

Math Connections: Algebra I by Sunburst: Exercises 11–13 *(optional)*

Fact of the Day

Mark Twain was the pseudonym of Samuel Langhorne Clemens (1835–1910), who achieved worldwide fame during his lifetime as an author, lecturer, satirist, and humorist. In 1865 he wrote "The Celebrated Jumping Frog of Calaveras County."

—ACADEMIC AMERICAN ENCYCLOPEDIA

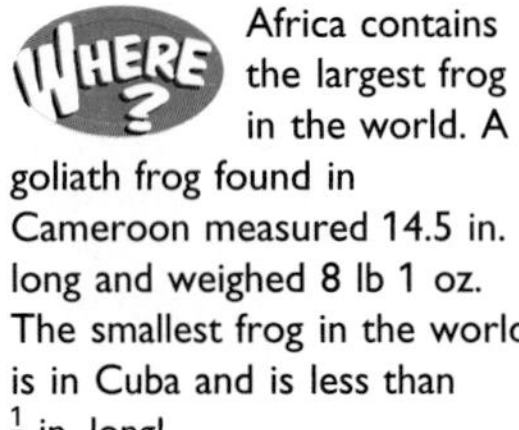

Africa contains the largest frog in the world. A goliath frog found in Cameroon measured 14.5 in. long and weighed 8 lb 1 oz. The smallest frog in the world is in Cuba and is less than $\frac{1}{2}$ in. long!

Source: *The Guinness Book of Records*

5. a. What do you notice about the sign of the sum of two negative integers? It is negative.

b. Complete: Adding two negative integers always results in a ■ integer. negative

Example 2 Use the table on page 455. What was the sum of Toadstool's jumps in his third attempt?

- Model each integer with tiles. Combine tiles to make zero pairs. Write the integer that the remaining tiles represent.

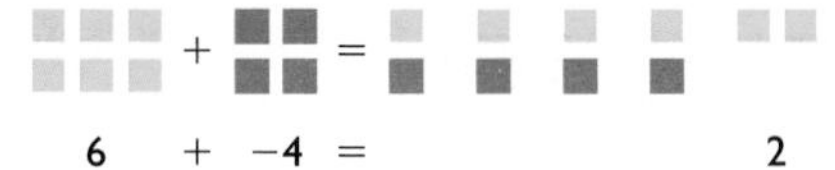

6 + −4 = 2

He jumped a total of 2 ft.

6. Use tiles to find each sum.

a. $-5 + 9$ 4 **b.** $-8 + 3$ −5 **c.** $7 + (-7)$ 0

7. What do you notice about the sign of the sum of a positive integer and a negative integer? It can be positive, negative, or zero.

8. Critical Thinking What is the sum of a number and its opposite? Give examples to justify your answer.
0; $-13 + 13 = 0$, $-12 + 12 = 0$

WORK TOGETHER

Check student's work.

Work with a partner. Place 20 yellow and 20 red algebra tiles in a paper bag. Make a scorecard like the sample at the left.

- Remove 1 tile from the bag. Write the integer that the tile represents. Replace the tile.
- Have your partner remove 1 tile, write the integer, and then replace the tile.
- Continue removing tiles and writing integers. During each round, increase the number of tiles you remove by 1.
- At the end of 8 rounds, find your score. Cross out any 0's or zero pairs. Model the remaining integers with tiles. Your score is the integer that these tiles represent.
- Compare your scores. Who had the greater score?

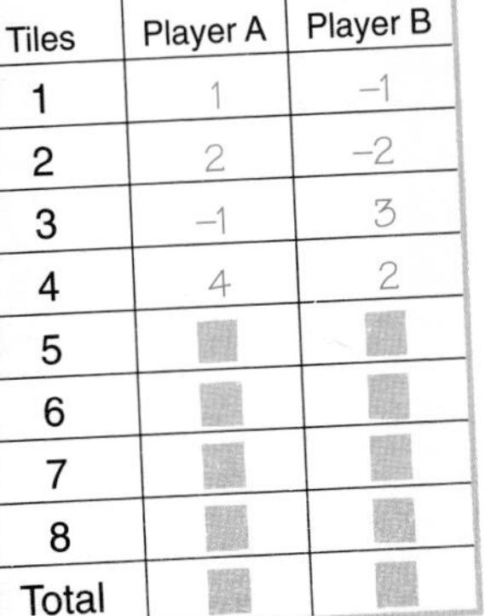

Tiles	Player A	Player B
1	1	−1
2	2	−2
3	−1	3
4	4	2
5	■	■
6	■	■
7	■	■
8	■	■
Total	■	■

Journal Ask students which they find easiest and which most difficult: adding positive integers, adding negative integers, or adding a combination of positive and negative integers. Have students explain their answers.

Connections Have a discussion about how adding integers is used. You may want to start with these examples:

- **Games and Tests** (adding positive, correct answers and negative, incorrect answers)
- **Travel** (estimating time of arrival or miles to go on a return trip)
- **Oceanography** (finding the depths of underwater trenches and mountains)

Reteaching Activity Place an equal number of two colors of tiles in a paper bag. Divide the class into two groups. Play a game in which each group will take turns guessing the color of tiles you will randomly draw from the bag. Award Team One 1 point for each correct answer and –1 for each incorrect answer. Award Team Two 2 points for each correct answer and –2 points for each incorrect answer. After about 20 draws, have students add up the scores and make conjectures comparing the scores. **(The integers 1 and –1 and 2 and –2 are zero pairs; the game is a 50/50 probability game. The odds are that both team's final score will be about the same: zero.)**

ON YOUR OWN

Students will need colored tiles for Exercises 20–34.

CONNECTION TO SCIENCE Exercise 30 has students use integers to evaluate weather data.

CHAPTER INVESTIGATION For Exercise 35, students can look through old yearbooks in the school's library or talk to teachers who have taught at the school for many years. Encourage students to start their timelines by choosing an appropriate date for zero.

Assignment Options

Core: 20–22, 26–30, 33–35, MR all, CH all	
Reinforce: 23–25, 31, 32, 36–39	**Enrich:** 40, 41

TRY THESE

Write a numerical expression for each model. Find the sum.

9. ■■■■■■ + ■■■■■ $-6 + 5$; -1

10. ■■ + ■■■■■■■■ $-2 + (-8)$; -10

Use tiles to find each sum.

11. $-1 + (-5)$ -6
12. $10 + (-10)$ 0
13. $-11 + 4$ -7

Mental Math **State whether the sum is positive or negative.**

14. $16 + 14$ positive
15. $-16 + (-14)$ negative
16. $-16 + 18$ positive

Work with a partner. Write an addition exercise involving a positive integer and a negative integer so that you can get each type of answer. Answers will vary. Sample given.

17. negative $5 + (-8)$
18. 0 $15 + (-15)$
19. positive $8 + (-5)$

ON YOUR OWN

Use tiles to find each sum.

20. $9 + (-4)$ 5
21. $-8 + (-7)$ -15
22. $-15 + 6$ -9
23. $-11 + 11$ 0
24. $0 + (-8)$ -8
25. $-6 + 11$ 5

Compare. Write <, >, or =.

26. $-7 + (-3)$ ■ $7 + 3$ $<$
27. $5 + (-5)$ ■ $-1 + 1$ $=$
28. $-2 + 8$ ■ $-8 + 2$ $>$
29. $6 + (-3) + (-4)$ ■ $6 + (-7)$ $=$

30. Weather What was the temperature in Spearfish, SD, at 7:32 A.M. on January 22, 1943? 45°F

31. Use the table on page 456. Did Player A or Player B have the greater score after 4 rounds? Explain why. A; $1 + 2 + (-1) + 4 > -1 + (-2) + 3 + 2$

32. Money On Saturday Tyrell earned \$12 running errands for the elderly center. On Monday he spent \$8 on a cassette. On Friday he earned \$7 baby-sitting. How much money did Tyrell have at the end of the week? \$11

At 7:30 A.M. on January 22, 1943, the temperature was −4°F in Spearfish, SD. Two minutes later the temperature had risen an amazing 49°F!

Source: *Guinness Book of World Records*

MENTAL MATH Have students keep notes of the opposites for Exercises 36–39.

WRITING For Exercise 41, have students provide an example for each type of addition operation.

CHECKPOINT

Students may need colored tiles for Questions 1–12.

Question 5: Have students list or draw the zero pairs.

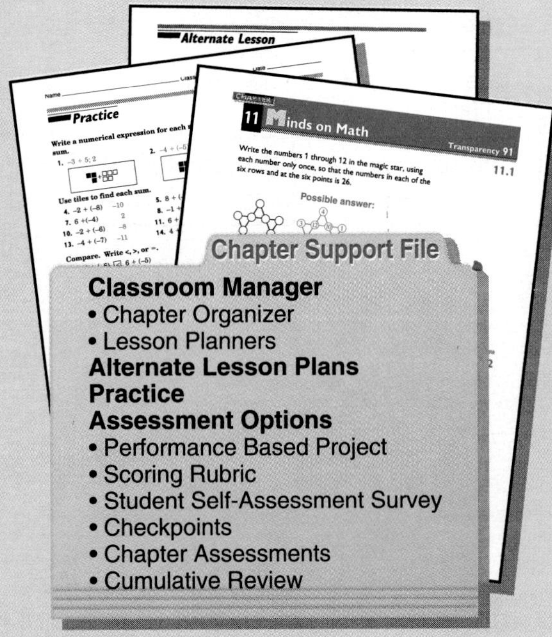

Minds on Math available in Teaching Transparencies

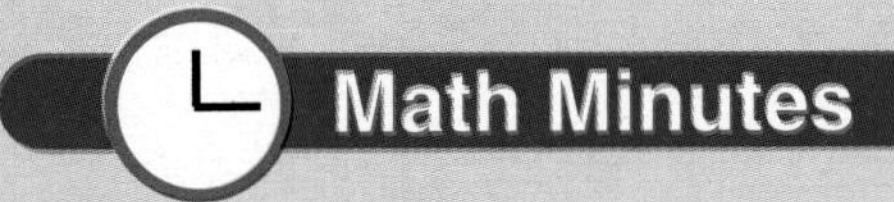

Math Minutes

Draw a triangle and place a dot directly above it. Then connect each vertex to that point. What three-dimensional figure have you drawn?
triangular pyramid

Materials for 11-4

- algebra tiles
- two dice of different colors

41. Answers may vary. Sample: The sum of two positive integers is positive, the sum of two negative integers is negative, and the sum of a positive and a negative integer can be positive, negative, or zero.

33. **Sports** A football team gained 6 yd on one play. On the next play the team lost 11 yd. Write the total gain or loss of yards as an integer. -5 yd

34. The mailroom of a large company is on the 15th floor. Linda delivers mail by first going up 5 floors in the elevator. She next goes down 3 floors. Then she goes down 4 floors. Where is she in relation to the mailroom? two floors below the mailroom

35. **Investigation (p. 448)** Research events that happened at your school before you entered. Assign a negative time line date to each event. Explain the time line dates. Check student's work.

Mental Math Group opposites to get a sum of 0. Add the remaining integers.

36. $-4 + 7 + 4 + (-2)$ 5
37. $6 + (-3) + (-8) + 3$ -2
38. $8 + (-9) + (-8) + 9$ 0
39. $-7 + 5 + (-1) + 7 + (-7)$ -3

Magic Integer Square

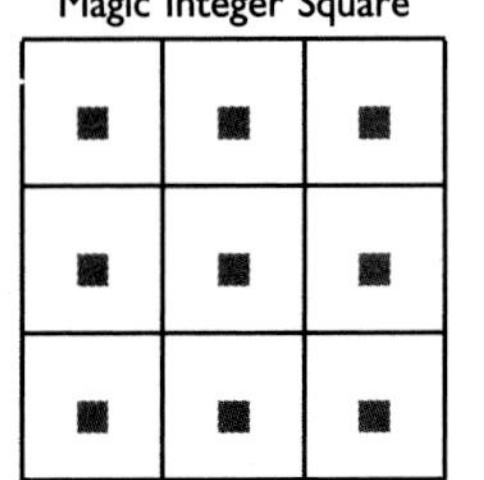

40. Copy the Magic Integer Square. Arrange the integers $-4, -3, -2, -1, 0, 1, 2, 3, 4$ so they add up to zero in all eight directions (vertically, horizontally, and on the diagonal). See Solution Key.

41. **Writing** Summarize what you know about adding 2 positive integers, 2 negative integers, and a positive integer and a negative integer. See left.

3. 4 in.: 20 ft
4. 80 in.^{2}; 48 in.

Mixed REVIEW

Write the integer that is represented by the tiles.

1. ■■■ -3
2. ■■■■■ 5

See above.

3. The length of a room in a blueprint is 4 in. The actual length is 20 ft. Find the scale of the blueprint.
4. A rectangle is 20 in. long. Its width is 4 in. What are its area and perimeter?
5. Find all combinations of 5 whole numbers that you can add to get a sum of 10. See Solution Key.

CHECKPOINT

Compare using <, >, or =.

1. 2 ■ 5 <
2. -4 ■ -8 >
3. -3 ■ 0 <
4. Graph on a number line: $2, -5, 3, 1, -7, -2$. See Solution Key.
5. What integer is represented by ■■■■■■■? 1

Use tiles to represent each integer and its opposite. See Solution Key.

6. 6   6, -6
7. -5 -5, 5
8. -2 -2, 2
9. 8   8, -8

Use tiles to find each sum.

10. $-2 + (-3)$ -5
11. $7 + (-5)$ 2
12. $-9 + 9$ 0

11-4

Connecting to Prior Knowledge

Ask students to compare *sum* and *difference* in their own words. Have students name situations in which it is useful to find the difference, such as when receiving change from a purchase.

THINK AND DISCUSS

ESL **VISUAL LEARNERS** Example 1 is an excellent demonstration of how the subtraction of negative integers results in a larger integer. Since this operation is difficult to visualize, model the problem on the chalkboard or overhead projector and go through it several times so that all students see what is being done.

Example 1

Point out to students that only negative tiles are used. The negative amount to be subtracted is merely removed from the starting negative integer. Compare the model to this situation: *You have a debt of $8 and your parent pays off $6 of it, or takes away $6 of your debt. How much do you still owe? Are you better off than when you started?* **($2; yes, you owe less.)**

Additional Example *Use tiles to subtract –7 – (–3).* **(Start with 7 negative tiles. Take away 3 negative tiles. There are 4 negative tiles. –7 – (–3) = –4)**

DIVERSITY Some students will grasp this concept quickly; others will struggle with it for a longer time. Allow plenty of time for students to practice with tiles, saying aloud the math procedures as they remove tiles as well as verbalizing the results.

Example 2

- *Use the results from Examples 1 and 2 to make a conjecture about what happens when you subtract a negative integer.* **(The answer is greater than the original number.)**

What's Ahead

- Subtracting integers using models

WHAT YOU'LL NEED

✓ Algebra tiles 

✓ Two dice of different colors 

11-4 Modeling Subtraction of Integers

THINK AND DISCUSS

Suppose you have $5 and want to spend $2. How much will you have left? You subtract to find the answer. Here's how you can use algebra tiles to subtract $5 - 2$.

Start with 5 positive tiles.
Take away 2 positive tiles.
Three positive tiles remain.

You have $3 left.

See Solution Key.

1. Show how to use tiles to find the difference $10 - 6$.

Example 1 Use tiles to subtract $-8 - (-6)$.

- Start with 8 negative tiles.
- Take away 6 negative tiles.

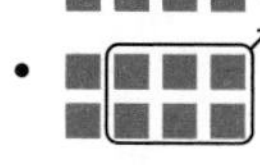

- There are 2 negative tiles.

$-8 - (-6) = -2$

2. Use tiles to find each difference.
   a. $12 - 4$ 8 b. $-10 - (-3)$ −7 c. $-15 - (-9)$ −6

Example 2 Use tiles to subtract $4 - (-3)$.

- There are not enough negative tiles to take 3 away. Add 3 zero pairs.

- Take away 3 negative tiles. There are 7 positive tiles left.

$4 - (-3) = 7$

3. a. What is the total value of the 3 zero pairs? Explain. 0; 0 + 0 + 0 = 0
   b. Did adding 3 zero pairs affect the value of −4? Explain. No; adding 0 to any number does not affect the value.

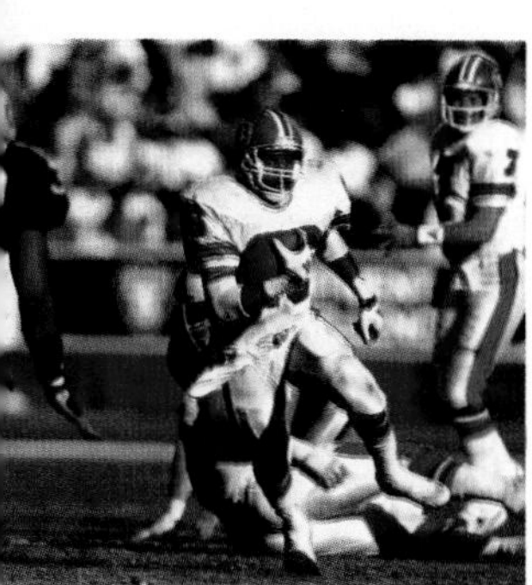

In the first half *of a game against the L.A. Raiders, the Denver Broncos ran for 79 yd and passed for −6 yd.* ***For how many more yards did the Broncos run than pass?*** 73 yd

> *"I recommend you to take care of the minutes for the hours will take care of themselves."*
>
> —Lord Chesterfield

Organizer

1. **Focus**
   Connecting to Prior Knowledge
2. **Teach**
   Think and Discuss
   Work Together
3. **Closure**
   Try These
   Wrap Up

Skills Reviewed in Context of Lesson

- modeling integers

Materials and Manipulatives

- algebra tiles (1 set per student)
- two dice of different colors (1 set per group)

On Your Own Exercises 15–20: algebra tiles

Student Resources

Extra Practice
Student Study Guide
Practice, TR Ch. 11, p. 25
Student Study Guide, Spanish Resources, TR
Alternate Lesson, TR Ch. 11, pp. 14–17

continues next page

Additional Example *Use tiles to subtract 7 – (–2).* **(Start with 7 positive tiles. There are not enough negative tiles to take 2 away. Add 2 zero pairs. Take away 2 negative tiles. There are 9 positive tiles left. 7 – (–2) = 9)**

Example 3

Point out how the data in the problem are represented: the starting temperature, 5°C, is the 5 positive tiles and the drop in temperature, –9°C, is the removal of 9 positive tiles. Make sure students understand why zero pairs are added and that they can add as many zero pairs as they like. However, any remaining zero pairs must be removed before they read the final answer.

Additional Example *The next day the high temperature was 6°C. By midnight the temperature had dropped 7°C. What was the temperature at midnight?* **(Start with 6 positive tiles. There are not enough positive tiles to take 7 away. Add a zero pair. Take away 7 positive tiles. There is 1 negative tile left. The temperature was –1°C at midnight.)**

Error Alert! For problems such as Examples 2 and 3, students may not understand when to add zero pairs or how many to add. ***Remediation*** Advise students to read the subtraction operations softly to themselves: 5 – 9 , for example, could be "five positive tiles take away nine positive tiles." By reading the operation, students will see what is missing to model the problem: 4 positive tiles.

WORK TOGETHER

Provide each group of three students with nine positive tiles, nine negative tiles, and two dice of different colors. You may wish to demonstrate several rounds of this game before students start.

TRY THESE

TECHNOLOGY OPTION For Exercises 8–10, students can use algebra software to subtract integers.

Organizer, continued

Teacher Resources

Teaching Transparency 92
Transparency Masters, TR p. 27
Overhead Manipulatives: algebra tiles
Lesson Planner, TR Ch. 11, p. 5

Prentice Hall Technology

Multimedia Math

- Math Tools, Frames
- Math Tools, Manipulatives

Computer Item Generator

- 11-4

Other Available Technology

Math Connections: Algebra I by Sunburst: Exercises 8–10 *(optional)*

Fact of the Day

The book *The Diary of a Young Girl* was based on Anne Frank's writings while she and her family hid from Nazi persecution in Amsterdam, Holland, during World War II. Her diary has been translated into more than 30 languages and was the basis for a prize-winning play and motion picture.

—ENCYCLOPAEDIA BRITANNICA

4. a. No; you would have only had 8 positive tiles to take away.

How wonderful it is that nobody need wait a single moment before starting to improve the world.

—Anne Frank (1929–1945)

Example 3 On January 15, the high temperature was 5°C. By midnight the temperature had dropped 9°C. What was the temperature at midnight?

- Use tiles to subtract 5 – 9.
- Start with 5 positive tiles.
- 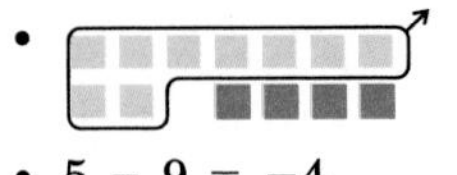 There are not enough positive tiles to take 9 away. Add 4 zero pairs.
- Take away 9 positive tiles. There are 4 negative tiles left.
- 5 – 9 = –4

The temperature was –4° C at midnight.

4. **Critical Thinking**
   a. Could 3 zero pairs have been added in the Example? Why or why not? See left.
   b. If 5 zero pairs had been added in the Example, would the answer be the same? Why or why not? Yes; adding 0 to any number does not affect the value.
5. Use tiles to find each difference.
   a. –5 – (–11) 6
   b. –10 –5 –15
   c. 12 – 19 –7

WORK TOGETHER

Work in groups of three. Start with 3 positive and 3 negative tiles each. Put the remaining tiles in a pile.

- Play the Great Integer Game. The object of the game is to be the first player to give away all his or her tiles.
- Decide which color die will be subtracted from the other. (For example, subtract a red die from a green die.)

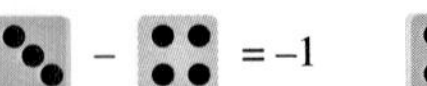

- Roll the dice. Put the resulting number of tiles in the pile.
- If you don't have enough tiles to put in the pot, you have to take zero pairs from the pile in order to make your number!
- The game is over when one player has no more tiles.

CONNECTION TO SCIENCE Exercise 14 has students use integers to evaluate weather data.

Ongoing Assessment Have students create a set of five word problems with integers to exchange with a partner.

Wrap Up

What's the Big Idea? Ask students: *How can you subtract integers using models?*

Journal Have students write conjectures about what other kinds of operations with integers might also be done, and how.

Reteaching Activity Assign students to groups of four. Have each student in a group write a subtraction operation involving integers, draw a model, and list the solution. Have students model and solve each other's subtraction problems. Ask students to compare answers.

Connections Have a discussion about how the subtraction of integers is used. You may want to start with these examples:

- **Navigation** (tracking descents in airplanes, balloons, or submarines)
- **Farming** (comparing the number of fields harvested or bushels sold)
- **Environment** (assessing losses to a herd or its range of land, describing decreases in pollution or poaching)

ON YOUR OWN

Students will need colored tiles for Exercises 15–20.

CRITICAL THINKING Encourage students to use tiles to model the patterns in Exercises 28 and 29.

Assignment Options

Core: 15–17, 21, 22, 28, 29, 31, 36–40, MR all	
Reinforce: 18–20, 23–27, 41–44	**Enrich:** 30, 32–35

TRY THESE

Write a numerical expression for each model. Find the difference.

6. 3 − (−2); 5

7. 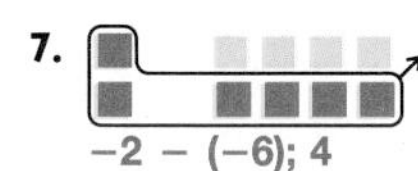
−2 − (−6); 4

Use tiles to find each difference.

8. 7 − 12 −5
9. −8 − 4 −12
10. −1 − (−5) 4

Model each situation with tiles. Give the result. −8°F

11. The temperature increases 9°F and then drops 17°F.
12. Elevator goes down 7 floors and then down 6 more floors. −13 floors
13. **Sports** Tasheka finished a golf game at 4 strokes over par (+4). Carmen scored 5 under par (−5). How many more golf strokes did Tasheka make than Carmen? 9 golf strokes
14. **Weather** One winter day the temperature rose from a low of −8° C to a high of 9° C. What was the temperature range for the day? 17°C

Mixed REVIEW

State whether the sum is positive or negative.

1. 2 + 5 positive
2. −2 + 5 positive

Find the prime factorization using a factor tree. See below.

3. 60
4. 1,240

5. I'm thinking of a number. If I multiply by 4 and add 7, the result is 51. What is the number? 11

3. 2 × 2 × 3 × 5
4. 2 × 2 × 2 × 5 × 31

ON YOUR OWN

Use tiles to find each sum or difference.

15. 1 − 6 −5
16. −13 − 8 −21
17. −4 − (−15) 11
18. −9 + 7 −2
19. 12 + (−3) 9
20. 0 − 10 −10

Compare. Write <, >, or =.

21. −1 − 5 ■ −5 − 1 =
22. 6 − 11 ■ 11 − 6 <
23. −4 − (−9) ■ −4 + 9 =
24. 8 − (−8) ■ −8 + 8 >

Weather **Find each average for the data at the right.**

25. median 6°C
26. mode(s) −6°C and 18°C
27. range 24°C

Average Low Temperatures (°C) for Boston, MA

Jan.	−6	July	18
Feb.	−6	Aug.	18
March	−1	Sept.	13
April	4	Oct.	8
May	9	Nov.	3
June	14	Dec.	−3

Critical Thinking **Find the next three integers in each pattern.**

28. 12, 7, 2, −3, ■, ■, ■ −8, −13, −18
29. 19, 13, 7, 1, ■, ■, ■ −5, −11, −17

CONNECTION TO PATTERNS Exercises 28 and 29 have students evaluate and continue patterns of integers.

WRITING For Exercise 30, have students write four types of subtraction examples: positive – positive, positive – negative, negative – positive, and negative – negative.

CHAPTER INVESTIGATION For Exercise 31, have students use zero to represent the day they entered school.

CONNECTION TO GEOGRAPHY Exercises 36–41 have students use integers to describe time zones.

RESEARCH For Exercise 41, students can consult an atlas. Ask students to find out about daylight savings time also, and to identify states that do not use it.

CRITICAL THINKING Encourage students to use colored tiles to model the sentences for Exercises 42–44.

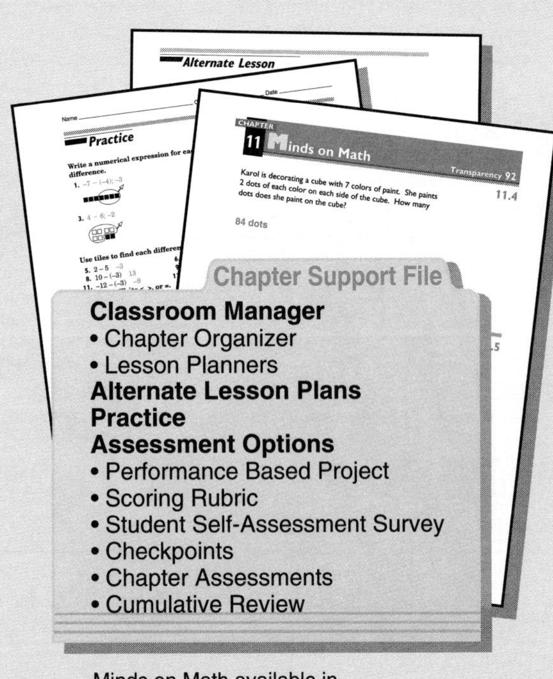

Minds on Math available in Teaching Transparencies

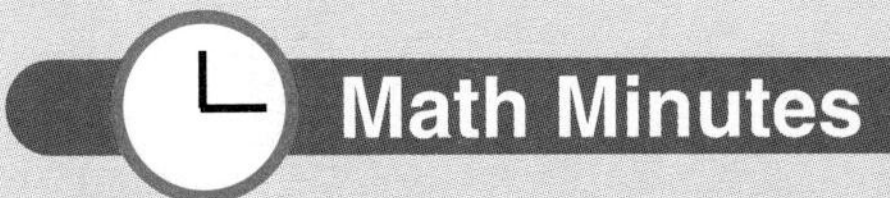

Harold spent $6.99 on a CD and twice that amount on a book. He has $9.03 left. How much did he have before making the purchases?
$30

30. Writing Describe how to use tiles to subtract integers. Include examples with both positive and negative integers. See Solution Key.

31. Investigation Name several pairs of events that happened at your school. In each pair, one event should occur before and one after you entered school. What are the time-line dates of the events? Find the amount of time that elapsed between the two events in each pair.
Check student's work.

Evaluate each expression when $a = -6$, $b = -1$, and $c = 9$.

32. $7 - a$ 13 **33.** $b - c$ −10 **34.** $-12 - b$ −11 **35.** $b - 11 - a$ −6

Geography **The map shows the time zones for North America. The starting point is a time zone through England, Spain, and Africa. The numbers indicate the time (in hours) compared to the starting zone's time.**

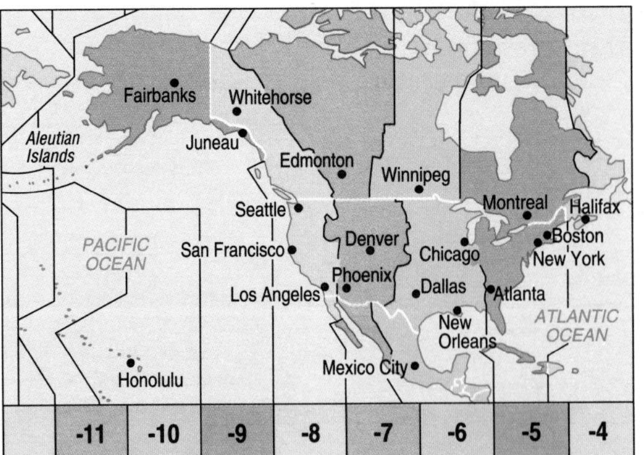

36. Complete with *add* or *subtract:* As you travel west, you ■ 1 h. As you travel east, you ■ 1 h.
subtract; add

37. It's 2:30 P.M. in the starting zone. What is the time in Denver? 7:30 A.M.

38. It's 8:15 A.M. in San Francisco. What time is it in Dallas? 10:15 A.M.

39. Times Square in New York is celebrating at midnight on New Year's Eve. What time is it in Los Angeles? 9:00 P.M.

40. How does the time in New Orleans compare to Honolulu?
Honolulu is 4 hours earlier.

41. a. Research Find the names of the time zones on the map above. See Solution Key.

b. In what time zone do you live? Check student's work.

c. Let t = the time at the starting zone. Write a variable expression to indicate the time in your time zone.
Check student's work.

WHEN? In 1884 an international conference established worldwide time zones. Before that, each place set its own time.

Source: *The World Book Encyclopedia*

Critical Thinking **Use positive and negative integers to write two different subtraction sentences.**
Answers will vary. Sample given.

42. ■ − ■ = 0
5, 5; −4, −4

43. ■ − ■ = 8
−2, −10; 12, 4

44. ■ − ■ = −5
12, 17; −4, 1

CHAPTER 11 PRACTICE

This page provides practice on the skills learned up to this point in the chapter. Daily cumulative practice can be found in the Mixed Reviews that appear in every lesson.

Students need tiles for Exercises 22–33, 40, and 41.

Practice

Graph each integer on a number line. See Solution Key.

1. −9 2. 4 3. −1 4. 7 5. 0

List the integers in order from least to greatest.

6. −3, 0, −8, 2 −8, −3, 0, 2
7. 5, −12, 1, −7 −12, −7, 1, 5
8. −9, 6, −4, 0, −2 −9, −4, −2, 0, 6
9. −72, −76, 72, −73, 71 −76, −73, −72, 71, 72

Name the opposite of each integer.

10. 5 −5 11. −3 3 12. 0 0 13. 6 −6 14. −6 6

Compare using $<$, $>$, or $=$.

15. −1 ■ −3 $>$ 16. 0 ■ −8 $>$ 17. 3 ■ 2 $>$ 18. −4 ■ −15 $>$

Write the integer represented by the tiles.

19. 0 20. −3 21. 5

Use tiles to represent each integer in two ways. See Solution Key.

22. 0 23. −2 24. −1 25. 4

Use tiles to find each sum or difference.

26. −7 + (−3) −10 27. −2 + (−5) −7 28. −4 + 7 3 29. 8 + (−8) 0

30. 2 − 5 −3 31. −12 − 9 −21 32. −3 − (−10) 7 33. 0 − 6 −6

Compare using $<$, $>$, or $=$.

34. −5 + (−3) ■ 5 + 3 $<$ 35. −7 + 10 ■ −10 + 7 $>$ 36. −3 + 3 ■ 1 + (−1) $=$

37. −2 − 4 ■ −4 − 2 $=$ 38. 5 − (−5) ■ −5 + 5 $>$ 39. 3 − 7 ■ 7 − 3 $<$

Model each situation with tiles. Give the result.

40. The temperature was 2°F below zero. The temperature then rose 9°F. 7°F

41. Chim ran 8 yd on a football play. On the next play he lost 13 yd. −5 yd

Resources

Extra Practice
Student Study Guide
Student Study Guide, Spanish Resources, TR

11-5

Connecting to Prior Knowledge

Have students name and describe problem-solving strategies they have used. If necessary, remind students of the following strategies: Make a Table, Logical Reasoning, Solve a Simpler Problem, Too Much/Too Little Information, Find a Pattern, Make a Model, Work Backward, Draw a Diagram, Guess and Test, Simulate a Problem.

Error Alert! For problems such as the one about the contest, students may try to start their solutions before assessing the information given in the problem. ***Remediation*** Encourage students always to begin a problem by noting the important information it gives them. Urge them not to begin combining numbers until they can clearly explain or represent the situation, or story, in the problem.

VISUAL LEARNERS Encourage students to draw diagrams for all problems so they can visualize what the problem is asking before they attempt to solve it.

ESL **DIVERSITY** Students may have trouble solving word problems because of reading or language difficulties. They may misinterpret the problem or simply not understand what the problem is asking. However, reading or language difficulties may not mean low math abilities. Pair students with high language skills with ESL students who understand the math but need help with the language.

Additional Problem *Sheila types 6 pages in an hour on her computer. Sherman types 6 pages in 20 minutes on his typewriter. If they both start at the same time and type continuously, how long would it take Sherman to be 100 pages ahead of Sheila?* **(Sherman will be 100 pages ahead in 8 h 20 min. Students can solve the problem with the Make a Table, Look for a Pattern, or Guess and Test strategies.)**

"Carry on every enterprise as if all depended on the success of it."
—Richelieu

Organizer

1. **Focus**
   Connecting to Prior Knowledge
2. **Teach**
3. **Closure**
   Try These
   Wrap Up

Skills Reviewed in Context of Lesson
- adding and multiplying whole numbers

Student Resources
Extra Practice
Student Study Guide
Practice, TR Ch. 11, p. 26
Student Study Guide, Spanish Resources, TR

Teacher Resources
Teaching Transparency 92
Lesson Planner, TR Ch. 11, p. 6

Prentice Hall Technology
Computer Item Generator
- 11-5

Other Available Technology
Label Land by Sunburst: Exercises 11–21 *(optional)*

PROBLEM SOLVING

11-5 Use Multiple Strategies

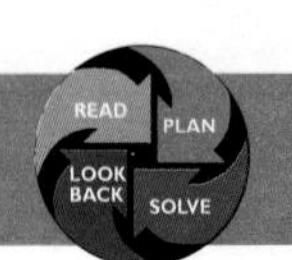

What's Ahead
- Solving problems using multiple strategies

Sometimes you need to use more than one strategy to solve a problem.

> Shamika finished first in the flying ring contest at the football field. The field had scoring zones worth 1, 3, 5, 7, and 9 points. Each zone was shaped like a semicircle. Shamika scored on all five of her throws. Which of these scores could be Shamika's total score: 4 24 37 47?

READ Read and understand the given information. Summarize the problem.

1. How many times did Shamika throw the ring? 5 times
2. What scores are possible on each throw? 1, 3, 5, 7, 9
3. Is 0 a possible score for one of Shamika's throws? no

PLAN Decide on a strategy to solve the problem.

First *draw a diagram* of the field to have a visual idea of the contest. Next *use logical reasoning* to eliminate as impossible some of the scores in the list above. Then *make a table* to keep track of the remaining throws and scores.

SOLVE Try out the strategy.

A diagram of the field shows the scoring sections as semicircles. Each section has a label showing the points received when a flying ring lands in that section.

The only possible scores for a throw are 1, 3, 5, 7, or 9 points. Think logically about the possible scores that Shamika can get altogether for her 5 throws.

TECHNOLOGY OPTION In problems such as the Additional Problem, students can use problem-solving software to practice using multiple strategies. Have students read and summarize the problem, decide on the strategy, and solve the problem.

TRY THESE

Ongoing Assessment Arrange students in groups of four. Have students in each group compare their answers and strategies for Exercises 11 and 12. Encourage students to take notes of others' methods and use the notes to evaluate their own solutions.

Wrap Up

What's the Big Idea? Ask students: *How can you solve problems using multiple strategies?*

Journal Have students name advantages and disadvantages of using multiple strategies.

Connections Have a discussion about how multiple strategies are used. You may want to start with these examples:

- **Field research** (compiling, organizing, and analyzing research data on animal behavior)
- **Carpentry** (assembling different materials, tools, and strategies for a project)
- **Sports** (combining offensive and defensive strategies in football)

Reteaching Activity Review the solution of the example problem with students. Have students draw up a list of steps that led to the solution. Have students compare the steps that belong to different strategies and describe the benefits of the strategies. Encourage students to share answers and observations.

4. What is the highest total score Shamika could get? 45
5. What is the lowest total score she could get? 5
6. Which two scores in the list can you now eliminate? 4 and 47

A table can help you to see if Shamika could get the remaining scores of 24 or 37. The table shows an example in which a player got 3 points on each of 2 throws, 5 points on 1 throw, 7 points on 1 throw, and 9 points on 1 throw.

	Points for Each Throw					Total Score
	1	3	5	7	9	
Number of Throws	0	2	1	1	1	$(0 \times 1) + (2 \times 3) + (1 \times 5) + (1 \times 7) + (1 \times 9) = $ **27**
	■	■	■	■	■	■
	■	■	■	■	■	■

Make a table like the one above to find which total score Shamika can receive. See Solution Key.

7. Experiment with possible ways to get the total score. Which problem solving strategy did you use? Answers may vary. Sample: Guess and Test
8. Which remaining score is impossible? Why? 24; no possible combination of five scores adds to 24.
9. Which is the only possible total score? 37
10. Find three ways Shamika's 5 throws could have landed to get the only possible score. Answers may vary. Sample: 9, 9, 9, 9, 1; 7, 7, 7, 7, 9; 9, 9, 9, 5, 5

Scott Zimmerman holds the world's record for throwing a flying ring. He threw a ring 1,257 ft across Niagara Falls from Canada to the United States.

Source: *Guinness Book of Records*

LOOK BACK

Think about how you solved this problem.

TRY THESE

Use any strategy to solve each problem. Show all your work.

11. The old clock tower loses 10 minutes every 2 days. The town residents have decided that eventually it will get back to the correct time on its own. Suppose that on May 1 the clock is correct. On what date will the clock show the correct time again? Sept. 22
12. A gardener wants to fence in the greatest possible area using 200 ft of fencing. What should be the length and the width of the garden? length = width = 50 ft

Fact of the Day

It is estimated that more Frisbees are sold in the United States each year than baseballs, basketballs, and footballs combined.

—ACADEMIC AMERICAN ENCYCLOPEDIA

Assignment Options

Core: 13, 15, 16, 18, MR all	
Reinforce: 14, 19, 20	**Enrich:** 17, 21

ON YOUR OWN

Exercises 13–21: Have students keep track of the strategies they use for each problem. Emphasize that being able to explain their strategies, and the steps they took to arrive at the solution (even those steps that didn't work) is the focus here, and not merely a correct solution. The answer probably can't be used again; the process will be useful forever.

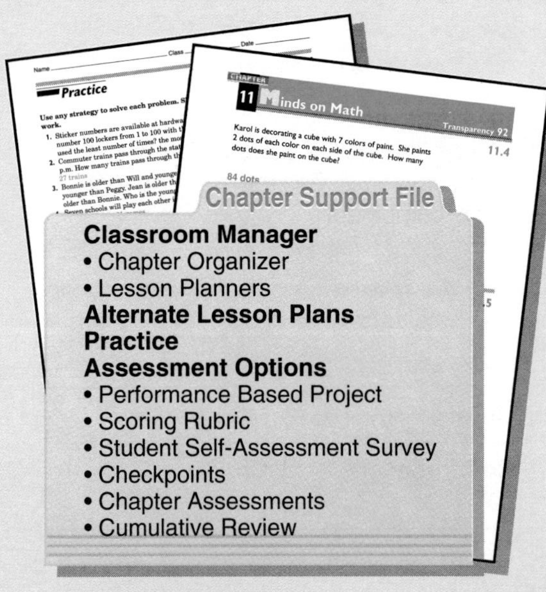

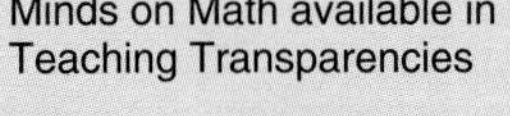

Minds on Math available in Teaching Transparencies

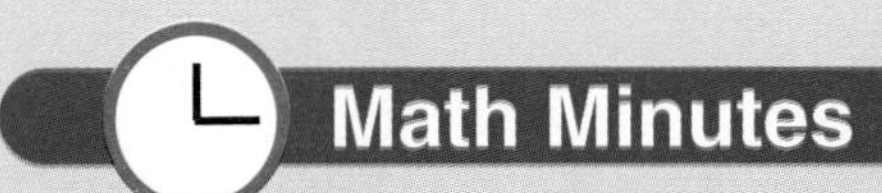

One out of every 15 students in Hill Country Middle School chooses to study Japanese. If the school has 900 students, how many students are taking Japanese? **60**

Materials for 11-6

- geoboard
- rubber bands

ON YOUR OWN

Use any strategy to solve each problem. Show all your work.

Thor Heyerdahl and five companions sailed a wooden raft named "Kon-Tiki" from South America to the Polynesian islands. The trip covered over 4,000 miles and lasted $3\frac{1}{2}$ months.

13. Suppose you launched a raft on the Ohio River at Three Rivers Stadium in Pittsburgh, PA. Your raft drifted at a steady 3 mi/h for 9 hours less than exactly 2 weeks. When your raft landed in Cairo, IL, you had traveled the entire length of the Ohio River. How long is the Ohio River? 981 mi

14. There are 48 students in the band. Of these students, 10 are left-handed and 19 have pierced ears. There are 27 students who are *not* left-handed and do *not* have pierced ears. How many students are left-handed and have pierced ears? 8 students

15. A couple who won the lottery gave their children half of the money. They gave their grandchildren half of the remaining money and kept $3.8 million for themselves. How much did the couple win? $15.2 million

16. Consumer Issues Suppose a customer will accept no more than 6 one-dollar bills in change. In how many different ways can you give the customer change from a $100 bill for a $79 purchase? 6 ways

17. Find the sum of all the odd whole numbers from 1 to 99. 2500

18. A young man jogs in the park every other day. His sister jogs every third day. They both jogged on July 1. How many more days in July can they jog together if they keep to this schedule? 5 more days

19. Suppose the average blink takes $\frac{1}{5}$ of a second and a person blinks 25 times per minute. You traveled at an average speed of 50 mi/h for 12 hours. How many miles would you have traveled with your eyes closed? 50 mi

20. A student spent $\frac{1}{2}$ of her money for a movie and then $3 on a snack for the movie. After the movie, she spent $\frac{1}{2}$ of her remaining money for a bus home. She then had $2. How much money did she have before the movie? $14

21. You have a stick 4 cm long and a stick 8 cm long. What are the possible whole-number lengths (in cm) of a third stick you could use with these sticks to form a triangle? 5, 6, 7, 8, 9, 10, 11

Mixed REVIEW

Use tiles to find each difference.

1. $5 - (-2)$ 7
2. $-3 - (-5)$ 2

Write each as a percent.

3. 18 boards out of 100 boards are warped 18%
4. 86 seats out of 100 seats are occupied 86%
5. Two numbers have a sum of 34 and a product of 273. What are the two numbers? 13 and 21

11-6

Connecting to Prior Knowledge

Ask students how many have taken motoring, biking, or hiking trips where they have had to rely on map readings to find or to stay on a particular route. Have volunteers locate various cities or sites on a map. **(Look up grid numbers or coordinates.)** Have students describe the process and give reasons why a grid system works so well.

WORK TOGETHER

Provide each pair of students with geoboards and rubber bands. Have students compare results.

AUDITORY LEARNERS The Work Together problem using a geoboard asks partners to describe to each other the shapes they made. From these descriptions, they have to take turns guessing what the shape is.

THINK AND DISCUSS

ESL **VISUAL LEARNERS** Have students label the different parts on a blank plane as you explain all the characteristics of the plane to them, such as *x*-axis and *y*-axis and quadrants.

Error Alert! For problems such as Examples 1 and 2 and Questions 4–6, students may be overwhelmed by the terminology and organization of a coordinate plane. ***Remediation*** Review each item separately. Compare the *origin* to a landmark for the plane and emphasize its central location. Point out that an ordered pair is alphabetical: the *x*-axis coordinate comes before the *y*-axis coordinate.

Example 1

Point out to students that the *x*-axis is the number line familiar to them by now, with negative to the left and positive to the right.

What's Ahead

- Using a coordinate plane to graph points
- Naming the coordinates of points on a coordinate plane

WHAT YOU'LL NEED

✓ Geoboard

✓ Rubber bands

11-6 Graphing on the Coordinate Plane

WORK TOGETHER

Work with a partner. Agree on a system for locating points on a geoboard.

- Create a shape on a geoboard with a rubber band. An example is at the left. Don't let your partner see your shape!
- Have your partner ask questions about the lines in your shape. Some topics might be the starting point, direction, distance, changes in direction, position, etc. Answer the questions using your location system.
- Your partner should use your answers to guess your shape and make a copy of it on his or her geoboard. Compare your partner's guess to your original shape.
- Switch roles and repeat the activity.

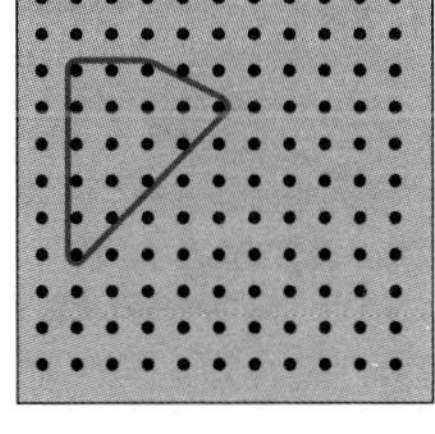

THINK AND DISCUSS

In mathematics you identify points by using a *coordinate plane.* The **coordinate plane** is formed by the intersection of two number lines. The horizontal number line is the **x-axis.** The vertical number line is the **y-axis.** The point where the 2 axes intersect is the **origin.**

You can graph points on a coordinate plane. Each point has 2 *coordinates,* which form an **ordered pair.** The *first coordinate* tells how far to move along the *x*-axis. The *second coordinate* tells how far to move along the *y*-axis.

1. What are the coordinates of the origin? **(0, 0)**
2. Do you move *left* or *right* from the origin to graph a point with a negative first coordinate? Explain. **left, because this is the negative direction on the *x*-axis.**
3. Do you move *up* or *down* from the origin to graph a point with a positive second coordinate? Explain. **up, because this is the positive direction on the *y*-axis.**

"They are never alone that are accompanied with noble thoughts."
—Sir Philip Sidney

Organizer

1. **Focus**
   Connecting to Prior Knowledge
2. **Teach**
   Work Together
   Think and Discuss
3. **Closure**
   Try These
   Wrap Up

Vocabulary/Symbols

coordinate plane
x-axis
y-axis
origin
coordinates
first coordinate
ordered pair
second coordinate
quadrants

Skills Reviewed in Context of Lesson

- using the number line

Materials and Manipulatives

- geoboard (1 per pair of students)
- rubber bands (per geoboard)

On Your Own Exercises 25–26: graph paper; Exercise 29: map of the U.S. or the world; Exercise 36: computer and spreadsheet software *(optional)*

continues next page

ESL Explain that the *y*-axis is the familiar number line placed vertically with positive up and negative down.

Additional Example
Graph point Q with coordinates (–2, –1). **(Move from the origin two units to the left. Move 1 unit down from the *x*-axis. Plot the point and label it Q.)**

Example 2
Encourage students to use a straightedge, or the edge of a sheet of paper, to line up the coordinates.

Additional Example
Find the coordinates of point R.

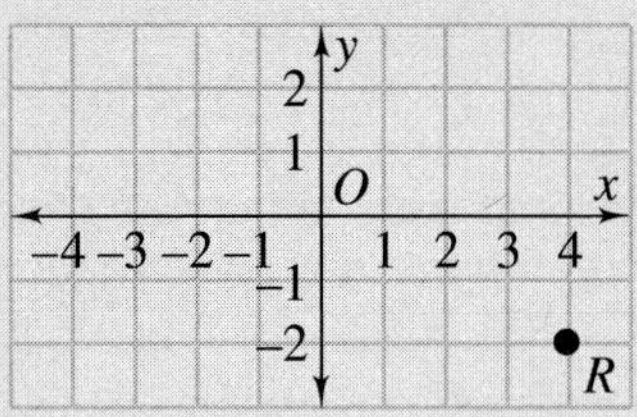

The coordinates of point *R* are (4, –2).

TRY THESE

TECHNOLOGY OPTION For Questions 7–16, students can use graphing software to practice graphing on a coordinate plane.

Ongoing Assessment
Have students meet in groups of four to compare their answers to Exercises 7–19. Make sure students check each other's answers and compare reasons for their answers to Exercises 18 and 19.

CONNECTION TO GEOMETRY Exercise 20 has students graph a square.

Wrap Up

What's the Big Idea?
Ask students: *How can you use a coordinate plane to graph points? How can you name the coordinates of points on a coordinate plane?*

Organizer, continued

Student Resources
Extra Practice
Student Study Guide
Practice, TR Ch. 11, p. 27
Student Study Guide, Spanish Resources, TR

Teacher Resources

Teaching Transparencies 3, 92
Overhead Manipulatives: geoboard
Lesson Planner, TR Ch. 11, p. 7

Prentice Hall Technology

Multimedia Math
- Math Investigations, Mission: Mars
- Hot Page 11-6

Computer Item Generator
- 11-6

Other Available Technology
Geometric Connections by Sunburst: Questions 7–16 *(optional)*

Fact of the Day

Miguel de Cervantes Saavedra (1547–1610), was a Spanish novelist, poet, and dramatist and the author of the novel *Don Quixote,* a masterpiece of world literature.

—ACADEMIC AMERICAN ENCYCLOPEDIA

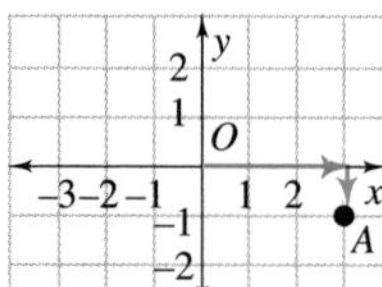

Example 1 Graph point *A* with coordinates $(3, -1)$.
- Move 3 units to the right from the origin.
- Move 1 unit down from the *x*-axis.
- Plot a point and label it *A*.

You can use a similar method to name the coordinates of points that are already graphed.

Example 2 Find the coordinates of point *B*.

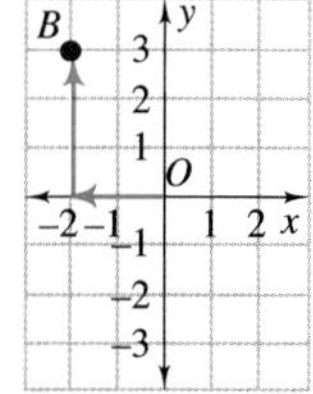

- Start at the origin.
- Move 2 units to the left. The first coordinate is -2.
- Then move 3 units up from the *x*-axis. The second coordinate is 3.

The coordinates of point *B* are $(-2, 3)$.

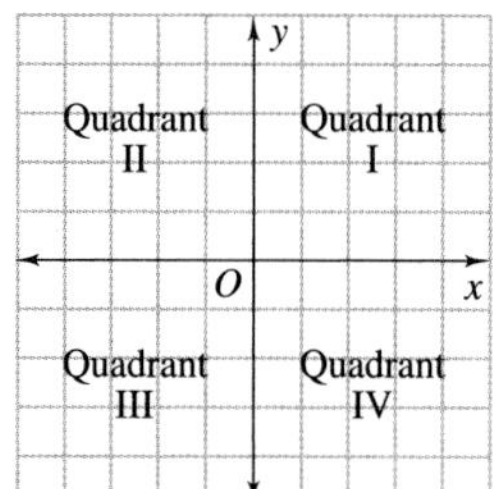

The axes separate the coordinate plane into four *quadrants.*

4. In which quadrant is the point $M(-2, 5)$ located? **II**
5. In which quadrants are the first coordinates of the points positive numbers? **I and IV**
6. In which quadrants are the second coordinates of the points negative numbers? **III and IV**

TRY THESE

Name the point with the given coordinates.

7. $(1, 2)$ **A** **8.** $(-2, -6)$ **G** **9.** $(3, -3)$ **J** **10.** $(0, -5)$ **H** **11.** $(3, 0)$ **L**

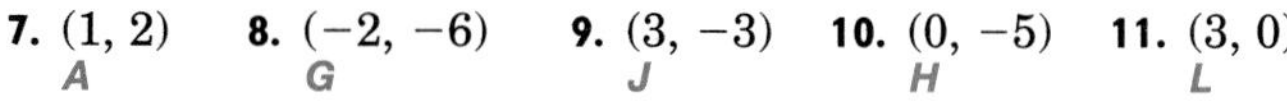

Write the coordinates of each point.

12. *C* **(–6, 4)** **13.** *D* **(–5, 0)** **14.** *K* **(6, –4)** **15.** *Q* **(0, 3)** **16.** *N* **(4, 6)**

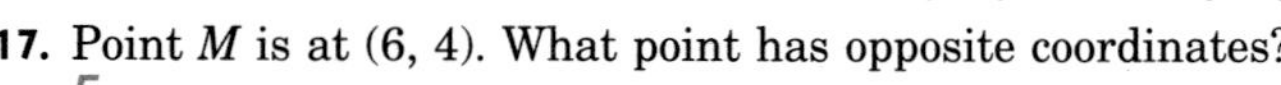

17. Point *M* is at $(6, 4)$. What point has opposite coordinates? **F**

18. What are the signs of the first and second coordinates of all the points in the second quadrant? **First coordinates are negative; second coordinates are positive.**

Reteaching Activity Have students examine the grids on a local map. Encourage students to compare the grids used on a map with a grid that uses coordinates. **(Map refers to a region, the other to an intersection.)** Ask students which is more precise. **(coordinates)** Encourage students to imagine what a coordinate plane map would look like.

Connections Have a discussion about how graphing on the coordinate plane is used. You may want to start with the following examples:

- **Navigation** (charts of coastlines, reefs, and shallows for ships)
- **Astronomy** (making maps of the stars)
- **Utilities** (electrical grids that divide up a city)

Journal Ask students to write a short story about someone who finds something by following directions given as coordinates.

ON YOUR OWN

Students will need graph paper for Exercises 25, 26, and 31.

CRITICAL THINKING For Exercise 26c, encourage students to write a definition of the figure.

CONNECTION TO GEOGRAPHY In Exercises 27–29 and 32–35, students compare coordinate planes to maps.

RESEARCH Have students check the library to find an atlas for Exercises 28 and 29.

CONNECTION TO ART Exercises 30 and 31 have students describe and create patterns by using coordinate planes.

WRITING For Exercise 35, have students organize their comparisons in a table.

COMPUTER You can also print a spreadsheet and make copies of it or have students draw their own.

Exercise 36b: Some students will choose to copy a map; others will want to create a place of their own.

19. In which quadrant are all coordinates positive? I

20. Three corners of a rectangle have coordinates (4, 2), (4, 7), and (−3, 2). Find the coordinates of the fourth corner. (−3, 7)

ON YOUR OWN

Identify the quadrant in which each point lies.

21. (3, 2) I **22.** (−17, 2) II **23.** (−6, −40) III **24.** (9, −11) IV

25. a. Graph the points $M(-5, -3)$, $N(2, -4)$, and $P(0, 1)$ on a coordinate plane. See Solution Key.

b. Connect the points in order. What shape do you see? a triangle

26. a. Graph the points $A(4, 3)$, $B(-1, 3)$, $C(-4, 0)$, and $D(1, 0)$. See Solution Key.

b. Connect the points in order. What shape do you see? a quadrilateral

c. **Critical Thinking** What is the most specific name you can use to describe figure $ABCD$? Explain. parallelogram; opposite sides and angles are equal, no right angles.

Where on Earth Are You?

How can you tell someone else where you are on Earth?

Scientists have put a coordinate system on Earth so that locations can be described easily. The equator is the "horizontal axis." The prime meridian is the "vertical axis" and runs from the North Pole to the South Pole through Greenwich, England.

Degrees are used to indicate distances from these axes. Degrees north or south of the equator are *degrees of latitude.* Degrees east or west of the prime meridian are *degrees of longitude.* You identify a place by the degrees. For example, New York City is at 41°N 74°W. Los Angeles is at 34°N 118°W.

27. **Data File 11 (pp. 446–447)** Estimate the location of each city using latitude and longitude. Estimates may vary.

a. Rivadavia, Argentina about 35°S 65°W **b.** Cloncurry, Australia about 20°S 140°E

28. **Research** Find a map of your state in an atlas or encyclopedia. Locate your town to the nearest degree of latitude and longitude. Answers may vary.

Mixed REVIEW

1. Payat bought 3 shirts for $14 each and a pair of pants for $23. How much of his clothing budget does Payat have left? See below.

2. The temperature is 70°F at 10:00 A.M. It increases 2°F every hour. What will the temperature be at 4:00 P.M.? 82°F

3. Write 45% as a decimal and as a fraction in simplest form. 0.45; $\frac{9}{20}$

4. Write $\frac{3}{8}$ as a decimal and as a percent. 0.375; 37.5%

5. A basketball player makes 80% of his foul shots. What is the probability that he makes two foul shots in a row? $\frac{16}{25}$

1. not enough information to solve

PH Multimedia Math Hot Page™ 11-6

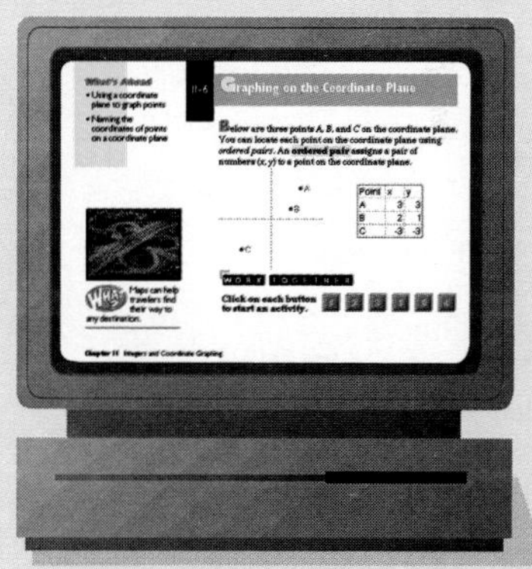

Assignment Options

Core: 21–24, 26, 27, 32–35, MR all	
Reinforce: 25, 29	**Enrich:** 28, 30, 31, 36

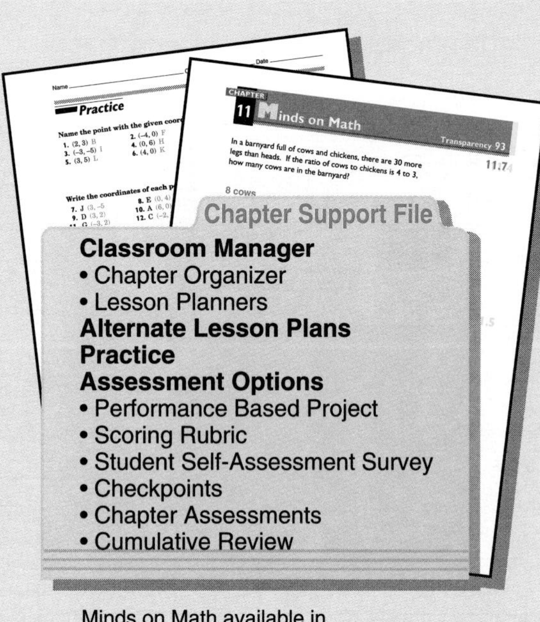

Minds on Math available in Teaching Transparencies

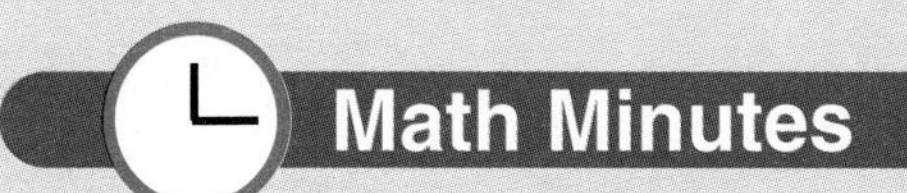

Solve the equation: $-4 + y = 2$.
$y = 6$

Materials for 11-7

- computer *(optional)*
- coordinate geometry software *(optional)*

29. a. **Research** Use a map to find the longitude and latitude of your birthplace to the nearest degree. Answers may vary.
    b. Compare these to your current town's location, which you found in Exercise 28. Answers may vary.

Crafts Some quilt makers use coordinate grids to plan their patterns before they stitch the quilt.

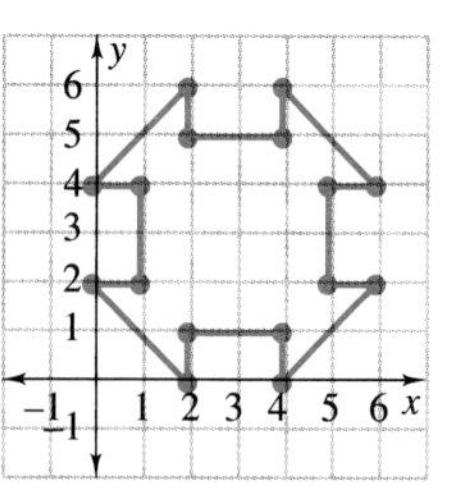

30. The Monkey Wrench pattern is from an African-American story quilt. Find the coordinates of the pattern points. See left.
31. Create your own quilt pattern. Draw the pattern on a grid and name the coordinates of the points. Answers may vary.

30. (2, 0), (2, 1), (4, 1), (4, 0), (6, 2), (5, 2), (5, 4), (6, 4), (4, 6), (4, 5), (2, 5), (2, 6), (0, 4), (1, 4), (1, 2), (0, 2).

Geography Mapmakers use a coordinate system so that people can locate places on a map. Coordinates on a map refer to a section of the map, not a point on the map.

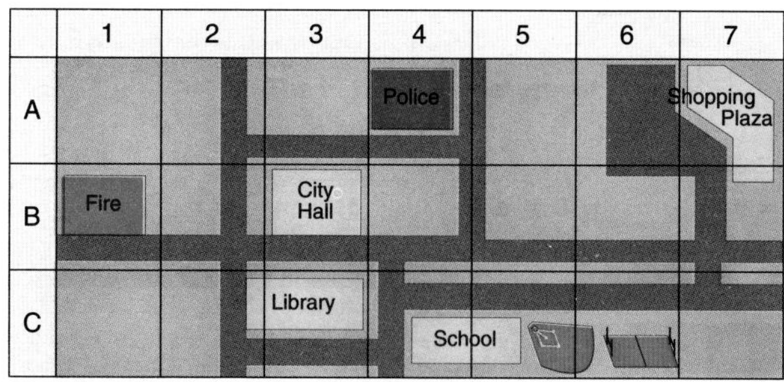

32. What do the letters A–C identify? the numbers 1–7? rows; columns
33. What is located in section B3? City Hall
34. What are the coordinates of the school and its fields? C4, C5, C6
35. **Writing** How are a map and the coordinate plane alike? How are they different? Sample: both have two coordinates; the map identifies regions, the coordinate plane identifies points
36. a. **Computer** Print out a blank spreadsheet. How are the rows, columns, and cells of a spreadsheet like a map?
    b. **Activity** Choose any town or create a place of your own. Draw a map of this place on the spreadsheet. Include names of places or items on the map. Answers may vary.
    c. Make a table listing the places or items on the map and their map coordinates. Answers may vary.

36a. Rows and columns of maps and spreadsheets identify spaces called regions or cells.

> *Journey over all the universe in a map, without the expense and fatigue of traveling.*
> —Miguel de Cervantes (1547–1616)

CHAPTER 11 PROBLEM SOLVING PRACTICE

This page provides a variety of problems that can be used to reinforce and enhance the students' problem solving skills. Encourage students to read each problem carefully. Then have them refer to the list of problem solving strategies to help them decide how to solve the problems.

Point out, however, that not all questions require a strategy for solving, nor are all the strategies in the list used on this page.

Exercise 1: Students may want to use graph paper.

Exercise 4: Have tiles available if students choose to make a model.

Problem Solving Practice

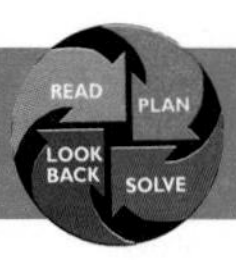

PROBLEM SOLVING STRATEGIES

Make a Table
Use Logical Reasoning
Solve a Simpler Problem
Too Much or Too Little Information
Look for a Pattern
Make a Model
Work Backward
Draw a Diagram
Guess and Test
Simulate a Problem
Use Multiple Strategies

Solve. The list at the left shows some possible strategies you can use.

1. Larry and Shamir want to build identical houses. They bought a rectangular piece of land and divided it into two identical squares. Each square piece of land has an area of 2500 m^2. What is the perimeter of the original rectangle? 300 m

2. A positive number is a *Perfect Square* whenever it is the square of a whole number. The first three perfect squares are 1, 4, and 9. What is the 100th perfect square? 10,000

3. After 5 tests, Pedro's average was 80%. Pedro thought he had a "B" wrapped up for his report card. He took the final exam and his final average dropped to 76% which is a "C." What must Pedro have scored on the final exam? 56%

4. Yoko and four friends divided a cake evenly among themselves. Yoko then shared her piece evenly with her four sisters. Yoko's youngest sister, Hoshi, gave half of her piece to her kitty, Leo. What percentage of the original cake did Leo get? 2%

5. Travel Walter started his U.S. tour with $250 to spend. Walter spent 5 times as much in Philadelphia as in New York. He spent $9.59 more in Washington, D.C. as in Philadelphia. In Boston, Walter spent $74.97. He spent 3¢ less in Boston than he did in Philadelphia. How much money did he have left? $.44

6. Weather On an unusual winter trip Mina Blackhawk left Helena, Montana, and watched the thermometer on the side of her plane rise 100°F as she stopped in Houston, Texas. She went on to Marshall, Minnesota, where she saw a −71°F drop in temperature. When she reached Portland, Maine, it was 12°F, a full 14°F warmer than Marshall. What was the temperature in Helena that morning? −31°F

11-7

Connecting to Prior Knowledge

Review plotting points on a coordinate plane, especially points in quadrants II, III, and IV. Tell the students they will be exploring how coordinates change when figures are moved around from one location to another.

THINK AND DISCUSS

Students may have seen shows in which people, vehicles, or planes move in formation, such as precision flying stunts performed by the Blue Angels. Ask students to imagine the practice that performers must do to prepare for the shows. Also discuss the preparation needed for designing such shows.

With translations and reflections, students will work with the transformations in context (ships moving in formation) before they are introduced to the formal vocabulary of transformations.

KINESTHETIC LEARNERS For Question 5, move the classroom chairs and desks to the perimeter of the room. Use masking tape (or the floor tiles) to designate a grid on the floor, labeling the x-axis and the y-axis. Have students stand on coordinates that represent the vertices of a rectangle. Ask the students to *slide* four points to the left. Have the students call out the new coordinates.

ESL **TACTILE LEARNERS** Have the students use blocks to model the movement of a figure on the coordinate plane such as a translation or reflection. Have the students place the block on a coordinate plane at certain coordinates and then have them move the figure to new coordinates.

DIVERSITY If you have students who are in a marching band, have them explain how they keep formations together as they march across a field. Perhaps show a videotape of a marching band translating a formation to different parts of the field. These examples of using translation of formations outside of the classroom might help students understand the concept.

"A moment's thinking is an hour in words."

—Thomas Hood

Answers to Problems Unique to Spanish Edition

5. Porque la figura se traslada de un lugar para otro sin hacer ningún otro cambio.

Organizer

1. **Focus**
   Connecting to Prior Knowledge
2. **Teach**
   Think and Discuss
   Work Together
3. **Closure**
   Wrap Up

Vocabulary/Symbols
translation
image
slide
reflection

Skills Reviewed in Context of Lesson
- using the coordinate plane

Materials and Manipulatives
- computer (1 per group; *optional*)
- coordinate geometry software (per computer; *optional*)

On Your Own Exercises 18, 21–22: computer and software *(optional)*

Student Resources
Extra Practice
Student Study Guide
Practice, TR Ch. 11, p. 28
Student Study Guide, Spanish Resources, TR
Checkpoint, TR Ch. 11, p. 34
Alternate Lesson, TR Ch. 11, pp. 18–21

continues next page

TECHNOLOGY

11-7 Translations and Reflections

What's Ahead
- Exploring translations and reflections on a coordinate plane using computers

WHAT YOU'LL NEED
✓ Computer
✓ Software

THINK AND DISCUSS

Band members march in step during half-time. Jets fly overhead in precise patterns. Tall ships sail in unison. On ground, in air, or on water, each formation moves as one, as though joined by invisible bonds.

The Valley Middle School marching band made a V on the football field at half-time of a game. They marched down the field and played the school song while keeping the V formation.

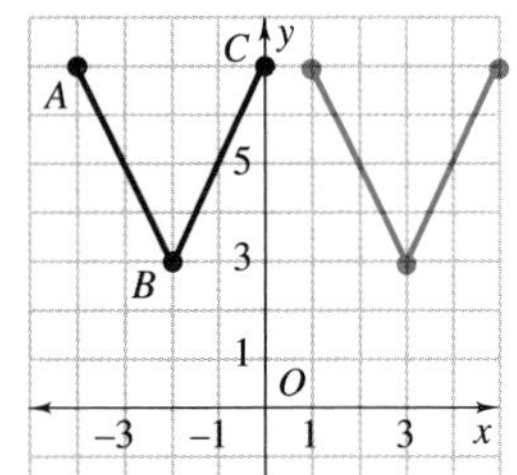

1. What are the coordinates of the vertices of the original V? (−4, 7), (−2, 3), (0, 7)
2. The V moved to the right. How many units did the V move? 5
3. What are the coordinates of the vertices of the new V? (1, 7), (3, 3), (5, 7)
4. Compare the size and shape of the new V to the original V. same size and shape

You can say that the V was *translated* to the right. A **translation** is moving a figure so that every point moves in the same direction and the same distance. Each new point is called the **image** of the original point.

5. **Discussion** Why is a translation also called a *slide*? You slide a figure when you translate it.
6. a. Copy and complete the table for the translation above.

	original x	new x	change in x	original y	new y	change in y
A	−4	1	+5	7	7	0
B	■ −2	■ 3	■ +5	■ 3	■ 3	■ 0
C	■ 0	■ 5	■ +5	■ 7	■ 7	■ 0

The largest marching band played at Dodger Stadium and consisted of 4,524 students from 52 schools in the Los Angeles area.

Source: *Guinness Book of Records*

Question 6a: Go over the data in the first row to make sure students understand the chart.

Error Alert! Students may still be confused when graphing points on the coordinate plane. Students may reverse the *x*- and *y*-coordinates. ***Remediation*** For students who are still having difficulty, it may help to discuss the *x*-coordinates separately from the *y*-coordinates.

Question 8c: Have students color the original figure one color and the reflected figure another color. Reflecting across an axis can sometimes confuse the students. Although the points are equidistant from the axis, the figure looks "different" because it has been flipped.

Question 8d: Ask students what the patterns they described in 8c and 6b have in common. For example, the amount of change in 8c is different from that in 6b, but in each case, all the coordinates of all the points change in the same way.

Question 9: Have the students use plastic mirrorlike rectangles to reflect about the *x*-axis. Students will be able to see the reflected figure and can find the line of symmetry more easily.

WORK TOGETHER

COMPUTER For Question 10a, show students how to enter and connect points and how to translate a figure. Students should take notes and make sketches to help them find patterns and draw conclusions. Use the software to find the coordinates of the image points. ***Alternate Approach*** If a computer is not available, have students use graph paper. You may wish to suggest that students use a different color when drawing the reflection.

WRITING For 10c students should be able to see the patterns in the *x*- and *y*-coordinates. **(The *x*-coordinates remain the same.)** Have them verbalize patterns they see before they write.

b. What patterns do you notice for the changes in x and the changes in y? All original x-values have 5 added to them; all y-values do not change.

7. Suppose part of the band also made an M with coordinates $(-1, -2)$, $(-1, 2)$, $(1, 0)$, $(3, 2)$, and $(3, -2)$. The M formation moved at the same time as the original V.

a. What would the M's coordinates be after the translation? Explain. (4, −2), (4, 2), (6, 0), (8, 2), (8, −2)

b. Draw a diagram to show the translation. See Solution Key.

Another way of moving a figure is to *reflect* it. A **reflection** is flipping a figure across a line. The new figure is a mirror image of the original.

8. At an air show, five fighter airplanes travel parallel to the grandstand. Their formation *DEFGH* changes as shown.

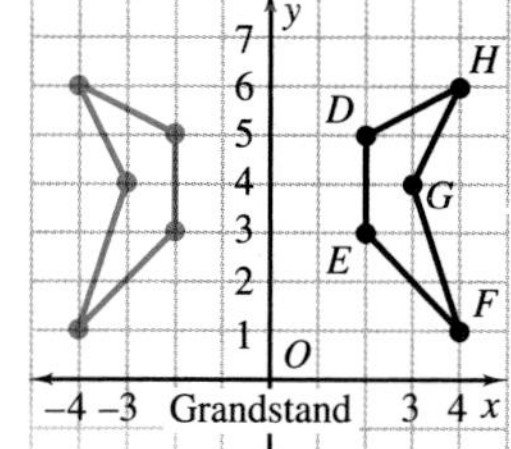

a. During the change, do all four airplanes move the same distance? Explain. No; D and E move the least, H and F the most.

b. What happens to the shape of the formation? It is the same.

c. Copy the diagram and fold along the center line. What do you notice about the original points and the image points? See Solution Key for diagram; the points and their image points are on top of each other.

d. **Discussion** Describe how the airplanes were reflected across the y-axis. The new figure is the mirror image of the original figure. Each point is the same distance from the y-axis as its image point.

9. Copy the original formation of the airplanes. Draw the formation after a reflection across the x-axis. See Solution Key.

WORK TOGETHER

Answers will vary.

10. a. **Computer** Draw a figure with three or more vertices to represent a formation of ships. Draw the reflection of the figure across the x-axis.

b. Make a table like the one in Question 6.

c. **Writing** Make a conjecture about how the coordinates of the points on a figure change when the figure is reflected across the x-axis.

d. **Critical Thinking** How would you test your conjecture?

e. Repeat parts (a)–(c) for a reflection across the y-axis.

WHAT? The Navy's demonstration flying team, The Blue Angels, fly in the F/A-18 Hornet, which has a top speed of Mach 2. The Air Force's Thunderbirds fly in the F-16 Fighting Falcon, which has a top speed of Mach 2.3.

Source: *The Kids' World Almanac of Transportation*

Organizer, continued

Teacher Resources

Teaching Transparencies 3, 93
Lesson Planner, TR Ch. 11, p. 8

Prentice Hall Technology

Computer Item Generator

- 11-7

Other Available Technology

Geometric Connections: Transformations by Sunburst *(optional)*

Fact of the Day

Jet propulsion is a type of propulsion in which thrust is produced by generating a high-velocity jet of hot gases inside an engine and expelling it through a nozzle in the rear. The action of the escaping gas causes an opposing reaction that propels the jet forward. The rocket engine is based on the same principle, except that it carries its own supply of oxygen so the fuel can burn when the rocket is outside the earth's atmosphere.

—*Academic American Encyclopedia*

CRITICAL THINKING For 10d have the students predict what will happen if a figure is reflected across the *x*-axis, then across the *y*-axis, then across the *x*-axis again, and finally across the *y*-axis again. Check the predictions by drawing a figure and carrying out the 4 transformations in that order. **(The figure will return to its original position.)**

Journal

Have the students describe how to use translations and reflections to create a design.

Ongoing Assessment

The coordinates of the vertices of △ABC are A(3, 1), B(3, −2), C(−1, −2). Which of the coordinates below represents a translation of the triangle, which represents a reflection, and which represents neither?

A(3, 2)	*B*(3, 5)	*C*(−1, 5)	**(reflection)**
A(−3, −1)	*B*(−3, −2)	*C*(−1, 2)	**(neither)**
A(6, −1)	*B*(6, −4)	*C*(2, −4)	**(translation)**

Wrap Up

What's the Big Idea?

Ask students: *How are translations and reflections similar? How are they different?*

Connections

Have a discussion about the purpose of graphing coordinates. You may wish to start with these examples:

- **Navigation** (graphing points of destination)
- **Manufacturing** (drilling holes on circuit boards)
- **Gardening** (planting at certain intervals)

Reteaching Activity

Have students use pattern blocks to act out translations and reflections. Students can work with a partner. One student models a translation or a reflection and challenges his or her partner to describe it mathematically.

Assignment Options

Core: 11–17, 19, 20, MR all, CH all	
Reinforce: 18, 21	**Enrich:** 22

ON YOUR OWN

Use the graph at the left.

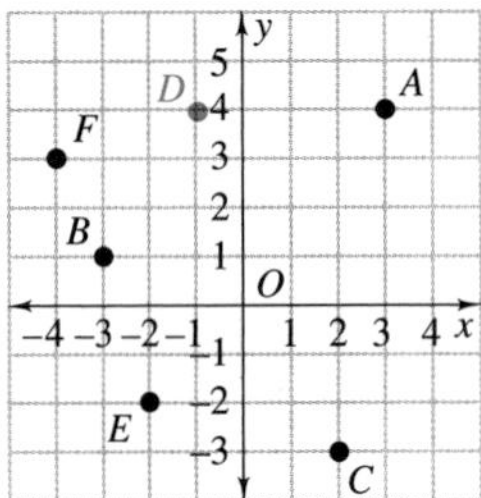

11. Translate point *A* to the left 5 units. What are its new coordinates? (−2, 4)

12. Translate point *B* down 3 units and to the right 2 units. What are its new coordinates? (−1, −2)

13. Point *C* is translated to point *D*. How far and in which directions has point *C* moved? 3 units to the left and 7 units up

14. Reflect point *E* across the *x*-axis. What are its new coordinates? (−2, 2)

15. Reflect point *F* across the *x*-axis and across the *y*-axis. What are its new coordinates? (4, −3)

Tell whether the graph shows a translation or a reflection. Describe the movement of the points.

16. 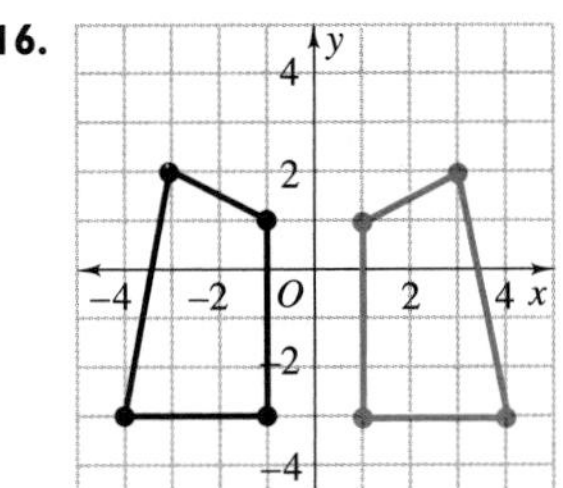

reflection across y-axis

17. 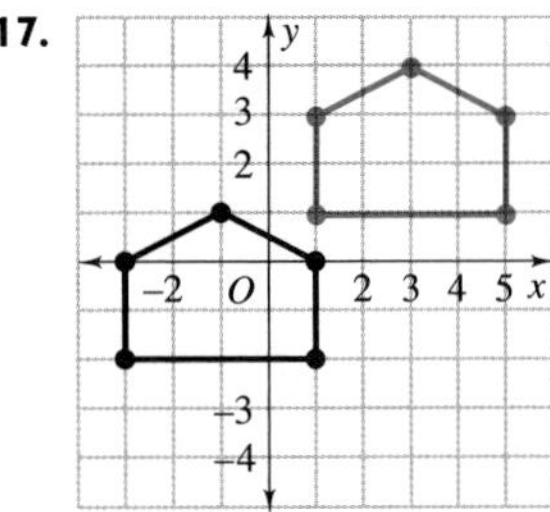

translation; 4 units right, 3 units

18. Four speed boats made an arrow formation. They moved in the same direction and the same distance as boat F.

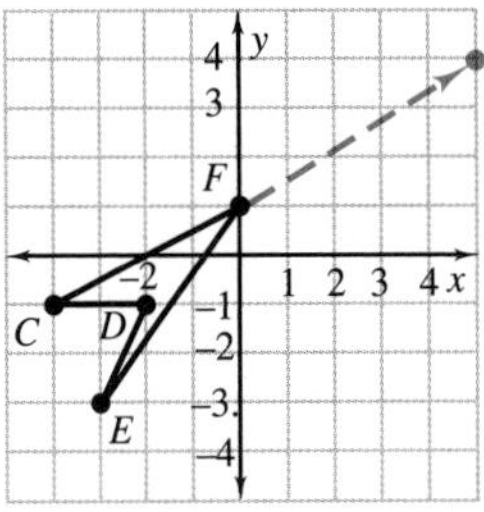

a. How can you find the new positions of *C*, *D*, and *E*? 5 right, 3 up

b. **Computer** Graph the original and the new positions of each boat. Connect each set of points. See Solution Key.

c. List the coordinates of the original positions of the boats and of the new positions. original: C(−4, −1), D(−2, −1), E(−3, −3), F(0, 1); new: (1, 2), (3, 2), (2, 0), (5, 4)

19. **Writing** Describe how translations and reflections are alike and how they are different. Include examples. See above.

19. Sample answer: Both are movements of figures on the coordinate plane. Both keep the same size and shape of the original figure. A translation slides the figure; a reflection flips the figure.

20. **Investigation (p. 448)** Draw a vertical line through year 0 on your time line. Explain how you could use your time line to show school enrollment through the years. Put a scale on the vertical axis indicating enrollment. Plot points showing enrollment using the time line as the horizontal axis.

ON YOUR OWN

COMPUTER For Exercise 18b, students can use software to graph the points. ***Alternate Approach*** If a computer is not available, students can use graph paper. The approach to this problem is different from other translations because the traveled distance becomes a diagonal, not a vertical or horizontal line. Have the students mark off vertical and horizontal coordinates (like the legs of a right triangle) in order to move to the translated coordinate.

WRITING For Exercise 19, students can summarize the objectives. If they correctly describe the changes to the coordinates on translations and reflections, they will have a thorough understanding of transformations.

CHAPTER INVESTIGATION For Exercise 20, have students discuss their various ideas.

COMPUTER For Exercise 21, students can use graphing software to graph the points and connect the points to form a geometric figure.

COMPUTER For Exercise 22, have students print the plans for their shows and display the translations and reflections on a poster board. ***Alternate Approach*** Students can graph translations and reflections on graph paper. To add interest to the exercise, enlarge the graph paper so that larger replicas of cars, planes, and people can be displayed.

CHECKPOINT

Exercises 11–13: Remind students using calculators to use the [+/-] rather than the [-] key to change the sign of a number.

21. a. Computer Graph the points (2, −6), (8, −6), and (4, −1). See Solution Key.
    b. Connect the points. What geometric figure have you drawn? triangle
    c. Computer Reflect the figure across the x-axis. What are the new coordinates? (2, 6), (8, 6), (4, 1)
    d. What is the area of the original figure? the new figure?
    e. Make a conjecture about what happens to the area of a figure after a reflection. nothing, area is the same.
    d. 15 sq. units; 15 sq. units
22. Computer Create your own show. Choose any kind of vehicles or performers for your formation. Your show must include at least 1 translation and 1 reflection.
    a. Graph the original position and shape of the formation. Label the coordinates of each object in the formation.
    b. Draw the formation after each translation or reflection. Describe how the formation moves after each translation or reflection.
    c. Write the coordinates of each point after each change.
    22. Answers will vary.

Mixed REVIEW

1. In which quadrant would you find the point (7, −8)? IV
2. In which quadrant are both coordinates of a point positive? I

Estimate a 5% sales tax for each item.

3. game: $8.99 $.45
4. bicycle: $135.95 $6.80
5. Kendra has 20 dimes and nickels altogether. The total value of the coins is $1.35. How many dimes does Kendra have? 7

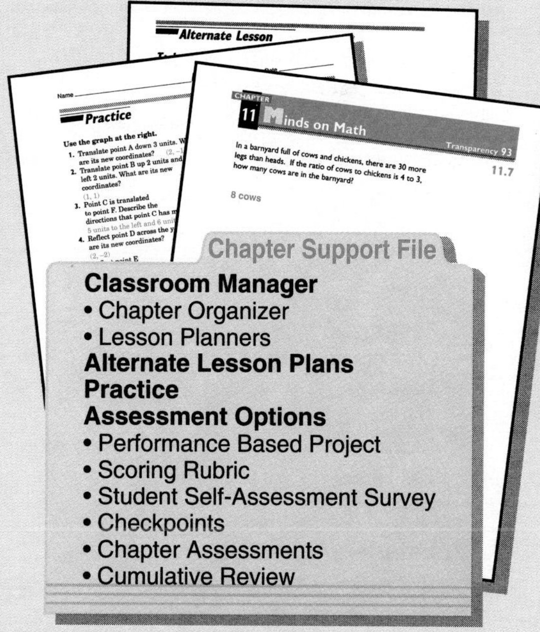

Minds on Math available in Teaching Transparencies

CHECKPOINT

1. Rachel numbered 235 tickets by hand starting with the number 1. How many digits did she write? 597

Name the point with the given coordinates.

2. (−1, −3) E 3. (0, 2) G 4. (2, −2) N 5. (−4, 1) A

Write the coordinates of each point.

6. J (4, 2) 7. M (4, −1) 8. C (−3, −1) 9. F (−1, 0)

10. **Choose A, B, C, or D.** The vertices of $\triangle ABC$ are $A(-4, 2)$, $B(-3, 4)$, and $C(-2, 2)$. This triangle is translated. The new coordinates for point A are (2, 2) and for point B are (3, 4). What are the new coordinates for point C? B

    A. (2, 8) **B.** (4, 2) **C.** (−2, 8) **D.** (−8, 2)

Use a calculator to find each sum or difference.

11. −215 + 343 128
12. 451 − (−134) 585
13. −1035 − 961 −1,996

Math Minutes

If the diameter of a bicycle wheel is 40 cm, how far will it go in one complete turn? **about 125.7 cm**

Materials for 11-8

- calculator

11-8

Connecting to Prior Knowledge

Ask students how they keep track of their own money received and money spent. Ask how they think businesses keep track of their income and expenses and what kind of records they must keep. Have students compare and evaluate the practicality of their answers.

THINK AND DISCUSS

ESL Students probably understand the concepts of profit and loss but they may not be familiar with the vocabulary. Explain that profit and loss are terms for making money and losing money. You may wish to point out the similarity between *lost* and *loss.* Help students understand that *balance,* as used here, refers to the difference between income and expenditures over a period of time.

TACTILE LEARNERS To demonstrate the concepts of profit and loss, give the students each a certain amount of play money. Then have one half of the class give a portion of the money to the other half. Ask students who made a profit and who suffered a loss from the transaction.

Example 1

Students may be confused about why a negative number is added to the balance instead of a positive number being subtracted. Tell students that either method will work, but that since the expenses are listed as negative integers, the method in the text is clearer and less likely to result in an error.

Error Alert! For problems such as Example 1, students may make a mistake in calculating the profit or loss. ***Remediation*** Encourage students first to determine if there is a profit or loss, which will tell them the sign of the balance. Then have students make an estimate with which to check their answers.

"Children need love, especially when they do not deserve it."

—Harold S. Hulbert

Organizer

1. **Focus**
   Connecting to Prior Knowledge
2. **Teach**
   Think and Discuss
3. **Closure**
   Try These
   Wrap Up

Vocabulary/Symbols
balance
balance sheet

Skills Reviewed in Context of Lesson
- plotting points on a graph

Materials and Manipulatives
- calculator (1 per student)

On Your Own Exercises 25–29: computer and spreadsheet software *(optional)*

Student Resources
Extra Practice
Student Study Guide
Practice, TR Ch. 11, p. 29
Student Study Guide, Spanish Resources, TR

Teacher Resources
Teaching Transparencies 19, 93
Lesson Planner, TR Ch. 11, p. 9

continues next page

MATH AND BUDGETS

11-8 Applying Integers and Graphs

What's Ahead
- Using a balance sheet to determine profit or loss
- Drawing and interpreting graphs involving integers

WHAT YOU'LL NEED
✓ Calculator 

THINK AND DISCUSS

Businesses keep track of not only the money they receive (income), but also any money they spend (expenses). The *balance* is the profit or loss that a company makes. A *balance sheet* is a table that helps keep track of income and expenses. Income is listed as a positive number. Expenses are listed as negative numbers. To find the balance, you add the income and expenses together.

positive balance → profit   negative balance → loss

1. **Discussion** What are some expenses that a business might have? **Answers may vary. Sample: product costs, rent, electricity, heat, parking**
2. Some expenses stay the same every month. Some vary every month. List some expenses of each type. **Sample: same: rent, parking; vary: product costs, heat, electricity**
3. List several different businesses. Describe the type of income each company would expect. **Answers may vary.**

You can use a calculator to find balances. Remember that pressing [+⁄-] will change the sign of a number.

Balance Sheet for Video Mania

Month	Income	Expenses
Jan.	\$11,917	−\$14,803
Feb.	\$12,739	−\$9,482
March	\$11,775	−\$10,954
April	\$13,620	−\$15,149

Example 1 Find the balance for the month of February for Video Mania. Did the company make a profit or a loss during February?

- Add the income and the expenses.

  12,739 [+] 9,482 [+⁄-] [=] 3257

- The balance is positive. So, there is a profit.

Video Mania made a profit of \$3,257 during February.

4. Find the balance for each month. Tell whether Video Mania made a profit or a loss during that month.
   a. January **−\$2,886; loss**
   b. March **\$821; profit**
   c. April **−\$1,529; loss**

Additional Example *Listed below are the income and expenses for the Most Music Store for the months of September through December. Find the balance for each month. Tell whether the store made a profit or loss for each month as well.*

Balance Sheet for The Most Music Store

Month	Income	Expenses
Sept.	$17,964	$18,111
Oct.	$16,048	$17,059
Nov.	$19,377	$16,236
Dec.	$31,404	$19,498

Sept: 17,964 [+] 18,111 [+/-] [=] −147 (loss)

Oct: 16,048 [+] 17,059 [+/-] [=] −1,011 (loss)

Nov: 19,377 [+] 16,236 [+/-] [=] 3,141 (profit)

Dec: 31,404 [+] 19,498 [+/-] [=] 11,906 (profit)

Example 2

Emphasize to students that they must plan their choices of scales and intervals. Encourage students to find each balance on the graph.

TECHNOLOGY OPTION For Example 2, students can use spreadsheet software to set up the balance sheet for Hobby and Toy Town. With the graphing capabilities of spreadsheet software, students can graph the data onto a line graph.

Journal Ask students to describe a business they would like to own, and to tell what kinds of profit or loss they might expect in the first six months.

TRY THESE

CALCULATOR With problems such as Exercises 10–12, students can avoid errors by first determining the sign of the answer and making an estimate before they press any keys.

After businesses calculate their monthly balances, they often make a line graph to look at trends. You can use what you know about coordinate grids to make line graphs showing data of balances, income, and expenses. Use the first and fourth quadrants to graph these types of data.

Example 2 Draw a line graph of the monthly balances for the Hobby & Toy Town store.

- Put the months on the horizontal axis. Put the dollar amounts on the vertical axis.
- The data goes from −1,917 to 1,945. Make a scale from −2,000 to 2,000. Use intervals of 500.
- Graph the data and connect the points.

Balances for Hobby & Toy Town

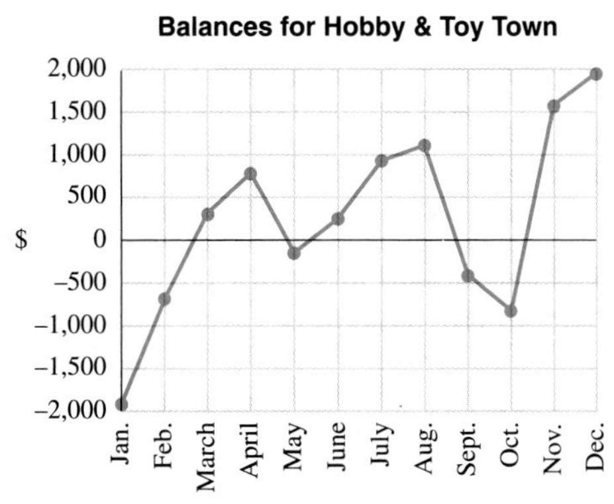

Balance Sheet for Hobby & Toy Town

Month	Balance (Profit/Loss)
January	−$1,917
February	−$682
March	$303
April	$781
May	−$150
June	$250
July	$933
August	$1,110
September	−$417
October	−$824
November	$1,566
December	$1,945

5. In which months was there a profit? March, April, June, July, August, November, December
6. In which month did the greatest loss occur? January
7. In which two months did the balance stay about the same? July and August
8. Which month showed the greatest change in the balance? November
9. Find the range of the balances. $3,862

TRY THESE

Calculator **Use a calculator to find each sum or difference.**

10. −435 + 628 193
11. 581 − (−57) 638
12. −2044 − (−1806) −238

Organizer, continued

Prentice Hall Technology

Multimedia Math
- Hot Page 11-8

Computer Item Generator
- 11-8

Other Available Technology

calculator

Excel; Works by Microsoft: Example 2 *(optional)*

1-2-3 by Lotus: Example 2 *(optional)*

ClarisWorks by Apple: Example 2 *(optional)*

Fact of the Day

Even though some audio cassette recorders require the tape to be flipped before recording on the other side, the recorder doesn't actually copy on both sides of the tape. Instead, it copies on both edges into the middle of the tape. Because video requires an audio and a video track, recorders use both sides of the tape each time, and so tapes cannot be flipped over.

—*When Do Fish Sleep?*

Ongoing Assessment Have students meet in groups of four to compare their answers to Exercises 13–16. Make sure students discuss their reasons for their choices. Have students take notes on alternate strategies.

Wrap Up

What's the Big Idea? Ask students: *How can you use a balance sheet to determine profit or loss? How can you draw and interpret graphs involving integers?*

Reteaching Activity Have students as a class create a list of expenses and income for a fictional business over a period of eight months. Have a volunteer write the balance sheet on the chalkboard. Then have students who require reteaching work in pairs or in small groups to find the profit or loss for each of the eight months Students can use Example 2 as a guide for making a line graph of the balances. Have pairs or groups of students compare graphs. You may wish to display the graphs for the class to share.

Connections Have a discussion about where balance sheets are used. You may want to start with these examples:

- **Small business**
- **Government agencies**
- **International corporations**
- **Schools**

ON YOUR OWN

Students will need graph paper for Exercise 23.

WRITING Challenge students also to make predictions about their potential profit for Exercise 24. Students could then list an example balance.

PH Multimedia Math Hot Page™ 11-8

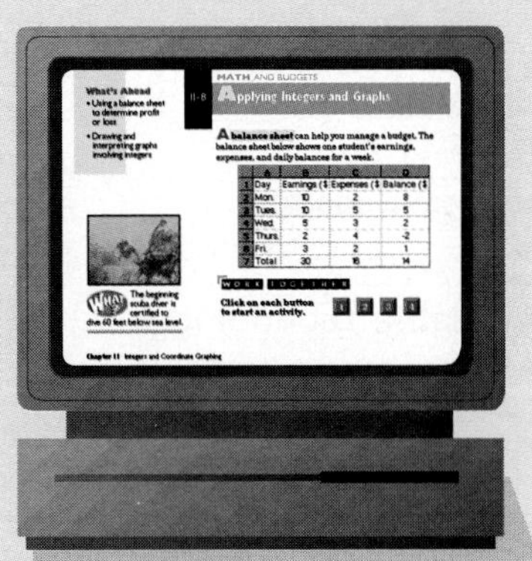

Assignment Options

Core: 17–19, 25–29, MR all	
Reinforce: 20–23	**Enrich:** 24

23a. Mon.: $9; Tues.: $18; Wed.: −$9; Thurs.: $17; Fri.: −$12; Sat.: −$1; Sun.: −$17

What scale and intervals would you use to graph the data set? Answers may vary. Sample given.

13. $-2, 3, 2, 4, -4, 1, -1, 3$
scale from −5 to 5; intervals of 1

14. $1, 7, -3, -4, 0, 9, -8, 0, -9$
scale from −10 to 10; intervals of 1

15. $-34, 98, 12, -71, 53, -95$
scale from −100 to 100; intervals of 10

16. $4, 68, 50, 41, -13, -18, 27$
scale from −20 to 80; intervals of 10

ON YOUR OWN

Choose **Use a calculator, mental math, or paper and pencil.**

17. $-12 + 5$ −7

18. $38 - 64$ −26

19. $-245 + 245$ 0

20. $1342 + (-672)$ 670

21. $29 - (-18)$ 47

22. $-86 + (-96)$ −182

Day	Expenses	Income
Mon.	−$85	$94
Tues.	−$60	$78
Wed.	−$22	$13
Thurs.	−$73	$90
Fri.	−$49	$37
Sat.	−$16	$15
Sun.	−$36	$19

23. a. Use the data at the left. Find the balance for each day. See left.

b. Draw a line graph to display the balances. See Solution Key.

24. Writing Describe a business that you would like to start. (You could sell some item or you could perform a service such as tutoring.) List all the expenses you would have. Answers may vary.

GREAT EXPECTATIONS

Video Game Producer

I would like to be a video game creator. I like challenging video games that you can play time after time and always try to beat your score from before. I think you would use math in this job. For example you would need to know how big the screen is to make the characters fit on the screen. If the characters took up the whole screen, there would be no room for background. If I made a game with many characters, I would need room for all of them to fit.

I have a few questions. After you think of your idea for a game, what do you do? Do you draw a diagram? How do you create one game and then put it at different levels? Where do you get your ideas?

Janna Mendoza

478

COMPUTER Help students with the mechanics of spreadsheets if they have difficulty. Exercises 25–29 can be done without actually using the computer.

Great Expectations

There are many resources available to students for gathering information about video game design. This list includes places to write for more information and publications to read.

- *The Art of Computer Game Design.* Chris Crawford. (Berkeley, CA: Osborne/McGraw Hill, 1984).
- *TCI: The Business of Entertainment Technology and Design.* (New York, NY: Theater Crafts Associates).
- *The Future of Video Recording.* (New York: TimeLife Video, 1982).

Students can also learn from discussions with experts. Here are some possible sources.

- Invite a video game designer to speak to the class.
- Ask the manager of a video game store to give a guided tour and explain the types of games that are available.
- Visit the computer science department of a university.

Encourage students to ask questions about the skills necessary for a career as a video game designer, including these topics.

- The training and college degrees necessary to qualify to become a video game designer
- How math is used on the job (discuss algebra algorithms, accounting, perspective, estimation, fractions, geometry, multi-dimensional figures)
- How computers are used to design special effects

Computer **Set up a spreadsheet like the one below.**

	A	B	C	D
1	Week	Income	Expenses	Balance
2	2/1–2/7	\$4,257	−\$6,513	■
3	2/8–2/14	\$3,840	−\$2,856	■
4	2/15–2/21	\$4,109	−\$3,915	■
5	2/22–2/28	\$3,725	−\$4,921	■
6	Totals	■	■	■

25. What formulas would you put in cells D2–D5? =B2+C2; =B3+C3; =B4+C4; =B5+C5

26. What formula goes in cell B6? Explain. =B2+B3+B4+B5

27. Fill in the formulas to find the unknown values. See Solution Key.

28. Did any weeks show a profit? Explain. Yes, week 2/8–2/14 and week 2/15–2/21 because income exceeded expenses.

29. What was the final balance for the month? Was it a loss or profit? −\$2,274; a loss

Mixed REVIEW

Find the number with the given prime factorization.

1. $2 \times 2 \times 3 \times 7 \times 13$ 1092
2. $2 \times 3 \times 3 \times 5 \times 23$ 2070

The coordinates of the vertices of $\triangle ABC$ are $A(-4, 1)$, $B(3, 5)$, and $C(3, 1)$. For each translation, give the new coordinates of each vertex.

3. up 4 units
4. right 6 units

See Solution Key.

5. Write a word problem with too little information.

Answers may vary.

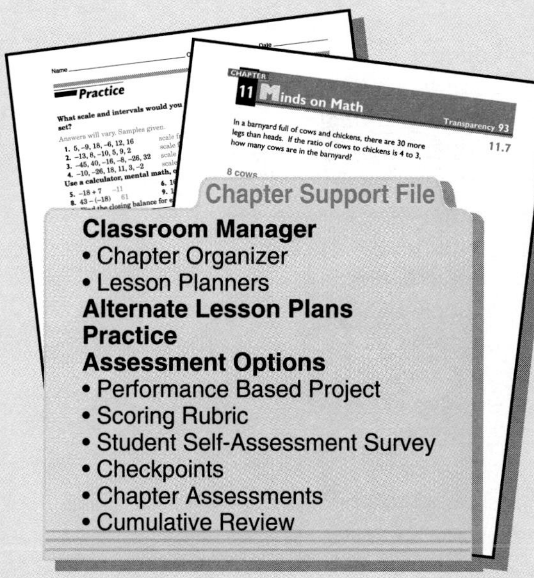

Minds on Math available in Teaching Transparencies

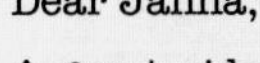

Math Minutes

Mr. Vega spent \$64.75 for five light fixtures and \$12.50 for four light switches. The light fixtures are all the same. How much did each light fixture cost?
\$12.95

Dear Janna,

A great video game usually starts with one person's idea. However, most creators work with groups of people. They prepare diagrams, animate people, objects, and animals, try ideas, solve problems, and write and test the game software.

When you finish college, computers will be quite different. Today's computer displays are colorful, but they are small and two-dimensional, and the computers used in games are slow. In ten years, creators will probably use three-dimensional (perhaps even holographic) displays. The software will animate figures realistically. Virtual reality may even make you part of the game.

To make games look life-like and operate realistically, creators should understand perspective, anatomy, structure, color, and lighting. To accomplish what they want their programs to do, math is important. Simple arithmetic is used everywhere in a game, but really good programmers also use trigonometry and advanced math.

Steven L. Cool

CHAPTER 11 WRAP UP

Ongoing Assessment Have students work in pairs on Exercises 18–29. Have partners take turns answering the questions and evaluating the answers. Circulate and act as referee when partners cannot agree on an answer.

Exercise 30: Some students may need to draw the two triangles in order to do this exercise.

Exercise 32: Encourage students to Make a Table, Draw a Diagram, and use the *Guess and Test* strategy to solve this problem.

Vocabulary/Symbols

balance
balance sheet
coordinate plane
coordinates
first coordinate
image
integers
negative integers
opposites
ordered pair
origin
positive integers
quadrants
reflection
second coordinate
slide
translation
x-axis
y-axis

Materials and Manipulatives

- algebra tiles
- graph paper

Integers and Opposites — 11-1, 11-2

Opposites are two numbers that are the same distance from 0 on the number line, but in opposite directions. The set of ***integers*** is the set of whole numbers and their opposites.

To compare integers, think of the number line. The integer farther to the right is the greater integer.

1. What integer represents 7°F below zero? −7
2. Name the opposite of each integer.
   a. −7 7 b. 1 −1 c. −8 8 d. −14 14
3. Write three numbers that are between −4 and −5. Are these numbers integers? Why or why not? Sample: $-4\frac{1}{2}$, $-4\frac{1}{3}$, $-4\frac{3}{4}$; no; These numbers have fractional parts.
4. Explain how to order the following integers from least to greatest: 3, −1, −13, 5, 0. −13, −1, 0, 3, 5; graph each number on a number line, then write the numbers in the order their points are from left to right.

Compare using <, >, or =.

5. −9 ■ −11 >
6. 4 ■ −13 >
7. −21 ■ 16 <
8. 0 ■ 9 <
9. 6 ■ 11 <

Write the integer represented by each set of tiles.

10. −1
11. 3
12. 1
13. 2

Modeling Addition and Subtraction of Integers — 11-3, 11-4

To add integers, model each integer with tiles. If possible, combine the tiles to make zero pairs and remove as many zero pairs as possible. Write the integer that the remaining tiles represent.

To subtract integers, model the first integer with tiles. Take away the second number of tiles. (You may need to add zero pairs to do this.) Write the integer that the remaining tiles represent.

Use tiles to find the sum or difference.

14. 9 + (−4) 5
15. −13 + 6 −7
16. 1 − (−7) 8
17. −2 − 8 −10

Graphing on the Coordinate Plane 11-6

The ***coordinate plane*** is formed by the intersection of the *x-axis* and the *y-axis.* Every point on the plane can be described by an ***ordered pair*** of numbers (*x*, *y*). These *coordinates* tell how far a point is from the origin, (0, 0).

Name the point with the given coordinates.

18. (0, 4) C **19.** (3, 1) G **20.** (−3, 3) N

21. (2, 3) A **22.** (−4, −3) H **23.** (1, 1) K

Write the coordinates of each point.

24. *B* (−3, −2) **25.** *F* (1, −3) **26.** *J* (0, −4)

27. *E* (−2, 2) **28.** *D* (4, 0) **29.** *M* (−1, −4)

Translations and Reflections 11-7

You can move figures in a coordinate plane by a ***translation*** or flip figures by a ***reflection.***

30. a. The vertices of triangle *ABC* are *A*(−4, −3), *B*(1, 4), and *C*(1, −3). Find the coordinates of the vertices of the triangle after it has been translated 4 units up. (−4, 1); (1, 8); (1, 1)

b. What can you say about the two triangles? They are congruent.

Strategies and Applications 11-5, 11-8

You can use multiple strategies to solve problems.

A *balance sheet* is a table that helps keep track of income and expenses. *Income* is listed as a positive number and *expenses* are listed as negative numbers.

31a. Jan.: $486, profit; Feb.: $2000, profit; March: −$266, loss; April: $673, profit

31. a. Find the balance for each month. Was there a profit or a loss? See right.

b. What scale and intervals would you use to graph the balances? scale from −500 to 2,000, intervals of 500

c. Draw a line graph to display the balances. See Solution Key.

32. Two people live 36 mi apart. They leave their homes on bicycles at 10:00 A.M. riding toward each other. The first person averages 8 mi/h and the second person averages 10 mi/h. At what time will they meet? 12:00 noon

Balance Sheet for Royale Bakery

Month	Income	Expenses
Jan.	$1,314	−$828
Feb.	$2,120	−$120
March	$1,019	−$1,285
April	$1,438	−$765

Student Resources

Practice, p. 463
Problem Solving Practice, p. 471
Extra Practice
Student Study Guide
Student Study Guide, Spanish Resources, TR
Tools for Studying Smarter, TR
Student Self-Assessment Survey, TR Ch. 11, p. 33 (see below)

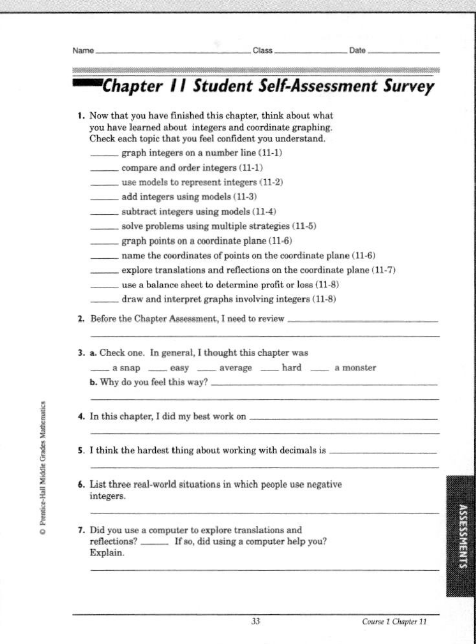

Name ______ Class ______ Date ______

Chapter 11 Student Self-Assessment Survey

1. Now that you have finished this chapter, think about what you have learned about integers and coordinate graphing. Check each topic that you feel confident you understand.
   ______ graph integers on a number line (11-1)
   ______ compare and order integers (11-1)
   ______ use models to represent integers (11-2)
   ______ add integers using models (11-3)
   ______ subtract integers using models (11-4)
   ______ solve problems using multiple strategies (11-5)
   ______ graph points on a coordinate plane (11-6)
   ______ name the coordinates of points on the coordinate plane (11-6)
   ______ explore translations and reflections on the coordinate plane (11-7)
   ______ use a balance sheet to determine profit or loss (11-8)
   ______ draw and interpret graphs involving integers (11-8)
2. Before the Chapter Assessment, I need to review ______
3. a. Check one. In general, I thought this chapter was
   ____ a snap ____ easy ____ average ____ hard ____ a monster
   b. Why do you feel this way? ______
4. In this chapter, I did my best work on ______
5. I think the hardest thing about working with decimals is ______
6. List three real-world situations in which people use negative integers.
7. Did you use a computer to explore translations and reflections? ______ If so, did using a computer help you? Explain.

ASSESSMENTS

33 Course 1 Chapter 11

CHAPTER 11 PUTTING IT ALL TOGETHER

The projects on these pages can be used in a variety of ways.

- alternative assessment
- portfolio ideas
- additional assignments for gifted and talented students
- extra credit for all students

Follow Up

- Timelines should show years and events occurring before Year Zero, but need not include vertical axes. Encourage imaginative depictions of time and events.
- You may wish to suggest that students project their timelines into the future to predict likely or hoped-for events.

EXCURSION To show all three events clearly, a very long line will be required. Even if the years of a student's birth and Einstein's death (1955) are separated by only $\frac{1}{2}$ in., a line more than a yard long will be needed to show the year of Pythagoras' death (around 500 B.C.).

Battle Grids

Do not direct students with ideas and strategies for the game. Let the students find patterns and follow deductive reasoning techniques on their own. After a few games, the students should have their strategy mapped out to win against their opponent. Students may want to play the game again, so don't give them strategies. Suggest that they discuss effective strategies with each other if they choose.

Sum It Up

Students should play at least one round of the game with the teacher or someone who understands how to add integers. Otherwise, the two students playing the summation game might have incorrect answers and neither of them might realize it.

Materials and Manipulatives

Follow Up
- paper for timeline

Battle Grids
- graph paper

Sum It Up
- heavy paper or index cards
- scissors
- tape

A Good Image
- heavy paper
- scissors
- paper bag
- drawing paper

Lining Up Time

At the beginning of the chapter you created a timeline that began with year zero, your first year in the school (or your first year as a member of your group). Now extend your timeline into the past (before year zero) based on your study of the chapter.

Convey as much information as possible on your timeline. You may wish to use negative numbers or a vertical axis to accomplish this. The problems preceded by the magnifying glass (p. 452, # 46; p. 458, # 35, p. 462, # 31; and p. 474, # 20) will help you complete your timeline.

Excursion: Suppose you decided to create a timeline of mathematics history that included the years of your birth, of Albert Einstein's death, and of the Greek mathematician Pythagoras's death. What difficulties would you encounter?

Where to Look:
- an encyclopedia

Try this with a partner. You will need graph paper.

- *Each player makes 2 grids on graph paper. Each grid must have a vertical y axis numbered 0-10 and a horizontal x axis numbered 0-10. Players keep the grids from their opponent's view.*
- *On the first grid, form a letter of the alphabet by placing Xs where the lines of the grid intersect. Use the other grid to guess your opponent's letter.*
- *Player A calls out to Player B an ordered pair of numbers. Player B tells whether or not the point plotted by the ordered pair is part of his or her letter. If so, Player A places an X on that spot on the blank grid. If not, an O is placed on that spot. Player B now takes a turn.*

The first player to correctly name the other player's letter wins.

482

Before they begin to play, have the students decide how many rounds of the game they will play before determining who is the winner.

EXCURSION Before they begin to play, students will have to make an extra cube that displays the operation. Have students create a table in which they can record the values and the operation determined from rolling the three cubes. Have them record the rounds as they play.

A Good Image

COOPERATIVE GROUPS If students use graph paper for the design, they can shade all the shapes and then calculate the area not covered.

Have students experiment with regular and irregular shapes.

Four, Three, Two, One, Zero!

There is more than one possible path that results in a sum of zero. Some students may give up too easily after unsuccessfully trying different paths. Encourage students to come up with a more efficient strategy. Ask students to find the sum of all the integers in the grid. **(25)** Have students find a set of numbers whose sum is this number (25). A path through the remaining numbers will result in a sum of zero.

EXCURSION Ask students to create their own 6×6 grid maze. Have students exchange mazes with a partner.

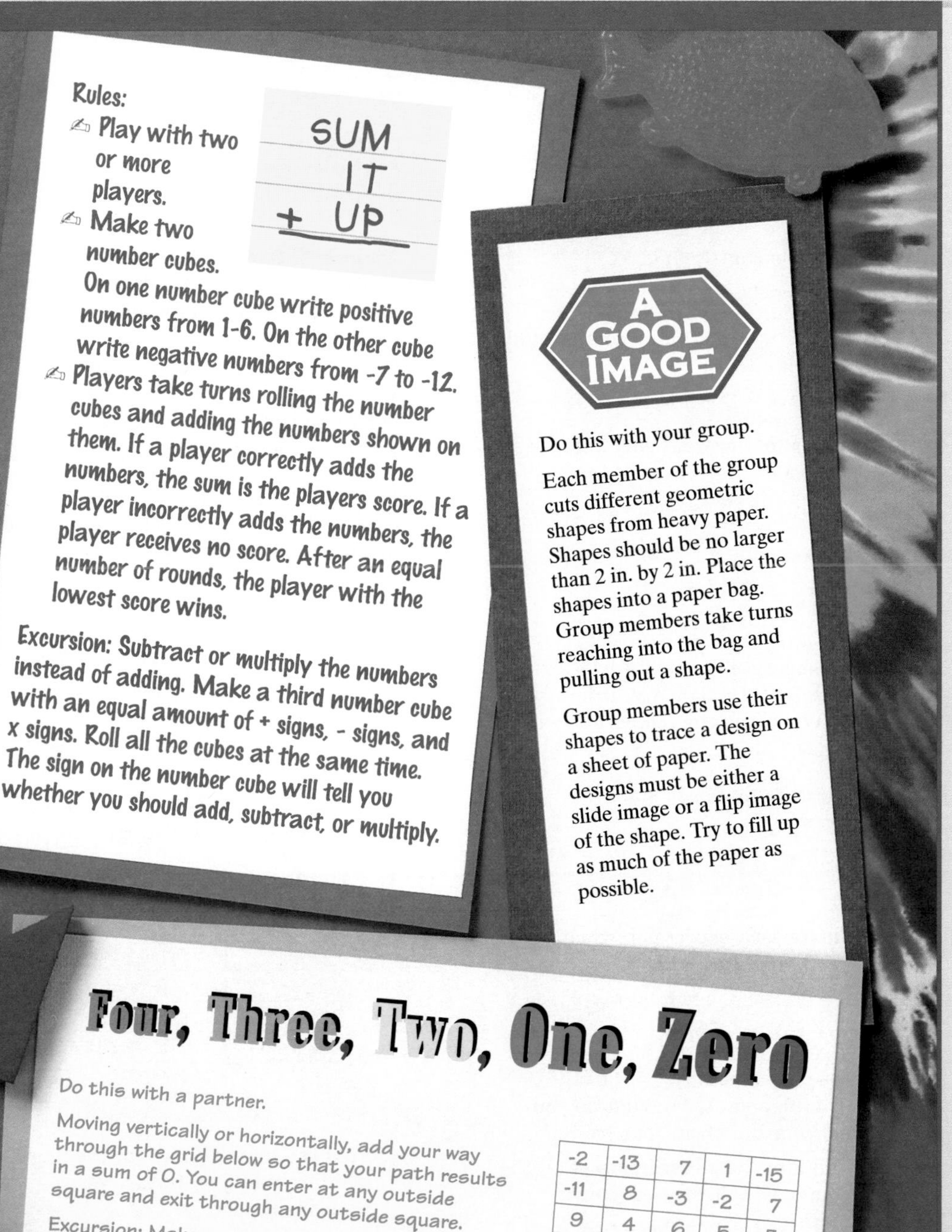

Rules:

- Play with two or more players.
- Make two number cubes. On one number cube write positive numbers from 1-6. On the other cube write negative numbers from -7 to -12.
- Players take turns rolling the number cubes and adding the numbers shown on them. If a player correctly adds the numbers, the sum is the players score. If a player incorrectly adds the numbers, the player receives no score. After an equal number of rounds, the player with the lowest score wins.

SUM IT + UP

Excursion: Subtract or multiply the numbers instead of adding. Make a third number cube with an equal amount of + signs, - signs, and x signs. Roll all the cubes at the same time. The sign on the number cube will tell you whether you should add, subtract, or multiply.

A GOOD IMAGE

Do this with your group.

Each member of the group cuts different geometric shapes from heavy paper. Shapes should be no larger than 2 in. by 2 in. Place the shapes into a paper bag. Group members take turns reaching into the bag and pulling out a shape.

Group members use their shapes to trace a design on a sheet of paper. The designs must be either a slide image or a flip image of the shape. Try to fill up as much of the paper as possible.

Four, Three, Two, One, Zero

Do this with a partner.

Moving vertically or horizontally, add your way through the grid below so that your path results in a sum of 0. You can enter at any outside square and exit through any outside square.

Excursion: Make your own maze, using a 6 by 6 grid. Exchange grids with a partner and solve.

-2	-13	7	1	-15
-11	8	-3	-2	7
9	4	6	5	-3
-3	2	12	-7	4
-4	14	-10	6	13

483

CHAPTER 11 ASSESSMENT

Writing Questions allow students to describe more fully their thinking and understanding of the concepts they've learned.
Exercises 8c and 13b are writing questions.

Enhanced Multiple Choice Questions are more complex than traditional multiple choice questions, which assess only one skill. Enhanced multiple choice questions assess the processes that students use as well as the end results. They are written so that students can use more than one strategy to solve the problem. Using multiple strategies is encouraged by the National Council of Teachers of Mathematics (NCTM).
Exercise 9 is an enhanced multiple choice question.

For Exercises 3 and 6, students are asked to use tiles to model integers.

Exercise 11: Students need calculators for this exercise.

Resources

Performance Based Project, TR Ch. 11, pp. 30–32
Chapter Assessment, Forms A and B, TR Ch. 11, pp. 35–38
Spanish Chapter Assessment, Spanish Resources, TR
Computer Item Generator

CHAPTER 11

Assessment

1. Compare using <, >, or =.

a. 18 ■ −24 > **b.** −15 ■ −9 <

2. Write the integer that is represented by the tiles.

a. ▪▪▪■ 2 **b.** ■■■■▪ −3

3. Use tiles to represent each integer and its opposite. See Solution Key.

a. −1 1 **b.** 6 −6 **c.** −2 2 **d.** −9 9

4. Compare using <, >, or =.

a. −13 + 4 ■ 13 + −4 <

b. 7 + (−8) + (−1) ■ 7 + (−9) =

5. The temperature was 4°F below zero at midnight. By 6:00 A.M. it had risen 22°F. What was the temperature at 6:00 A.M.? 18°F

6. Use tiles to find each sum or difference.

a. −11 + (−4) −15 **b.** −12 − 4 −16

c. 6 − (−3) 9 **d.** −5 + 5 0

7. Evaluate each expression when $x = 4$, $y = -3$, and $z = -12$.

a. $9 - y$ 12 **b.** $x + y + z$ −11

c. $z - y - x$ −13 **d.** $-8 + y - x$ −15

8. a. Graph the points (−4, 1), (1, 6), (−4, 6), and (1, 1). What do you notice about these four points?

b. Add 2 to the x-coordinate of all the points. Graph the new points.

c. **Writing** How do these two graphs compare? They are congruent rectangles.

a. They make a rectangle.
b. See Solution Key.

9. Choose A, B, C, or D. On his corrected math quiz Emilio had −2 points on the first question, −1 on the second, −3 on the third, −2 on the fourth, and −1 on the fifth. The quiz was worth 50 points. How many points did Emilio get on the quiz? B

A. 50 **B.** 41 **C.** 32 **D.** 12

10. Fai bought 3 birthday cards for $1.50 each and 2 posters for $2.75 each. How much did he spend in all? $10

11. Use a calculator to find each sum or difference.

a. −85 + 54 −31 **b.** −112 − (−792) 680

c. 384 + (−556) −172 **d.** 3,077 − (−1,902) 4979

12. Identify the quadrant in which each point lies.

a. (4, 2) I **b.** (−6, −5) III

c. (9, −15) IV **d.** (−8, 3) II

13. The data below shows the balance sheet for Balloons Galore.

Month	Balance
January	−$985
February	$10,241
March	−$209
April	$17,239

a. Find the total balance for the four months ending with April for Balloons Galore. $26,286

b. **Writing** Did the company make a profit or loss? Explain. profit; because February and April gained more than January and March lost.

CHAPTER

11 CUMULATIVE REVIEW

Exercises 2, 4, and 8 are enhanced multiple choice questions.

Exercise 2: Some students may need to copy and cut out the four figures.

Exercise 4: You may want to review the definitions of square, rectangle, quadrilateral, rhombus, and parallelogram. Encourage students to draw diagrams.

Item(s)	Review Topic	Chapter
1	perimeter of a square	6
2	nets of rectangular prisms	6
3	estimating percent of a number	9
4	special quadrilaterals	2
5	ratios	9
6, 9	probability	10
7	variables and expressions	5
8	modeling addition of integers	11
10	exploring arrangements	10

CHAPTER 11

Cumulative Review

Choose A, B, C, or D.

1. Find the perimeter of a square with sides 5 m. A

A. 20 m **B.** 25 m
C. 10 m **D.** 125 m

2. Which could be a net for a rectangular prism? C

A. 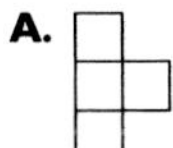 **B.** 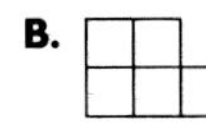

C. 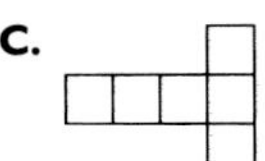 **D.** 

3. Find the best estimate for 43% of 87. B

A. 50 **B.** 36
C. 30 **D.** 25

4. Which statement is false? C

A. A square is always a rectangle.
B. Some rectangles are rhombuses.
C. All quadrilaterals are parallelograms.
D. Parallelograms can be divided into two congruent triangles.

5. Rehema bought 9 apples, 6 oranges, 12 pears, and 8 plums. What was the ratio of number of plums bought to number of pears bought? A

A. $\frac{2}{3}$ **B.** 9 to 12
C. 12:8 **D.** 4:2

6. You roll a number cube three times. Find the probability of getting either a 3 or a 4 all three times. D

A. 1 **B.** $\frac{1}{8}$
C. $\frac{1}{216}$ **D.** $\frac{1}{27}$

7. Evaluate the expression $b - a - 8$ when $a = -7$ and $b = -4$. C

A. -19 **B.** -11
C. -5 **D.** 11

8. Write the numerical expression that is represented by the set of tiles. Then find the sum. B

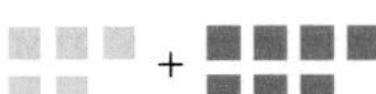

A. $-5 + 7; -2$ **B.** $5 + (-7); -2$
C. $5 + 7; 12$ **D.** $-5 + (-7); -12$

9. Four students are chosen at random. Find the probability that all four were born on a Monday. C

A. $\frac{4}{365}$ **B.** $\frac{1}{343}$
C. $\frac{1}{2401}$ **D.** $\frac{1}{7}$

10. How many different six-digit numbers can be formed using the digits 1, 2, 3, 4, 5, and 6 if no digit is repeated in a number? D

A. 5040 **B.** 36
C. 21 **D.** 720

Resources

Cumulative Review, TR Ch. 11, pp. 39–40
Transparency Masters, TR p. 35

Chapter 1

Extra Practice

The table at the right shows the number of books Lee read each month for 1 year.

Number of books Lee read					
3	1	4	2	4	1
3	2	4	4	2	1

1. a. Make a line plot. See Sol. Key.
   b. Find the median and mode. 2.5, 4

Make a frequency table and find the mean, median, and mode.

2. 23, 26, 22, 25, 22, 28, 22, 10, 11
   21, 22, 22
3. 102, 202, 102, 302, 102, 402, 102, 402, 201
   213, 201, 102

Name the type of graph most appropriate for each situation.

4. amount of rainfall in Costa Rica each month for 1 year line graph
5. cost of six different cars bar graph
6. number of students from each grade who play soccer circle graph
7. Data File 1 (pp. 2–3) Name the most appropriate type of graph to represent the data given in the chart "How Much TV Do We Watch?" circle graph
8. a. Data File 8 (pp. 316–317) Using the most appropriate type of graph, show the number of different types of medals won by Cuba in 1992. bar graph
   b. How will increasing the scale in your graph affect the appearance of the data? The differences will appear smaller.
9. Data File 1 (pp. 2–3) Draw 2 different line graphs using the data in "Persons Viewing in Prime Time." Draw the first graph using the scale shown. Draw a second graph using a scale of 5, starting at 80 and ending at 110. How does the change in scale affect each representation? See Sol. Key.
10. Mr. Yee deposited $710 into his account. He gave the teller twice as many $5's as $1's and three times as many $10's as $5's. Find the number of $1, $5, and $10 bills Mr. Yee deposited. 10 $1 bills, 20 $5 bills, 60 $10 bills
11. Data File 3 (pp. 92–93) Terry owns three of the cards listed in the table "Valuable Baseball Cards." The total value of the cards is $43,500. What are the cards that Terry owns? Mantle, Roberts, and Ruth

Chapter 2

Extra Practice

Use the figure at the right for Exercises 1–9. Name each of the following. Answers may vary. Samples are given.

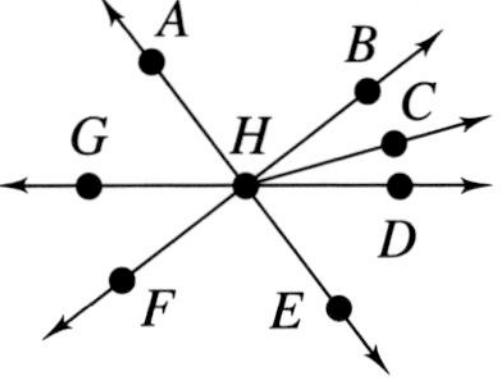

1. 3 acute angles
   ∠BHC, ∠BHD, ∠CHD
2. 4 obtuse angles
   ∠AHD, ∠DHF, ∠EHG, ∠FHC
3. 3 noncollinear points
   E, D, C
4. 6 rays
   $\overrightarrow{HB}$, $\overrightarrow{HC}$, $\overrightarrow{HD}$, $\overrightarrow{HE}$, $\overrightarrow{HF}$, $\overrightarrow{HG}$

Use a protractor to find the measure of each angle.

5. ∠*BHF* 180°
6. ∠*FHC* 158°
7. ∠*FHG* 36°
8. ∠*CHD* 15°
9. ∠*AHC* 112°

10. Draw a segment $\overline{RS}$. Construct a segment three times as long as $\overline{RS}$. See Sol. Key.

11. Draw an acute ∠*F*. Construct an angle congruent to ∠*F*. See Sol. Key.

Classify the triangle with the given side lengths as scalene, isosceles, or equilateral.

12. 7 cm, 9 cm, 7 cm
    isosceles
13. 3 m, 3 m, 3 m
    equilateral
14. 18 in., 16 in., 5 in.
    scalene

Classify the triangle with the given angle measures as acute, obtuse, or right.

15. 2°, 176°, 2°
    obtuse
16. 30°, 60°, 90°
    right
17. 45°, 65°, 70°
    acute

18. Find the number of lines of symmetry in this octagon. 2

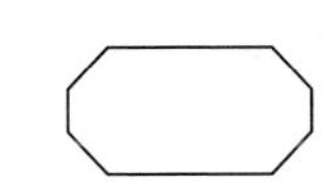

19. Draw a circle with a chord, central angle, and diameter. Check students' work.

20. In October, 65 middle school students visited the science museum. Of these students, 24 viewed an Omni theatre movie, 29 went to the planetarium, and 12 walked around the dinosaur exhibit. No students signed up for two choices. How many must have signed up for all three? too little information

21. Tickets at the Highview theatre cost \$2 for children and \$5 for adults. One afternoon, the theatre took in \$100 for one showing. List the possible combinations of ticket sales involving children and/or adults. Describe the pattern you see. See Sol. Key.

Extra Practice

Draw a model for each decimal. See Solution Key.

1. 0.8 **2.** 0.35 **3.** 1.2 **4.** three tenths **5.** seven hundredths

Write each decimal in words.

6. 0.10 ten hundredths
7. 0.8 eight tenths
8. 0.51 fifty-one hundredths
9. 0.30 thirty hundredths
10. 3.25 three and twenty-five hundredths
11. 33.05 thirty-three and five hundredths

Write each number in standard form.

12. four tenths 0.4
13. fifty-seven hundredths 0.57
14. sixty-six and seven hundredths 66.07
15. one hundred forty-two thousandths 0.142
16. two hundred twenty-two thousandths 0.222

Find the value of the digit 9 in each number.

17. 0.9 9 tenths
18. 1.009 9 thousandths
19. 52.39 9 hundredths
20. 0.4829 9 ten-thousandths
21. 351.09 9 hundredths

Compare. Use >, <, or =.

22. 1.11 ■ 1.09 >
23. 0.2357 ■ 0.23 >
24. 11.521 ■ 11.53 <
25. 13.10 ■ 13.1 =

Round to the nearest whole number. Estimate the sum or difference.

26. 0.8 + 3.5 5
27. 6.2 − 0.625 5
28. 5.001 − 0.67 4
29. 13.41 + 7.61 21
30. 1.14 + 9.3 10
31. 9 − 3.5 5
32. 4.11 − 2.621 1
33. 3.541 + 1.333 5

34. Measure each side of the triangle in millimeters and find its perimeter.
15 mm + 11 mm + 23 mm = 49 mm

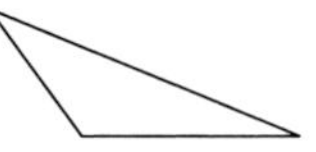

35. What metric unit would you use to measure each item?

a. height of a house m
b. length of a pencil cm
c. length of a river km

36. In one month, Rachel wants to buy a new pair of $170 in-line skates. She works 10 h a week for $5/h. She also spends $15 a week. Can Rachel buy the skates in one month? No

37. Judith found a picture of her mother at 3 years of age dated 1960. Judith was 12 years old in 1993. In what year will she be half her mother's age? 2005

Chapter 4

Extra Practice

Extra Practice

Round each factor to the nearest whole number to estimate the product.

1. 3.7×6.8 28
2. 4.8×3.2 15
3. 11.69×8.49 96

Use compatible numbers to estimate. Accept reasonable estimates.

4. $3{,}126.38 \div 26.01$ 125
5. $21.49 \div 3.76$ 7
6. 2.28×5.59 12

Use order of operations to evaluate.

7. $7 + 5 \times 6 \div 3$ 17
8. $(17 + 1) \div 3 \times 2$ 12
9. $6 \div 2 + 5 \times 3$ 18
10. $(3 \times 5) \times (6 \div 2)$ 45
11. $26 - 6 \div 3 \times (3 + 5)$ 10
12. $8 \div (1.25 + 0.75)$ 4

Use the distributive property to evaluate.

13. $3 \times (10 + 5)$ 45
14. $4 \times (50 - 5)$ 180
15. $5 \times (7 - 5)$ 10
16. $6 \times (8 + 5)$ 78

Use the distributive property to rewrite and evaluate.

17. 7×78 546
18. 8×503 4,024
19. 6×66 396
20. 9×12 108

Find each product.

21. 0.35×0.07 0.0245
22. 100×0.069 6.9
23. 7.9×0.03 0.237
24. 9.9×1.2 11.88

Draw a model to find each quotient.

25. $0.6 \div 0.05$ 12
26. $1.5 \div 3$ 0.5
27. $0.24 \div 6$ 0.04
28. $1.8 \div 0.09$ 20

Find each quotient.

29. $6.72 \div 4.2$ 1.6
30. $6.2\overline{)0.5952}$ 0.096
31. $7.5\overline{)64.5}$ 8.6
32. $21.12 \div 4.4$ 4.8

33. What information is missing or given but not needed?

    Symphony tickets cost $12 for orchestra seats or $7 for balcony seats. Programs cost $3. Madeline bought two tickets. How much did she spend?
    Cannot tell which type of ticket she bought. Do not need to know how much programs cost.

34. Hameen bought two shirts on sale for a total of $28.50. Earlier in the week the store offered the shirts for $18.99 apiece. Find how much money Hameen saved by buying the shirts on sale. $9.48

Chapter 5

Extra Practice

Find the next three terms in each number pattern. Write a rule to describe each number pattern.

1. 1, 4, 16, 64 256, 1024, 4096 Begin with 1. Mult. by 4.
2. 0, 3, 6, 9 12, 15, 18 Begin with 0. Add 3.
3. 0.3, 2.3, 4.3, 6.3 8.3, 10.3, 12.3 Begin with 0.3. Add 2.

Name the base and the exponent.

4. 2^{16} 2, 16
5. 4^7 4, 7
6. 4^2 4, 2
7. 7^4 7, 4
8. 1^0 1, 0

Choose **Use a calculator, mental math, or paper and pencil to evaluate.**

9. $(8^2 - 4) \div 10$ 6
10. $6(5 + 5)$ 60
11. $5^8 \div 2$ 195,312.5
12. $144 + 56 \div 4$ 158

Mental Math **Evaluate each expression for the given values of the variables.**

13. $7x$ for $x = 7$ 49
14. $a + 0.30$ for $a = 1.70$ 2
15. $b^2 - 24$ for $b = 8$ 40

Write a variable expression for each word phrase.

16. one less than b $b - 1$
17. twice as many p $2p$
18. four greater than b $b + 4$

Solve each equation.

19. $3b = 21$ 7
20. $20 = y + 1$ 19
21. $27 + a = 163$ 136
22. $n - 35 = 75$ 110
23. $178 = 10d$ 17.8
24. $b \div 7 = 7$ 49
25. $25 = p - 4.2$ 29.2
26. $1.5t = 6$ 4
27. $40 = k \div 5$ 200

28. Sunscreen carries an SPF number. To find how long you can sunbathe while wearing sunscreen, you multiply the SPF number by the number of minutes you can safely stay in the sun *without* sunscreen. Suppose you can be in the sun safely without sunscreen for n min. Write a variable expression for the amount of time you can sunbathe while wearing a 15 SPF sunscreen. $15n$

29. In 1990, the population of Hillsboro was 25,000. The population increases by 5,000 people every 5 years. What will be the population in the year 2005? 40,000

Chapter 6

Extra Practice

Find the area of each figure. Use 3.14 for π.

1. 9.5 in. 5.5 in. 52.25 in.^{2}

2. 4 m 5 m 6 m 12 m^2

3. 18 cm 10 cm 8 cm 144 cm^2

4. 22 yd 379.94 yd^2

5. The area of a triangle equals 36 cm^2. The base equals 12 cm. Find the height of the triangle. 6 cm

6. The area of a rectangle equals 64 cm^2. The height equals 4 cm. Find the width. 16 cm

Find the circumference and area of a circle with the given radius or diameter. First estimate using 3 for π, then use a calculator.

7. $d = 26$ C = 78; 81.68 A = 507; 530.93

8. $d = 10.6$ C = 31.8; 33.3 A = 84.27; 88.25

9. $r = 30$ C = 180; 188.5 A = 2700; 2827.43

10. $r = 11$ C = 66; 69.12 A = 363; 380.13

11. a. Identify the figure below. pentagonal prism
    b. Find the number of faces, edges, and vertices. 7, 15, 10

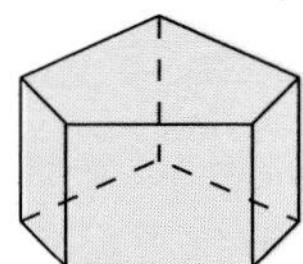

12. Find the volume and surface area of the rectangular prism below. SA = 340 sq. units V = 400 cu. units

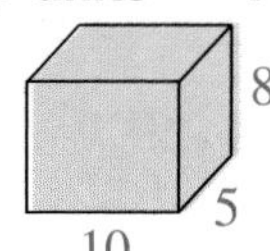

13. Identify the figure formed by the net at the right. Then find its surface area. triangular prism; 72 sq. units

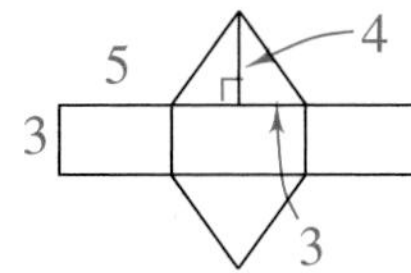

14. Martina wants to trim her bulletin board with ribbon. The bulletin board measures 90 cm by 150 cm. How much ribbon does Martina need? 480 cm

15. Triangles are worth 9 points, quadrilaterals 16 points, and pentagons 25 points. Find the total number of points contained in the figure below. Use only convex shapes. convex only 125 pts

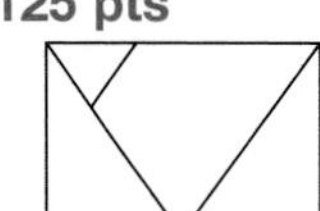

Extra Practice

Chapter 7

Extra Practice

Mental Math **Decide whether each number is divisible by 1, 2, 3, 5, 9, or 10.**

1. 324 1, 2, 3, 9
2. 2685 1, 3, 5
3. 540 1, 2, 3, 5, 9, 10
4. 114 1, 2, 3
5. 31 1
6. 981 1, 3, 9

Tell whether each number is prime or composite.

7. 24 composite
8. 49 composite
9. 7 prime
10. 81 composite
11. 37 prime
12. 23 prime

Use prime factorization to find the GCF of each set of numbers.

13. 16, 36 4
14. 25, 75 25
15. 16, 24, 8 8
16. 54, 63 9
17. 15, 25, 30 5
18. 17, 23 1

Write two fractions equivalent to each fraction. Then write each fraction as a decimal.

19. $\frac{2}{3}$ $\frac{4}{6}$, $\frac{6}{9}$ 0.6
20. $\frac{3}{4}$ $\frac{6}{8}$, $\frac{9}{12}$ 0.75
21. $\frac{2}{5}$ $\frac{4}{10}$, $\frac{6}{15}$ 0.4
22. $\frac{1}{4}$ $\frac{2}{8}$, $\frac{3}{12}$ 0.25
23. $\frac{1}{2}$ $\frac{2}{4}$, $\frac{3}{6}$ 0.5
24. $\frac{3}{5}$ $\frac{6}{10}$, $\frac{9}{15}$ 0.6

Find the GCF of each numerator and denominator. Then simplify each fraction.

25. $\frac{30}{35}$ 5, $\frac{6}{7}$
26. $\frac{27}{36}$ 9, $\frac{3}{4}$
27. $\frac{40}{50}$ 10, $\frac{4}{5}$
28. $\frac{32}{48}$ 16, $\frac{2}{3}$
29. $\frac{6}{60}$ 6, $\frac{1}{10}$

Write each improper fraction as a mixed number.

30. $\frac{25}{7}$ $3\frac{4}{7}$
31. $\frac{39}{12}$ $3\frac{1}{4}$
32. $\frac{12}{5}$ $2\frac{2}{5}$
33. $\frac{10}{7}$ $1\frac{3}{7}$
34. $\frac{7}{2}$ $3\frac{1}{2}$

Write each mixed number as an improper fraction.

35. $1\frac{7}{8}$ $\frac{15}{8}$
36. $2\frac{3}{5}$ $\frac{13}{5}$
37. $11\frac{1}{9}$ $\frac{100}{9}$
38. $5\frac{6}{8}$ $\frac{46}{8} = \frac{23}{4}$
39. $10\frac{1}{8}$ $\frac{81}{8}$

40. I am thinking of a two-digit prime number. The product of the digits in the number equals 12. Find the number. 43

41. Complete the number below with the digits 5, 3, and 1 so that the number is divisible by 6. How many different ways can you do this? If you completed the number with any other digits from 0 to 9, will the number still be divisible by 2? 3 ■ 6 ■ 2 ■ 1 2 4
6; yes 531, 135, 351 513, 153, 315

Chapter 8

Extra Practice

Find each sum or difference.

1. $\frac{1}{2} + \frac{1}{3}$ $\frac{5}{6}$
2. $\frac{1}{6} - \frac{1}{8}$ $\frac{1}{24}$
3. $\frac{3}{4} - \frac{1}{3}$ $\frac{5}{12}$
4. $\frac{7}{10} + \frac{3}{10}$ 1
5. $\frac{7}{8} + \frac{1}{7}$ $\frac{57}{56}$ or $1\frac{1}{56}$
6. $\frac{3}{5} - \frac{1}{2}$ $\frac{1}{10}$
7. $6\frac{2}{3} + 1\frac{1}{2}$ $\frac{49}{6}$ or $8\frac{1}{6}$
8. $3\frac{2}{3} - 3\frac{2}{7}$ $\frac{8}{21}$
9. $7\frac{4}{5} + 1\frac{2}{3}$ $\frac{142}{15}$ or $9\frac{7}{15}$
10. $11\frac{15}{16} - 2\frac{3}{4}$ $\frac{147}{16}$ or $9\frac{3}{16}$
11. $7\frac{5}{6} - 2\frac{1}{12}$ $\frac{69}{12}$ or $5\frac{3}{4}$
12. $4\frac{2}{3} + 4\frac{1}{5}$ $\frac{133}{15}$ or $8\frac{13}{15}$

Estimate **Then find the product and simplify.**

13. $\frac{1}{2} \times \frac{2}{3}$ $\frac{1}{3}$
14. $4\frac{1}{4} \times 3\frac{5}{6}$ $\frac{391}{24}$ or $16\frac{7}{24}$
15. $6\frac{1}{3} \times 7\frac{1}{5}$ $\frac{228}{5}$ or $45\frac{3}{5}$
16. $5\frac{7}{8} \times 2\frac{3}{4}$ $\frac{517}{32}$ or $16\frac{5}{32}$
17. $8 \times \frac{1}{4}$ 2
18. $\frac{1}{20} \times 100$ 5
19. $\frac{8}{7} \times \frac{4}{9}$ $\frac{32}{63}$
20. $4\frac{7}{6} \times 2\frac{2}{3}$ $\frac{124}{9}$ or $13\frac{7}{9}$

Divide. Write each answer in simplest form.

21. $\frac{4}{5} \div 2$ $\frac{2}{5}$
22. $\frac{6}{7} \div \frac{2}{5}$ $\frac{15}{7}$ or $2\frac{1}{7}$
23. $2\frac{1}{7} \div \frac{2}{3}$ $\frac{45}{14}$ or $3\frac{3}{14}$
24. $4\frac{1}{2} \div 3\frac{1}{4}$ $\frac{18}{13}$ or $1\frac{5}{13}$
25. $\frac{2}{5} \div \frac{2}{25}$ 5
26. $\frac{13}{16} \div \frac{1}{16}$ 13
27. $\frac{5}{6} \div \frac{5}{6}$ 1
28. $\frac{1}{4} \div \frac{4}{4}$ $\frac{1}{4}$

Draw a model for each equation. See Sol. Key.

29. $\frac{2}{5} - \frac{1}{10} = \frac{3}{10}$
30. $\frac{1}{4} + \frac{1}{2} = \frac{3}{4}$
31. $\frac{5}{6} - \frac{2}{3} = \frac{1}{6}$
32. $\frac{2}{5} + \frac{1}{2} = \frac{9}{10}$

Write the reciprocal of each number.

33. $\frac{3}{4}$ $\frac{4}{3}$
34. 5 $\frac{1}{5}$
35. $\frac{3}{9}$ 3
36. $\frac{1}{3}$ 3
37. $4\frac{1}{3}$ $\frac{3}{13}$
38. $5\frac{3}{4}$ $\frac{4}{23}$

39. Complete the table at the right. Then add another row and describe the pattern in the "Sum" column. The sum increases by $\frac{1}{2}$.

Expression	Sum
$\frac{1}{2}$	$\frac{1}{2}$
$\frac{1}{2} + \frac{2}{4}$	■ 1
$\frac{1}{2} + \frac{2}{4} + \frac{3}{6}$	■ $1\frac{1}{2}$
$\frac{1}{2} + \frac{2}{4} + \frac{3}{6} + \frac{4}{8}$	2

40. Maria wants to plant a row of pine trees to form a hedge. Her yard measures 44 ft long. Trees must be 4 ft apart. Draw a diagram to find the number of trees she can plant. 12 trees

41. Jules Verne wrote the classic tale *20,000 Leagues Under the Sea.* One league equals 3 miles. How many miles equals 20,000 leagues? 60,000 mi

Chapter 9

Extra Practice

Write each ratio as a fraction in simplest form.

1. 30 to 60 $\frac{1}{2}$
2. 5 : 15 $\frac{1}{3}$
3. 13 to 52 $\frac{1}{4}$
4. 7 : 77 $\frac{1}{11}$
5. 18 : 72 $\frac{1}{4}$

Find the value of *n*.

6. $\frac{n}{30} = \frac{3}{15}$ 6
7. $\frac{64}{n} = \frac{5}{10}$ 128
8. $\frac{13}{3} = \frac{n}{6}$ 26
9. $\frac{5}{225} = \frac{2}{n}$ 90
10. $\frac{9}{12} = \frac{12}{n}$ 16
11. $\frac{n}{50} = \frac{3}{75}$ 2
12. $\frac{18}{n} = \frac{3}{10}$ 60
13. $\frac{51}{17} = \frac{n}{3}$ 9
14. $\frac{2}{16} = \frac{n}{24}$ 3
15. $\frac{3}{45} = \frac{4}{n}$ 60

Write each as a percent.

16. 0.77 77%
17. $\frac{10}{25}$ 40%
18. 0.06 6%
19. 0.9 90%
20. $\frac{13}{50}$ 26%
21. $\frac{18}{60}$ 30%
22. 0.03 3%
23. $\frac{3}{50}$ 6%
24. 0.39 39%
25. 0.17 17%
26. $\frac{12}{75}$ 16%
27. $\frac{4}{5}$ 80%

Write each as a fraction in lowest terms.

28. 42% $\frac{21}{50}$
29. 0.66 $\frac{33}{50}$
30. 96% $\frac{24}{25}$
31. 0.24 $\frac{6}{25}$
32. 80% $\frac{4}{5}$
33. 0.56 $\frac{14}{25}$

Express each as a decimal.

34. 1% 0.01
35. $\frac{7}{10}$ 0.7
36. 87% 0.87
37. $\frac{8}{40}$ 0.2
38. 88% 0.88
39. $\frac{15}{25}$ 0.6

Find each percent.

40. 48% of 200 96
41. 5% of 80 4
42. 62% of 150 93
43. 35% of 50 17.5
44. 20% of 80 16
45. 15% of $17.50 $2.63
46. 50% of 86 43
47. 90% of 100 90

48. A diorama of Minute Man National Historic Park in Concord, MA, shows the road from the Old North Bridge to the visitor center as 12 in. long. One inch on the model represents $\frac{1}{16}$ mi. How far is the bridge from the center? 0.75 mi

49. Data File 5 (pp. 182–183) Compare the average number of hours pigs sleep to the average number of hours two-toed sloths sleep. Write the comparison as a fraction, as a percent, and as a decimal. $\frac{13}{20}$, 65%, 0.65

Chapter 10

Extra Practice

1. Harvey rolls a number cube. If he rolls an even number, he wins. If he rolls an odd number, his sister wins. Is this a fair game? Explain. Yes; it is fair. See Sol. Key

2. Solve by simulation. Suppose you take a four-question true-false test. You guess all the answers. What is the probability you will get 3 out of 4 correct? $\frac{1}{4}$

3. Nina took a true-false test. She did not know any of the answers but got 4 correct and 6 incorrect. Use this data to find the experimental probability of getting a question right. 0.4

4. Use the number 3,486,335,206 to find the following probabilities. Write the probabilities as a percent and fraction.
   a. probability that a digit selected at random is a 3 30%, $\frac{3}{10}$
   b. probability that a digit selected at random is a 2 10%, $\frac{1}{10}$
   c. probability that a digit selected at random is a multiple of 2 50%, $\frac{1}{2}$

5. Make a tree diagram to show all possible sandwich combinations. Assume you choose one in each category. See Solution Key.

Sandwiches	
Meats:	Turkey, Roast Beef
Breads:	Bagel, Whole Wheat, White
Toppings:	Lettuce, Tomatoes, Onions

Is each sample random? representative? Explain.

6. A school district wants to find out what fruits to sell in its school cafeterias. They survey all the students in one school. No; possibly

7. A teacher wants to know the opinions of all her students on the upcoming elections. She places each student's name in a box and draws 15 names. Yes; possibly

Extra Practice

List the integers in order from least to greatest.

1. $-7, -6, 7, 6$
   $-7, -6, 6, 7$
2. $0, -14, -15, -13$
   $-15, -14, -13, 0$
3. $15, -7, 71, 1$
   $-7, 1, 15, 71$
4. $5, -4, -1, 1$
   $-4, -1, 1, 5$

Compare using $<$, $>$, $=$.

5. -3 ■ -1
   $<$
6. 5 ■ 7
   $<$
7. -5 ■ -7
   $>$
8. -6 ■ 0
   $<$
9. $-3 - 1$ ■ $-3 + (-1)$
   $=$
10. $4 - 8$ ■ $8 - 4$
    $<$
11. $-5 - (-2)$ ■ $-5 - 2$
    $>$

Use the graph at the right for Exercises 12–23. Name the coordinates of each point.

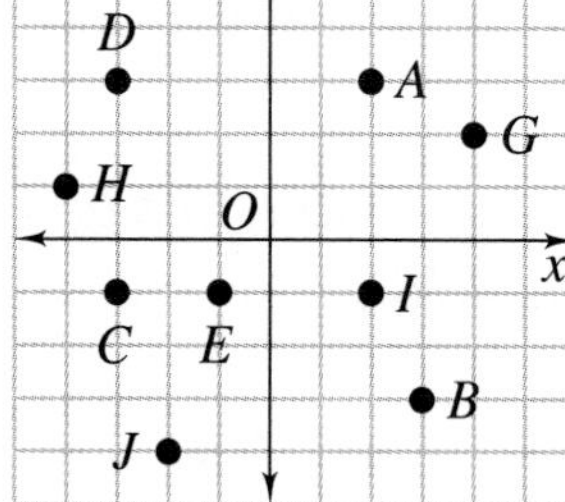

12. A (2, 3)
13. B (3, −3)
14. C (−3, −1)
15. D (−3, 3)
16. E (−1, −1)

Name the point with the given coordinates.

17. (4, 2) G
18. (4, 5) F
19. (2, −1) I
20. (−4, 1) H
21. In which quadrant are points C, E, and J?
    3rd quadrant
22. Translate point G to the left 4 units and down 2 units. What are its new coordinates? (0, 0)
23. Reflect point D across the y-axis. What are its new coordinates? (3, 3)
24. Graph the points $X(-3, 2)$, $Y(5, -4)$, and $Z(0, 5)$. See Sol. Key.

Use any method to evaluate.

25. $-14 + 28$
    14
26. $31 - (-52)$
    83
27. $-72 + (-53)$
    −125
28. $-217 - (-217)$
    0

What scale and intervals would you use to graph the data set?

29. $0, -35, 25, 15, -17, 5, -4.1$
    scale: −35 to 25; intervals: 5 or 10
30. $-12, 0, 12, -7, -6, 3, -8, 6$
    scale: −12 to 12; intervals: 4
31. Mars travels around the Sun in 687 days. Earth journeys around the Sun in 365 days. About how many times will Mars and Earth travel around the Sun in twenty years?
    Mars: about $10\frac{1}{2}$ times
    Earth: 20 times
32. Data File 4 (pp. 138–139) Bernie and Bernice are twins. They turn twelve in two months. Each is 140 cm tall. Estimate each twin's adult height.
    Bernie: about 168 cm tall;
    Bernice: about 153 cm tall

Tables

Table 1 Measures

Metric

Length
10 millimeters (mm) = 1 centimeter (cm)
100 cm = 1 meter (m)
1,000 m = 1 kilometer (km)

Area
100 square millimeters (mm^2) = 1 square centimeter (cm^2)
10,000 cm^2 = 1 square meter (m^2)

Volume
1,000 cubic millimeters (mm^3) = 1 cubic centimeter (cm^3)
1,000,000 cm^3 = 1 cubic meter (m^3)

Mass
1,000 milligrams (mg) = 1 gram (g)
1,000 g = 1 kilogram (kg)

Capacity
1,000 milliliters (mL) = 1 liter (L)

United States Customary

Length
12 inches (in.) = 1 foot (ft)
3 feet = 1 yard (yd)
36 in. = 1 yd
5,280 ft = 1 mile (mi)
1,760 yd = 1 mi

Area
144 square inches ($in.^2$) = 1 square foot (ft^2)
9 ft^2 = 1 square yard (yd^2)
4,840 yd^2 = 1 acre

Volume
1,728 cubic inches ($in.^3$) = 1 cubic foot (ft^3)
27 ft^3 = 1 cubic yard (yd^3)

Weight
16 ounces (oz) = 1 pound (lb)
2,000 lb = 1 ton (T)

Capacity
8 fluid ounces (fl oz) = 1 cup (c)
2 c = 1 pint (pt)
2 pt = 1 quart (qt)
4 qt = 1 gallon (gal)

Time
1 minute (min) = 60 seconds (s)
1 hour (h) = 60 min
1 day (da) = 24 h
1 year (y) = 365 da

Table 2 Formulas

Circumference of a circle
$C = \pi d$ or $C = 2\pi r$

Area	parallelogram:	$A = bh$	**Volume**	rectangular prism:	$V = lwh$
	rectangle:	$A = bh$			
	triangle:	$A = \frac{1}{2}bh$			
	circle:	$A = \pi r^2$			

Table 3 Symbols

$>$	is greater than	$\approx$	is approximately equal to
$<$	is less than	$\overline{AB}$	segment AB
$=$	is equal to	$\overrightarrow{AB}$	ray AB
$^\circ$	degrees	$\overleftrightarrow{AB}$	line AB
%	percent	$\angle ABC$	angle ABC
$a : b$	ratio of a to b, $\frac{a}{b}$	AB	length of segment AB
$P(E)$	probability of an event E	mi/h	miles per hour
π	pi		

Student Study Guide and Glossary

A

Acute angle (p. 46)

An acute angle is any angle that measures less than 90°.

Example $0° < m\angle 1 < 90°$

Acute triangle (p. 54)

A triangle that contains all acute angles is an acute triangle.

Example $m\angle 1, m\angle 2, m\angle 3 < 90°$

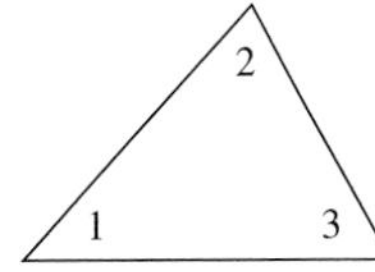

Angle (p. 45)

An angle is made up of two rays with a common endpoint.

Example

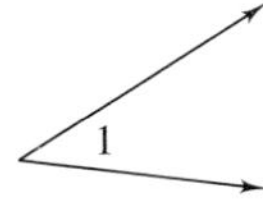

Area (p. 151)

The number of square units inside a figure is the area.

Example $l = 6$ ft, and $w = 4$ ft, so the area is 24 ft^2.

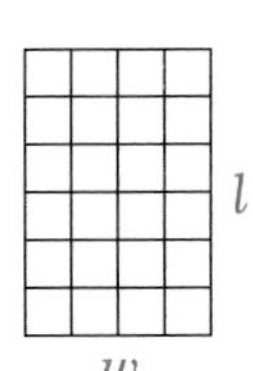

Each square equals 1 ft^2.

B

Bar graph (p. 20)

A bar graph compares amounts.

Example This bar graph represents class sizes for grades 6, 7, and 8.

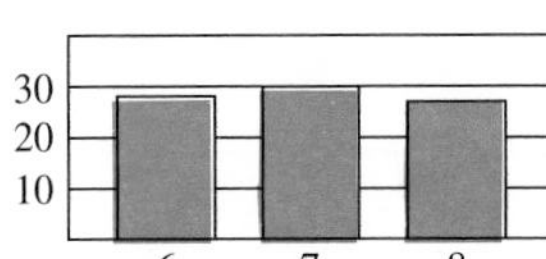

Base (p. 192)

When a number is written in exponential form the number that is used as a factor is the base.

$5^4 = 5 \times 5 \times 5 \times 5$

↑ base

C

Chord (p. 78)

A chord is a segment with endpoints on a circle.

Example $\overline{BC}$ is a chord of circle O.

Circle (p. 78)

A circle is a set of points on a plane that are all the same distance from a given point, called the center.

Example Circle O

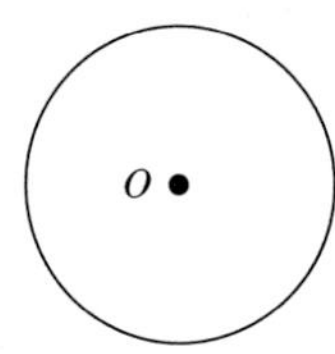

Circle graphs (pp. 21, 399)

The entire circle represents the whole. Each wedge in the circle graph represents a part of the whole.

Example The circle graph represents the different types of plays William Shakespeare wrote.

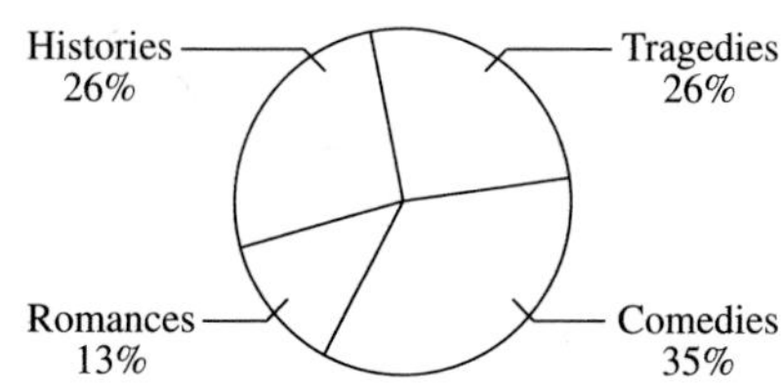

Circumference (p. 242)

Circumference is the distance around a circle. You calculate the circumference of a circle by multiplying the diameter by pi (π) ($C = \pi \times d$). Pi is approximately equal to 3.14.

Example The circumference of a circle with a diameter of 10 cm is approximately 31.4 cm.

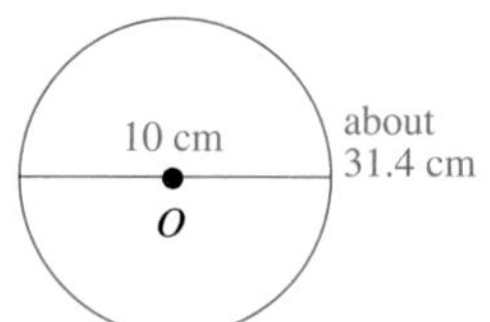

Collinear points (p. 42)

If there is a line that goes through a set of points, the points are collinear.

Example Points B, C, R and S are collinear.

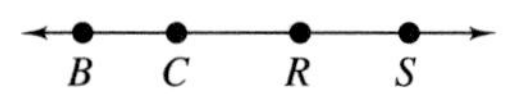

Compass (p. 51) A compass is a tool that is used to draw circles or parts of circles called arcs.

Example

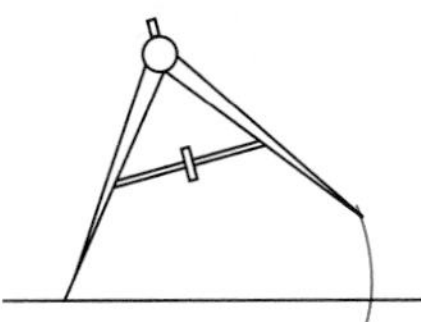

Compatible numbers (p. 141) Estimating products or quotients is easier when you use compatible numbers. Compatible numbers are numbers close in value to the numbers you want to multiply or divide. Compatible numbers are easy to multiply or divide mentally.

Example Estimate the quotient $151 \div 14.6$.

$151 \approx 150$
$14.6 \approx 15$
$150 \div 15 = 10$, so $151 \div 14.6 \approx 10$

Composite number (p. 278) A number that has more than two factors is called a composite number.

Example 24 is a composite number that has 1, 2, 3, 4, 6, 8, 12, and 24 as factors.

Congruent figures (p. 70) Figures that have the same size and shape are congruent.

Example $AB = QS$, $CB = RS$, and $AC = QR$. $m\angle A = m\angle Q$, $m\angle C = m\angle R$, and $m\angle B = m\angle S$. Triangles ABC and QSR are congruent.

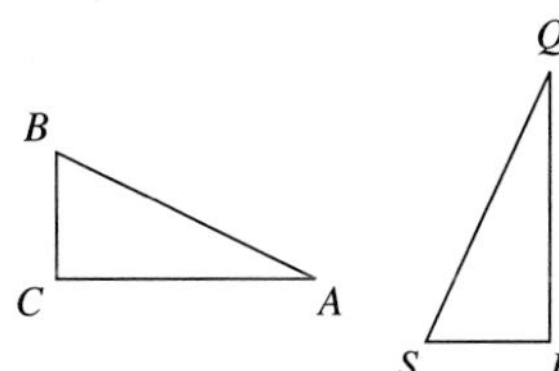

Congruent angles (p. 52) Congruent angles are angles that have the same measure.

Example $\angle C$ and $\angle B$ are both 60° so $\angle C$ is congruent to $\angle B$.

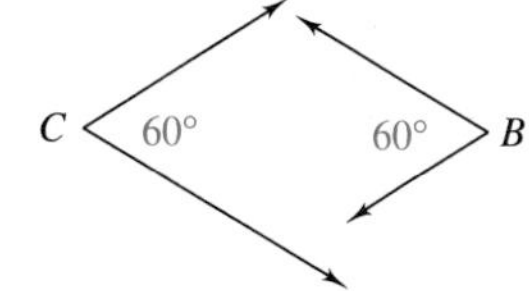

Student Study Guide

Congruent polygons (p. 70) Polygons whose corresponding parts (sides and angles) are congruent are congruent polygons.

Example triangle *HOT* is congruent to triangle *PIE*

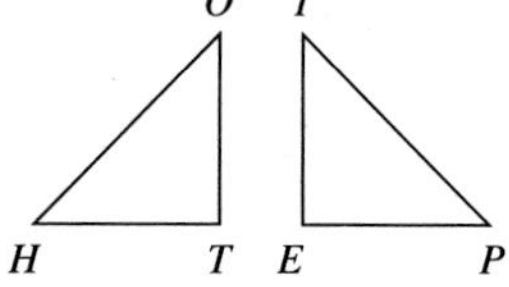

Congruent segments (p. 51) Congruent segments are segments that have the same length.

Example $\overline{AB}$ is congruent to $\overline{WX}$.

Coordinate plane (p. 467) A coordinate plane is formed by the intersection of a horizontal number line, called the x-axis, and a vertical number line, called the y-axis.

Example

Coordinates (p. 467) Each point on the coordinate plane is identified by a unique ordered pair of numbers called its coordinates. The first coordinate tells you how to move from the origin along the x-axis. The second coordinate tells you how to move from the origin along the y-axis.

Example The ordered pair $(-2, 1)$ describes the point that is two units to the left of the origin and one unit above the x-axis.

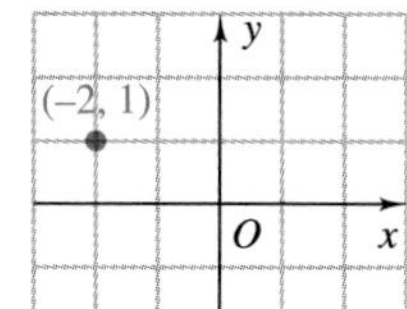

Counting principle (p. 426) The number of outcomes for an event with two or more stages is the product of the number of outcomes at each stage.

Example Flip a coin and roll a number cube. The total number of possible outcomes $= 2 \times 6 = 12$.

Cross products (p. 369) The cross products of the proportion $\frac{a}{b} = \frac{c}{d}$ are $a \times d$ and $b \times c$.

Example The cross products of the proportion $\frac{2}{15} = \frac{6}{45}$ are 2×45 and 15×6.

Cube (p. 252) A cube is a rectangular prism with six congruent faces.

Example

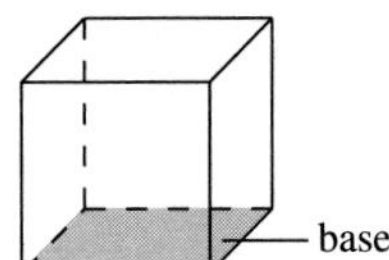

D

Diameter (p. 78) A diameter is a segment that passes through the center of a circle and has both endpoints on the circle.

Example $\overline{RS}$ is a diameter of circle O.

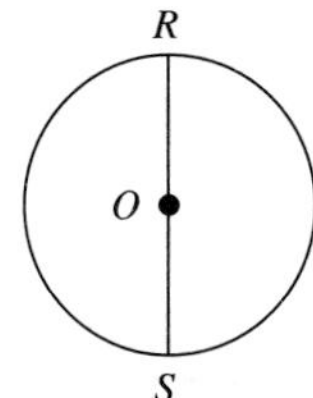

Distributive Property (p. 152) Each term inside a set of parentheses can be multiplied by a factor outside the parentheses.

Example $a \times (b + c) = a \times b + a \times c$.
Likewise, $a \times (b - c) = a \times b - a \times c$.

Divisibility (p. 275) Divisibility is the ability of one number to divide into another with no remainder.

Example 15 and 20 are both divisible by 5.

E

Equal ratios (p. 365) Ratios that make the same comparison or describe the same rate are equal ratios.

Example $\frac{2}{3}$, $\frac{4}{6}$, and $\frac{24}{36}$ are equal ratios.

Equation (p. 212) A mathematical sentence that contains an equal sign, =, is an equation.

Example $2(6 + 17) = 46$

Equilateral triangle (p. 54) An equilateral triangle is a triangle with three congruent sides.

Example $\overline{SL} \cong \overline{LW} \cong \overline{WS}$

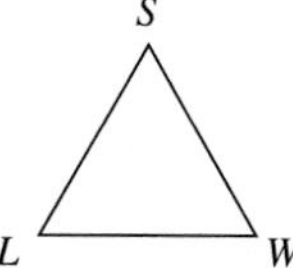

Equivalent fractions (p. 286) Fractions that are equal to each other are equivalent fractions.

Example $\frac{1}{2} = \frac{25}{50}$

Evaluate an expression (p. 197) To evaluate an expression, replace each variable with a number. Then compute, following the order of operations.

Example Evaluate the expression $2^3 + (y - 5)$ for $y = 17$.
$2^3 + (17 - 5) = 8 + 12 = 20$

Expanded form (p. 98) Expanded form shows the place and value of each digit.

Example 0.85 can be written in expanded form as $0.8 + 0.05$.

Exponent (p. 192) An exponent tells you how many times a base is used as a factor.

Example $3^4 = 3 \times 3 \times 3 \times 3$ (exponent)

F

Factor (p. 278) One number is a factor of another if it divides that number with no remainder.

Example 1, 2, 3, 4, 6, 9, 12, 18, and 36 are factors of 36.

Factor tree (p. 279) A factor tree is used to find a number's prime factors.

Example

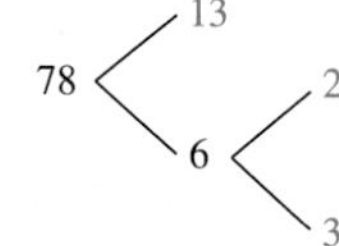

Fair game (p. 411) A game is fair if each player has the same chance of winning.

Example Predicting whether a coin will land "heads" or "tails" is a game where each player has the same chance of winning, so it is a fair game.

Frequency table (p. 5)

A frequency table lists items together with the number of times, or frequency, they occur.

Example

Phones	Tally	Frequency
1	~~||||~~ |||	8
2	~~||||~~ |	6
3	||||	4

Front-end estimation (p. 112)

To use front-end estimation to estimate sums, first add the front-end digits. Then adjust by estimating the sum of the remaining digits. Add the two values.

Example Estimate \$3.49 + \$2.29.

$$3 + 2 = 5$$
$$0.49 + 0.29 \approx 1$$
$$5 + 1 = 6$$

Function (p. 209)

A function is a relationship in which each member of one set is paired with exactly one member of another set.

Example

No. of nickels	Value in cents
0	0
1	5
2	10
3	15

G

Gram (p. 260)

A gram is the basic unit of mass, or weight, in the metric system.

Example A paper clip weighs about 1 g.

Greatest common factor (p. 282)

The greatest common factor (GCF) of two or more numbers is the greatest number that is a factor of all the numbers.

Example 12 and 30 have a GCF of 6.

I

Image (p. 472) A point, line, or figure that is transformed to a new set of coordinates is the image of the original point, line, or figure.

Example Rectangle $A'B'C'D'$ is the image of rectangle $ABCD$.

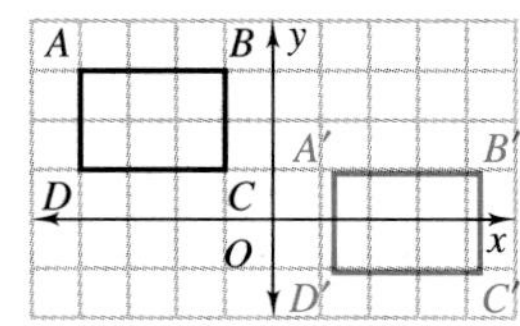

Improper fraction (p. 294) A fraction whose numerator is greater than its denominator is called an improper fraction.

Example $\frac{73}{16}$ is an improper fraction.

Independent events (p. 429) Two events are independent if the outcome of one event has no effect on the outcome of the other.

Example Rolling a number cube and tossing a coin are independent events.

Integers (p. 449) Integers are the set of whole numbers and their opposites.

Example $\ldots -3, -2, -1, 0, 1, 2, 3, \ldots$ are integers.

Isosceles triangle (p. 54) An isosceles triangle is a triangle with at least two congruent sides.

Example $\overline{LM} \cong \overline{LB}$

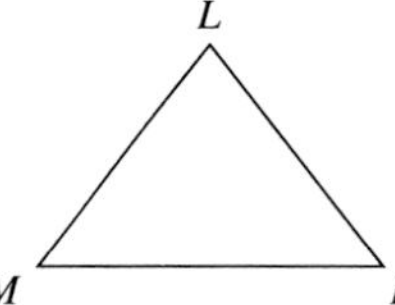

L

Least common denominator (p. 301) The least common denominator (LCD) of two or more fractions is the least common multiple (LCM) of their denominators.

Example The LCD of the fractions $\frac{3}{8}$ and $\frac{7}{10}$ is 40.

Least common multiple (p. 297) The smallest number that is a common multiple of two or more numbers is the least common multiple (LCM).

Example The LCM of 15 and 6 is 30.

Line (p. 41) A line continues without end in opposite directions.

Example $\overleftrightarrow{AB}$ represents a line.

Line graph (p. 21)

A line graph shows how an amount changes over time.

Example This line graph represents seasonal snow blower sales (in thousands) for a large chain of department stores.

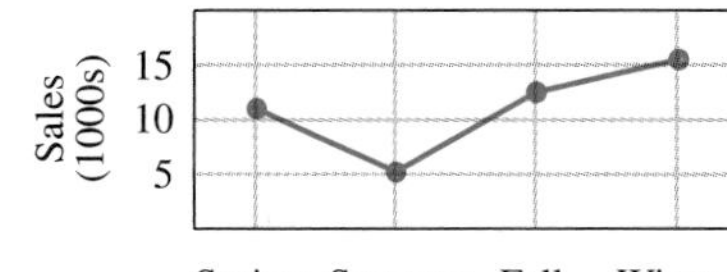

Line plot (p. 5)

A line plot displays data on a horizontal line.

Example This line plot shows video game scores during 13 sessions of play.

45	46	47	48	49	50
				×	
			×	×	
		×	×	×	×
×	×	×	×	×	×

Line symmetry (p. 74)

A figure has line symmetry if a line can be drawn through the figure so that one side is a mirror image of the other.

Example The figure shown has one line of symmetry, l.

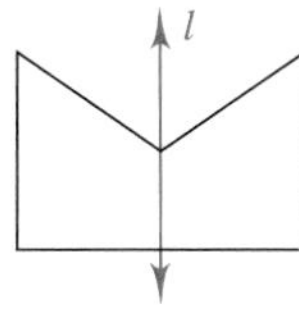

Liter (p. 262)

A liter (L) is the basic unit of capacity, or volume, in the metric system.

Example A pitcher holds about 2 L of juice.

M

Mean (p. 11)

The mean of a set of data is the sum of the data divided by the number of pieces of data.

Example The mean temperature (°F) for the set of temperatures, 44, 52, 48, 55, 60, 67, and 58, is approximately 54.86°F.

Median (p. 12)

The median is the middle number in a set of data when the data are arranged in numerical order.

Example Temperatures (°F) for one week arranged in numerical order are 44, 48, 52, 55, 58, 60, and 67. 55 is the median temperature because it is the middle number in the set of data.

Meter (p. 124) A meter (m) is the basic unit of length in the metric system.

Example A doorknob is about 1 m from the floor.

Mixed number (p. 294) A mixed number shows the sum of a whole number and a fraction.

Example $3\frac{11}{16}$ is a mixed number; $3\frac{11}{16} = 3 + \frac{11}{16}$

Mode (p. 12) The mode is the data item that appears most often.

Example The mode of the set of wages \$2.50, \$3.75, \$3.60, \$2.75, \$2.75, \$3.70, is \$2.75.

Multiple (p. 297) A multiple of a number is the product of that number and any nonzero whole number.

Example The number 39 is a multiple of 13.

N

Net (p. 253) The pattern that you cut out and fold to form a three-dimensional figure is called a net.

Example This net can be folded to make a cube.

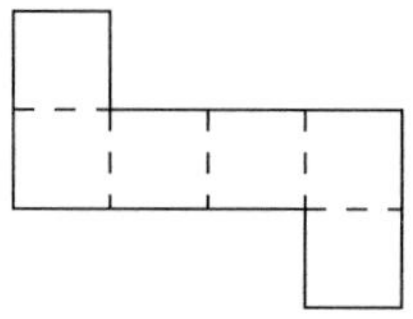

Noncollinear points (p. 42) If there is no line that goes through all the points in a set, the points are noncollinear.

Example Points S, Q, R, and T are noncollinear.

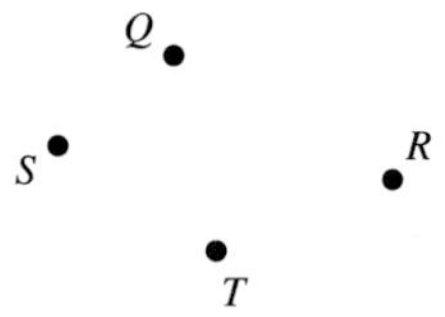

Q

S

R

T

Numerical expression (p. 196) An expression that contains only numbers and mathematical symbols is a numerical expression.

Example $2(5 + 7) - 14$ is a numerical expression.

O

Obtuse angle (p. 47)

An obtuse angle is any angle that measures greater than 90° and less than 180°.

Example

Order of operations (p. 148)

1. Do all operations within parentheses.
2. Do all work with exponents.
3. Multiply and divide from left to right.
4. Add and subtract from left to right.

Example $2^3(7 - 4) = 2^3 \cdot 3 = 8 \cdot 3 = 24$

Ordered pair (p. 467)

An ordered pair is a pair of numbers that describe the location of a point on a coordinate plane. The first value is the x-coordinate and the second value is the y-coordinate.

Example $(-2, 1)$. The x-coordinate is -2; the y-coordinate is 1.

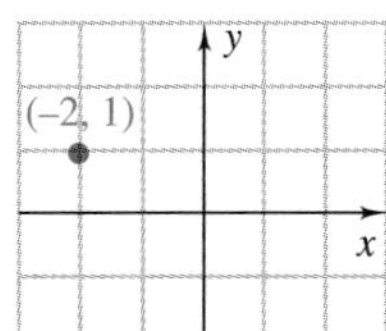

Origin (p. 467)

The origin is the point of intersection of the x- and y-axes on a coordinate plane.

Example The ordered pair that describes the origin is (0, 0).

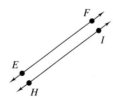

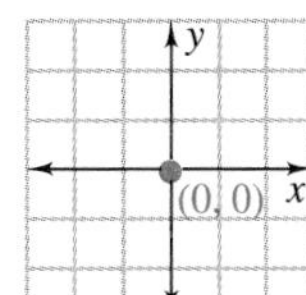

P

Parallel lines (p. 43)

Parallel lines are lines on the same plane that do not intersect.

Example $\overleftrightarrow{EF} \parallel \overleftrightarrow{HI}$

Parallelogram (p. 62) A parallelogram has both pairs of opposite sides parallel.

Example $\overline{KV}$ is parallel to $\overline{AD}$ and $\overline{AK}$ is parallel to $\overline{DV}$.

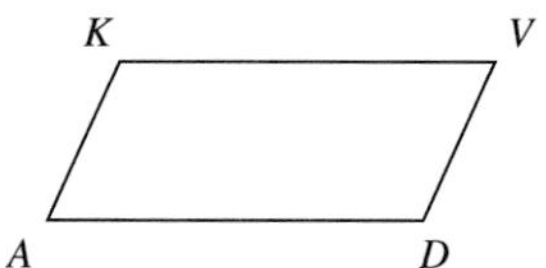

Percent (p. 384) A percent is a ratio that compares a number to 100. The symbol for percent is %.

Example The ratio 50 to 100 is a percent because 50 is compared to 100.
$\frac{50}{100} = 50\%$

Perimeter (p. 125) The perimeter of a figure is the distance around it.

Example The perimeter of $ABCD$=
2 ft + 4 ft + 2 ft + 4 ft = 12 ft.

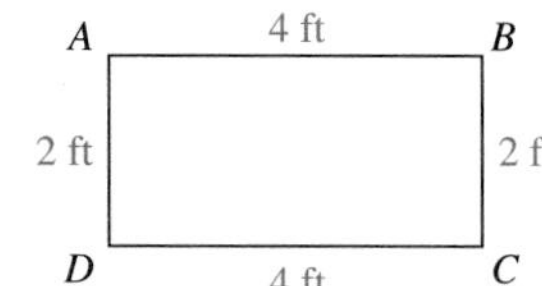

Perpendicular lines (p. 47) Perpendicular lines are lines that intersect to form right angles.

Example $\overleftrightarrow{DE} \perp \overleftrightarrow{RS}$

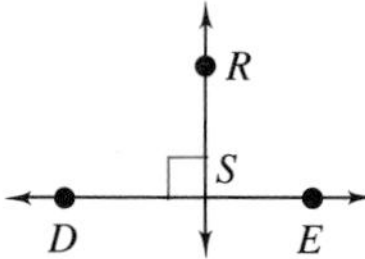

Point (p. 41) A point is a position in space. It has no size, only location.

Example D, B, and N represent points.

Polygon (p. 58) A polygon is a closed plane figure formed by three or more line segments.

Example The figure $CDEFG$ is a convex polygon. The figure $VWXYZ$ is not convex.

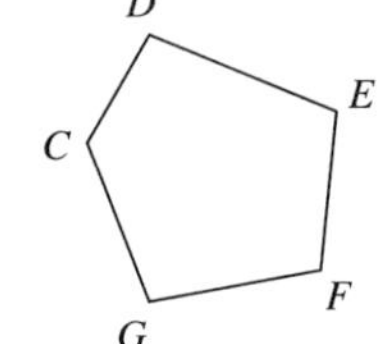

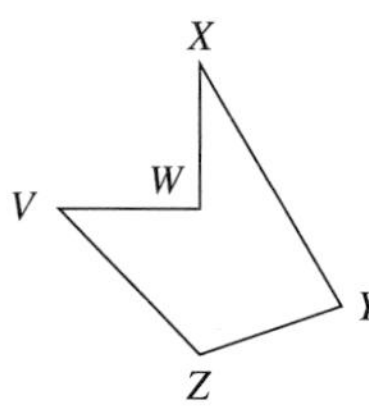

Population (p. 436)	A population is a group of people or objects about whom information is gathered.
Example	A quality control inspector examines a sample of the population, which is the output of a factory.
Power (p. 192)	A number that is expressed using an exponent is called a power.
Example	2^4 is two to the fourth power; $2^4 = 2 \times 2 \times 2 \times 2$
Prime factorization (p. 279)	Writing a composite number as the product of its prime factors is called prime factorization.
Example	The prime factorization of 30 is $2 \times 3 \times 5$.
Prime number (p. 278)	A number that has exactly two factors, 1 and the number itself, is a prime number.
Example	13 is a prime number because its only factors are 1 and 13.
Probability (p. 421)	Probability is used to describe how likely it is that an event will happen. The ratio for probability, P(E), is: $P(E) = \dfrac{\text{number of favorable outcomes}}{\text{number of possible outcomes}}$.
Example	The probability of spinning the number 4 is $\frac{1}{8}$.
Proportion (p. 369)	A proportion is an equation stating that two ratios are equal. The cross products of a proportion are always equal.
Example	The equation $\frac{3}{12} = \frac{12}{48}$ is a proportion because $3 \times 48 = 12 \times 12$.
Protractor (p. 45)	A protractor is a tool used to measure and draw angles.
Example	$m\angle A = 40°$
Pyramid (p. 252)	Pyramids are three-dimensional figures with only one base. The base is a polygon and the other faces are triangles. A pyramid is named by the shape of its base.
Example	The figure shown is a rectangular pyramid.

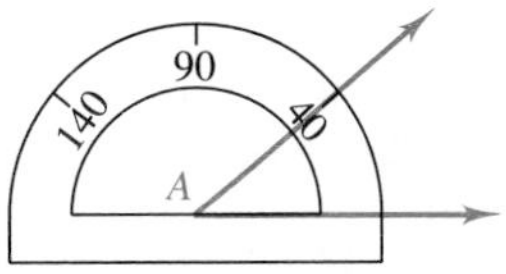

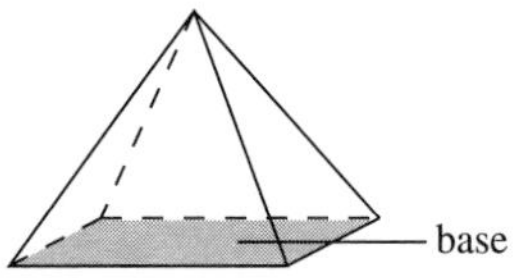

Q

Quadrant (p. 468) The x- and y-axes divide the coordinate plane into four regions, called quadrants.

Example

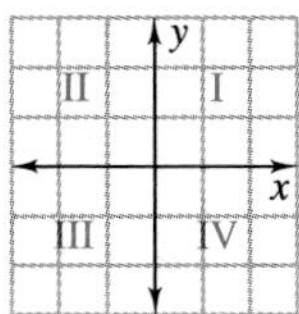

R

Radius (p. 78) A radius is a segment that has one endpoint at the center and the other endpoint on the circle.

Example $\overline{OA}$ is a radius of circle O.

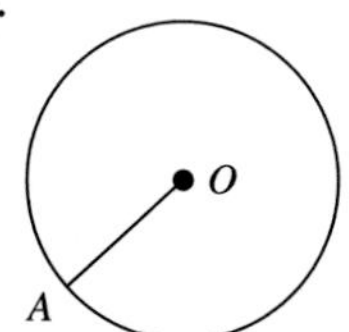

Range (p. 6) The range of a set of data is the difference between the greatest and the least values in the set.

Example Data set: 62, 109, 234, 35, 96, 49, 201
Range: $234 - 35 = 199$

Rate (p. 366) A rate is a ratio that compares two quantities measured in two different units.

Example A student typed an 1,100 word essay in 50 min, or 22 words/min.

Ratio (p. 363) A ratio is a comparison of two numbers.

Example A ratio can be written in three different ways: 72 to 100, 72 : 100, and $\frac{72}{100}$.

Ray (p. 42) A ray is a part of a line. It consists of one endpoint and all the points of the line on one side of the endpoint.

Example $\overrightarrow{SW}$ represents a ray.

Reciprocal (p. 347) Two numbers are reciprocals if their product is 1. Dividing by a number is the same as multiplying by the reciprocal of that number.

Example The numbers 5 and $\frac{1}{5}$ are reciprocals because $5 \times \frac{1}{5} = 1$.

Rectangle (p. 62) A rectangle is a parallelogram with four right angles.

Example

Reflection (p. 473) A reflection flips a figure across a line.

Example $K'L'M'N'$ is a reflection of $KLMN$ over the y-axis.

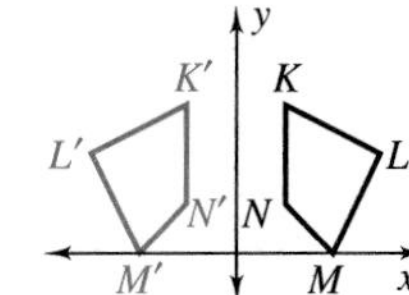

Repeating decimal (p. 304) A decimal whose digits repeat without end is a repeating decimal. A bar indicates the digits that repeat.

Example $0.6666\ldots$ or $0.\overline{6}$

Rhombus (p. 62) A rhombus is a parallelogram with four congruent sides.

Example

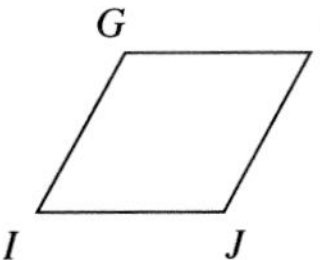

Right angle (p. 46) A right angle is an angle with a measure of 90°.

Example $m\angle D = 90°$.

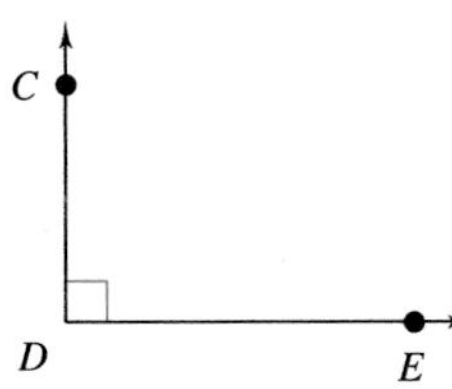

Right triangle (p. 54) A right triangle is a triangle with a right angle.

Example $m\angle B = 90°$.

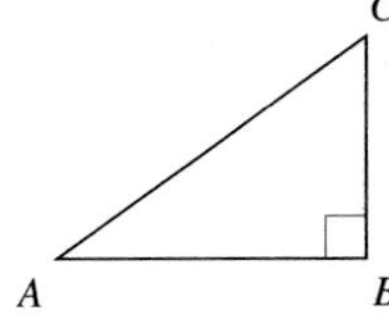

Student Study Guide

S

Sample (p. 436)

A sample of a group is a smaller subgroup selected from within the group. A representative sample of a group is a subgroup that has the same characteristics as the larger group. A random sample of a group is a subgroup selected at random from the group.

Example A representative sample of last week's math quizzes would include quizzes from each of several math classes. A random sample could be obtained by shuffling all the quizzes together and selecting a certain number of them without looking at them.

Scalene triangle (p. 54)

A scalene triangle is a triangle with no congruent sides.

Example

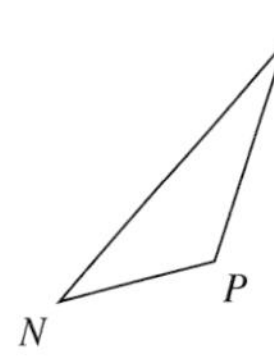

Segment (p. 41)

A segment is part of a line. It consists of two points and all the points on the line that are between the two points.

Example $\overline{CB}$ represents a segment.

Similar (p. 71)

Figures that have the same shape are similar.

Example $\triangle ABC \sim \triangle RTS.$

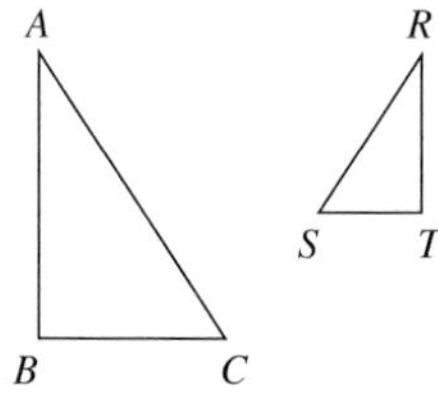

Simplest form of a fraction (p. 289)

A fraction is in simplest form when the GCF of the numerator and denominator is 1.

Example The fraction $\frac{3}{7}$ is in simplest form because the GCF of 3 and 7 is 1.

Simulation (p. 414)

A simulation is a model of a real-world situation.

Example A baseball team has an equal chance of winning or losing the next game. You can toss a coin to simulate the outcome.

Solution of an equation (p. 213)

A value of the variable that makes the equation true is called a solution of the equation.

Example 4 is the solution of $x + 5 = 9$.

Spreadsheet (p. 16) A spreadsheet is a tool used for organizing and analyzing data. Spreadsheets are arranged in rows and columns. A cell is the box on a spreadsheet where a row and a column meet. The names of the row and column determine the name of the cell. A cell may contain data values, labels, or formulas.

Example In the spreadsheet shown, column C and row 2 meet at the shaded box, cell C2. The value of cell C2 is 2.75.

	A	B	C	D	E
1	0.50	0.70	0.60	0.50	2.30
2	1.50	0.50	2.75	2.50	7.25

Square (p. 62) A square is a parallelogram with four right angles and four congruent sides.

Example

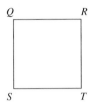

Straight angle (p. 47) An angle that measures 180° is called a straight angle.

Example $m\angle TPL = 180°$

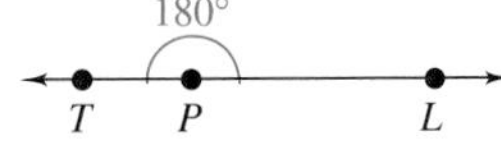

Straightedge (p. 51) A straightedge is a tool used to draw lines, rays, and segments. It is similar to a ruler, but does not have marks to indicate measure.

Example A ruler, if you ignore the markings, can be used as a straightedge.

Surface area of a rectangular prism (p. 256) The surface area of a rectangular prism is the sum of the areas of the faces.

Example Surface area $= 4 \times 12 + 2 \times 9 = 66$ in^2.

Each square = 1 in.^{2}

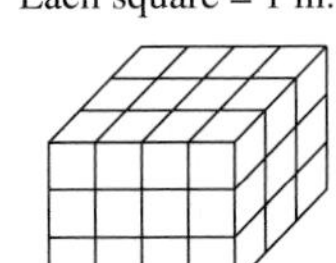

T

Terminating decimal (p. 304) A terminating decimal is a decimal that stops or terminates.

Example Both 0.6 and 0.7265 are terminating decimals.

Student Study Guide

Tessellations (p. 82) Tessellations are repeated geometric designs that cover a plane with no gaps and no overlaps.

Example

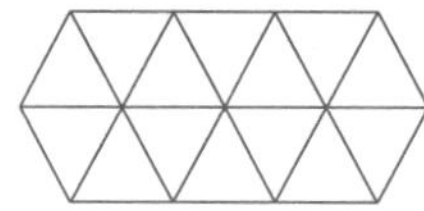

Translation (p. 472) A transformation that slides points, lines, or figures on a coordinate plane is a translation.

Example Rectangle *ABCD* has been translated to rectangle *A′B′C′D′*.

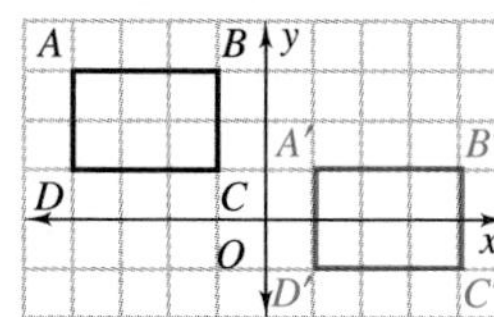

Trapezoid (p. 62) A trapezoid has exactly one pair of parallel sides.

Example

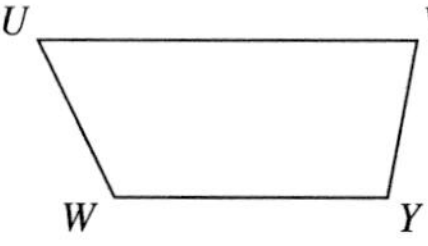

Tree diagram (p. 425) A tree diagram displays all the possible outcomes of an event.

Example There are for 4 possible outcomes for tossing 2 coins: HH, HT, TH, TT.

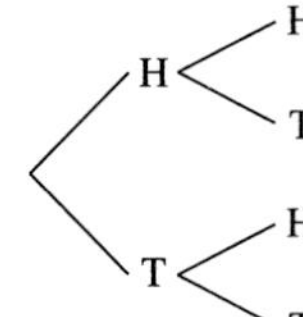

U

Unit rate (p. 366) A unit rate compares a quantity to a unit of one.

Example Miles per hour is a unit rate that compares distance traveled, in miles, to one unit of time, one hour.

V

Variable (p. 196) A variable is a symbol, usually a letter, that stands for a number.

Example x is a variable in the equation $9 - x = 3$.

Variable expression (p. 196) A variable expression is an expression that contains at least one variable.

Example $7 + x$

Vertex of a polygon (p. 237) A vertex of a polygon is any point where two sides of the polygon meet.

Example C, D, E, F, and G are all vertices of the pentagon shown.

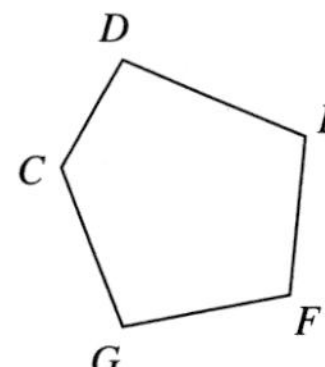

Volume (p. 259) The volume of a three-dimensional figure is the number of cubic units needed to fill the space inside the figure.

Example The volume of the rectangular prism is 36 in.^{3}.

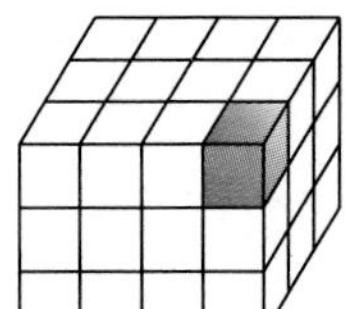

each cube = 1 in.^{3}

X

***x*-axis (p. 467)** The x-axis is the horizontal number line that, together with the y-axis, forms the coordinate plane.

Example

Y

***y*-axis (p. 467)** The y-axis is the vertical number line that, together with the x-axis, forms the coordinate plane.

Example

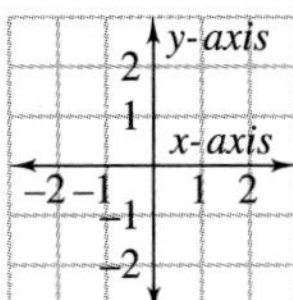

Z

Zero pairs (p. 453) Zero pairs are pairs of tiles that represent the number zero.

Example 

Index

Selected Answers

CHAPTER 1

1-1 pages 5–7

On Your Own **7. a.** 1, 3, 6, 0 **9.** 17.5 in. **13. b.** VA, MA, NY, OH **c.** No; the data are not numerical

Mixed Review **1.** 1,139 **2.** 218 **3.** 18,629 **4.** 174 **5.** 1 quarter, 2 dimes, 1 nickel, and 2 pennies

1-2 pages 8–10

On Your Own **15.** Carmen **17.** 16 triangles **19.** 65 numbered pages **21.** 1:10 P.M.

Mixed Review **3.** 8 in. **4.** 4,096 members

1-3 pages 11–14

On Your Own **9. a.** 11 songs; 12 songs **b.** mode; it is the most frequent number of songs appearing on CDs.

Mixed Review **1.** 764 **2.** 1,488 **3.** 1,368 **4.** 31 **5.** 7,600 ft

Checkpoint

1.

grams fat	tally	freq
0	卌 III	8
1	卌 IIII	9
2	卌	5
3	III	3

2.

```
   ×
×  ×
×  ×
×  ×
×  ×  ×
×  ×  ×
×  ×  ×  ×
×  ×  ×  ×
×  ×  ×  ×
-----------
0  1  2  3
```

3. 8.6 players **4.** 9 players **5.** 11 players

Problem Solving Practice page 15

1. $2 **3.** 6 y and 9 y **5.** 7

1-4 pages 16–19

On Your Own **9.** Subtract the value in cell B2 from the value in cell C2; multiply the value in cell D2 by 6. **11. a.** No; it would calculate Tamara working a negative ten hours instead of the two hours she worked. **13.** =B2 + C2 + D2; =B3 + C3 + D3; =B4 + C4 + D4; =B5 + C5 + D5; =B6 + C6 + D6 **15.** No; she could have added the scores for each group and divided by 3. **17. b.** yellow **c.** green **d.** yellow; they had the highest mean score.

Mixed Review **1.** 26 **2.** 17 **3.** 15. **4.** 11 **5.** 49°F

1-5 pages 20–23

On Your Own **17.** the number of balloons in the Fiesta has increased over the past 20 y. **19.** 1980 to 1981 **21.** 5 teachers **23.** circle graph; two parts are being compared to a whole. **25.** bar graph; several life spans are being compared.

Mixed Review **1.** spreadsheet **2.** cell **3.** formula **4.** Yes; the mean of the test scores is 85.

Practice page 24

1.

```
 ×
 ×    ×              ×
 ×    ×    ×    ×    ×    ×
-----------------------------
196  197  199  202  205  210
```

3. 14 mi/h **7.** 3,523; 3,662; no mode **9.** line graph **11.** ME; RI **13.** Maine has about 3 times as much land as Vermont.

1-6 pages 25–28

On Your Own **7.** Answers may vary. Sample: intervals of 200 **9.** The population declined from 1950 to 1990 **11. c.** Both the cost of a public college education and a private college education are increasing.

Mixed Review **1.** bar graph **2.** bar graph **3.** line graph **4.** 21 and 22

Checkpoint **1.** c **2.**

Mean Scores: 100, 80, 60, 40, 20, 0; J, E, N

3. Army **4.** 238 medals of honor

1-7 pages 29–31

Mixed Review **2.** 20 h

Wrap Up pages 32–33

1.

vowel	tally	freq
a	卌卌卌	15
e	卌卌卌	15
i	卌||	7
o	卌卌	10
u	||||	4

2.

x x x x x x (the: x; and: x; a: x x x x; are)

the and a are

3. 9 ways **4.** 6 ways **5.** 45; 49; 50 **6.** 6; 7; 9 **7.** String sales on 9/10/93 totaled $65. **8.** =B2 + C2 + D2 **9.** $940.00 **10.** bar graph **11.** line graph **12.** circle graph

Getting Ready for Chapter 2 **1.** triangle **2.** rhombus, parallelogram, square, rectangle **3.** rectangle, parallelogram **4.** circle **5.** Sample: tip of an Indian arrowhead. **6.** Sample: tile **7.** Sample: pizza **8.** Sample: photograph

Cumulative Review page 37

1. A **2.** A **3.** C **4.** C **5.** C **6.** D **7.** B **8.** C

CHAPTER 2

On Your Own **21.** *A*, *B*, and *C* **23.** Sample: $\overline{AC}$, $\overline{BD}$, $\overline{DE}$ **25.** Sample: $\overleftrightarrow{AC}$ and $\overleftrightarrow{DE}$ **27.** $\overline{XY}$ and $\overline{WZ}$ **29.** • • • • • *A B C D E* **31.** always **33.** sometimes **35.** never

Mixed Review **1.** 120 **2.** 20 **3.** 52 **4.** 50 **5.** 12

2-2 pages 45–49

On Your Own **11. a.** $\overrightarrow{LK}$, $\overrightarrow{LM}$, $\overrightarrow{LN}$ **b.** $\angle MLN$: acute; $\angle KLM$: right; $\angle KLN$: obtuse

13.

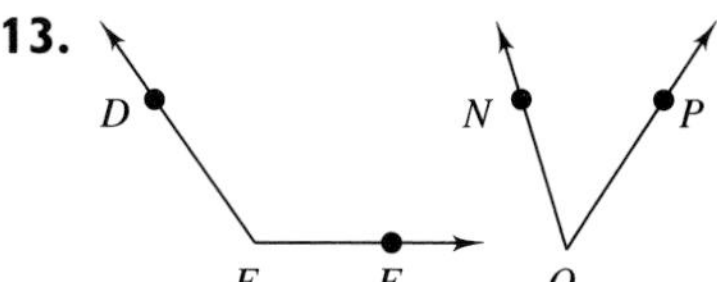

15. Samples: 90°, 180° You need only a straight edge to draw a straight angle; a corner to draw a right angle. **17.** 60° **19.** 150° **21.** about 120°; 125°; obtuse **27.** 45° **29.** A **31. a.** 180° **b.** 70° **c.** 120° **d.** 90° **e.** $\angle AGE$, $\angle BGE$, $\angle BGF$, $\angle CGF$ **f.** $\angle AGD$, $\angle DGF$, $\angle CGE$ **g.** $\angle AGF$

Mixed Review **1.** 997 **2.** 1,494 **3.** mode **4.** Sample: *A*, *B*, *C* **5.** Sample $\overrightarrow{BC}$, $\overrightarrow{CB}$ **6.** 12 books

Problem Solving Practice page 50

1. C; E **3.** 7 days

2-3 pages 51–53

On Your Own **7., 9.** Answers may vary.

Mixed Review **1.** < **2.** =

3.

data	tally	freq
0	||	2
1	||	2
2	||	2
3	||	2
4	||	2

4. 4 **5.** $\angle 1$ **6.** 145° **7.** 10,880 ft

2-4 pages 54–57

On Your Own **13.** isosceles **15.** equilateral **17.** acute **19.** Yes; it has at least two congruent sides; no; it may only have two congruent sides

21. **27.**

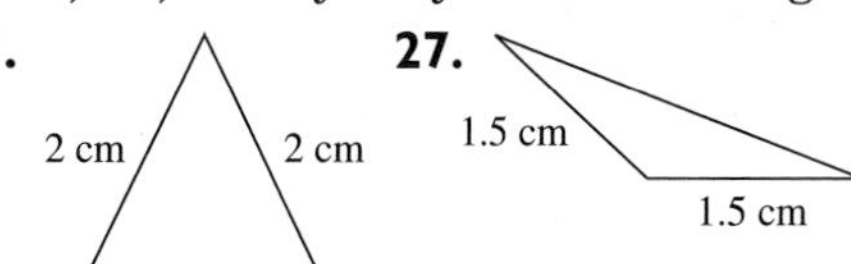

29. Not possible; an acute △ has three acute angles.

Selected Answers

Mixed Review **1.** 4,527; 3,201; 3,097; 2,852; 2,684; 978 **2.** about 88 million **3.** compass **4.** congruent **5.** 6

Checkpoint **1.** $\overleftrightarrow{LM}$, $\overleftrightarrow{KN}$ **2.** Sample: $\overrightarrow{JK}$, $\overrightarrow{JL}$, $\overrightarrow{JP}$ **3.** Sample: $\overline{LM}$, $\overline{JP}$, $\overline{JN}$ **4.** Sample: $\angle LJK$ **5.** Sample $\angle KJM$ **6.** Sample $\angle LJP$ **7.** Sample $\angle LJM$ **8.** Sample: L, J, M **9.** Sample: J, P, M **10.** 47° **13.** B **14.** Answers may vary. Sample: quilt designs, tile floors, sails

2-5 pages 58–61

On Your Own **7.** hexagon **9.** decagon **11.** octagon **13. a.** 3 congruent sides and 3 congruent angles **b.** 4 congruent sides and 4 congruent angles **c.** 5 congruent sides and 5 congruent angles **d.** equal sides and equal angles **15.** Sample: quadruplet, quadrant, quadriceps **19.** D

Mixed Review **1.** 230 **2.** 15 **3.** acute **4.** obtuse **5.** 12 packages

2-6 pages 62–65

On Your Own **13.** **15.**

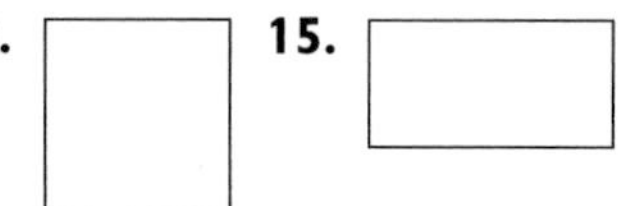

17.

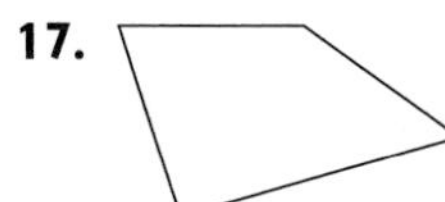

19. parallelogram, (rectangle)

23. a. congruent **b.** isosceles **c.** Isosceles trapezoid because two of its sides are congruent. **25.** parallelogram, rectangle, rhombus, square, trapezoid **27.** rectangle, rhombus, square **29.** Some **31.** All **33.** Some

Mixed Review **1.** 29 **2.** 25,000 **3.** octagon **4.** pentagon **5.** 15°

2-7 pages 66–68

On Your Own **11. a.** 17 **b.** 4 **13.** 17 pennies; 12 pennies, 1 nickel; 7 pennies, 1 dime; 7 pennies, 2 nickels; 2 pennies, 1 dime, 1 nickel; 2 pennies, 3 nickels

Mixed Review **1.** 630 **2.** 380 **3.** 11 **4.** 9 **5.** trapezoid **6.** parallelogram **7.** 82

Practice page 69

1. S, R, P **3.** $\overline{RQ}$, $\overline{SR}$, $\overline{PR}$ **5.** $\angle QRP$ **7.** 50° **9.** 140° **11.** 40° **17.** isosceles **19.** right **21.** acute **25.** true **27.** true

2-8 pages 70–73

On Your Own **7.** a, d **9.** similar **11.** congruent, similar **15.** Congruent; The window must be the same size and shape to fit in the window opening. **17. b.** No; Rhombuses can be different shapes. **c.** Yes; They are always the same shape. **19.** They appear to be similar.

Mixed Review **1.** = **2.** = **3.** circle graph **4.** 38 **5.** 18

2-9 pages 74–77

On Your Own

7. **9.**

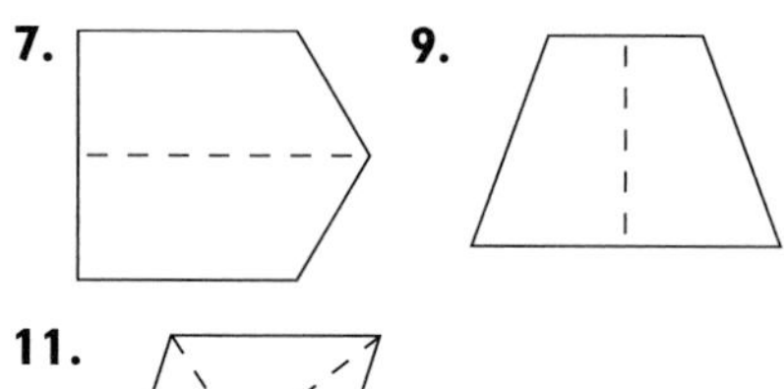

11.

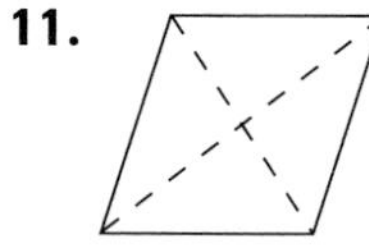

13.

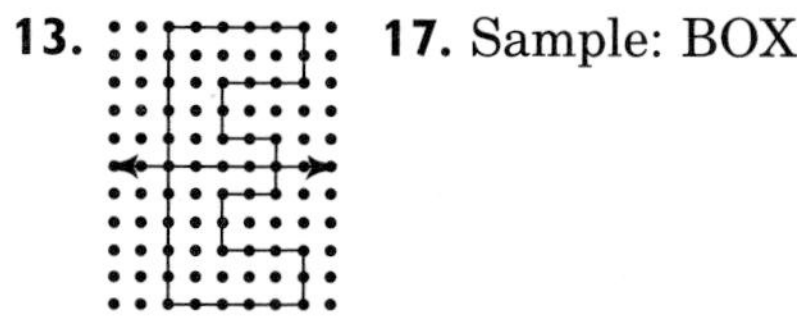

17. Sample: BOX

Mixed Review **1.** 332 **2.** 332 **3.** equilateral **4.** scalene **5.** c, b **6.** a, b, c **7.** 5 and 7

Checkpoint **1.** 10 **2.** 8 **3.** 4 **5. a.** 6 **b.** 21 **6. a.** A, B, E **b.** A, B, D, E **7.** A

2-10 pages 78–81

On Your Own **11.** $\overline{RT}$ **13.** $\overline{RT}$, $\overline{ST}$ **15.** 5 in. **19.** 125 ft **21.** 360 ÷ no. of cars **23.** $\angle ACB$ is always a right angle.

528

Mixed Review **1.** = **2.** > **3.** 0 **4.** 1 **5.** 16 **6.** 8

2-11 pages 82–85

On Your Own **7.** yes **9.** yes **13.** D

Mixed Review **1.** 37,442 **2.** 7,079 **3.** 4 **4.** 7 **5.** twice **6.** diameter

Wrap Up pages 86–87

1. A C B **2.** J M K N **3.** 3; 6; 1 **4.** straight **5.** acute **6.** obtuse **7.** Sample: $\overline{OX}$, $\overline{OY}$, $\overline{OV}$ **8.** $\overline{XV}$ **9.** $\angle XOY$, $\angle VOY$ **10.** $\overline{VW}$, $\overline{WY}$, $\overline{VX}$ **13.** B **14.** similar **15.** neither **16.** 2 **18.** 5

Getting Ready for Chapter 3 **1.** hundreds' **2.** 6

Cumulative Review page 91

1. A **2.** C **3.** B **4.** D **5.** D **6.** A **7.** A **8.** B **9.** C **10.** C

CHAPTER 3

3-1 pages 95–97

On Your Own **13.** eight hundredths **15.** fifty-six hundredths **19.** 0.4 **21.** 0.6 **23.** 0.8 **25.** about 0.25

Mixed Review **1.** 2 **2.** 95 **3.** yes **4.** no **5.** 4,250 lb

3-2 pages 98–100

On Your Own **19. a.** 0.22 **b.** 2 tenths; 2 hundredths; 0.2 + 0.02 **21.** $.06 **23.** $.75 **25.** 5 tenths **27.** 5 millionths **35.** 0.2 + 0.04 + 0.009 + 0.0008 **37.** Every 4 years a day is added. These years are called leap years. **39.** 4.7 pt **41.** 0.001 s

Mixed Review **1.** acute **2.** acute **3.** 0.9 **4.** 1.05 **5.** thirty-five hundredths **6.** two and thirty-three hundredths **7.** $19.50

3-3 pages 101–104

On Your Own **13.** > **15.** > **17.** > **21.** No, the number of decimals between 0.4 and 0.5 is unlimited. Other decimal places can be added to 0.4 such as thousandths, ten thousandths, etc. **23.** 0.4; 0.8; 1.1 **25.** 4.28, 4.37, 8.7, 11.09, 11.4 **27.** Light-year is the distance light travels in one year; i.e., approx. 6 trillion miles. This unit enables astronomers to measure vast solar distances with smaller, more understandable numbers.

Mixed Review **1.** 68° **2.** 31° **3.** 3 tenths **4.** 3 tens **5.** 25 lb

Checkpoint **1.** nine tenths **2.** one hundredth **3.** seventy-three hundredths **4.** sixty hundredths **5.** 0.3 **6.** 0.02 **7.** 0.92 **8.** 6 tenths **9.** 7 hundredths **10.** 8 ones **11.** 3 thousandths **12.** < **13.** = **14.** >

3-4 pages 105–107

On Your Own **9.** No; 1,320 people will get in **11.** About 2.97 qt **13.** $14.77

Mixed Review **1.** 78° **2.** 25° **3.** < **4.** > **5.** 243 passengers

3-5 pages 108–110

On Your Own **11.** 0.95 **13.** 47, 4, 7 **15.** 11 **17.** 0.7 **19.** 0.3 **21.** 1.09 **23.** 1.55 **25.** 2.00 **27.** 1.76

Mixed Review **1.** yes **2.** no **3.** false **4.** true **5.** 60 times (61 times in a leap year)

3-6 pages 111–114

On Your Own **19.** 0.1 **21.** 2.7084 **23.** $14.00 **25.** $45.00 **27. a.** about 1.8 oz; about 5.2 oz **b.** about 0.2 oz **c.** about 3.7 oz **29.** about $118 **31.** Answers may vary. Sample: Two adults, one child—Cedar Point **33.** B **35. a.** 3.158 and 6.8 **b.** 13.228 and 6.8 **37.** higher; all numbers have been rounded up. **39.** $226,000 more

Mixed Review **1.** Sample: $\overleftrightarrow{ST}$, $\overleftrightarrow{SU}$, $\overleftrightarrow{SV}$ **2.** Sample: $\overrightarrow{TS}$, $\overrightarrow{TU}$, $\overrightarrow{UV}$ **3.** 2.6 **4.** 0.1 **5.** 60 books

Problem Solving Practice page 115

1. 7,282 mi **3.** Steve, Sara, Sam, Sue **7.** Yes; the total cost of the tickets is $28. The estimated discount total is $3.50. $28 − $3.50 = $24.50

3-7 pages 116–119

On Your Own **15.** 6; 5.1 **17.** 9; 8.561 **19.** 3; 2.7 **21.** 14; 13.87 **23.** 0.27 **27.** gas and firewood/charcoal **29.** 0 **31.** $4.25 **33.** C **35.** Charges based on the dollar amount of the order are less.

Mixed Review **1.** True **2.** False **3.** 1.949 **4.** 23.0 **5.** $269.50

3-8 pages 120–122

On Your Own **15. a.** Answers may vary. Sample: Data is organized into cells. **b.** Put In; Took Out; End of Day **c.** $24.50 **d.** less; Start of Day equaled $20 **e.** $24.50 **f.** Start of Day: 20.00, 24.50, 19.49, 23.99, 33.24; End of Day: 17.50, 19.49, 23.99, 33.24, 8.24

Mixed Review **1.** 45.25 **2.** 4.6 **3.** 22.35 **4.** 4.16 **5.** $70

Practice page 123

7. five tenths **9.** seventy hundredths **11.** seventy-five and three hundredths **13.** 0.45 **15.** 7 tenths **17.** 7 tens **19.** 7 hundredths **21.** 100.051 **23.** 30 + 8 + 0.8 + 0.001 + 0.0005 **25.** > **27.** < **31.** 6.188 **33.** 95.36 **35.** 3 **37.** $9.00 **39.** $1.00 **41.** 3; 3.0 **43.** 8; 8.461 **45.** 11; 11.53 **47.** 5; 5.909

3-9 pages 124–127

On Your Own **13.** 28 mm **15.** 91 mm **17.** 110 mm **19.** 18 m **21.** no; 30 m **23.** no; 18 cm **27.** centimeter **29.** kilometer

Mixed Review **1.** 82° **2.** 136° **3.** False **4.** True **5.** $99.63

Checkpoint **1–4.** Samples given. **1.** 7; 7.32 **2.** 8; 8.26 **3.** 19; 18.19 **4.** 29; 29.2 **5.** 12.04 **6.** 2 **7.** 9.066 **8.** 53.9 **9.** A

3-10 pages 128–131

On Your Own **9. a.** 25 min **13.** Captain EO, Red Baron

Mixed Review **1.** right **2.** acute **3.** 6 mm **4.** meter **5.** 6:00 P.M.

Wrap Up pages 132–133

1. 0.5 **2.** 0.48 **3.** 9.0008 **4.** > **5.** > **6.** = **7.** > **8.** 5.698 **9.** 0.88 **10.** 9.236 **11.** 4.0 **12.** 44 **13.** 0.7 **14.** 1.68 **15.** 0.931 **16.** 53.642 **17.** 357.48 **18.** 85.62 **19.** 65.62 **20.** 0.40 **21.** meter **22.** centimeter **23.** meter **24.** yes; 8:15 P.M. **25.** 1,440 times

Getting Ready for Chapter 4 **1.** about 8 **2.** about 54 **3.** about 1,190 **4.** about 9 **5.** about 8 **6.** about 10 **7.** about 33 **8.** about 231 **9.** about 1,920 **10.** about 3 **11.** about 210 **12.** about 3

Cumulative Review page 137

1. B **2.** C **3.** B **4.** D **5.** A **6.** A **7.** C **8.** D **9.** B **10.** B

CHAPTER 4

4-1 pages 141–144

On Your Own **19.** about 36 **21.** about 0 **23.** about 93 **25.** about 5 **27.** about 8 **29.** about 6 **31.** about 50 ft/s **33.** about 64 g **35. a.** about $300 **b.** about $9 **37.** B **39.** about 60 km

Mixed Review **1.** 1:32 P.M. **2.** 0.54 **3.** 18,000 **4.** 40 **5.** Feb. and Mar.

4-2 pages 145–147

On Your Own **9. a.** Coin, Composition, Condition, Cost **b.** 5 **c.** Answers may vary **e.** $86.75

Mixed Review **1.** about 200 **2.** about 28 **4.** 0.65 **5.** 3.016 **6.** yes

4-3 pages 148–150

On Your Own **9.** subtraction **11.** multiplication **13.** 12 **15.** 7.9 **17.** 60 **19.** 5 **21.** 1.5 **25.** $>$ **27.** $<$ **29.** When the subtraction is in parentheses. **31.** $14 \div (2 + 5) - 1 = 1$ **33.** $(11 - 7) \div 2 = 2$ **35.** no parentheses needed **37.** 28 **39.** 8 **41.** $\div, +, +$ **43.** $-, \times, \div$ or $-, \times, \times$

Mixed Review **1.** \$240 **2.** 28 **3.** about 120 **4.** about 1000 **5.** about 10 **6.** 176 lockers

4-4 pages 151–154

On Your Own **23.** $(3 \times 6) + (3 \times 2)$; $3 \times (6 + 2)$; 24 **25.** 8; 3 **27.** 336 **29.** 560 **31.** 80 **33.** 77

Mixed Review **1.** 15 **2.** 3 **3.** 0 **6.** Exercise 4: 12.25; 11.5; 9 Exercise 5: 8.58; 8.5; 8.5

Checkpoint **1.** about 18 **2.** about 52 **3.** about 60 **4.** about 80 **5.** about 39 **6.** about 1500 **7.** 29 **8.** 6 **9.** 8 **10.** C

Problem Solving Practice page 155

1. 10 calls **3.** 19 rows **5.** May 7 **7.** 204

4-5 pages 156–157

On Your Own **7.** $0.6 \times 0.9 = 0.54$ **9.** $0.5 \times 0.5 = 0.25$ **11.** 0.6 **13.** 1.8 **15.** 0.14 **17.** 0.6 **19.** 0.72 **21.** One and five-tenths times one tenth equals fifteen hundredths.

Mixed Review **1.** $>$ **2.** $<$ **4.** 120 **5.** 2,574 **6.** 82.6

4-6 pages 158–161

On Your Own **21.** 14.72 **23.** 15.857 **25.** 62 **27.** 3500 **29.** 24.78 **31.** 0.124 **33.** 4.5 **35.** 0.1152 **37.** Yes; answers may vary. **39.** False; Sample: $2 \times 3 = 6$, $3 \times 2 = 6$ **43.** 5 cm **45.** 105 calories **47.** 196 calories; more

Mixed Review **1.** 544 **2.** 380 **3.**

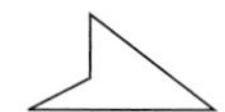

4. **5.** 4.97 L **6.** 8 h 27 min

4-7 pages 162–164

On Your Own **9.** The amount she was charged is needed to solve the problem **11.** about 19.5 hands **13.** The number of stores is needed to solve the problem **17.** Not enough information; The tidal range is 39.4. The water level at low tide is needed.

Mixed Review **1.** 1.52 **2.** 5.7 **3.** 8 **4.** 4 and 24 **5.** 0.05, 0.505, 0.55, 5.55 **6.** 9.004, 9.04, 90.4, 900.4 **7.** 11

Practice page 165

1. about 32 **3.** about 3 **5.** about 5 **7.** about 100 **9.** about 4 **11.** 20 **13.** 1 **15.** 9 **17.** $\div, -$ **19.** $-, \times$ **21.** 6, 4 **23.** 33 **25.** 14 **27.** 60 **29.** 228 **31.** 801 **33.** 0.636 **35.** 6.916 **37.** 0.492 **39.** 0.0252

4-8 pages 166–167

On Your Own **9.** 10 **11.** 0.25 **13.** 1.6 **15.** 16 **17.** 4 **19.** 2 **21.** 3

Mixed Review **1.** 2.714 **2.** 0.0072 **3.** 0.06 **4.** Pool record needed. **5.**

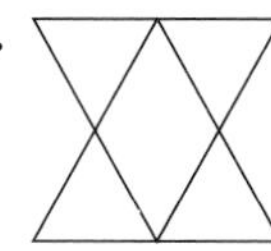

4-9 pages 168–171

On Your Own **23.** 2.5 **25.** 0.003 **27.** 0.02 **29.** 0.05 **31.** 0.073 **33.** 38 **35.** 6,450 **37.** 32 **39.** 0.079 in. **43. a.** 5 **b.** greater than both 3.5 and 0.7

Mixed Review **1.** 15 **2.** 9 **3.** \$12.50/h **4.** 0.336 **5.** 3.5

Checkpoint **1.** 9; 8 **2.** 5; 6; 2 **3.** 32.76 **4.** 1.9598 **5.** \$48.75 **6.** 4.25 **7.** \$14.20 **8.** 16.4

4-10 pages 172–175

On Your Own **7. a.** about \$20.20 **b.** \$9.44

Mixed Review **1.** 0.39 **2.** 1.91 **3.** 0.00082 **4.** RF **5.** $\angle M$

Wrap Up pages 176–177

1. 125 **2.** 30 **3.** 5 **4.** 100 **6.** 72 **7.** 12.3 **8.** 105 **9.** 360 **10.** A **11.** 90; 485 **12.** 30; 216 **13.** $0.3 \times 0.1 = 0.03$ **14.** $0.5 \div 0.1 = 5$ **15.** 0.1286 **16.** 46.08 **17.** 0.75 **18.** 30 **23.** The number of students riding the bus is needed **24.** 153.5 cm tall

Getting Ready for Chapter 5 **2.** x; y; z

Cumulative Review page 181

1. A **2.** C **3.** A **4.** D **5.** D **6.** B **7.** C **8.** D **9.** C **10.** C

CHAPTER 5

5-1 pages 185–187

On Your Own **9.** 35, 42, 49 **11.** 1, 1.25, 1.5 **13.** $\frac{1}{16}, \frac{1}{32}, \frac{1}{64}$ **15.** 1, 1.5, 2.25, 3.375, 5.0625

Mixed Review **1.** 44.7 **2.** 8.1 **3.** \$8 **4.** \$223.11 **5.** seventy-three hundredths **6.** three hundred eighty-six and nine hundred eight thousandths. **7.** \$77

5-2 pages 188–191

On Your Own **13.** 301 **15.** 3,632 **17.** 256,758 **19.** 261,992 **21.** 140 min

Mixed Review **1.** 3.2 **2.** 19.52 **3.** 256; 1,024; 4,096 **4.** 1.1, 1.4, 1.7 **5.** 7 **6.** 12 **7.** 5, 12

5-3 pages 192–195

On Your Own **19.** 7, 9 **21.** 10, 3 **23.** 4^6 **25.** 35 **27.** 183 **29.** 82 **31.** 500 **33.** 2^3 **35. a.** 10,000; 10^5; 100,000 **c.** 100,000,000; 10,000,000,000; 1,000,000,000,000

Mixed Review **1.** 10,000 **2.** 2,400 **3.** 8, 10, 12 **4.** 24, 30, 36 **5.** 5 blocks

Checkpoint **1.** 4, 8, 16, 32, 64 **2.** 10^6 **3.** 4,782,969 **4.** 468 **5.** 6 **6.** 4 **7.** 14

5-4 pages 196–199

On Your Own **19.** 8 **21.** 193 **23.** 3 **25.** 216 **27.** 4 **29.** $r = 8, s = 11, t = 10$ **31.** $x = 10$; 14, 28, 42, 56 **33.** A **35.** 110 + 630

Mixed Review **1.** 15 **2.** 16 **3.** 5^4 **4.** 9^3 **5.** 2, 9, 16, 23, 30 **6.** 95 people

5-5 pages 200–202

On Your Own **13.** 7 h **15.** yes; no; yes **17.** 7 and 9 **19.** 24 and 25

21.

	hat	coat
Anita	Althea	Beth
Cheryl	Anita	Althea
Beth	Cheryl	Anita
Althea	Beth	Cheryl

Mixed Review **1.** 52.27 **2.** 2.689 **3.** n **4.** f **5.** 45 **6.** 38 **7.** 6 outfits

Practice page 203

1. 10, 12, 14 **3.** 3.2, 4.2, 5.2 **5.** 7, 4 **7.** 2, 8 **9.** 24^2 **11.** 6 **13.** 14,348,907 **15.** 4 **17.** 468 **19.** 2r + 4 **21.** 2s + 3 **23.** 5 **25.** 21 **27.** 12 **29.** 30

5-6 pages 204–206

On Your Own **17.** h less than 18, 18 minus h **19.** quotient of 21 and m, 21 divided by m. **21.** $k - 22$ **23.** $3m$ **25.** $3b$ **27.** $a + 3$ **29. a.** 37; 43 **b.** 57 **c.** $n + 10, n - 10, n - 2, n + 2$ **31. a.** $x - 3$ **b.** $x + 10$ **c.** $x - z$ **d.** $x + t$ **33. a.** $15t$ **b.** $15t \div 60$

Mixed Review **1.** 144.72 **2.** 5.176 **3.** = **4.** > **5.** 32 pieces

Problem Solving Practice Page 207

1. 6 days **3.** Joe: 2.5 km; Frank: 1.25 km; Steve: 2.25 km **5.** 15 push pins **7.** 16 s

5-7 pages 208-211

On Your Own **7. a.** 11, 14, 17; 6, 10, 14 **b.** $3n + 5$; $4n - 2$ **c.** Yes; the price increases at a constant rate. **d.** No; you would not order zero tees.

Mixed Review **1.** false **2.** false **3.** x divided by 5 **4.** 14 more than s **5.** $t - 3$ **6.** $n + 8$ **7.** 7 games

5-8 pages 212–216

On Your Own **19.** True **21.** True **23.** yes **25.** yes **27.** no **29.** 88 **31.** 48 **33.** 26.6 **35.** 389 **37.** 74.578

41. a. $1 + 3 + 5 + 7 + 9 = 25$ or 5^2
$1 + 3 + 5 + 7 + 9 + 11 = 36$ or 6^2
$1 + 3 + 5 + 7 + 9 + 11 + 13 = 49$ or 7^2
b. The number of addends is equal to the base of the power. **c.** Use 10 as the base of the power; 10^2 or 100 **d.** 20^2 or 400
43. $p + 1{,}200 = 2{,}250$; 1,050 mi

Mixed Review **1.** hexagon **2.** decagon **5.** ninth stop

Checkpoint **1.** B **2.** $y + 12$ **3.** $b + 5$ **4.** $6 - w$ **5.** $22 - r$ **6.** 50 **7.** 385 **8.** 2

5-9 pages 217–219

On Your Own **13.** no **15.** no **17.** 125 **19.** 18 **21.** 51,772 **23.** 1.65 **25.** 162.5 **29. a.** $1.28g = 16$ **b.** 12.5 gal **31.** 1,188; 1,287; 1,386; 1,485; $99 \times 16 = 1{,}584$; $99 \times 17 = 1{,}683$

Mixed Review **1.** 26 cm **2.** 116 m **3.** 6 **4.** 17 **5.** 18 numbers

Wrap Up pages 220–221

1. 162; 486; 1,458; start with the number 2 and multiply by 3 repeatedly **2.** 9 **3.** 89 **4.** 16 **5.** 1.25 **6.** $x - 5$ **7.** $y \div p$ **8.** D **9.** $.39 **11.** subtraction; 5 **12.** addition; 23 **13.** division; 8 **14.** multiplication; 128 **15.** D

Getting Ready for Chapter 6 **1.** Perimeter: add the lengths of the sides. Area: multiply the length and width. **2.** 15.6 **3.** 289 **4.** 120

Cumulative Review page 225

1. C **2.** C **3.** D **4.** A **5.** B **6.** B **7.** B **8.** B **9.** D **10.** A **11.** C

CHAPTER 6

6-1 pages 229–232

On Your Own **7.** 8 cm^2 **9.** sample given: about 21 in.^{2} **11.** Sample given: about 56 cm^2 **15.** B; A **17.** Sample given: about 41 in.^{2}

Mixed Review **1.** 400 **2.** 9 **3.** 153 **4.** 16 **5.** 25 **6.** 93×751

6-2 pages 233–236

On Your Own **13.** 7 cm; 3 cm^2 **15. a.** 200 in.^{2} **b.** 60 in. **17.** 9 in.^{2} **19.** 7 ft **21. a.** 2 m **b.** 0.25 m^2 **23. a.** 5 m **b.** 1 m^2 **25.** D **27.** 4 by 1, 3 by 2

Mixed Review **1.** 368 **2.** 8,208 **3.** about 11 square units **4. a.** 3.6 **b.** $70.15

6-3 pages 237–240

On Your Own **11.** 54 cm; 90 cm^2 **13.** 9 square units **15.** 16 square units **17. a.** 30 square units **b.** 25.8 square units **c.** 21 square units **d.** As the measure of $\angle B$ decreases, so does the area of the parallelogram. **19. a.** 12 cm^2

Checkpoint **1.** 175 in.^{2}; 80 in. **2.** 240 in. **3.** 38 in.; 84 in.^{2} **4.** 34 cm; 72.25 cm^2

Problem Solving Practice page 241

1. 8 weeks **3.** 1 by 17, 2 by 16, 3 by 15, 4 by 14, 5 by 13, 6 by 12, 7 by 11, 8 by 10, 9 by 9 **5.** 4, 5, 25; 9, 10, 15; 9, 12, 13 **7.** 64 in.; 64 in.

6-4 pages 242–245

On Your Own **11.** about 33 m **13.** about 18 m **15.** 157 m **17.** 402 m **19.** 55 ft **21.** 2 m **23.** 27 cm **25.** 18 m **27.** 22 cm **29.** 6 m **31.** Yes **33. a.** Neither; Every point on the stage turns simultaneously **b.** The keyboard player; She is on a circle with greater diameter. **c.** 94.2 ft **d.** yes; $2 \times 3.14 \times 30 = 2 \times 2 \times 3.14 \times 15$

Mixed Review **1.** 4.54 **2.** 0.82 **3.** 289 **4.** 27.04 **5.** 21 cm^2 **6.** 11 m^2 **7.** 7

6-5 pages 246–249

On Your Own **11.** 254.5 cm^2 **13.** 1,963.5 m^2 **15.** 14.1 square units; 15.4 units **17.** about 3 m^2 **21.** 74 m^2 **23.** 19 m^2 **27.** 52 y

Mixed Review **1.** 3.96 **2.** 345 **3.** about 31.4 m **4.** about 100.5 cm **5.** 16

Practice page 250

1. Sample: 50 cm^2 **3.** Sample: 50 cm^2 **5.** 245 m^2; 63 m **7.** 24 ft^2; 24 ft **9.** 48 in. **11.** 30 cm; 75 cm^2 **13.** 12 cm; 12 cm^2 **15.** 65.97 in.; 346.36 in.^{2} **17.** 452.39 m; 16,286.02 m^2 **19.** 452.16 cm^2 **21.** 5,941.67 yd^2

6-6 pages 251–255

On Your Own **17.** cylinder **19.** cone **25.** rectangular prism **27.** triangular prism

Mixed Review **1.** 1.68 **2.** 2.05 **3.** 254.34 ft^2 **4.** 153.86 m^2 **5.** 45 **6.** 45 **7.** $1.92

6-7 pages 256–258

On Your Own **5.** 406 in.^{2} **7.** 1,440 cm^2 **9.** 3,150 mm^2 **11.** 80 m^2 **15. a.** 240 ft^2 **b.** 207 ft^2 **c.** 447 ft^2 **d.** 2

Mixed Review **1.** 50 **2.** 4 **3.** sphere **4.** rectangular prism **5.** 1,260 **6.** 83.325 **7.** the square pizza

6-8 pages 259–262

On Your Own **9.** 600 in.^{3} **11.** 180 mm^3 **13.** 42 ft^3 **15.** l = 5 cm **17. a.** 125 cm^3 **19.** C **21.** 1 by 1 by 32, 2 by 1 by 16, 2 by 2 by 8, 2 by 4 by 4, 4 by 1 by 8 **23. a.** about 960 m^3 **b.** about 960,000 L **c.** at least 24 m by 16 m

Mixed Review **3. a.** rectangular prism **b.** 64 in.^{2} **4.** Jerry; 15¢

Checkpoint **1.** rectangular prism; 6 faces, 12 edges, 8 vertices **2.** triangular prism; 5 faces, 9 edges, 6 vertices **3.** 62 cm^2 **4.** 54 cm^2

6-9 pages 263–265

On Your Own **9. a.** Answers may vary. Sample: 8, 16, 32 **b.** 7, 11, 16 or 7, 12, 20 **11.** 9.5 square units **13.** 1 by 1 by 12 **15. a.** 6 **b.** 27 **c.** 1

Mixed Review **1.** 6^4 **2.** 22^3 **3.** 56 cm^3 **4.** 105 ft^3 **5.** makes $7

Wrap Up pages 266–267

1. about 18 m^2 **2.** 13.5 cm^2; 22 cm **3.** 34 m **4.** 45.6 cm^2 **5.** 37.7 in.; 113.0 in.^{2} **6.** 23.9 m; 45.3 m^2 **7.** 76.9 cm; 471.2 cm^2 **8.** 118.1 ft; 1,109.8 ft^2 **9.** 31.4 in.; 78.5 in.^{2} **10.** 81.7 m; 530.9 m^2 **11.** 29.5 m; 69.4 m^2 **12. a.** rectangular pyramid **b.** 5, 8, 5 **14.** 64 m^2; 28 m^3 **15.** B **16.** 36 **17.** The dimensions of the box are 8 in. by 8 in. by 4 in.

Getting Ready for Chapter 7 **1.** 2 **2.** 2, 5, 10 **3.** no **4.** 5 **5.** 2, 5, 10 **6.** no

Cumulative Review page 271

1. C **2.** C **3.** B **4.** A **5.** A **6.** C **7.** D **8.** C **9.** D

CHAPTER 7

7-1 pages 275-277

On Your Own **11.** 1, 3, 5 **13.** 1, 2, 3, 5, 10 **15.** 1, 2 **17.** 1, 2, 3, 9 **19.** 7 **21.** 4 **23.** Sample: 330 **25.** Sample: 1,200,000,000 **27.** C **29. a.** 78; 8,010; 21,822 **b.** 78; 8,010; 21,822 **c.** A number is divisible by 6 if it is divisible by both 2 and 3.

Mixed Review **1.** 9 **2.** 26 **3.** 1 **4.** 30 **5.** 16 **6.** 18 **7.** 270

7-2 pages 278–281

On Your Own **27.** 1, 3; prime **29.** 1, 3, 7, 21; composite **31.** prime **33.** composite **35.** prime **37.** composite **39.** prime **41.** composite **43.** 34; 2; 17 **45.** $2 \times 5 \times 5$ **47.** $3 \times 3 \times 5$ **49.** 11×13 **51.** $2 \times 2 \times 3 \times 3 \times 3$ **53.** 692,733 **55.** 3, 5; 5, 7; 11, 13; 17, 19; 29, 31; 41, 43; 59, 61; 71, 73

Mixed Review **1.** 3, 9 **2.** 3, 5, 9 **3.** 3, 5, 9 **4.** 3 **5.** 24 m^2 **6.** 5.76 cm^2 **7.** 975

7-3 pages 282–284

On Your Own **13.** 7 **15.** 3 **17.** 1 **19.** 2 **21.** 3 **23.** 17

Mixed Review **1.** $2 \times 2 \times 3 \times 3 \times 3 \times 3$ **2.** $2 \times 2 \times 2 \times 3 \times 5 \times 5$ **5.** 153.86 m^2 **6.** 200.96 $in.^2$ **7.** 12 h 11 min

Checkpoint **1.** 1, 2, 3, 5, 10 **2.** 1, 3, 9 **3.** 1, 2, 3, 5, 10 **4.** 1, 2, 3, 5, 10 **5.** $2 \times 2 \times 2 \times 2 \times 2 \times 2 \times 3 \times 5$ **6.** $3 \times 3 \times 3 \times 3 \times 3$ **7.** $2 \times 3 \times 5 \times 7 \times 11$ **8.** $2 \times 3 \times 5 \times 13 \times 13$ **9.** 8 **10.** 6 **11.** 150

Problem Solving Practice page 285

1. 3 times **3.** 8 students **5.** \$8 **9.** 5:50 P.M.

7-4 pages 286–287

On Your Own **11.** $\frac{3}{4}$ **13.** $\frac{2}{4}, \frac{3}{6}, \frac{5}{10}$, or $\frac{6}{12}$ **15.** $\frac{4}{6}, \frac{6}{9}$, or $\frac{8}{12}$

Mixed Review **1.** 6 **2.** 15 **3.** 4 **4.** $n - 10$ **5.** $2n + 5$ **6.** $6n$ **7.** 12 m × 4 m

7-5 pages 288–290

On Your Own **15.** $\frac{47}{64}$ **17.** $\frac{2}{6}, \frac{1}{3}$; yes **19.** $\frac{5}{5}$ **21.** Sample: $\frac{1}{2}, \frac{2}{4}$ **23.** Sample: $\frac{1}{3}, \frac{2}{6}$ **25.** no; $\frac{3}{7}$ **27.** no; $\frac{1}{6}$ **29.** no; $\frac{1}{3}$ **31.** no; $\frac{2}{13}$ **35.** $\frac{2}{6}, \frac{4}{12}; \frac{2}{4}, \frac{6}{12}$

Mixed Review **1.** 1 **2.** 0 **3.** $\frac{1}{2}$ **4.** 600 cm^2 **5.** 148 $in.^2$ **6.** 12 people

Practice page 291

1. 1, 2 **3.** 1, 2, 3, 5, 10 **5.** 1, 2, 3 **7.** composite **9.** composite **11.** 5×7 **13.** $3 \times 7 \times 13$ **15.** $2 \times 2 \times 2 \times 2 \times 3 \times 3$ **17.** 5 **19.** 7 **21.** $\frac{2}{4}$ **23.** $\frac{1}{3}$ **25.** $\frac{6}{8}, \frac{9}{12}$ **27.** $\frac{4}{10}$ **29.** $\frac{2}{12}, \frac{3}{18}$ **31.** $\frac{1}{4}, \frac{6}{24}$ **33.** $\frac{22}{24}, \frac{33}{36}$ **35.** $\frac{3}{6}, \frac{2}{4}$; yes **37.** $\frac{2}{3}$ **39.** $\frac{1}{6}$ **41.** $\frac{3}{7}$

7-6 pages 292–293

On Your Own **13.** $\frac{4}{13}$ **15.** $\frac{2}{5}$ **17.** $\frac{5}{8}$ **19.** $\frac{1}{3}$

Mixed Review **1.** ≠ **2.** = **3.** 20 **4.** 4 **5.** 1 **6.** 50 **7.** 11th floor

7-7 pages 294–296

On Your Own **15.** B **17.** $1\frac{6}{7}$ **19.** $3\frac{1}{12}$ **21.** $\frac{33}{5}$ **23.** $\frac{9}{2}$ **25.** $\frac{9}{5}$; $1\frac{4}{5}$

Mixed Review **1.** $\frac{3}{4}$ **2.** $\frac{9}{16}$ **3.** 1,728 cm^3 **4.** 180 cm^3 **5.** ×, + or +, ×

Checkpoint **1.** $\frac{3}{4}$ **2.** $\frac{2}{3}$ **3.** $\frac{7}{9}$ **4.** $\frac{1}{6}$ **5.** $\frac{1}{2}$ **6.** $9\frac{4}{5}$ **7.** $2\frac{5}{8}$ **8.** $8\frac{1}{6}$ **9.** $4\frac{1}{4}$ **10.** $2\frac{1}{2}$ **11.** $\frac{17}{3}$ **12.** $\frac{51}{4}$ **13.** $\frac{53}{6}$ **14.** $\frac{21}{2}$

7-8 pages 297–299

On Your Own **5.** 660 **7.** 60 **9.** 462 **11.** in 48 days **13.** D

Mixed Review **1.** $2\frac{1}{2}$ **2.** $7\frac{7}{8}$ **3.** $6\frac{3}{4}$ **4.** 14 **5.** $A = 11.52$ cm^2; $P = 14.4$ cm **6.** $A = 225$ m^2; $P = 60$ m **7.** about 1,256 ft^2

7-9 pages 300–302

On Your Own **13.** < **15.** > **17.** Timothy **19.** $\frac{8}{15}, \frac{23}{40}, \frac{7}{12}, \frac{19}{30}$ **23.** B

Mixed Review **1.** 24 **2.** 30 **3.** 90 **4.** 360 **5.** 686 **6.** 424 **7.** π

7-10 pages 303–306

On Your Own **17.** $\frac{113}{200}$ **19.** $\frac{7}{100}$ **21.** $1.\overline{1}$ **23.** $0.4\overline{6}$ **25.** $0.208\overline{3}$ **27.** $3.\overline{36}$ **29.** 0.25 **31.** $\frac{11}{20}$ **33. a.** 0.34, $0.\overline{3}$, 0.32, $0.34\overline{6}$ **b.** $\frac{8}{25}, \frac{1}{3}, \frac{17}{50}, \frac{26}{75}$

Mixed Review **1.** $\frac{2}{3}, \frac{7}{10}, \frac{3}{4}$ **2.** $\frac{1}{6}, \frac{1}{5}, \frac{3}{10}$ **3.** $\frac{32}{10}, 3\frac{3}{8}, \frac{7}{2}$ **4.** Sample: $\frac{18}{20}, \frac{27}{30}, \frac{36}{40}$ **5.** Sample: $\frac{6}{8}, \frac{9}{12}, \frac{12}{16}$ **6.** Jan $2.00; Leah $3.25

Checkpoint **1.** 96 **2.** 504 **3.** 360 **4.** 0.4 **5.** 0.07 **6.** 0.375 **7.** $0.1\overline{6}$ **8.** $\frac{13}{25}$ **9.** $\frac{1}{25}$ **10.** $\frac{3}{4}$ **11.** $15\frac{1}{40}$ **12.** D

7-11 pages 307–309

On Your Own **11.** 8 **13.** 18 muffins **15.** Saturday **23.** 1 h 54 min

Mixed Review **1.** 0.85 **2.** 0.12 **3.** $\frac{12}{25}$ **4.** $\frac{3}{50}$ **5.** $\frac{19}{20}$ **6.** $\frac{19}{125}$ **7.** Sample: 1 tricycle, 3 bicycles, 3 unicycles

Wrap Up pages 312–313

1. 1, 3 **2.** 1, 2 **3.** 1, 3, 9 **4.** 1, 3, 5, 9 **5.** 1, 2 **6.** 1, 2, 5, 10 **7.** B **8.** $2 \times 2 \times 2 \times 3 \times 3$ **9.** $2 \times 2 \times 2 \times 3 \times 5$ **10.** 3×11 **11.** $2 \times 2 \times 2 \times 2 \times 5$ **12.** $2 \times 3 \times 3 \times 13$ **13.** $3 \times 5 \times 23$ **14.** 20; 280 **15.** 1; 294 **16.** 3; 72 **17.** 5; 75 **18.** 6; 1,260 **19.** 2; 240 **20.** $\frac{8}{9}$ **21.** $\frac{2}{5}$ **22.** $\frac{3}{10}$ **23.** $\frac{3}{8}$ **24.** $\frac{4}{11}$ **25.** $\frac{2}{7}$ **26.** Sample: $\frac{2}{16}, \frac{3}{24}$ **27.** Sample: $\frac{1}{5}, \frac{4}{20}$ **28.** Sample: $\frac{1}{5}, \frac{10}{50}$ **29.** Sample: $\frac{6}{10}, \frac{9}{15}$ **30.** Sample: $\frac{1}{2}, \frac{2}{4}$ **31.** Sample: $\frac{3}{5}, \frac{6}{10}$ **32.** $\frac{19}{4}$ **33.** $4\frac{2}{5}$ **34.** $8\frac{1}{7}$ **35.** $\frac{17}{7}$ **36.** $2\frac{2}{14}$ or $2\frac{1}{7}$ **37.** $\frac{57}{11}$ **38.** $\frac{35}{36}, 1\frac{3}{4}, 1\frac{7}{9}, 1\frac{5}{6}$ **39.** $\frac{1}{25}$ **40.** $3\frac{7}{8}$ **41.** $2\frac{7}{50}$ **42.** 0.425 **43.** $0.\overline{8}$ **44.** $0.\overline{54}$ **45.** $39

Getting Ready for Chapter 8 **1.** $\frac{1}{2}$ **2.** 1 **3.** 0 **4.** 0 **5.** $\frac{1}{2}$ **6.** $\frac{1}{2}$

Cumulative Review page 315

1. B **2.** A **3.** B; acute **4.** C **5.** B **6.** C **7.** D **8.** C **9.** C **10.** A **11.** D

CHAPTER 8

8-1 pages 319–321

On Your Own **13.** 10 **15.** $100\frac{1}{2}$ **17.** about 4 innings **19.** $\frac{3}{10}; \frac{1}{2}$ **21.** about 1 ft **23.** $1\frac{1}{2}$ **25.** 3 **27.** 13 **29.** Answers will vary. Sample: $\frac{1}{10}, \frac{2}{10}, \frac{8}{10}$ **33.** about 24 ft

Mixed Review **1.** 0.1 **2.** 5.618 **3.** Saturday **4.** 24 **5.** The cost of each juice.

8-2 pages 322–325

On Your Own **17.** $\frac{1}{5} + \frac{3}{5} = \frac{4}{5}$ **19.** $\frac{2}{6} + \frac{3}{6} = \frac{5}{6}$ **21.** $\frac{4}{6} - \frac{1}{6} = \frac{3}{6}$ or $\frac{1}{2}$ **23.** $\frac{8}{10}$ or $\frac{4}{5}$ **25. a.** $\frac{1}{2}$ tablespoon **b.** $\frac{1}{4}$ cup **27.** no; $\frac{2}{5}$ **29.** no; $\frac{4}{9}$ **31.** no; $\frac{2}{3}$ **33.** yes; $\frac{1}{3}$ **39.** $\frac{5}{10}$ **41.** $\frac{7}{8}$ **43.** $\frac{2}{3}$

Mixed Review **1.** triangular pyramid; 4; 6; 4 **2.** cube; 6; 12; 8 **3.** 2 **4.** 4 **5.** $21

8-3 pages 326–329

On Your Own **27.** $\frac{1}{3} - \frac{1}{6} = \frac{1}{6}$ **29.** > **31.** $1\frac{9}{24}$ or $1\frac{3}{8}$ **33.** $\frac{9}{10}$ **35.** $\frac{5}{6}$ **39.** $\frac{1}{10}$ **41.** $\frac{3}{8}$ **43.** no

Mixed Review **1.** $\frac{2}{3}$ **2.** $\frac{1}{9}$ **3.** 3 **4.** 1.91 **5.** Wahkuna—pharmacist; Alma—stock broker; Yuji—teacher

Problem Solving Practice page 330

1. 19 boxes **3.** 6,000 mi **5.** 8:45 A.M. **7.** $.80

8-4 pages 331–333

On Your Own **21.** $\frac{5}{16}$; $\frac{21}{64}$; $\frac{1}{4} + \frac{1}{16} + \frac{1}{64} + \frac{1}{256}$; $\frac{85}{256}$ **25.** D; In the eleventh minute, you would receive more than $1\frac{1}{2}$ oz.

Mixed Review **1.** $1\frac{11}{15}$ **2.** $\frac{11}{48}$ **3.** $\overline{CA}$ **4.** $\overline{OB}$, $\overline{OA}$, or $\overline{OC}$ **5.** 47 min 50 s

Checkpoint **1.** $\frac{5}{12}$; $\frac{1}{2}$ **2.** $\frac{4}{5}$; 1 **3.** $\frac{6}{7}$ **4.** $\frac{4}{8}$; $\frac{1}{2}$ **5.** $\frac{3}{9}$; $\frac{1}{3}$ **6.** $\frac{1}{12}$ **7.** $\frac{38}{45}$ **8.** $\frac{9}{8}$ or $1\frac{1}{8}$ **9.** $\frac{9}{20}$ **10.** $\frac{8}{39}$ **11. a.** $\frac{6}{25}$; $\frac{31}{125}$ **b.** $\frac{1}{5} + \frac{1}{25} + \frac{1}{125} + \frac{1}{625}$; $\frac{156}{625}$

8-5 pages 334–337

On Your Own **19.** coyote; $\frac{1}{4}$ in. **21.** 4 **23.** $4\frac{2}{3}$ **25.** Black, Red, White, Norway **27.** White and Red; Red and Black **29.** $3\frac{1}{8}$ **31.** $4\frac{7}{15}$ **33.** $3\frac{1}{4}$ **35.** $13\frac{7}{12}$ **37.** \$77.50 **39.** $10\frac{1}{4}$ in. **41.** $3\frac{1}{2}$; $2\frac{1}{3}$

Mixed Review **1.** $\frac{7}{5}$; $\frac{9}{5}$; $\frac{11}{5}$ **2.** $\frac{7}{10}$; $\frac{3}{5}$; $\frac{1}{2}$ **3.** equilateral **4.** isosceles **5.** \$7.25

8-6 pages 338–340

On Your Own **15.** about 80 gifts **17.** yes **19.** 30 s **21.** 230 ft

Mixed Review **1.** $6\frac{9}{14}$ **2.** $2\frac{1}{2}$

3.

```
x       x
x   x   x
x   x   x   x   x
-----------------
A   B   C   D   F
```

4. 8 students **5.** 28 handshakes

Practice page 341

1. $1\frac{1}{2}$ **3.** $\frac{1}{2}$ **5.** 8 in. **7.** $3\frac{1}{2}$ in. **9.** 10 in. **11.** $\frac{4}{8}$; $\frac{1}{2}$ **13.** $\frac{2}{4}$; $\frac{1}{2}$ **15.** $\frac{1}{10}$ **17.** $\frac{73}{168}$ **19.** $\frac{17}{60}$ **21.** $1\frac{1}{10}$ **23.** $8\frac{1}{6}$ **25.** $2\frac{11}{12}$ **27.** $9\frac{1}{16}$ **29.** $15\frac{1}{8}$ **31.** $1\frac{1}{2}$ mi

8-7 pages 342–345

On Your Own **25.** 18 **27.** 60 **29.** $119\frac{3}{4}$ in. **33.** 10 **35.** 4 **37.** $13\frac{7}{8}$ **39.** $\frac{1}{15}$ **41.** 90 out of 191 million **43.** about 1,270,000; about $\frac{1}{18}$

Mixed Review **1.** 26 **2.** 18 **3.** 5 **5.** 744 times

8-8 pages 346–349

On Your Own **27.** 6 pieces **29.** $1\frac{7}{10}$ mi **31.** McKinley **33.** 2 **35.** $1\frac{1}{8}$ **37.** $1\frac{1}{2}$ **39.** $\frac{2}{15}$ **41.** 12 **43.** 24 **47.** 16 **49.** 24 pieces **51.** $6\frac{2}{3}$ **53.** $2\frac{5}{7}$ **55.** $\frac{2}{5}$ **57.** $1\frac{5}{7}$

Mixed Review **1.** 0.05 **2.** 0.047 **3.** $11\frac{1}{5}$ **4.** 28 **5.** 3 students

Checkpoint **1.** 8 pieces **2.** $\frac{8}{7}$; $\frac{1}{4}$; 3; $\frac{6}{13}$ **3.** $8\frac{3}{4}$ **4.** $\frac{20}{27}$ **5.** $2\frac{1}{4}$ **6.** 6 **7.** $\frac{1}{9}$ **8.** $1\frac{5}{9}$ **9.** $16\frac{2}{3}$ **10.** $1\frac{11}{15}$ **11.** C

8-9 pages 350–353

On Your Own **15.** 9,240 **17.** $1\frac{1}{2}$ **19.** 34 **21.** yes **23.** > **25.** < **27.** $6{,}665\frac{1}{8}$ in. **29. a.** 45,000,000 gallons **b.** 3,000 T **31.** 3 yd 2 ft

Mixed Review **1.** 9 **2.** 12 **3.** $3\frac{1}{2}$ **4.** $\frac{15}{49}$ **5.** \$17

Wrap Up pages 354–355

1. $\frac{1}{2}$ **2.** $1\frac{1}{2}$ **3.** $4\frac{1}{2}$ **4.** 6 **5.** $\frac{1}{5} + \frac{1}{2} = \frac{7}{10}$

6. $\frac{5}{6} - \frac{2}{6} = \frac{3}{6} = \frac{1}{2}$ **7.** $\frac{5}{9}$ **8.** $2\frac{1}{2}$ **9.** $1\frac{1}{12}$ **10.** $1\frac{2}{7}$

11. $\frac{11}{16}$ **12.** $3\frac{13}{20}$ **13.** $5\frac{1}{24}$ **14.** $\frac{1}{15}$

15.

$\frac{1}{3}$	$\frac{1}{3}$
$\frac{1}{3} + \frac{1}{6}$	$\frac{3}{6}$
$\frac{1}{3} + \frac{1}{6} + \frac{1}{12}$	$\frac{7}{12}$
$\frac{1}{3} + \frac{1}{6} + \frac{1}{12} + \frac{1}{24}$	$\frac{15}{24}$

Each successive numerator is the sum of the first *n* terms in the pattern 1, 2, 4, 8, 16, . . .
Each successive denominator is twice the previous denominator.

16. $\frac{1}{2}$ **17.** $\frac{1}{12}$ **18.** $8\frac{1}{8}$ **19.** $\frac{19}{20}$ **20.** 1 **21.** $24\frac{6}{7}$

22. 6 **23.** $2\frac{1}{2}$ **24. b.** living room: 8 ft × 10 ft, dining room: 8 ft × 8 ft **c.** living room: 80 ft^2, dining room: 64 ft^2, hallway: 72 ft^2, total area: 216 ft^2 **25.** 20 yd **26.** 96 pancakes

Getting Ready for Chapter 9 **1.** 7 **2.** 6 **3.** 18 **4.** 2

Cumulative Review page 359

1. A **2.** D **3.** A **4.** C **5.** B **6.** B **7.** D **8.** C **9.** C **10.** A **11.** D **12.** D **13.** A

CHAPTER 9

9-1 pages 363–364

On Your Own **9.** 2 to 1, 2 : 1, $\frac{2}{1}$ **11.** 3 to 2, 3 : 2, $\frac{3}{2}$ **13.** 5 : 7 **21.** hexagon to triangle **23.** trapezoid to triangle or hexagon to rhombus

Mixed Review **1.** About 25.12 cm **2.** About 50.24 cm^2 **3.** 2 ft 4 in. **4.** 1 ft **5.** Answers may vary. Samples: $\frac{4}{6}, \frac{6}{9}$ **6.** Answers may vary. Samples: $\frac{6}{10}, \frac{9}{15}$ **7.** 5 birds and 3 squirrels

9-2 pages 365–368

On Your Own **15.** $\frac{1}{2}, \frac{5}{10}, \frac{100}{200}$ **17.** 4 : 7, 16 : 28, 24 : 42 **19.** 10 **21.** 2 **23.** 21 **27.** $\frac{2}{3}$ **29.** 0 **31.** 25 mi/da **33.** 2 pears/child **35.** 12 players/team **37.** $\frac{2}{5}$ **39.** $\frac{3}{4}$

Mixed Review **1.** $\frac{2}{5}$ **2.** $3\frac{9}{16}$ **3. a.** 3 : 1 **b.** 1 : 6 **4.** 2 dimes, 1 nickel

9-3 pages 369–372

On Your Own **15.** yes **17.** yes **19.** 112.5 **21.** 9 **23.** Sample answer: $\frac{2}{6} = \frac{5}{15}$ **27.** 27 coaches **29.** about 112 people

Mixed Review **1.** 9 **2.** 26 **3.** 28 **4.** 28 : 70, 42 : 105 **5.** $\frac{3}{4}, \frac{12}{16}$ **6.** 2 to 5, 16 to 40 **7.** Julio: roast beef, Stella: chicken, Ted: tuna

Checkpoint **1.** C **2.** $\frac{2}{3}, \frac{20}{30}$ **3.** 10 to 17, 40 to 68 **4.** 9 : 20, 36 : 80 **5.** $\frac{46}{88}, \frac{69}{132}$ **6.** $\frac{14}{19}$ **7.** 11 : 30 **8.** $\frac{1}{3}$ **9.** 9 : 19 **10.** $.89/taco **11.** $.35/battery **12.** no **13.** yes **14.** no **15.** no **16.** 108 in.

9-4 pages 373–375

On Your Own **9.** 80 adult tickets **11.** Bob **13.** Sums and placement of digits may vary. **15.** 24 **17.** 13 **19.** 14 **21.** ↑← or ←↑ **23.** 30

Mixed Review **1.** 55 **2.** 27 **3.** F **4.** T **5.** T **6.** F **7.** 6:58 A.M.

Problem Solving Practice page 376

1. 111, 112 **3.** $4.89
5. Sample: 974 + 82 = 1,056 **7.** Marla, Jon, Noel, Dana **9.** 75 cm^2

9-5 pages 377–379

Mixed Review **1.** 22 ft **2.** 28 ft^2 **3.** 60 **4.** 125 **5.** 8, 13

9-6 pages 380–383

On Your Own **9.** 12 m **11.** 120 cm **13.** 0.075 in. **15.** 1.08 in.

Mixed Review **1.** > **2.** < **3.** $\angle D$, $\angle E$, $\angle F$ **4.** EF **5.** $\frac{27}{100}$ **6.** $\frac{56}{100}$ **7.** 140.8 ft/sec

9-7 pages 384–386

On Your Own **15.** 31% **17.** 11% **19.** 4% **21.** 33% **23.** 25% **25.** 1% **27.** \$.05; \$.50 **29.** 25%

Mixed Review **1.** $1\frac{5}{16}$ **2.** $\frac{3}{8}$ **3.** 2 m × 5 m **4.** 2.4 m **5.** 0.25 **6.** 0.5625 **7.** 13 students

9-8 pages 387–389

On Your Own **11.** $\frac{11}{50}$; 0.22 **13.** 0.88; 88% **15.** 0.8; 80% **17.** D **19. a.** 25%; 34%; 44%, 55%; 69%, 77% **c.** Sample answer: about 87%

Mixed Review **1.** 2,197 **2.** 729 **3.** 40% **4.** 92% **5.** \$10.50

Practice page 390

1. $\frac{5}{34}$, 5 : 34, 5 to 34 **3.** $\frac{5}{3}$, 5 : 3, 5 to 3 **5.** $\frac{1}{4}$ **7.** $\frac{3}{7}$ **9.** $\frac{1}{3}$ **11.** Answers may vary. **13.** 21 **15.** 5 **17.** 60 **19.** 1.1 m **21.** 55%, $\frac{11}{20}$, 0.55 **23.** 25%, $\frac{1}{4}$, 0.25 **25.** 20%, $\frac{1}{5}$, 0.2

9-9 pages 391–394

On Your Own **25.** Sample answers: **a.** \$70 **b.** \$105 **c.** \$262.50 **27.** c **a.** \$.63 **b.** \$.48 **c.** \$.72 **37.** rounding to \$16, \$9.20 each

Mixed Review **1.** $\frac{11}{15}$ **2.** $\frac{5}{24}$ **3.** 25% **4.** 75% **5.** $\frac{2}{5}$ **6.** $\frac{17}{20}$ **7.** 69, sample method: truncate $1{,}000 \div 13 \approx 76$, and subtract the no. of 2-digit numbers, $76 - 7 = 69$

9-10 pages 395–398

On Your Own **5.** 393 **7.** 5.6 **9.** 51.8 **11.** 8.64 **13.** 65.34 **15.** \$380 **17.** about 39 **19.** about 7 **21.** Answers may vary. Consonants also occur. **23.** 647 children and teenagers **25.** males—about 225; females—about 319

Mixed Review **1.** < **2.** < **3.** Sample answer: \$.60 **4.** Sample answer: \$2.33 **5.** 120 **6.** 135 **7.** 60 singers

Checkpoint **1.** 8, 9, 10 **2.** $x = 10$ **3.** 262.5 km **8.** 75% **9.** 45% **10.** 67% **11.** 60% **12.** C **13.** 41.76 **14.** 35.26 **15.** 3.2

9-11 pages 399–401

Mixed Review **1.** $\frac{15}{16}$ **2.** $\frac{4}{5}$ **3.** 212.3 **4.** 19.14 **5.** Answers may vary. Sample: 2992 does not have alternating digits.

Wrap Up pages 402–403

1. 45 to 100, $\frac{45}{100}$, 45 : 100 **2.** three tapes: \$1.99, two tapes: \$1.88; The tape in the package of three. **3.** 21 **4.** 27 **5.** 3 **6.** 16 **7.** 3 **8.** 9 **10.** 24 ft **11.** 1.5 m **12.** 0.65, $\frac{13}{20}$ **13.** about \$70 **14.** C **15.** 30 **16.** 4.37 **17.** 48 **18.** 23.5 **19.** \$.80 **21.** 11 small feeders

Getting Ready for Chapter 10 **1.** 100

Cumulative Review page 407

1. B **2.** C **3.** B **4.** C **5.** D **6.** A **7.** B **8.** C **9.** A **10.** D

CHAPTER 10

10-1 pages 411–413

On Your Own **15.** the game seems fair **17.** unfair; There are 15 possible prime sums and 21 possible composite sums.

Mixed Review **1.** $1\frac{23}{170}$ **2.** $1\frac{7}{20}$ **3.**

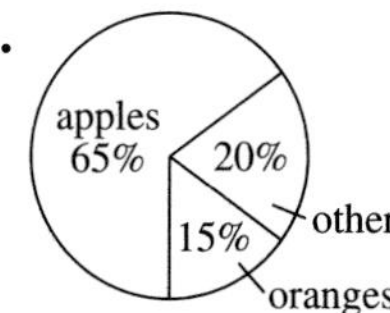

4. 16, 22, 29 **5.** 1.95, 2.25, 2.55

Selected Answers

10-2 pages 414–416

On Your Own **15.** He spends only $\frac{5}{56}$ of the time in school. **19.** No; two non-adjacent squares would always be left uncovered **21.** Use a simulation. Answers may vary.

Mixed Review

1. 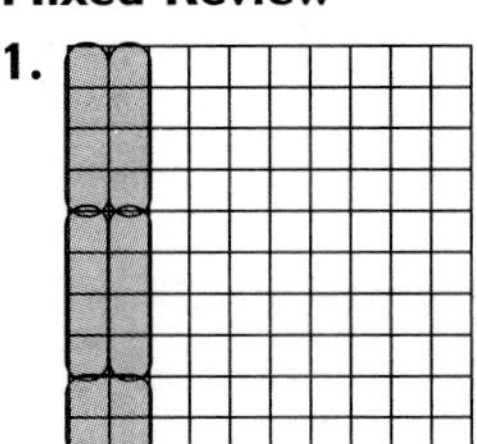 **2.** 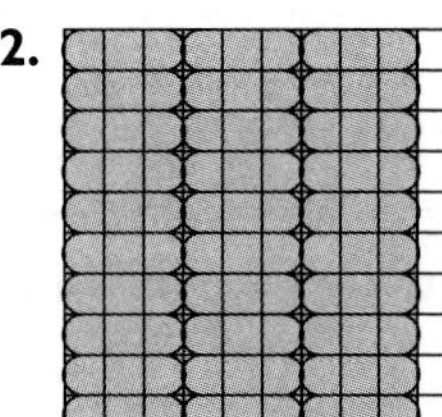

5. 18

10-3 pages 417–419

On Your Own **13.** about 22 **15.** unfair

Mixed Review **1.** $\frac{2}{3}, \frac{4}{6}$ **2.** $\frac{1}{3}, \frac{2}{6}$ **3.** Nov. 1 **4.** $\frac{8}{125}$ **5.** 18

Problem Solving Practice page 420

1. 1768 **2.** about 1,384.74 sq ft **3. a.** about 525 **b.** \$551.25 **6.** 120

10-4 pages 421–424

On Your Own **21.** 0, 0.0, 0% **23.** $\frac{1}{2}$, 0.5, 50% **25.** 5 **29.** Answers may vary. Sample: A, B, E, G, C, D, F

Mixed Review **1.** 30 m **2.** 11 ft **3.** They all have an equal chance. **4.** no

Checkpoint **1. a.** $\frac{1}{5}$, 0.2, 20% **b.** $\frac{3}{5}$, 0.6, 60% **c.** $\frac{2}{5}$, 0.4, 40% **d.** $\frac{4}{5}$, 0.8, 80% **2. a.** $\frac{7}{15}$ **b.** $\frac{8}{15}$ **c.** The game seems fair because the probabilities are close to $\frac{1}{2}$. **3.** D

10-5 pages 425–428

On Your Own **15.** 9 **17.** 40

Mixed Review **1.** 1,485 **2.** 24,003 **3.** $\frac{1}{3}$ **4.** $\frac{3}{7}$ **5.** 580

10-6 pages 429–431

On Your Own **13.** Yes; The second spin is independent of the first spin. **15.** $\frac{9}{25}$ **17.** $\frac{1}{10}$ **19. a.** 2 **b.** 6 **c.** 12 **d.** 72 **21.** B

Mixed Review **1.** 45° **2.** 130°

4. $\frac{1}{4}$ **5.** 10 **6.** 2

10-7 pages 432–434

On Your Own **15.** 120 **17. a.** 5,040 **b.** $\frac{1}{5{,}040}$ **19.** 5,040

Mixed Review **1.** 17 **2.** 30 **3.** $\frac{1}{12}$ **4.** $\frac{1}{36}$ **5.** 28, 13

Checkpoint **1. a.** B < H, T; R < H, T; Y < H, T **b.** $\frac{1}{6}$ **2.** 12 **3.** $\frac{16}{49}$ **4.** 720

Practice page 435

1. unfair **3.** $\frac{3}{5}$ **5.** $\frac{1}{2}$ **7.** $\frac{11}{12}$ **9.** $\frac{3}{4}$ **13.** 120 **15.** no **17.** yes **19.** 39,916,800

10-8 pages 436–439

On Your Own **13.** no; no **15.** yes; possibly **17. a.** 47% **b.** about 93

Mixed Review **1.** 23 **2.** 21 **3.** 5,040 **4.** 24 **5.** 30

Wrap Up pages 440–441

1. a.

	1	2	3	4	5	6
1	2	3	4	5	6	7
2	3	4	5	6	7	8
3	4	5	6	7	8	9
4	5	6	7	8	9	10
5	6	7	8	9	10	11
6	7	8	9	10	11	12

2. a. $\frac{3}{10}$; $\frac{7}{10}$ **b.** unfair **4.** $\frac{2}{9}$ **5. a.** $\frac{2}{11}$ **b.** 0 **c.** $\frac{4}{11}$ **6.** 240 cars **7.** $\frac{15}{64}$ **8.** 120 **9.** No; not all boys in school have an equal chance of being surveyed.

Getting Ready for Chapter 11 **1.** negative **2.** positive **3.** negative **4.** positive

Cumulative Review page 445

1. C **2.** B **3.** D **4.** D **5.** B **6.** C **7.** A **8.** A **9.** B **10.** D

CHAPTER 11

11-1 pages 449–452

On Your Own **25.** Answers may vary. Sample: +210,000 **27. a.** teacher aide, cook, lawyer, bank teller, typist, farmer **29.** −3 **31.** −8 **33.** 8 **35.** 212 **37.** −2 **39.** −7 **41.** −89°C, −68°C, −63°C, −59°C, −33°C, −24°C, −22°C **43.** −8 **45.** −6

Mixed Review **1.** $8\frac{5}{6}$ **2.** $1\frac{5}{24}$ **4.** 43% **5.** 110

11-2 pages 453–454

On Your Own
15. −2 **17.** −6 **19. a.** 64 ways **b.** −6, −5, −4, −3, −2, 1, 0, 1, 2, 3, 4, 5, 6

Mixed Review **1.** 60 **2.** 56 **3.** 4 **4.** −21

11-3 pages 455–458

On Your Own **21.** −15 **23.** 0 **25.** 5 **27.** = **29.** = **31.** A **33.** −5 yd **37.** −2 **39.** −3

Mixed Review **1.** −3 **2.** 5 **3.** 4 in. : 20 ft **4.** 80 in.^{2}; 48 in.

Checkpoint
1. < **2.** > **3.** < **4.**
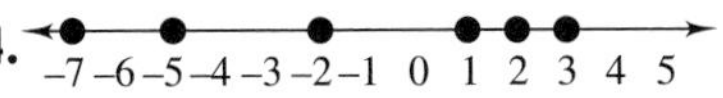

5. 1 **6.** 6, −6 **7.** −5, 5 **8.** −2, 2 **9.** 8, −8 **10.** −5 **11.** 2 **12.** 0

11-4 pages 459–462

On Your Own **15.** −5 **17.** 11 **19.** 9 **21.** = **23.** = **25.** 6°C **27.** 24°C **29.** −5, −11, −17 **33.** −10 **35.** −6 **37.** 7:30 A.M. **39.** 9:00 P.M.

Mixed Review **1.** positive **2.** positive **3.** 2 × 2 × 3 × 5 **4.** 2 × 2 × 2 × 5 × 31 **5.** 11

Practice page 463

7. −12, −7, 1, 5 **9.** −76, −73, −72, 71, 72 **11.** 3 **13.** −6 **15.** > **17.** > **19.** 0 **21.** 5 **23.** Answers may vary. **25.** Answers may vary. **27.** −7 **29.** 0 **31.** −21 **33.** −6 **35.** > **37.** = **39.** < **41.** −5 yd

11-5 pages 464–466

On Your Own **13.** 981 mi **15.** $15.2 million **17.** 2500 **19.** 50 mi **21.** 5, 6, 7, 8, 9, 10, 11

Mixed Review **1.** 7 **2.** 2 **3.** 18% **4.** 86% **5.** 13 and 21

11-6 pages 467–470

On Your Own **21.** I **23.** III **27. a.** Estimates may vary. about 35°S, 65°W **b.** about 20°S, 140°E **33.** City Hall

Mixed Review **1.** not enough information to solve **2.** 82°F **3.** 0.45; $\frac{9}{20}$ **4.** 0.375; 37.5% **5.** $\frac{16}{25}$

Problem Solving Practice page 471

1. 300 m **3.** 56% **5.** $.44

11-7 pages 472–475

On Your Own **11.** (−2, 4) **13.** 3 units to the left and 7 units up **15.** (4, −3) **17.** translation, 4 units right, 3 units up **21. b.** triangle **c.** (2, 6), (8, 6), (4, 1) **d.** 15 sq. units; 15 sq. units

Mixed Review **1.** IV **2.** I **3.** $.45 **4.** $6.80 **5.** 7

Checkpoint **1.** 597 **2.** *E* **3.** *G* **4.** *N* **5.** *A* **6.** (4, 2) **7.** (4, −1) **8.** (−3, −1) **9.** (−1, 0) **10.** B **11.** 128 **12.** 585 **13.** −1,996

11-8 pages 476–479

On Your Own **17.** −7 **19.** 0 **21.** 47 **23. a.** Mon.: $9; Tues.: $18; Wed.: −$9; Thurs.: $17; Fri.: −$12; Sat.: −$1; Sun.: −$17 **25.** =B2 + C2; =B3 + C3; =B4 + C4; =B5 + C5 **27.** Balances 2: −$2,256; 3: $984; 4: $194; 5: −$1,196 Totals Income: $15,931; Expenses: −$18,205; Balance: −$2,274

Mixed Review **1.** 1,092 **2.** 2,070 **3.** $A(-4, 5)$ $B(3, 9)$ $C(3, 5)$ **4.** $A(2, 1)$ $B(9, 5)$ $C(9, 1)$

Wrap Up pages 480–481

1. −7 **2. a.** 7 **b.** −1 **c.** 8 **d.** 14 **5.** > **6.** > **7.** < **8.** < **9.** < **10.** −1 **11.** 3 **12.** 1 **13.** 2 **14.** 5 **15.** −7 **16.** 8 **17.** −10 **18.** C **19.** G **20.** N **21.** A **22.** H **23.** K **24.** (−3, −2) **25.** (1, −3) **26.** (0, −4) **27.** (−2, 2) **28.** (4, 0) **29.** (−1, −4) **30. a.** (−4, 1); (1, 8); (1, 1) **b.** They are congruent. **31. a.** Jan.: $486, profit; Feb.: $2,000, profit; March: −$266, loss; April: $673, profit **b.** scale from −500 to 2,000; intervals of 500. **32.** 12:00 P.M.

Cumulative Review page 485

1. A **2.** C **3.** B **4.** C **5.** A **6.** D **7.** C **8.** B **9.** C **10.** D

Extra Practice 1 page 486

1. a.

			x
x	x		x
x	x	x	x
x	x	x	x
1	2	3	4

b. 2.5; 4

3.

num	tally	total
102	||||	4
201	|	1
202	|	1
302	|	1
402	||	2

mean: 213
median: 201
mode: 102

5. bar graph **7.** circle graph
11. Mantle, Roberts, and Ruth

Extra Practice 2 page 487

1. Answers may vary. Sample: $\angle BHC$, $\angle BHD$, $\angle CHD$ **3.** Sample: E, D, C **5.** 180° **7.** 36° **9.** 112° **13.** equilateral **15.** obtuse **17.** acute
19.

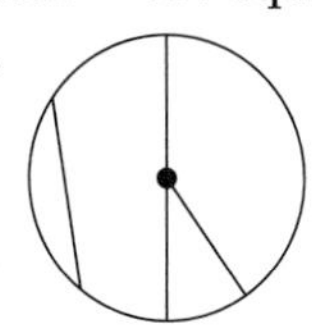

Extra Practice 3 page 488

1. **5.**

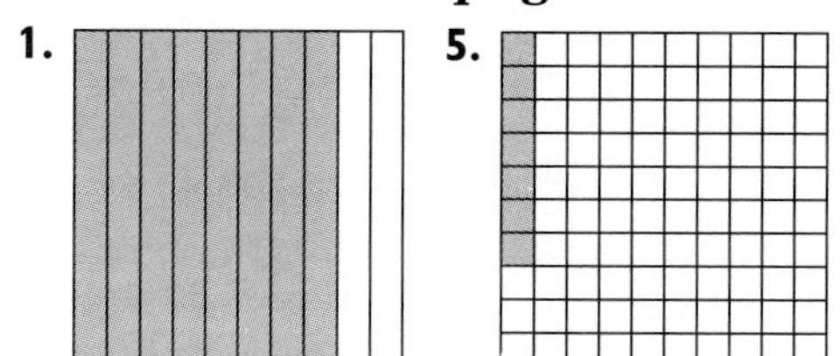

7. eight tenths **9.** thirty hundredths **11.** thirty-three and five hundredths **13.** 0.57 **15.** 0.142 **17.** 9 tenths **19.** 9 hundredths **21.** 9 hundredths **23.** > **25.** = **27.** 5 **29.** 21 **31.** 5 **33.** 5 **35. a.** m **b.** cm **c.** km **37.** 2005

Extra Practice 4 page 489

1. 28 **3.** 96 **5.** 7 **7.** 17 **9.** 18 **11.** 10 **13.** 45 **15.** 10 **17.** 546 **19.** 396 **21.** 0.0245 **23.** 0.237 **25.** 12 **27.** 0.04 **29.** 1.6 **31.** 8.6 **33.** Cannot tell which type of ticket she bought. Do not need to know how much programs cost.

Extra Practice 5 page 490

1. 256, 1,024, 4,096; Begin with 1 and multiply by 4. **3.** 8.3, 10.3, 12.3; Begin with 0.3 and add 2 to each preceding number. **5.** 4, 7 **7.** 7, 4 **9.** 6 **11.** 195,312.5 **13.** 49 **15.** 40 **17.** $2p$ **19.** 7 **21.** 136 **23.** 17.8 **25.** 29.2 **27.** 200 **29.** 40,000

Extra Practice 6 page 491

1. 52.25 in.^{2} **3.** 144 cm^2 **5.** 6 cm **7.** $C = 78$; 81.68; $A = 507$; 530.93 **9.** $C = 180$; 188.5; $A = 2{,}700$; 2,827.43 **11. a.** pentagonal prism **b.** 7, 15, 10 **13.** triangular prism; 72 sq. units **15.** 4 triangles, 4 quadrilaterals, 1 pentagon; 125 points

Extra Practice 7 page 492

1. 1, 2, 3, 9 **3.** 1, 2, 3, 5, 9, 10 **5.** 1 **7.** composite **9.** prime **11.** prime **13.** 4 **15.** 8 **17.** 5 **19.** $\frac{4}{6}, \frac{6}{9}$; $0.\overline{6}$ **21.** $\frac{4}{10}, \frac{6}{15}$; 0.4 **23.** $\frac{2}{4}, \frac{3}{6}$; 0.5

25. 5, $\frac{6}{7}$ **27.** 10, $\frac{4}{5}$ **29.** 6, $\frac{1}{10}$ **31.** $3\frac{1}{4}$ **33.** $1\frac{3}{7}$ **35.** $\frac{15}{8}$ **37.** $\frac{100}{9}$ **39.** $\frac{81}{8}$ **41.** 6; 531, 135, 351 and 513, 153, 315; yes

Extra Practice 8 page 493

1. $\frac{5}{6}$ **3.** $\frac{5}{12}$ **5.** $\frac{57}{56}$ or $1\frac{1}{56}$ **7.** $\frac{49}{6}$ or $8\frac{1}{6}$ **9.** $\frac{142}{15}$ or $9\frac{7}{15}$ **11.** $\frac{69}{12}$ or $5\frac{3}{4}$ **13.** $\frac{1}{3}$ **15.** $\frac{228}{5}$ or $45\frac{3}{5}$ **17.** 2 **19.** $\frac{32}{63}$ **21.** $\frac{2}{5}$ **23.** $\frac{45}{14}$ or $3\frac{3}{14}$ **25.** 5 **27.** 1 **33.** $\frac{4}{3}$ **35.** 3 **37.** $\frac{3}{13}$ **41.** 60,000 mi

Extra Practice 9 page 494

1. $\frac{1}{2}$ **3.** $\frac{1}{4}$ **5.** $\frac{1}{4}$ **7.** 128 **9.** 90 **11.** 2 **13.** 9 **15.** 60 **17.** 40% **19.** 90% **21.** 30% **23.** 6% **25.** 17% **27.** 80% **29.** $\frac{33}{50}$ **31.** $\frac{6}{25}$ **33.** $\frac{14}{25}$ **35.** 0.7 **37.** 0.2 **39.** 0.6 **41.** 4 **43.** 17.5 **45.** \$2.63 **47.** 90 **49.** $\frac{13}{20}$, 65%, 0.65

Extra Practice 10 page 495

1. Yes, it is fair **3.** 0.4

5.

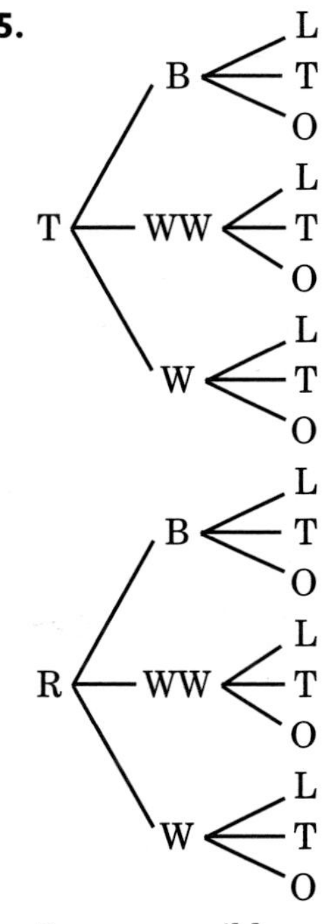

7. yes, possibly

Extra Practice 11 page 496

1. −7, −6, 6, 7 **3.** −7, 1, 15, 71 **5.** < **7.** > **9.** = **11.** > **13.** (3, −3) **15.** (−3, 3) **17.** *G* **19.** *I* **21.** 3rd quadrant **23.** (3, 3) **25.** 14 **27.** −125 **29.** scale: −35 to 25; intervals: 5 or 10 **31.** Mars: about $10\frac{1}{2}$ times; Earth: 20 times

Selected Answers

Acknowledgments

Cover Design
Martucci Studio and L. Christopher Valente

Front Cover Photo Martucci Studio

Back Cover Photo Ken O'Donoghue

Book Design DECODE, Inc.

Technical Illustration ANCO/Outlook

Illustration

Anco/OUTLOOK: 15, 118, 119, 121, 122, 128, 129, 130, 133, 141, 142, 145, 162, 200, 230 T, 231, 264, 265, 277, 287, 301, 302, 319, 325, 331, 332, 333, 336, 352, 365, 376, 380, 382, 384, 412, 431, 433, 450, 456, 460, 464, 470, 476, 477, 478, 481, 484

Eliot Bergman: 195

Arnold Bombay: 28, 118, 172, 426, 451

DECODE, Inc.: vii TL, viii TL, ix TL, x TL, xi TL, xii TL, xiii TL, xiv TL, xv TL, xvi TL, xvii TL, 2 TL, 34 B, 35 BL, 35 C, 35 TL, 40, 88 C, 89 B, 89 C, 89 T, 92 TL, 134,B, 135 BR, 135 T, 135,BL, 138 TR, 178 B, 179 B, 179 TL, 179 TL, 182 TL, 222 B, 223 CL, 223 CR, 223 T, 226 TL, 228, 268 B, 269 B, 269 CR, 269 T, 272 TL, 312 BR, 313, 313 B, 313 C, 316 TL, 318, 356 B, 357 R, 357 TL, 360 TL, 380 TR, 404 B, 405 T, 405,BR, 408 TL, 442 B, 443 C, 443 T, 446 TL, 482 B, 483 B, 483 TL, 483 TR

Jim DeLapine: 41, 47, 54, 99, 279, 288

Donald Doyle: 384

Horizon Design/John Sanderson: 229, 230 B, 329, 462

Dave Joly: 455, 457

Rick Lovell: viii TR, 38–39, 126, 205

Scott MacNEILL: 21, 164, 174, 397, 398, 413, 461

Steve Moscowitz: 63, 73, 78, 275, 292, 338, 364, 400

Matthew Pippin: 242, 256, 259, 411, 422

Precision Graphics: vii TR, x TR, xi TR, xiii TR, xv TR, xvi TR, xvii TR, 2–3, 138 C, 139 L, 182-183, 272-273, 274, 317, 361, 408–409, 409 T, 446–447, 447 T

Pat Rossi: 25, 100, 186, 199, 212, 337

Schneck-DePippo Graphics: 59, 75, 82, 84, 208

Schneck-DePippo Graphics and Anco/OUTLOOK: 49, 59, 75, 185, 186, 187, 196, 201, 202, 210

Ned Shaw: xv B, 13, 105, 112, 113, 173, 200, 219, 241, 280, 289, 377, 378, 392

DAYS OF THUNDER™, 299; drawing courtesy of Paramount Parks. TM and © 1994 Paramount Pictures. All rights reserved. DAYS OF THUNDER is a trademark of Paramount Pictures

Photography

Front Matter: i, ii, iii, Martucci Studio; **iv–v,** Bill DeSimone Photography; **vii BL,** C.C. Lockwood/Cactus Productions; **viii TR,** Josef Beck/FPG; **ix TR,** PH Photo; **x L,** Lee Celano/Sipa Press; **xii L,** R. Ian Lloyd/Stock Market; **xii TR,** Steve Greenberg Photography; **xiv TR,** Mike Powell/Allsport; **xiv L,** William R. Sallaz/duomo; **xvi L,** PH Photo.

Chapter One: 4, Ken O'Donoghue; **7,** Courtesy, The Franklin D. Roosevelt Library; **9,** Museum of the American Indian; **12,** C.C. Lockwood/Cactus Clyde Productions; **16,** Dan McCoy/Rainbow; **17,** The Metropolitan Museum of Art, Rogers Fund, 1903, Photograph by Schecter Lee; **18,** Russ Lappa; **19,** Carol Halebian/The Gamma Liaison Network; **23,** Bob Burch/Bruce Coleman, Inc.; **30,** A. Tannenbaum/Sygma; **31,** Christopher Brown/Stock Boston; **35,** David Young-Wolf/PhotoEdit.

Chapter Two: 43, Steven E. Sutton/© duomo; **45,** Ken O'Donoghue; **46,** S. N. Nielsen/Bruce Coleman, Inc.; **50,** Courtesy, Jay E. Frick; **55,** Rob Crandall/Stock Boston; **57,** Ken O'Donoghue; **58 both,** The Granger Collection; **59,** Dr. Jeremy Burgess/Science Photo Library/Photo Researchers, Inc.; **60,** © Staller Studios; **61,** Raphael Gaillarde/Gamma Liaison; **65,** Josef Beck/FPG International; **70,** Bryce Flynn/Stock Boston; **71,** J. Messerschmidt/Bruce Coleman, Inc.; **74,** John Shaw/Bruce Coleman, Inc.; **75,** © Boltin Picture Library; **77,** Philippe Sion/The Image Bank; **81,** The Granger Collection; **82,** Reproduced with permission from *Geometry in Our World*; **85,** Courtesy, Roma Tile Company, Watertown, MA., photo by Ken O'Donoghue; **89,** Sybil Shackman/Monkmeyer Press.

Chapter Three: 92 BL, Annie Hunter; **92,** Courtesy, Prentice Hall; **94,** Ken O'Donoghue; **96,** Photo by Gary Gengozian, Fort Payne, AL.; **102,** Louis Goldman/Photo Researchers, Inc.; **107, 109,** The Granger Collection; **111,** © Jerry Jacka Photography; **114,** Courtesy, Paramount's Great America; **115,** The National Museum of Photography, Film & Television/The Science Museum; **116,** Ken Levine/Allsport; **117,** UPI/Bettmann; **120,** Paula Friedland; **122,** Robb Kendrick/National Geographic Society; **125,** Bob Daemmrich/The Image Works; **128,** Lawrence Migdale; **130,** Courtesy, Evin Demirel; **131,** © NASA (Dan McCoy)/Rainbow; **132,** Annie Hunter.

Chapter Four: 140, Mark Thayer; **143,** D. Mainzer Photography, Inc.; **144,** Richard Hutchings/Photo Researchers, Inc.; **146,** Willie Hill, Jr./Stock Boston; **148,** The Bettmann Archive; **150,** Arthur Grace/Stock Boston; **152,** The Granger Collection; **153,** Derek Berwin/ The Image Bank; **155,** Richard J. Green/Photo Researchers, Inc.; **158,** Lee Celano/Sipa Press; **159,** Hans Reinhard/Bruce Coleman, Inc.; **161,** Bob Daemmrich/ Stock Boston; **164,** Robert Maier/Animals Animals; **169,** Courtesy, Ringling Brothers, Barnum and Bailey; **171 L,** © M.M. Heaton; **171 R,** The Granger Collection; **174,** Courtesy, Justin Rankin; **175,** Ken O'Donoghue; **179,** Tony Freeman/PhotoEdit.

Chapter Five: **184,** David Young-Wolff/PhotoEdit; **186,** The Science Museum; **187,** ESA/Phototake; **188,** The Science Museum, London; **190,** Courtesy, Katherine Shell; **191 both,** Lee Boltin; **192,** Kindra Clineff; **193,** The Granger Collection; **198,** Mary Evans Picture Library; **199,** Wolfgang Kaehler; **204,** Peter Morenus/ Cornell University Photo; **208,** Lon Photography/NFL Photos; **209,** Rosanne Olson; **214,** Association for Women in Mathematics; **216 both,** Mark Greenberg/Visions; **218,** UPI/Bettmann; **223,** Bob Daemmrich/The Image Works.

Chapter Six: **229,** Steve Greenberg; **232,** Solomon D. Butcher Collection/Nebraska State Historical Society; **233,** The Bettmann Archive; **234,** Comstock; **236,** R. Ian Lloyd/TSM; **238,** V. Wilkinson/Valan Photos; **239,** Abe Frajndlich/Sygma; **245,** Mary Evans Picture Library; **247,** Jock Montgomery/Bruce Coleman, Inc., **249,** Museo de Anthropologia, Mexica City, Mexico/Superstock; **251 L,** Hazel Hankin/Stock Boston; **251 R,** Kunio Owaki/The Stock Market; **252,** J. Messerschmidt/The Stock Market; **253 TL,** Gordon R. Gainer/The Stock Market; **253 TR,** Bill Gallery/Stock Boston; **253 BL,** Halle Flygare Photos LTD/Bruce Coleman, Inc.; **253 BR,** Peter Campbell/The Bettmann Archive; **254 T,** Rene Burri/Magnum Photos; **254 B,** Courtesy, Jane Broussard; **255,** Laurence Gould - Oxford Scientific Films/Earth Scenes; **258,** Debra P. Hershkowitz/Bruce Coleman, Inc.; **260,** Annie Hunter; **264,** Mike Moreland/Custom Medical Stock Photo; **268,** Lawrence Migdale/Stock Boston.

Chapter Seven: **275,** Norman Owen Tomalin/ Bruce Coleman, Inc.; **276,** Scala/Art Resource; **282,** Ken O'Donoghue; **283,** E. Adams/Sygma; **286,** Kent Wood/ Peter Arnold, Inc.; **290,** T. Campion/Sygma; **294,** Eddie Hironaka/The Image Bank; **297,** CNRI/Science Photo Library/Photo Researchers, Inc.; **298,** Courtesy, Stephen Horel; **305,** NASA; **308,** AP Photo/Wide World; **309,** Emerson/NARAS/Sygma; **312,** David R. Frazier/ Photo Researchers, Inc.

Chapter Eight: **316,** Mike Powell/Allsport; **320,** Jim Gund/Allsport; **321,** Wendell Metzen/Bruce Coleman, Inc.; **323,** Ken O'Donoghue; **325,** Jean-Pierre/ Sygma; **328,** E.R. Degginger/Bruce Coleman, Inc.; **330,** William R. Sallaz/© duomo; **335,** K&K Ammann/Bruce Coleman, Inc.; **336,** Lynne M. Stone/Bruce Coleman, Inc.; **339,** The Granger Collection; **344,** Bruce Roberts/ Photo Reserachers, Inc.; **347,** © duomo; **348,** David pMadison/Bruce Coleman, Inc.; **351,** James P. McCoy Photography; **352,** Courtesy, Lisa Mollmann; **353,** Norvia Behling/Animals Animals; **354,** Mike Powell/Allsport; **357,** PhotoEdit.

Chapter Nine: **360,** Victah Sailer/Agence Shot; **366,** Mitchell Layton/© duomo; **367,** Darek Karp/Animals Animals; **369,** Mike James/Photo Researchers, Inc.; **370,** Ken O'Donoghue; **371,** The Granger Collection; **372,** Bjorn Bolstad/Photo Researchers, Inc.; **383,** George Goodwin/Monkmeyer Press; **387,** Tom McHugh/Photo Researchers, Inc.; **388,** Michael Simpson/FPG International; **395,** Ken O'Donoghue; **402,** Victah Sailer/ Agence Shot; **405,** David Young-Wolf/PhotoEdit.

Chapter Ten: **410,** Keith Kent/Science Photo Library/Photo Researchers, Inc.; **416,** Mik Dakin/Bruce Coleman, Inc.; **419,** Fred Lyon/Photo Researchers, Inc.; **421,** Ken O'Donoghue; **424,** J. David Taylor/Bruce Coleman, Inc.; **425,** Kevin Larkin/AP/Wide World Photos; **427,** Tony Freeman/PhotoEdit; **432,** Rhoda Sidney/ Stock Boston; **434,** David Madison/© duomo; **437,** UPI/ Bettmann; **438,** Russ Lappa; **439,** Thomas Kitchin/ Tom Stack & Associates; **443,** Jock Montgomery/Bruce Coleman, Inc.

Chapter Eleven: **449,** AP/Wide World Photos; **450,** Dan Helms/© duomo; **452,** David Madison/© duomo; **459,** Sportschrome East/West; **460,** The Granger Collection; **465,** Denis Cahill/The St. Catharines Standard; **466,** Courtesy, The Kon-Tiki Museum, Oslo; **469,** Courtesy, The First Church of Christ Scientist; **472,** C.V. Faint/The Image Bank; **478,** Courtesy, Janna Mendoza; **479,** Gregory MacNicol/Photo Researchers, Inc.; **482,** Mary Mate Denny/PhotoEdit.

Photo Research Toni Michaels

Contributing Author Paul Curtis, Hollis Public Schools, Hollis NH

Editorial, Design, and Electronic Prepress Production, for the Teaching Resources
The Wheetley Company

Editorial Services for the Teacher's Edition
Publishers Resource Group, Inc.

Index

A

B

C

D

E

F

G

Index

H

I

J

K

L

M

Index

N

O

P

Q

R

S

T

Acknowledgments

Technical Art, ANCO/Outlook

Bulletin Boards, Andrea Maginnis

Photo on page T13, Dean Abramson

Acknowledgments

Technical Art, ANCO/Outlook

Bulletin Boards, Andrea Maginnis

Photo on page 13, Dean Abramson